DIFFERENTIATION RULES

General Formulas

Assume u and v are differentiable functions of x.

Constant:
$$\frac{d}{dx}(c) = 0$$

Sum:
$$\frac{d}{dx}(u + v) = \frac{du}{dx} + \frac{dv}{dx}$$

Difference:
$$\frac{d}{dx}(u - v) = \frac{du}{dx} - \frac{dv}{dx}$$

Constant Multiple:
$$\frac{d}{dx}(cu) = c\frac{du}{dx}$$

Product:
$$\frac{d}{dx}(uv) = u\frac{dv}{dx} + v\frac{du}{dx}$$

Quotient:
$$\frac{d}{dx}\left(\frac{u}{v}\right) = \frac{v\dfrac{du}{dx} - u\dfrac{dv}{dx}}{v^2}$$

Power:
$$\frac{d}{dx}x^n = nx^{n-1}$$

Chain Rule:
$$\frac{d}{dx}(f(g(x))) = f'(g(x)) \cdot g'(x)$$

Trigonometric Functions

$$\frac{d}{dx}(\sin x) = \cos x \qquad \frac{d}{dx}(\cos x) = -\sin x$$

$$\frac{d}{dx}(\tan x) = \sec^2 x \qquad \frac{d}{dx}(\sec x) = \sec x \tan x$$

$$\frac{d}{dx}(\cot x) = -\csc^2 x \qquad \frac{d}{dx}(\csc x) = -\csc x \cot x$$

Exponential and Logarithmic Functions

$$\frac{d}{dx}e^x = e^x \qquad \frac{d}{dx}\ln x = \frac{1}{x}$$

$$\frac{d}{dx}a^x = a^x \ln a \qquad \frac{d}{dx}(\log_a x) = \frac{1}{x \ln a}$$

Inverse Trigonometric Functions

$$\frac{d}{dx}(\sin^{-1} x) = \frac{1}{\sqrt{1 - x^2}} \qquad \frac{d}{dx}(\cos^{-1} x) = -\frac{1}{\sqrt{1 - x^2}}$$

$$\frac{d}{dx}(\tan^{-1} x) = \frac{1}{1 + x^2} \qquad \frac{d}{dx}(\sec^{-1} x) = \frac{1}{|x|\sqrt{x^2 - 1}}$$

$$\frac{d}{dx}(\cot^{-1} x) = -\frac{1}{1 + x^2} \qquad \frac{d}{dx}(\csc^{-1} x) = -\frac{1}{|x|\sqrt{x^2 - 1}}$$

Hyperbolic Functions

$$\frac{d}{dx}(\sinh x) = \cosh x \qquad \frac{d}{dx}(\cosh x) = \sinh x$$

$$\frac{d}{dx}(\tanh x) = \operatorname{sech}^2 x \qquad \frac{d}{dx}(\operatorname{sech} x) = -\operatorname{sech} x \tanh x$$

$$\frac{d}{dx}(\coth x) = -\operatorname{csch}^2 x \qquad \frac{d}{dx}(\operatorname{csch} x) = -\operatorname{csch} x \coth x$$

Inverse Hyperbolic Functions

$$\frac{d}{dx}(\sinh^{-1} x) = \frac{1}{\sqrt{1 + x^2}} \qquad \frac{d}{dx}(\cosh^{-1} x) = \frac{1}{\sqrt{x^2 - 1}}$$

$$\frac{d}{dx}(\tanh^{-1} x) = \frac{1}{1 - x^2} \qquad \frac{d}{dx}(\operatorname{sech}^{-1} x) = -\frac{1}{x\sqrt{1 - x^2}}$$

$$\frac{d}{dx}(\coth^{-1} x) = \frac{1}{1 - x^2} \qquad \frac{d}{dx}(\operatorname{csch}^{-1} x) = -\frac{1}{|x|\sqrt{1 + x^2}}$$

Parametric Equations

If $x = f(t)$ and $y = g(t)$ are differentiable, then

$$y' = \frac{dy}{dx} = \frac{dy/dt}{dx/dt} \qquad \text{and} \qquad \frac{d^2y}{dx^2} = \frac{dy'/dt}{dx/dt}$$

Thomas' Calculus

VOLUME 1

Based on the original work by George B. Thomas, Jr.
As revised by Maurice D. Weir, Joel Hass, and Frank R. Giordano

Custom Edition for York College

Taken from:
Thomas' Calculus, Eleventh Edition
Based on the original work by George B. Thomas, Jr.
As revised by Maurice D. Weir, Joel Hass, and Frank R. Giordano

PEARSON
Custom
Publishing

PEARSON
Addison
Wesley

Cover Art: *Zakim Bridge 3*, by S. Olsen/K. Mizra

Taken from:

Thomas' Calculus, Eleventh Edition
Based on the original work by George B. Thomas, Jr.
As revised by Maurice D. Weir, Joel Hass, and Frank R. Giordano
Copyright © 2005 by Addison Wesley, Inc.
A Pearson Education Company
Boston, Massachusetts, 02116

This special edition published in cooperation with Pearson Custom Publishing.

Printed in the United States of America

10 9 8 7 6 5 4 3

ISBN 0-536-97012-2

2005360332

AK

Please visit our web site at *www.pearsoncustom.com*

PEARSON CUSTOM PUBLISHING
75 Arlington Street, Suite 300, Boston, MA 02116
A Pearson Education Company

CONTENTS

4   Applications of Derivatives   244

5   Integration   325

6   Applications of Definite Integrals   396

| **7** | **Transcendental Functions** | **466** |

| **Appendices** | **AP-1** |

| **Answers** | **A-1** |

| **Index** | **I-1** |

| **A Brief Table of Integrals** | **T-1** |

| **Credits** | **C-1** |

PREFACE

OVERVIEW In preparing the eleventh edition of *Thomas' Calculus*, we have worked to capture the style and strengths of earlier editions. Our goal has been to revisit the best features of the *Thomas' Calculus* classic editions while listening carefully to the suggestions of our many users and reviewers. With these high standards in mind, we have reconstructed the exercises and clarified some difficult topics. In the words of George Thomas, "(We) have tried to write the book as clearly and precisely as is possible." In addition, we have restructured the contents to be more logical and in alignment with the standard syllabus. In looking backward, we have learned much to help us create a useful and appealing calculus text for the next generation of engineers and scientists.

In the eleventh edition the text introduces students not just to the methods and applications of calculus, but also to a mathematical way of thinking. From the exercises to the examples to the narrative that develops the concepts and reveals the theory in readable language, this book is about thinking and communicating mathematical ideas. Calculus contains many of the key paradigms of mathematics, and it marks the real beginnings of how to think about physical and mathematical subjects in a precise and logical way. We try to help students achieve the mathematical maturity required to master the material and apply its power. The insights that come from a deep understanding are well worth the effort.

After completing this book, students should be well versed in the mathematical language needed for applying the concepts of calculus to numerous applications in science and engineering. They should also be well prepared for courses in differential equations, linear algebra, or advanced calculus.

Changes for the Eleventh Edition

EXERCISES Exercises and examples play a crucial role in learning calculus. We have included in this new edition many of the exercises that appeared in previous editions of *Thomas' Calculus*, and which constituted a great strength of those editions. Within each section we have organized and grouped the exercises by topic, progressing from computational problems to applied and theoretical problems. This arrangement gives students the opportunity to develop skills in using the methods of calculus and to deepen their appreciation and understanding of its applications and coherent mathematical structure.

RIGOR The level of rigor, while comparable to earlier editions, is more consistent throughout. We give both formal and informal discussions, making clear the distinction between the two, and we include precise definitions and accessible proofs for the students.

The text is organized so the material can be covered informally, giving the instructor a degree of flexibility. For example, while we do not prove that a continuous function on a closed and bounded interval has a maximum there, we do state this theorem carefully and use it to prove several subsequent results. Moreover, the chapter on limits has been substantially reorganized, with greater attention to both clarity and precision. As in previous editions, the limit concept is still motivated by the important idea of obtaining the slope of the line tangent to a curve at a point on it.

CONTENT   During the preparation of this edition, we have paid considerable attention to the suggestions and comments from users of previous *Thomas' Calculus* editions and from our reviewers. This has resulted in extensive revisions and changes to several chapters.

- **Preliminaries**   We have rewritten Chapter 1 as a brief review of the elementary functions. While many instructors may choose to skip the chapter, it allows for easy reference and review by the student, standardizes notation, and indicates what is assumed as background material. It also contains some helpful material that many students may not have seen, such as the pitfalls of relying entirely on a calculator or computer to give the graph of a function.

- **Limits**   Included in Chapter 2 are epsilon-delta definitions, proofs of many theorems, limits at infinity and infinite limits (and their relationship to asymptotes of a graph).

- **Antiderivatives**   We present the derivative and its important applications in Chapters 3 and 4, concluding with the antiderivative concept, which sets the stage for integration.

- **Integration**   After discussing several examples of finite sums, we introduce in Chapter 5 the definite integral in its traditional setting of the area under a curve. Following the treatment of the Fundamental Theorem of Calculus, bridging derivatives and antiderivatives, we present the indefinite integral, along with the Substitution Rule for integration. The traditional chapter on applications of definite integrals follows.

- **Techniques of integration**   The main techniques of integration, including numerical integration, are presented in Chapter 8. This follows the introduction of the transcendental functions, where we define the natural logarithm as an integral and the exponential function as its inverse.

- **Differential equations**   The bulk of the material on solving basic differential equations is now organized into a single Chapter 9. This organization allows for greater instructor flexibility in the coverage of those topics.

- **Conics**   At the request of many users, Chapter 10 on the conic sections has been fully restored. This chapter also completes the material on parametric equations by giving parametrizations of parabolas, hyperbolas, and cycloids.

- **Series**   In Chapter 11 we have restored the more complete development of the series' convergence tests that appeared in the ninth edition. We also include a brief section introducing Fourier series (which may be omitted) at the end of the chapter.

- **Vectors**   To avoid repetition of the central algebraic and geometric ideas, we have combined the treatment of two- and three-dimensional vectors into a single Chapter 12. This presentation is followed by a chapter on vector-valued functions in the plane and in space.

- **The real numbers**   We have written a brief new appendix on the theory of real numbers as it applies to calculus.

ART We realize that figures and illustrations are a critical component to learning calculus, so we have taken a fresh look at all of the figures in the book. When revising existing figures and creating new ones, we worked to improve the clarity with which the figures illustrate their associated concepts. This is especially evident with the three-dimensional graphics, where we were able to better indicate depth, layering, and rotation (see figures below). We also attempted to ensure a consistent and pedagogical use of color and assembled a team dedicated to proofreading the completed pieces.

FIGURE 6.11, page 402

Finding the volume of the solid generated by revolving the region (a) about the y-axis.

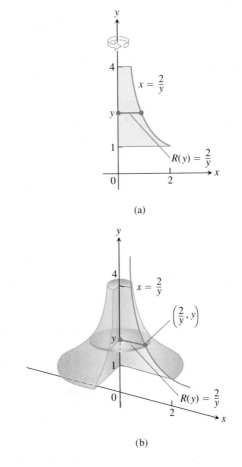

FIGURE 6.13, page 403

The cross-sections of the solid of revolution generated here are washers, not disks.

Continuing Features

END-OF-CHAPTER REVIEWS AND PROJECTS   In addition to problems appearing after each section, each chapter culminates with review questions, practice exercises covering the entire chapter, and a series of Additional and Advanced Exercises serving to include more challenging or synthesizing problems. Most chapters also include descriptions of several student projects that can be worked on by individual students, or groups of students, over a longer period of time. These projects require the use of a computer and additional material that is available over the Internet at **www.aw-bc.com/thomas**.

WRITING EXERCISES   Writing exercises placed throughout the text ask students to explore and explain a variety of calculus concepts and applications. In addition, each chapter end contains a list of questions for students to review and summarize what they have learned. Many of these exercises make good writing assignments.

ANSWERS   Answers are provided for all odd-numbered exercises when appropriate, and these have been carefully checked for correctness.

MATHEMATICAL CORRECTNESS   As in previous editions, we have been careful to say only what is true and mathematically sound. Every definition, theorem, corollary, and proof has been reviewed for clarity and mathematical correctness.

WRITING AND APPLICATIONS   As always, this text continues to be easy to read, conversational, and mathematically rich. Each new topic is motivated by clear, easy-to-understand examples and is then reinforced by its application to real-world problems of immediate interest to students. A hallmark of this book has been the application of calculus to science and engineering. These applied problems have been updated, improved, and extended continually over the last several editions.

TECHNOLOGY   In a course using the text, technology can be incorporated according to the taste of the instructor. Each section contains exercises requiring the use of technology; these are marked with a **T** if suitable for calculator or computer usage or are labeled **Computer Explorations** if a computer algebra system (CAS, such as *Maple* or *Mathematica*) is required. While we continue to provide support for technology, we have toned down its visibility within the chapters from the tenth edition.

EARLY TRANSCENDENTALS   For instructors who require an earlier treatment of the calculus of transcendental functions, we have prepared an *Early Transcendentals* version of this text, in which the exponential and logarithmic functions are introduced in the first chapter. Their limits, derivatives, and integrals are given in Chapters 2 through 5, along with those for polynomials and other algebraic functions. Examples and exercises involving the transcendental functions are then interlaced throughout those chapters as the various calculus topics are developed.

Text Versions

STUDENT EDITION OF THOMAS' CALCULUS, Eleventh Edition
Complete (Chapters 1–16), ISBN 0-321-18558-7
Part One, Single Variable Calculus (Chapters 1–11), ISBN 0-321-22642-9
Part Two, Multivariable Calculus (Chapters 11–16), ISBN 0-321-22651-8

STUDENT EDITION OF THOMAS' CALCULUS: EARLY TRANSCENDENTALS, Eleventh Edition
Complete (Chapters 1–16), ISBN 0-321-19800-X
Part One, Single Variable Calculus (Chapters 1–11), ISBN 0-321-22633-X
Part Two, Multivariable Calculus (Chapters 11–16), ISBN 0-321-22651-8
The *Early Transcendentals* version of *Thomas' Calculus* introduces and integrates transcendental functions (such as inverse trigonometric, exponential, and logarithmic functions) into the exposition, examples, and exercises of the early chapters alongside the algebraic functions. Part Two for *Thomas' Calculus: Early Transcendentals* is the same text as Part Two for *Thomas' Calculus.*

Print Supplements

INSTRUCTOR'S SOLUTIONS MANUAL
Part One (Chapters 1–11), ISBN 0-321-22653-4
Part Two (Chapters 11–16), ISBN 0-321-22650-X
The *Instructor's Solutions Manual* by William Ardis, Joseph Borzellino, Linda Buchanan, Alexis T. Mogill, and Patricia Nelson contains complete worked-out solutions to all of the exercises in the text.

ANSWER BOOK
ISBN 0-321-22649-6
The *Answer Book* by William Ardis, Joseph Borzellino, Linda Buchanan, Alexis T. Mogill, and Patricia Nelson contains short answers to most of the exercises in the text.

STUDENT OUTLINES
Part One (Chapters 1–11), ISBN 0-321-22640-2
Part Two (Chapters 11–16), ISBN 0-321-22641-0
Organized to correspond to the text, the *Student Outlines* by Joseph Borzellino and Patricia Nelson reinforces important concepts and provides an outline of the important topics, theorems, and definitions, as well as study tips and additional practice problems.

STUDENT'S SOLUTIONS MANUAL
Part One (Chapters 1–11), ISBN 0-321-22646-1
Part Two (Chapters 11–16), ISBN 0-321-22647-X
The *Student's Solutions Manual* by William Ardis, Joseph Borzellino, Linda Buchanan, Alexis T. Mogill, and Patricia Nelson is designed for the student and contains carefully worked-out solutions to all the odd-numbered exercises in the text.

JUST-IN-TIME ALGEBRA AND TRIGONOMETRY FOR CALCULUS, Third Edition
ISBN 0-321-26943-8
Sharp algebra and trigonometry skills are critical to mastering calculus, and *Just-in-Time Algebra and Trigonometry for Calculus,* Third Edition, by Guntram Mueller and Ronald I. Brent is designed to bolster these skills while students study calculus. As students make their way through calculus, this text is with them every step of the way, showing them the necessary algebra or trigonometry topics and pointing out potential problem spots. The easy-to-use contents has algebra and trigonometry topics arranged in the order in which students will need them as they study calculus.

ADDISON-WESLEY'S CALCULUS REVIEW CARD
The Calculus Review Card is a resource for students containing important formulas, functions, definitions, and theorems that correspond precisely to *Thomas' Calculus.* This card

can work as a reference for completing homework assignments or as an aid in studying and is available bundled with a new text. Contact your Addison-Wesley sales representative for more information.

Media and Online Supplements

TECHNOLOGY RESOURCE MANUALS

Maple Manual by Donald Hartig, California Polytechnic State University
Mathematica Manual by Marie Vanisko, California State University Stanislaus, and Lyle Cochran, Whitworth College
TI-Graphing Calculator Manual by Luz DeAlba, Drake University
These manuals cover *Maple* 9, *Mathematica* 5, and the TI-83 Plus/TI-84 Plus, TI-85/TI-86, and TI-89/TI-92 Plus, respectively. Each manual provides detailed guidance for integrating a specific software package or graphing calculator throughout the course, including syntax and commands. These manuals are available to qualified instructors through **http://suppscentral.aw.com.**

MYMATHLAB™

MyMathLab is a series of text-specific, easily customizable online courses for Addison-Wesley textbooks in mathematics and statistics. MyMathLab is powered by CourseCompass™—Pearson Education's online teaching and learning environment—and by MathXL—Addison-Wesley's online homework, tutorial, and assessment system. MyMathLab gives you the tools you need to deliver all or a portion of your course online, whether your students are in a lab setting or working from home. MyMathLab provides a rich and flexible set of course materials, featuring free-response exercises that are algorithmically generated for unlimited practice and mastery. Students can also use online tools, such as video lectures, animations, multimedia textbook, and Maple/Mathematica projects, to independently improve their understanding and performance. Instructors can use MyMathLab's homework and test managers to select and assign online exercises correlated directly to the textbook, and they can import TestGen tests into MyMathLab for added flexibility. MyMathLab's online gradebook—designed specifically for mathematics and statistics—automatically tracks students' homework and test results and gives the instructor control over how to calculate final grades. MyMathLab is available to qualified adopters. For more information, visit our Web site at **www.mymathlab.com** or contact your Addison-Wesley sales representative for a product demonstration.

MATHXL®

MathXL is a powerful online homework, tutorial, and assessment system that accompanies your Addison-Wesley textbook in mathematics or statistics. With MathXL, instructors can create, edit, and assign online homework and tests using algorithmically generated exercises correlated at the objective level to the textbook. All student work is tracked in MathXL's online gradebook. Students can take chapter tests in MathXL and receive personalized study plans based on their test results. The study plan diagnoses weaknesses and links students directly to tutorial exercises for the objectives they need to study and retest. Students can also access supplemental animations and video clips directly from selected exercises. MathXL is available to qualified adopters. For more information, visit our Web site at **www.mathxl.com** or contact your Addison-Wesley sales representative for a product demonstration.

TESTGEN WITH QUIZMASTER

TestGen enables instructors to build, edit, print, and administer tests using a computerized bank of questions developed to cover all the objectives of the text. TestGen is algorithmically based, allowing instructors to create multiple but equivalent versions of the same question or test with the click of a button. Instructors can also modify test bank questions or add new questions by using the built-in question editor, which allows users to create graphs, import graphics, and insert math notation, variable numbers, or text. Tests can be printed or administered online via the Internet or another network. TestGen comes packaged with QuizMaster, which allows students to take tests on a local area network. The software is available on a dual-platform Windows/Macintosh CD-ROM.

DIGITAL VIDEO TUTOR

The Digital Video Tutor features an engaging team of mathematics instructors who present comprehensive coverage of topics in the text. The lecturers' presentations include examples and exercises from the text and support an approach that emphasizes visualization and problem solving. The video lectures are available on CD-ROM, making it easy and convenient for students to watch the videos from a computer at home or on campus. The complete digitized video set, affordable and portable for students, is ideal for distance learning or supplemental instruction.

WEB SITE   www.aw-bc.com/thomas

The *Thomas' Calculus* Web site provides the expanded historical biographies and essays referenced in the text. Also available is a collection of *Maple* and *Mathematica* modules that can be used as projects by individual students or groups of students.

ADDISON-WESLEY MATH TUTOR CENTER

The Addison-Wesley Math Tutor Center is staffed by qualified mathematics and statistics instructors who provide students with tutoring on examples and odd-numbered exercises from the textbook. Tutoring is available via toll-free telephone, toll-free fax, e-mail, and the Internet. Interactive, Web-based technology allows tutors and students to view and work through problems together in real time over the Internet. The Addison-Wesley Math Tutor Center is available to qualified adopters. For more information, please visit our Web site at **www.aw-bc.com/tutorcenter** or call us at 1-888-777-0463.

Acknowledgments

We would like to express our thanks to the people who made many valuable contributions to this edition as it developed through its various stages:

Development Editors
Elka Block
David Chelton
Frank Purcell

Accuracy Checkers
William Ardis
Karl Kattchee
Douglas B. Meade
Robert Pierce
Frank Purcell
Marie Vanisko
Thomas Wegleitner

Super Reviewers
Harry Allen, *Ohio State University*
Rebecca Goldin, *George Mason University*
Christopher Heil, *Georgia Institute of Technology*
Dominic Naughton, *Purdue University*
Maria Terrell, *Cornell University*
Clifford Weil, *Michigan State University*

Reviewers
Robert Andersen, *University of Wisconsin–Eau Claire*
Charles Ashley, *Villanova University*
David Bachman, *California Polytechnic State University*
Elizabeth Bator, *University of North Texas*

William Bogley, *Oregon State University*

Kaddour Boukaabar, *California University of Pennsylvania*

Deborah Brandon, *Carnegie Mellon University*

Mark Bridger, *Northeastern University*

Sean Cleary, *City College of New York*

Edward Crotty, *University of Pennsylvania*

Mark Davidson, *Louisiana State University*

Richard Davitt, *University of Louisville*

Elias Deeba, *University of Houston, Downtown Campus*

Anne Dougherty, *University of Colorado*

Rafael Espericueta, *Bakersfield College*

Klaus Fischer, *George Mason University*

William Fitzgibbon, *University of Houston*

Carol Flakus, *Lower Columbia College*

Tim Flood, *Pittsburg State University*

Robert Gardner, *East Tennessee State University*

John Gilbert, *University of Texas at Austin*

Mark Hanisch, *Calvin College*

Zahid Hasan, *California State University, San Bernardino*

Jo W. Heath, *Auburn University*

Ken Holladay, *University of New Orleans*

Hugh Howards, *Wake Forest University*

Dwayne Jennings, *Union University*

Matthias Kawski, *Arizona State University*

Bill Kincaid, *Wilmington College*

Mark M. Maxwell, *Robert Morris University*

Jack Mealy, *Austin College*

Richard Mercer, *Wright State University*

Victor Nistor, *Pennsylvania State University*

Michael O'Leary, *Towson University*

Bogdan Oporowski, *Louisiana State University*

Troy Riggs, *Union University*

Ferdinand Rivera, *San Jose State University*

Mohammed Saleem, *San Jose State University*

Tatiana Shubin, *San Jose State University*

Alex Smith, *University of Wisconsin-Eau Claire*

Donald Solomon, *University of Wisconsin–Milwaukee*

Chia Chi Tung, *Minnesota State University*

William L. Van Alstine, *Aiken Technical College*

Bobby Winters, *Pittsburg State University*

Dennis Wortman, *University of Massachusetts at Boston*

Survey Participants

Omar Adawi, *Parkland College*

Siham Alfred, *Raritan Valley Community College*

Donna J. Bailey, *Truman State University*

Rajesh K. Barnwal, *Middle Tennessee State University*

Robert C. Brigham, *University of Central Florida (retired)*

Thomas A. Carnevale, *Valdosta State University*

Leonard Chastkofsky, *University of Georgia*

Richard Dalrymple, *Minnesota West Community & Technical College*

W. Lloyd Davis, *College of San Mateo*

Will-Matthis Dunn III, *Montgomery College*

George F. Feissner, *SUNY College at Cortland*

Bruno Harris, *Brown University*

Celeste Hernandez, *Richland College*

Wei-Min Huang, *Lehigh University*

Herbert E. Kasube, *Bradley University*

Frederick W. Keene, *Pasadena City College*

Michael Kent, *Borough of Manhattan Community College*

Robert Levine, *Community College of Allegheny County, Boyce Campus*

John Martin, *Santa Rosa Junior College*

Michael Scott McClendon, *University of Central Oklahoma*

Ching-Tsuan Pan, *Northern Illinois University*

Emma Previato, *Boston University*

S.S. Ravindran, *University of Alabama*

Dan Rothe, *Alpena Community College*

John T. Saccoman, *Seton Hall University*

Mansour Samimi, *Winston-Salem State University*

Ned W. Schillow, *Lehigh Carbon Community College*

W.R. Schrank, *Angelina College*

Mark R. Woodard, *Furman University*

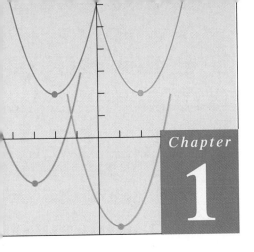

1

PRELIMINARIES

OVERVIEW This chapter reviews the basic ideas you need to start calculus. The topics include the real number system, Cartesian coordinates in the plane, straight lines, parabolas, circles, functions, and trigonometry. We also discuss the use of graphing calculators and computer graphing software.

1.1 Real Numbers and the Real Line

This section reviews real numbers, inequalities, intervals, and absolute values.

Real Numbers

Much of calculus is based on properties of the real number system. **Real numbers** are numbers that can be expressed as decimals, such as

$$-\frac{3}{4} = -0.75000\ldots$$

$$\frac{1}{3} = 0.33333\ldots$$

$$\sqrt{2} = 1.4142\ldots$$

The dots ... in each case indicate that the sequence of decimal digits goes on forever. Every conceivable decimal expansion represents a real number, although some numbers have two representations. For instance, the infinite decimals .999... and 1.000... represent the same real number 1. A similar statement holds for any number with an infinite tail of 9's.

The real numbers can be represented geometrically as points on a number line called the **real line**.

The symbol $\mathbb{R}$ denotes either the real number system or, equivalently, the real line.

The properties of the real number system fall into three categories: algebraic properties, order properties, and completeness. The **algebraic properties** say that the real numbers can be added, subtracted, multiplied, and divided (except by 0) to produce more real numbers under the usual rules of arithmetic. *You can never divide by* 0.

The **order properties** of real numbers are given in Appendix 4. The following useful rules can be derived from them, where the symbol $\Rightarrow$ means "implies."

Rules for Inequalities

If a, b, and c are real numbers, then:

1. $a < b \Rightarrow a + c < b + c$
2. $a < b \Rightarrow a - c < b - c$
3. $a < b$ and $c > 0 \Rightarrow ac < bc$
4. $a < b$ and $c < 0 \Rightarrow bc < ac$
    Special case: $a < b \Rightarrow -b < -a$
5. $a > 0 \Rightarrow \dfrac{1}{a} > 0$

6. If a and b are both positive or both negative, then $a < b \Rightarrow \dfrac{1}{b} < \dfrac{1}{a}$

Notice the rules for multiplying an inequality by a number. Multiplying by a positive number preserves the inequality; multiplying by a negative number reverses the inequality. Also, reciprocation reverses the inequality for numbers of the same sign. For example, $2 < 5$ but $-2 > -5$ and $1/2 > 1/5$.

The **completeness property** of the real number system is deeper and harder to define precisely. However, the property is essential to the idea of a limit (Chapter 2). Roughly speaking, it says that there are enough real numbers to "complete" the real number line, in the sense that there are no "holes" or "gaps" in it. Many theorems of calculus would fail if the real number system were not complete. The topic is best saved for a more advanced course, but Appendix 4 hints about what is involved and how the real numbers are constructed.

We distinguish three special subsets of real numbers.

1. The **natural numbers,** namely 1, 2, 3, 4, ...
2. The **integers,** namely 0, ± 1, ± 2, ± 3, ...
3. The **rational numbers,** namely the numbers that can be expressed in the form of a fraction m/n, where m and n are integers and $n \neq 0$. Examples are

$$\frac{1}{3}, \quad -\frac{4}{9} = \frac{-4}{9} = \frac{4}{-9}, \quad \frac{200}{13}, \quad \text{and} \quad 57 = \frac{57}{1}.$$

The rational numbers are precisely the real numbers with decimal expansions that are either

(a) terminating (ending in an infinite string of zeros), for example,

$$\frac{3}{4} = 0.75000\ldots = 0.75 \qquad \text{or}$$

(b) eventually repeating (ending with a block of digits that repeats over and over), for example

$$\frac{23}{11} = 2.090909\ldots = 2.\overline{09}$$

The bar indicates the block of repeating digits.

A terminating decimal expansion is a special type of repeating decimal since the ending zeros repeat.

The set of rational numbers has all the algebraic and order properties of the real numbers but lacks the completeness property. For example, there is no rational number whose square is 2; there is a "hole" in the rational line where $\sqrt{2}$ should be.

Real numbers that are not rational are called **irrational numbers**. They are characterized by having nonterminating and nonrepeating decimal expansions. Examples are π, $\sqrt{2}$, $\sqrt[3]{5}$, and $\log_{10} 3$. Since every decimal expansion represents a real number, it should be clear that there are infinitely many irrational numbers. Both rational and irrational numbers are found arbitrarily close to any point on the real line.

Set notation is very useful for specifying a particular subset of real numbers. A **set** is a collection of objects, and these objects are the **elements** of the set. If S is a set, the notation $a \in S$ means that a is an element of S, and $a \notin S$ means that a is not an element of S. If S and T are sets, then $S \cup T$ is their **union** and consists of all elements belonging either to S or T (or to both S and T). The **intersection** $S \cap T$ consists of all elements belonging to both S and T. The **empty set** $\varnothing$ is the set that contains no elements. For example, the intersection of the rational numbers and the irrational numbers is the empty set.

Some sets can be described by *listing* their elements in braces. For instance, the set A consisting of the natural numbers (or positive integers) less than 6 can be expressed as

$$A = \{1, 2, 3, 4, 5\}.$$

The entire set of integers is written as

$$\{0, \pm 1, \pm 2, \pm 3, \dots\}.$$

Another way to describe a set is to enclose in braces a rule that generates all the elements of the set. For instance, the set

$$A = \{x \mid x \text{ is an integer and } 0 < x < 6\}$$

is the set of positive integers less than 6.

Intervals

A subset of the real line is called an **interval** if it contains at least two numbers and contains all the real numbers lying between any two of its elements. For example, the set of all real numbers x such that $x > 6$ is an interval, as is the set of all x such that $-2 \le x \le 5$. The set of all nonzero real numbers is not an interval; since 0 is absent, the set fails to contain every real number between -1 and 1 (for example).

Geometrically, intervals correspond to rays and line segments on the real line, along with the real line itself. Intervals of numbers corresponding to line segments are **finite intervals**; intervals corresponding to rays and the real line are **infinite intervals**.

A finite interval is said to be **closed** if it contains both of its endpoints, **half-open** if it contains one endpoint but not the other, and **open** if it contains neither endpoint. The endpoints are also called **boundary points**; they make up the interval's **boundary**. The remaining points of the interval are **interior points** and together comprise the interval's **interior**. Infinite intervals are closed if they contain a finite endpoint, and open otherwise. The entire real line $\mathbb{R}$ is an infinite interval that is both open and closed.

Solving Inequalities

The process of finding the interval or intervals of numbers that satisfy an inequality in x is called **solving** the inequality.

TABLE 1.1   Types of intervals

	Notation	Set description	Type	Picture
Finite:	(a, b)	$\{x \mid a < x < b\}$	Open	
	$[a, b]$	$\{x \mid a \leq x \leq b\}$	Closed	
	$[a, b)$	$\{x \mid a \leq x < b\}$	Half-open	
	$(a, b]$	$\{x \mid a < x \leq b\}$	Half-open	
Infinite:	(a, ∞)	$\{x \mid x > a\}$	Open	
	$[a, \infty)$	$\{x \mid x \geq a\}$	Closed	
	$(-\infty, b)$	$\{x \mid x < b\}$	Open	
	$(-\infty, b]$	$\{x \mid x \leq b\}$	Closed	
	$(-\infty, \infty)$	$\mathbb{R}$ (set of all real numbers)	Both open and closed	

EXAMPLE 1   Solve the following inequalities and show their solution sets on the real line.

(a) $2x - 1 < x + 3$ **(b)** $-\dfrac{x}{3} < 2x + 1$ **(c)** $\dfrac{6}{x - 1} \geq 5$

Solution

(a)
$$2x - 1 < x + 3$$
$$2x < x + 4 \qquad \text{Add 1 to both sides.}$$
$$x < 4 \qquad \text{Subtract } x \text{ from both sides.}$$

The solution set is the open interval $(-\infty, 4)$ (Figure 1.1a).

(b)
$$-\frac{x}{3} < 2x + 1$$
$$-x < 6x + 3 \qquad \text{Multiply both sides by 3.}$$
$$0 < 7x + 3 \qquad \text{Add } x \text{ to both sides.}$$
$$-3 < 7x \qquad \text{Subtract 3 from both sides.}$$
$$-\frac{3}{7} < x \qquad \text{Divide by 7.}$$

(a)

(b)

(c)

FIGURE 1.1   Solution sets for the inequalities in Example 1.

The solution set is the open interval $(-3/7, \infty)$ (Figure 1.1b).

(c) The inequality $6/(x - 1) \geq 5$ can hold only if $x > 1$, because otherwise $6/(x - 1)$ is undefined or negative. Therefore, $(x - 1)$ is positive and the inequality will be preserved if we multiply both sides by $(x - 1)$, and we have

$$\frac{6}{x - 1} \geq 5$$

$$6 \geq 5x - 5 \qquad \text{Multiply both sides by } (x - 1).$$

$$11 \geq 5x \qquad \text{Add 5 to both sides.}$$

$$\frac{11}{5} \geq x. \qquad \text{Or } x \leq \frac{11}{5}.$$

The solution set is the half-open interval $(1, 11/5]$ (Figure 1.1c). ∎

Absolute Value

The **absolute value** of a number x, denoted by $|x|$, is defined by the formula

$$|x| = \begin{cases} x, & x \geq 0 \\ -x, & x < 0. \end{cases}$$

EXAMPLE 2   Finding Absolute Values

$$|3| = 3, \quad |0| = 0, \quad |-5| = -(-5) = 5, \quad |-|a|| = |a| \qquad ∎$$

Geometrically, the absolute value of x is the distance from x to 0 on the real number line. Since distances are always positive or 0, we see that $|x| \geq 0$ for every real number x, and $|x| = 0$ if and only if $x = 0$. Also,

$$|x - y| = \text{the distance between } x \text{ and } y$$

on the real line (Figure 1.2).

Since the symbol $\sqrt{a}$ always denotes the *nonnegative* square root of a, an alternate definition of $|x|$ is

$$|x| = \sqrt{x^2}.$$

It is important to remember that $\sqrt{a^2} = |a|$. Do not write $\sqrt{a^2} = a$ unless you already know that $a \geq 0$.

The absolute value has the following properties. (You are asked to prove these properties in the exercises.)

FIGURE 1.2 Absolute values give distances between points on the number line.

Absolute Value Properties

1. $|-a| = |a|$ — A number and its additive inverse or negative have the same absolute value.

2. $|ab| = |a||b|$ — The absolute value of a product is the product of the absolute values.

3. $\left|\dfrac{a}{b}\right| = \dfrac{|a|}{|b|}$ — The absolute value of a quotient is the quotient of the absolute values.

4. $|a + b| \leq |a| + |b|$ — The **triangle inequality**. The absolute value of the sum of two numbers is less than or equal to the sum of their absolute values.

Note that $|-a| \neq -|a|$. For example, $|-3| = 3$, whereas $-|3| = -3$. If a and b differ in sign, then $|a + b|$ is less than $|a| + |b|$. In all other cases, $|a + b|$ equals $|a| + |b|$. Absolute value bars in expressions like $|-3 + 5|$ work like parentheses: We do the arithmetic inside *before* taking the absolute value.

FIGURE 1.3 $|x| < a$ means x lies between $-a$ and a.

EXAMPLE 3   Illustrating the Triangle Inequality

$$|-3 + 5| = |2| = 2 < |-3| + |5| = 8$$
$$|3 + 5| = |8| = |3| + |5|$$
$$|-3 - 5| = |-8| = 8 = |-3| + |-5|$$

∎

The inequality $|x| < a$ says that the distance from x to 0 is less than the positive number a. This means that x must lie between $-a$ and a, as we can see from Figure 1.3.

The following statements are all consequences of the definition of absolute value and are often helpful when solving equations or inequalities involving absolute values.

Absolute Values and Intervals
If a is any positive number, then

5. $|x| = a$ if and only if $x = \pm a$
6. $|x| < a$ if and only if $-a < x < a$
7. $|x| > a$ if and only if $x > a$ or $x < -a$
8. $|x| \leq a$ if and only if $-a \leq x \leq a$
9. $|x| \geq a$ if and only if $x \geq a$ or $x \leq -a$

The symbol $\Leftrightarrow$ is often used by mathematicians to denote the "if and only if" logical relationship. It also means "implies and is implied by."

EXAMPLE 4   Solving an Equation with Absolute Values

Solve the equation $|2x - 3| = 7$.

Solution   By Property 5, $2x - 3 = \pm 7$, so there are two possibilities:

$$2x - 3 = 7 \qquad 2x - 3 = -7 \qquad \text{Equivalent equations}$$
$$2x = 10 \qquad\quad 2x = -4 \qquad \text{without absolute values}$$
$$x = 5 \qquad\qquad x = -2 \qquad\text{Solve as usual.}$$

The solutions of $|2x - 3| = 7$ are $x = 5$ and $x = -2$.   ∎

EXAMPLE 5   Solving an Inequality Involving Absolute Values

Solve the inequality $\left| 5 - \dfrac{2}{x} \right| < 1$.

Solution   We have

$$\left| 5 - \frac{2}{x} \right| < 1 \Leftrightarrow -1 < 5 - \frac{2}{x} < 1 \qquad \text{Property 6}$$

$$\Leftrightarrow -6 < -\frac{2}{x} < -4 \qquad \text{Subtract 5.}$$

$$\Leftrightarrow 3 > \frac{1}{x} > 2 \qquad \text{Multiply by } -\frac{1}{2}.$$

$$\Leftrightarrow \frac{1}{3} < x < \frac{1}{2}. \qquad \text{Take reciprocals.}$$

Notice how the various rules for inequalities were used here. Multiplying by a negative number reverses the inequality. So does taking reciprocals in an inequality in which both sides are positive. The original inequality holds if and only if $(1/3) < x < (1/2)$. The solution set is the open interval $(1/3, 1/2)$. ∎

EXAMPLE 6   Solve the inequality and show the solution set on the real line:

(a) $|2x - 3| \le 1$ **(b)** $|2x - 3| \ge 1$

(a)

(b)

FIGURE 1.4   The solution sets (a) $[1, 2]$ and (b) $(-\infty, 1] \cup [2, \infty)$ in Example 6.

Solution

(a)
$$|2x - 3| \le 1$$
$$-1 \le 2x - 3 \le 1 \qquad \text{Property 8}$$
$$2 \le 2x \le 4 \qquad \text{Add 3.}$$
$$1 \le x \le 2 \qquad \text{Divide by 2.}$$

The solution set is the closed interval $[1, 2]$ (Figure 1.4a).

(b)
$$|2x - 3| \ge 1$$

$$2x - 3 \ge 1 \quad \text{or} \quad 2x - 3 \le -1 \qquad \text{Property 9}$$

$$x - \frac{3}{2} \ge \frac{1}{2} \quad \text{or} \quad x - \frac{3}{2} \le -\frac{1}{2} \qquad \text{Divide by 2.}$$

$$x \ge 2 \quad \text{or} \quad x \le 1 \qquad \text{Add } \frac{3}{2}.$$

The solution set is $(-\infty, 1] \cup [2, \infty)$ (Figure 1.4b). ∎

EXERCISES 1.1

Decimal Representations

1. Express 1/9 as a repeating decimal, using a bar to indicate the repeating digits. What are the decimal representations of 2/9? 3/9? 8/9? 9/9?

2. Express 1/11 as a repeating decimal, using a bar to indicate the repeating digits. What are the decimal representations of 2/11? 3/11? 9/11? 11/11?

Inequalities

3. If $2 < x < 6$, which of the following statements about x are necessarily true, and which are not necessarily true?

a. $0 < x < 4$

b. $0 < x - 2 < 4$

c. $1 < \frac{x}{2} < 3$

d. $\frac{1}{6} < \frac{1}{x} < \frac{1}{2}$

e. $1 < \frac{6}{x} < 3$

f. $|x - 4| < 2$

g. $-6 < -x < 2$

h. $-6 < -x < -2$

4. If $-1 < y - 5 < 1$, which of the following statements about y are necessarily true, and which are not necessarily true?

  a. $4 < y < 6$ **b.** $-6 < y < -4$

  c. $y > 4$ **d.** $y < 6$

  e. $0 < y - 4 < 2$ **f.** $2 < \dfrac{y}{2} < 3$

  g. $\dfrac{1}{6} < \dfrac{1}{y} < \dfrac{1}{4}$ **h.** $|y - 5| < 1$

In Exercises 5–12, solve the inequalities and show the solution sets on the real line.

5. $-2x > 4$ **6.** $8 - 3x \geq 5$

7. $5x - 3 \leq 7 - 3x$ **8.** $3(2 - x) > 2(3 + x)$

9. $2x - \dfrac{1}{2} \geq 7x + \dfrac{7}{6}$ **10.** $\dfrac{6 - x}{4} < \dfrac{3x - 4}{2}$

11. $\dfrac{4}{5}(x - 2) < \dfrac{1}{3}(x - 6)$ **12.** $-\dfrac{x + 5}{2} \leq \dfrac{12 + 3x}{4}$

Absolute Value

Solve the equations in Exercises 13–18.

13. $|y| = 3$ **14.** $|y - 3| = 7$ **15.** $|2t + 5| = 4$

16. $|1 - t| = 1$ **17.** $|8 - 3s| = \dfrac{9}{2}$ **18.** $\left|\dfrac{s}{2} - 1\right| = 1$

Solve the inequalities in Exercises 19–34, expressing the solution sets as intervals or unions of intervals. Also, show each solution set on the real line.

19. $|x| < 2$ **20.** $|x| \leq 2$ **21.** $|t - 1| \leq 3$

22. $|t + 2| < 1$ **23.** $|3y - 7| < 4$ **24.** $|2y + 5| < 1$

25. $\left|\dfrac{z}{5} - 1\right| \leq 1$ **26.** $\left|\dfrac{3}{2}z - 1\right| \leq 2$ **27.** $\left|3 - \dfrac{1}{x}\right| < \dfrac{1}{2}$

28. $\left|\dfrac{2}{x} - 4\right| < 3$ **29.** $|2s| \geq 4$ **30.** $|s + 3| \geq \dfrac{1}{2}$

31. $|1 - x| > 1$ **32.** $|2 - 3x| > 5$ **33.** $\left|\dfrac{r + 1}{2}\right| \geq 1$

34. $\left|\dfrac{3r}{5} - 1\right| > \dfrac{2}{5}$

Quadratic Inequalities

Solve the inequalities in Exercises 35–42. Express the solution sets as intervals or unions of intervals and show them on the real line. Use the result $\sqrt{a^2} = |a|$ as appropriate.

35. $x^2 < 2$ **36.** $4 \leq x^2$ **37.** $4 < x^2 < 9$

38. $\dfrac{1}{9} < x^2 < \dfrac{1}{4}$ **39.** $(x - 1)^2 < 4$ **40.** $(x + 3)^2 < 2$

41. $x^2 - x < 0$ **42.** $x^2 - x - 2 \geq 0$

Theory and Examples

43. Do not fall into the trap $|-a| = a$. For what real numbers a is this equation true? For what real numbers is it false?

44. Solve the equation $|x - 1| = 1 - x$.

45. A proof of the triangle inequality   Give the reason justifying each of the numbered steps in the following proof of the triangle inequality.

$$|a + b|^2 = (a + b)^2 \tag{1}$$
$$= a^2 + 2ab + b^2$$
$$\leq a^2 + 2|a||b| + b^2 \tag{2}$$
$$= |a|^2 + 2|a||b| + |b|^2 \tag{3}$$
$$= (|a| + |b|)^2$$
$$|a + b| \leq |a| + |b| \tag{4}$$

46. Prove that $|ab| = |a||b|$ for any numbers a and b.

47. If $|x| \leq 3$ and $x > -1/2$, what can you say about x?

48. Graph the inequality $|x| + |y| \leq 1$.

49. Let $f(x) = 2x + 1$ and let $\delta > 0$ be any positive number. Prove that $|x - 1| < \delta$ implies $|f(x) - f(1)| < 2\delta$. Here the notation $f(a)$ means the value of the expression $2x + 1$ when $x = a$. This *function notation* is explained in Section 1.3.

50. Let $f(x) = 2x + 3$ and let $\epsilon > 0$ be any positive number. Prove that $|f(x) - f(0)| < \epsilon$ whenever $|x - 0| < \dfrac{\epsilon}{2}$. Here the notation $f(a)$ means the value of the expression $2x + 3$ when $x = a$. (See Section 1.3.)

51. For any number a, prove that $|-a| = |a|$.

52. Let a be any positive number. Prove that $|x| > a$ if and only if $x > a$ or $x < -a$.

53. a. If b is any nonzero real number, prove that $|1/b| = 1/|b|$.

  b. Prove that $\left|\dfrac{a}{b}\right| = \dfrac{|a|}{|b|}$ for any numbers a and $b \neq 0$.

54. Using mathematical induction (see Appendix 1), prove that $|a^n| = |a|^n$ for any number a and positive integer n.

1.2 Lines, Circles, and Parabolas

This section reviews coordinates, lines, distance, circles, and parabolas in the plane. The notion of increment is also discussed.

Cartesian Coordinates in the Plane

In the previous section we identified the points on the line with real numbers by assigning them coordinates. Points in the plane can be identified with ordered pairs of real numbers. To begin, we draw two perpendicular coordinate lines that intersect at the 0-point of each line. These lines are called **coordinate axes** in the plane. On the horizontal x-axis, numbers are denoted by x and increase to the right. On the vertical y-axis, numbers are denoted by y and increase upward (Figure 1.5). Thus "upward" and "to the right" are positive directions, whereas "downward" and "to the left" are considered as negative. The **origin** O, also labeled 0, of the coordinate system is the point in the plane where x and y are both zero.

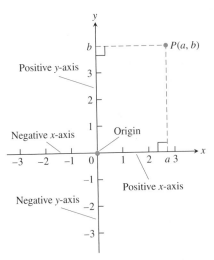

FIGURE 1.5 Cartesian coordinates in the plane are based on two perpendicular axes intersecting at the origin.

If P is any point in the plane, it can be located by exactly one ordered pair of real numbers in the following way. Draw lines through P perpendicular to the two coordinate axes. These lines intersect the axes at points with coordinates a and b (Figure 1.5). The ordered pair (a, b) is assigned to the point P and is called its **coordinate pair**. The first number a is the **x-coordinate** (or **abscissa**) of P; the second number b is the **y-coordinate** (or **ordinate**) of P. The x-coordinate of every point on the y-axis is 0. The y-coordinate of every point on the x-axis is 0. The origin is the point (0, 0).

Starting with an ordered pair (a, b), we can reverse the process and arrive at a corresponding point P in the plane. Often we identify P with the ordered pair and write $P(a, b)$. We sometimes also refer to "the point (a, b)" and it will be clear from the context when (a, b) refers to a point in the plane and not to an open interval on the real line. Several points labeled by their coordinates are shown in Figure 1.6.

This coordinate system is called the **rectangular coordinate system** or **Cartesian coordinate system** (after the sixteenth century French mathematician René Descartes). The coordinate axes of this coordinate or Cartesian plane divide the plane into four regions called **quadrants**, numbered counterclockwise as shown in Figure 1.6.

The **graph** of an equation or inequality in the variables x and y is the set of all points $P(x, y)$ in the plane whose coordinates satisfy the equation or inequality. When we plot data in the coordinate plane or graph formulas whose variables have different units of measure, we do not need to use the same scale on the two axes. If we plot time vs. thrust for a rocket motor, for example, there is no reason to place the mark that shows 1 sec on the time axis the same distance from the origin as the mark that shows 1 lb on the thrust axis.

Usually when we graph functions whose variables do not represent physical measurements and when we draw figures in the coordinate plane to study their geometry and trigonometry, we try to make the scales on the axes identical. A vertical unit of distance then looks the same as a horizontal unit. As on a surveyor's map or a scale drawing, line segments that are supposed to have the same length will look as if they do and angles that are supposed to be congruent will look congruent.

Computer displays and calculator displays are another matter. The vertical and horizontal scales on machine-generated graphs usually differ, and there are corresponding distortions in distances, slopes, and angles. Circles may look like ellipses, rectangles may look like squares, right angles may appear to be acute or obtuse, and so on. We discuss these displays and distortions in greater detail in Section 1.7.

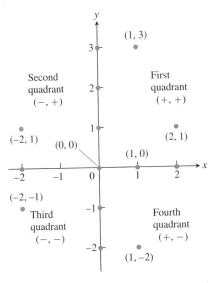

FIGURE 1.6 Points labeled in the xy-coordinate or Cartesian plane. The points on the axes all have coordinate pairs but are usually labeled with single real numbers, (so (1, 0) on the x-axis is labeled as 1). Notice the coordinate sign patterns of the quadrants.

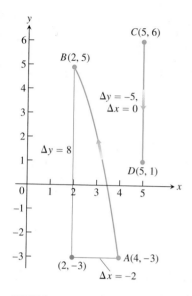

FIGURE 1.7 Coordinate increments may be positive, negative, or zero (Example 1).

HISTORICAL BIOGRAPHY*

René Descartes
(1596–1650)

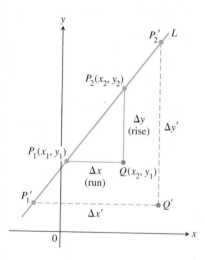

FIGURE 1.8 Triangles P_1QP_2 and $P_1'Q'P_2'$ are similar, so the ratio of their sides has the same value for any two points on the line. This common value is the line's slope.

Increments and Straight Lines

When a particle moves from one point in the plane to another, the net changes in its coordinates are called *increments*. They are calculated by subtracting the coordinates of the starting point from the coordinates of the ending point. If x changes from x_1 to x_2, the **increment** in x is

$$\Delta x = x_2 - x_1.$$

EXAMPLE 1   In going from the point $A(4, -3)$ to the point $B(2, 5)$ the increments in the x- and y-coordinates are

$$\Delta x = 2 - 4 = -2, \qquad \Delta y = 5 - (-3) = 8.$$

From $C(5, 6)$ to $D(5, 1)$ the coordinate increments are

$$\Delta x = 5 - 5 = 0, \qquad \Delta y = 1 - 6 = -5.$$

See Figure 1.7.   ∎

Given two points $P_1(x_1, y_1)$ and $P_2(x_2, y_2)$ in the plane, we call the increments $\Delta x = x_2 - x_1$ and $\Delta y = y_2 - y_1$ the **run** and the **rise**, respectively, between P_1 and P_2. Two such points always determine a unique straight line (usually called simply a line) passing through them both. We call the line P_1P_2.

Any nonvertical line in the plane has the property that the ratio

$$m = \frac{\text{rise}}{\text{run}} = \frac{\Delta y}{\Delta x} = \frac{y_2 - y_1}{x_2 - x_1}$$

has the same value for every choice of the two points $P_1(x_1, y_1)$ and $P_2(x_2, y_2)$ on the line (Figure 1.8). This is because the ratios of corresponding sides for similar triangles are equal.

DEFINITION   Slope
The constant

$$m = \frac{\text{rise}}{\text{run}} = \frac{\Delta y}{\Delta x} = \frac{y_2 - y_1}{x_2 - x_1}$$

is the **slope** of the nonvertical line P_1P_2.

The slope tells us the direction (uphill, downhill) and steepness of a line. A line with positive slope rises uphill to the right; one with negative slope falls downhill to the right (Figure 1.9). The greater the absolute value of the slope, the more rapid the rise or fall. The slope of a vertical line is *undefined*. Since the run Δx is zero for a vertical line, we cannot evaluate the slope ratio m.

The direction and steepness of a line can also be measured with an angle. The **angle of inclination** of a line that crosses the x-axis is the smallest counterclockwise angle from the x-axis to the line (Figure 1.10). The inclination of a horizontal line is 0°. The inclination of a vertical line is 90°. If ϕ (the Greek letter phi) is the inclination of a line, then $0 \le \phi < 180°$.

The relationship between the slope m of a nonvertical line and the line's angle of inclination ϕ is shown in Figure 1.11:

$$m = \tan \phi.$$

Straight lines have relatively simple equations. All points on the *vertical line* through the point a on the x-axis have x-coordinates equal to a. Thus, $x = a$ is an equation for the vertical line. Similarly, $y = b$ is an equation for the *horizontal line* meeting the y-axis at b. (See Figure 1.12.)

We can write an equation for a nonvertical straight line L if we know its slope m and the coordinates of one point $P_1(x_1, y_1)$ on it. If $P(x, y)$ is *any* other point on L, then we can use the two points P_1 and P to compute the slope,

$$m = \frac{y - y_1}{x - x_1}$$

so that

$$y - y_1 = m(x - x_1) \qquad \text{or} \qquad y = y_1 + m(x - x_1).$$

The equation

$$y = y_1 + m(x - x_1)$$

is the **point-slope equation** of the line that passes through the point (x_1, y_1) and has slope m.

EXAMPLE 2   Write an equation for the line through the point $(2, 3)$ with slope $-3/2$.

Solution   We substitute $x_1 = 2, y_1 = 3$, and $m = -3/2$ into the point-slope equation and obtain

$$y = 3 - \frac{3}{2}(x - 2), \qquad \text{or} \qquad y = -\frac{3}{2}x + 6.$$

When $x = 0, y = 6$ so the line intersects the y-axis at $y = 6$.   ∎

EXAMPLE 3   A Line Through Two Points

Write an equation for the line through $(-2, -1)$ and $(3, 4)$.

Solution   The line's slope is

$$m = \frac{-1 - 4}{-2 - 3} = \frac{-5}{-5} = 1.$$

We can use this slope with either of the two given points in the point-slope equation:

With $(x_1, y_1) = (-2, -1)$	**With $(x_1, y_1) = (3, 4)$**
$y = -1 + 1 \cdot (x - (-2))$	$y = 4 + 1 \cdot (x - 3)$
$y = -1 + x + 2$	$y = 4 + x - 3$
$y = x + 1$	$y = x + 1$

Same result

Either way, $y = x + 1$ is an equation for the line (Figure 1.13).   ∎

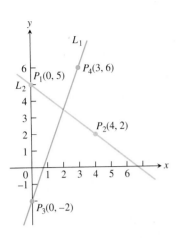

FIGURE 1.9   The slope of L_1 is

$$m = \frac{\Delta y}{\Delta x} = \frac{6 - (-2)}{3 - 0} = \frac{8}{3}.$$

That is, y increases 8 units every time x increases 3 units. The slope of L_2 is

$$m = \frac{\Delta y}{\Delta x} = \frac{2 - 5}{4 - 0} = \frac{-3}{4}.$$

That is, y decreases 3 units every time x increases 4 units.

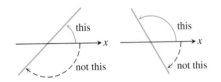

FIGURE 1.10   Angles of inclination are measured counterclockwise from the x-axis.

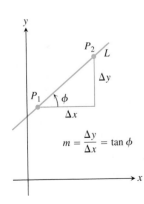

$$m = \frac{\Delta y}{\Delta x} = \tan \phi$$

FIGURE 1.11   The slope of a nonvertical line is the tangent of its angle of inclination.

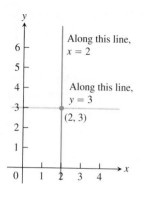

FIGURE 1.12   The standard equations for the vertical and horizontal lines through (2, 3) are $x = 2$ and $y = 3$.

The y-coordinate of the point where a nonvertical line intersects the y-axis is called the **y-intercept** of the line. Similarly, the **x-intercept** of a nonhorizontal line is the x-coordinate of the point where it crosses the x-axis (Figure 1.14). A line with slope m and y-intercept b passes through the point $(0, b)$, so it has equation

$$y = b + m(x - 0), \qquad \text{or, more simply,} \qquad y = mx + b.$$

The equation

$$y = mx + b$$

is called the **slope-intercept equation** of the line with slope m and y-intercept b.

Lines with equations of the form $y = mx$ have y-intercept 0 and so pass through the origin. Equations of lines are called **linear** equations.

The equation

$$Ax + By = C \qquad (A \text{ and } B \text{ not both } 0)$$

is called the **general linear equation** in x and y because its graph always represents a line and every line has an equation in this form (including lines with undefined slope).

EXAMPLE 4   Finding the Slope and y-Intercept

Find the slope and y-intercept of the line $8x + 5y = 20$.

Solution   Solve the equation for y to put it in slope-intercept form:

$$8x + 5y = 20$$
$$5y = -8x + 20$$
$$y = -\frac{8}{5}x + 4.$$

The slope is $m = -8/5$. The y-intercept is $b = 4$.   ∎

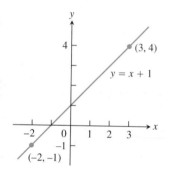

FIGURE 1.13   The line in Example 3.

Parallel and Perpendicular Lines

Lines that are parallel have equal angles of inclination, so they have the same slope (if they are not vertical). Conversely, lines with equal slopes have equal angles of inclination and so are parallel.

If two nonvertical lines L_1 and L_2 are perpendicular, their slopes m_1 and m_2 satisfy $m_1 m_2 = -1$, so each slope is the *negative reciprocal* of the other:

$$m_1 = -\frac{1}{m_2}, \qquad m_2 = -\frac{1}{m_1}.$$

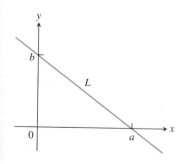

FIGURE 1.14   Line L has x-intercept a and y-intercept b.

To see this, notice by inspecting similar triangles in Figure 1.15 that $m_1 = a/h$, and $m_2 = -h/a$. Hence, $m_1 m_2 = (a/h)(-h/a) = -1$.

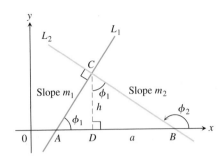

FIGURE 1.15 $\triangle ADC$ is similar to $\triangle CDB$. Hence ϕ_1 is also the upper angle in $\triangle CDB$. From the sides of $\triangle CDB$, we read $\tan \phi_1 = a/h$.

Distance and Circles in the Plane

The distance between points in the plane is calculated with a formula that comes from the Pythagorean theorem (Figure 1.16).

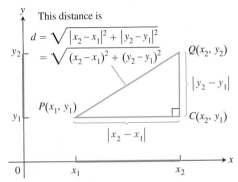

FIGURE 1.16 To calculate the distance between $P(x_1, y_1)$ and $Q(x_2, y_2)$, apply the Pythagorean theorem to triangle PCQ.

Distance Formula for Points in the Plane
The distance between $P(x_1, y_1)$ and $Q(x_2, y_2)$ is
$$d = \sqrt{(\Delta x)^2 + (\Delta y)^2} = \sqrt{(x_2 - x_1)^2 + (y_2 - y_1)^2}.$$

EXAMPLE 5   Calculating Distance

(a) The distance between $P(-1, 2)$ and $Q(3, 4)$ is
$$\sqrt{(3 - (-1))^2 + (4 - 2)^2} = \sqrt{(4)^2 + (2)^2} = \sqrt{20} = \sqrt{4 \cdot 5} = 2\sqrt{5}.$$

(b) The distance from the origin to $P(x, y)$ is
$$\sqrt{(x - 0)^2 + (y - 0)^2} = \sqrt{x^2 + y^2}. \qquad \blacksquare$$

By definition, a **circle** of radius a is the set of all points $P(x, y)$ whose distance from some center $C(h, k)$ equals a (Figure 1.17). From the distance formula, P lies on the circle if and only if
$$\sqrt{(x - h)^2 + (y - k)^2} = a,$$

so

$$(x - h)^2 + (y - k)^2 = a^2. \tag{1}$$

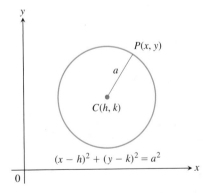

FIGURE 1.17 A circle of radius a in the xy-plane, with center at (h, k).

Equation (1) is the **standard equation** of a circle with center (h, k) and radius a. The circle of radius $a = 1$ and centered at the origin is the **unit circle** with equation
$$x^2 + y^2 = 1.$$

EXAMPLE 6

(a) The standard equation for the circle of radius 2 centered at $(3, 4)$ is

$$(x - 3)^2 + (y - 4)^2 = 2^2 = 4.$$

(b) The circle

$$(x - 1)^2 + (y + 5)^2 = 3$$

has $h = 1$, $k = -5$, and $a = \sqrt{3}$. The center is the point $(h, k) = (1, -5)$ and the radius is $a = \sqrt{3}$. ∎

If an equation for a circle is not in standard form, we can find the circle's center and radius by first converting the equation to standard form. The algebraic technique for doing so is *completing the square* (see Appendix 9).

EXAMPLE 7   Finding a Circle's Center and Radius

Find the center and radius of the circle

$$x^2 + y^2 + 4x - 6y - 3 = 0.$$

Solution   We convert the equation to standard form by completing the squares in x and y:

$x^2 + y^2 + 4x - 6y - 3 = 0$	Start with the given equation.
$(x^2 + 4x \quad) + (y^2 - 6y \quad) = 3$	Gather terms. Move the constant to the right-hand side.
$\left(x^2 + 4x + \left(\dfrac{4}{2}\right)^2\right) + \left(y^2 - 6y + \left(\dfrac{-6}{2}\right)^2\right) =$ $3 + \left(\dfrac{4}{2}\right)^2 + \left(\dfrac{-6}{2}\right)^2$	Add the square of half the coefficient of x to each side of the equation. Do the same for y. The parenthetical expressions on the left-hand side are now perfect squares.
$(x^2 + 4x + 4) + (y^2 - 6y + 9) = 3 + 4 + 9$	
$(x + 2)^2 + (y - 3)^2 = 16$	Write each quadratic as a squared linear expression.

The center is $(-2, 3)$ and the radius is $a = 4$. ∎

The points (x, y) satisfying the inequality

$$(x - h)^2 + (y - k)^2 < a^2$$

make up the **interior** region of the circle with center (h, k) and radius a (Figure 1.18). The circle's **exterior** consists of the points (x, y) satisfying

$$(x - h)^2 + (y - k)^2 > a^2.$$

Exterior: $(x - h)^2 + (y - k)^2 > a^2$

On: $(x - h)^2 + (y - k)^2 = a^2$

(h, k)

a

Interior: $(x - h)^2 + (y - k)^2 < a^2$

FIGURE 1.18   The interior and exterior of the circle $(x - h)^2 + (y - k)^2 = a^2$.

Parabolas

The geometric definition and properties of general parabolas are reviewed in Section 10.1. Here we look at parabolas arising as the graphs of equations of the form $y = ax^2 + bx + c$.

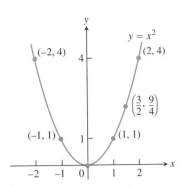

FIGURE 1.19 The parabola $y = x^2$ (Example 8).

EXAMPLE 8   The Parabola $y = x^2$

Consider the equation $y = x^2$. Some points whose coordinates satisfy this equation are $(0, 0), (1, 1), \left(\dfrac{3}{2}, \dfrac{9}{4}\right), (-1, 1), (2, 4)$, and $(-2, 4)$. These points (and all others satisfying the equation) make up a smooth curve called a parabola (Figure 1.19).   ∎

The graph of an equation of the form

$$y = ax^2$$

is a **parabola** whose **axis** (axis of symmetry) is the y-axis. The parabola's **vertex** (point where the parabola and axis cross) lies at the origin. The parabola opens upward if $a > 0$ and downward if $a < 0$. The larger the value of $|a|$, the narrower the parabola (Figure 1.20).

Generally, the graph of $y = ax^2 + bx + c$ is a shifted and scaled version of the parabola $y = x^2$. We discuss shifting and scaling of graphs in more detail in Section 1.5.

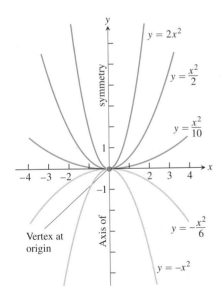

FIGURE 1.20 Besides determining the direction in which the parabola $y = ax^2$ opens, the number a is a scaling factor. The parabola widens as a approaches zero and narrows as $|a|$ becomes large.

The Graph of $y = ax^2 + bx + c$, $a \neq 0$

The graph of the equation $y = ax^2 + bx + c, a \neq 0$, is a parabola. The parabola opens upward if $a > 0$ and downward if $a < 0$. The **axis** is the line

$$x = -\frac{b}{2a}. \tag{2}$$

The **vertex** of the parabola is the point where the axis and parabola intersect. Its x-coordinate is $x = -b/2a$; its y-coordinate is found by substituting $x = -b/2a$ in the parabola's equation.

Notice that if $a = 0$, then we have $y = bx + c$ which is an equation for a line. The axis, given by Equation (2), can be found by completing the square or by using a technique we study in Section 4.1.

EXAMPLE 9   Graphing a Parabola

Graph the equation $y = -\dfrac{1}{2}x^2 - x + 4$.

Solution   Comparing the equation with $y = ax^2 + bx + c$ we see that

$$a = -\frac{1}{2}, \qquad b = -1, \qquad c = 4.$$

Since $a < 0$, the parabola opens downward. From Equation (2) the axis is the vertical line

$$x = -\frac{b}{2a} = -\frac{(-1)}{2(-1/2)} = -1.$$

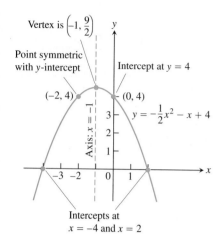

Vertex is $\left(-1, \frac{9}{2}\right)$

Point symmetric with y-intercept

Intercept at $y = 4$

$(-2, 4)$ $(0, 4)$

$y = -\frac{1}{2}x^2 - x + 4$

Axis: $x = -1$

-3 -2 0 1

Intercepts at $x = -4$ and $x = 2$

FIGURE 1.21 The parabola in Example 9.

When $x = -1$, we have

$$y = -\frac{1}{2}(-1)^2 - (-1) + 4 = \frac{9}{2}.$$

The vertex is $(-1, 9/2)$.

The x-intercepts are where $y = 0$:

$$-\frac{1}{2}x^2 - x + 4 = 0$$
$$x^2 + 2x - 8 = 0$$
$$(x - 2)(x + 4) = 0$$
$$x = 2, \qquad x = -4$$

We plot some points, sketch the axis, and use the direction of opening to complete the graph in Figure 1.21. ■

EXERCISES 1.2

Increments and Distance

In Exercises 1–4, a particle moves from A to B in the coordinate plane. Find the increments Δx and Δy in the particle's coordinates. Also find the distance from A to B.

1. $A(-3, 2)$, $B(-1, -2)$ **2.** $A(-1, -2)$, $B(-3, 2)$
3. $A(-3.2, -2)$, $B(-8.1, -2)$ **4.** $A(\sqrt{2}, 4)$, $B(0, 1.5)$

Describe the graphs of the equations in Exercises 5–8.

5. $x^2 + y^2 = 1$ **6.** $x^2 + y^2 = 2$
7. $x^2 + y^2 \le 3$ **8.** $x^2 + y^2 = 0$

Slopes, Lines, and Intercepts

Plot the points in Exercises 9–12 and find the slope (if any) of the line they determine. Also find the common slope (if any) of the lines perpendicular to line AB.

9. $A(-1, 2)$, $B(-2, -1)$ **10.** $A(-2, 1)$, $B(2, -2)$
11. $A(2, 3)$, $B(-1, 3)$ **12.** $A(-2, 0)$, $B(-2, -2)$

In Exercises 13–16, find an equation for (a) the vertical line and (b) the horizontal line through the given point.

13. $(-1, 4/3)$ **14.** $\left(\sqrt{2}, -1.3\right)$
15. $\left(0, -\sqrt{2}\right)$ **16.** $(-\pi, 0)$

In Exercises 17–30, write an equation for each line described.

17. Passes through $(-1, 1)$ with slope -1

18. Passes through $(2, -3)$ with slope $1/2$
19. Passes through $(3, 4)$ and $(-2, 5)$
20. Passes through $(-8, 0)$ and $(-1, 3)$
21. Has slope $-5/4$ and y-intercept 6
22. Has slope $1/2$ and y-intercept -3
23. Passes through $(-12, -9)$ and has slope 0
24. Passes through $(1/3, 4)$, and has no slope
25. Has y-intercept 4 and x-intercept -1
26. Has y-intercept -6 and x-intercept 2
27. Passes through $(5, -1)$ and is parallel to the line $2x + 5y = 15$
28. Passes through $\left(-\sqrt{2}, 2\right)$ parallel to the line $\sqrt{2}x + 5y = \sqrt{3}$
29. Passes through $(4, 10)$ and is perpendicular to the line $6x - 3y = 5$
30. Passes through $(0, 1)$ and is perpendicular to the line $8x - 13y = 13$

In Exercises 31–34, find the line's x- and y-intercepts and use this information to graph the line.

31. $3x + 4y = 12$ **32.** $x + 2y = -4$
33. $\sqrt{2}x - \sqrt{3}y = \sqrt{6}$ **34.** $1.5x - y = -3$
35. Is there anything special about the relationship between the lines $Ax + By = C_1$ and $Bx - Ay = C_2$ $(A \ne 0, B \ne 0)$? Give reasons for your answer.
36. Is there anything special about the relationship between the lines $Ax + By = C_1$ and $Ax + By = C_2$ $(A \ne 0, B \ne 0)$? Give reasons for your answer.

Increments and Motion

37. A particle starts at $A(-2, 3)$ and its coordinates change by increments $\Delta x = 5$, $\Delta y = -6$. Find its new position.

38. A particle starts at $A(6, 0)$ and its coordinates change by increments $\Delta x = -6$, $\Delta y = 0$. Find its new position.

39. The coordinates of a particle change by $\Delta x = 5$ and $\Delta y = 6$ as it moves from $A(x, y)$ to $B(3, -3)$. Find x and y.

40. A particle started at $A(1, 0)$, circled the origin once counterclockwise, and returned to $A(1, 0)$. What were the net changes in its coordinates?

Circles

In Exercises 41–46, find an equation for the circle with the given center $C(h, k)$ and radius a. Then sketch the circle in the xy-plane. Include the circle's center in your sketch. Also, label the circle's x- and y-intercepts, if any, with their coordinate pairs.

41. $C(0, 2)$, $a = 2$ **42.** $C(-3, 0)$, $a = 3$

43. $C(-1, 5)$, $a = \sqrt{10}$ **44.** $C(1, 1)$, $a = \sqrt{2}$

45. $C\left(-\sqrt{3}, -2\right)$, $a = 2$ **46.** $C(3, 1/2)$, $a = 5$

Graph the circles whose equations are given in Exercises 47–52. Label each circle's center and intercepts (if any) with their coordinate pairs.

47. $x^2 + y^2 + 4x - 4y + 4 = 0$

48. $x^2 + y^2 - 8x + 4y + 16 = 0$

49. $x^2 + y^2 - 3y - 4 = 0$

50. $x^2 + y^2 - 4x - (9/4) = 0$

51. $x^2 + y^2 - 4x + 4y = 0$

52. $x^2 + y^2 + 2x = 3$

Parabolas

Graph the parabolas in Exercises 53–60. Label the vertex, axis, and intercepts in each case.

53. $y = x^2 - 2x - 3$ **54.** $y = x^2 + 4x + 3$

55. $y = -x^2 + 4x$ **56.** $y = -x^2 + 4x - 5$

57. $y = -x^2 - 6x - 5$ **58.** $y = 2x^2 - x + 3$

59. $y = \frac{1}{2}x^2 + x + 4$ **60.** $y = -\frac{1}{4}x^2 + 2x + 4$

Inequalities

Describe the regions defined by the inequalities and pairs of inequalities in Exercises 61–68.

61. $x^2 + y^2 > 7$

62. $x^2 + y^2 < 5$

63. $(x - 1)^2 + y^2 \le 4$

64. $x^2 + (y - 2)^2 \ge 4$

65. $x^2 + y^2 > 1$, $x^2 + y^2 < 4$

66. $x^2 + y^2 \le 4$, $(x + 2)^2 + y^2 \le 4$

67. $x^2 + y^2 + 6y < 0$, $y > -3$

68. $x^2 + y^2 - 4x + 2y > 4$, $x > 2$

69. Write an inequality that describes the points that lie inside the circle with center $(-2, 1)$ and radius $\sqrt{6}$.

70. Write an inequality that describes the points that lie outside the circle with center $(-4, 2)$ and radius 4.

71. Write a pair of inequalities that describe the points that lie inside or on the circle with center $(0, 0)$ and radius $\sqrt{2}$, and on or to the right of the vertical line through $(1, 0)$.

72. Write a pair of inequalities that describe the points that lie outside the circle with center $(0, 0)$ and radius 2, and inside the circle that has center $(1, 3)$ and passes through the origin.

Intersecting Lines, Circles, and Parabolas

In Exercises 73–80, graph the two equations and find the points in which the graphs intersect.

73. $y = 2x$, $x^2 + y^2 = 1$

74. $x + y = 1$, $(x - 1)^2 + y^2 = 1$

75. $y - x = 1$, $y = x^2$

76. $x + y = 0$, $y = -(x - 1)^2$

77. $y = -x^2$, $y = 2x^2 - 1$

78. $y = \frac{1}{4}x^2$, $y = (x - 1)^2$

79. $x^2 + y^2 = 1$, $(x - 1)^2 + y^2 = 1$

80. $x^2 + y^2 = 1$, $x^2 + y = 1$

Applications

81. Insulation By measuring slopes in the accompanying figure, estimate the temperature change in degrees per inch for (a) the gypsum wallboard; (b) the fiberglass insulation; (c) the wood sheathing.

The temperature changes in the wall in Exercises 81 and 82.

82. Insulation   According to the figure in Exercise 81, which of the materials is the best insulator? the poorest? Explain.

83. Pressure under water   The pressure p experienced by a diver under water is related to the diver's depth d by an equation of the form $p = kd + 1$ (k a constant). At the surface, the pressure is 1 atmosphere. The pressure at 100 meters is about 10.94 atmospheres. Find the pressure at 50 meters.

84. Reflected light   A ray of light comes in along the line $x + y = 1$ from the second quadrant and reflects off the x-axis (see the accompanying figure). The angle of incidence is equal to the angle of reflection. Write an equation for the line along which the departing light travels.

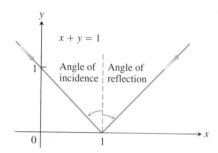

The path of the light ray in Exercise 84. Angles of incidence and reflection are measured from the perpendicular.

85. Fahrenheit vs. Celsius   In the FC-plane, sketch the graph of the equation

$$C = \frac{5}{9}(F - 32)$$

linking Fahrenheit and Celsius temperatures. On the same graph sketch the line $C = F$. Is there a temperature at which a Celsius thermometer gives the same numerical reading as a Fahrenheit thermometer? If so, find it.

86. The Mt. Washington Cog Railway   Civil engineers calculate the slope of roadbed as the ratio of the distance it rises or falls to the distance it runs horizontally. They call this ratio the **grade** of the roadbed, usually written as a percentage. Along the coast, commercial railroad grades are usually less than 2%. In the mountains, they may go as high as 4%. Highway grades are usually less than 5%.

   The steepest part of the Mt. Washington Cog Railway in New Hampshire has an exceptional 37.1% grade. Along this part of the track, the seats in the front of the car are 14 ft above those in the rear. About how far apart are the front and rear rows of seats?

Theory and Examples

87. By calculating the lengths of its sides, show that the triangle with vertices at the points $A(1, 2)$, $B(5, 5)$, and $C(4, -2)$ is isosceles but not equilateral.

88. Show that the triangle with vertices $A(0, 0)$, $B\left(1, \sqrt{3}\right)$, and $C(2, 0)$ is equilateral.

89. Show that the points $A(2, -1)$, $B(1, 3)$, and $C(-3, 2)$ are vertices of a square, and find the fourth vertex.

90. The rectangle shown here has sides parallel to the axes. It is three times as long as it is wide, and its perimeter is 56 units. Find the coordinates of the vertices A, B, and C.

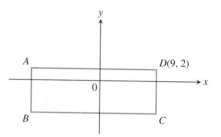

91. Three different parallelograms have vertices at $(-1, 1)$, $(2, 0)$, and $(2, 3)$. Sketch them and find the coordinates of the fourth vertex of each.

92. A $90°$ rotation counterclockwise about the origin takes $(2, 0)$ to $(0, 2)$, and $(0, 3)$ to $(-3, 0)$, as shown in the accompanying figure. Where does it take each of the following points?

   a. $(4, 1)$ **b.** $(-2, -3)$ **c.** $(2, -5)$

   d. $(x, 0)$ **e.** $(0, y)$ **f.** (x, y)

   g. What point is taken to $(10, 3)$?

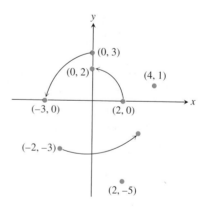

93. For what value of k is the line $2x + ky = 3$ perpendicular to the line $4x + y = 1$? For what value of k are the lines parallel?

94. Find the line that passes through the point $(1, 2)$ and through the point of intersection of the two lines $x + 2y = 3$ and $2x - 3y = -1$.

95. Midpoint of a line segment   Show that the point with coordinates

$$\left(\frac{x_1 + x_2}{2}, \frac{y_1 + y_2}{2}\right)$$

is the midpoint of the line segment joining $P(x_1, y_1)$ to $Q(x_2, y_2)$.

96. The distance from a point to a line We can find the distance from a point $P(x_0, y_0)$ to a line $L: Ax + By = C$ by taking the following steps (there is a somewhat faster method in Section 12.5):

1. Find an equation for the line M through P perpendicular to L.
2. Find the coordinates of the point Q in which M and L intersect.
3. Find the distance from P to Q.

Use these steps to find the distance from P to L in each of the following cases.

a. $P(2, 1)$, $\quad L: y = x + 2$
b. $P(4, 6)$, $\quad L: 4x + 3y = 12$
c. $P(a, b)$, $\quad L: x = -1$
d. $P(x_0, y_0)$, $\quad L: Ax + By = C$

1.3 Functions and Their Graphs

Functions are the key to describing the real world in mathematical terms. This section reviews the ideas of functions, their graphs, and ways of representing them.

Functions; Domain and Range

The temperature at which water boils depends on the elevation above sea level (the boiling point drops as you ascend). The interest paid on a cash investment depends on the length of time the investment is held. The area of a circle depends on the radius of the circle. The distance an object travels at constant speed from an initial location along a straight line path depends on the elapsed time.

In each case, the value of one variable quantity, which we might call y, depends on the value of another variable quantity, which we might call x. Since the value of y is completely determined by the value of x, we say that y is a function of x. Often the value of y is given by a *rule* or formula that says how to calculate it from the variable x. For instance, the equation $A = \pi r^2$ is a rule that calculates the area A of a circle from its radius r.

In calculus we may want to refer to an unspecified function without having any particular formula in mind. A symbolic way to say "y is a function of x" is by writing

$$y = f(x) \qquad (\text{"}y \text{ equals } f \text{ of } x\text{"})$$

In this notation, the symbol f represents the function. The letter x, called the **independent variable**, represents the input value of f, and y, the **dependent variable**, represents the corresponding output **value** of f at x.

> **DEFINITION** **Function**
>
> A **function** from a set D to a set Y is a rule that assigns a *unique* (single) element $f(x) \in Y$ to each element $x \in D$.

The set D of all possible input values is called the **domain** of the function. The set of all values of $f(x)$ as x varies throughout D is called the **range** of the function. The range may not include every element in the set Y.

The domain and range of a function can be any sets of objects, but often in calculus they are sets of real numbers. (In Chapters 13–16 many variables may be involved.)

Think of a function f as a kind of machine that produces an output value $f(x)$ in its range whenever we feed it an input value x from its domain (Figure 1.22). The function

FIGURE 1.22 A diagram showing a function as a kind of machine.

keys on a calculator give an example of a function as a machine. For instance, the $\sqrt{x}$ key on a calculator gives an output value (the square root) whenever you enter a nonnegative number x and press the $\sqrt{x}$ key. The output value appearing in the display is usually a decimal approximation to the square root of x. If you input a number $x < 0$, then the calculator will indicate an error because $x < 0$ is not in the domain of the function and cannot be accepted as an input. The $\sqrt{x}$ key on a calculator is not the same as the exact mathematical function f defined by $f(x) = \sqrt{x}$ because it is limited to decimal outputs and has only finitely many inputs.

A function can also be pictured as an **arrow diagram** (Figure 1.23). Each arrow associates an element of the domain D to a unique or single element in the set Y. In Figure 1.23, the arrows indicate that $f(a)$ is associated with a, $f(x)$ is associated with x, and so on.

The domain of a function may be restricted by context. For example, the domain of the area function given by $A = \pi r^2$ only allows the radius r to be positive. When we define a function $y = f(x)$ with a formula and the domain is not stated explicitly or restricted by context, the domain is assumed to be the largest set of real x-values for which the formula gives real y-values, the so-called **natural domain**. If we want to restrict the domain in some way, we must say so. The domain of $y = x^2$ is the entire set of real numbers. To restrict the function to, say, positive values of x, we would write "$y = x^2, x > 0$."

Changing the domain to which we apply a formula usually changes the range as well. The range of $y = x^2$ is $[0, \infty)$. The range of $y = x^2, x \geq 2$, is the set of all numbers obtained by squaring numbers greater than or equal to 2. In set notation, the range is $\{x^2 \mid x \geq 2\}$ or $\{y \mid y \geq 4\}$ or $[4, \infty)$.

When the range of a function is a set of real numbers, the function is said to be **real-valued**. The domains and ranges of many real-valued functions of a real variable are intervals or combinations of intervals. The intervals may be open, closed, or half open, and may be finite or infinite.

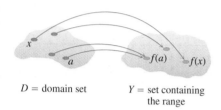

D = domain set Y = set containing the range

FIGURE 1.23   A function from a set D to a set Y assigns a unique element of Y to each element in D.

EXAMPLE 1   Identifying Domain and Range

Verify the domains and ranges of these functions.

Function	Domain (x)	Range (y)
$y = x^2$	$(-\infty, \infty)$	$[0, \infty)$
$y = 1/x$	$(-\infty, 0) \cup (0, \infty)$	$(-\infty, 0) \cup (0, \infty)$
$y = \sqrt{x}$	$[0, \infty)$	$[0, \infty)$
$y = \sqrt{4 - x}$	$(-\infty, 4]$	$[0, \infty)$
$y = \sqrt{1 - x^2}$	$[-1, 1]$	$[0, 1]$

Solution   The formula $y = x^2$ gives a real y-value for any real number x, so the domain is $(-\infty, \infty)$. The range of $y = x^2$ is $[0, \infty)$ because the square of any real number is nonnegative and every nonnegative number y is the square of its own square root, $y = \left(\sqrt{y}\right)^2$ for $y \geq 0$.

The formula $y = 1/x$ gives a real y-value for every x except $x = 0$. *We cannot divide any number by zero.* The range of $y = 1/x$, the set of reciprocals of all nonzero real numbers, is the set of all nonzero real numbers, since $y = 1/(1/y)$.

The formula $y = \sqrt{x}$ gives a real y-value only if $x \geq 0$. The range of $y = \sqrt{x}$ is $[0, \infty)$ because every nonnegative number is some number's square root (namely, it is the square root of its own square).

In $y = \sqrt{4 - x}$, the quantity $4 - x$ cannot be negative. That is, $4 - x \geq 0$, or $x \leq 4$. The formula gives real y-values for all $x \leq 4$. The range of $\sqrt{4 - x}$ is $[0, \infty)$, the set of all nonnegative numbers.

The formula $y = \sqrt{1 - x^2}$ gives a real y-value for every x in the closed interval from -1 to 1. Outside this domain, $1 - x^2$ is negative and its square root is not a real number. The values of $1 - x^2$ vary from 0 to 1 on the given domain, and the square roots of these values do the same. The range of $\sqrt{1 - x^2}$ is $[0, 1]$. ∎

Graphs of Functions

Another way to visualize a function is its graph. If f is a function with domain D, its **graph** consists of the points in the Cartesian plane whose coordinates are the input-output pairs for f. In set notation, the graph is

$$\{(x, f(x)) \mid x \in D\}.$$

The graph of the function $f(x) = x + 2$ is the set of points with coordinates (x, y) for which $y = x + 2$. Its graph is sketched in Figure 1.24.

The graph of a function f is a useful picture of its behavior. If (x, y) is a point on the graph, then $y = f(x)$ is the height of the graph above the point x. The height may be positive or negative, depending on the sign of $f(x)$ (Figure 1.25).

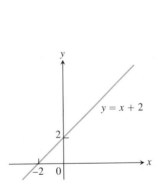

FIGURE 1.24 The graph of $f(x) = x + 2$ is the set of points (x, y) for which y has the value $x + 2$.

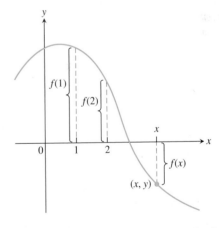

FIGURE 1.25 If (x, y) lies on the graph of f, then the value $y = f(x)$ is the height of the graph above the point x (or below x if $f(x)$ is negative).

x	$y = x^2$
-2	4
-1	1
0	0
1	1
$\dfrac{3}{2}$	$\dfrac{9}{4}$
2	4

EXAMPLE 2   Sketching a Graph

Graph the function $y = x^2$ over the interval $[-2, 2]$.

Solution

1.   Make a table of xy-pairs that satisfy the function rule, in this case the equation $y = x^2$.

2. Plot the points (x, y) whose coordinates appear in the table. Use fractions when they are convenient computationally.

3. Draw a smooth curve through the plotted points. Label the curve with its equation.

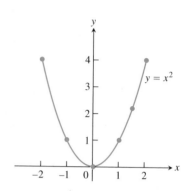

Computers and graphing calculators graph functions in much this way—by stringing together plotted points—and the same question arises.

How do we know that the graph of $y = x^2$ doesn't look like one of these curves?

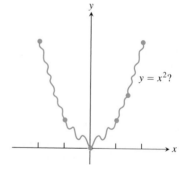

To find out, we could plot more points. But how would we then connect *them*? The basic question still remains: How do we know for sure what the graph looks like between the points we plot? The answer lies in calculus, as we will see in Chapter 4. There we will use the *derivative* to find a curve's shape between plotted points. Meanwhile we will have to settle for plotting points and connecting them as best we can.

EXAMPLE 3   Evaluating a Function from Its Graph

The graph of a fruit fly population p is shown in Figure 1.26.

(a) Find the populations after 20 and 45 days.

(b) What is the (approximate) range of the population function over the time interval $0 \le t \le 50$?

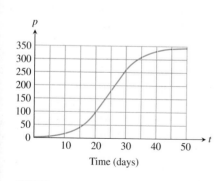

FIGURE 1.26   Graph of a fruit fly population versus time (Example 3).

Solution

(a) We see from Figure 1.26 that the point $(20, 100)$ lies on the graph, so the value of the population p at 20 is $p(20) = 100$. Likewise, $p(45)$ is about 340.

(b) The range of the population function over $0 \le t \le 50$ is approximately $[0, 345]$. We also observe that the population appears to get closer and closer to the value $p = 350$ as time advances.

Representing a Function Numerically

We have seen how a function may be represented algebraically by a formula (the area function) and visually by a graph (Examples 2 and 3). Another way to represent a function is **numerically**, through a table of values. Numerical representations are often used by engineers and applied scientists. From an appropriate table of values, a graph of the function can be obtained using the method illustrated in Example 2, possibly with the aid of a computer. The graph of only the tabled points is called a **scatterplot**.

EXAMPLE 4 A Function Defined by a Table of Values

Musical notes are pressure waves in the air that can be recorded. The data in Table 1.2 give recorded pressure displacement versus time in seconds of a musical note produced by a tuning fork. The table provides a representation of the pressure function over time. If we first make a scatterplot and then connect the data points (t, p) from the table, we obtain the graph shown in Figure 1.27.

TABLE 1.2 Tuning fork data

Time	Pressure	Time	Pressure
0.00091	−0.080	0.00362	0.217
0.00108	0.200	0.00379	0.480
0.00125	0.480	0.00398	0.681
0.00144	0.693	0.00416	0.810
0.00162	0.816	0.00435	0.827
0.00180	0.844	0.00453	0.749
0.00198	0.771	0.00471	0.581
0.00216	0.603	0.00489	0.346
0.00234	0.368	0.00507	0.077
0.00253	0.099	0.00525	−0.164
0.00271	−0.141	0.00543	−0.320
0.00289	−0.309	0.00562	−0.354
0.00307	−0.348	0.00579	−0.248
0.00325	−0.248	0.00598	−0.035
0.00344	−0.041		

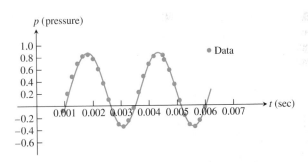

FIGURE 1.27 A smooth curve through the plotted points gives a graph of the pressure function represented by Table 1.2.

The Vertical Line Test

Not every curve you draw is the graph of a function. A function f can have only one value $f(x)$ for each x in its domain, so no *vertical line* can intersect the graph of a function more than once. Thus, a circle cannot be the graph of a function since some vertical lines intersect the circle twice (Figure 1.28a). If a is in the domain of a function f, then the vertical line $x = a$ will intersect the graph of f in the single point $(a, f(a))$.

The circle in Figure 1.28a, however, does contain the graphs of *two* functions of x; the upper semicircle defined by the function $f(x) = \sqrt{1 - x^2}$ and the lower semicircle defined by the function $g(x) = -\sqrt{1 - x^2}$ (Figures 1.28b and 1.28c).

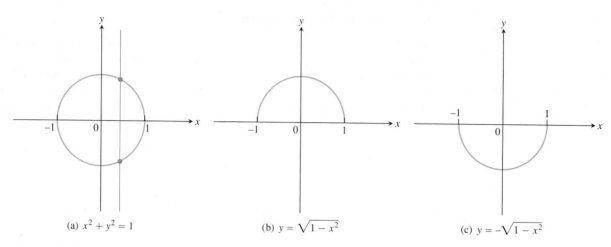

(a) $x^2 + y^2 = 1$ (b) $y = \sqrt{1 - x^2}$ (c) $y = -\sqrt{1 - x^2}$

FIGURE 1.28   (a) The circle is not the graph of a function; it fails the vertical line test.   (b) The upper semicircle is the graph of a function $f(x) = \sqrt{1 - x^2}$.   (c) The lower semicircle is the graph of a function $g(x) = -\sqrt{1 - x^2}$.

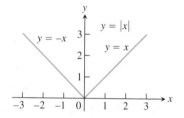

FIGURE 1.29   The absolute value function has domain $(-\infty, \infty)$ and range $[0, \infty)$.

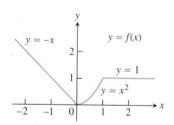

FIGURE 1.30   To graph the function $y = f(x)$ shown here, we apply different formulas to different parts of its domain (Example 5).

Piecewise-Defined Functions

Sometimes a function is described by using different formulas on different parts of its domain. One example is the **absolute value function**

$$|x| = \begin{cases} x, & x \geq 0 \\ -x, & x < 0, \end{cases}$$

whose graph is given in Figure 1.29. Here are some other examples.

EXAMPLE 5   Graphing Piecewise-Defined Functions

The function

$$f(x) = \begin{cases} -x, & x < 0 \\ x^2, & 0 \leq x \leq 1 \\ 1, & x > 1 \end{cases}$$

is defined on the entire real line but has values given by different formulas depending on the position of x. The values of f are given by: $y = -x$ when $x < 0$, $y = x^2$ when $0 \leq x \leq 1$, and $y = 1$ when $x > 1$. The function, however, is *just one function* whose domain is the entire set of real numbers (Figure 1.30).   ∎

EXAMPLE 6   The Greatest Integer Function

The function whose value at any number x is the *greatest integer less than or equal to x* is called the **greatest integer function** or the **integer floor function**. It is denoted $\lfloor x \rfloor$, or, in some books, $[x]$ or $[[x]]$ or int x. Figure 1.31 shows the graph. Observe that

$$\lfloor 2.4 \rfloor = 2, \qquad \lfloor 1.9 \rfloor = 1, \qquad \lfloor 0 \rfloor = 0, \qquad \lfloor -1.2 \rfloor = -2,$$
$$\lfloor 2 \rfloor = 2, \qquad \lfloor 0.2 \rfloor = 0, \qquad \lfloor -0.3 \rfloor = -1, \qquad \lfloor -2 \rfloor = -2.$$
    ∎

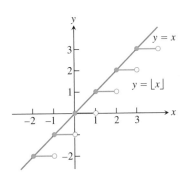

FIGURE 1.31   The graph of the greatest integer function $y = \lfloor x \rfloor$ lies on or below the line $y = x$, so it provides an integer floor for x (Example 6).

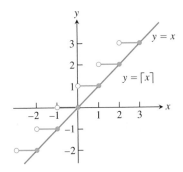

FIGURE 1.32   The graph of the least integer function $y = \lceil x \rceil$ lies on or above the line $y = x$, so it provides an integer ceiling for x (Example 7).

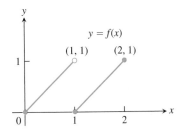

FIGURE 1.33   The segment on the left contains (0, 0) but not (1, 1). The segment on the right contains both of its endpoints (Example 8).

EXAMPLE 7   The Least Integer Function

The function whose value at any number x is the *smallest integer greater than or equal to* x is called the **least integer function** or the **integer ceiling function**. It is denoted $\lceil x \rceil$. Figure 1.32 shows the graph. For positive values of x, this function might represent, for example, the cost of parking x hours in a parking lot which charges \$1 for each hour or part of an hour.

EXAMPLE 8   Writing Formulas for Piecewise-Defined Functions

Write a formula for the function $y = f(x)$ whose graph consists of the two line segments in Figure 1.33.

Solution   We find formulas for the segments from (0, 0) to (1, 1), and from (1, 0) to (2, 1) and piece them together in the manner of Example 5.

Segment from (0, 0) to (1, 1)   The line through (0, 0) and (1, 1) has slope $m = (1 - 0)/(1 - 0) = 1$ and y-intercept $b = 0$. Its slope-intercept equation is $y = x$. The segment from (0, 0) to (1, 1) that includes the point (0, 0) but not the point (1, 1) is the graph of the function $y = x$ restricted to the half-open interval $0 \leq x < 1$, namely,

$$y = x, \qquad 0 \leq x < 1.$$

Segment from (1, 0) to (2, 1)   The line through (1, 0) and (2, 1) has slope $m = (1 - 0)/(2 - 1) = 1$ and passes through the point (1, 0). The corresponding point-slope equation for the line is

$$y = 0 + 1(x - 1), \qquad \text{or} \qquad y = x - 1.$$

The segment from (1, 0) to (2, 1) that includes both endpoints is the graph of $y = x - 1$ restricted to the closed interval $1 \leq x \leq 2$, namely,

$$y = x - 1, \qquad 1 \leq x \leq 2.$$

Piecewise formula   Combining the formulas for the two pieces of the graph, we obtain

$$f(x) = \begin{cases} x, & 0 \leq x < 1 \\ x - 1, & 1 \leq x \leq 2. \end{cases}$$

EXERCISES 1.3

Functions

In Exercises 1–6, find the domain and range of each function.

1. $f(x) = 1 + x^2$

2. $f(x) = 1 - \sqrt{x}$

3. $F(t) = \dfrac{1}{\sqrt{t}}$

4. $F(t) = \dfrac{1}{1 + \sqrt{t}}$

5. $g(z) = \sqrt{4 - z^2}$

6. $g(z) = \dfrac{1}{\sqrt{4 - z^2}}$

In Exercises 7 and 8, which of the graphs are graphs of functions of x, and which are not? Give reasons for your answers.

7. a.

b.

8. a.

b.
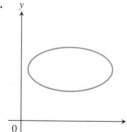

9. Consider the function $y = \sqrt{(1/x) - 1}$.

   a. Can x be negative?

   b. Can $x = 0$?

   c. Can x be greater than 1?

   d. What is the domain of the function?

10. Consider the function $y = \sqrt{2 - \sqrt{x}}$.

   a. Can x be negative?

   b. Can $\sqrt{x}$ be greater than 2?

   c. What is the domain of the function?

Finding Formulas for Functions

11. Express the area and perimeter of an equilateral triangle as a function of the triangle's side length x.

12. Express the side length of a square as a function of the length d of the square's diagonal. Then express the area as a function of the diagonal length.

13. Express the edge length of a cube as a function of the cube's diagonal length d. Then express the surface area and volume of the cube as a function of the diagonal length.

14. A point P in the first quadrant lies on the graph of the function $f(x) = \sqrt{x}$. Express the coordinates of P as functions of the slope of the line joining P to the origin.

Functions and Graphs

Find the domain and graph the functions in Exercises 15–20.

15. $f(x) = 5 - 2x$

16. $f(x) = 1 - 2x - x^2$

17. $g(x) = \sqrt{|x|}$

18. $g(x) = \sqrt{-x}$

19. $F(t) = t/|t|$

20. $G(t) = 1/|t|$

21. Graph the following equations and explain why they are not graphs of functions of x.

   a. $|y| = x$

   b. $y^2 = x^2$

22. Graph the following equations and explain why they are not graphs of functions of x.

   a. $|x| + |y| = 1$

   b. $|x + y| = 1$

Piecewise-Defined Functions

Graph the functions in Exercises 23–26.

23. $f(x) = \begin{cases} x, & 0 \le x \le 1 \\ 2 - x, & 1 < x \le 2 \end{cases}$

24. $g(x) = \begin{cases} 1 - x, & 0 \le x \le 1 \\ 2 - x, & 1 < x \le 2 \end{cases}$

25. $F(x) = \begin{cases} 3 - x, & x \le 1 \\ 2x, & x > 1 \end{cases}$

26. $G(x) = \begin{cases} 1/x, & x < 0 \\ x, & 0 \le x \end{cases}$

27. Find a formula for each function graphed.

a.
b.

28. a.

b.

29. a.

b.

30. a.

b.

T **31. a.** Graph the functions $f(x) = x/2$ and $g(x) = 1 + (4/x)$ together to identify the values of x for which

$$\frac{x}{2} > 1 + \frac{4}{x}.$$

  b. Confirm your findings in part (a) algebraically.

T **32. a.** Graph the functions $f(x) = 3/(x - 1)$ and $g(x) = 2/(x + 1)$ together to identify the values of x for which

$$\frac{3}{x - 1} < \frac{2}{x + 1}.$$

  b. Confirm your findings in part (a) algebraically.

The Greatest and Least Integer Functions

33. For what values of x is

  a. $\lfloor x \rfloor = 0$?   **b.** $\lceil x \rceil = 0$?

34. What real numbers x satisfy the equation $\lfloor x \rfloor = \lceil x \rceil$?

35. Does $\lceil -x \rceil = -\lfloor x \rfloor$ for all real x? Give reasons for your answer.

36. Graph the function

$$f(x) = \begin{cases} \lfloor x \rfloor, & x \geq 0 \\ \lceil x \rceil, & x < 0 \end{cases}$$

Why is $f(x)$ called the *integer part* of x?

Theory and Examples

37. A box with an open top is to be constructed from a rectangular piece of cardboard with dimensions 14 in. by 22 in. by cutting out equal squares of side x at each corner and then folding up the sides as in the figure. Express the volume V of the box as a function of x.

38. The figure shown here shows a rectangle inscribed in an isosceles right triangle whose hypotenuse is 2 units long.

  a. Express the y-coordinate of P in terms of x. (You might start by writing an equation for the line AB.)

  b. Express the area of the rectangle in terms of x.

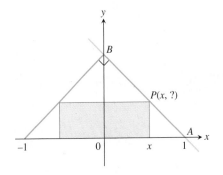

39. A cone problem   Begin with a circular piece of paper with a 4 in. radius as shown in part (a). Cut out a sector with an arc length of x. Join the two edges of the remaining portion to form a cone with radius r and height h, as shown in part (b).

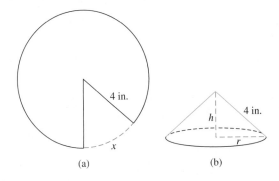

  a. Explain why the circumference of the base of the cone is $8\pi - x$.

  b. Express the radius r as a function of x.

  c. Express the height h as a function of x.

  d. Express the volume V of the cone as a function of x.

40. Industrial costs Dayton Power and Light, Inc., has a power plant on the Miami River where the river is 800 ft wide. To lay a new cable from the plant to a location in the city 2 mi downstream on the opposite side costs $180 per foot across the river and $100 per foot along the land.

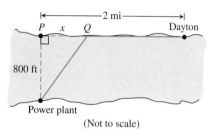

(Not to scale)

a. Suppose that the cable goes from the plant to a point Q on the opposite side that is x ft from the point P directly opposite the plant. Write a function $C(x)$ that gives the cost of laying the cable in terms of the distance x.

b. Generate a table of values to determine if the least expensive location for point Q is less than 2000 ft or greater than 2000 ft from point P.

41. For a curve to be *symmetric about the x-axis*, the point (x, y) must lie on the curve if and only if the point $(x, -y)$ lies on the curve. Explain why a curve that is symmetric about the x-axis is not the graph of a function, unless the function is $y = 0$.

42. A magic trick You may have heard of a magic trick that goes like this: Take any number. Add 5. Double the result. Subtract 6. Divide by 2. Subtract 2. Now tell me your answer, and I'll tell you what you started with. Pick a number and try it.

You can see what is going on if you let x be your original number and follow the steps to make a formula $f(x)$ for the number you end up with.

1.4   Identifying Functions; Mathematical Models

There are a number of important types of functions frequently encountered in calculus. We identify and briefly summarize them here.

Linear Functions   A function of the form $f(x) = mx + b$, for constants m and b, is called a **linear function**. Figure 1.34 shows an array of lines $f(x) = mx$ where $b = 0$, so these lines pass through the origin. Constant functions result when the slope $m = 0$ (Figure 1.35).

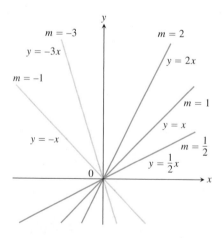

FIGURE 1.34   The collection of lines $y = mx$ has slope m and all lines pass through the origin.

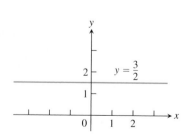

FIGURE 1.35   A constant function has slope $m = 0$.

Power Functions   A function $f(x) = x^a$, where a is a constant, is called a **power function**. There are several important cases to consider.

(a) $a = n$, a positive integer.

The graphs of $f(x) = x^n$, for $n = 1, 2, 3, 4, 5$, are displayed in Figure 1.36. These functions are defined for all real values of x. Notice that as the power n gets larger, the curves tend to flatten toward the x-axis on the interval $(-1, 1)$, and also rise more steeply for $|x| > 1$. Each curve passes through the point $(1, 1)$ and through the origin.

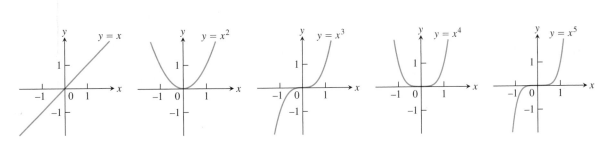

FIGURE 1.36   Graphs of $f(x) = x^n$, $n = 1, 2, 3, 4, 5$ defined for $-\infty < x < \infty$.

(b) $a = -1$ or $a = -2$.

The graphs of the functions $f(x) = x^{-1} = 1/x$ and $g(x) = x^{-2} = 1/x^2$ are shown in Figure 1.37. Both functions are defined for all $x \neq 0$ (you can never divide by zero). The graph of $y = 1/x$ is the hyperbola $xy = 1$ which approaches the coordinate axes far from the origin. The graph of $y = 1/x^2$ also approaches the coordinate axes.

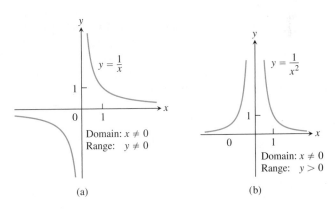

FIGURE 1.37   Graphs of the power functions $f(x) = x^a$ for part
(a) $a = -1$ and for part (b) $a = -2$.

(c) $a = \dfrac{1}{2}, \dfrac{1}{3}, \dfrac{3}{2}$, and $\dfrac{2}{3}$.

The functions $f(x) = x^{1/2} = \sqrt{x}$ and $g(x) = x^{1/3} = \sqrt[3]{x}$ are the **square root** and **cube root** functions, respectively. The domain of the square root function is $[0, \infty)$, but the cube root function is defined for all real x. Their graphs are displayed in Figure 1.38 along with the graphs of $y = x^{3/2}$ and $y = x^{2/3}$. (Recall that $x^{3/2} = (x^{1/2})^3$ and $x^{2/3} = (x^{1/3})^2$.)

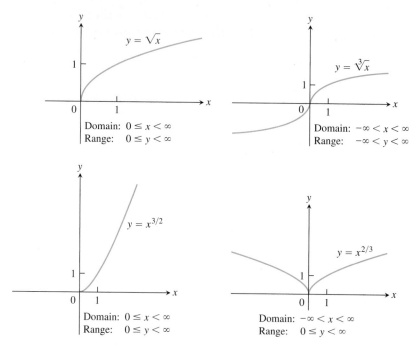

FIGURE 1.38 Graphs of the power functions $f(x) = x^a$ for $a = \dfrac{1}{2}, \dfrac{1}{3}, \dfrac{3}{2},$ and $\dfrac{2}{3}$.

Polynomials A function p is a **polynomial** if

$$p(x) = a_n x^n + a_{n-1} x^{n-1} + \cdots + a_1 x + a_0$$

where n is a nonnegative integer and the numbers $a_0, a_1, a_2, \ldots, a_n$ are real constants (called the **coefficients** of the polynomial). All polynomials have domain $(-\infty, \infty)$. If the leading coefficient $a_n \neq 0$ and $n > 0$, then n is called the **degree** of the polynomial. Linear functions with $m \neq 0$ are polynomials of degree 1. Polynomials of degree 2, usually written as $p(x) = ax^2 + bx + c$, are called **quadratic functions**. Likewise, **cubic functions** are polynomials $p(x) = ax^3 + bx^2 + cx + d$ of degree 3. Figure 1.39 shows the graphs of three polynomials. You will learn how to graph polynomials in Chapter 4.

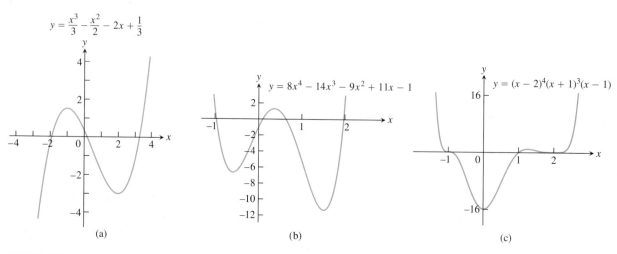

FIGURE 1.39 Graphs of three polynomial functions.

Rational Functions   A **rational function** is a quotient or ratio of two polynomials:

$$f(x) = \frac{p(x)}{q(x)}$$

where p and q are polynomials. The domain of a rational function is the set of all real x for which $q(x) \neq 0$. For example, the function

$$f(x) = \frac{2x^2 - 3}{7x + 4}$$

is a rational function with domain $\{x \mid x \neq -4/7\}$. Its graph is shown in Figure 1.40a with the graphs of two other rational functions in Figures 1.40b and 1.40c.

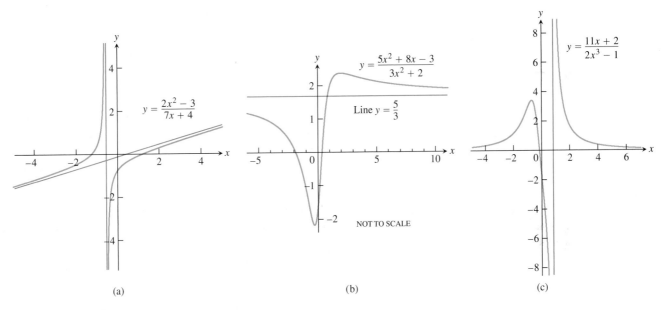

(a)　　　　　　　　　(b)　　　　　　　　　(c)

FIGURE 1.40   Graphs of three rational functions.

Algebraic Functions   Any function constructed from polynomials using algebraic operations (addition, subtraction, multiplication, division, and taking roots) lies within the class of **algebraic functions**. All rational functions are algebraic, but also included are more complicated functions (such as those satisfying an equation like $y^3 - 9xy + x^3 = 0$, studied in Section 3.6). Figure 1.41 displays the graphs of three algebraic functions.

Trigonometric Functions   We review trigonometric functions in Section 1.6. The graphs of the sine and cosine functions are shown in Figure 1.42.

Exponential Functions   Functions of the form $f(x) = a^x$, where the base $a > 0$ is a positive constant and $a \neq 1$, are called **exponential functions**. All exponential functions have domain $(-\infty, \infty)$ and range $(0, \infty)$. So an exponential function never assumes the value 0. The graphs of some exponential functions are shown in Figure 1.43. The calculus of exponential functions is studied in Chapter 7.

Logarithmic Functions   These are the functions $f(x) = \log_a x$, where the base $a \neq 1$ is a positive constant. They are the *inverse functions* of the exponential functions, and the

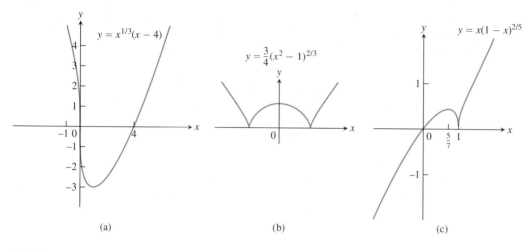

FIGURE 1.41   Graphs of three algebraic functions.

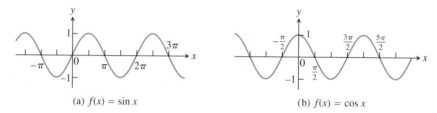

FIGURE 1.42   Graphs of the sine and cosine functions.

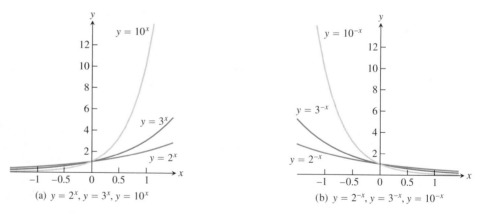

FIGURE 1.43   Graphs of exponential functions.

calculus of these functions is studied in Chapter 7. Figure 1.44 shows the graphs of four logarithmic functions with various bases. In each case the domain is $(0, \infty)$ and the range is $(-\infty, \infty)$.

Transcendental Functions   These are functions that are not algebraic. They include the trigonometric, inverse trigonometric, exponential, and logarithmic functions, and many

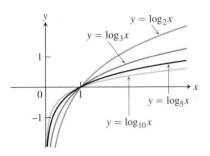

FIGURE 1.44 Graphs of four logarithmic functions.

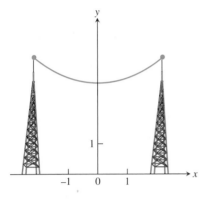

FIGURE 1.45 Graph of a catenary or hanging cable. (The Latin word *catena* means "chain.")

other functions as well (such as the hyperbolic functions studied in Chapter 7). An example of a transcendental function is a **catenary**. Its graph takes the shape of a cable, like a telephone line or TV cable, strung from one support to another and hanging freely under its own weight (Figure 1.45).

EXAMPLE 1 Recognizing Functions

Identify each function given here as one of the types of functions we have discussed. Keep in mind that some functions can fall into more than one category. For example, $f(x) = x^2$ is both a power function and a polynomial of second degree.

(a) $f(x) = 1 + x - \frac{1}{2}x^5$ **(b)** $g(x) = 7^x$ **(c)** $h(z) = z^7$

(d) $y(t) = \sin\left(t - \frac{\pi}{4}\right)$

Solution

(a) $f(x) = 1 + x - \frac{1}{2}x^5$ is a polynomial of degree 5.

(b) $g(x) = 7^x$ is an exponential function with base 7. Notice that the variable x is the exponent.

(c) $h(z) = z^7$ is a power function. (The variable z is the base.)

(d) $y(t) = \sin\left(t - \frac{\pi}{4}\right)$ is a trigonometric function. ∎

Increasing Versus Decreasing Functions

If the graph of a function *climbs* or *rises* as you move from left to right, we say that the function is *increasing*. If the graph *descends* or *falls* as you move from left to right, the function is *decreasing*. We give formal definitions of increasing functions and decreasing functions in Section 4.3. In that section, you will learn how to find the intervals over which a function is increasing and the intervals where it is decreasing. Here are examples from Figures 1.36, 1.37, and 1.38.

Function	Where increasing	Where decreasing
$y = x^2$	$0 \le x < \infty$	$-\infty < x \le 0$
$y = x^3$	$-\infty < x < \infty$	Nowhere
$y = 1/x$	Nowhere	$-\infty < x < 0$ and $0 < x < \infty$
$y = 1/x^2$	$-\infty < x < 0$	$0 < x < \infty$
$y = \sqrt{x}$	$0 \le x < \infty$	Nowhere
$y = x^{2/3}$	$0 \le x < \infty$	$-\infty < x \le 0$

Even Functions and Odd Functions: Symmetry

The graphs of *even* and *odd* functions have characteristic symmetry properties.

> **DEFINITIONS** Even Function, Odd Function
>
> A function $y = f(x)$ is an
>
> $$\textbf{even function of } x \quad \text{if } f(-x) = f(x),$$
> $$\textbf{odd function of } x \quad \text{if } f(-x) = -f(x),$$
>
> for every x in the function's domain.

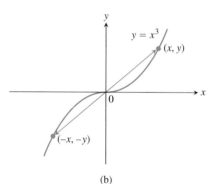

(a)

(b)

FIGURE 1.46 In part (a) the graph of $y = x^2$ (an even function) is symmetric about the y-axis. The graph of $y = x^3$ (an odd function) in part (b) is symmetric about the origin.

The names even and odd come from powers of x. If y is an even power of x, as in $y = x^2$ or $y = x^4$, it is an even function of x (because $(-x)^2 = x^2$ and $(-x)^4 = x^4$). If y is an odd power of x, as in $y = x$ or $y = x^3$, it is an odd function of x (because $(-x)^1 = -x$ and $(-x)^3 = -x^3$).

The graph of an even function is **symmetric about the y-axis**. Since $f(-x) = f(x)$, a point (x, y) lies on the graph if and only if the point $(-x, y)$ lies on the graph (Figure 1.46a). A reflection across the y-axis leaves the graph unchanged.

The graph of an odd function is **symmetric about the origin**. Since $f(-x) = -f(x)$, a point (x, y) lies on the graph if and only if the point $(-x, -y)$ lies on the graph (Figure 1.46b). Equivalently, a graph is symmetric about the origin if a rotation of 180° about the origin leaves the graph unchanged. Notice that the definitions imply both x and $-x$ must be in the domain of f.

EXAMPLE 2 Recognizing Even and Odd Functions

$f(x) = x^2$ Even function: $(-x)^2 = x^2$ for all x; symmetry about y-axis.

$f(x) = x^2 + 1$ Even function: $(-x)^2 + 1 = x^2 + 1$ for all x; symmetry about y-axis (Figure 1.47a).

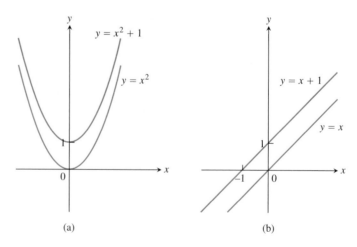

(a)   (b)

FIGURE 1.47 (a) When we add the constant term 1 to the function $y = x^2$, the resulting function $y = x^2 + 1$ is still even and its graph is still symmetric about the y-axis. (b) When we add the constant term 1 to the function $y = x$, the resulting function $y = x + 1$ is no longer odd. The symmetry about the origin is lost (Example 2).

$f(x) = x$ Odd function: $(-x) = -x$ for all x; symmetry about the origin.

$f(x) = x + 1$ Not odd: $f(-x) = -x + 1$, but $-f(x) = -x - 1$. The two are not equal.
Not even: $(-x) + 1 \neq x + 1$ for all $x \neq 0$ (Figure 1.47b).   ∎

Mathematical Models

To help us better understand our world, we often describe a particular phenomenon mathematically (by means of a function or an equation, for instance). Such a **mathematical model** is an idealization of the real-world phenomenon and is seldom a completely accurate representation. Although any model has its limitations, a good one can provide valuable results and conclusions. A model allows us to reach conclusions, as illustrated in Figure 1.48.

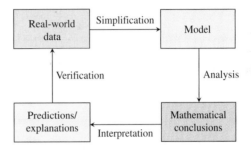

FIGURE 1.48 A flow of the modeling process beginning with an examination of real-world data.

Most models simplify reality and can only *approximate* real-world behavior. One simplifying relationship is *proportionality*.

DEFINITION   Proportionality

Two variables y and x are **proportional** (to one another) if one is always a constant multiple of the other; that is, if

$$y = kx$$

for some nonzero constant k.

The definition means that the graph of y versus x lies along a straight line through the origin. This graphical observation is useful in testing whether a given data collection reasonably assumes a proportionality relationship. If a proportionality is reasonable, a plot of one variable against the other should approximate a straight line through the origin.

EXAMPLE 3   Kepler's Third Law

A famous proportionality, postulated by the German astronomer Johannes Kepler in the early seventeenth century, is his third law. If T is the period in days for a planet to complete one full orbit around the sun, and R is the mean distance of the planet to the sun, then Kepler postulated that T is proportional to R raised to the 3/2 power. That is, for some constant k,

$$T = kR^{3/2}.$$

Let's compare his law to the data in Table 1.3 taken from the *1993 World Almanac*.

TABLE 1.3 Orbital periods and mean distances of planets from the sun

Planet	T Period (days)	R Mean distance (millions of miles)
Mercury	88.0	36
Venus	224.7	67.25
Earth	365.3	93
Mars	687.0	141.75
Jupiter	4,331.8	483.80
Saturn	10,760.0	887.97
Uranus	30,684.0	1,764.50
Neptune	60,188.3	2,791.05
Pluto	90,466.8	3,653.90

The graphing principle in this example may be new to you. To plot T versus $R^{3/2}$ we first calculate the value of $R^{3/2}$ for each value in Table 1.3. For example, $3653.90^{3/2} \approx 220{,}869.1$ and $36^{3/2} = 216$. The horizontal axis represents $R^{3/2}$ (not R values) and we plot the ordered pairs $(R^{3/2}, T)$ in the coordinate system in Figure 1.49. This plot of ordered pairs or scatterplot gives a graph of the period versus the mean distance to the $3/2$ power. We observe that the scatterplot in the figure does lie approximately along a straight line that projects through the origin. By picking two points that lie on that line we can easily estimate the slope, which is the constant of proportionality (in days per miles $\times 10^{-4}$).

$$k = slope = \frac{90{,}466.8 - 88}{220{,}869.1 - 216} \approx 0.410$$

We estimate the model of Kepler's third law to be $T = 0.410R^{3/2}$ (which depends on our choice of units). We need to be careful to point out that this is *not a proof* of Kepler's third

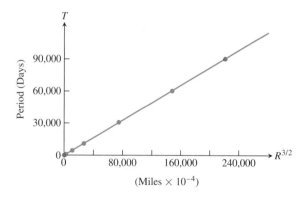

FIGURE 1.49 Graph of Kepler's third law as a proportionality: $T = 0.410R^{3/2}$ (Example 3).

law. We cannot prove or verify a theorem by just looking at some examples. Nevertheless, Figure 1.49 suggests that Kepler's third law is reasonable. ∎

The concept of proportionality is one way to test the reasonableness of a conjectured relationship between two variables, as in Example 3. It can also provide the basis for an **empirical model** which comes entirely from a table of collected data.

EXERCISES 1.4

Recognizing Functions

In Exercises 1–4, identify each function as a constant function, linear function, power function, polynomial (state its degree), rational function, algebraic function, trigonometric function, exponential function, or logarithmic function. Remember that some functions can fall into more than one category.

1. a. $f(x) = 7 - 3x$ **b.** $g(x) = \sqrt[5]{x}$

    c. $h(x) = \dfrac{x^2 - 1}{x^2 + 1}$ **d.** $r(x) = 8^x$

2. a. $F(t) = t^4 - t$ **b.** $G(t) = 5^t$

    c. $H(z) = \sqrt{z^3 + 1}$ **d.** $R(z) = \sqrt[3]{z^7}$

3. a. $y = \dfrac{3 + 2x}{x - 1}$ **b.** $y = x^{5/2} - 2x + 1$

    c. $y = \tan \pi x$ **d.** $y = \log_7 x$

4. a. $y = \log_5 \left(\dfrac{1}{t}\right)$ **b.** $f(z) = \dfrac{z^5}{\sqrt{z} + 1}$

    c. $g(x) = 2^{1/x}$ **d.** $w = 5 \cos\left(\dfrac{t}{2} + \dfrac{\pi}{6}\right)$

In Exercises 5 and 6, match each equation with its graph. Do not use a graphing device, and give reasons for your answer.

5. a. $y = x^4$ **b.** $y = x^7$ **c.** $y = x^{10}$

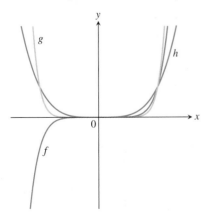

6. a. $y = 5x$ **b.** $y = 5^x$ **c.** $y = x^5$

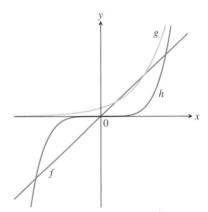

Increasing and Decreasing Functions

Graph the functions in Exercises 7–18. What symmetries, if any, do the graphs have? Specify the intervals over which the function is increasing and the intervals where it is decreasing.

7. $y = -x^3$ **8.** $y = -\dfrac{1}{x^2}$

9. $y = -\dfrac{1}{x}$ **10.** $y = \dfrac{1}{|x|}$

11. $y = \sqrt{|x|}$ **12.** $y = \sqrt{-x}$

13. $y = x^3/8$ **14.** $y = -4\sqrt{x}$

15. $y = -x^{3/2}$ **16.** $y = (-x)^{3/2}$

17. $y = (-x)^{2/3}$ **18.** $y = -x^{2/3}$

Even and Odd Functions

In Exercises 19–30, say whether the function is even, odd, or neither. Give reasons for your answer.

19. $f(x) = 3$ **20.** $f(x) = x^{-5}$

21. $f(x) = x^2 + 1$ **22.** $f(x) = x^2 + x$

23. $g(x) = x^3 + x$ **24.** $g(x) = x^4 + 3x^2 - 1$

25. $g(x) = \dfrac{1}{x^2 - 1}$

26. $g(x) = \dfrac{x}{x^2 - 1}$

27. $h(t) = \dfrac{1}{t - 1}$

28. $h(t) = |t^3|$

29. $h(t) = 2t + 1$

30. $h(t) = 2|t| + 1$

Proportionality

In Exercises 31 and 32, assess whether the given data sets reasonably support the stated proportionality assumption. Graph an appropriate scatterplot for your investigation and, if the proportionality assumption seems reasonable, estimate the constant of proportionality.

31. a. y is proportional to x

y	1	2	3	4	5	6	7	8
x	5.9	12.1	17.9	23.9	29.9	36.2	41.8	48.2

b. y is proportional to $x^{1/2}$

y	3.5	5	6	7	8
x	3	6	9	12	15

32. a. y is proportional to 3^x

y	5	15	45	135	405	1215	3645	10,935
x	0	1	2	3	4	5	6	7

b. y is proportional to $\ln x$

y	2	4.8	5.3	6.5	8.0	10.5	14.4	15.0
x	2.0	5.0	6.0	9.0	14.0	35.0	120.0	150.0

T 33. The accompanying table shows the distance a car travels during the time the driver is reacting before applying the brakes, and the distance the car travels after the brakes are applied. The distances (in feet) depend on the speed of the car (in miles per hour). Test the reasonableness of the following proportionality assumptions and estimate the constants of proportionality.

a. reaction distance is proportional to speed.

b. braking distance is proportional to the square of the speed.

Speed (mph)	20	25	30	35	40	45	50	55	60	65	70	75	80
Reaction distance (ft)	22	28	33	39	44	50	55	61	66	72	77	83	88
Braking distance (ft)	20	28	41	53	72	93	118	149	182	221	266	318	376

34. In October 2002, astronomers discovered a rocky, icy mini-planet tentatively named "Quaoar" circling the sun far beyond Neptune. The new planet is about 4 billion miles from Earth in an outer fringe of the solar system known as the Kuiper Belt. Using Kepler's third law, estimate the time T it takes Quaoar to complete one full orbit around the sun.

T 35. Spring elongation The response of a spring to various loads must be modeled to design a vehicle such as a dump truck, utility vehicle, or a luxury car that responds to road conditions in a desired way. We conducted an experiment to measure the stretch y of a spring in inches as a function of the number x of units of mass placed on the spring.

x (number of units of mass)	0	1	2	3	4	5
y (elongation in inches)	0	0.875	1.721	2.641	3.531	4.391

x (number of units of mass)	6	7	8	9	10
y (elongation in inches)	5.241	6.120	6.992	7.869	8.741

a. Make a scatterplot of the data to test the reasonableness of the hypothesis that stretch y is proportional to the mass x.

b. Estimate the constant of proportionality from your graph obtained in part (a).

c. Predict the elongation of the spring for 13 units of mass.

36. Ponderosa pines In the table, x represents the girth (distance around) of a pine tree measured in inches (in.) at shoulder height; y represents the board feet (bf) of lumber finally obtained.

x (in.)	17	19	20	23	25	28	32	38	39	41
y (bf)	19	25	32	57	71	113	123	252	259	294

Formulate and test the following two models: that usable board feet is proportional to **(a)** the square of the girth and **(b)** the cube of the girth. Does one model provide a better "explanation" than the other?

1.5 Combining Functions; Shifting and Scaling Graphs

In this section we look at the main ways functions are combined or transformed to form new functions.

Sums, Differences, Products, and Quotients

Like numbers, functions can be added, subtracted, multiplied, and divided (except where the denominator is zero) to produce new functions. If f and g are functions, then for every x that belongs to the domains of both f and g (that is, for $x \in D(f) \cap D(g)$), we define functions $f + g$, $f - g$, and fg by the formulas

$$(f + g)(x) = f(x) + g(x).$$
$$(f - g)(x) = f(x) - g(x).$$
$$(fg)(x) = f(x)g(x).$$

Notice that the $+$ sign on the left-hand side of the first equation represents the operation of addition of *functions*, whereas the $+$ on the right-hand side of the equation means addition of the real numbers $f(x)$ and $g(x)$.

At any point of $D(f) \cap D(g)$ at which $g(x) \neq 0$, we can also define the function f/g by the formula

$$\left(\frac{f}{g}\right)(x) = \frac{f(x)}{g(x)} \qquad (\text{where } g(x) \neq 0).$$

Functions can also be multiplied by constants: If c is a real number, then the function cf is defined for all x in the domain of f by

$$(cf)(x) = cf(x).$$

EXAMPLE 1   Combining Functions Algebraically

The functions defined by the formulas

$$f(x) = \sqrt{x} \qquad \text{and} \qquad g(x) = \sqrt{1 - x},$$

have domains $D(f) = [0, \infty)$ and $D(g) = (-\infty, 1]$. The points common to these domains are the points

$$[0, \infty) \cap (-\infty, 1] = [0, 1].$$

The following table summarizes the formulas and domains for the various algebraic combinations of the two functions. We also write $f \cdot g$ for the product function fg.

Function	Formula	Domain
$f + g$	$(f + g)(x) = \sqrt{x} + \sqrt{1 - x}$	$[0, 1] = D(f) \cap D(g)$
$f - g$	$(f - g)(x) = \sqrt{x} - \sqrt{1 - x}$	$[0, 1]$
$g - f$	$(g - f)(x) = \sqrt{1 - x} - \sqrt{x}$	$[0, 1]$
$f \cdot g$	$(f \cdot g)(x) = f(x)g(x) = \sqrt{x(1 - x)}$	$[0, 1]$
f/g	$\dfrac{f}{g}(x) = \dfrac{f(x)}{g(x)} = \sqrt{\dfrac{x}{1 - x}}$	$[0, 1)$ $(x = 1$ excluded$)$
g/f	$\dfrac{g}{f}(x) = \dfrac{g(x)}{f(x)} = \sqrt{\dfrac{1 - x}{x}}$	$(0, 1]$ $(x = 0$ excluded$)$

■

The graph of the function $f + g$ is obtained from the graphs of f and g by adding the corresponding y-coordinates $f(x)$ and $g(x)$ at each point $x \in D(f) \cap D(g)$, as in Figure 1.50. The graphs of $f + g$ and $f \cdot g$ from Example 1 are shown in Figure 1.51.

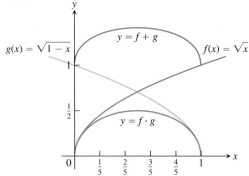

FIGURE 1.50 Graphical addition of two functions.

FIGURE 1.51 The domain of the function $f + g$ is the intersection of the domains of f and g, the interval $[0, 1]$ on the x-axis where these domains overlap. This interval is also the domain of the function $f \cdot g$ (Example 1).

Composite Functions

Composition is another method for combining functions.

DEFINITION   Composition of Functions

If f and g are functions, the **composite** function $f \circ g$ ("f composed with g") is defined by

$$(f \circ g)(x) = f(g(x)).$$

The domain of $f \circ g$ consists of the numbers x in the domain of g for which $g(x)$ lies in the domain of f.

The definition says that $f \circ g$ can be formed when the range of g lies in the domain of f. To find $(f \circ g)(x)$, *first* find $g(x)$ and *second* find $f(g(x))$. Figure 1.52 pictures $f \circ g$ as a machine diagram and Figure 1.53 shows the composite as an arrow diagram.

FIGURE 1.52 Two functions can be composed at x whenever the value of one function at x lies in the domain of the other. The composite is denoted by $f \circ g$.

FIGURE 1.53 Arrow diagram for $f \circ g$.

EXAMPLE 2   Viewing a Function as a Composite

The function $y = \sqrt{1 - x^2}$ can be thought of as first calculating $1 - x^2$ and then taking the square root of the result. The function y is the composite of the function $g(x) = 1 - x^2$ and the function $f(x) = \sqrt{x}$. Notice that $1 - x^2$ cannot be negative. The domain of the composite is $[-1, 1]$. ∎

To evaluate the composite function $g \circ f$ (when defined), we reverse the order, finding $f(x)$ first and then $g(f(x))$. The domain of $g \circ f$ is the set of numbers x in the domain of f such that $f(x)$ lies in the domain of g.

The functions $f \circ g$ and $g \circ f$ are usually quite different.

EXAMPLE 3   Finding Formulas for Composites

If $f(x) = \sqrt{x}$ and $g(x) = x + 1$, find

(a) $(f \circ g)(x)$ **(b)** $(g \circ f)(x)$ **(c)** $(f \circ f)(x)$ **(d)** $(g \circ g)(x)$.

Solution

Composite	Domain
(a) $(f \circ g)(x) = f(g(x)) = \sqrt{g(x)} = \sqrt{x + 1}$	$[-1, \infty)$
(b) $(g \circ f)(x) = g(f(x)) = f(x) + 1 = \sqrt{x} + 1$	$[0, \infty)$
(c) $(f \circ f)(x) = f(f(x)) = \sqrt{f(x)} = \sqrt{\sqrt{x}} = x^{1/4}$	$[0, \infty)$
(d) $(g \circ g)(x) = g(g(x)) = g(x) + 1 = (x + 1) + 1 = x + 2$	$(-\infty, \infty)$

To see why the domain of $f \circ g$ is $[-1, \infty)$, notice that $g(x) = x + 1$ is defined for all real x but belongs to the domain of f only if $x + 1 \geq 0$, that is to say, when $x \geq -1$. ∎

Notice that if $f(x) = x^2$ and $g(x) = \sqrt{x}$, then $(f \circ g)(x) = \left(\sqrt{x}\right)^2 = x$. However, the domain of $f \circ g$ is $[0, \infty)$, not $(-\infty, \infty)$.

Shifting a Graph of a Function

To shift the graph of a function $y = f(x)$ straight up, add a positive constant to the right-hand side of the formula $y = f(x)$.

To shift the graph of a function $y = f(x)$ straight down, add a negative constant to the right-hand side of the formula $y = f(x)$.

To shift the graph of $y = f(x)$ to the left, add a positive constant to x. To shift the graph of $y = f(x)$ to the right, add a negative constant to x.

Shift Formulas

Vertical Shifts

$y = f(x) + k$ Shifts the graph of f *up* k units if $k > 0$

Shifts it *down* $|k|$ units if $k < 0$

Horizontal Shifts

$y = f(x + h)$ Shifts the graph of f *left* h units if $h > 0$

Shifts it *right* $|h|$ units if $h < 0$

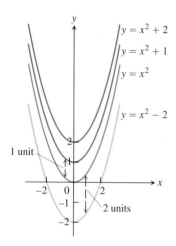

FIGURE 1.54 To shift the graph of $f(x) = x^2$ up (or down), we add positive (or negative) constants to the formula for f (Example 4a and b).

EXAMPLE 4   Shifting a Graph

(a) Adding 1 to the right-hand side of the formula $y = x^2$ to get $y = x^2 + 1$ shifts the graph up 1 unit (Figure 1.54).

(b) Adding -2 to the right-hand side of the formula $y = x^2$ to get $y = x^2 - 2$ shifts the graph down 2 units (Figure 1.54).

(c) Adding 3 to x in $y = x^2$ to get $y = (x + 3)^2$ shifts the graph 3 units to the left (Figure 1.55).

(d) Adding -2 to x in $y = |x|$, and then adding -1 to the result, gives $y = |x - 2| - 1$ and shifts the graph 2 units to the right and 1 unit down (Figure 1.56).

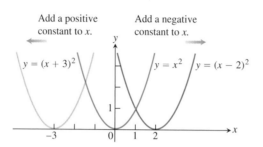

FIGURE 1.55 To shift the graph of $y = x^2$ to the left, we add a positive constant to x. To shift the graph to the right, we add a negative constant to x (Example 4c).

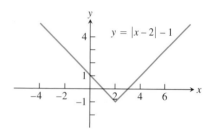

FIGURE 1.56 Shifting the graph of $y = |x|$ 2 units to the right and 1 unit down (Example 4d).

Scaling and Reflecting a Graph of a Function

To scale the graph of a function $y = f(x)$ is to stretch or compress it, vertically or horizontally. This is accomplished by multiplying the function f, or the independent variable x, by an appropriate constant c. Reflections across the coordinate axes are special cases where $c = -1$.

Vertical and Horizontal Scaling and Reflecting Formulas

For $c > 1$,

$y = cf(x)$ Stretches the graph of f vertically by a factor of c.

$y = \dfrac{1}{c} f(x)$ Compresses the graph of f vertically by a factor of c.

$y = f(cx)$ Compresses the graph of f horizontally by a factor of c.

$y = f(x/c)$ Stretches the graph of f horizontally by a factor of c.

For $c = -1$,

$y = -f(x)$ Reflects the graph of f across the x-axis.

$y = f(-x)$ Reflects the graph of f across the y-axis.

EXAMPLE 5 Scaling and Reflecting a Graph

(a) Vertical: Multiplying the right-hand side of $y = \sqrt{x}$ by 3 to get $y = 3\sqrt{x}$ stretches the graph vertically by a factor of 3, whereas multiplying by $1/3$ compresses the graph by a factor of 3 (Figure 1.57).

(b) Horizontal: The graph of $y = \sqrt{3x}$ is a horizontal compression of the graph of $y = \sqrt{x}$ by a factor of 3, and $y = \sqrt{x/3}$ is a horizontal stretching by a factor of 3 (Figure 1.58). Note that $y = \sqrt{3x} = \sqrt{3}\sqrt{x}$ so a horizontal compression *may* correspond to a vertical stretching by a different scaling factor. Likewise, a horizontal stretching may correspond to a vertical compression by a different scaling factor.

(c) Reflection: The graph of $y = -\sqrt{x}$ is a reflection of $y = \sqrt{x}$ across the x-axis, and $y = \sqrt{-x}$ is a reflection across the y-axis (Figure 1.59).

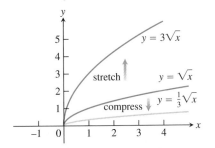

FIGURE 1.57 Vertically stretching and compressing the graph $y = \sqrt{x}$ by a factor of 3 (Example 5a).

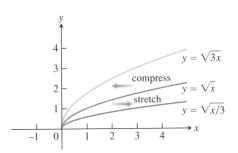

FIGURE 1.58 Horizontally stretching and compressing the graph $y = \sqrt{x}$ by a factor of 3 (Example 5b).

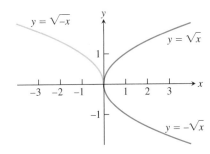

FIGURE 1.59 Reflections of the graph $y = \sqrt{x}$ across the coordinate axes (Example 5c). ∎

EXAMPLE 6 Combining Scalings and Reflections

Given the function $f(x) = x^4 - 4x^3 + 10$ (Figure 1.60a), find formulas to

(a) compress the graph horizontally by a factor of 2 followed by a reflection across the y-axis (Figure 1.60b).

(b) compress the graph vertically by a factor of 2 followed by a reflection across the x-axis (Figure 1.60c).

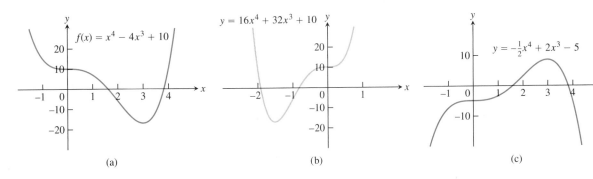

FIGURE 1.60 (a) The original graph of f. (b) The horizontal compression of $y = f(x)$ in part (a) by a factor of 2, followed by a reflection across the y-axis. (c) The vertical compression of $y = f(x)$ in part (a) by a factor of 2, followed by a reflection across the x-axis (Example 6).

Solution

(a) The formula is obtained by substituting $-2x$ for x in the right-hand side of the equation for f

$$y = f(-2x) = (-2x)^4 - 4(-2x)^3 + 10$$
$$= 16x^4 + 32x^3 + 10.$$

(b) The formula is

$$y = -\frac{1}{2}f(x) = -\frac{1}{2}x^4 + 2x^3 - 5.$$ ∎

Ellipses

Substituting cx for x in the standard equation for a circle of radius r centered at the origin gives

$$c^2x^2 + y^2 = r^2. \tag{1}$$

If $0 < c < 1$, the graph of Equation (1) horizontally stretches the circle; if $c > 1$ the circle is compressed horizontally. In either case, the graph of Equation (1) is an ellipse (Figure 1.61). Notice in Figure 1.61 that the y-intercepts of all three graphs are always $-r$ and r. In Figure 1.61b, the line segment joining the points $(\pm r/c, 0)$ is called the **major axis** of the ellipse; the **minor axis** is the line segment joining $(0, \pm r)$. The axes of the ellipse are reversed in Figure 1.61c: the major axis is the line segment joining the points $(0, \pm r)$ and the minor axis is the line segment joining the points $(\pm r/c, 0)$. In both cases, the major axis is the line segment having the longer length.

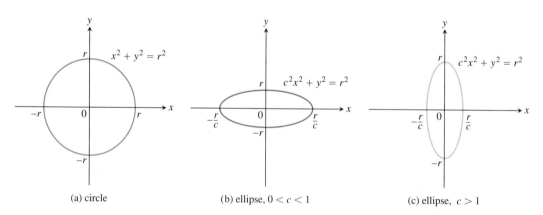

(a) circle   (b) ellipse, $0 < c < 1$ (c) ellipse, $c > 1$

FIGURE 1.61   Horizontal stretchings or compressions of a circle produce graphs of ellipses.

If we divide both sides of Equation (1) by r^2, we obtain

$$\frac{x^2}{a^2} + \frac{y^2}{b^2} = 1. \tag{2}$$

where $a = r/c$ and $b = r$. If $a > b$, the major axis is horizontal; if $a < b$, the major axis is vertical. The **center** of the ellipse given by Equation (2) is the origin (Figure 1.62).

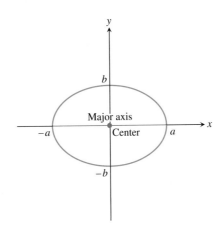

FIGURE 1.62 Graph of the ellipse $\dfrac{x^2}{a^2} + \dfrac{y^2}{b^2} = 1, a > b$, where the major axis is horizontal.

Substituting $x - h$ for x, and $y - k$ for y, in Equation (2) results in

$$\frac{(x - h)^2}{a^2} + \frac{(y - k)^2}{b^2} = 1. \tag{3}$$

Equation (3) is the **standard equation of an ellipse** with center at (h, k). The geometric definition and properties of ellipses are reviewed in Section 10.1.

EXERCISES 1.5

Sums, Differences, Products, and Quotients

In Exercises 1 and 2, find the domains and ranges of $f, g, f + g$, and $f \cdot g$.

1. $f(x) = x, \quad g(x) = \sqrt{x - 1}$

2. $f(x) = \sqrt{x + 1}, \quad g(x) = \sqrt{x - 1}$

In Exercises 3 and 4, find the domains and ranges of $f, g, f/g$, and g/f.

3. $f(x) = 2, \quad g(x) = x^2 + 1$

4. $f(x) = 1, \quad g(x) = 1 + \sqrt{x}$

Composites of Functions

5. If $f(x) = x + 5$ and $g(x) = x^2 - 3$, find the following.

a. $f(g(0))$

b. $g(f(0))$

c. $f(g(x))$

d. $g(f(x))$

e. $f(f(-5))$

f. $g(g(2))$

g. $f(f(x))$

h. $g(g(x))$

6. If $f(x) = x - 1$ and $g(x) = 1/(x + 1)$, find the following.

a. $f(g(1/2))$

b. $g(f(1/2))$

c. $f(g(x))$

d. $g(f(x))$

e. $f(f(2))$

f. $g(g(2))$

g. $f(f(x))$

h. $g(g(x))$

7. If $u(x) = 4x - 5, v(x) = x^2$, and $f(x) = 1/x$, find formulas for the following.

a. $u(v(f(x)))$

b. $u(f(v(x)))$

c. $v(u(f(x)))$

d. $v(f(u(x)))$

e. $f(u(v(x)))$

f. $f(v(u(x)))$

8. If $f(x) = \sqrt{x}, g(x) = x/4$, and $h(x) = 4x - 8$, find formulas for the following.

a. $h(g(f(x)))$

b. $h(f(g(x)))$

c. $g(h(f(x)))$

d. $g(f(h(x)))$

e. $f(g(h(x)))$

f. $f(h(g(x)))$

Let $f(x) = x - 3, \quad g(x) = \sqrt{x}, \quad h(x) = x^3$, and $j(x) = 2x$. Express each of the functions in Exercises 9 and 10 as a composite involving one or more of f, g, h, and j.

9. a. $y = \sqrt{x} - 3$

b. $y = 2\sqrt{x}$

c. $y = x^{1/4}$

d. $y = 4x$

e. $y = \sqrt{(x - 3)^3}$

f. $y = (2x - 6)^3$

10. a. $y = 2x - 3$

b. $y = x^{3/2}$

c. $y = x^9$

d. $y = x - 6$

e. $y = 2\sqrt{x - 3}$

f. $y = \sqrt{x^3 - 3}$

11. Copy and complete the following table.

g(x)	f(x)	(f ∘ g)(x)
a. $x - 7$	$\sqrt{x}$	
b. $x + 2$	$3x$	
c.	$\sqrt{x - 5}$	$\sqrt{x^2 - 5}$
d. $\dfrac{x}{x - 1}$	$\dfrac{x}{x - 1}$	
e.	$1 + \dfrac{1}{x}$	x
f. $\dfrac{1}{x}$		x

12. Copy and complete the following table.

g(x)	f(x)	(f ∘ g)(x)
a. $\dfrac{1}{x - 1}$	$\lvert x \rvert$	?
b. ?	$\dfrac{x - 1}{x}$	$\dfrac{x}{x + 1}$
c. ?	$\sqrt{x}$	$\lvert x \rvert$
d. $\sqrt{x}$	?	$\lvert x \rvert$

In Exercises 13 and 14, **(a)** write a formula for $f \circ g$ and $g \circ f$ and find the **(b)** domain and **(c)** range of each.

13. $f(x) = \sqrt{x + 1}, \quad g(x) = \dfrac{1}{x}$

14. $f(x) = x^2, \quad g(x) = 1 - \sqrt{x}$

Shifting Graphs

15. The accompanying figure shows the graph of $y = -x^2$ shifted to two new positions. Write equations for the new graphs.

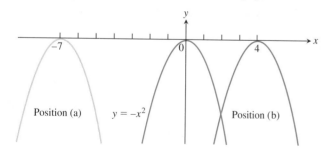

16. The accompanying figure shows the graph of $y = x^2$ shifted to two new positions. Write equations for the new graphs.

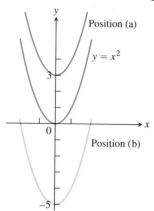

17. Match the equations listed in parts (a)–(d) to the graphs in the accompanying figure.

a. $y = (x - 1)^2 - 4$ **b.** $y = (x - 2)^2 + 2$

c. $y = (x + 2)^2 + 2$ **d.** $y = (x + 3)^2 - 2$

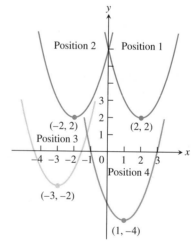

18. The accompanying figure shows the graph of $y = -x^2$ shifted to four new positions. Write an equation for each new graph.

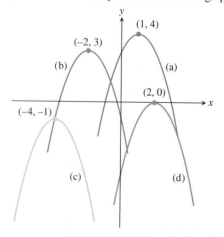

Exercises 19–28 tell how many units and in what directions the graphs of the given equations are to be shifted. Give an equation for the shifted graph. Then sketch the original and shifted graphs together, labeling each graph with its equation.

19. $x^2 + y^2 = 49$ Down 3, left 2

20. $x^2 + y^2 = 25$ Up 3, left 4

21. $y = x^3$ Left 1, down 1

22. $y = x^{2/3}$ Right 1, down 1

23. $y = \sqrt{x}$ Left 0.81

24. $y = -\sqrt{x}$ Right 3

25. $y = 2x - 7$ Up 7

26. $y = \frac{1}{2}(x + 1) + 5$ Down 5, right 1

27. $y = 1/x$ Up 1, right 1

28. $y = 1/x^2$ Left 2, down 1

Graph the functions in Exercises 29–48.

29. $y = \sqrt{x + 4}$

30. $y = \sqrt{9 - x}$

31. $y = |x - 2|$

32. $y = |1 - x| - 1$

33. $y = 1 + \sqrt{x - 1}$

34. $y = 1 - \sqrt{x}$

35. $y = (x + 1)^{2/3}$

36. $y = (x - 8)^{2/3}$

37. $y = 1 - x^{2/3}$

38. $y + 4 = x^{2/3}$

39. $y = \sqrt[3]{x - 1} - 1$

40. $y = (x + 2)^{3/2} + 1$

41. $y = \dfrac{1}{x - 2}$

42. $y = \dfrac{1}{x} - 2$

43. $y = \dfrac{1}{x} + 2$

44. $y = \dfrac{1}{x + 2}$

45. $y = \dfrac{1}{(x - 1)^2}$

46. $y = \dfrac{1}{x^2} - 1$

47. $y = \dfrac{1}{x^2} + 1$

48. $y = \dfrac{1}{(x + 1)^2}$

49. The accompanying figure shows the graph of a function $f(x)$ with domain $[0, 2]$ and range $[0, 1]$. Find the domains and ranges of the following functions, and sketch their graphs.

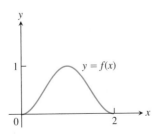

a. $f(x) + 2$

b. $f(x) - 1$

c. $2f(x)$

d. $-f(x)$

e. $f(x + 2)$

f. $f(x - 1)$

g. $f(-x)$

h. $-f(x + 1) + 1$

50. The accompanying figure shows the graph of a function $g(t)$ with domain $[-4, 0]$ and range $[-3, 0]$. Find the domains and ranges of the following functions, and sketch their graphs.

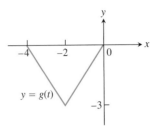

a. $g(-t)$

b. $-g(t)$

c. $g(t) + 3$

d. $1 - g(t)$

e. $g(-t + 2)$

f. $g(t - 2)$

g. $g(1 - t)$

h. $-g(t - 4)$

Vertical and Horizontal Scaling

Exercises 51–60 tell by what factor and direction the graphs of the given functions are to be stretched or compressed. Give an equation for the stretched or compressed graph.

51. $y = x^2 - 1$,   stretched vertically by a factor of 3

52. $y = x^2 - 1$,   compressed horizontally by a factor of 2

53. $y = 1 + \dfrac{1}{x^2}$,   compressed vertically by a factor of 2

54. $y = 1 + \dfrac{1}{x^2}$,   stretched horizontally by a factor of 3

55. $y = \sqrt{x + 1}$,   compressed horizontally by a factor of 4

56. $y = \sqrt{x + 1}$,   stretched vertically by a factor of 3

57. $y = \sqrt{4 - x^2}$,   stretched horizontally by a factor of 2

58. $y = \sqrt{4 - x^2}$,   compressed vertically by a factor of 3

59. $y = 1 - x^3$,   compressed horizontally by a factor of 3

60. $y = 1 - x^3$,   stretched horizontally by a factor of 2

Graphing

In Exercises 61–68, graph each function, not by plotting points, but by starting with the graph of one of the standard functions presented in Figures 1.36–1.38, and applying an appropriate transformation.

61. $y = -\sqrt{2x + 1}$

62. $y = \sqrt{1 - \dfrac{x}{2}}$

63. $y = (x - 1)^3 + 2$

64. $y = (1 - x)^3 + 2$

65. $y = \dfrac{1}{2x} - 1$

66. $y = \dfrac{2}{x^2} + 1$

67. $y = -\sqrt[3]{x}$

68. $y = (-2x)^{2/3}$

69. Graph the function $y = |x^2 - 1|$.

70. Graph the function $y = \sqrt{|x|}$.

Ellipses

Exercises 71–76 give equations of ellipses. Put each equation in standard form and sketch the ellipse.

71. $9x^2 + 25y^2 = 225$ **72.** $16x^2 + 7y^2 = 112$

73. $3x^2 + (y - 2)^2 = 3$ **74.** $(x + 1)^2 + 2y^2 = 4$

75. $3(x - 1)^2 + 2(y + 2)^2 = 6$

76. $6\left(x + \frac{3}{2}\right)^2 + 9\left(y - \frac{1}{2}\right)^2 = 54$

77. Write an equation for the ellipse $(x^2/16) + (y^2/9) = 1$ shifted 4 units to the left and 3 units up. Sketch the ellipse and identify its center and major axis.

78. Write an equation for the ellipse $(x^2/4) + (y^2/25) = 1$ shifted 3 units to the right and 2 units down. Sketch the ellipse and identify its center and major axis.

Even and Odd Functions

79. Assume that f is an even function, g is an odd function, and both f and g are defined on the entire real line $\mathbb{R}$. Which of the following (where defined) are even? odd?

    a. fg **b.** f/g **c.** g/f

    d. $f^2 = ff$ **e.** $g^2 = gg$ **f.** $f \circ g$

    g. $g \circ f$ **h.** $f \circ f$ **i.** $g \circ g$

80. Can a function be both even and odd? Give reasons for your answer.

T 81. (*Continuation of Example* 1.) Graph the functions $f(x) = \sqrt{x}$ and $g(x) = \sqrt{1 - x}$ together with their (a) sum, (b) product, (c) two differences, (d) two quotients.

T 82. Let $f(x) = x - 7$ and $g(x) = x^2$. Graph f and g together with $f \circ g$ and $g \circ f$.

1.6 Trigonometric Functions

This section reviews the basic trigonometric functions. The trigonometric functions are important because they are periodic, or repeating, and therefore model many naturally occurring periodic processes.

Radian Measure

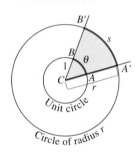

FIGURE 1.63 The radian measure of angle ACB is the length θ of arc AB on the unit circle centered at C. The value of θ can be found from any other circle, however, as the ratio s/r. Thus $s = r\theta$ is the length of arc on a circle of radius r when θ is measured in radians.

In navigation and astronomy, angles are measured in degrees, but in calculus it is best to use units called *radians* because of the way they simplify later calculations.

The **radian measure** of the angle ACB at the center of the unit circle (Figure 1.63) equals the length of the arc that ACB cuts from the unit circle. Figure 1.63 shows that $s = r\theta$ is the **length of arc** cut from a circle of radius r when the subtending angle θ producing the arc is measured in radians.

Since the circumference of the circle is 2π and one complete revolution of a circle is $360°$, the relation between radians and degrees is given by

$$\pi \text{ radians} = 180°.$$

For example, $45°$ in radian measure is

$$45 \cdot \frac{\pi}{180} = \frac{\pi}{4} \text{ rad},$$

and $\pi/6$ radians is

$$\frac{\pi}{6} \cdot \frac{180}{\pi} = 30°.$$

Figure 1.64 shows the angles of two common triangles in both measures.

An angle in the xy-plane is said to be in **standard position** if its vertex lies at the origin and its initial ray lies along the positive x-axis (Figure 1.65). Angles measured counterclockwise from the positive x-axis are assigned positive measures; angles measured clockwise are assigned negative measures.

Conversion Formulas

1 degree $= \dfrac{\pi}{180} \, (\approx 0.02)$ radians

Degrees to radians: multiply by $\dfrac{\pi}{180}$

1 radian $= \dfrac{180}{\pi} \, (\approx 57)$ degrees

Radians to degrees: multiply by $\dfrac{180}{\pi}$

Degrees	Radians
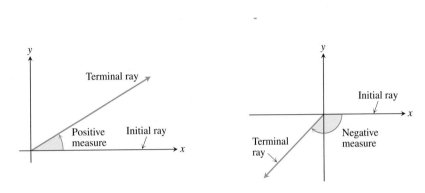	

FIGURE 1.64   The angles of two common triangles, in degrees and radians.

FIGURE 1.65   Angles in standard position in the *xy*-plane.

When angles are used to describe counterclockwise rotations, our measurements can go arbitrarily far beyond 2π radians or 360°. Similarly, angles describing clockwise rotations can have negative measures of all sizes (Figure 1.66).

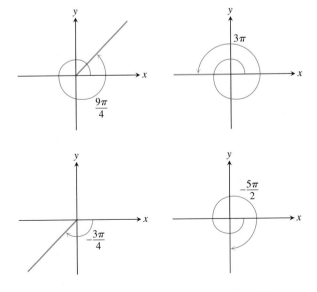

FIGURE 1.66   Nonzero radian measures can be positive or negative and can go beyond 2π.

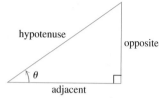

$$\sin \theta = \frac{\text{opp}}{\text{hyp}} \qquad \csc \theta = \frac{\text{hyp}}{\text{opp}}$$

$$\cos \theta = \frac{\text{adj}}{\text{hyp}} \qquad \sec \theta = \frac{\text{hyp}}{\text{adj}}$$

$$\tan \theta = \frac{\text{opp}}{\text{adj}} \qquad \cot \theta = \frac{\text{adj}}{\text{opp}}$$

FIGURE 1.67 Trigonometric ratios of an acute angle.

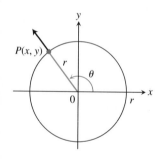

FIGURE 1.68 The trigonometric functions of a general angle θ are defined in terms of x, y, and r.

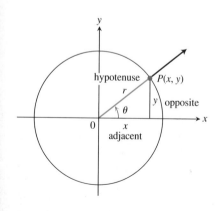

FIGURE 1.69 The new and old definitions agree for acute angles.

> **Angle Convention: Use Radians**
> From now on in this book it is assumed that all angles are measured in radians unless degrees or some other unit is stated explicitly. When we talk about the angle $\pi/3$, we mean $\pi/3$ radians (which is $60°$), not $\pi/3$ degrees. When you do calculus, keep your calculator in radian mode.

The Six Basic Trigonometric Functions

You are probably familiar with defining the trigonometric functions of an acute angle in terms of the sides of a right triangle (Figure 1.67). We extend this definition to obtuse and negative angles by first placing the angle in standard position in a circle of radius r. We then define the trigonometric functions in terms of the coordinates of the point $P(x, y)$ where the angle's terminal ray intersects the circle (Figure 1.68).

$$\textbf{sine:} \quad \sin \theta = \frac{y}{r} \qquad\qquad \textbf{cosecant:} \quad \csc \theta = \frac{r}{y}$$

$$\textbf{cosine:} \quad \cos \theta = \frac{x}{r} \qquad\qquad \textbf{secant:} \quad \sec \theta = \frac{r}{x}$$

$$\textbf{tangent:} \quad \tan \theta = \frac{y}{x} \qquad\qquad \textbf{cotangent:} \quad \cot \theta = \frac{x}{y}$$

These extended definitions agree with the right-triangle definitions when the angle is acute (Figure 1.69).

Notice also the following definitions, whenever the quotients are defined.

$$\tan \theta = \frac{\sin \theta}{\cos \theta} \qquad\qquad \cot \theta = \frac{1}{\tan \theta}$$

$$\sec \theta = \frac{1}{\cos \theta} \qquad\qquad \csc \theta = \frac{1}{\sin \theta}$$

As you can see, $\tan \theta$ and $\sec \theta$ are not defined if $x = 0$. This means they are not defined if θ is $\pm \pi/2, \pm 3\pi/2, \ldots$. Similarly, $\cot \theta$ and $\csc \theta$ are not defined for values of θ for which $y = 0$, namely $\theta = 0, \pm \pi, \pm 2\pi, \ldots$.

The exact values of these trigonometric ratios for some angles can be read from the triangles in Figure 1.64. For instance,

$$\sin \frac{\pi}{4} = \frac{1}{\sqrt{2}} \qquad \sin \frac{\pi}{6} = \frac{1}{2} \qquad \sin \frac{\pi}{3} = \frac{\sqrt{3}}{2}$$

$$\cos \frac{\pi}{4} = \frac{1}{\sqrt{2}} \qquad \cos \frac{\pi}{6} = \frac{\sqrt{3}}{2} \qquad \cos \frac{\pi}{3} = \frac{1}{2}$$

$$\tan \frac{\pi}{4} = 1 \qquad \tan \frac{\pi}{6} = \frac{1}{\sqrt{3}} \qquad \tan \frac{\pi}{3} = \sqrt{3}$$

The CAST rule (Figure 1.70) is useful for remembering when the basic trigonometric functions are positive or negative. For instance, from the triangle in Figure 1.71, we see that

$$\sin \frac{2\pi}{3} = \frac{\sqrt{3}}{2}, \qquad \cos \frac{2\pi}{3} = -\frac{1}{2}, \qquad \tan \frac{2\pi}{3} = -\sqrt{3}.$$

Using a similar method we determined the values of $\sin \theta$, $\cos \theta$, and $\tan \theta$ shown in Table 1.4.

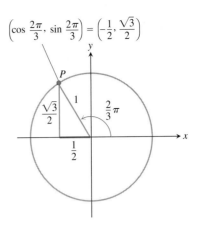

FIGURE 1.70 The CAST rule, remembered by the statement "All Students Take Calculus," tells which trigonometric functions are positive in each quadrant.

FIGURE 1.71 The triangle for calculating the sine and cosine of $2\pi/3$ radians. The side lengths come from the geometry of right triangles.

Most calculators and computers readily provide values of the trigonometric functions for angles given in either radians or degrees.

TABLE 1.4 Values of $\sin \theta$, $\cos \theta$, and $\tan \theta$ for selected values of θ

Degrees	−180	−135	−90	−45	0	30	45	60	90	120	135	150	180	270	360
θ (radians)	$-\pi$	$\dfrac{-3\pi}{4}$	$\dfrac{-\pi}{2}$	$\dfrac{-\pi}{4}$	0	$\dfrac{\pi}{6}$	$\dfrac{\pi}{4}$	$\dfrac{\pi}{3}$	$\dfrac{\pi}{2}$	$\dfrac{2\pi}{3}$	$\dfrac{3\pi}{4}$	$\dfrac{5\pi}{6}$	π	$\dfrac{3\pi}{2}$	2π
$\sin \theta$	0	$\dfrac{-\sqrt{2}}{2}$	−1	$\dfrac{-\sqrt{2}}{2}$	0	$\dfrac{1}{2}$	$\dfrac{\sqrt{2}}{2}$	$\dfrac{\sqrt{3}}{2}$	1	$\dfrac{\sqrt{3}}{2}$	$\dfrac{\sqrt{2}}{2}$	$\dfrac{1}{2}$	0	−1	0
$\cos \theta$	−1	$\dfrac{-\sqrt{2}}{2}$	0	$\dfrac{\sqrt{2}}{2}$	1	$\dfrac{\sqrt{3}}{2}$	$\dfrac{\sqrt{2}}{2}$	$\dfrac{1}{2}$	0	$-\dfrac{1}{2}$	$\dfrac{-\sqrt{2}}{2}$	$\dfrac{-\sqrt{3}}{2}$	−1	0	1
$\tan \theta$	0	1		−1	0	$\dfrac{\sqrt{3}}{3}$	1	$\sqrt{3}$		$-\sqrt{3}$	−1	$\dfrac{-\sqrt{3}}{3}$	0		0

EXAMPLE 1 Finding Trigonometric Function Values

If $\tan \theta = 3/2$ and $0 < \theta < \pi/2$, find the five other trigonometric functions of θ.

Solution From $\tan \theta = 3/2$, we construct the right triangle of height 3 (opposite) and base 2 (adjacent) in Figure 1.72. The Pythagorean theorem gives the length of the hypotenuse, $\sqrt{4 + 9} = \sqrt{13}$. From the triangle we write the values of the other five trigonometric functions:

$$\cos \theta = \frac{2}{\sqrt{13}}, \qquad \sin \theta = \frac{3}{\sqrt{13}}, \qquad \sec \theta = \frac{\sqrt{13}}{2}, \qquad \csc \theta = \frac{\sqrt{13}}{3}, \qquad \cot \theta = \frac{2}{3}$$

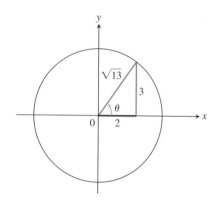

FIGURE 1.72 The triangle for calculating the trigonometric functions in Example 1.

Periodicity and Graphs of the Trigonometric Functions

When an angle of measure θ and an angle of measure $\theta + 2\pi$ are in standard position, their terminal rays coincide. The two angles therefore have the same trigonometric function values:

$$\cos(\theta + 2\pi) = \cos\theta \qquad \sin(\theta + 2\pi) = \sin\theta \qquad \tan(\theta + 2\pi) = \tan\theta$$
$$\sec(\theta + 2\pi) = \sec\theta \qquad \csc(\theta + 2\pi) = \csc\theta \qquad \cot(\theta + 2\pi) = \cot\theta$$

Similarly, $\cos(\theta - 2\pi) = \cos\theta$, $\sin(\theta - 2\pi) = \sin\theta$, and so on. We describe this repeating behavior by saying that the six basic trigonometric functions are *periodic*.

DEFINITION **Periodic Function**

A function $f(x)$ is **periodic** if there is a positive number p such that $f(x + p) = f(x)$ for every value of x. The smallest such value of p is the **period** of f.

When we graph trigonometric functions in the coordinate plane, we usually denote the independent variable by x instead of θ. See Figure 1.73.

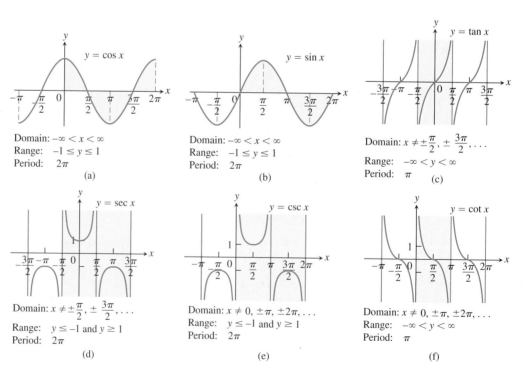

FIGURE 1.73 Graphs of the (a) cosine, (b) sine, (c) tangent, (d) secant, (e) cosecant, and (f) cotangent functions using radian measure. The shading for each trigonometric function indicates its periodicity.

Periods of Trigonometric Functions

Period π:
$\tan(x + \pi) = \tan x$
$\cot(x + \pi) = \cot x$

Period 2π:
$\sin(x + 2\pi) = \sin x$
$\cos(x + 2\pi) = \cos x$
$\sec(x + 2\pi) = \sec x$
$\csc(x + 2\pi) = \csc x$

As we can see in Figure 1.73, the tangent and cotangent functions have period $p = \pi$. The other four functions have period 2π. Periodic functions are important because many behaviors studied in science are approximately periodic. A theorem from advanced calculus says that every periodic function we want to use in mathematical modeling can be written as an algebraic combination of sines and cosines. We show how to do this in Section 11.11.

The symmetries in the graphs in Figure 1.73 reveal that the cosine and secant functions are even and the other four functions are odd:

Even	Odd
$\cos(-x) = \cos x$	$\sin(-x) = -\sin x$
$\sec(-x) = \sec x$	$\tan(-x) = -\tan x$
	$\csc(-x) = -\csc x$
	$\cot(-x) = -\cot x$

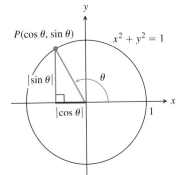

FIGURE 1.74 The reference triangle for a general angle θ.

Identities

The coordinates of any point $P(x, y)$ in the plane can be expressed in terms of the point's distance from the origin and the angle that ray OP makes with the positive x-axis (Figure 1.69). Since $x/r = \cos\theta$ and $y/r = \sin\theta$, we have

$$x = r\cos\theta, \qquad y = r\sin\theta.$$

When $r = 1$ we can apply the Pythagorean theorem to the reference right triangle in Figure 1.74 and obtain the equation

$$\cos^2\theta + \sin^2\theta = 1. \tag{1}$$

This equation, true for all values of θ, is the most frequently used identity in trigonometry. Dividing this identity in turn by $\cos^2\theta$ and $\sin^2\theta$ gives

$$1 + \tan^2\theta = \sec^2\theta.$$
$$1 + \cot^2\theta = \csc^2\theta.$$

The following formulas hold for all angles A and B (Exercises 53 and 54).

Addition Formulas

$$\cos(A + B) = \cos A\cos B - \sin A\sin B$$
$$\sin(A + B) = \sin A\cos B + \cos A\sin B \tag{2}$$

There are similar formulas for $\cos(A - B)$ and $\sin(A - B)$ (Exercises 35 and 36). All the trigonometric identities needed in this book derive from Equations (1) and (2). For example, substituting θ for both A and B in the addition formulas gives

---

Double-Angle Formulas

$$\cos 2\theta = \cos^2 \theta - \sin^2 \theta$$

$$\sin 2\theta = 2 \sin \theta \cos \theta$$

(3)

Additional formulas come from combining the equations

$$\cos^2 \theta + \sin^2 \theta = 1, \qquad \cos^2 \theta - \sin^2 \theta = \cos 2\theta.$$

We add the two equations to get $2 \cos^2 \theta = 1 + \cos 2\theta$ and subtract the second from the first to get $2 \sin^2 \theta = 1 - \cos 2\theta$. This results in the following identities, which are useful in integral calculus.

Half-Angle Formulas

$$\cos^2 \theta = \frac{1 + \cos 2\theta}{2}$$

(4)

$$\sin^2 \theta = \frac{1 - \cos 2\theta}{2}$$

(5)

The Law of Cosines

If a, b, and c are sides of a triangle ABC and if θ is the angle opposite c, then

---

$$c^2 = a^2 + b^2 - 2ab \cos \theta.$$

(6)

This equation is called the **law of cosines**.

We can see why the law holds if we introduce coordinate axes with the origin at C and the positive x-axis along one side of the triangle, as in Figure 1.75. The coordinates of A are $(b, 0)$; the coordinates of B are $(a \cos \theta, a \sin \theta)$. The square of the distance between A and B is therefore

$$c^2 = (a \cos \theta - b)^2 + (a \sin \theta)^2$$

$$= a^2(\underbrace{\cos^2 \theta + \sin^2 \theta}_{1}) + b^2 - 2ab \cos \theta$$

$$= a^2 + b^2 - 2ab \cos \theta.$$

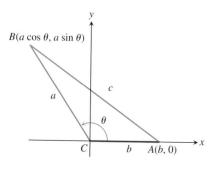

FIGURE 1.75 The square of the distance between A and B gives the law of cosines.

The law of cosines generalizes the Pythagorean theorem. If $\theta = \pi/2$, then $\cos \theta = 0$ and $c^2 = a^2 + b^2$.

Transformations of Trigonometric Graphs

The rules for shifting, stretching, compressing, and reflecting the graph of a function apply to the trigonometric functions. The following diagram will remind you of the controlling parameters.

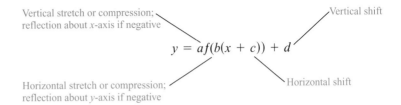

Vertical stretch or compression; reflection about x-axis if negative

Vertical shift

$$y = af(b(x + c)) + d$$

Horizontal stretch or compression; reflection about y-axis if negative

Horizontal shift

EXAMPLE 2   Modeling Temperature in Alaska

The builders of the Trans-Alaska Pipeline used insulated pads to keep the pipeline heat from melting the permanently frozen soil beneath. To design the pads, it was necessary to take into account the variation in air temperature throughout the year. The variation was represented in the calculations by a **general sine function** or **sinusoid** of the form

$$f(x) = A \sin\left[\frac{2\pi}{B}(x - C)\right] + D,$$

where $|A|$ is the *amplitude*, $|B|$ is the *period*, C is the *horizontal shift*, and D is the *vertical shift* (Figure 1.76).

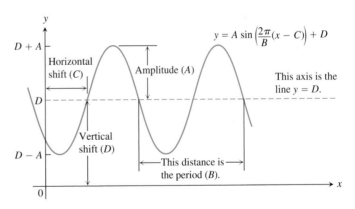

FIGURE 1.76   The general sine curve $y = A \sin\left[(2\pi/B)(x - C)\right] + D$, shown for *A, B, C,* and *D* positive (Example 2).

Figure 1.77 shows how to use such a function to represent temperature data. The data points in the figure are plots of the mean daily air temperatures for Fairbanks, Alaska, based on records of the National Weather Service from 1941 to 1970. The sine function used to fit the data is

$$f(x) = 37 \sin\left[\frac{2\pi}{365}(x - 101)\right] + 25,$$

where f is temperature in degrees Fahrenheit and x is the number of the day counting from the beginning of the year. The fit, obtained by using the sinusoidal regression feature on a calculator or computer, as we discuss in the next section, is very good at capturing the trend of the data.

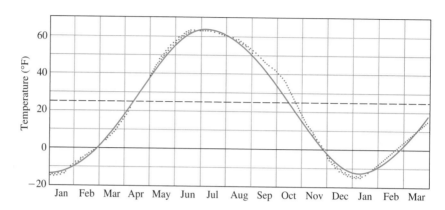

FIGURE 1.77   Normal mean air temperatures for Fairbanks, Alaska, plotted as data points (red). The approximating sine function (blue) is

$$f(x) = 37 \sin [(2\pi/365)(x - 101)] + 25.$$

EXERCISES 1.6

Radians, Degrees, and Circular Arcs

1. On a circle of radius 10 m, how long is an arc that subtends a central angle of (a) $4\pi/5$ radians? (b) $110°$?

2. A central angle in a circle of radius 8 is subtended by an arc of length 10π. Find the angle's radian and degree measures.

3. You want to make an $80°$ angle by marking an arc on the perimeter of a 12-in.-diameter disk and drawing lines from the ends of the arc to the disk's center. To the nearest tenth of an inch, how long should the arc be?

4. If you roll a 1-m-diameter wheel forward 30 cm over level ground, through what angle will the wheel turn? Answer in radians (to the nearest tenth) and degrees (to the nearest degree).

Evaluating Trigonometric Functions

5. Copy and complete the following table of function values. If the function is undefined at a given angle, enter "UND." Do not use a calculator or tables.

θ	$-\pi$	$-2\pi/3$	0	$\pi/2$	$3\pi/4$
$\sin \theta$					
$\cos \theta$					
$\tan \theta$					
$\cot \theta$					
$\sec \theta$					
$\csc \theta$					

6. Copy and complete the following table of function values. If the function is undefined at a given angle, enter "UND." Do not use a calculator or tables.

θ	$-3\pi/2$	$-\pi/3$	$-\pi/6$	$\pi/4$	$5\pi/6$
$\sin \theta$					
$\cos \theta$					
$\tan \theta$					
$\cot \theta$					
$\sec \theta$					
$\csc \theta$					

In Exercises 7–12, one of $\sin x$, $\cos x$, and $\tan x$ is given. Find the other two if x lies in the specified interval.

7. $\sin x = \dfrac{3}{5}, \quad x \in \left[\dfrac{\pi}{2}, \pi\right]$ 8. $\tan x = 2, \quad x \in \left[0, \dfrac{\pi}{2}\right]$

9. $\cos x = \dfrac{1}{3}, \quad x \in \left[-\dfrac{\pi}{2}, 0\right]$ 10. $\cos x = -\dfrac{5}{13}, \quad x \in \left[\dfrac{\pi}{2}, \pi\right]$

11. $\tan x = \dfrac{1}{2}, \quad x \in \left[\pi, \dfrac{3\pi}{2}\right]$ 12. $\sin x = -\dfrac{1}{2}, \quad x \in \left[\pi, \dfrac{3\pi}{2}\right]$

Graphing Trigonometric Functions

Graph the functions in Exercises 13–22. What is the period of each function?

13. $\sin 2x$ 14. $\sin (x/2)$

15. $\cos \pi x$

16. $\cos \dfrac{\pi x}{2}$

17. $-\sin \dfrac{\pi x}{3}$

18. $-\cos 2\pi x$

19. $\cos\left(x - \dfrac{\pi}{2}\right)$

20. $\sin\left(x + \dfrac{\pi}{2}\right)$

21. $\sin\left(x - \dfrac{\pi}{4}\right) + 1$

22. $\cos\left(x + \dfrac{\pi}{4}\right) - 1$

Graph the functions in Exercises 23–26 in the ts-plane (t-axis horizontal, s-axis vertical). What is the period of each function? What symmetries do the graphs have?

23. $s = \cot 2t$

24. $s = -\tan \pi t$

25. $s = \sec\left(\dfrac{\pi t}{2}\right)$

26. $s = \csc\left(\dfrac{t}{2}\right)$

T 27. a. Graph $y = \cos x$ and $y = \sec x$ together for $-3\pi/2 \leq x \leq 3\pi/2$. Comment on the behavior of $\sec x$ in relation to the signs and values of $\cos x$.

b. Graph $y = \sin x$ and $y = \csc x$ together for $-\pi \leq x \leq 2\pi$. Comment on the behavior of $\csc x$ in relation to the signs and values of $\sin x$.

T 28. Graph $y = \tan x$ and $y = \cot x$ together for $-7 \leq x \leq 7$. Comment on the behavior of $\cot x$ in relation to the signs and values of $\tan x$.

29. Graph $y = \sin x$ and $y = \lfloor \sin x \rfloor$ together. What are the domain and range of $\lfloor \sin x \rfloor$?

30. Graph $y = \sin x$ and $y = \lceil \sin x \rceil$ together. What are the domain and range of $\lceil \sin x \rceil$?

Additional Trigonometric Identities

Use the addition formulas to derive the identities in Exercises 31–36.

31. $\cos\left(x - \dfrac{\pi}{2}\right) = \sin x$

32. $\cos\left(x + \dfrac{\pi}{2}\right) = -\sin x$

33. $\sin\left(x + \dfrac{\pi}{2}\right) = \cos x$

34. $\sin\left(x - \dfrac{\pi}{2}\right) = -\cos x$

35. $\cos(A - B) = \cos A \cos B + \sin A \sin B$ (Exercise 53 provides a different derivation.)

36. $\sin(A - B) = \sin A \cos B - \cos A \sin B$

37. What happens if you take $B = A$ in the identity $\cos(A - B) = \cos A \cos B + \sin A \sin B$? Does the result agree with something you already know?

38. What happens if you take $B = 2\pi$ in the addition formulas? Do the results agree with something you already know?

Using the Addition Formulas

In Exercises 39–42, express the given quantity in terms of $\sin x$ and $\cos x$.

39. $\cos(\pi + x)$

40. $\sin(2\pi - x)$

41. $\sin\left(\dfrac{3\pi}{2} - x\right)$

42. $\cos\left(\dfrac{3\pi}{2} + x\right)$

43. Evaluate $\sin \dfrac{7\pi}{12}$ as $\sin\left(\dfrac{\pi}{4} + \dfrac{\pi}{3}\right)$.

44. Evaluate $\cos \dfrac{11\pi}{12}$ as $\cos\left(\dfrac{\pi}{4} + \dfrac{2\pi}{3}\right)$.

45. Evaluate $\cos \dfrac{\pi}{12}$.

46. Evaluate $\sin \dfrac{5\pi}{12}$.

Using the Double-Angle Formulas

Find the function values in Exercises 47–50.

47. $\cos^2 \dfrac{\pi}{8}$

48. $\cos^2 \dfrac{\pi}{12}$

49. $\sin^2 \dfrac{\pi}{12}$

50. $\sin^2 \dfrac{\pi}{8}$

Theory and Examples

51. The tangent sum formula The standard formula for the tangent of the sum of two angles is

$$\tan(A + B) = \frac{\tan A + \tan B}{1 - \tan A \tan B}.$$

Derive the formula.

52. *(Continuation of Exercise 51.)* Derive a formula for $\tan(A - B)$.

53. Apply the law of cosines to the triangle in the accompanying figure to derive the formula for $\cos(A - B)$.

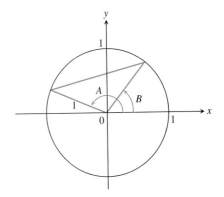

54. a. Apply the formula for $\cos(A - B)$ to the identity $\sin\theta = \cos\left(\dfrac{\pi}{2} - \theta\right)$ to obtain the addition formula for $\sin(A + B)$.

b. Derive the formula for $\cos(A + B)$ by substituting $-B$ for B in the formula for $\cos(A - B)$ from Exercise 35.

55. A triangle has sides $a = 2$ and $b = 3$ and angle $C = 60°$. Find the length of side c.

56. A triangle has sides $a = 2$ and $b = 3$ and angle $C = 40°$. Find the length of side c.

57. The law of sines   The *law of sines* says that if a, b, and c are the sides opposite the angles A, B, and C in a triangle, then

$$\frac{\sin A}{a} = \frac{\sin B}{b} = \frac{\sin C}{c}.$$

Use the accompanying figures and the identity $\sin(\pi - \theta) = \sin \theta$, if required, to derive the law.

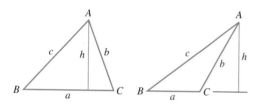

58. A triangle has sides $a = 2$ and $b = 3$ and angle $C = 60°$ (as in Exercise 55). Find the sine of angle B using the law of sines.

59. A triangle has side $c = 2$ and angles $A = \pi/4$ and $B = \pi/3$. Find the length a of the side opposite A.

T **60. The approximation $\sin x \approx x$**   It is often useful to know that, when x is measured in radians, $\sin x \approx x$ for numerically small values of x. In Section 3.8, we will see why the approximation holds. The approximation error is less than 1 in 5000 if $|x| < 0.1$.

  a. With your grapher in radian mode, graph $y = \sin x$ and $y = x$ together in a viewing window about the origin. What do you see happening as x nears the origin?

  b. With your grapher in degree mode, graph $y = \sin x$ and $y = x$ together about the origin again. How is the picture different from the one obtained with radian mode?

  c. A quick radian mode check   Is your calculator in radian mode? Evaluate $\sin x$ at a value of x near the origin, say $x = 0.1$. If $\sin x \approx x$, the calculator is in radian mode; if not, it isn't. Try it.

General Sine Curves

For

$$f(x) = A \sin\left(\frac{2\pi}{B}(x - C)\right) + D,$$

identify A, B, C, and D for the sine functions in Exercises 61–64 and sketch their graphs (see Figure 1.76).

61. $y = 2 \sin(x + \pi) - 1$

62. $y = \dfrac{1}{2} \sin(\pi x - \pi) + \dfrac{1}{2}$

63. $y = -\dfrac{2}{\pi} \sin\left(\dfrac{\pi}{2} t\right) + \dfrac{1}{\pi}$

64. $y = \dfrac{L}{2\pi} \sin \dfrac{2\pi t}{L}$, $L > 0$

65. Temperature in Fairbanks, Alaska   Find the **(a)** amplitude, **(b)** period, **(c)** horizontal shift, and **(d)** vertical shift of the general sine function

$$f(x) = 37 \sin\left(\frac{2\pi}{365}(x - 101)\right) + 25.$$

66. Temperature in Fairbanks, Alaska   Use the equation in Exercise 65 to approximate the answers to the following questions about the temperature in Fairbanks, Alaska, shown in Figure 1.77. Assume that the year has 365 days.

  a. What are the highest and lowest mean daily temperatures shown?

  b. What is the average of the highest and lowest mean daily temperatures shown? Why is this average the vertical shift of the function?

COMPUTER EXPLORATIONS

In Exercises 67–70, you will explore graphically the general sine function

$$f(x) = A \sin\left(\frac{2\pi}{B}(x - C)\right) + D$$

as you change the values of the constants A, B, C, and D. Use a CAS or computer grapher to perform the steps in the exercises.

67. The period B   Set the constants $A = 3$, $C = D = 0$.

  a. Plot $f(x)$ for the values $B = 1, 3, 2\pi, 5\pi$ over the interval $-4\pi \le x \le 4\pi$. Describe what happens to the graph of the general sine function as the period increases.

  b. What happens to the graph for negative values of B? Try it with $B = -3$ and $B = -2\pi$.

68. The horizontal shift C   Set the constants $A = 3$, $B = 6$, $D = 0$.

  a. Plot $f(x)$ for the values $C = 0, 1$, and 2 over the interval $-4\pi \le x \le 4\pi$. Describe what happens to the graph of the general sine function as C increases through positive values.

  b. What happens to the graph for negative values of C?

  c. What smallest positive value should be assigned to C so the graph exhibits no horizontal shift? Confirm your answer with a plot.

69. The vertical shift D   Set the constants $A = 3$, $B = 6$, $C = 0$.

  a. Plot $f(x)$ for the values $D = 0, 1$, and 3 over the interval $-4\pi \le x \le 4\pi$. Describe what happens to the graph of the general sine function as D increases through positive values.

  b. What happens to the graph for negative values of D?

70. The amplitude A   Set the constants $B = 6$, $C = D = 0$.

  a. Describe what happens to the graph of the general sine function as A increases through positive values. Confirm your answer by plotting $f(x)$ for the values $A = 1, 5$, and 9.

  b. What happens to the graph for negative values of A?

1.7 Graphing with Calculators and Computers

A graphing calculator or a computer with graphing software enables us to graph very complicated functions with high precision. Many of these functions could not otherwise be easily graphed. However, care must be taken when using such devices for graphing purposes and we address those issues in this section. In Chapter 4 we will see how calculus helps us to be certain we are viewing accurately all the important features of a function's graph.

Graphing Windows

When using a graphing calculator or computer as a graphing tool, a portion of the graph is displayed in a rectangular **display** or **viewing window**. Often the default window gives an incomplete or misleading picture of the graph. We use the term *square window* when the units or scales on both axis are the same. This term does not mean that the display window itself is square in shape (usually it is rectangular), but means instead that the x-unit is the same as the y-unit.

When a graph is displayed in the default window, the x-unit may differ from the y-unit of scaling in order to fit the graph in the display. The viewing window in the display is set by specifying the minimum and maximum values of the independent and dependent variables. That is, an interval $a \leq x \leq b$ is specified as well as a range $c \leq y \leq d$. The machine selects a certain number of equally spaced values of x between a and b. Starting with a first value for x, if it lies within the domain of the function f being graphed, and if f(x) lies inside the range [c, d], then the point (x, f(x)) is plotted. If x lies outside the domain of f, or f(x) lies outside the specified range [c, d], the machine just moves on to the next x-value since it cannot plot (x, f(x)) in that case. The machine plots a large number of points (x, f(x)) in this way and approximates the curve representing the graph by drawing a short line segment between each plotted point and its next neighboring point, as we might do by hand. Usually, adjacent points are so close together that the graphical representation has the appearance of a smooth curve. Things can go wrong with this procedure and we illustrate the most common problems through the following examples.

EXAMPLE 1 Choosing a Viewing Window

Graph the function $f(x) = x^3 - 7x^2 + 28$ in each of the following display or viewing windows:

(a) $[-10, 10]$ by $[-10, 10]$ **(b)** $[-4, 4]$ by $[-50, 10]$ **(c)** $[-4, 10]$ by $[-60, 60]$

Solution

(a) We select $a = -10$, $b = 10$, $c = -10$, and $d = 10$ to specify the interval of x-values and the range of y-values for the window. The resulting graph is shown in Figure 1.78a. It appears that the window is cutting off the bottom part of the graph and that the interval of x-values is too large. Let's try the next window.

(b) Now we see more features of the graph (Figure 1.78b), but the top is missing and we need to view more to the right of $x = 4$ as well. The next window should help.

(c) Figure 1.78c shows the graph in this new viewing window. Observe that we get a more complete picture of the graph in this window and it is a reasonable graph of a third-degree polynomial. Choosing a good viewing window is a trial-and-error process which may require some troubleshooting as well.

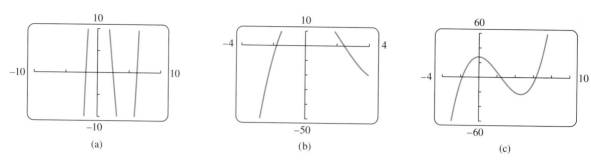

FIGURE 1.78 The graph of $f(x) = x^3 - 7x^2 + 28$ in different viewing windows (Example 1).

EXAMPLE 2   Square Windows

When a graph is displayed, the x-unit may differ from the y-unit, as in the graphs shown in Figures 1.78b and 1.78c. The result is distortion in the picture, which may be misleading. The display window can be made square by compressing or stretching the units on one axis to match the scale on the other, giving the true graph. Many systems have built-in functions to make the window "square." If yours does not, you will have to do some calculations and set the window size manually to get a square window, or bring to your viewing some foreknowledge of the true picture.

Figure 1.79a shows the graphs of the perpendicular lines $y = x$ and $y = -x + 3\sqrt{2}$, together with the semicircle $y = \sqrt{9 - x^2}$, in a nonsquare $[-6, 6]$ by $[-6, 8]$ display window. Notice the distortion. The lines do not appear to be perpendicular, and the semicircle appears to be elliptical in shape.

Figure 1.79b shows the graphs of the same functions in a square window in which the x-units are scaled to be the same as the y-units. Notice that the $[-6, 6]$ by $[-4, 4]$ viewing window has the same x-axis in both figures, but the scaling on the x-axis has been compressed in Figure 1.79b to make the window square. Figure 1.79c gives an enlarged view with a square $[-3, 3]$ by $[0, 4]$ window.

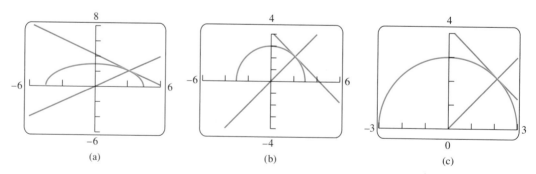

FIGURE 1.79 Graphs of the perpendicular lines $y = x$ and $y = -x + 3\sqrt{2}$, and the semicircle $y = \sqrt{9 - x^2}$, in (a) a nonsquare window, and (b) and (c) square windows (Example 2).

If the denominator of a rational function is zero at some x-value within the viewing window, a calculator or graphing computer software may produce a steep near-vertical line segment from the top to the bottom of the window. Here is an example.

EXAMPLE 3   Graph of a Rational Function

Graph the function $y = \dfrac{1}{2 - x}$.

Solution   Figure 1.80a shows the graph in the $[-10, 10]$ by $[-10, 10]$ default square window with our computer graphing software. Notice the near-vertical line segment at $x = 2$. It is not truly a part of the graph and $x = 2$ does not belong to the domain of the function. By trial and error we can eliminate the line by changing the viewing window to the smaller $[-6, 6]$ by $[-4, 4]$ view, revealing a better graph (Figure 1.80b).

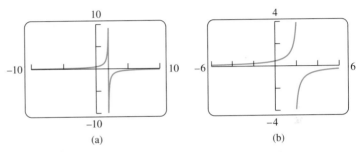

FIGURE 1.80   Graphs of the function $y = \dfrac{1}{2 - x}$ (Example 3).

Sometimes the graph of a trigonometric function oscillates very rapidly. When a calculator or computer software plots the points of the graph and connects them, many of the maximum and minimum points are actually missed. The resulting graph is then very misleading.

EXAMPLE 4   Graph of a Rapidly Oscillating Function

Graph the function $f(x) = \sin 100x$.

Solution   Figure 1.81a shows the graph of f in the viewing window $[-12, 12]$ by $[-1, 1]$. We see that the graph looks very strange because the sine curve should oscillate periodically between -1 and 1. This behavior is not exhibited in Figure 1.81a. We might experiment with a smaller viewing window, say $[-6, 6]$ by $[-1, 1]$, but the graph is not better (Figure 1.81b). The difficulty is that the period of the trigonometric function $y = \sin 100x$ is very small $(2\pi/100 \approx 0.063)$. If we choose the much smaller viewing window $[-0.1, 0.1]$ by $[-1, 1]$ we get the graph shown in Figure 1.81c. This graph reveals the expected oscillations of a sine curve.

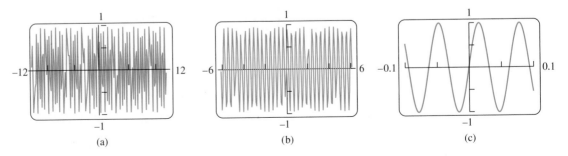

FIGURE 1.81   Graphs of the function $y = \sin 100x$ in three viewing windows. Because the period is $2\pi/100 \approx 0.063$, the smaller window in (c) best displays the true aspects of this rapidly oscillating function (Example 4).

EXAMPLE 5 Another Rapidly Oscillating Function

Graph the function $y = \cos x + \dfrac{1}{50} \sin 50x$.

Solution In the viewing window $[-6, 6]$ by $[-1, 1]$ the graph appears much like the cosine function with some small sharp wiggles on it (Figure 1.82a). We get a better look when we significantly reduce the window to $[-0.6, 0.6]$ by $[0.8, 1.02]$, obtaining the graph in Figure 1.82b. We now see the small but rapid oscillations of the second term, $1/50 \sin 50x$, added to the comparatively larger values of the cosine curve.

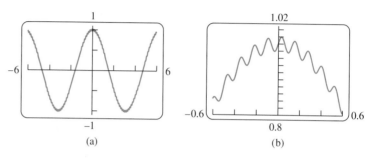

(a)   (b)

FIGURE 1.82 In (b) we see a close-up view of the function

$y = \cos x + \dfrac{1}{50} \sin 50x$ graphed in (a). The term $\cos x$ clearly dominates the

second term, $\dfrac{1}{50} \sin 50x$, which produces the rapid oscillations along the

cosine curve (Example 5). ∎

EXAMPLE 6 Graphing an Odd Fractional Power

Graph the function $y = x^{1/3}$.

Solution Many graphing devices display the graph shown in Figure 1.83a. When we compare it with the graph of $y = x^{1/3} = \sqrt[3]{x}$ in Figure 1.38, we see that the left branch for $x < 0$ is missing. The reason the graphs differ is that many calculators and computer soft-

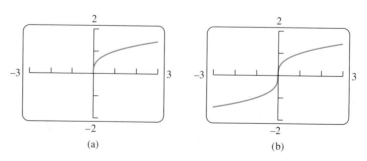

(a)   (b)

FIGURE 1.83 The graph of $y = x^{1/3}$ is missing the left branch in (a). In

(b) we graph the function $f(x) = \dfrac{x}{|x|} \cdot |x|^{1/3}$ obtaining both branches. (See

Example 6.)

ware programs calculate $x^{1/3}$ as $e^{(1/3)\ln x}$. (The exponential and logarithmic functions are studied in Chapter 7.) Since the logarithmic function is not defined for negative values of x, the computing device can only produce the right branch where $x > 0$.

To obtain the full picture showing both branches, we can graph the function

$$f(x) = \frac{x}{|x|} \cdot |x|^{1/3}.$$

This function equals $x^{1/3}$ except at $x = 0$ (where f is undefined, although $0^{1/3} = 0$). The graph of f is shown in Figure 1.83b. ∎

Empirical Modeling: Capturing the Trend of Collected Data

In Example 3 of Section 1.4, we verified the reasonableness of Kepler's hypothesis that the period of a planet's orbit is proportional to its mean distance from the sun raised to the 3/2 power. If we cannot hypothesize a relationship between a dependent variable and an independent variable, we might collect data points and try to find a curve that "fits" the data and captures the trend of the scatterplot. The process of finding a curve to fit data is called **regression analysis** and the curve is called a **regression curve**. A computer or graphing calculator finds the regression curve by finding the particular curve which minimizes the sum of the squares of the vertical distances between the data points and the curve. This method of **least squares** is discussed in the Section 14.7 exercises.

There are many useful types of regression curves, such as straight lines, power, polynomial, exponential, logarithmic, and sinusoidal curves. Many computers or graphing calculators have a regression analysis feature to fit a variety of regression curve types. The next example illustrates using a graphing calculator's linear regression feature to fit data from Table 1.5 with a linear equation.

EXAMPLE 7   Fitting a Regression Line

Starting with the data in Table 1.5, build a model for the price of a postage stamp as a function of time. After verifying that the model is "reasonable," use it to predict the price in 2010.

Solution   We are building a model for the price of a stamp since 1968. There were two increases in 1981, one of three cents followed by another of two cents. To make 1981 comparable with the other listed years, we lump them together as a single five-cent increase, giving the data in Table 1.6. Figure 1.84a gives the scatterplot for Table 1.6.

TABLE 1.5 Price of a U.S. postage stamp	
Year x	**Cost y**
1968	0.06
1971	0.08
1974	0.10
1975	0.13
1977	0.15
1981	0.18
1981	0.20
1985	0.22
1987	0.25
1991	0.29
1995	0.32
1998	0.33
2002	0.37

TABLE 1.6 Price of a U.S postage stamp since 1968

x	0	3	6	7	9	13	17	19	23	27	30	34
y	6	8	10	13	15	20	22	25	29	32	33	37

Since the scatterplot is fairly linear, we investigate a linear model. Upon entering the data into a graphing calculator (or computer software) and selecting the linear regression option, we find the regression line to be

$$y = 0.94x + 6.10.$$

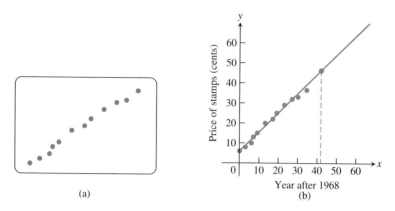

FIGURE 1.84   (a) Scatterplot of (x, y) data in Table 1.6. (b) Using the regression line to estimate the price of a stamp in 2010. (Example 7).

Figure 1.84b shows the line and scatterplot together. The fit is remarkably good, so the model seems reasonable.

Evaluating the regression line, we conclude that in 2010 ($x = 42$), the price of a stamp will be

$$y = 0.94(42) + 6.10 \approx 46 \text{ cents}.$$

The prediction is shown as the red point on the regression line in Figure 1.84b.   ■

EXAMPLE 8   Finding a Curve to Predict Population Levels

We may want to predict the future size of a population, such as the number of trout or catfish living in a fish farm. Figure 1.85 shows a scatterplot of the data collected by R. Pearl for a collection of yeast cells (measured as **biomass**) growing over time (measured in hours) in a nutrient.

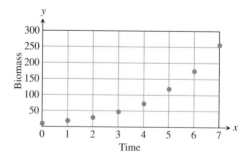

FIGURE 1.85   Biomass of a yeast culture versus elapsed time (Example 8).
(Data from R. Pearl, "The Growth of Population," *Quart. Rev. Biol.*, Vol. 2 (1927), pp. 532–548.)

The plot of points appears to be reasonably smooth with an upward curving trend. We might attempt to capture this trend by fitting a polynomial (for example, a quadratic $y = ax^2 + bx + c$), a power curve ($y = ax^b$), or an exponential curve ($y = ae^{bx}$). Figure 1.86 shows the result of using a calculator to fit a quadratic model.

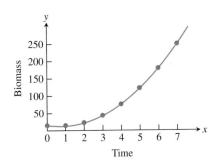

FIGURE 1.86 Fitting a quadratic to Pearl's data gives the equation $y = 6.10x^2 - 9.28x + 16.43$ and the prediction $y(17) = 1622.65$ (Example 8).

The quadratic model $y = 6.10x^2 - 9.28x + 16.43$ appears to fit the collected data reasonably well (Figure 1.86). Using this model, we predict the population after 17 hours as $y(17) = 1622.65$. Let us examine more of Pearl's data to see if our quadratic model continues to be a good one.

In Figure 1.87, we display all of Pearl's data. Now you see that the prediction of $y(17) = 1622.65$ grossly overestimates the observed population of 659.6. Why did the quadratic model fail to predict a more accurate value?

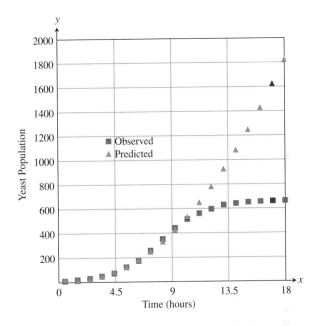

FIGURE 1.87 The rest of Pearl's data (Example 8).

The problem lies in the danger of predicting beyond the range of data used to build the empirical model. (The range of data creating our model was $0 \le x \le 7$.) Such *extrapolation* is especially dangerous when the model selected is not supported by some underlying rationale suggesting the form of the model. In our yeast example, why would we expect a quadratic function as underlying population growth? Why not an exponential function? In the face of this, how then do we predict future values? Often, calculus can help, and in Chapter 9 we use it to model population growth. ∎

Regression Analysis

Regression analysis has four steps:

1. Plot the data (scatterplot).
2. Find a regression equation. For a line, it has the form $y = mx + b$, and for a quadratic, the form $y = ax^2 + bx + c$.
3. Superimpose the graph of the regression equation on the scatterplot to see the fit.
4. If the fit is satisfactory, use the regression equation to predict y-values for values of x not in the table.

EXERCISES 1.7

Choosing a Viewing Window

In Exercises 1–4, use a graphing calculator or computer to determine which of the given viewing windows displays the most appropriate graph of the specified function.

1. $f(x) = x^4 - 7x^2 + 6x$
   a. $[-1, 1]$ by $[-1, 1]$
   b. $[-2, 2]$ by $[-5, 5]$
   c. $[-10, 10]$ by $[-10, 10]$
   d. $[-5, 5]$ by $[-25, 15]$

2. $f(x) = x^3 - 4x^2 - 4x + 16$
   a. $[-1, 1]$ by $[-5, 5]$
   b. $[-3, 3]$ by $[-10, 10]$
   c. $[-5, 5]$ by $[-10, 20]$
   d. $[-20, 20]$ by $[-100, 100]$

3. $f(x) = 5 + 12x - x^3$
   a. $[-1, 1]$ by $[-1, 1]$
   b. $[-5, 5]$ by $[-10, 10]$
   c. $[-4, 4]$ by $[-20, 20]$
   d. $[-4, 5]$ by $[-15, 25]$

4. $f(x) = \sqrt{5 + 4x - x^2}$
   a. $[-2, 2]$ by $[-2, 2]$
   b. $[-2, 6]$ by $[-1, 4]$
   c. $[-3, 7]$ by $[0, 10]$
   d. $[-10, 10]$ by $[-10, 10]$

Determining a Viewing Window

In Exercises 5–30, determine an appropriate viewing window for the given function and use it to display its graph.

5. $f(x) = x^4 - 4x^3 + 15$

6. $f(x) = \dfrac{x^3}{3} - \dfrac{x^2}{2} - 2x + 1$

7. $f(x) = x^5 - 5x^4 + 10$

8. $f(x) = 4x^3 - x^4$

9. $f(x) = x\sqrt{9 - x^2}$

10. $f(x) = x^2(6 - x^3)$

11. $y = 2x - 3x^{2/3}$

12. $y = x^{1/3}(x^2 - 8)$

13. $y = 5x^{2/5} - 2x$

14. $y = x^{2/3}(5 - x)$

15. $y = |x^2 - 1|$

16. $y = |x^2 - x|$

17. $y = \dfrac{x + 3}{x + 2}$

18. $y = 1 - \dfrac{1}{x + 3}$

19. $f(x) = \dfrac{x^2 + 2}{x^2 + 1}$

20. $f(x) = \dfrac{x^2 - 1}{x^2 + 1}$

21. $f(x) = \dfrac{x - 1}{x^2 - x - 6}$

22. $f(x) = \dfrac{8}{x^2 - 9}$

23. $f(x) = \dfrac{6x^2 - 15x + 6}{4x^2 - 10x}$

24. $f(x) = \dfrac{x^2 - 3}{x - 2}$

25. $y = \sin 250x$

26. $y = 3 \cos 60x$

27. $y = \cos\left(\dfrac{x}{50}\right)$

28. $y = \dfrac{1}{10} \sin\left(\dfrac{x}{10}\right)$

29. $y = x + \dfrac{1}{10} \sin 30x$

30. $y = x^2 + \dfrac{1}{50} \cos 100x$

31. Graph the lower half of the circle defined by the equation $x^2 + 2x = 4 + 4y - y^2$.

32. Graph the upper branch of the hyperbola $y^2 - 16x^2 = 1$.

33. Graph four periods of the function $f(x) = -\tan 2x$.

34. Graph two periods of the function $f(x) = 3 \cot \dfrac{x}{2} + 1$.

35. Graph the function $f(x) = \sin 2x + \cos 3x$.

36. Graph the function $f(x) = \sin^3 x$.

Graphing in Dot Mode

Another way to avoid incorrect connections when using a graphing device is through the use of a "dot mode," which plots only the points. If your graphing utility allows that mode, use it to plot the functions in Exercises 37–40.

37. $y = \dfrac{1}{x - 3}$

38. $y = \sin \dfrac{1}{x}$

39. $y = x \lfloor x \rfloor$

40. $y = \dfrac{x^3 - 1}{x^2 - 1}$

Regression Analysis

T 41. Table 1.7 shows the mean annual compensation of construction workers.

TABLE 1.7 Construction workers' average annual compensation

Year	Annual compensation (dollars)
1980	22,033
1985	27,581
1988	30,466
1990	32,836
1992	34,815
1995	37,996
1999	42,236
2002	45,413

Source: U.S. Bureau of Economic Analysis.

a. Find a linear regression equation for the data.

b. Find the slope of the regression line. What does the slope represent?

c. Superimpose the graph of the linear regression equation on a scatterplot of the data.

d. Use the regression equation to predict the construction workers' average annual compensation in 2010.

T **42.** The median price of existing single-family homes has increased consistently since 1970. The data in Table 1.8, however, show that there have been differences in various parts of the country.

a. Find a linear regression equation for home cost in the Northeast.

b. What does the slope of the regression line represent?

c. Find a linear regression equation for home cost in the Midwest.

d. Where is the median price increasing more rapidly, in the Northeast or the Midwest?

TABLE 1.8 Median price of single-family homes

Year	Northeast (dollars)	Midwest (dollars)
1970	25,200	20,100
1975	39,300	30,100
1980	60,800	51,900
1985	88,900	58,900
1990	141,200	74,000
1995	197,100	88,300
2000	264,700	97,000

Source: National Association of Realtors®

T **43. Vehicular stopping distance** Table 1.9 shows the total stopping distance of a car as a function of its speed.

a. Find the quadratic regression equation for the data in Table 1.9.

b. Superimpose the graph of the quadratic regression equation on a scatterplot of the data.

c. Use the graph of the quadratic regression equation to predict the average total stopping distance for speeds of 72 and 85 mph. Confirm algebraically.

d. Now use *linear* regression to predict the average total stopping distance for speeds of 72 and 85 mph. Superimpose the regression line on a scatterplot of the data. Which gives the better fit, the line here or the graph in part (b)?

TABLE 1.9 Vehicular stopping distance

Speed (mph)	Average total stopping distance (ft)
20	42
25	56
30	73.5
35	91.5
40	116
45	142.5
50	173
55	209.5
60	248
65	292.5
70	343
75	401
80	464

Source: U.S. Bureau of Public Roads.

T **44. Stern waves** Observations of the stern waves that follow a boat at right angles to its course have disclosed that the distance between the crests of these waves (their *wave length*) increases with the speed of the boat. Table 1.10 shows the relationship between wave length and the speed of the boat.

TABLE 1.10 Wave lengths

Wave length (m)	Speed (km/h)
0.20	1.8
0.65	3.6
1.13	5.4
2.55	7.2
4.00	9.0
5.75	10.8
7.80	12.6
10.20	14.4
12.90	16.2
16.00	18.0
18.40	19.8

a. Find a power regression equation $y = ax^b$ for the data in Table 1.10, where x is the wave length, and y the speed of the boat.

b. Superimpose the graph of the power regression equation on a scatterplot of the data.

c. Use the graph of the power regression equation to predict the speed of the boat when the wave length is 11 m. Confirm algebraically.

d. Now use *linear* regression to predict the speed when the wave length is 11 m. Superimpose the regression line on a scatterplot of the data. Which gives the better fit, the line here or the curve in part (b)?

Chapter 1   Questions to Guide Your Review

1. How are the real numbers represented? What are the main categories characterizing the properties of the real number system? What are the primary subsets of the real numbers?

2. How are the rational numbers described in terms of decimal expansions? What are the irrational numbers? Give examples.

3. What are the order properties of the real numbers? How are they used in solving equations?

4. What is a number's absolute value? Give examples? How are $|-a|$, $|ab|$, $|a/b|$, and $|a + b|$ related to $|a|$ and $|b|$?

5. How are absolute values used to describe intervals or unions of intervals? Give examples.

6. How do we identify points in the plane using the Cartesian coordinate system? What is the graph of an equation in the variables x and y?

7. How can you write an equation for a line if you know the coordinates of two points on the line? The line's slope and the coordinates of one point on the line? The line's slope and y-intercept? Give examples.

8. What are the standard equations for lines perpendicular to the coordinate axes?

9. How are the slopes of mutually perpendicular lines related? What about parallel lines? Give examples.

10. When a line is not vertical, what is the relation between its slope and its angle of inclination?

11. How do you find the distance between two points in the coordinate plane?

12. What is the standard equation of a circle with center (h, k) and radius a? What is the unit circle and what is its equation?

13. Describe the steps you would take to graph the circle $x^2 + y^2 + 4x - 6y + 12 = 0$.

14. What inequality describes the points in the coordinate plane that lie inside the circle of radius a centered at the point (h, k)? That lie inside or on the circle? That lie outside the circle? That lie outside or on the circle?

15. If a, b, and c are constants and $a \neq 0$, what can you say about the graph of the equation $y = ax^2 + bx + c$? In particular, how would you go about sketching the curve $y = 2x^2 + 4x$?

16. What is a function? What is its domain? Its range? What is an arrow diagram for a function? Give examples.

17. What is the graph of a real-valued function of a real variable? What is the vertical line test?

18. What is a piecewise-defined function? Give examples.

19. What are the important types of functions frequently encountered in calculus? Give an example of each type.

20. In terms of its graph, what is meant by an increasing function? A decreasing function? Give an example of each.

21. What is an even function? An odd function? What symmetry properties do the graphs of such functions have? What advantage can we take of this? Given an example of a function that is neither even nor odd.

22. What does it mean to say that y is proportional to x? To $x^{3/2}$? What is the geometric interpretation of proportionality? How can this interpretation be used to test a proposed proportionality?

23. If f and g are real-valued functions, how are the domains of $f + g, f - g, fg$, and f/g related to the domains of f and g? Give examples.

24. When is it possible to compose one function with another? Give examples of composites and their values at various points. Does the order in which functions are composed ever matter?

25. How do you change the equation $y = f(x)$ to shift its graph vertically up or down by a factor $k > 0$? Horizontally to the left or right? Give examples.

26. How do you change the equation $y = f(x)$ to compress or stretch the graph by $c > 1$? Reflect the graph across a coordinate axis? Give examples.

27. What is the standard equation of an ellipse with center (h, k)? What is its major axis? Its minor axis? Give examples.

28. What is radian measure? How do you convert from radians to degrees? Degrees to radians?

29. Graph the six basic trigonometric functions. What symmetries do the graphs have?

30. What is a periodic function? Give examples. What are the periods of the six basic trigonometric functions?

31. Starting with the identity $\sin^2 \theta + \cos^2 \theta = 1$ and the formulas for $\cos(A + B)$ and $\sin(A + B)$, show how a variety of other trigonometric identities may be derived.

32. How does the formula for the general sine function $f(x) = A \sin((2\pi/B)(x - C)) + D$ relate to the shifting, stretching, compressing, and reflection of its graph? Give examples. Graph the general sine curve and identify the constants A, B, C, and D.

33. Name three issues that arise when functions are graphed using a calculator or computer with graphing software. Give examples.

Chapter 1 Practice Exercises

Inequalities

In Exercises 1–4, solve the inequalities and show the solution sets on the real line.

1. $7 + 2x \geq 3$

2. $-3x < 10$

3. $\frac{1}{5}(x - 1) < \frac{1}{4}(x - 2)$

4. $\frac{x - 3}{2} \geq -\frac{4 + x}{3}$

Absolute Value

Solve the equations or inequalities in Exercises 5–8.

5. $|x + 1| = 7$

6. $|y - 3| < 4$

7. $\left| 1 - \frac{x}{2} \right| > \frac{3}{2}$

8. $\left| \frac{2x + 7}{3} \right| \leq 5$

Coordinates

9. A particle in the plane moved from $A(-2, 5)$ to the y-axis in such a way that Δy equaled $3\Delta x$. What were the particle's new coordinates?

10. a. Plot the points $A(8, 1)$, $B(2, 10)$, $C(-4, 6)$, $D(2, -3)$, and $E(14/3, 6)$.

b. Find the slopes of the lines AB, BC, CD, DA, CE, and BD.

c. Do any four of the five points A, B, C, D, and E form a parallelogram?

d. Are any three of the five points collinear? How do you know?

e. Which of the lines determined by the five points pass through the origin?

11. Do the points $A(6, 4)$, $B(4, -3)$, and $C(-2, 3)$ form an isosceles triangle? A right triangle? How do you know?

12. Find the coordinates of the point on the line $y = 3x + 1$ that is equidistant from $(0, 0)$ and $(-3, 4)$.

Lines

In Exercises 13–24, write an equation for the specified line.

13. through $(1, -6)$ with slope 3

14. through $(-1, 2)$ with slope $-1/2$

15. the vertical line through $(0, -3)$

16. through $(-3, 6)$ and $(1, -2)$

17. the horizontal line through $(0, 2)$

18. through $(3, 3)$ and $(-2, 5)$

19. with slope -3 and y-intercept 3

20. through $(3, 1)$ and parallel to $2x - y = -2$

21. through $(4, -12)$ and parallel to $4x + 3y = 12$

22. through $(-2, -3)$ and perpendicular to $3x - 5y = 1$

23. through $(-1, 2)$ and perpendicular to $(1/2)x + (1/3)y = 1$

24. with x-intercept 3 and y-intercept -5

Functions and Graphs

25. Express the area and circumference of a circle as functions of the circle's radius. Then express the area as a function of the circumference.

26. Express the radius of a sphere as a function of the sphere's surface area. Then express the surface area as a function of the volume.

27. A point P in the first quadrant lies on the parabola $y = x^2$. Express the coordinates of P as functions of the angle of inclination of the line joining P to the origin.

28. A hot-air balloon rising straight up from a level field is tracked by a range finder located 500 ft from the point of liftoff. Express the balloon's height as a function of the angle the line from the range finder to the balloon makes with the ground.

In Exercises 29–32, determine whether the graph of the function is symmetric about the y-axis, the origin, or neither.

29. $y = x^{1/5}$

30. $y = x^{2/5}$

31. $y = x^2 - 2x - 1$

32. $y = e^{-x^2}$

In Exercises 33–40, determine whether the function is even, odd, or neither.

33. $y = x^2 + 1$

34. $y = x^5 - x^3 - x$

35. $y = 1 - \cos x$

36. $y = \sec x \tan x$

37. $y = \frac{x^4 + 1}{x^3 - 2x}$

38. $y = 1 - \sin x$

39. $y = x + \cos x$

40. $y = \sqrt{x^4 - 1}$

In Exercises 41–50, find the (a) domain and (b) range.

41. $y = |x| - 2$

42. $y = -2 + \sqrt{1 - x}$

43. $y = \sqrt{16 - x^2}$

44. $y = 3^{2-x} + 1$

45. $y = 2e^{-x} - 3$

46. $y = \tan(2x - \pi)$

47. $y = 2\sin(3x + \pi) - 1$

48. $y = x^{2/5}$

49. $y = \ln(x - 3) + 1$

50. $y = -1 + \sqrt[3]{2 - x}$

Piecewise-Defined Functions

In Exercises 51 and 52, find the (a) domain and (b) range.

51. $y = \begin{cases} \sqrt{-x}, & -4 \le x \le 0 \\ \sqrt{x}, & 0 < x \le 4 \end{cases}$

52. $y = \begin{cases} -x - 2, & -2 \le x \le -1 \\ x, & -1 < x \le 1 \\ -x + 2, & 1 < x \le 2 \end{cases}$

In Exercises 53 and 54, write a piecewise formula for the function.

53.

54.

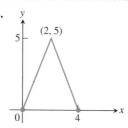

Composition of Functions

In Exercises 55 and 56, find

a. $(f \circ g)(-1)$.

b. $(g \circ f)(2)$.

c. $(f \circ f)(x)$.

d. $(g \circ g)(x)$.

55. $f(x) = \dfrac{1}{x}, \quad g(x) = \dfrac{1}{\sqrt{x + 2}}$

56. $f(x) = 2 - x, \quad g(x) = \sqrt[3]{x + 1}$

In Exercises 57 and 58, (a) write a formula for $f \circ g$ and $g \circ f$ and find the (b) domain and (c) range of each.

57. $f(x) = 2 - x^2, \quad g(x) = \sqrt{x + 2}$

58. $f(x) = \sqrt{x}, \quad g(x) = \sqrt{1 - x}$

Composition with absolute values In Exercises 59–64, graph f_1 and f_2 together. Then describe how applying the absolute value function before applying f_1 affects the graph.

$f_1(x)$	$f_2(x) = f_1(|x|)$
59. x	$|x|$
60. x^3	$|x|^3$
61. x^2	$|x|^2$
62. $\dfrac{1}{x}$	$\dfrac{1}{|x|}$
63. $\sqrt{x}$	$\sqrt{|x|}$
64. $\sin x$	$\sin|x|$

Composition with absolute values In Exercises 65–68, graph g_1 and g_2 together. Then describe how taking absolute values after applying g_1 affects the graph.

$g_1(x)$	$g_2(x) = |g_1(x)|$
65. x^3	$|x^3|$
66. $\sqrt{x}$	$|\sqrt{x}|$
67. $4 - x^2$	$|4 - x^2|$
68. $x^2 + x$	$|x^2 + x|$

Trigonometry

In Exercises 69–72, sketch the graph of the given function. What is the period of the function?

69. $y = \cos 2x$

70. $y = \sin\dfrac{x}{2}$

71. $y = \sin \pi x$

72. $y = \cos\dfrac{\pi x}{2}$

73. Sketch the graph $y = 2\cos\left(x - \dfrac{\pi}{3}\right)$.

74. Sketch the graph $y = 1 + \sin\left(x + \dfrac{\pi}{4}\right)$.

In Exercises 75–78, ABC is a right triangle with the right angle at C. The sides opposite angles A, B, and C are a, b, and c, respectively.

75. a. Find a and b if $c = 2$, $B = \pi/3$.

    b. Find a and c if $b = 2$, $B = \pi/3$.

76. a. Express a in terms of A and c.

    b. Express a in terms of A and b.

77. a. Express a in terms of B and b.

    b. Express c in terms of A and a.

78. a. Express $\sin A$ in terms of a and c.

    b. Express $\sin A$ in terms of b and c.

79. Height of a pole Two wires stretch from the top T of a vertical pole to points B and C on the ground, where C is 10 m closer to the base of the pole than is B. If wire BT makes an angle of 35° with the horizontal and wire CT makes an angle of 50° with the horizontal, how high is the pole?

80. Height of a weather balloon Observers at positions A and B 2 km apart simultaneously measure the angle of elevation of a weather balloon to be 40° and 70°, respectively. If the balloon is directly above a point on the line segment between A and B, find the height of the balloon.

T **81. a.** Graph the function $f(x) = \sin x + \cos(x/2)$.

    b. What appears to be the period of this function?

    c. Confirm your finding in part (b) algebraically.

T **82. a.** Graph $f(x) = \sin(1/x)$.

    b. What are the domain and range of f?

    c. Is f periodic? Give reasons for your answer.

Chapter 1   Additional and Advanced Exercises

Functions and Graphs

1. The graph of f is shown. Draw the graph of each function.

  a. $y = f(-x)$ **b.** $y = -f(x)$

  c. $y = -2f(x + 1) + 1$ **d.** $y = 3f(x - 2) - 2$

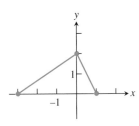

2. A portion of the graph of a function defined on $[-3, 3]$ is shown. Complete the graph assuming that the function is

  a. even.   **b.** odd.

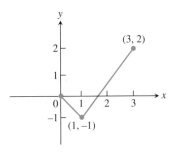

3. Are there two functions f and g such that $f \circ g = g \circ f$? Give reasons for your answer.

4. Are there two functions f and g with the following property? The graphs of f and g are not straight lines but the graph of $f \circ g$ is a straight line. Give reasons for your answer.

5. If $f(x)$ is odd, can anything be said of $g(x) = f(x) - 2$? What if f is even instead? Give reasons for your answer.

6. If $g(x)$ is an odd function defined for all values of x, can anything be said about $g(0)$? Give reasons for your answer.

7. Graph the equation $|x| + |y| = 1 + x$.

8. Graph the equation $y + |y| = x + |x|$.

Trigonometry

In Exercises 9–14, ABC is an arbitrary triangle with sides a, b, and c opposite angles A, B, and C, respectively.

9. Find b if $a = \sqrt{3}, A = \pi/3, B = \pi/4$.

10. Find $\sin B$ if $a = 4, b = 3, A = \pi/4$.

11. Find $\cos A$ if $a = 2, b = 2, c = 3$.

12. Find c if $a = 2, b = 3, C = \pi/4$.

13. Find $\sin B$ if $a = 2, b = 3, c = 4$.

14. Find $\sin C$ if $a = 2, b = 4, c = 5$.

Derivations and Proofs

15. Prove the following identities.

  a. $\dfrac{1 - \cos x}{\sin x} = \dfrac{\sin x}{1 + \cos x}$

  b. $\dfrac{1 - \cos x}{1 + \cos x} = \tan^2 \dfrac{x}{2}$

16. Explain the following "proof without words" of the law of cosines. (Source: "Proof without Words: The Law of Cosines," Sidney H. Kung, *Mathematics Magazine*, Vol. 63, No. 5, Dec. 1990, p. 342.)

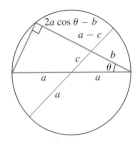

17. Show that the area of triangle ABC is given by $(1/2)ab \sin C = (1/2)bc \sin A = (1/2)ca \sin B$.

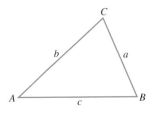

18. Show that the area of triangle ABC is given by $\sqrt{s(s - a)(s - b)(s - c)}$ where $s = (a + b + c)/2$ is the semiperimeter of the triangle.

19. **Properties of inequalities**   If a and b are real numbers, we say that a **is less than** b and write $a < b$ if (and only if) $b - a$ is positive. Use this definition to prove the following properties of inequalities.

  If a, b, and c are real numbers, then:

  1. $a < b \Rightarrow a + c < b + c$

  2. $a < b \Rightarrow a - c < b - c$

  3. $a < b$ and $c > 0 \Rightarrow ac < bc$

  4. $a < b$ and $c < 0 \Rightarrow bc < ac$

    (Special case: $a < b \Rightarrow -b < -a$)

5. $a > 0 \Rightarrow \dfrac{1}{a} > 0$

6. $0 < a < b \Rightarrow \dfrac{1}{b} < \dfrac{1}{a}$

7. $a < b < 0 \Rightarrow \dfrac{1}{b} < \dfrac{1}{a}$

20. Prove that the following inequalities hold for any real numbers a and b.

 a. $|a| < |b|$ if and only if $a^2 < b^2$

 b. $|a - b| \geq ||a| - |b||$

Generalizing the triangle inequality   Prove by mathematical induction that the inequalities in Exercises 21 and 22 hold for any n real numbers $a_1, a_2, \ldots, a_n$. (Mathematical induction is reviewed in Appendix 1.)

21. $|a_1 + a_2 + \cdots + a_n| \leq |a_1| + |a_2| + \cdots + |a_n|$

22. $|a_1 + a_2 + \cdots + a_n| \geq |a_1| - |a_2| - \cdots - |a_n|$

23. Show that if f is both even and odd, then $f(x) = 0$ for every x in the domain of f.

24. a. Even-odd decompositions   Let f be a function whose domain is symmetric about the origin, that is, $-x$ belongs to the domain whenever x does. Show that f is the sum of an even function and an odd function:

$$f(x) = E(x) + O(x),$$

where E is an even function and O is an odd function. (*Hint:* Let $E(x) = (f(x) + f(-x))/2$. Show that $E(-x) = E(x)$, so that E is even. Then show that $O(x) = f(x) - E(x)$ is odd.)

 b. Uniqueness   Show that there is only one way to write f as the sum of an even and an odd function. (*Hint:* One way is given in part (a). If also $f(x) = E_1(x) + O_1(x)$ where E_1 is even and O_1 is odd, show that $E - E_1 = O_1 - O$. Then use Exercise 23 to show that $E = E_1$ and $O = O_1$.)

Grapher Explorations—Effects of Parameters

25. What happens to the graph of $y = ax^2 + bx + c$ as

 a. a changes while b and c remain fixed?

 b. b changes (a and c fixed, $a \neq 0$)?

 c. c changes (a and b fixed, $a \neq 0$)?

26. What happens to the graph of $y = a(x + b)^3 + c$ as

 a. a changes while b and c remain fixed?

 b. b changes (a and c fixed, $a \neq 0$)?

 c. c changes (a and b fixed, $a \neq 0$)?

27. Find all values of the slope of the line $y = mx + 2$ for which the x-intercept exceeds $1/2$.

Geometry

28. An object's center of mass moves at a constant velocity v along a straight line past the origin. The accompanying figure shows the coordinate system and the line of motion. The dots show positions that are 1 sec apart. Why are the areas $A_1, A_2, \ldots, A_5$ in the figure all equal? As in Kepler's equal area law (see Section 13.6), the line that joins the object's center of mass to the origin sweeps out equal areas in equal times.

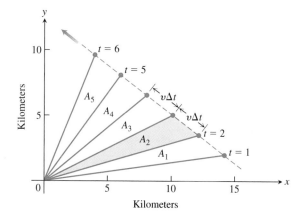

29. a. Find the slope of the line from the origin to the midpoint P, of side AB in the triangle in the accompanying figure ($a, b > 0$).

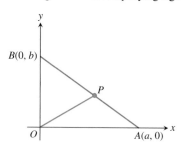

 b. When is OP perpendicular to AB?

Chapter 1   Technology Application Projects

An Overview of Mathematica
An overview of *Mathematica* sufficient to complete the *Mathematica* modules appearing on the Web site.

Mathematica/Maple Module
Modeling Change: Springs, Driving Safety, Radioactivity, Trees, Fish, and Mammals.
Construct and interpret mathematical models, analyze and improve them, and make predictions using them.

2

LIMITS AND CONTINUITY

OVERVIEW The concept of a limit is a central idea that distinguishes calculus from algebra and trigonometry. It is fundamental to finding the tangent to a curve or the velocity of an object.

In this chapter we develop the limit, first intuitively and then formally. We use limits to describe the way a function *f* varies. Some functions vary continuously; small changes in *x* produce only small changes in *f(x)*. Other functions can have values that jump or vary erratically. The notion of limit gives a precise way to distinguish between these behaviors. The geometric application of using limits to define the tangent to a curve leads at once to the important concept of the derivative of a function. The derivative, which we investigate thoroughly in Chapter 3, quantifies the way a function's values change.

2.1 Rates of Change and Limits

In this section, we introduce average and instantaneous rates of change. These lead to the main idea of the section, the idea of limit.

Average and Instantaneous Speed

A moving body's **average speed** during an interval of time is found by dividing the distance covered by the time elapsed. The unit of measure is length per unit time: kilometers per hour, feet per second, or whatever is appropriate to the problem at hand.

EXAMPLE 1 Finding an Average Speed

A rock breaks loose from the top of a tall cliff. What is its average speed

(a) during the first 2 sec of fall?

(b) during the 1-sec interval between second 1 and second 2?

Solution In solving this problem we use the fact, discovered by Galileo in the late sixteenth century, that a solid object dropped from rest (not moving) to fall freely near the surface of the earth will fall a distance proportional to the square of the time it has been falling. (This assumes negligible air resistance to slow the object down and that gravity is

HISTORICAL BIOGRAPHY*

Galileo Galilei
(1564–1642)

the only force acting on the falling body. We call this type of motion **free fall**.) If y denotes the distance fallen in feet after t seconds, then Galileo's law is

$$y = 16t^2,$$

where 16 is the constant of proportionality.

The average speed of the rock during a given time interval is the change in distance, Δy, divided by the length of the time interval, Δt.

(a) For the first 2 sec: $\dfrac{\Delta y}{\Delta t} = \dfrac{16(2)^2 - 16(0)^2}{2 - 0} = 32\,\dfrac{\text{ft}}{\text{sec}}$

(b) From sec 1 to sec 2: $\dfrac{\Delta y}{\Delta t} = \dfrac{16(2)^2 - 16(1)^2}{2 - 1} = 48\,\dfrac{\text{ft}}{\text{sec}}$ ∎

The next example examines what happens when we look at the average speed of a falling object over shorter and shorter time intervals.

EXAMPLE 2 Finding an Instantaneous Speed

Find the speed of the falling rock at $t = 1$ and $t = 2$ sec.

Solution   We can calculate the average speed of the rock over a time interval $[t_0, t_0 + h]$, having length $\Delta t = h$, as

$$\frac{\Delta y}{\Delta t} = \frac{16(t_0 + h)^2 - 16t_0^2}{h}. \tag{1}$$

We cannot use this formula to calculate the "instantaneous" speed at t_0 by substituting $h = 0$, because we cannot divide by zero. But we *can* use it to calculate average speeds over increasingly short time intervals starting at $t_0 = 1$ and $t_0 = 2$. When we do so, we see a pattern (Table 2.1).

TABLE 2.1 Average speeds over short time intervals		
Average speed: $\dfrac{\Delta y}{\Delta t} = \dfrac{16(t_0 + h)^2 - 16t_0^2}{h}$		
Length of time interval h	**Average speed over interval of length h starting at $t_0 = 1$**	**Average speed over interval of length h starting at $t_0 = 2$**
1	48	80
0.1	33.6	65.6
0.01	32.16	64.16
0.001	32.016	64.016
0.0001	32.0016	64.0016

The average speed on intervals starting at $t_0 = 1$ seems to approach a limiting value of 32 as the length of the interval decreases. This suggests that the rock is falling at a speed of 32 ft/sec at $t_0 = 1$ sec. Let's confirm this algebraically.

To learn more about the historical figures and the development of the major elements and topics of calculus, visit **www.aw-bc.com/thomas**.

If we set $t_0 = 1$ and then expand the numerator in Equation (1) and simplify, we find that

$$\frac{\Delta y}{\Delta t} = \frac{16(1+h)^2 - 16(1)^2}{h} = \frac{16(1 + 2h + h^2) - 16}{h}$$

$$= \frac{32h + 16h^2}{h} = 32 + 16h.$$

For values of h different from 0, the expressions on the right and left are equivalent and the average speed is $32 + 16h$ ft/sec. We can now see why the average speed has the limiting value $32 + 16(0) = 32$ ft/sec as h approaches 0.

Similarly, setting $t_0 = 2$ in Equation (1), the procedure yields

$$\frac{\Delta y}{\Delta t} = 64 + 16h$$

for values of h different from 0. As h gets closer and closer to 0, the average speed at $t_0 = 2$ sec has the limiting value 64 ft/sec.   ∎

Average Rates of Change and Secant Lines

Given an arbitrary function $y = f(x)$, we calculate the average rate of change of y with respect to x over the interval $[x_1, x_2]$ by dividing the change in the value of y, $\Delta y = f(x_2) - f(x_1)$, by the length $\Delta x = x_2 - x_1 = h$ of the interval over which the change occurs.

DEFINITION   Average Rate of Change over an Interval

The **average rate of change** of $y = f(x)$ with respect to x over the interval $[x_1, x_2]$ is

$$\frac{\Delta y}{\Delta x} = \frac{f(x_2) - f(x_1)}{x_2 - x_1} = \frac{f(x_1 + h) - f(x_1)}{h}, \qquad h \neq 0.$$

Geometrically, the rate of change of f over $[x_1, x_2]$ is the slope of the line through the points $P(x_1, f(x_1))$ and $Q(x_2, f(x_2))$ (Figure 2.1). In geometry, a line joining two points of a curve is a **secant** to the curve. Thus, the average rate of change of f from x_1 to x_2 is identical with the slope of secant PQ.

Experimental biologists often want to know the rates at which populations grow under controlled laboratory conditions.

EXAMPLE 3   The Average Growth Rate of a Laboratory Population

Figure 2.2 shows how a population of fruit flies (*Drosophila*) grew in a 50-day experiment. The number of flies was counted at regular intervals, the counted values plotted with respect to time, and the points joined by a smooth curve (colored blue in Figure 2.2). Find the average growth rate from day 23 to day 45.

Solution   There were 150 flies on day 23 and 340 flies on day 45. Thus the number of flies increased by $340 - 150 = 190$ in $45 - 23 = 22$ days. The average rate of change of the population from day 23 to day 45 was

$$\text{Average rate of change: } \frac{\Delta p}{\Delta t} = \frac{340 - 150}{45 - 23} = \frac{190}{22} \approx 8.6 \text{ flies/day}.$$

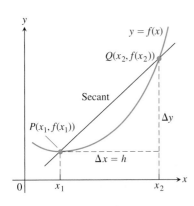

FIGURE 2.1 A secant to the graph $y = f(x)$. Its slope is $\Delta y / \Delta x$, the average rate of change of f over the interval $[x_1, x_2]$.

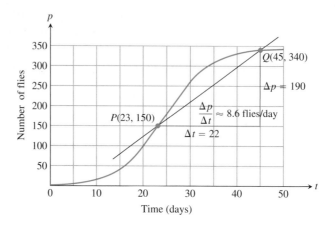

FIGURE 2.2 Growth of a fruit fly population in a controlled experiment. The average rate of change over 22 days is the slope $\Delta p / \Delta t$ of the secant line.

This average is the slope of the secant through the points P and Q on the graph in Figure 2.2. ∎

The average rate of change from day 23 to day 45 calculated in Example 3 does not tell us how fast the population was changing on day 23 itself. For that we need to examine time intervals closer to the day in question.

EXAMPLE 4   The Growth Rate on Day 23

How fast was the number of flies in the population of Example 3 growing on day 23?

Solution   To answer this question, we examine the average rates of change over increasingly short time intervals starting at day 23. In geometric terms, we find these rates by calculating the slopes of secants from P to Q, for a sequence of points Q approaching P along the curve (Figure 2.3).

Q	Slope of $PQ = \Delta p / \Delta t$ (flies/day)
$(45, 340)$	$\dfrac{340 - 150}{45 - 23} \approx 8.6$
$(40, 330)$	$\dfrac{330 - 150}{40 - 23} \approx 10.6$
$(35, 310)$	$\dfrac{310 - 150}{35 - 23} \approx 13.3$
$(30, 265)$	$\dfrac{265 - 150}{30 - 23} \approx 16.4$

FIGURE 2.3 The positions and slopes of four secants through the point P on the fruit fly graph (Example 4).

The values in the table show that the secant slopes rise from 8.6 to 16.4 as the t-coordinate of Q decreases from 45 to 30, and we would expect the slopes to rise slightly higher as t continued on toward 23. Geometrically, the secants rotate about P and seem to approach the red line in the figure, a line that goes through P in the same direction that the curve goes through P. We will see that this line is called the *tangent* to the curve at P. Since the line appears to pass through the points $(14, 0)$ and $(35, 350)$, it has slope

$$\frac{350 - 0}{35 - 14} = 16.7 \text{ flies/day (approximately)}.$$

On day 23 the population was increasing at a rate of about 16.7 flies/day. ∎

The rates at which the rock in Example 2 was falling at the instants $t = 1$ and $t = 2$ and the rate at which the population in Example 4 was changing on day $t = 23$ are called *instantaneous rates of change*. As the examples suggest, we find instantaneous rates as limiting values of average rates. In Example 4, we also pictured the tangent line to the population curve on day 23 as a limiting position of secant lines. Instantaneous rates and tangent lines, intimately connected, appear in many other contexts. To talk about the two constructively, and to understand the connection further, we need to investigate the process by which we determine limiting values, or *limits*, as we will soon call them.

Limits of Function Values

Our examples have suggested the limit idea. Let's begin with an informal definition of limit, postponing the precise definition until we've gained more insight.

Let $f(x)$ be defined on an open interval about x_0, *except possibly at x_0 itself*. If $f(x)$ gets arbitrarily close to L (as close to L as we like) for all x sufficiently close to x_0, we say that f approaches the **limit** L as x approaches x_0, and we write

$$\lim_{x \to x_0} f(x) = L,$$

which is read "the limit of $f(x)$ as x approaches x_0 is L". Essentially, the definition says that the values of $f(x)$ are close to the number L whenever x is close to x_0 (on either side of x_0). This definition is "informal" because phrases like *arbitrarily close* and *sufficiently close* are imprecise; their meaning depends on the context. To a machinist manufacturing a piston, *close* may mean *within a few thousandths of an inch*. To an astronomer studying distant galaxies, *close* may mean *within a few thousand light-years*. The definition is clear enough, however, to enable us to recognize and evaluate limits of specific functions. We will need the precise definition of Section 2.3, however, when we set out to prove theorems about limits.

EXAMPLE 5   Behavior of a Function Near a Point

How does the function

$$f(x) = \frac{x^2 - 1}{x - 1}$$

behave near $x = 1$?

Solution   The given formula defines f for all real numbers x except $x = 1$ (we cannot divide by zero). For any $x \neq 1$, we can simplify the formula by factoring the numerator and canceling common factors:

$$f(x) = \frac{(x - 1)(x + 1)}{x - 1} = x + 1 \qquad \text{for} \qquad x \neq 1.$$

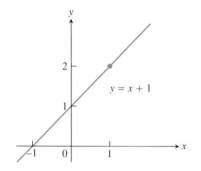

FIGURE 2.4 The graph of f is identical with the line $y = x + 1$ except at $x = 1$, where f is not defined (Example 5).

The graph of f is thus the line $y = x + 1$ with the point $(1, 2)$ *removed*. This removed point is shown as a "hole" in Figure 2.4. Even though $f(1)$ is not defined, it is clear that we can make the value of $f(x)$ *as close as we want* to 2 by choosing x *close enough* to 1 (Table 2.2).

TABLE 2.2 The closer x gets to 1, the closer $f(x) = (x^2 - 1)/(x - 1)$ seems to get to 2	
Values of x below and above 1	$f(x) = \dfrac{x^2 - 1}{x - 1} = x + 1, \qquad x \ne 1$
0.9	1.9
1.1	2.1
0.99	1.99
1.01	2.01
0.999	1.999
1.001	2.001
0.999999	1.999999
1.000001	2.000001

We say that $f(x)$ approaches the *limit* 2 as x approaches 1, and write

$$\lim_{x \to 1} f(x) = 2, \qquad \text{or} \qquad \lim_{x \to 1} \frac{x^2 - 1}{x - 1} = 2.$$ ∎

EXAMPLE 6   The Limit Value Does Not Depend on How the Function Is Defined at x_0

The function f in Figure 2.5 has limit 2 as $x \to 1$ even though f is not defined at $x = 1$. The function g has limit 2 as $x \to 1$ even though $2 \ne g(1)$. The function h is the only one

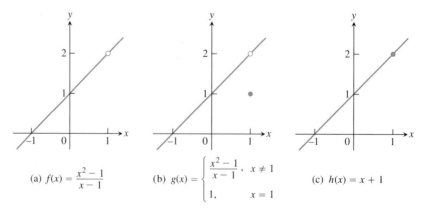

(a) $f(x) = \dfrac{x^2 - 1}{x - 1}$

(b) $g(x) = \begin{cases} \dfrac{x^2 - 1}{x - 1}, & x \ne 1 \\ 1, & x = 1 \end{cases}$

(c) $h(x) = x + 1$

FIGURE 2.5   The limits of $f(x)$, $g(x)$, and $h(x)$ all equal 2 as x approaches 1. However, only $h(x)$ has the same function value as its limit at $x = 1$ (Example 6).

(a) Identity function

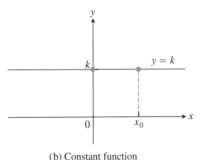

(b) Constant function

FIGURE 2.6 The functions in Example 8.

whose limit as $x \to 1$ equals its value at $x = 1$. For h, we have $\lim_{x \to 1} h(x) = h(1)$. This equality of limit and function value is special, and we return to it in Section 2.6. ■

Sometimes $\lim_{x \to x_0} f(x)$ can be evaluated by calculating $f(x_0)$. This holds, for example, whenever $f(x)$ is an algebraic combination of polynomials and trigonometric functions for which $f(x_0)$ is defined. (We will say more about this in Sections 2.2 and 2.6.)

EXAMPLE 7   Finding Limits by Calculating $f(x_0)$

(a) $\lim\limits_{x \to 2} (4) = 4$

(b) $\lim\limits_{x \to -13} (4) = 4$

(c) $\lim\limits_{x \to 3} x = 3$

(d) $\lim\limits_{x \to 2} (5x - 3) = 10 - 3 = 7$

(e) $\lim\limits_{x \to -2} \dfrac{3x + 4}{x + 5} = \dfrac{-6 + 4}{-2 + 5} = -\dfrac{2}{3}$ ■

EXAMPLE 8   The Identity and Constant Functions Have Limits at Every Point

(a) If f is the **identity function** $f(x) = x$, then for any value of x_0 (Figure 2.6a),

$$\lim_{x \to x_0} f(x) = \lim_{x \to x_0} x = x_0.$$

(b) If f is the **constant function** $f(x) = k$ (function with the constant value k), then for any value of x_0 (Figure 2.6b),

$$\lim_{x \to x_0} f(x) = \lim_{x \to x_0} k = k.$$

For instance,

$$\lim_{x \to 3} x = 3 \qquad \text{and} \qquad \lim_{x \to -7} (4) = \lim_{x \to 2} (4) = 4.$$

We prove these results in Example 3 in Section 2.3. ■

Some ways that limits can fail to exist are illustrated in Figure 2.7 and described in the next example.

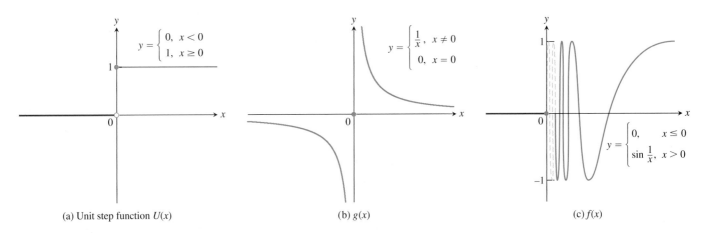

(a) Unit step function $U(x)$

(b) $g(x)$

(c) $f(x)$

FIGURE 2.7   None of these functions has a limit as x approaches 0 (Example 9).

EXAMPLE 9   A Function May Fail to Have a Limit at a Point in Its Domain

Discuss the behavior of the following functions as $x \to 0$.

(a) $U(x) = \begin{cases} 0, & x < 0 \\ 1, & x \geq 0 \end{cases}$

(b) $g(x) = \begin{cases} \dfrac{1}{x}, & x \neq 0 \\ 0, & x = 0 \end{cases}$

(c) $f(x) = \begin{cases} 0, & x \leq 0 \\ \sin \dfrac{1}{x}, & x > 0 \end{cases}$

Solution

(a) It *jumps:* The **unit step function** $U(x)$ has no limit as $x \to 0$ because its values jump at $x = 0$. For negative values of x arbitrarily close to zero, $U(x) = 0$. For positive values of x arbitrarily close to zero, $U(x) = 1$. There is no *single* value L approached by $U(x)$ as $x \to 0$ (Figure 2.7a).

(b) It *grows too large to have a limit:* $g(x)$ has no limit as $x \to 0$ because the values of g grow arbitrarily large in absolute value as $x \to 0$ and do not stay close to *any* real number (Figure 2.7b).

(c) It *oscillates too much to have a limit:* $f(x)$ has no limit as $x \to 0$ because the function's values oscillate between $+1$ and -1 in every open interval containing 0. The values do not stay close to any one number as $x \to 0$ (Figure 2.7c). ∎

Using Calculators and Computers to Estimate Limits

Tables 2.1 and 2.2 illustrate using a calculator or computer to guess a limit numerically as x gets closer and closer to x_0. That procedure would also be successful for the limits of functions like those in Example 7 (these are *continuous* functions and we study them in Section 2.6). However, calculators and computers can give *false values and misleading impressions* for functions that are undefined at a point or fail to have a limit there. The differential calculus will help us know when a calculator or computer is providing strange or ambiguous information about a function's behavior near some point (see Sections 4.4 and 4.6). For now, we simply need to be attentive to the fact that pitfalls may occur when using computing devices to guess the value of a limit. Here's one example.

EXAMPLE 10   Guessing a Limit

Guess the value of $\lim\limits_{x \to 0} \dfrac{\sqrt{x^2 + 100} - 10}{x^2}$.

Solution   Table 2.3 lists values of the function for several values near $x = 0$. As x approaches 0 through the values ± 1, ± 0.5, ± 0.10, and ± 0.01, the function seems to approach the number 0.05.

As we take even smaller values of x, ± 0.0005, ± 0.0001, ± 0.00001, and ± 0.000001, the function appears to approach the value 0.

So what is the answer? Is it 0.05 or 0, or some other value? The calculator/computer values are ambiguous, but the theorems on limits presented in the next section will confirm the correct limit value to be $0.05 \left(= 1/20\right)$. Problems such as these demonstrate the

TABLE 2.3 Computer values of $f(x) = \dfrac{\sqrt{x^2 + 100} - 10}{x^2}$ Near $x = 0$

x	$f(x)$	
± 1	0.049876	
± 0.5	0.049969	approaches 0.05?
± 0.1	0.049999	
± 0.01	0.050000	
± 0.0005	0.080000	
± 0.0001	0.000000	approaches 0?
± 0.00001	0.000000	
± 0.000001	0.000000	

power of mathematical reasoning, once it is developed, over the conclusions we might draw from making a few observations. Both approaches have advantages and disadvantages in revealing nature's realities. ∎

EXERCISES 2.1

Limits from Graphs

1. For the function $g(x)$ graphed here, find the following limits or explain why they do not exist.

   a. $\lim\limits_{x \to 1} g(x)$ **b.** $\lim\limits_{x \to 2} g(x)$ **c.** $\lim\limits_{x \to 3} g(x)$

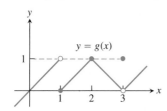

2. For the function $f(t)$ graphed here, find the following limits or explain why they do not exist.

   a. $\lim\limits_{t \to -2} f(t)$ **b.** $\lim\limits_{t \to -1} f(t)$ **c.** $\lim\limits_{t \to 0} f(t)$

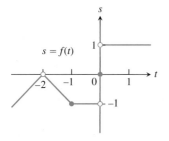

3. Which of the following statements about the function $y = f(x)$ graphed here are true, and which are false?

   a. $\lim\limits_{x \to 0} f(x)$ exists.

   b. $\lim\limits_{x \to 0} f(x) = 0$.

   c. $\lim\limits_{x \to 0} f(x) = 1$.

   d. $\lim\limits_{x \to 1} f(x) = 1$.

   e. $\lim\limits_{x \to 1} f(x) = 0$.

   f. $\lim\limits_{x \to x_0} f(x)$ exists at every point x_0 in $(-1, 1)$.

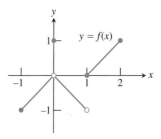

4. Which of the following statements about the function $y = f(x)$ graphed here are true, and which are false?

   a. $\lim\limits_{x \to 2} f(x)$ does not exist.

   b. $\lim\limits_{x \to 2} f(x) = 2$.

c. $\lim_{x \to 1} f(x)$ does not exist.

d. $\lim_{x \to x_0} f(x)$ exists at every point x_0 in $(-1, 1)$.

e. $\lim_{x \to x_0} f(x)$ exists at every point x_0 in $(1, 3)$.

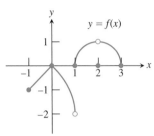

Existence of Limits

In Exercises 5 and 6, explain why the limits do not exist.

5. $\lim_{x \to 0} \dfrac{x}{|x|}$

6. $\lim_{x \to 1} \dfrac{1}{x - 1}$

7. Suppose that a function $f(x)$ is defined for all real values of x except $x = x_0$. Can anything be said about the existence of $\lim_{x \to x_0} f(x)$? Give reasons for your answer.

8. Suppose that a function $f(x)$ is defined for all x in $[-1, 1]$. Can anything be said about the existence of $\lim_{x \to 0} f(x)$? Give reasons for your answer.

9. If $\lim_{x \to 1} f(x) = 5$, must f be defined at $x = 1$? If it is, must $f(1) = 5$? Can we conclude *anything* about the values of f at $x = 1$? Explain.

10. If $f(1) = 5$, must $\lim_{x \to 1} f(x)$ exist? If it does, then must $\lim_{x \to 1} f(x) = 5$? Can we conclude *anything* about $\lim_{x \to 1} f(x)$? Explain.

Estimating Limits

T You will find a graphing calculator useful for Exercises 11–20.

11. Let $f(x) = (x^2 - 9)/(x + 3)$.

a. Make a table of the values of f at the points $x = -3.1$, -3.01, -3.001, and so on as far as your calculator can go. Then estimate $\lim_{x \to -3} f(x)$. What estimate do you arrive at if you evaluate f at $x = -2.9, -2.99, -2.999, \ldots$ instead?

b. Support your conclusions in part (a) by graphing f near $x_0 = -3$ and using Zoom and Trace to estimate y-values on the graph as $x \to -3$.

c. Find $\lim_{x \to -3} f(x)$ algebraically, as in Example 5.

12. Let $g(x) = (x^2 - 2)/\left(x - \sqrt{2}\right)$.

a. Make a table of the values of g at the points $x = 1.4, 1.41$, 1.414, and so on through successive decimal approximations of $\sqrt{2}$. Estimate $\lim_{x \to \sqrt{2}} g(x)$.

b. Support your conclusion in part (a) by graphing g near $x_0 = \sqrt{2}$ and using Zoom and Trace to estimate y-values on the graph as $x \to \sqrt{2}$.

c. Find $\lim_{x \to \sqrt{2}} g(x)$ algebraically.

13. Let $G(x) = (x + 6)/(x^2 + 4x - 12)$.

a. Make a table of the values of G at $x = -5.9, -5.99, -5.999$, and so on. Then estimate $\lim_{x \to -6} G(x)$. What estimate do you arrive at if you evaluate G at $x = -6.1, -6.01, -6.001, \ldots$ instead?

b. Support your conclusions in part (a) by graphing G and using Zoom and Trace to estimate y-values on the graph as $x \to -6$.

c. Find $\lim_{x \to -6} G(x)$ algebraically.

14. Let $h(x) = (x^2 - 2x - 3)/(x^2 - 4x + 3)$.

a. Make a table of the values of h at $x = 2.9, 2.99, 2.999$, and so on. Then estimate $\lim_{x \to 3} h(x)$. What estimate do you arrive at if you evaluate h at $x = 3.1, 3.01, 3.001, \ldots$ instead?

b. Support your conclusions in part (a) by graphing h near $x_0 = 3$ and using Zoom and Trace to estimate y-values on the graph as $x \to 3$.

c. Find $\lim_{x \to 3} h(x)$ algebraically.

15. Let $f(x) = (x^2 - 1)/(|x| - 1)$.

a. Make tables of the values of f at values of x that approach $x_0 = -1$ from above and below. Then estimate $\lim_{x \to -1} f(x)$.

b. Support your conclusion in part (a) by graphing f near $x_0 = -1$ and using Zoom and Trace to estimate y-values on the graph as $x \to -1$.

c. Find $\lim_{x \to -1} f(x)$ algebraically.

16. Let $F(x) = (x^2 + 3x + 2)/(2 - |x|)$.

a. Make tables of values of F at values of x that approach $x_0 = -2$ from above and below. Then estimate $\lim_{x \to -2} F(x)$.

b. Support your conclusion in part (a) by graphing F near $x_0 = -2$ and using Zoom and Trace to estimate y-values on the graph as $x \to -2$.

c. Find $\lim_{x \to -2} F(x)$ algebraically.

17. Let $g(\theta) = (\sin \theta)/\theta$.

a. Make a table of the values of g at values of θ that approach $\theta_0 = 0$ from above and below. Then estimate $\lim_{\theta \to 0} g(\theta)$.

b. Support your conclusion in part (a) by graphing g near $\theta_0 = 0$.

18. Let $G(t) = (1 - \cos t)/t^2$.

a. Make tables of values of G at values of t that approach $t_0 = 0$ from above and below. Then estimate $\lim_{t \to 0} G(t)$.

b. Support your conclusion in part (a) by graphing G near $t_0 = 0$.

19. Let $f(x) = x^{1/(1-x)}$.

a. Make tables of values of f at values of x that approach $x_0 = 1$ from above and below. Does f appear to have a limit as $x \to 1$? If so, what is it? If not, why not?

b. Support your conclusions in part (a) by graphing f near $x_0 = 1$.

20. Let $f(x) = (3^x - 1)/x$.

   a. Make tables of values of f at values of x that approach $x_0 = 0$ from above and below. Does f appear to have a limit as $x \to 0$? If so, what is it? If not, why not?

   b. Support your conclusions in part (a) by graphing f near $x_0 = 0$.

Limits by Substitution

In Exercises 21–28, find the limits by substitution. *Support your answers with a computer or calculator if available.*

21. $\lim\limits_{x \to 2} 2x$

22. $\lim\limits_{x \to 0} 2x$

23. $\lim\limits_{x \to 1/3} (3x - 1)$

24. $\lim\limits_{x \to 1} \dfrac{-1}{(3x - 1)}$

25. $\lim\limits_{x \to -1} 3x(2x - 1)$

26. $\lim\limits_{x \to -1} \dfrac{3x^2}{2x - 1}$

27. $\lim\limits_{x \to \pi/2} x \sin x$

28. $\lim\limits_{x \to \pi} \dfrac{\cos x}{1 - \pi}$

Average Rates of Change

In Exercises 29–34, find the average rate of change of the function over the given interval or intervals.

29. $f(x) = x^3 + 1$;

   a. $[2, 3]$ **b.** $[-1, 1]$

30. $g(x) = x^2$;

   a. $[-1, 1]$ **b.** $[-2, 0]$

31. $h(t) = \cot t$;

   a. $[\pi/4, 3\pi/4]$ **b.** $[\pi/6, \pi/2]$

32. $g(t) = 2 + \cos t$;

   a. $[0, \pi]$ **b.** $[-\pi, \pi]$

33. $R(\theta) = \sqrt{4\theta + 1}$; $[0, 2]$

34. $P(\theta) = \theta^3 - 4\theta^2 + 5\theta$; $[1, 2]$

35. A Ford Mustang Cobra's speed The accompanying figure shows the time-to-distance graph for a 1994 Ford Mustang Cobra accelerating from a standstill.

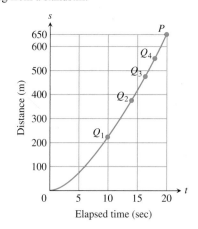

a. Estimate the slopes of secants PQ_1, PQ_2, PQ_3, and PQ_4, arranging them in order in a table like the one in Figure 2.3. What are the appropriate units for these slopes?

b. Then estimate the Cobra's speed at time $t = 20$ sec.

36. The accompanying figure shows the plot of distance fallen versus time for an object that fell from the lunar landing module a distance 80 m to the surface of the moon.

   a. Estimate the slopes of the secants PQ_1, PQ_2, PQ_3, and PQ_4, arranging them in a table like the one in Figure 2.3.

   b. About how fast was the object going when it hit the surface?

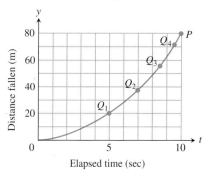

T 37. The profits of a small company for each of the first five years of its operation are given in the following table:

Year	Profit in $1000s
1990	6
1991	27
1992	62
1993	111
1994	174

   a. Plot points representing the profit as a function of year, and join them by as smooth a curve as you can.

   b. What is the average rate of increase of the profits between 1992 and 1994?

   c. Use your graph to estimate the rate at which the profits were changing in 1992.

T 38. Make a table of values for the function $F(x) = (x + 2)/(x - 2)$ at the points $x = 1.2$, $x = 11/10$, $x = 101/100$, $x = 1001/1000$, $x = 10001/10000$, and $x = 1$.

   a. Find the average rate of change of $F(x)$ over the intervals $[1, x]$ for each $x \neq 1$ in your table.

   b. Extending the table if necessary, try to determine the rate of change of $F(x)$ at $x = 1$.

T 39. Let $g(x) = \sqrt{x}$ for $x \geq 0$.

   a. Find the average rate of change of $g(x)$ with respect to x over the intervals $[1, 2]$, $[1, 1.5]$ and $[1, 1 + h]$.

   b. Make a table of values of the average rate of change of g with respect to x over the interval $[1, 1 + h]$ for some values of h

approaching zero, say $h = 0.1, 0.01, 0.001, 0.0001, 0.00001$, and 0.000001.

c. What does your table indicate is the rate of change of $g(x)$ with respect to x at $x = 1$?

d. Calculate the limit as h approaches zero of the average rate of change of $g(x)$ with respect to x over the interval $[1, 1 + h]$.

T **40.** Let $f(t) = 1/t$ for $t \neq 0$.

a. Find the average rate of change of f with respect to t over the intervals (i) from $t = 2$ to $t = 3$, and (ii) from $t = 2$ to $t = T$.

b. Make a table of values of the average rate of change of f with respect to t over the interval $[2, T]$, for some values of T approaching 2, say $T = 2.1, 2.01, 2.001, 2.0001, 2.00001$, and 2.000001.

c. What does your table indicate is the rate of change of f with respect to t at $t = 2$?

d. Calculate the limit as T approaches 2 of the average rate of change of f with respect to t over the interval from 2 to T. You will have to do some algebra before you can substitute $T = 2$.

COMPUTER EXPLORATIONS

Graphical Estimates of Limits

In Exercises 41–46, use a CAS to perform the following steps:

a. Plot the function near the point x_0 being approached.

b. From your plot guess the value of the limit.

41. $\lim\limits_{x \to 2} \dfrac{x^4 - 16}{x - 2}$

42. $\lim\limits_{x \to -1} \dfrac{x^3 - x^2 - 5x - 3}{(x + 1)^2}$

43. $\lim\limits_{x \to 0} \dfrac{\sqrt[3]{1 + x} - 1}{x}$

44. $\lim\limits_{x \to 3} \dfrac{x^2 - 9}{\sqrt{x^2 + 7} - 4}$

45. $\lim\limits_{x \to 0} \dfrac{1 - \cos x}{x \sin x}$

46. $\lim\limits_{x \to 0} \dfrac{2x^2}{3 - 3 \cos x}$

2.2   Calculating Limits Using the Limit Laws

HISTORICAL ESSAY*

Limits

In Section 2.1 we used graphs and calculators to guess the values of limits. This section presents theorems for calculating limits. The first three let us build on the results of Example 8 in the preceding section to find limits of polynomials, rational functions, and powers. The fourth and fifth prepare for calculations later in the text.

The Limit Laws

The next theorem tells how to calculate limits of functions that are arithmetic combinations of functions whose limits we already know.

THEOREM 1   Limit Laws

If L, M, c and k are real numbers and

$$\lim\limits_{x \to c} f(x) = L \qquad \text{and} \qquad \lim\limits_{x \to c} g(x) = M, \quad \text{then}$$

1. *Sum Rule*: $\qquad\qquad\qquad\qquad \lim\limits_{x \to c} (f(x) + g(x)) = L + M$

The limit of the sum of two functions is the sum of their limits.

2. *Difference Rule*: $\qquad\qquad\quad\;\; \lim\limits_{x \to c} (f(x) - g(x)) = L - M$

The limit of the difference of two functions is the difference of their limits.

3. *Product Rule*: $\qquad\qquad\qquad\;\; \lim\limits_{x \to c} (f(x) \cdot g(x)) = L \cdot M$

The limit of a product of two functions is the product of their limits.

To learn more about the historical figures and the development of the major elements and topics of calculus, visit **www.aw-bc.com/thomas**.

4. *Constant Multiple Rule:* $\qquad\qquad \lim_{x \to c}(k \cdot f(x)) = k \cdot L$

The limit of a constant times a function is the constant times the limit of the function.

5. *Quotient Rule:* $\qquad\qquad\qquad \lim_{x \to c} \dfrac{f(x)}{g(x)} = \dfrac{L}{M}, \quad M \neq 0$

The limit of a quotient of two functions is the quotient of their limits, provided the limit of the denominator is not zero.

6. *Power Rule*: If r and s are integers with no common factor and $s \neq 0$, then

$$\lim_{x \to c}(f(x))^{r/s} = L^{r/s}$$

provided that $L^{r/s}$ is a real number. (If s is even, we assume that $L > 0$.)

The limit of a rational power of a function is that power of the limit of the function, provided the latter is a real number.

It is easy to convince ourselves that the properties in Theorem 1 are true (although these intuitive arguments do not constitute proofs). If x is sufficiently close to c, then $f(x)$ is close to L and $g(x)$ is close to M, from our informal definition of a limit. It is then reasonable that $f(x) + g(x)$ is close to $L + M$; $f(x) - g(x)$ is close to $L - M$; $f(x)g(x)$ is close to LM; $kf(x)$ is close to kL; and that $f(x)/g(x)$ is close to L/M if M is not zero. We prove the Sum Rule in Section 2.3, based on a precise definition of limit. Rules 2–5 are proved in Appendix 2. Rule 6 is proved in more advanced texts.

Here are some examples of how Theorem 1 can be used to find limits of polynomial and rational functions.

EXAMPLE 1   Using the Limit Laws

Use the observations $\lim_{x \to c} k = k$ and $\lim_{x \to c} x = c$ (Example 8 in Section 2.1) and the properties of limits to find the following limits.

(a) $\lim_{x \to c}(x^3 + 4x^2 - 3)$ **(b)** $\lim_{x \to c} \dfrac{x^4 + x^2 - 1}{x^2 + 5}$ **(c)** $\lim_{x \to -2} \sqrt{4x^2 - 3}$

Solution

(a) $\lim_{x \to c}(x^3 + 4x^2 - 3) = \lim_{x \to c} x^3 + \lim_{x \to c} 4x^2 - \lim_{x \to c} 3$ Sum and Difference Rules

$\qquad\qquad\qquad\qquad = c^3 + 4c^2 - 3$ Product and Multiple Rules

(b) $\lim_{x \to c} \dfrac{x^4 + x^2 - 1}{x^2 + 5} = \dfrac{\lim_{x \to c}(x^4 + x^2 - 1)}{\lim_{x \to c}(x^2 + 5)}$ Quotient Rule

$\qquad\qquad\qquad = \dfrac{\lim_{x \to c} x^4 + \lim_{x \to c} x^2 - \lim_{x \to c} 1}{\lim_{x \to c} x^2 + \lim_{x \to c} 5}$ Sum and Difference Rules

$\qquad\qquad\qquad = \dfrac{c^4 + c^2 - 1}{c^2 + 5}$ Power or Product Rule

(c) $\lim\limits_{x \to -2} \sqrt{4x^2 - 3} = \sqrt{\lim\limits_{x \to -2} (4x^2 - 3)}$

Power Rule with $r/s = \frac{1}{2}$

$$= \sqrt{\lim\limits_{x \to -2} 4x^2 - \lim\limits_{x \to -2} 3}$$

Difference Rule

$$= \sqrt{4(-2)^2 - 3}$$

Product and Multiple Rules

$$= \sqrt{16 - 3}$$

$$= \sqrt{13} \qquad\blacksquare$$

Two consequences of Theorem 1 further simplify the task of calculating limits of polynomials and rational functions. To evaluate the limit of a polynomial function as x approaches c, merely substitute c for x in the formula for the function. To evaluate the limit of a rational function as x approaches a point c *at which the denominator is not zero*, substitute c for x in the formula for the function. (See Examples 1a and 1b.)

THEOREM 2 **Limits of Polynomials Can Be Found by Substitution**

If $P(x) = a_n x^n + a_{n-1} x^{n-1} + \cdots + a_0$, then

$$\lim\limits_{x \to c} P(x) = P(c) = a_n c^n + a_{n-1} c^{n-1} + \cdots + a_0.$$

THEOREM 3 **Limits of Rational Functions Can Be Found by Substitution If the Limit of the Denominator Is Not Zero**

If $P(x)$ and $Q(x)$ are polynomials and $Q(c) \neq 0$, then

$$\lim\limits_{x \to c} \frac{P(x)}{Q(x)} = \frac{P(c)}{Q(c)}.$$

EXAMPLE 2 Limit of a Rational Function

$$\lim\limits_{x \to -1} \frac{x^3 + 4x^2 - 3}{x^2 + 5} = \frac{(-1)^3 + 4(-1)^2 - 3}{(-1)^2 + 5} = \frac{0}{6} = 0$$

This result is similar to the second limit in Example 1 with $c = -1$, now done in one step. $\blacksquare$

Identifying Common Factors

It can be shown that if $Q(x)$ is a polynomial and $Q(c) = 0$, then $(x - c)$ is a factor of $Q(x)$. Thus, if the numerator and denominator of a rational function of x are both zero at $x = c$, they have $(x - c)$ as a common factor.

Eliminating Zero Denominators Algebraically

Theorem 3 applies only if the denominator of the rational function is not zero at the limit point c. If the denominator is zero, canceling common factors in the numerator and denominator may reduce the fraction to one whose denominator is no longer zero at c. If this happens, we can find the limit by substitution in the simplified fraction.

EXAMPLE 3 Canceling a Common Factor

Evaluate

$$\lim\limits_{x \to 1} \frac{x^2 + x - 2}{x^2 - x}.$$

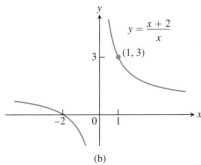

FIGURE 2.8 The graph of $f(x) = (x^2 + x - 2)/(x^2 - x)$ in part (a) is the same as the graph of $g(x) = (x + 2)/x$ in part (b) except at $x = 1$, where f is undefined. The functions have the same limit as $x \to 1$ (Example 3).

Solution We cannot substitute $x = 1$ because it makes the denominator zero. We test the numerator to see if it, too, is zero at $x = 1$. It is, so it has a factor of $(x - 1)$ in common with the denominator. Canceling the $(x - 1)$'s gives a simpler fraction with the same values as the original for $x \neq 1$:

$$\frac{x^2 + x - 2}{x^2 - x} = \frac{(x - 1)(x + 2)}{x(x - 1)} = \frac{x + 2}{x}, \quad \text{if } x \neq 1.$$

Using the simpler fraction, we find the limit of these values as $x \to 1$ by substitution:

$$\lim_{x \to 1} \frac{x^2 + x - 2}{x^2 - x} = \lim_{x \to 1} \frac{x + 2}{x} = \frac{1 + 2}{1} = 3.$$

See Figure 2.8. ∎

EXAMPLE 4 Creating and Canceling a Common Factor

Evaluate

$$\lim_{x \to 0} \frac{\sqrt{x^2 + 100} - 10}{x^2}.$$

Solution This is the limit we considered in Example 10 of the preceding section. We cannot substitute $x = 0$, and the numerator and denominator have no obvious common factors. We can create a common factor by multiplying both numerator and denominator by the expression $\sqrt{x^2 + 100} + 10$ (obtained by changing the sign after the square root). The preliminary algebra rationalizes the numerator:

$$\frac{\sqrt{x^2 + 100} - 10}{x^2} = \frac{\sqrt{x^2 + 100} - 10}{x^2} \cdot \frac{\sqrt{x^2 + 100} + 10}{\sqrt{x^2 + 100} + 10}$$

$$= \frac{x^2 + 100 - 100}{x^2\left(\sqrt{x^2 + 100} + 10\right)}$$

$$= \frac{x^2}{x^2\left(\sqrt{x^2 + 100} + 10\right)} \quad \text{Common factor } x^2$$

$$= \frac{1}{\sqrt{x^2 + 100} + 10}. \quad \text{Cancel } x^2 \text{ for } x \neq 0$$

Therefore,

$$\lim_{x \to 0} \frac{\sqrt{x^2 + 100} - 10}{x^2} = \lim_{x \to 0} \frac{1}{\sqrt{x^2 + 100} + 10}$$

$$= \frac{1}{\sqrt{0^2 + 100} + 10} \quad \begin{array}{l}\text{Denominator}\\ \text{not 0 at } x = 0;\\ \text{substitute}\end{array}$$

$$= \frac{1}{20} = 0.05.$$

This calculation provides the correct answer to the ambiguous computer results in Example 10 of the preceding section. ∎

The Sandwich Theorem

The following theorem will enable us to calculate a variety of limits in subsequent chapters. It is called the Sandwich Theorem because it refers to a function f whose values are

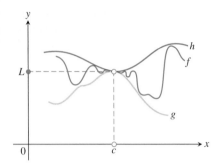

FIGURE 2.9 The graph of f is sandwiched between the graphs of g and h.

sandwiched between the values of two other functions g and h that have the same limit L at a point c. Being trapped between the values of two functions that approach L, the values of f must also approach L (Figure 2.9). You will find a proof in Appendix 2.

THEOREM 4   The Sandwich Theorem

Suppose that $g(x) \leq f(x) \leq h(x)$ for all x in some open interval containing c, except possibly at $x = c$ itself. Suppose also that

$$\lim_{x \to c} g(x) = \lim_{x \to c} h(x) = L.$$

Then $\lim_{x \to c} f(x) = L$.

The Sandwich Theorem is sometimes called the Squeeze Theorem or the Pinching Theorem.

EXAMPLE 5   Applying the Sandwich Theorem

Given that

$$1 - \frac{x^2}{4} \leq u(x) \leq 1 + \frac{x^2}{2} \qquad \text{for all } x \neq 0,$$

find $\lim_{x \to 0} u(x)$, no matter how complicated u is.

Solution   Since

$$\lim_{x \to 0} (1 - (x^2/4)) = 1 \qquad \text{and} \qquad \lim_{x \to 0} (1 + (x^2/2)) = 1,$$

the Sandwich Theorem implies that $\lim_{x \to 0} u(x) = 1$ (Figure 2.10).   ∎

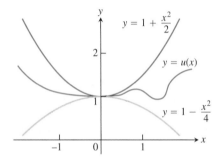

FIGURE 2.10 Any function $u(x)$ whose graph lies in the region between $y = 1 + (x^2/2)$ and $y = 1 - (x^2/4)$ has limit 1 as $x \to 0$ (Example 5).

EXAMPLE 6   More Applications of the Sandwich Theorem

(a) (Figure 2.11a). It follows from the definition of $\sin \theta$ that $-|\theta| \leq \sin \theta \leq |\theta|$ for all θ, and since $\lim_{\theta \to 0} (-|\theta|) = \lim_{\theta \to 0} |\theta| = 0$, we have

$$\lim_{\theta \to 0} \sin \theta = 0.$$

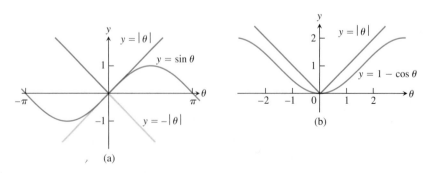

FIGURE 2.11 The Sandwich Theorem confirms that (a) $\lim_{\theta \to 0} \sin \theta = 0$ and (b) $\lim_{\theta \to 0} (1 - \cos \theta) = 0$ (Example 6).

(b) (Figure 2.11b). From the definition of $\cos \theta$, $0 \le 1 - \cos \theta \le |\theta|$ for all θ, and we have $\lim_{\theta \to 0} (1 - \cos \theta) = 0$ or

$$\lim_{\theta \to 0} \cos \theta = 1.$$

(c) For any function $f(x)$, if $\lim_{x \to c} |f(x)| = 0$, then $\lim_{x \to c} f(x) = 0$. The argument: $-|f(x)| \le f(x) \le |f(x)|$ and $-|f(x)|$ and $|f(x)|$ have limit 0 as $x \to c$. ∎

Another important property of limits is given by the next theorem. A proof is given in the next section.

THEOREM 5   If $f(x) \le g(x)$ for all x in some open interval containing c, except possibly at $x = c$ itself, and the limits of f and g both exist as x approaches c, then

$$\lim_{x \to c} f(x) \le \lim_{x \to c} g(x).$$

The assertion resulting from replacing the less than or equal to $\le$ inequality by the strict $<$ inequality in Theorem 5 is false. Figure 2.11a shows that for $\theta \ne 0$, $-|\theta| < \sin \theta < |\theta|$, but in the limit as $\theta \to 0$, equality holds.

EXERCISES 2.2

Limit Calculations

Find the limits in Exercises 1–18.

1. $\lim_{x \to -7} (2x + 5)$

2. $\lim_{x \to 12} (10 - 3x)$

3. $\lim_{x \to 2} (-x^2 + 5x - 2)$

4. $\lim_{x \to -2} (x^3 - 2x^2 + 4x + 8)$

5. $\lim_{t \to 6} 8(t - 5)(t - 7)$

6. $\lim_{s \to 2/3} 3s(2s - 1)$

7. $\lim_{x \to 2} \dfrac{x + 3}{x + 6}$

8. $\lim_{x \to 5} \dfrac{4}{x - 7}$

9. $\lim_{y \to -5} \dfrac{y^2}{5 - y}$

10. $\lim_{y \to 2} \dfrac{y + 2}{y^2 + 5y + 6}$

11. $\lim_{x \to -1} 3(2x - 1)^2$

12. $\lim_{x \to -4} (x + 3)^{1984}$

13. $\lim_{y \to -3} (5 - y)^{4/3}$

14. $\lim_{z \to 0} (2z - 8)^{1/3}$

15. $\lim_{h \to 0} \dfrac{3}{\sqrt{3h + 1} + 1}$

16. $\lim_{h \to 0} \dfrac{5}{\sqrt{5h + 4} + 2}$

17. $\lim_{h \to 0} \dfrac{\sqrt{3h + 1} - 1}{h}$

18. $\lim_{h \to 0} \dfrac{\sqrt{5h + 4} - 2}{h}$

Find the limits in Exercises 19–36.

19. $\lim_{x \to 5} \dfrac{x - 5}{x^2 - 25}$

20. $\lim_{x \to -3} \dfrac{x + 3}{x^2 + 4x + 3}$

21. $\lim_{x \to -5} \dfrac{x^2 + 3x - 10}{x + 5}$

22. $\lim_{x \to 2} \dfrac{x^2 - 7x + 10}{x - 2}$

23. $\lim_{t \to 1} \dfrac{t^2 + t - 2}{t^2 - 1}$

24. $\lim_{t \to -1} \dfrac{t^2 + 3t + 2}{t^2 - t - 2}$

25. $\lim_{x \to -2} \dfrac{-2x - 4}{x^3 + 2x^2}$

26. $\lim_{y \to 0} \dfrac{5y^3 + 8y^2}{3y^4 - 16y^2}$

27. $\lim_{u \to 1} \dfrac{u^4 - 1}{u^3 - 1}$

28. $\lim_{v \to 2} \dfrac{v^3 - 8}{v^4 - 16}$

29. $\lim_{x \to 9} \dfrac{\sqrt{x} - 3}{x - 9}$

30. $\lim_{x \to 4} \dfrac{4x - x^2}{2 - \sqrt{x}}$

31. $\lim_{x \to 1} \dfrac{x - 1}{\sqrt{x + 3} - 2}$

32. $\lim_{x \to -1} \dfrac{\sqrt{x^2 + 8} - 3}{x + 1}$

33. $\lim_{x \to 2} \dfrac{\sqrt{x^2 + 12} - 4}{x - 2}$

34. $\lim_{x \to -2} \dfrac{x + 2}{\sqrt{x^2 + 5} - 3}$

35. $\lim\limits_{x \to -3} \dfrac{2 - \sqrt{x^2 - 5}}{x + 3}$

36. $\lim\limits_{x \to 4} \dfrac{4 - x}{5 - \sqrt{x^2 + 9}}$

Using Limit Rules

37. Suppose $\lim_{x \to 0} f(x) = 1$ and $\lim_{x \to 0} g(x) = -5$. Name the rules in Theorem 1 that are used to accomplish steps (a), (b), and (c) of the following calculation.

$$\lim_{x \to 0} \frac{2f(x) - g(x)}{(f(x) + 7)^{2/3}} = \frac{\lim\limits_{x \to 0}(2f(x) - g(x))}{\lim\limits_{x \to 0}(f(x) + 7)^{2/3}} \quad \text{(a)}$$

$$= \frac{\lim\limits_{x \to 0} 2f(x) - \lim\limits_{x \to 0} g(x)}{\left(\lim\limits_{x \to 0}(f(x) + 7)\right)^{2/3}} \quad \text{(b)}$$

$$= \frac{2 \lim\limits_{x \to 0} f(x) - \lim\limits_{x \to 0} g(x)}{\left(\lim\limits_{x \to 0} f(x) + \lim\limits_{x \to 0} 7\right)^{2/3}} \quad \text{(c)}$$

$$= \frac{(2)(1) - (-5)}{(1 + 7)^{2/3}} = \frac{7}{4}$$

38. Let $\lim_{x \to 1} h(x) = 5$, $\lim_{x \to 1} p(x) = 1$, and $\lim_{x \to 1} r(x) = 2$. Name the rules in Theorem 1 that are used to accomplish steps (a), (b), and (c) of the following calculation.

$$\lim_{x \to 1} \frac{\sqrt{5h(x)}}{p(x)(4 - r(x))} = \frac{\lim\limits_{x \to 1}\sqrt{5h(x)}}{\lim\limits_{x \to 1}(p(x)(4 - r(x)))} \quad \text{(a)}$$

$$= \frac{\sqrt{\lim\limits_{x \to 1} 5h(x)}}{\left(\lim\limits_{x \to 1} p(x)\right)\left(\lim\limits_{x \to 1}\left(4 - r(x)\right)\right)} \quad \text{(b)}$$

$$= \frac{\sqrt{5 \lim\limits_{x \to 1} h(x)}}{\left(\lim\limits_{x \to 1} p(x)\right)\left(\lim\limits_{x \to 1} 4 - \lim\limits_{x \to 1} r(x)\right)} \quad \text{(c)}$$

$$= \frac{\sqrt{(5)(5)}}{(1)(4 - 2)} = \frac{5}{2}$$

39. Suppose $\lim_{x \to c} f(x) = 5$ and $\lim_{x \to c} g(x) = -2$. Find

a. $\lim\limits_{x \to c} f(x)g(x)$ **b.** $\lim\limits_{x \to c} 2f(x)g(x)$

c. $\lim\limits_{x \to c}(f(x) + 3g(x))$ **d.** $\lim\limits_{x \to c} \dfrac{f(x)}{f(x) - g(x)}$

40. Suppose $\lim_{x \to 4} f(x) = 0$ and $\lim_{x \to 4} g(x) = -3$. Find

a. $\lim\limits_{x \to 4}(g(x) + 3)$ **b.** $\lim\limits_{x \to 4} xf(x)$

c. $\lim\limits_{x \to 4}(g(x))^2$ **d.** $\lim\limits_{x \to 4} \dfrac{g(x)}{f(x) - 1}$

41. Suppose $\lim_{x \to b} f(x) = 7$ and $\lim_{x \to b} g(x) = -3$. Find

a. $\lim\limits_{x \to b}(f(x) + g(x))$ **b.** $\lim\limits_{x \to b} f(x) \cdot g(x)$

c. $\lim\limits_{x \to b} 4g(x)$ **d.** $\lim\limits_{x \to b} f(x)/g(x)$

42. Suppose that $\lim_{x \to -2} p(x) = 4$, $\lim_{x \to -2} r(x) = 0$, and $\lim_{x \to -2} s(x) = -3$. Find

a. $\lim\limits_{x \to -2}(p(x) + r(x) + s(x))$

b. $\lim\limits_{x \to -2} p(x) \cdot r(x) \cdot s(x)$

c. $\lim\limits_{x \to -2}(-4p(x) + 5r(x))/s(x)$

Limits of Average Rates of Change

Because of their connection with secant lines, tangents, and instantaneous rates, limits of the form

$$\lim_{h \to 0} \frac{f(x + h) - f(x)}{h}$$

occur frequently in calculus. In Exercises 43–48, evaluate this limit for the given value of x and function f.

43. $f(x) = x^2, \quad x = 1$ **44.** $f(x) = x^2, \quad x = -2$

45. $f(x) = 3x - 4, \quad x = 2$ **46.** $f(x) = 1/x, \quad x = -2$

47. $f(x) = \sqrt{x}, \quad x = 7$ **48.** $f(x) = \sqrt{3x + 1}, \quad x = 0$

Using the Sandwich Theorem

49. If $\sqrt{5 - 2x^2} \le f(x) \le \sqrt{5 - x^2}$ for $-1 \le x \le 1$, find $\lim_{x \to 0} f(x)$.

50. If $2 - x^2 \le g(x) \le 2 \cos x$ for all x, find $\lim_{x \to 0} g(x)$.

51. a. It can be shown that the inequalities

$$1 - \frac{x^2}{6} < \frac{x \sin x}{2 - 2 \cos x} < 1$$

hold for all values of x close to zero. What, if anything, does this tell you about

$$\lim_{x \to 0} \frac{x \sin x}{2 - 2 \cos x}?$$

Give reasons for your answer.

T b. Graph

$$y = 1 - (x^2/6), \, y = (x \sin x)/(2 - 2 \cos x), \text{ and } y = 1$$

together for $-2 \le x \le 2$. Comment on the behavior of the graphs as $x \to 0$.

52. a. Suppose that the inequalities

$$\frac{1}{2} - \frac{x^2}{24} < \frac{1 - \cos x}{x^2} < \frac{1}{2}$$

hold for values of x close to zero. (They do, as you will see in Section 11.9.) What, if anything, does this tell you about

$$\lim_{x \to 0} \frac{1 - \cos x}{x^2}?$$

Give reasons for your answer.

b. Graph the equations $y = (1/2) - (x^2/24)$, $y = (1 - \cos x)/x^2$, and $y = 1/2$ together for $-2 \le x \le 2$. Comment on the behavior of the graphs as $x \to 0$.

Theory and Examples

53. If $x^4 \le f(x) \le x^2$ for x in $[-1, 1]$ and $x^2 \le f(x) \le x^4$ for $x < -1$ and $x > 1$, at what points c do you automatically know $\lim_{x \to c} f(x)$? What can you say about the value of the limit at these points?

54. Suppose that $g(x) \le f(x) \le h(x)$ for all $x \ne 2$ and suppose that

$$\lim_{x \to 2} g(x) = \lim_{x \to 2} h(x) = -5.$$

Can we conclude anything about the values of f, g, and h at $x = 2$? Could $f(2) = 0$? Could $\lim_{x \to 2} f(x) = 0$? Give reasons for your answers.

55. If $\lim_{x \to 4} \dfrac{f(x) - 5}{x - 2} = 1$, find $\lim_{x \to 4} f(x)$.

56. If $\lim_{x \to -2} \dfrac{f(x)}{x^2} = 1$, find

    a. $\lim_{x \to -2} f(x)$ **b.** $\lim_{x \to -2} \dfrac{f(x)}{x}$

57. **a.** If $\lim_{x \to 2} \dfrac{f(x) - 5}{x - 2} = 3$, find $\lim_{x \to 2} f(x)$.

    b. If $\lim_{x \to 2} \dfrac{f(x) - 5}{x - 2} = 4$, find $\lim_{x \to 2} f(x)$.

58. If $\lim_{x \to 0} \dfrac{f(x)}{x^2} = 1$, find

    a. $\lim_{x \to 0} f(x)$ **b.** $\lim_{x \to 0} \dfrac{f(x)}{x}$

T **59.** **a.** Graph $g(x) = x \sin(1/x)$ to estimate $\lim_{x \to 0} g(x)$, zooming in on the origin as necessary.

    b. Confirm your estimate in part (a) with a proof.

T **60.** **a.** Graph $h(x) = x^2 \cos(1/x^3)$ to estimate $\lim_{x \to 0} h(x)$, zooming in on the origin as necessary.

    b. Confirm your estimate in part (a) with a proof.

2.3 The Precise Definition of a Limit

Now that we have gained some insight into the limit concept, working intuitively with the informal definition, we turn our attention to its precise definition. We replace vague phrases like "gets arbitrarily close to" in the informal definition with specific conditions that can be applied to any particular example. With a precise definition we will be able to prove conclusively the limit properties given in the preceding section, and we can establish other particular limits important to the study of calculus.

To show that the limit of $f(x)$ as $x \to x_0$ equals the number L, we need to show that the gap between $f(x)$ and L can be made "as small as we choose" if x is kept "close enough" to x_0. Let us see what this would require if we specified the size of the gap between $f(x)$ and L.

EXAMPLE 1   A Linear Function

Consider the function $y = 2x - 1$ near $x_0 = 4$. Intuitively it is clear that y is close to 7 when x is close to 4, so $\lim_{x \to 4}(2x - 1) = 7$. However, how close to $x_0 = 4$ does x have to be so that $y = 2x - 1$ differs from 7 by, say, less than 2 units?

Solution   We are asked: For what values of x is $|y - 7| < 2$? To find the answer we first express $|y - 7|$ in terms of x:

$$|y - 7| = |(2x - 1) - 7| = |2x - 8|.$$

The question then becomes: what values of x satisfy the inequality $|2x - 8| < 2$? To find out, we solve the inequality:

$$|2x - 8| < 2$$
$$-2 < 2x - 8 < 2$$
$$6 < 2x < 10$$
$$3 < x < 5$$
$$-1 < x - 4 < 1.$$

Keeping x within 1 unit of $x_0 = 4$ will keep y within 2 units of $y_0 = 7$ (Figure 2.12).   ∎

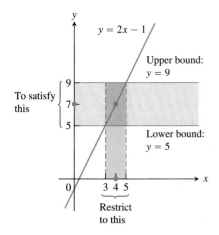

FIGURE 2.12 Keeping x within 1 unit of $x_0 = 4$ will keep y within 2 units of $y_0 = 7$ (Example 1).

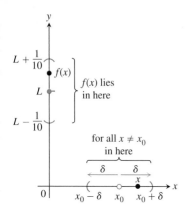

FIGURE 2.13 How should we define $\delta > 0$ so that keeping x within the interval $(x_0 - \delta, x_0 + \delta)$ will keep $f(x)$ within the interval $\left(L - \dfrac{1}{10}, L + \dfrac{1}{10} \right)$?

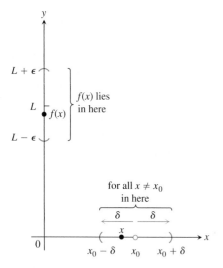

FIGURE 2.14 The relation of δ and ϵ in the definition of limit.

In the previous example we determined how close x must be to a particular value x_0 to ensure that the outputs $f(x)$ of some function lie within a prescribed interval about a limit value L. To show that the limit of $f(x)$ as $x \rightarrow x_0$ actually equals L, we must be able to show that the gap between $f(x)$ and L can be made less than *any prescribed error*, no matter how small, by holding x close enough to x_0.

Definition of Limit

Suppose we are watching the values of a function $f(x)$ as x approaches x_0 (without taking on the value of x_0 itself). Certainly we want to be able to say that $f(x)$ stays within one-tenth of a unit of L as soon as x stays within some distance δ of x_0 (Figure 2.13). But that in itself is not enough, because as x continues on its course toward x_0, what is to prevent $f(x)$ from jittering about within the interval from $L - (1/10)$ to $L + (1/10)$ without tending toward L?

We can be told that the error can be no more than $1/100$ or $1/1000$ or $1/100,000$. Each time, we find a new δ-interval about x_0 so that keeping x within that interval satisfies the new error tolerance. And each time the possibility exists that $f(x)$ jitters away from L at some stage.

The figures on the next page illustrate the problem. You can think of this as a quarrel between a skeptic and a scholar. The skeptic presents ϵ-challenges to prove that the limit does not exist or, more precisely, that there is room for doubt, and the scholar answers every challenge with a δ-interval around x_0.

How do we stop this seemingly endless series of challenges and responses? By proving that for every error tolerance ϵ that the challenger can produce, we can find, calculate, or conjure a matching distance δ that keeps x "close enough" to x_0 to keep $f(x)$ within that tolerance of L (Figure 2.14). This leads us to the precise definition of a limit.

DEFINITION   Limit of a Function

Let $f(x)$ be defined on an open interval about x_0, except possibly at x_0 itself. We say that the **limit of $f(x)$ as x approaches x_0 is the number L**, and write

$$\lim_{x \to x_0} f(x) = L,$$

if, for every number $\epsilon > 0$, there exists a corresponding number $\delta > 0$ such that for all x,

$$0 < |x - x_0| < \delta \quad \Rightarrow \quad |f(x) - L| < \epsilon.$$

One way to think about the definition is to suppose we are machining a generator shaft to a close tolerance. We may try for diameter L, but since nothing is perfect, we must be satisfied with a diameter $f(x)$ somewhere between $L - \epsilon$ and $L + \epsilon$. The δ is the measure of how accurate our control setting for x must be to guarantee this degree of accuracy in the diameter of the shaft. Notice that as the tolerance for error becomes stricter, we may have to adjust δ. That is, the value of δ, how tight our control setting must be, depends on the value of ϵ, the error tolerance.

Examples: Testing the Definition

The formal definition of limit does not tell how to find the limit of a function, but it enables us to verify that a suspected limit is correct. The following examples show how the

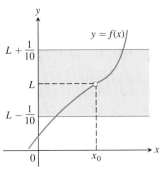

The challenge:

Make $\left| f(x) - L \right| < \epsilon = \dfrac{1}{10}$

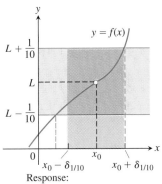

Response:

$\left| x - x_0 \right| < \delta_{1/10}$ (a number)

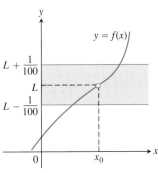

New challenge:

Make $\left| f(x) - L \right| < \epsilon = \dfrac{1}{100}$

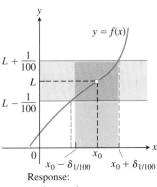

Response:

$\left| x - x_0 \right| < \delta_{1/100}$

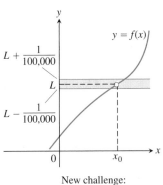

New challenge:

$\epsilon = \dfrac{1}{1000}$

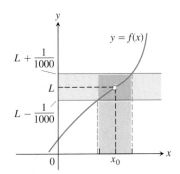

Response:

$\left| x - x_0 \right| < \delta_{1/1000}$

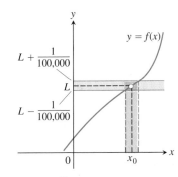

New challenge:

$\epsilon = \dfrac{1}{100,000}$

Response:

$\left| x - x_0 \right| < \delta_{1/100,000}$

New challenge:

$\epsilon = \cdots$

definition can be used to verify limit statements for specific functions. (The first two examples correspond to parts of Examples 7 and 8 in Section 2.1.) However, the real purpose of the definition is not to do calculations like this, but rather to prove general theorems so that the calculation of specific limits can be simplified.

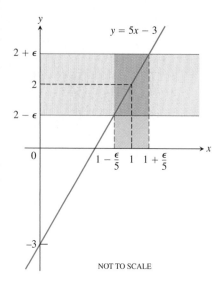

FIGURE 2.15 If $f(x) = 5x - 3$, then $0 < |x - 1| < \epsilon/5$ guarantees that $|f(x) - 2| < \epsilon$ (Example 2).

EXAMPLE 2   Testing the Definition

Show that

$$\lim_{x \to 1} (5x - 3) = 2.$$

Solution   Set $x_0 = 1$, $f(x) = 5x - 3$, and $L = 2$ in the definition of limit. For any given $\epsilon > 0$, we have to find a suitable $\delta > 0$ so that if $x \neq 1$ and x is within distance δ of $x_0 = 1$, that is, whenever

$$0 < |x - 1| < \delta,$$

it is true that $f(x)$ is within distance ϵ of $L = 2$, so

$$|f(x) - 2| < \epsilon.$$

We find δ by working backward from the ϵ-inequality:

$$|(5x - 3) - 2| = |5x - 5| < \epsilon$$
$$5|x - 1| < \epsilon$$
$$|x - 1| < \epsilon/5.$$

Thus, we can take $\delta = \epsilon/5$ (Figure 2.15). If $0 < |x - 1| < \delta = \epsilon/5$, then

$$|(5x - 3) - 2| = |5x - 5| = 5|x - 1| < 5(\epsilon/5) = \epsilon,$$

which proves that $\lim_{x \to 1}(5x - 3) = 2$.

The value of $\delta = \epsilon/5$ is not the only value that will make $0 < |x - 1| < \delta$ imply $|5x - 5| < \epsilon$. Any smaller positive δ will do as well. The definition does not ask for a "best" positive δ, just one that will work.   ∎

EXAMPLE 3   Limits of the Identity and Constant Functions

Prove:

(a) $\lim_{x \to x_0} x = x_0$ **(b)** $\lim_{x \to x_0} k = k$ (k constant).

Solution

(a) Let $\epsilon > 0$ be given. We must find $\delta > 0$ such that for all x

$$0 < |x - x_0| < \delta \quad \text{implies} \quad |x - x_0| < \epsilon.$$

The implication will hold if δ equals ϵ or any smaller positive number (Figure 2.16). This proves that $\lim_{x \to x_0} x = x_0$.

(b) Let $\epsilon > 0$ be given. We must find $\delta > 0$ such that for all x

$$0 < |x - x_0| < \delta \quad \text{implies} \quad |k - k| < \epsilon.$$

Since $k - k = 0$, we can use any positive number for δ and the implication will hold (Figure 2.17). This proves that $\lim_{x \to x_0} k = k$.   ∎

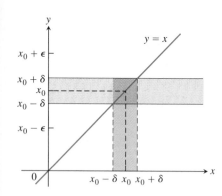

FIGURE 2.16 For the function $f(x) = x$, we find that $0 < |x - x_0| < \delta$ will guarantee $|f(x) - x_0| < \epsilon$ whenever $\delta \leq \epsilon$ (Example 3a).

Finding Deltas Algebraically for Given Epsilons

In Examples 2 and 3, the interval of values about x_0 for which $|f(x) - L|$ was less than ϵ was symmetric about x_0 and we could take δ to be half the length of that interval. When

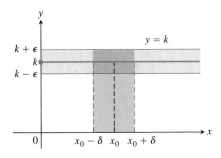

FIGURE 2.17 For the function $f(x) = k$, we find that $|f(x) - k| < \epsilon$ for any positive δ (Example 3b).

such symmetry is absent, as it usually is, we can take δ to be the distance from x_0 to the interval's *nearer* endpoint.

EXAMPLE 4   Finding Delta Algebraically

For the limit $\lim_{x \to 5} \sqrt{x - 1} = 2$, find a $\delta > 0$ that works for $\epsilon = 1$. That is, find a $\delta > 0$ such that for all x

$$0 < |x - 5| < \delta \quad \Rightarrow \quad |\sqrt{x - 1} - 2| < 1.$$

Solution   We organize the search into two steps, as discussed below.

1. *Solve the inequality* $|\sqrt{x - 1} - 2| < 1$ *to find an interval containing* $x_0 = 5$ *on which the inequality holds for all* $x \neq x_0$.

$$|\sqrt{x - 1} - 2| < 1$$
$$-1 < \sqrt{x - 1} - 2 < 1$$
$$1 < \sqrt{x - 1} < 3$$
$$1 < x - 1 < 9$$
$$2 < x < 10$$

The inequality holds for all x in the open interval $(2, 10)$, so it holds for all $x \neq 5$ in this interval as well (see Figure 2.19).

2. *Find a value of* $\delta > 0$ *to place the centered interval* $5 - \delta < x < 5 + \delta$ (centered at $x_0 = 5$) *inside the interval* $(2, 10)$. The distance from 5 to the nearer endpoint of $(2, 10)$ is 3 (Figure 2.18). If we take $\delta = 3$ or any smaller positive number, then the inequality $0 < |x - 5| < \delta$ will automatically place x between 2 and 10 to make $|\sqrt{x - 1} - 2| < 1$ (Figure 2.19)

$$0 < |x - 5| < 3 \quad \Rightarrow \quad |\sqrt{x - 1} - 2| < 1.$$

FIGURE 2.18 An open interval of radius 3 about $x_0 = 5$ will lie inside the open interval $(2, 10)$.

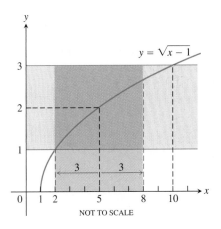

FIGURE 2.19 The function and intervals in Example 4.

How to Find Algebraically a δ for a Given f, L, x_0, and $\epsilon > 0$

The process of finding a $\delta > 0$ such that for all x

$$0 < |x - x_0| < \delta \quad \Rightarrow \quad |f(x) - L| < \epsilon$$

can be accomplished in two steps.

1. *Solve the inequality* $|f(x) - L| < \epsilon$ to find an open interval (a, b) containing x_0 on which the inequality holds for all $x \neq x_0$.

2. *Find a value of* $\delta > 0$ that places the open interval $(x_0 - \delta, x_0 + \delta)$ centered at x_0 inside the interval (a, b). The inequality $|f(x) - L| < \epsilon$ will hold for all $x \neq x_0$ in this δ-interval.

EXAMPLE 5   Finding Delta Algebraically

Prove that $\lim_{x \to 2} f(x) = 4$ if

$$f(x) = \begin{cases} x^2, & x \neq 2 \\ 1, & x = 2. \end{cases}$$

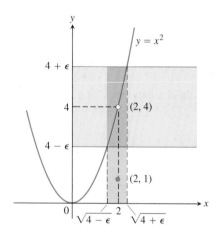

Solution   Our task is to show that given $\epsilon > 0$ there exists a $\delta > 0$ such that for all x

$$0 < |x - 2| < \delta \quad \Rightarrow \quad |f(x) - 4| < \epsilon.$$

1. *Solve the inequality* $|f(x) - 4| < \epsilon$ *to find an open interval containing $x_0 = 2$ on which the inequality holds for all $x \neq x_0$.*

   For $x \neq x_0 = 2$, we have $f(x) = x^2$, and the inequality to solve is $|x^2 - 4| < \epsilon$:

   $$|x^2 - 4| < \epsilon$$
   $$-\epsilon < x^2 - 4 < \epsilon$$
   $$4 - \epsilon < x^2 < 4 + \epsilon$$
   $$\sqrt{4 - \epsilon} < |x| < \sqrt{4 + \epsilon} \qquad \text{Assumes } \epsilon < 4; \text{ see below.}$$
   $$\sqrt{4 - \epsilon} < x < \sqrt{4 + \epsilon}. \qquad \text{An open interval about } x_0 = 2 \text{ that solves the inequality}$$

   The inequality $|f(x) - 4| < \epsilon$ holds for all $x \neq 2$ in the open interval $\left(\sqrt{4 - \epsilon}, \sqrt{4 + \epsilon}\right)$ (Figure 2.20).

FIGURE 2.20 An interval containing $x = 2$ so that the function in Example 5 satisfies $|f(x) - 4| < \epsilon$.

2. *Find a value of* $\delta > 0$ *that places the centered interval $(2 - \delta, 2 + \delta)$ inside the interval $\left(\sqrt{4 - \epsilon}, \sqrt{4 + \epsilon}\right)$.*

   Take δ to be the distance from $x_0 = 2$ to the nearer endpoint of $\left(\sqrt{4 - \epsilon}, \sqrt{4 + \epsilon}\right)$. In other words, take $\delta = \min\left\{2 - \sqrt{4 - \epsilon}, \sqrt{4 + \epsilon} - 2\right\}$, the *minimum* (the smaller) of the two numbers $2 - \sqrt{4 - \epsilon}$ and $\sqrt{4 + \epsilon} - 2$. If δ has this or any smaller positive value, the inequality $0 < |x - 2| < \delta$ will automatically place x between $\sqrt{4 - \epsilon}$ and $\sqrt{4 + \epsilon}$ to make $|f(x) - 4| < \epsilon$. For all x,

$$0 < |x - 2| < \delta \quad \Rightarrow \quad |f(x) - 4| < \epsilon.$$

This completes the proof for $\epsilon > 4$.

If $\epsilon \geq 4$, then we take δ to be the distance from $x_0 = 2$ to the nearer endpoint of the interval $\left(0, \sqrt{4 + \epsilon}\right)$. In other words, take $\delta = \min\left\{2\sqrt{4 + \epsilon} - 2\right\}$. (See Figure 2.20) ■

Using the Definition to Prove Theorems

We do not usually rely on the formal definition of limit to verify specific limits such as those in the preceding examples. Rather we appeal to general theorems about limits, in particular the theorems of Section 2.2. The definition is used to prove these theorems (Appendix 2). As an example, we prove part 1 of Theorem 1, the Sum Rule.

EXAMPLE 6   Proving the Rule for the Limit of a Sum

Given that $\lim_{x \to c} f(x) = L$ and $\lim_{x \to c} g(x) = M$, prove that

$$\lim_{x \to c} (f(x) + g(x)) = L + M.$$

Solution   Let $\epsilon > 0$ be given. We want to find a positive number δ such that for all x

$$0 < |x - c| < \delta \quad \Rightarrow \quad |f(x) + g(x) - (L + M)| < \epsilon.$$

Regrouping terms, we get

$$|f(x) + g(x) - (L + M)| = |(f(x) - L) + (g(x) - M)|$$
$$\leq |f(x) - L| + |g(x) - M|. \qquad \text{Triangle Inequality:}$$
$$|a + b| \leq |a| + |b|$$

Since $\lim_{x \to c} f(x) = L$, there exists a number $\delta_1 > 0$ such that for all x

$$0 < |x - c| < \delta_1 \quad \Rightarrow \quad |f(x) - L| < \epsilon/2.$$

Similarly, since $\lim_{x \to c} g(x) = M$, there exists a number $\delta_2 > 0$ such that for all x

$$0 < |x - c| < \delta_2 \quad \Rightarrow \quad |g(x) - M| < \epsilon/2.$$

Let $\delta = \min\{\delta_1, \delta_2\}$, the smaller of δ_1 and δ_2. If $0 < |x - c| < \delta$ then $|x - c| < \delta_1$, so $|f(x) - L| < \epsilon/2$, and $|x - c| < \delta_2$, so $|g(x) - M| < \epsilon/2$. Therefore

$$|f(x) + g(x) - (L + M)| < \frac{\epsilon}{2} + \frac{\epsilon}{2} = \epsilon.$$

This shows that $\lim_{x \to c} (f(x) + g(x)) = L + M.$ ■

Let's also prove Theorem 5 of Section 2.2.

EXAMPLE 7   Given that $\lim_{x \to c} f(x) = L$ and $\lim_{x \to c} g(x) = M$, and that $f(x) \leq g(x)$ for all x in an open interval containing c (except possibly c itself), prove that $L \leq M$.

Solution   We use the method of proof by contradiction. Suppose, on the contrary, that $L > M$. Then by the limit of a difference property in Theorem 1,

$$\lim_{x \to c} (g(x) - f(x)) = M - L.$$

Therefore, for any $\epsilon > 0$, there exists $\delta > 0$ such that

$$|(g(x) - f(x)) - (M - L)| < \epsilon \qquad \text{whenever} \quad 0 < |x - c| < \delta.$$

Since $L - M > 0$ by hypothesis, we take $\epsilon = L - M$ in particular and we have a number $\delta > 0$ such that

$$|(g(x) - f(x)) - (M - L)| < L - M \qquad \text{whenever} \quad 0 < |x - c| < \delta.$$

Since $a \leq |a|$ for any number a, we have

$$(g(x) - f(x)) - (M - L) < L - M \qquad \text{whenever} \quad 0 < |x - c| < \delta$$

which simplifies to

$$g(x) < f(x) \qquad \text{whenever} \quad 0 < |x - c| < \delta.$$

But this contradicts $f(x) \leq g(x)$. Thus the inequality $L > M$ must be false. Therefore $L \leq M$. ∎

EXERCISES 2.3

Centering Intervals About a Point

In Exercises 1–6, sketch the interval (a, b) on the x-axis with the point x_0 inside. Then find a value of $\delta > 0$ such that for all x, $0 < |x - x_0| < \delta \implies a < x < b$.

1. $a = 1$, $b = 7$, $x_0 = 5$

2. $a = 1$, $b = 7$, $x_0 = 2$

3. $a = -7/2$, $b = -1/2$, $x_0 = -3$

4. $a = -7/2$, $b = -1/2$, $x_0 = -3/2$

5. $a = 4/9$, $b = 4/7$, $x_0 = 1/2$

6. $a = 2.7591$, $b = 3.2391$, $x_0 = 3$

Finding Deltas Graphically

In Exercises 7–14, use the graphs to find a $\delta > 0$ such that for all x

$$0 < |x - x_0| < \delta \qquad \implies \qquad |f(x) - L| < \epsilon.$$

7.

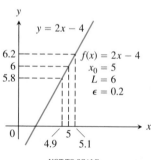

$y = 2x - 4$
$f(x) = 2x - 4$
$x_0 = 5$
$L = 6$
$\epsilon = 0.2$

6.2
6
5.8

4.9 5 5.1

NOT TO SCALE

8.

$f(x) = -\dfrac{3}{2}x + 3$
$x_0 = -3$
$L = 7.5$
$\epsilon = 0.15$

$y = -\dfrac{3}{2}x + 3$

7.65
7.5
7.35

−3.1   −3   −2.9   0

NOT TO SCALE

9.

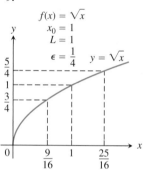

$f(x) = \sqrt{x}$
$x_0 = 1$
$L = 1$
$\epsilon = \dfrac{1}{4}$

$y = \sqrt{x}$

$\dfrac{5}{4}$
1
$\dfrac{3}{4}$

0   $\dfrac{9}{16}$ 1 $\dfrac{25}{16}$

10.

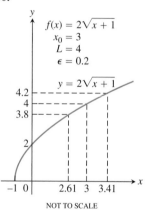

$f(x) = 2\sqrt{x + 1}$
$x_0 = 3$
$L = 4$
$\epsilon = 0.2$

$y = 2\sqrt{x + 1}$

4.2
4
3.8

2

−1 0   2.61 3 3.41

NOT TO SCALE

11.

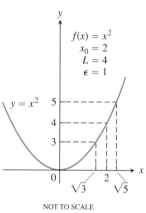

$f(x) = x^2$
$x_0 = 2$
$L = 4$
$\epsilon = 1$

$y = x^2$

5
4
3

0   $\sqrt{3}$ 2 $\sqrt{5}$

NOT TO SCALE

12.

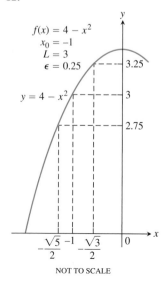

$f(x) = 4 - x^2$
$x_0 = -1$
$L = 3$
$\epsilon = 0.25$

3.25

$y = 4 - x^2$ 3

2.75

$-\dfrac{\sqrt{5}}{2}$ −1 $-\dfrac{\sqrt{3}}{2}$ 0

NOT TO SCALE

13.   **14.**

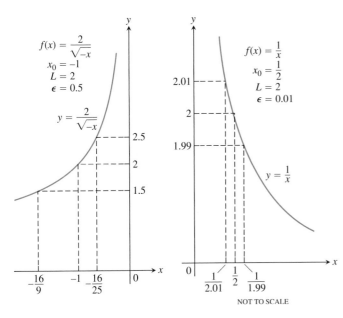

$f(x) = \dfrac{2}{\sqrt{-x}}$

$x_0 = -1$

$L = 2$

$\epsilon = 0.5$

$y = \dfrac{2}{\sqrt{-x}}$

$f(x) = \dfrac{1}{x}$

$x_0 = \dfrac{1}{2}$

$L = 2$

$\epsilon = 0.01$

$y = \dfrac{1}{x}$

NOT TO SCALE

Finding Deltas Algebraically

Each of Exercises 15–30 gives a function $f(x)$ and numbers L, x_0 and $\epsilon > 0$. In each case, find an open interval about x_0 on which the inequality $|f(x) - L| < \epsilon$ holds. Then give a value for $\delta > 0$ such that for all x satisfying $0 < |x - x_0| < \delta$ the inequality $|f(x) - L| < \epsilon$ holds.

15. $f(x) = x + 1,$ $L = 5,$ $x_0 = 4,$ $\epsilon = 0.01$

16. $f(x) = 2x - 2,$ $L = -6,$ $x_0 = -2,$ $\epsilon = 0.02$

17. $f(x) = \sqrt{x + 1},$ $L = 1,$ $x_0 = 0,$ $\epsilon = 0.1$

18. $f(x) = \sqrt{x},$ $L = 1/2,$ $x_0 = 1/4,$ $\epsilon = 0.1$

19. $f(x) = \sqrt{19 - x},$ $L = 3,$ $x_0 = 10,$ $\epsilon = 1$

20. $f(x) = \sqrt{x - 7},$ $L = 4,$ $x_0 = 23,$ $\epsilon = 1$

21. $f(x) = 1/x,$ $L = 1/4,$ $x_0 = 4,$ $\epsilon = 0.05$

22. $f(x) = x^2,$ $L = 3,$ $x_0 = \sqrt{3},$ $\epsilon = 0.1$

23. $f(x) = x^2,$ $L = 4,$ $x_0 = -2,$ $\epsilon = 0.5$

24. $f(x) = 1/x,$ $L = -1,$ $x_0 = -1,$ $\epsilon = 0.1$

25. $f(x) = x^2 - 5,$ $L = 11,$ $x_0 = 4,$ $\epsilon = 1$

26. $f(x) = 120/x,$ $L = 5,$ $x_0 = 24,$ $\epsilon = 1$

27. $f(x) = mx,$ $m > 0,$ $L = 2m,$ $x_0 = 2,$ $\epsilon = 0.03$

28. $f(x) = mx,$ $m > 0,$ $L = 3m,$ $x_0 = 3,$
$\epsilon = c > 0$

29. $f(x) = mx + b,$ $m > 0,$ $L = (m/2) + b,$
$x_0 = 1/2,$ $\epsilon = c > 0$

30. $f(x) = mx + b,$ $m > 0,$ $L = m + b,$ $x_0 = 1,$
$\epsilon = 0.05$

More on Formal Limits

Each of Exercises 31–36 gives a function $f(x)$, a point x_0, and a positive number ϵ. Find $L = \lim\limits_{x \to x_0} f(x)$. Then find a number $\delta > 0$ such that for all x

$$0 < |x - x_0| < \delta \quad \Rightarrow \quad |f(x) - L| < \epsilon.$$

31. $f(x) = 3 - 2x,$ $x_0 = 3,$ $\epsilon = 0.02$

32. $f(x) = -3x - 2,$ $x_0 = -1,$ $\epsilon = 0.03$

33. $f(x) = \dfrac{x^2 - 4}{x - 2},$ $x_0 = 2,$ $\epsilon = 0.05$

34. $f(x) = \dfrac{x^2 + 6x + 5}{x + 5},$ $x_0 = -5,$ $\epsilon = 0.05$

35. $f(x) = \sqrt{1 - 5x},$ $x_0 = -3,$ $\epsilon = 0.5$

36. $f(x) = 4/x,$ $x_0 = 2,$ $\epsilon = 0.4$

Prove the limit statements in Exercises 37–50.

37. $\lim\limits_{x \to 4} (9 - x) = 5$ **38.** $\lim\limits_{x \to 3} (3x - 7) = 2$

39. $\lim\limits_{x \to 9} \sqrt{x - 5} = 2$ **40.** $\lim\limits_{x \to 0} \sqrt{4 - x} = 2$

41. $\lim\limits_{x \to 1} f(x) = 1$ if $f(x) = \begin{cases} x^2, & x \neq 1 \\ 2, & x = 1 \end{cases}$

42. $\lim\limits_{x \to -2} f(x) = 4$ if $f(x) = \begin{cases} x^2, & x \neq -2 \\ 1, & x = -2 \end{cases}$

43. $\lim\limits_{x \to 1} \dfrac{1}{x} = 1$

44. $\lim\limits_{x \to \sqrt{3}} \dfrac{1}{x^2} = \dfrac{1}{3}$

45. $\lim\limits_{x \to -3} \dfrac{x^2 - 9}{x + 3} = -6$ **46.** $\lim\limits_{x \to 1} \dfrac{x^2 - 1}{x - 1} = 2$

47. $\lim\limits_{x \to 1} f(x) = 2$ if $f(x) = \begin{cases} 4 - 2x, & x < 1 \\ 6x - 4, & x \geq 1 \end{cases}$

48. $\lim\limits_{x \to 0} f(x) = 0$ if $f(x) = \begin{cases} 2x, & x < 0 \\ x/2, & x \geq 0 \end{cases}$

49. $\lim\limits_{x \to 0} x \sin \dfrac{1}{x} = 0$

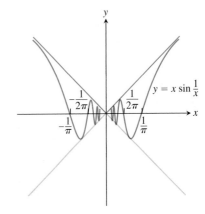

$y = x \sin \dfrac{1}{x}$

50. $\lim\limits_{x \to 0} x^2 \sin \dfrac{1}{x} = 0$

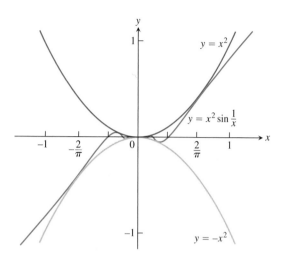

---

volts and I is to be 5 ± 0.1 amp. In what interval does R have to lie for I to be within 0.1 amp of the value $I_0 = 5$?

When Is a Number L Not the Limit of $f(x)$ as $x \to x_0$?

We can prove that $\lim_{x \to x_0} f(x) \neq L$ by providing an $\epsilon > 0$ such that no possible $\delta > 0$ satisfies the condition

$$\text{For all } x, \quad 0 < |x - x_0| < \delta \quad \Rightarrow \quad |f(x) - L| < \epsilon.$$

We accomplish this for our candidate ϵ by showing that for each $\delta > 0$ there exists a value of x such that

$$0 < |x - x_0| < \delta \quad \text{and} \quad |f(x) - L| \geq \epsilon.$$

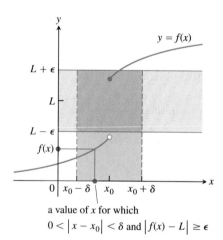

a value of x for which
$$0 < |x - x_0| < \delta \text{ and } |f(x) - L| \geq \epsilon$$

Theory and Examples

51. Define what it means to say that $\lim\limits_{x \to 0} g(x) = k$.

52. Prove that $\lim\limits_{x \to c} f(x) = L$ if and only if $\lim\limits_{h \to 0} f(h + c) = L$.

53. A wrong statement about limits Show by example that the following statement is wrong.

The number L is the limit of $f(x)$ as x approaches x_0 if $f(x)$ gets closer to L as x approaches x_0.

Explain why the function in your example does not have the given value of L as a limit as $x \to x_0$.

54. Another wrong statement about limits Show by example that the following statement is wrong.

The number L is the limit of $f(x)$ as x approaches x_0 if, given any $\epsilon > 0$, there exists a value of x for which $|f(x) - L| < \epsilon$.

Explain why the function in your example does not have the given value of L as a limit as $x \to x_0$.

T 55. Grinding engine cylinders Before contracting to grind engine cylinders to a cross-sectional area of 9 in^2, you need to know how much deviation from the ideal cylinder diameter of $x_0 = 3.385$ in. you can allow and still have the area come within 0.01 in^2 of the required 9 in^2. To find out, you let $A = \pi(x/2)^2$ and look for the interval in which you must hold x to make $|A - 9| \leq 0.01$. What interval do you find?

56. Manufacturing electrical resistors Ohm's law for electrical circuits like the one shown in the accompanying figure states that $V = RI$. In this equation, V is a constant voltage, I is the current in amperes, and R is the resistance in ohms. Your firm has been asked to supply the resistors for a circuit in which V will be 120

57. Let $f(x) = \begin{cases} x, & x < 1 \\ x + 1, & x > 1. \end{cases}$

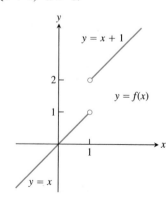

a. Let $\epsilon = 1/2$. Show that no possible $\delta > 0$ satisfies the following condition:

For all x, $\quad 0 < |x - 1| < \delta \quad \Rightarrow \quad |f(x) - 2| < 1/2$.

That is, for each $\delta > 0$ show that there is a value of x such that

$$0 < |x - 1| < \delta \quad \text{and} \quad |f(x) - 2| \geq 1/2.$$

This will show that $\lim_{x \to 1} f(x) \neq 2$.

b. Show that $\lim_{x \to 1} f(x) \neq 1$.

c. Show that $\lim_{x \to 1} f(x) \neq 1.5$.

58. Let $h(x) = \begin{cases} x^2, & x < 2 \\ 3, & x = 2 \\ 2, & x > 2. \end{cases}$

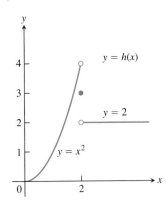

Show that

a. $\lim_{x \to 2} h(x) \neq 4$

b. $\lim_{x \to 2} h(x) \neq 3$

c. $\lim_{x \to 2} h(x) \neq 2$

59. For the function graphed here, explain why

a. $\lim_{x \to 3} f(x) \neq 4$

b. $\lim_{x \to 3} f(x) \neq 4.8$

c. $\lim_{x \to 3} f(x) \neq 3$

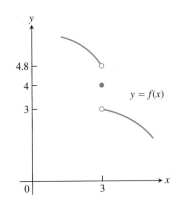

60. a. For the function graphed here, show that $\lim_{x \to -1} g(x) \neq 2$.

b. Does $\lim_{x \to -1} g(x)$ appear to exist? If so, what is the value of the limit? If not, why not?

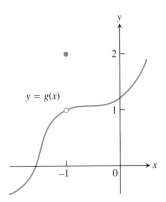

COMPUTER EXPLORATIONS

In Exercises 61–66, you will further explore finding deltas graphically. Use a CAS to perform the following steps:

a. Plot the function $y = f(x)$ near the point x_0 being approached.

b. Guess the value of the limit L and then evaluate the limit symbolically to see if you guessed correctly.

c. Using the value $\epsilon = 0.2$, graph the banding lines $y_1 = L - \epsilon$ and $y_2 = L + \epsilon$ together with the function f near x_0.

d. From your graph in part (c), estimate a $\delta > 0$ such that for all x

$$0 < |x - x_0| < \delta \quad \Rightarrow \quad |f(x) - L| < \epsilon.$$

Test your estimate by plotting f, y_1, and y_2 over the interval $0 < |x - x_0| < \delta$. For your viewing window use $x_0 - 2\delta \leq x \leq x_0 + 2\delta$ and $L - 2\epsilon \leq y \leq L + 2\epsilon$. If any function values lie outside the interval $[L - \epsilon, L + \epsilon]$, your choice of δ was too large. Try again with a smaller estimate.

e. Repeat parts (c) and (d) successively for $\epsilon = 0.1, 0.05$, and 0.001.

61. $f(x) = \dfrac{x^4 - 81}{x - 3}, \quad x_0 = 3$

62. $f(x) = \dfrac{5x^3 + 9x^2}{2x^5 + 3x^2}, \quad x_0 = 0$

63. $f(x) = \dfrac{\sin 2x}{3x}, \quad x_0 = 0$

64. $f(x) = \dfrac{x(1 - \cos x)}{x - \sin x}, \quad x_0 = 0$

65. $f(x) = \dfrac{\sqrt[3]{x} - 1}{x - 1}, \quad x_0 = 1$

66. $f(x) = \dfrac{3x^2 - (7x + 1)\sqrt{x} + 5}{x - 1}, \quad x_0 = 1$

2.4 One-Sided Limits and Limits at Infinity

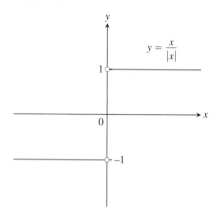

FIGURE 2.21 Different right-hand and left-hand limits at the origin.

In this section we extend the limit concept to *one-sided limits*, which are limits as x approaches the number x_0 from the left-hand side (where $x < x_0$) or the right-hand side ($x > x_0$) only. We also analyze the graphs of certain rational functions as well as other functions with limit behavior as $x \to \pm\infty$.

One-Sided Limits

To have a limit L as x approaches c, a function f must be defined on *both sides* of c and its values $f(x)$ must approach L as x approaches c from either side. Because of this, ordinary limits are called **two-sided**.

If f fails to have a two-sided limit at c, it may still have a one-sided limit, that is, a limit if the approach is only from one side. If the approach is from the right, the limit is a **right-hand limit**. From the left, it is a **left-hand limit**.

The function $f(x) = x/|x|$ (Figure 2.21) has limit 1 as x approaches 0 from the right, and limit -1 as x approaches 0 from the left. Since these one-sided limit values are not the same, there is no single number that $f(x)$ approaches as x approaches 0. So $f(x)$ does not have a (two-sided) limit at 0.

Intuitively, if $f(x)$ is defined on an interval (c, b), where $c < b$, and approaches arbitrarily close to L as x approaches c from within that interval, then f has **right-hand limit** L at c. We write

$$\lim_{x \to c^+} f(x) = L.$$

The symbol "$x \to c^+$" means that we consider only values of x greater than c.

Similarly, if $f(x)$ is defined on an interval (a, c), where $a < c$ and approaches arbitrarily close to M as x approaches c from within that interval, then f has **left-hand limit** M at c. We write

$$\lim_{x \to c^-} f(x) = M.$$

The symbol "$x \to c^-$" means that we consider only x values less than c.

These informal definitions are illustrated in Figure 2.22. For the function $f(x) = x/|x|$ in Figure 2.21 we have

$$\lim_{x \to 0^+} f(x) = 1 \qquad \text{and} \qquad \lim_{x \to 0^-} f(x) = -1.$$

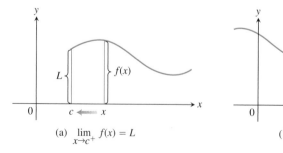

(a) $\lim_{x \to c^+} f(x) = L$

(b) $\lim_{x \to c^-} f(x) = M$

FIGURE 2.22 (a) Right-hand limit as x approaches c. (b) Left-hand limit as x approaches c.

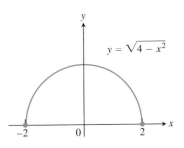

FIGURE 2.23 $\lim_{x \to 2^-} \sqrt{4 - x^2} = 0$ and $\lim_{x \to -2^+} \sqrt{4 - x^2} = 0$ (Example 1).

EXAMPLE 1   One-Sided Limits for a Semicircle

The domain of $f(x) = \sqrt{4 - x^2}$ is $[-2, 2]$; its graph is the semicircle in Figure 2.23. We have

$$\lim_{x \to -2^+} \sqrt{4 - x^2} = 0 \quad \text{and} \quad \lim_{x \to 2^-} \sqrt{4 - x^2} = 0.$$

The function does not have a left-hand limit at $x = -2$ or a right-hand limit at $x = 2$. It does not have ordinary two-sided limits at either -2 or 2.   ∎

One-sided limits have all the properties listed in Theorem 1 in Section 2.2. The right-hand limit of the sum of two functions is the sum of their right-hand limits, and so on. The theorems for limits of polynomials and rational functions hold with one-sided limits, as does the Sandwich Theorem and Theorem 5. One-sided limits are related to limits in the following way.

THEOREM 6

A function $f(x)$ has a limit as x approaches c if and only if it has left-hand and right-hand limits there and these one-sided limits are equal:

$$\lim_{x \to c} f(x) = L \quad \Leftrightarrow \quad \lim_{x \to c^-} f(x) = L \quad \text{and} \quad \lim_{x \to c^+} f(x) = L.$$

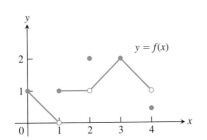

FIGURE 2.24 Graph of the function in Example 2.

EXAMPLE 2   Limits of the Function Graphed in Figure 2.24

At $x = 0$: $\lim_{x \to 0^+} f(x) = 1$,

$\lim_{x \to 0^-} f(x)$ and $\lim_{x \to 0} f(x)$ do not exist. The function is not defined to the left of $x = 0$.

At $x = 1$: $\lim_{x \to 1^-} f(x) = 0$ even though $f(1) = 1$,

$\lim_{x \to 1^+} f(x) = 1$,

$\lim_{x \to 1} f(x)$ does not exist. The right- and left-hand limits are not equal.

At $x = 2$: $\lim_{x \to 2^-} f(x) = 1$,

$\lim_{x \to 2^+} f(x) = 1$,

$\lim_{x \to 2} f(x) = 1$ even though $f(2) = 2$.

At $x = 3$: $\lim_{x \to 3^-} f(x) = \lim_{x \to 3^+} f(x) = \lim_{x \to 3} f(x) = f(3) = 2$.

At $x = 4$: $\lim_{x \to 4^-} f(x) = 1$ even though $f(4) \neq 1$,

$\lim_{x \to 4^+} f(x)$ and $\lim_{x \to 4} f(x)$ do not exist. The function is not defined to the right of $x = 4$.

At every other point c in $[0, 4]$, $f(x)$ has limit $f(c)$.   ∎

Precise Definitions of One-Sided Limits

The formal definition of the limit in Section 2.3 is readily modified for one-sided limits.

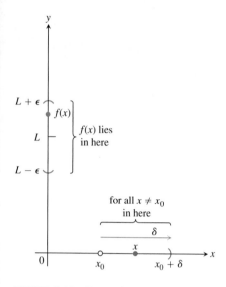

FIGURE 2.25 Intervals associated with the definition of right-hand limit.

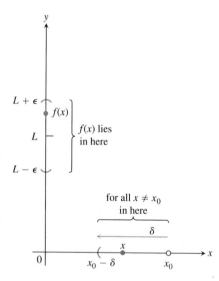

FIGURE 2.26 Intervals associated with the definition of left-hand limit.

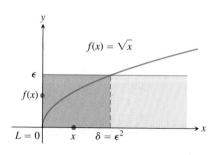

FIGURE 2.27 $\lim_{x \to 0^+} \sqrt{x} = 0$ in Example 3.

DEFINITIONS   Right-Hand, Left-Hand Limits

We say that $f(x)$ has **right-hand limit L at x_0**, and write

$$\lim_{x \to x_0^+} f(x) = L \qquad \text{(See Figure 2.25)}$$

if for every number $\epsilon > 0$ there exists a corresponding number $\delta > 0$ such that for all x

$$x_0 < x < x_0 + \delta \qquad \Rightarrow \qquad |f(x) - L| < \epsilon.$$

We say that f has **left-hand limit L at x_0**, and write

$$\lim_{x \to x_0^-} f(x) = L \qquad \text{(See Figure 2.26)}$$

if for every number $\epsilon > 0$ there exists a corresponding number $\delta > 0$ such that for all x

$$x_0 - \delta < x < x_0 \qquad \Rightarrow \qquad |f(x) - L| < \epsilon.$$

EXAMPLE 3   Applying the Definition to Find Delta

Prove that

$$\lim_{x \to 0^+} \sqrt{x} = 0.$$

Solution   Let $\epsilon > 0$ be given. Here $x_0 = 0$ and $L = 0$, so we want to find a $\delta > 0$ such that for all x

$$0 < x < \delta \qquad \Rightarrow \qquad |\sqrt{x} - 0| < \epsilon,$$

or

$$0 < x < \delta \qquad \Rightarrow \qquad \sqrt{x} < \epsilon.$$

Squaring both sides of this last inequality gives

$$x < \epsilon^2 \qquad \text{if} \qquad 0 < x < \delta.$$

If we choose $\delta = \epsilon^2$ we have

$$0 < x < \delta = \epsilon^2 \qquad \Rightarrow \qquad \sqrt{x} < \epsilon,$$

or

$$0 < x < \epsilon^2 \qquad \Rightarrow \qquad |\sqrt{x} - 0| < \epsilon.$$

According to the definition, this shows that $\lim_{x \to 0^+} \sqrt{x} = 0$ (Figure 2.27). ∎

The functions examined so far have had some kind of limit at each point of interest. In general, that need not be the case.

EXAMPLE 4   A Function Oscillating Too Much

Show that $y = \sin(1/x)$ has no limit as x approaches zero from either side (Figure 2.28).

Solution   As x approaches zero, its reciprocal, $1/x$, grows without bound and the values of $\sin(1/x)$ cycle repeatedly from -1 to 1. There is no single number L that the function's

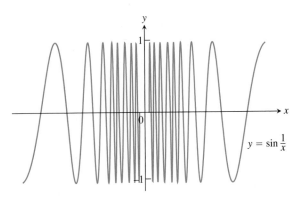

FIGURE 2.28 The function $y = \sin(1/x)$ has neither a right-hand nor a left-hand limit as x approaches zero (Example 4).

values stay increasingly close to as x approaches zero. This is true even if we restrict x to positive values or to negative values. The function has neither a right-hand limit nor a left-hand limit at $x = 0$. ∎

Limits Involving $(\sin\theta)/\theta$

A central fact about $(\sin\theta)/\theta$ is that in radian measure its limit as $\theta \to 0$ is 1. We can see this in Figure 2.29 and confirm it algebraically using the Sandwich Theorem. You will see the importance of this limit in Section 3.4, where instantaneous rates of change of the trigonometric functions are studied.

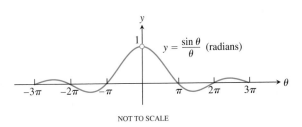

FIGURE 2.29 The graph of $f(\theta) = (\sin\theta)/\theta$.

THEOREM 7

$$\lim_{\theta \to 0} \frac{\sin\theta}{\theta} = 1 \qquad (\theta \text{ in radians}) \qquad (1)$$

Proof The plan is to show that the right-hand and left-hand limits are both 1. Then we will know that the two-sided limit is 1 as well.

To show that the right-hand limit is 1, we begin with positive values of θ less than $\pi/2$ (Figure 2.30). Notice that

$$\text{Area } \Delta OAP < \text{ area sector } OAP < \text{ area } \Delta OAT.$$

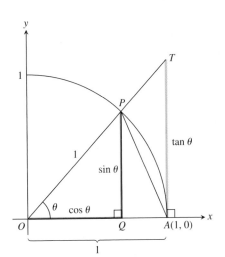

FIGURE 2.30 The figure for the proof of Theorem 7. $TA/OA = \tan\theta$, but $OA = 1$, so $TA = \tan\theta$.

Equation (2) is where radian measure comes in: The area of sector OAP is $\theta/2$ only if θ is measured in radians.

We can express these areas in terms of θ as follows:

$$\text{Area } \Delta OAP = \frac{1}{2} \text{ base} \times \text{height} = \frac{1}{2}(1)(\sin \theta) = \frac{1}{2} \sin \theta$$

$$\text{Area sector } OAP = \frac{1}{2} r^2 \theta = \frac{1}{2}(1)^2 \theta = \frac{\theta}{2} \tag{2}$$

$$\text{Area } \Delta OAT = \frac{1}{2} \text{ base} \times \text{height} = \frac{1}{2}(1)(\tan \theta) = \frac{1}{2} \tan \theta.$$

Thus,

$$\frac{1}{2} \sin \theta < \frac{1}{2} \theta < \frac{1}{2} \tan \theta.$$

This last inequality goes the same way if we divide all three terms by the number $(1/2) \sin \theta$, which is positive since $0 < \theta < \pi/2$:

$$1 < \frac{\theta}{\sin \theta} < \frac{1}{\cos \theta}.$$

Taking reciprocals reverses the inequalities:

$$1 > \frac{\sin \theta}{\theta} > \cos \theta.$$

Since $\lim_{\theta \to 0^+} \cos \theta = 1$ (Example 6b, Section 2.2), the Sandwich Theorem gives

$$\lim_{\theta \to 0^+} \frac{\sin \theta}{\theta} = 1.$$

Recall that $\sin \theta$ and θ are both *odd functions* (Section 1.4). Therefore, $f(\theta) = (\sin \theta)/\theta$ is an *even function*, with a graph symmetric about the y-axis (see Figure 2.29). This symmetry implies that the left-hand limit at 0 exists and has the same value as the right-hand limit:

$$\lim_{\theta \to 0^-} \frac{\sin \theta}{\theta} = 1 = \lim_{\theta \to 0^+} \frac{\sin \theta}{\theta},$$

so $\lim_{\theta \to 0} (\sin \theta)/\theta = 1$ by Theorem 6.   ■

EXAMPLE 5   Using $\lim\limits_{\theta \to 0} \dfrac{\sin \theta}{\theta} = 1$

Show that **(a)** $\lim\limits_{h \to 0} \dfrac{\cos h - 1}{h} = 0$ and **(b)** $\lim\limits_{x \to 0} \dfrac{\sin 2x}{5x} = \dfrac{2}{5}$.

Solution

(a) Using the half-angle formula $\cos h = 1 - 2 \sin^2(h/2)$, we calculate

$$\lim_{h \to 0} \frac{\cos h - 1}{h} = \lim_{h \to 0} -\frac{2 \sin^2(h/2)}{h}$$

$$= -\lim_{\theta \to 0} \frac{\sin \theta}{\theta} \sin \theta \qquad \text{Let } \theta = h/2.$$

$$= -(1)(0) = 0.$$

(b) Equation (1) does not apply to the original fraction. We need a $2x$ in the denominator, not a $5x$. We produce it by multiplying numerator and denominator by $2/5$:

$$\lim_{x\to0}\frac{\sin 2x}{5x} = \lim_{x\to0}\frac{(2/5)\cdot\sin 2x}{(2/5)\cdot 5x}$$

$$= \frac{2}{5}\lim_{x\to0}\frac{\sin 2x}{2x} \qquad \text{Now, Eq. (1) applies with } \theta = 2x.$$

$$= \frac{2}{5}(1) = \frac{2}{5} \qquad\blacksquare$$

Finite Limits as $x \to \pm\infty$

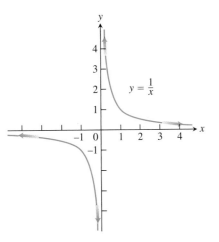

$y = \frac{1}{x}$

FIGURE 2.31 The graph of $y = 1/x$.

The symbol for infinity (∞) does not represent a real number. We use ∞ to describe the behavior of a function when the values in its domain or range outgrow all finite bounds. For example, the function $f(x) = 1/x$ is defined for all $x \neq 0$ (Figure 2.31). When x is positive and becomes increasingly large, $1/x$ becomes increasingly small. When x is negative and its magnitude becomes increasingly large, $1/x$ again becomes small. We summarize these observations by saying that $f(x) = 1/x$ has limit 0 as $x \to \pm\infty$ or that 0 is a *limit of $f(x) = 1/x$ at infinity and negative infinity*. Here is a precise definition.

DEFINITIONS Limit as x approaches ∞ or $-\infty$

1. We say that $f(x)$ has the **limit L as x approaches infinity** and write

$$\lim_{x\to\infty} f(x) = L$$

if, for every number $\epsilon > 0$, there exists a corresponding number M such that for all x

$$x > M \qquad\Rightarrow\qquad |f(x) - L| < \epsilon.$$

2. We say that $f(x)$ has the **limit L as x approaches minus infinity** and write

$$\lim_{x\to-\infty} f(x) = L$$

if, for every number $\epsilon > 0$, there exists a corresponding number N such that for all x

$$x < N \qquad\Rightarrow\qquad |f(x) - L| < \epsilon.$$

Intuitively, $\lim_{x\to\infty} f(x) = L$ if, as x moves increasingly far from the origin in the positive direction, $f(x)$ gets arbitrarily close to L. Similarly, $\lim_{x\to-\infty} f(x) = L$ if, as x moves increasingly far from the origin in the negative direction, $f(x)$ gets arbitrarily close to L.

The strategy for calculating limits of functions as $x \to \pm\infty$ is similar to the one for finite limits in Section 2.2. There we first found the limits of the constant and identity functions $y = k$ and $y = x$. We then extended these results to other functions by applying a theorem about limits of algebraic combinations. Here we do the same thing, except that the starting functions are $y = k$ and $y = 1/x$ instead of $y = k$ and $y = x$.

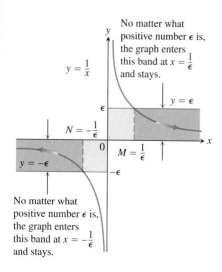

No matter what positive number ϵ is, the graph enters this band at $x = \frac{1}{\epsilon}$ and stays.

$y = \frac{1}{x}$

$y = \epsilon$

$N = -\frac{1}{\epsilon}$

$M = \frac{1}{\epsilon}$

$y = -\epsilon$

No matter what positive number ϵ is, the graph enters this band at $x = -\frac{1}{\epsilon}$ and stays.

FIGURE 2.32 The geometry behind the argument in Example 6.

The basic facts to be verified by applying the formal definition are

$$\lim_{x \to \pm\infty} k = k \qquad \text{and} \qquad \lim_{x \to \pm\infty} \frac{1}{x} = 0. \qquad (3)$$

We prove the latter and leave the former to Exercises 71 and 72.

EXAMPLE 6   Limits at Infinity for $f(x) = \frac{1}{x}$

Show that

(a) $\lim\limits_{x \to \infty} \frac{1}{x} = 0$
(b) $\lim\limits_{x \to -\infty} \frac{1}{x} = 0.$

Solution

(a) Let $\epsilon > 0$ be given. We must find a number M such that for all x

$$x > M \qquad \Rightarrow \qquad \left| \frac{1}{x} - 0 \right| = \left| \frac{1}{x} \right| < \epsilon.$$

The implication will hold if $M = 1/\epsilon$ or any larger positive number (Figure 2.32). This proves $\lim_{x \to \infty} (1/x) = 0$.

(b) Let $\epsilon > 0$ be given. We must find a number N such that for all x

$$x < N \qquad \Rightarrow \qquad \left| \frac{1}{x} - 0 \right| = \left| \frac{1}{x} \right| < \epsilon.$$

The implication will hold if $N = -1/\epsilon$ or any number less than $-1/\epsilon$ (Figure 2.32). This proves $\lim_{x \to -\infty} (1/x) = 0$. ∎

Limits at infinity have properties similar to those of finite limits.

THEOREM 8   Limit Laws as $x \to \pm\infty$

If L, M, and k, are real numbers and

$$\lim_{x \to \pm\infty} f(x) = L \qquad \text{and} \qquad \lim_{x \to \pm\infty} g(x) = M, \quad \text{then}$$

1. *Sum Rule:* $\qquad\qquad\qquad \lim\limits_{x \to \pm\infty} (f(x) + g(x)) = L + M$

2. *Difference Rule:* $\qquad\quad \lim\limits_{x \to \pm\infty} (f(x) - g(x)) = L - M$

3. *Product Rule:* $\qquad\qquad \lim\limits_{x \to \pm\infty} (f(x) \cdot g(x)) = L \cdot M$

4. *Constant Multiple Rule:* $\quad \lim\limits_{x \to \pm\infty} (k \cdot f(x)) = k \cdot L$

5. *Quotient Rule:* $\qquad\qquad \lim\limits_{x \to \pm\infty} \dfrac{f(x)}{g(x)} = \dfrac{L}{M}, \quad M \neq 0$

6. *Power Rule:* If r and s are integers with no common factors, $s \neq 0$, then

$$\lim_{x \to \pm\infty} (f(x))^{r/s} = L^{r/s}$$

provided that $L^{r/s}$ is a real number. (If s is even, we assume that $L > 0$.)

These properties are just like the properties in Theorem 1, Section 2.2, and we use them the same way.

EXAMPLE 7 Using Theorem 8

(a) $\displaystyle\lim_{x\to\infty}\left(5+\frac{1}{x}\right) = \lim_{x\to\infty} 5 + \lim_{x\to\infty}\frac{1}{x}$ Sum Rule

$$= 5 + 0 = 5 \qquad \text{Known limits}$$

(b) $\displaystyle\lim_{x\to-\infty}\frac{\pi\sqrt{3}}{x^2} = \lim_{x\to-\infty} \pi\sqrt{3}\cdot\frac{1}{x}\cdot\frac{1}{x}$

$$= \lim_{x\to-\infty} \pi\sqrt{3}\cdot \lim_{x\to-\infty}\frac{1}{x}\cdot \lim_{x\to-\infty}\frac{1}{x} \qquad \text{Product rule}$$

$$= \pi\sqrt{3}\cdot 0\cdot 0 = 0 \qquad \text{Known limits} \qquad ■$$

Limits at Infinity of Rational Functions

To determine the limit of a rational function as $x \to \pm\infty$, we can divide the numerator and denominator by the highest power of x in the denominator. What happens then depends on the degrees of the polynomials involved.

EXAMPLE 8 Numerator and Denominator of Same Degree

$$\lim_{x\to\infty}\frac{5x^2+8x-3}{3x^2+2} = \lim_{x\to\infty}\frac{5+(8/x)-(3/x^2)}{3+(2/x^2)} \qquad \begin{array}{l}\text{Divide numerator and}\\ \text{denominator by } x^2.\end{array}$$

$$= \frac{5+0-0}{3+0} = \frac{5}{3} \qquad \text{See Fig. 2.33.} \qquad ▨$$

EXAMPLE 9 Degree of Numerator Less Than Degree of Denominator

$$\lim_{x\to-\infty}\frac{11x+2}{2x^3-1} = \lim_{x\to-\infty}\frac{(11/x^2)+(2/x^3)}{2-(1/x^3)} \qquad \begin{array}{l}\text{Divide numerator and}\\ \text{denominator by } x^3.\end{array}$$

$$= \frac{0+0}{2-0} = 0 \qquad \text{See Fig. 2.34.} \qquad ■$$

We give an example of the case when the degree of the numerator is greater than the degree of the denominator in the next section (Example 8, Section 2.5).

Horizontal Asymptotes

If the distance between the graph of a function and some fixed line approaches zero as a point on the graph moves increasingly far from the origin, we say that the graph approaches the line *asymptotically* and that the line is an *asymptote* of the graph.

Looking at $f(x) = 1/x$ (See Figure 2.31), we observe that the x-axis is an asymptote of the curve on the right because

$$\lim_{x\to\infty}\frac{1}{x} = 0$$

and on the left because

$$\lim_{x\to-\infty}\frac{1}{x} = 0.$$

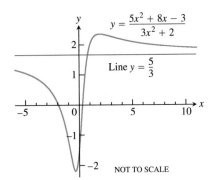

FIGURE 2.33 The graph of the function in Example 8. The graph approaches the line $y = 5/3$ as $|x|$ increases.

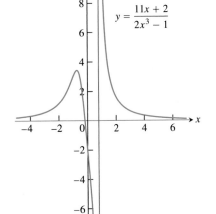

FIGURE 2.34 The graph of the function in Example 9. The graph approaches the x-axis as $|x|$ increases.

We say that the x-axis is a *horizontal asymptote* of the graph of $f(x) = 1/x$.

DEFINITION   Horizontal Asymptote

A line $y = b$ is a **horizontal asymptote** of the graph of a function $y = f(x)$ if either

$$\lim_{x \to \infty} f(x) = b \qquad \text{or} \qquad \lim_{x \to -\infty} f(x) = b.$$

The curve

$$f(x) = \frac{5x^2 + 8x - 3}{3x^2 + 2}$$

sketched in Figure 2.33 (Example 8) has the line $y = 5/3$ as a horizontal asymptote on both the right and the left because

$$\lim_{x \to \infty} f(x) = \frac{5}{3} \qquad \text{and} \qquad \lim_{x \to -\infty} f(x) = \frac{5}{3}.$$

EXAMPLE 10   Substituting a New Variable

Find $\lim\limits_{x \to \infty} \sin(1/x)$.

Solution   We introduce the new variable $t = 1/x$. From Example 6, we know that $t \to 0^+$ as $x \to \infty$ (see Figure 2.31). Therefore,

$$\lim_{x \to \infty} \sin \frac{1}{x} = \lim_{t \to 0^+} \sin t = 0. \qquad \blacksquare$$

The Sandwich Theorem Revisited

The Sandwich Theorem also holds for limits as $x \to \pm\infty$.

EXAMPLE 11   A Curve May Cross Its Horizontal Asymptote

Using the Sandwich Theorem, find the horizontal asymptote of the curve

$$y = 2 + \frac{\sin x}{x}.$$

Solution   We are interested in the behavior as $x \to \pm\infty$. Since

$$0 \le \left| \frac{\sin x}{x} \right| \le \left| \frac{1}{x} \right|$$

and $\lim_{x \to \pm\infty} |1/x| = 0$, we have $\lim_{x \to \pm\infty} (\sin x)/x = 0$ by the Sandwich Theorem. Hence,

$$\lim_{x \to \pm\infty} \left(2 + \frac{\sin x}{x} \right) = 2 + 0 = 2,$$

and the line $y = 2$ is a horizontal asymptote of the curve on both left and right (Figure 2.35).

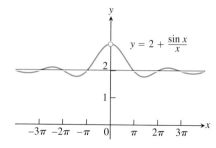

FIGURE 2.35   A curve may cross one of its asymptotes infinitely often (Example 11).

This example illustrates that a curve may cross one of its horizontal asymptotes, perhaps many times. ∎

Oblique Asymptotes

If the degree of the numerator of a rational function is one greater than the degree of the denominator, the graph has an **oblique (slanted) asymptote**. We find an equation for the asymptote by dividing numerator by denominator to express f as a linear function plus a remainder that goes to zero as $x \to \pm\infty$. Here's an example.

EXAMPLE 12 Finding an Oblique Asymptote

Find the oblique asymptote for the graph of

$$f(x) = \frac{2x^2 - 3}{7x + 4}$$

in Figure 2.36.

Solution By long division, we find

$$f(x) = \frac{2x^2 - 3}{7x + 4}$$

$$= \underbrace{\left(\frac{2}{7}x - \frac{8}{49}\right)}_{\text{linear function } g(x)} + \underbrace{\frac{-115}{49(7x + 4)}}_{\text{remainder}}$$

As $x \to \pm\infty$, the remainder, whose magnitude gives the vertical distance between the graphs of f and g, goes to zero, making the (slanted) line

$$g(x) = \frac{2}{7}x - \frac{8}{49}$$

an asymptote of the graph of f (Figure 2.36). The line $y = g(x)$ is an asymptote both to the right and to the left. In the next section you will see that the function $f(x)$ grows arbitrarily large in absolute value as x approaches $-4/7$, where the denominator becomes zero (Figure 2.36). ∎

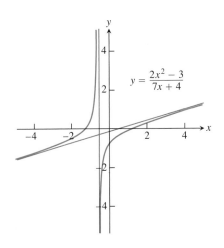

FIGURE 2.36 The function in Example 12 has an oblique asymptote.

EXERCISES 2.4

Finding Limits Graphically

1. Which of the following statements about the function $y = f(x)$ graphed here are true, and which are false?

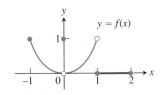

a. $\displaystyle\lim_{x \to -1^+} f(x) = 1$

b. $\displaystyle\lim_{x \to 0^-} f(x) = 0$

c. $\displaystyle\lim_{x \to 0^-} f(x) = 1$

d. $\displaystyle\lim_{x \to 0^-} f(x) = \lim_{x \to 0^+} f(x)$

e. $\displaystyle\lim_{x \to 0} f(x)$ exists

f. $\displaystyle\lim_{x \to 0} f(x) = 0$

g. $\displaystyle\lim_{x \to 0} f(x) = 1$

h. $\displaystyle\lim_{x \to 1} f(x) = 1$

i. $\displaystyle\lim_{x \to 1} f(x) = 0$

j. $\displaystyle\lim_{x \to 2^-} f(x) = 2$

k. $\displaystyle\lim_{x \to -1^-} f(x)$ does not exist.

l. $\displaystyle\lim_{x \to 2^+} f(x) = 0$

2. Which of the following statements about the function $y = f(x)$ graphed here are true, and which are false?

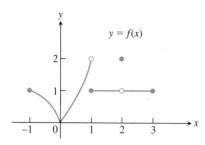

$y = f(x)$

a. $\lim_{x \to -1^+} f(x) = 1$

b. $\lim_{x \to 2} f(x)$ does not exist.

c. $\lim_{x \to 2} f(x) = 2$

d. $\lim_{x \to 1^-} f(x) = 2$

e. $\lim_{x \to 1^+} f(x) = 1$

f. $\lim_{x \to 1} f(x)$ does not exist.

g. $\lim_{x \to 0^+} f(x) = \lim_{x \to 0^-} f(x)$

h. $\lim_{x \to c} f(x)$ exists at every c in the open interval $(-1, 1)$.

i. $\lim_{x \to c} f(x)$ exists at every c in the open interval $(1, 3)$.

j. $\lim_{x \to -1^-} f(x) = 0$

k. $\lim_{x \to 3^+} f(x)$ does not exist.

3. Let $f(x) = \begin{cases} 3 - x, & x < 2 \\ \dfrac{x}{2} + 1, & x > 2. \end{cases}$

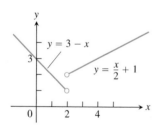

$y = 3 - x$

$y = \dfrac{x}{2} + 1$

a. Find $\lim_{x \to 2^+} f(x)$ and $\lim_{x \to 2^-} f(x)$.

b. Does $\lim_{x \to 2} f(x)$ exist? If so, what is it? If not, why not?

c. Find $\lim_{x \to 4^-} f(x)$ and $\lim_{x \to 4^+} f(x)$.

d. Does $\lim_{x \to 4} f(x)$ exist? If so, what is it? If not, why not?

4. Let $f(x) = \begin{cases} 3 - x, & x < 2 \\ 2, & x = 2 \\ \dfrac{x}{2}, & x > 2. \end{cases}$

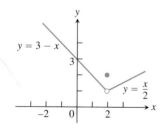

$y = 3 - x$

$y = \dfrac{x}{2}$

a. Find $\lim_{x \to 2^+} f(x)$, $\lim_{x \to 2^-} f(x)$, and $f(2)$.

b. Does $\lim_{x \to 2} f(x)$ exist? If so, what is it? If not, why not?

c. Find $\lim_{x \to -1^-} f(x)$ and $\lim_{x \to -1^+} f(x)$.

d. Does $\lim_{x \to -1} f(x)$ exist? If so, what is it? If not, why not?

5. Let $f(x) = \begin{cases} 0, & x \le 0 \\ \sin \dfrac{1}{x}, & x > 0. \end{cases}$

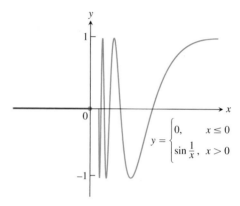

$y = \begin{cases} 0, & x \le 0 \\ \sin \dfrac{1}{x}, & x > 0 \end{cases}$

a. Does $\lim_{x \to 0^+} f(x)$ exist? If so, what is it? If not, why not?

b. Does $\lim_{x \to 0^-} f(x)$ exist? If so, what is it? If not, why not?

c. Does $\lim_{x \to 0} f(x)$ exist? If so, what is it? If not, why not?

6. Let $g(x) = \sqrt{x} \sin(1/x)$.

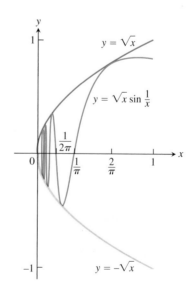

$y = \sqrt{x}$

$y = \sqrt{x} \sin \dfrac{1}{x}$

$y = -\sqrt{x}$

a. Does $\lim_{x \to 0^+} g(x)$ exist? If so, what is it? If not, why not?

b. Does $\lim_{x \to 0^-} g(x)$ exist? If so, what is it? If not, why not?

c. Does $\lim_{x \to 0} g(x)$ exist? If so, what is it? If not, why not?

7. a. Graph $f(x) = \begin{cases} x^3, & x \neq 1 \\ 0, & x = 1. \end{cases}$

  b. Find $\lim_{x \to 1^-} f(x)$ and $\lim_{x \to 1^+} f(x)$.

  c. Does $\lim_{x \to 1} f(x)$ exist? If so, what is it? If not, why not?

8. a. Graph $f(x) = \begin{cases} 1 - x^2, & x \neq 1 \\ 2, & x = 1. \end{cases}$

  b. Find $\lim_{x \to 1^+} f(x)$ and $\lim_{x \to 1^-} f(x)$.

  c. Does $\lim_{x \to 1} f(x)$ exist? If so, what is it? If not, why not?

Graph the functions in Exercises 9 and 10. Then answer these questions.

  a. What are the domain and range of f?

  b. At what points c, if any, does $\lim_{x \to c} f(x)$ exist?

  c. At what points does only the left-hand limit exist?

  d. At what points does only the right-hand limit exist?

9. $f(x) = \begin{cases} \sqrt{1 - x^2}, & 0 \leq x < 1 \\ 1, & 1 \leq x < 2 \\ 2, & x = 2 \end{cases}$

10. $f(x) = \begin{cases} x, & -1 \leq x < 0, \quad \text{or} \quad 0 < x \leq 1 \\ 1, & x = 0 \\ 0, & x < -1, \quad \text{or} \quad x > 1 \end{cases}$

Finding One-Sided Limits Algebraically

Find the limits in Exercises 11–18.

11. $\lim_{x \to -0.5^-} \sqrt{\dfrac{x + 2}{x + 1}}$

12. $\lim_{x \to 1^+} \sqrt{\dfrac{x - 1}{x + 2}}$

13. $\lim_{x \to -2^+} \left(\dfrac{x}{x + 1} \right) \left(\dfrac{2x + 5}{x^2 + x} \right)$

14. $\lim_{x \to 1^-} \left(\dfrac{1}{x + 1} \right) \left(\dfrac{x + 6}{x} \right) \left(\dfrac{3 - x}{7} \right)$

15. $\lim_{h \to 0^+} \dfrac{\sqrt{h^2 + 4h + 5} - \sqrt{5}}{h}$

16. $\lim_{h \to 0^-} \dfrac{\sqrt{6} - \sqrt{5h^2 + 11h + 6}}{h}$

17. a. $\lim_{x \to -2^+} (x + 3) \dfrac{|x + 2|}{x + 2}$ **b.** $\lim_{x \to -2^-} (x + 3) \dfrac{|x + 2|}{x + 2}$

18. a. $\lim_{x \to 1^+} \dfrac{\sqrt{2x} (x - 1)}{|x - 1|}$ **b.** $\lim_{x \to 1^-} \dfrac{\sqrt{2x} (x - 1)}{|x - 1|}$

Use the graph of the greatest integer function $y = \lfloor x \rfloor$ (sometimes written $y = \text{int } x$), Figure 1.31 in Section 1.3, to help you find the limits in Exercises 19 and 20.

19. a. $\lim_{\theta \to 3^+} \dfrac{\lfloor \theta \rfloor}{\theta}$ **b.** $\lim_{\theta \to 3^-} \dfrac{\lfloor \theta \rfloor}{\theta}$

20. a. $\lim_{t \to 4^+} (t - \lfloor t \rfloor)$ **b.** $\lim_{t \to 4^-} (t - \lfloor t \rfloor)$

Using $\lim_{\theta \to 0} \dfrac{\sin \theta}{\theta} = 1$

Find the limits in Exercises 21–36.

21. $\lim_{\theta \to 0} \dfrac{\sin \sqrt{2\theta}}{\sqrt{2\theta}}$

22. $\lim_{t \to 0} \dfrac{\sin kt}{t}$ (k constant)

23. $\lim_{y \to 0} \dfrac{\sin 3y}{4y}$

24. $\lim_{h \to 0^-} \dfrac{h}{\sin 3h}$

25. $\lim_{x \to 0} \dfrac{\tan 2x}{x}$

26. $\lim_{t \to 0} \dfrac{2t}{\tan t}$

27. $\lim_{x \to 0} \dfrac{x \csc 2x}{\cos 5x}$

28. $\lim_{x \to 0} 6x^2 (\cot x)(\csc 2x)$

29. $\lim_{x \to 0} \dfrac{x + x \cos x}{\sin x \cos x}$

30. $\lim_{x \to 0} \dfrac{x^2 - x + \sin x}{2x}$

31. $\lim_{t \to 0} \dfrac{\sin (1 - \cos t)}{1 - \cos t}$

32. $\lim_{h \to 0} \dfrac{\sin (\sin h)}{\sin h}$

33. $\lim_{\theta \to 0} \dfrac{\sin \theta}{\sin 2\theta}$

34. $\lim_{x \to 0} \dfrac{\sin 5x}{\sin 4x}$

35. $\lim_{x \to 0} \dfrac{\tan 3x}{\sin 8x}$

36. $\lim_{y \to 0} \dfrac{\sin 3y \cot 5y}{y \cot 4y}$

Calculating Limits as $x \to \pm \infty$

In Exercises 37–42, find the limit of each function (a) as $x \to \infty$ and (b) as $x \to -\infty$. (You may wish to visualize your answer with a graphing calculator or computer.)

37. $f(x) = \dfrac{2}{x} - 3$

38. $f(x) = \pi - \dfrac{2}{x^2}$

39. $g(x) = \dfrac{1}{2 + (1/x)}$

40. $g(x) = \dfrac{1}{8 - (5/x^2)}$

41. $h(x) = \dfrac{-5 + (7/x)}{3 - (1/x^2)}$

42. $h(x) = \dfrac{3 - (2/x)}{4 + \left(\sqrt{2}/x^2 \right)}$

Find the limits in Exercises 43–46.

43. $\lim_{x \to \infty} \dfrac{\sin 2x}{x}$

44. $\lim_{\theta \to -\infty} \dfrac{\cos \theta}{3\theta}$

45. $\lim_{t \to -\infty} \dfrac{2 - t + \sin t}{t + \cos t}$

46. $\lim_{r \to \infty} \dfrac{r + \sin r}{2r + 7 - 5 \sin r}$

Limits of Rational Functions

In Exercises 47–56, find the limit of each rational function (a) as $x \to \infty$ and (b) as $x \to -\infty$.

47. $f(x) = \dfrac{2x + 3}{5x + 7}$

48. $f(x) = \dfrac{2x^3 + 7}{x^3 - x^2 + x + 7}$

49. $f(x) = \dfrac{x + 1}{x^2 + 3}$

50. $f(x) = \dfrac{3x + 7}{x^2 - 2}$

51. $h(x) = \dfrac{7x^3}{x^3 - 3x^2 + 6x}$

52. $g(x) = \dfrac{1}{x^3 - 4x + 1}$

53. $g(x) = \dfrac{10x^5 + x^4 + 31}{x^6}$

54. $h(x) = \dfrac{9x^4 + x}{2x^4 + 5x^2 - x + 6}$

55. $h(x) = \dfrac{-2x^3 - 2x + 3}{3x^3 + 3x^2 - 5x}$

56. $h(x) = \dfrac{-x^4}{x^4 - 7x^3 + 7x^2 + 9}$

Limits with Noninteger or Negative Powers

The process by which we determine limits of rational functions applies equally well to ratios containing noninteger or negative powers of x: divide numerator and denominator by the highest power of x in the denominator and proceed from there. Find the limits in Exercises 57–62.

57. $\lim\limits_{x \to \infty} \dfrac{2\sqrt{x} + x^{-1}}{3x - 7}$

58. $\lim\limits_{x \to \infty} \dfrac{2 + \sqrt{x}}{2 - \sqrt{x}}$

59. $\lim\limits_{x \to -\infty} \dfrac{\sqrt[3]{x} - \sqrt[5]{x}}{\sqrt[3]{x} + \sqrt[5]{x}}$

60. $\lim\limits_{x \to \infty} \dfrac{x^{-1} + x^{-4}}{x^{-2} - x^{-3}}$

61. $\lim\limits_{x \to \infty} \dfrac{2x^{5/3} - x^{1/3} + 7}{x^{8/5} + 3x + \sqrt{x}}$

62. $\lim\limits_{x \to -\infty} \dfrac{\sqrt[3]{x} - 5x + 3}{2x + x^{2/3} - 4}$

Theory and Examples

63. Once you know $\lim_{x \to a^+} f(x)$ and $\lim_{x \to a^-} f(x)$ at an interior point of the domain of f, do you then know $\lim_{x \to a} f(x)$? Give reasons for your answer.

64. If you know that $\lim_{x \to c} f(x)$ exists, can you find its value by calculating $\lim_{x \to c^+} f(x)$? Give reasons for your answer.

65. Suppose that f is an odd function of x. Does knowing that $\lim_{x \to 0^+} f(x) = 3$ tell you anything about $\lim_{x \to 0^-} f(x)$? Give reasons for your answer.

66. Suppose that f is an even function of x. Does knowing that $\lim_{x \to 2^-} f(x) = 7$ tell you anything about either $\lim_{x \to -2^-} f(x)$ or $\lim_{x \to -2^+} f(x)$? Give reasons for your answer.

67. Suppose that $f(x)$ and $g(x)$ are polynomials in x and that $\lim_{x \to \infty} (f(x)/g(x)) = 2$. Can you conclude anything about $\lim_{x \to -\infty} (f(x)/g(x))$? Give reasons for your answer.

68. Suppose that $f(x)$ and $g(x)$ are polynomials in x. Can the graph of $f(x)/g(x)$ have an asymptote if $g(x)$ is never zero? Give reasons for your answer.

69. How many horizontal asymptotes can the graph of a given rational function have? Give reasons for your answer.

70. Find $\lim\limits_{x \to \infty} \left(\sqrt{x^2 + x} - \sqrt{x^2 - x} \right)$.

Use the formal definitions of limits as $x \to \pm\infty$ to establish the limits in Exercises 71 and 72.

71. If f has the constant value $f(x) = k$, then $\lim\limits_{x \to \infty} f(x) = k$.

72. If f has the constant value $f(x) = k$, then $\lim\limits_{x \to -\infty} f(x) = k$.

Formal Definitions of One-Sided Limits

73. Given $\epsilon > 0$, find an interval $I = (5, 5 + \delta)$, $\delta > 0$, such that if x lies in I, then $\sqrt{x - 5} < \epsilon$. What limit is being verified and what is its value?

74. Given $\epsilon > 0$, find an interval $I = (4 - \delta, 4)$, $\delta > 0$, such that if x lies in I, then $\sqrt{4 - x} < \epsilon$. What limit is being verified and what is its value?

Use the definitions of right-hand and left-hand limits to prove the limit statements in Exercises 75 and 76.

75. $\lim\limits_{x \to 0^-} \dfrac{x}{|x|} = -1$

76. $\lim\limits_{x \to 2^+} \dfrac{x - 2}{|x - 2|} = 1$

77. Greatest integer function Find **(a)** $\lim_{x \to 400^+} \lfloor x \rfloor$ and **(b)** $\lim_{x \to 400^-} \lfloor x \rfloor$; then use limit definitions to verify your findings. **(c)** Based on your conclusions in parts (a) and (b), can anything be said about $\lim_{x \to 400} \lfloor x \rfloor$? Give reasons for your answers.

78. One-sided limits Let $f(x) = \begin{cases} x^2 \sin(1/x), & x < 0 \\ \sqrt{x}, & x > 0. \end{cases}$

Find **(a)** $\lim_{x \to 0^+} f(x)$ and **(b)** $\lim_{x \to 0^-} f(x)$; then use limit definitions to verify your findings. **(c)** Based on your conclusions in parts (a) and (b), can anything be said about $\lim_{x \to 0} f(x)$? Give reasons for your answer.

Grapher Explorations—"Seeing" Limits at Infinity

Sometimes a change of variable can change an unfamiliar expression into one whose limit we know how to find. For example,

$$\lim_{x \to \infty} \sin \frac{1}{x} = \lim_{\theta \to 0^+} \sin \theta \qquad \text{Substitute } \theta = 1/x$$

$$= 0.$$

This suggests a creative way to "see" limits at infinity. Describe the procedure and use it to picture and determine limits in Exercises 79–84.

79. $\lim\limits_{x \to \pm\infty} x \sin \dfrac{1}{x}$

80. $\lim\limits_{x \to -\infty} \dfrac{\cos(1/x)}{1 + (1/x)}$

81. $\lim\limits_{x \to \pm\infty} \dfrac{3x + 4}{2x - 5}$

82. $\lim\limits_{x \to \infty} \left(\dfrac{1}{x} \right)^{1/x}$

83. $\lim\limits_{x \to \pm\infty} \left(3 + \dfrac{2}{x} \right) \left(\cos \dfrac{1}{x} \right)$

84. $\lim\limits_{x \to \infty} \left(\dfrac{3}{x^2} - \cos \dfrac{1}{x} \right) \left(1 + \sin \dfrac{1}{x} \right)$

2.5 Infinite Limits and Vertical Asymptotes

In this section we extend the concept of limit to *infinite limits*, which are not limits as before, but rather an entirely new use of the term limit. Infinite limits provide useful symbols and language for describing the behavior of functions whose values become arbitrarily large, positive or negative. We continue our analysis of graphs of rational functions from the last section, using vertical asymptotes and dominant terms for numerically large values of x.

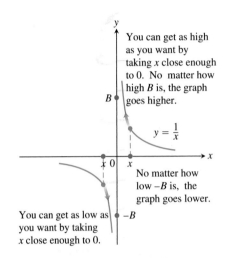

You can get as high as you want by taking x close enough to 0. No matter how high B is, the graph goes higher.

$y = \frac{1}{x}$

No matter how low $-B$ is, the graph goes lower.

You can get as low as you want by taking x close enough to 0.

FIGURE 2.37 One-sided infinite limits:

$$\lim_{x \to 0^+} \frac{1}{x} = \infty \qquad \text{and} \qquad \lim_{x \to 0^-} \frac{1}{x} = -\infty$$

Infinite Limits

Let us look again at the function $f(x) = 1/x$. As $x \to 0^+$, the values of f grow without bound, eventually reaching and surpassing every positive real number. That is, given any positive real number B, however large, the values of f become larger still (Figure 2.37). Thus, f has no limit as $x \to 0^+$. It is nevertheless convenient to describe the behavior of f by saying that $f(x)$ approaches ∞ as $x \to 0^+$. We write

$$\lim_{x \to 0^+} f(x) = \lim_{x \to 0^+} \frac{1}{x} = \infty.$$

In writing this, we are *not* saying that the limit exists. Nor are we saying that there is a real number ∞, for there is no such number. Rather, we are saying that $\lim_{x \to 0^+} (1/x)$ *does not exist because $1/x$ becomes arbitrarily large and positive as $x \to 0^+$.*

As $x \to 0^-$, the values of $f(x) = 1/x$ become arbitrarily large and negative. Given any negative real number $-B$, the values of f eventually lie below $-B$. (See Figure 2.37.) We write

$$\lim_{x \to 0^-} f(x) = \lim_{x \to 0^-} \frac{1}{x} = -\infty.$$

Again, we are not saying that the limit exists and equals the number $-\infty$. There *is* no real number $-\infty$. We are describing the behavior of a function whose limit as $x \to 0^-$ *does not exist because its values become arbitrarily large and negative.*

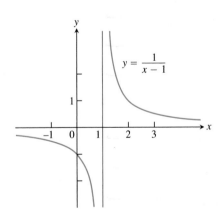

$y = \frac{1}{x - 1}$

FIGURE 2.38 Near $x = 1$, the function $y = 1/(x - 1)$ behaves the way the function $y = 1/x$ behaves near $x = 0$. Its graph is the graph of $y = 1/x$ shifted 1 unit to the right (Example 1).

EXAMPLE 1   One-Sided Infinite Limits

Find $\displaystyle\lim_{x \to 1^+} \frac{1}{x - 1}$ and $\displaystyle\lim_{x \to 1^-} \frac{1}{x - 1}$.

Geometric Solution   The graph of $y = 1/(x - 1)$ is the graph of $y = 1/x$ shifted 1 unit to the right (Figure 2.38). Therefore, $y = 1/(x - 1)$ behaves near 1 exactly the way $y = 1/x$ behaves near 0:

$$\lim_{x \to 1^+} \frac{1}{x - 1} = \infty \qquad \text{and} \qquad \lim_{x \to 1^-} \frac{1}{x - 1} = -\infty.$$

Analytic Solution   Think about the number $x - 1$ and its reciprocal. As $x \to 1^+$, we have $(x - 1) \to 0^+$ and $1/(x - 1) \to \infty$. As $x \to 1^-$, we have $(x - 1) \to 0^-$ and $1/(x - 1) \to -\infty$. ∎

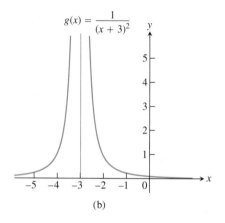

FIGURE 2.39 The graphs of the functions in Example 2. (a) $f(x)$ approaches infinity as $x \to 0$. (b) $g(x)$ approaches infinity as $x \to -3$.

EXAMPLE 2   Two-Sided Infinite Limits

Discuss the behavior of

(a) $f(x) = \dfrac{1}{x^2}$ near $x = 0$,

(b) $g(x) = \dfrac{1}{(x+3)^2}$ near $x = -3$.

Solution

(a) As x approaches zero from either side, the values of $1/x^2$ are positive and become arbitrarily large (Figure 2.39a):

$$\lim_{x \to 0} f(x) = \lim_{x \to 0} \frac{1}{x^2} = \infty.$$

(b) The graph of $g(x) = 1/(x+3)^2$ is the graph of $f(x) = 1/x^2$ shifted 3 units to the left (Figure 2.39b). Therefore, g behaves near -3 exactly the way f behaves near 0.

$$\lim_{x \to -3} g(x) = \lim_{x \to -3} \frac{1}{(x+3)^2} = \infty.$$

The function $y = 1/x$ shows no consistent behavior as $x \to 0$. We have $1/x \to \infty$ if $x \to 0^+$, but $1/x \to -\infty$ if $x \to 0^-$. All we can say about $\lim_{x \to 0} (1/x)$ is that it does not exist. The function $y = 1/x^2$ is different. Its values approach infinity as x approaches zero from either side, so we can say that $\lim_{x \to 0} (1/x^2) = \infty$.

EXAMPLE 3   Rational Functions Can Behave in Various Ways Near Zeros of Their Denominators

(a) $\displaystyle\lim_{x \to 2} \frac{(x-2)^2}{x^2-4} = \lim_{x \to 2} \frac{(x-2)^2}{(x-2)(x+2)} = \lim_{x \to 2} \frac{x-2}{x+2} = 0$

(b) $\displaystyle\lim_{x \to 2} \frac{x-2}{x^2-4} = \lim_{x \to 2} \frac{x-2}{(x-2)(x+2)} = \lim_{x \to 2} \frac{1}{x+2} = \frac{1}{4}$

(c) $\displaystyle\lim_{x \to 2^+} \frac{x-3}{x^2-4} = \lim_{x \to 2^+} \frac{x-3}{(x-2)(x+2)} = -\infty$ The values are negative for $x > 2$, x near 2.

(d) $\displaystyle\lim_{x \to 2^-} \frac{x-3}{x^2-4} = \lim_{x \to 2^-} \frac{x-3}{(x-2)(x+2)} = \infty$ The values are positive for $x < 2$, x near 2.

(e) $\displaystyle\lim_{x \to 2} \frac{x-3}{x^2-4} = \lim_{x \to 2} \frac{x-3}{(x-2)(x+2)}$ does not exist.   See parts (c) and (d).

(f) $\displaystyle\lim_{x \to 2} \frac{2-x}{(x-2)^3} = \lim_{x \to 2} \frac{-(x-2)}{(x-2)^3} = \lim_{x \to 2} \frac{-1}{(x-2)^2} = -\infty$

In parts (a) and (b) the effect of the zero in the denominator at $x = 2$ is canceled because the numerator is zero there also. Thus a finite limit exists. This is not true in part (f), where cancellation still leaves a zero in the denominator.

Precise Definitions of Infinite Limits

Instead of requiring $f(x)$ to lie arbitrarily close to a finite number L for all x sufficiently close to x_0, the definitions of infinite limits require $f(x)$ to lie arbitrarily far from the ori-

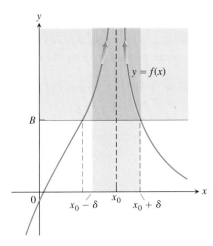

FIGURE 2.40 For $x_0 - \delta < x < x_0 + \delta$, the graph of $f(x)$ lies above the line $y = B$.

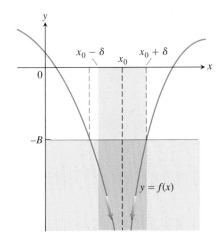

FIGURE 2.41 For $x_0 - \delta < x < x_0 + \delta$, the graph of $f(x)$ lies below the line $y = -B$.

gin. Except for this change, the language is identical with what we have seen before. Figures 2.40 and 2.41 accompany these definitions.

DEFINITIONS Infinity, Negative Infinity as Limits

1. We say that $f(x)$ **approaches infinity as x approaches x_0**, and write

$$\lim_{x \to x_0} f(x) = \infty,$$

if for every positive real number B there exists a corresponding $\delta > 0$ such that for all x

$$0 < |x - x_0| < \delta \quad \Rightarrow \quad f(x) > B.$$

2. We say that $f(x)$ **approaches negative infinity as x approaches x_0**, and write

$$\lim_{x \to x_0} f(x) = -\infty,$$

if for every negative real number $-B$ there exists a corresponding $\delta > 0$ such that for all x

$$0 < |x - x_0| < \delta \quad \Rightarrow \quad f(x) < -B.$$

The precise definitions of one-sided infinite limits at x_0 are similar and are stated in the exercises.

EXAMPLE 4 Using the Definition of Infinite Limits

Prove that $\lim_{x \to 0} \dfrac{1}{x^2} = \infty$.

Solution Given $B > 0$, we want to find $\delta > 0$ such that

$$0 < |x - 0| < \delta \quad \text{implies} \quad \frac{1}{x^2} > B.$$

Now,

$$\frac{1}{x^2} > B \qquad \text{if and only if } x^2 < \frac{1}{B}$$

or, equivalently,

$$|x| < \frac{1}{\sqrt{B}}.$$

Thus, choosing $\delta = 1/\sqrt{B}$ (or any smaller positive number), we see that

$$|x| < \delta \quad \text{implies} \quad \frac{1}{x^2} > \frac{1}{\delta^2} \geq B.$$

Therefore, by definition,

$$\lim_{x \to 0} \frac{1}{x^2} = \infty.$$

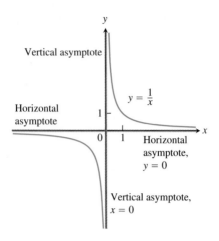

FIGURE 2.42 The coordinate axes are asymptotes of both branches of the hyperbola $y = 1/x$.

Vertical Asymptotes

Notice that the distance between a point on the graph of $y = 1/x$ and the y-axis approaches zero as the point moves vertically along the graph and away from the origin (Figure 2.42). This behavior occurs because

$$\lim_{x \to 0^+} \frac{1}{x} = \infty \qquad \text{and} \qquad \lim_{x \to 0^-} \frac{1}{x} = -\infty.$$

We say that the line $x = 0$ (the y-axis) is a *vertical asymptote* of the graph of $y = 1/x$. Observe that the denominator is zero at $x = 0$ and the function is undefined there.

> **DEFINITION** Vertical Asymptote
>
> A line $x = a$ is a **vertical asymptote** of the graph of a function $y = f(x)$ if either
>
> $$\lim_{x \to a^+} f(x) = \pm\infty \qquad \text{or} \qquad \lim_{x \to a^-} f(x) = \pm\infty.$$

EXAMPLE 5   Looking for Asymptotes

Find the horizontal and vertical asymptotes of the curve

$$y = \frac{x + 3}{x + 2}.$$

Solution   We are interested in the behavior as $x \to \pm\infty$ and as $x \to -2$, where the denominator is zero.

The asymptotes are quickly revealed if we recast the rational function as a polynomial with a remainder, by dividing $(x + 2)$ into $(x + 3)$.

$$\begin{array}{r} 1 \\ x + 2 \overline{) x + 3} \\ \underline{x + 2} \\ 1 \end{array}$$

This result enables us to rewrite y:

$$y = 1 + \frac{1}{x + 2}.$$

We now see that the curve in question is the graph of $y = 1/x$ shifted 1 unit up and 2 units left (Figure 2.43). The asymptotes, instead of being the coordinate axes, are now the lines $y = 1$ and $x = -2$.   ∎

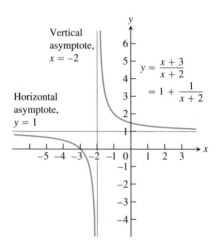

FIGURE 2.43 The lines $y = 1$ and $x = -2$ are asymptotes of the curve $y = (x + 3)/(x + 2)$ (Example 5).

EXAMPLE 6   Asymptotes Need Not Be Two-Sided

Find the horizontal and vertical asymptotes of the graph of

$$f(x) = -\frac{8}{x^2 - 4}.$$

Solution   We are interested in the behavior as $x \to \pm\infty$ and as $x \to \pm2$, where the denominator is zero. Notice that f is an even function of x, so its graph is symmetric with respect to the y-axis.

(a) *The behavior as $x \to \pm\infty$*. Since $\lim_{x \to \infty} f(x) = 0$, the line $y = 0$ is a horizontal asymptote of the graph to the right. By symmetry it is an asymptote to the left as well

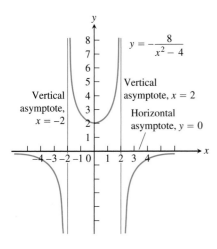

FIGURE 2.44 Graph of
$y = -8/(x^2 - 4)$. Notice that the curve
approaches the x-axis from only one side.
Asymptotes do not have to be two-sided
(Example 6).

(Figure 2.44). Notice that the curve approaches the x-axis from only the negative side
(or from below).

(b) *The behavior as $x \to \pm 2$.* Since

$$\lim_{x \to 2^+} f(x) = -\infty \quad \text{and} \quad \lim_{x \to 2^-} f(x) = \infty,$$

the line $x = 2$ is a vertical asymptote both from the right and from the left. By symmetry, the same holds for the line $x = -2$.

There are no other asymptotes because f has a finite limit at every other point. ∎

EXAMPLE 7 Curves with Infinitely Many Asymptotes

The curves

$$y = \sec x = \frac{1}{\cos x} \quad \text{and} \quad y = \tan x = \frac{\sin x}{\cos x}$$

both have vertical asymptotes at odd-integer multiples of $\pi/2$, where $\cos x = 0$ (Figure 2.45).

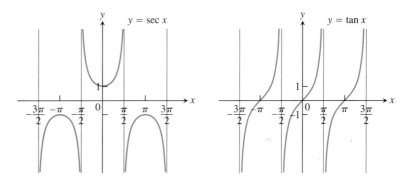

FIGURE 2.45 The graphs of $\sec x$ and $\tan x$ have infinitely many vertical
asymptotes (Example 7).

The graphs of

$$y = \csc x = \frac{1}{\sin x} \quad \text{and} \quad y = \cot x = \frac{\cos x}{\sin x}$$

have vertical asymptotes at integer multiples of π, where $\sin x = 0$ (Figure 2.46).

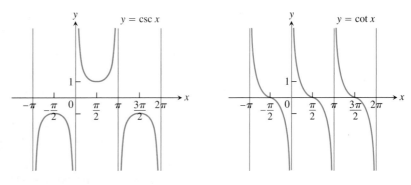

FIGURE 2.46 The graphs of $\csc x$ and $\cot x$ (Example 7). ∎

EXAMPLE 8   A Rational Function with Degree of Numerator Greater than Degree of Denominator

Find the asymptotes of the graph of

$$f(x) = \frac{x^2 - 3}{2x - 4}.$$

Solution   We are interested in the behavior as $x \to \pm\infty$ and also as $x \to 2$, where the denominator is zero. We divide $(2x - 4)$ into $(x^2 - 3)$:

$$
\begin{array}{r}
\frac{x}{2} + 1 \\
2x - 4 \overline{)x^2 - 3 } \\
\underline{x^2 - 2x } \\
2x - 3 \\
\underline{2x - 4} \\
1
\end{array}
$$

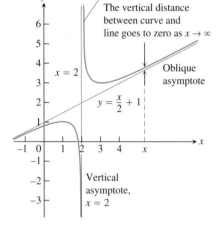

$y = \dfrac{x^2 - 3}{2x - 4} = \dfrac{x}{2} + 1 + \dfrac{1}{2x - 4}$

The vertical distance between curve and line goes to zero as $x \to \infty$

$x = 2$

Oblique asymptote

$y = \dfrac{x}{2} + 1$

Vertical asymptote, $x = 2$

FIGURE 2.47   The graph of $f(x) = (x^2 - 3)/(2x - 4)$ has a vertical asymptote and an oblique asymptote (Example 8).

This tells us that

$$f(x) = \frac{x^2 - 3}{2x - 4} = \underbrace{\frac{x}{2} + 1}_{\text{linear}} + \underbrace{\frac{1}{2x - 4}}_{\text{remainder}}.$$

Since $\lim_{x \to 2^+} f(x) = \infty$ and $\lim_{x \to 2^-} f(x) = -\infty$, the line $x = 2$ is a two-sided vertical asymptote. As $x \to \pm\infty$, the remainder approaches 0 and $f(x) \to (x/2) + 1$. The line $y = (x/2) + 1$ is an oblique asymptote both to the right and to the left (Figure 2.47). ∎

Notice in Example 8, that if the degree of the numerator in a rational function is greater than the degree of the denominator, then the limit is $+\infty$ or $-\infty$, depending on the signs assumed by the numerator and denominator as $|x|$ becomes large.

Dominant Terms

Of all the observations we can make quickly about the function

$$f(x) = \frac{x^2 - 3}{2x - 4}$$

in Example 8, probably the most useful is that

$$f(x) = \frac{x}{2} + 1 + \frac{1}{2x - 4}.$$

This tells us immediately that

$$f(x) \approx \frac{x}{2} + 1 \qquad \text{For } x \text{ numerically large}$$

$$f(x) \approx \frac{1}{2x - 4} \qquad \text{For } x \text{ near } 2$$

If we want to know how f behaves, this is the way to find out. It behaves like $y = (x/2) + 1$ when x is numerically large and the contribution of $1/(2x - 4)$ to the total value of f is insignificant. It behaves like $1/(2x - 4)$ when x is so close to 2 that $1/(2x - 4)$ makes the dominant contribution.

We say that $(x/2) + 1$ **dominates** when x is numerically large, and we say that $1/(2x - 4)$ dominates when x is near 2. **Dominant terms** like these are the key to predicting a function's behavior. Here's another example.

EXAMPLE 9   Two Graphs Appearing Identical on a Large Scale

Let $f(x) = 3x^4 - 2x^3 + 3x^2 - 5x + 6$ and $g(x) = 3x^4$. Show that although f and g are quite different for numerically small values of x, they are virtually identical for $|x|$ very large.

Solution   The graphs of f and g behave quite differently near the origin (Figure 2.48a), but appear as virtually identical on a larger scale (Figure 2.48b).

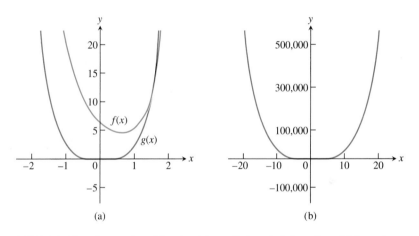

(a)   (b)

FIGURE 2.48   The graphs of f and g, (a) are distinct for $|x|$ small, and (b) nearly identical for $|x|$ large (Example 9).

We can test that the term $3x^4$ in f, represented graphically by g, dominates the polynomial f for numerically large values of x by examining the ratio of the two functions as $x \to \pm\infty$. We find that

$$\lim_{x \to \pm\infty} \frac{f(x)}{g(x)} = \lim_{x \to \pm\infty} \frac{3x^4 - 2x^3 + 3x^2 - 5x + 6}{3x^4}$$

$$= \lim_{x \to \pm\infty} \left(1 - \frac{2}{3x} + \frac{1}{x^2} - \frac{5}{3x^3} + \frac{2}{x^4} \right)$$

$$= 1,$$

so that f and g are nearly identical for $|x|$ large.   ■

EXERCISES 2.5

Infinite Limits

Find the limits in Exercises 1–12.

1. $\lim_{x \to 0^+} \dfrac{1}{3x}$

2. $\lim_{x \to 0^-} \dfrac{5}{2x}$

3. $\lim_{x \to 2^-} \dfrac{3}{x - 2}$

4. $\lim_{x \to 3^+} \dfrac{1}{x - 3}$

5. $\lim_{x \to -8^+} \dfrac{2x}{x + 8}$

6. $\lim_{x \to -5^-} \dfrac{3x}{2x + 10}$

7. $\lim_{x \to 7} \dfrac{4}{(x - 7)^2}$

8. $\lim_{x \to 0} \dfrac{-1}{x^2(x + 1)}$

9. a. $\lim_{x \to 0^+} \dfrac{2}{3x^{1/3}}$
   b. $\lim_{x \to 0^-} \dfrac{2}{3x^{1/3}}$

10. a. $\lim_{x \to 0^+} \dfrac{2}{x^{1/5}}$
   b. $\lim_{x \to 0^-} \dfrac{2}{x^{1/5}}$

11. $\lim_{x \to 0} \dfrac{4}{x^{2/5}}$

12. $\lim_{x \to 0} \dfrac{1}{x^{2/3}}$

Find the limits in Exercises 13–16.

13. $\lim_{x \to (\pi/2)^-} \tan x$

14. $\lim_{x \to (-\pi/2)^+} \sec x$

15. $\lim_{\theta \to 0^-} (1 + \csc \theta)$

16. $\lim_{\theta \to 0} (2 - \cot \theta)$

Additional Calculations

Find the limits in Exercises 17–22.

17. $\lim \dfrac{1}{x^2 - 4}$ as

   a. $x \to 2^+$
   b. $x \to 2^-$
   c. $x \to -2^+$
   d. $x \to -2^-$

18. $\lim \dfrac{x}{x^2 - 1}$ as

   a. $x \to 1^+$
   b. $x \to 1^-$
   c. $x \to -1^+$
   d. $x \to -1^-$

19. $\lim \left(\dfrac{x^2}{2} - \dfrac{1}{x} \right)$ as

   a. $x \to 0^+$
   b. $x \to 0^-$
   c. $x \to \sqrt[3]{2}$
   d. $x \to -1$

20. $\lim \dfrac{x^2 - 1}{2x + 4}$ as

   a. $x \to -2^+$
   b. $x \to -2^-$
   c. $x \to 1^+$
   d. $x \to 0^-$

21. $\lim \dfrac{x^2 - 3x + 2}{x^3 - 2x^2}$ as

   a. $x \to 0^+$
   b. $x \to 2^+$
   c. $x \to 2^-$
   d. $x \to 2$
   e. What, if anything, can be said about the limit as $x \to 0$?

22. $\lim \dfrac{x^2 - 3x + 2}{x^3 - 4x}$ as

   a. $x \to 2^+$
   b. $x \to -2^+$
   c. $x \to 0^-$
   d. $x \to 1^+$
   e. What, if anything, can be said about the limit as $x \to 0$?

Find the limits in Exercises 23–26.

23. $\lim \left(2 - \dfrac{3}{t^{1/3}} \right)$ as

   a. $t \to 0^+$
   b. $t \to 0^-$

24. $\lim \left(\dfrac{1}{t^{3/5}} + 7 \right)$ as

   a. $t \to 0^+$
   b. $t \to 0^-$

25. $\lim \left(\dfrac{1}{x^{2/3}} + \dfrac{2}{(x - 1)^{2/3}} \right)$ as

   a. $x \to 0^+$
   b. $x \to 0^-$
   c. $x \to 1^+$
   d. $x \to 1^-$

26. $\lim \left(\dfrac{1}{x^{1/3}} - \dfrac{1}{(x - 1)^{4/3}} \right)$ as

   a. $x \to 0^+$
   b. $x \to 0^-$
   c. $x \to 1^+$
   d. $x \to 1^-$

Graphing Rational Functions

Graph the rational functions in Exercises 27–38. Include the graphs and equations of the asymptotes and dominant terms.

27. $y = \dfrac{1}{x - 1}$

28. $y = \dfrac{1}{x + 1}$

29. $y = \dfrac{1}{2x + 4}$

30. $y = \dfrac{-3}{x - 3}$

31. $y = \dfrac{x + 3}{x + 2}$

32. $y = \dfrac{2x}{x + 1}$

33. $y = \dfrac{x^2}{x - 1}$

34. $y = \dfrac{x^2 + 1}{x - 1}$

35. $y = \dfrac{x^2 - 4}{x - 1}$

36. $y = \dfrac{x^2 - 1}{2x + 4}$

37. $y = \dfrac{x^2 - 1}{x}$

38. $y = \dfrac{x^3 + 1}{x^2}$

Inventing Graphs from Values and Limits

In Exercises 39–42, sketch the graph of a function $y = f(x)$ that satisfies the given conditions. No formulas are required—just label the coordinate axes and sketch an appropriate graph. (The answers are not unique, so your graphs may not be exactly like those in the answer section.)

39. $f(0) = 0, f(1) = 2, f(-1) = -2, \lim\limits_{x \to -\infty} f(x) = -1,$ and
$$\lim\limits_{x \to \infty} f(x) = 1$$

40. $f(0) = 0, \lim\limits_{x \to \pm\infty} f(x) = 0, \lim\limits_{x \to 0^+} f(x) = 2,$ and
$$\lim\limits_{x \to 0^-} f(x) = -2$$

41. $f(0) = 0, \lim\limits_{x \to \pm\infty} f(x) = 0, \lim\limits_{x \to 1^-} f(x) = \lim\limits_{x \to -1^+} f(x) = \infty,$
$$\lim\limits_{x \to 1^+} f(x) = -\infty, \text{ and } \lim\limits_{x \to -1^-} f(x) = -\infty$$

42. $f(2) = 1, f(-1) = 0, \lim\limits_{x \to \infty} f(x) = 0, \lim\limits_{x \to 0^+} f(x) = \infty,$
$$\lim\limits_{x \to 0^-} f(x) = -\infty, \text{ and } \lim\limits_{x \to -\infty} f(x) = 1$$

Inventing Functions

In Exercises 43–46, find a function that satisfies the given conditions and sketch its graph. (The answers here are not unique. Any function that satisfies the conditions is acceptable. Feel free to use formulas defined in pieces if that will help.)

43. $\lim\limits_{x \to \pm\infty} f(x) = 0, \lim\limits_{x \to 2^-} f(x) = \infty, \text{ and } \lim\limits_{x \to 2^+} f(x) = \infty$

44. $\lim\limits_{x \to \pm\infty} g(x) = 0, \lim\limits_{x \to 3^-} g(x) = -\infty, \text{ and } \lim\limits_{x \to 3^+} g(x) = \infty$

45. $\lim\limits_{x \to -\infty} h(x) = -1, \lim\limits_{x \to \infty} h(x) = 1, \lim\limits_{x \to 0^-} h(x) = -1, \text{ and }$
$$\lim\limits_{x \to 0^+} h(x) = 1$$

46. $\lim\limits_{x \to \pm\infty} k(x) = 1, \lim\limits_{x \to 1^-} k(x) = \infty, \text{ and } \lim\limits_{x \to 1^+} k(x) = -\infty$

The Formal Definition of Infinite Limit

Use formal definitions to prove the limit statements in Exercises 47–50.

47. $\lim\limits_{x \to 0} \dfrac{-1}{x^2} = -\infty$

48. $\lim\limits_{x \to 0} \dfrac{1}{|x|} = \infty$

49. $\lim\limits_{x \to 3} \dfrac{-2}{(x-3)^2} = -\infty$

50. $\lim\limits_{x \to -5} \dfrac{1}{(x+5)^2} = \infty$

Formal Definitions of Infinite One-Sided Limits

51. Here is the definition of **infinite right-hand limit**.

> We say that $f(x)$ approaches infinity as x approaches x_0 from the right, and write
> $$\lim\limits_{x \to x_0^+} f(x) = \infty,$$
> if, for every positive real number B, there exists a corresponding number $\delta > 0$ such that for all x
> $$x_0 < x < x_0 + \delta \quad \Rightarrow \quad f(x) > B.$$

Modify the definition to cover the following cases.

a. $\lim\limits_{x \to x_0^-} f(x) = \infty$

b. $\lim\limits_{x \to x_0^+} f(x) = -\infty$

c. $\lim\limits_{x \to x_0^-} f(x) = -\infty$

Use the formal definitions from Exercise 51 to prove the limit statements in Exercises 52–56.

52. $\lim\limits_{x \to 0^+} \dfrac{1}{x} = \infty$

53. $\lim\limits_{x \to 0^-} \dfrac{1}{x} = -\infty$

54. $\lim\limits_{x \to 2^-} \dfrac{1}{x-2} = -\infty$

55. $\lim\limits_{x \to 2^+} \dfrac{1}{x-2} = \infty$

56. $\lim\limits_{x \to 1^-} \dfrac{1}{1-x^2} = \infty$

Graphing Terms

Each of the functions in Exercises 57–60 is given as the sum or difference of two terms. First graph the terms (with the same set of axes). Then, using these graphs as guides, sketch in the graph of the function.

57. $y = \sec x + \dfrac{1}{x}, \quad -\dfrac{\pi}{2} < x < \dfrac{\pi}{2}$

58. $y = \sec x - \dfrac{1}{x^2}, \quad -\dfrac{\pi}{2} < x < \dfrac{\pi}{2}$

59. $y = \tan x + \dfrac{1}{x^2}, \quad -\dfrac{\pi}{2} < x < \dfrac{\pi}{2}$

60. $y = \dfrac{1}{x} - \tan x, \quad -\dfrac{\pi}{2} < x < \dfrac{\pi}{2}$

Grapher Explorations—Comparing Graphs with Formulas

Graph the curves in Exercises 61–64. Explain the relation between the curve's formula and what you see.

61. $y = \dfrac{x}{\sqrt{4 - x^2}}$

62. $y = \dfrac{-1}{\sqrt{4 - x^2}}$

63. $y = x^{2/3} + \dfrac{1}{x^{1/3}}$

64. $y = \sin\left(\dfrac{\pi}{x^2 + 1}\right)$

2.6   Continuity

FIGURE 2.49 Connecting plotted points by an unbroken curve from experimental data $Q_1, Q_2, Q_3, \ldots$ for a falling object.

When we plot function values generated in a laboratory or collected in the field, we often connect the plotted points with an unbroken curve to show what the function's values are likely to have been at the times we did not measure (Figure 2.49). In doing so, we are assuming that we are working with a *continuous function*, so its outputs vary continuously with the inputs and do not jump from one value to another without taking on the values in between. The limit of a continuous function as x approaches c can be found simply by calculating the value of the function at c. (We found this to be true for polynomials in Section 2.2.)

Any function $y = f(x)$ whose graph can be sketched over its domain in one continuous motion without lifting the pencil is an example of a continuous function. In this section we investigate more precisely what it means for a function to be continuous. We also study the properties of continuous functions, and see that many of the function types presented in Section 1.4 are continuous.

Continuity at a Point

To understand continuity, we need to consider a function like the one in Figure 2.50 whose limits we investigated in Example 2, Section 2.4.

EXAMPLE 1   Investigating Continuity

Find the points at which the function f in Figure 2.50 is continuous and the points at which f is discontinuous.

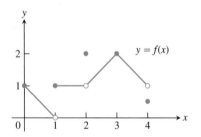

FIGURE 2.50 The function is continuous on $[0, 4]$ except at $x = 1, x = 2,$ and $x = 4$ (Example 1).

Solution   The function f is continuous at every point in its domain $[0, 4]$ except at $x = 1, x = 2,$ and $x = 4$. At these points, there are breaks in the graph. Note the relationship between the limit of f and the value of f at each point of the function's domain.

Points at which f is continuous:

At $x = 0$,	$\lim\limits_{x \to 0^+} f(x) = f(0)$.
At $x = 3$,	$\lim\limits_{x \to 3} f(x) = f(3)$.
At $0 < c < 4, c \neq 1, 2,$	$\lim\limits_{x \to c} f(x) = f(c)$.

Points at which f is discontinuous:

At $x = 1$,	$\lim\limits_{x \to 1} f(x)$ does not exist.
At $x = 2$,	$\lim\limits_{x \to 2} f(x) = 1$, but $1 \neq f(2)$.
At $x = 4$,	$\lim\limits_{x \to 4^-} f(x) = 1$, but $1 \neq f(4)$.
At $c < 0, c > 4,$	these points are not in the domain of f. ∎

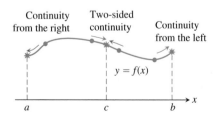

FIGURE 2.51 Continuity at points a, b, and c.

To define continuity at a point in a function's domain, we need to define continuity at an interior point (which involves a two-sided limit) and continuity at an endpoint (which involves a one-sided limit) (Figure 2.51).

DEFINITION Continuous at a Point

Interior point: A function $y = f(x)$ is **continuous at an interior point c** of its domain if

$$\lim_{x \to c} f(x) = f(c).$$

Endpoint: A function $y = f(x)$ is **continuous at a left endpoint a** or is **continuous at a right endpoint b** of its domain if

$$\lim_{x \to a^+} f(x) = f(a) \quad \text{or} \quad \lim_{x \to b^-} f(x) = f(b), \quad \text{respectively}.$$

If a function f is not continuous at a point c, we say that f is **discontinuous** at c and c is a **point of discontinuity** of f. Note that c need not be in the domain of f.

A function f is **right-continuous (continuous from the right)** at a point $x = c$ in its domain if $\lim_{x \to c^+} f(x) = f(c)$. It is **left-continuous (continuous from the left)** at c if $\lim_{x \to c^-} f(x) = f(c)$. Thus, a function is continuous at a left endpoint a of its domain if it is right-continuous at a and continuous at a right endpoint b of its domain if it is left-continuous at b. A function is continuous at an interior point c of its domain if and only if it is both right-continuous and left-continuous at c (Figure 2.51).

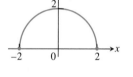

$y = \sqrt{4 - x^2}$

FIGURE 2.52 A function that is continuous at every domain point (Example 2).

EXAMPLE 2 A Function Continuous Throughout Its Domain

The function $f(x) = \sqrt{4 - x^2}$ is continuous at every point of its domain, $[-2, 2]$ (Figure 2.52), including $x = -2$, where f is right-continuous, and $x = 2$, where f is left-continuous. ∎

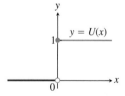

$y = U(x)$

FIGURE 2.53 A function that is right-continuous, but not left-continuous, at the origin. It has a jump discontinuity there (Example 3).

EXAMPLE 3 The Unit Step Function Has a Jump Discontinuity

The unit step function $U(x)$, graphed in Figure 2.53, is right-continuous at $x = 0$, but is neither left-continuous nor continuous there. It has a jump discontinuity at $x = 0$. ∎

We summarize continuity at a point in the form of a test.

Continuity Test

A function $f(x)$ is continuous at $x = c$ if and only if it meets the following three conditions.

1. $f(c)$ exists   (c lies in the domain of f)
2. $\lim_{x \to c} f(x)$ exists   (f has a limit as $x \to c$)
3. $\lim_{x \to c} f(x) = f(c)$ (the limit equals the function value)

For one-sided continuity and continuity at an endpoint, the limits in parts 2 and 3 of the test should be replaced by the appropriate one-sided limits.

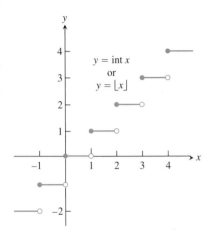

FIGURE 2.54 The greatest integer function is continuous at every noninteger point. It is right-continuous, but not left-continuous, at every integer point (Example 4).

EXAMPLE 4   The Greatest Integer Function

The function $y = \lfloor x \rfloor$ or $y = \text{int } x$, introduced in Chapter 1, is graphed in Figure 2.54. It is discontinuous at every integer because the limit does not exist at any integer n:

$$\lim_{x \to n^-} \text{int } x = n - 1 \qquad \text{and} \qquad \lim_{x \to n^+} \text{int } x = n$$

so the left-hand and right-hand limits are not equal as $x \to n$. Since int $n = n$, the greatest integer function is right-continuous at every integer n (but not left-continuous).

The greatest integer function is continuous at every real number other than the integers. For example,

$$\lim_{x \to 1.5} \text{int } x = 1 = \text{int } 1.5.$$

In general, if $n - 1 < c < n$, n an integer, then

$$\lim_{x \to c} \text{int } x = n - 1 = \text{int } c. \qquad \blacksquare$$

Figure 2.55 is a catalog of discontinuity types. The function in Figure 2.55a is continuous at $x = 0$. The function in Figure 2.55b would be continuous if it had $f(0) = 1$. The function in Figure 2.55c would be continuous if $f(0)$ were 1 instead of 2. The discontinuities in Figure 2.55b and c are **removable**. Each function has a limit as $x \to 0$, and we can remove the discontinuity by setting $f(0)$ equal to this limit.

The discontinuities in Figure 2.55d through f are more serious: $\lim_{x \to 0} f(x)$ does not exist, and there is no way to improve the situation by changing f at 0. The step function in Figure 2.55d has a **jump discontinuity**: The one-sided limits exist but have different values. The function $f(x) = 1/x^2$ in Figure 2.55e has an **infinite discontinuity**. The function in Figure 2.55f has an **oscillating discontinuity**: It oscillates too much to have a limit as $x \to 0$.

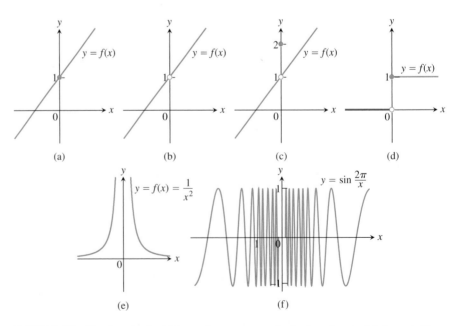

FIGURE 2.55 The function in (a) is continuous at $x = 0$; the functions in (b) through (f) are not.

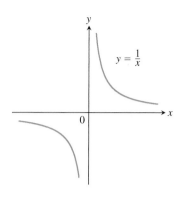

FIGURE 2.56 The function $y = 1/x$ is continuous at every value of x except $x = 0$. It has a point of discontinuity at $x = 0$ (Example 5).

Continuous Functions

A function is **continuous on an interval** if and only if it is continuous at every point of the interval. For example, the semicircle function graphed in Figure 2.52 is continuous on the interval $[-2, 2]$, which is its domain. A **continuous function** is one that is continuous at every point of its domain. A continuous function need not be continuous on every interval. For example, $y = 1/x$ is not continuous on $[-1, 1]$ (Figure 2.56), but it is continuous over its domain $(-\infty, 0) \cup (0, \infty)$.

EXAMPLE 5   Identifying Continuous Functions

(a) The function $y = 1/x$ (Figure 2.56) is a continuous function because it is continuous at every point of its domain. It has a point of discontinuity at $x = 0$, however, because it is not defined there.

(b) The identity function $f(x) = x$ and constant functions are continuous everywhere by Example 3, Section 2.3. ∎

Algebraic combinations of continuous functions are continuous wherever they are defined.

THEOREM 9   Properties of Continuous Functions

If the functions f and g are continuous at $x = c$, then the following combinations are continuous at $x = c$.

1. *Sums*: $f + g$
2. *Differences*: $f - g$
3. *Products*: $f \cdot g$
4. *Constant multiples*: $k \cdot f$, for any number k
5. *Quotients*: f/g provided $g(c) \neq 0$
6. *Powers*: $f^{r/s}$, provided it is defined on an open interval containing c, where r and s are integers

---

Most of the results in Theorem 9 are easily proved from the limit rules in Theorem 1, Section 2.2. For instance, to prove the sum property we have

$$
\begin{aligned}
\lim_{x \to c} (f + g)(x) &= \lim_{x \to c} (f(x) + g(x)) \\
&= \lim_{x \to c} f(x) + \lim_{x \to c} g(x), &&\text{Sum Rule, Theorem 1} \\
&= f(c) + g(c) &&\text{Continuity of } f, g \text{ at } c \\
&= (f + g)(c).
\end{aligned}
$$

This shows that $f + g$ is continuous.

EXAMPLE 6   Polynomial and Rational Functions Are Continuous

(a) Every polynomial $P(x) = a_n x^n + a_{n-1} x^{n-1} + \cdots + a_0$ is continuous because $\lim_{x \to c} P(x) = P(c)$ by Theorem 2, Section 2.2.

(b) If $P(x)$ and $Q(x)$ are polynomials, then the rational function $P(x)/Q(x)$ is continuous wherever it is defined ($Q(c) \neq 0$) by the Quotient Rule in Theorem 9.

EXAMPLE 7   Continuity of the Absolute Value Function

The function $f(x) = |x|$ is continuous at every value of x. If $x > 0$, we have $f(x) = x$, a polynomial. If $x < 0$, we have $f(x) = -x$, another polynomial. Finally, at the origin, $\lim_{x \to 0} |x| = 0 = |0|$.   ∎

The functions $y = \sin x$ and $y = \cos x$ are continuous at $x = 0$ by Example 6 of Section 2.2. Both functions are, in fact, continuous everywhere (see Exercise 62). It follows from Theorem 9 that all six trigonometric functions are then continuous wherever they are defined. For example, $y = \tan x$ is continuous on $\cdots \cup (-\pi/2, \pi/2) \cup (\pi/2, 3\pi/2) \cup \cdots$.

Composites

All composites of continuous functions are continuous. The idea is that if $f(x)$ is continuous at $x = c$ and $g(x)$ is continuous at $x = f(c)$, then $g \circ f$ is continuous at $x = c$ (Figure 2.57). In this case, the limit as $x \to c$ is $g(f(c))$.

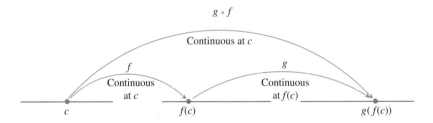

FIGURE 2.57   Composites of continuous functions are continuous.

THEOREM 10   Composite of Continuous Functions

If f is continuous at c and g is continuous at $f(c)$, then the composite $g \circ f$ is continuous at c.

Intuitively, Theorem 10 is reasonable because if x is close to c, then $f(x)$ is close to $f(c)$, and since g is continuous at $f(c)$, it follows that $g(f(x))$ is close to $g(f(c))$.

The continuity of composites holds for any finite number of functions. The only requirement is that each function be continuous where it is applied. For an outline of the proof of Theorem 10, see Exercise 6 in Appendix 2.

EXAMPLE 8   Applying Theorems 9 and 10

Show that the following functions are continuous everywhere on their respective domains.

(a) $y = \sqrt{x^2 - 2x - 5}$

(b) $y = \dfrac{x^{2/3}}{1 + x^4}$

(c) $y = \left| \dfrac{x - 2}{x^2 - 2} \right|$

(d) $y = \left| \dfrac{x \sin x}{x^2 + 2} \right|$

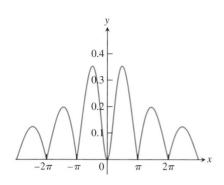

FIGURE 2.58 The graph suggests that $y = |(x \sin x)/(x^2 + 2)|$ is continuous (Example 8d).

Solution

(a) The square root function is continuous on $[0, \infty)$ because it is a rational power of the continuous identity function $f(x) = x$ (Part 6, Theorem 9). The given function is then the composite of the polynomial $f(x) = x^2 - 2x - 5$ with the square root function $g(t) = \sqrt{t}$.

(b) The numerator is a rational power of the identity function; the denominator is an everywhere-positive polynomial. Therefore, the quotient is continuous.

(c) The quotient $(x - 2)/(x^2 - 2)$ is continuous for all $x \neq \pm\sqrt{2}$, and the function is the composition of this quotient with the continuous absolute value function (Example 7).

(d) Because the sine function is everywhere-continuous (Exercise 62), the numerator term $x \sin x$ is the product of continuous functions, and the denominator term $x^2 + 2$ is an everywhere-positive polynomial. The given function is the composite of a quotient of continuous functions with the continuous absolute value function (Figure 2.58). ■

Continuous Extension to a Point

The function $y = (\sin x)/x$ is continuous at every point except $x = 0$. In this it is like the function $y = 1/x$. But $y = (\sin x)/x$ is different from $y = 1/x$ in that it has a finite limit as $x \to 0$ (Theorem 7). It is therefore possible to extend the function's domain to include the point $x = 0$ in such a way that the extended function is continuous at $x = 0$. We define

$$F(x) = \begin{cases} \dfrac{\sin x}{x}, & x \neq 0 \\ 1, & x = 0. \end{cases}$$

The function $F(x)$ is continuous at $x = 0$ because

$$\lim_{x \to 0} \frac{\sin x}{x} = F(0)$$

(Figure 2.59).

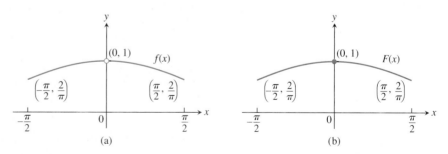

FIGURE 2.59 The graph (a) of $f(x) = (\sin x)/x$ for $-\pi/2 \leq x \leq \pi/2$ does not include the point $(0, 1)$ because the function is not defined at $x = 0$. (b) We can remove the discontinuity from the graph by defining the new function $F(x)$ with $F(0) = 1$ and $F(x) = f(x)$ everywhere else. Note that $F(0) = \lim_{x \to 0} f(x)$.

More generally, a function (such as a rational function) may have a limit even at a point where it is not defined. If $f(c)$ is not defined, but $\lim_{x \to c} f(x) = L$ exists, we can define a new function $F(x)$ by the rule

$$F(x) = \begin{cases} f(x), & \text{if } x \text{ is in the domain of } f \\ L, & \text{if } x = c. \end{cases}$$

The function F is continuous at $x = c$. It is called the **continuous extension** of f to $x = c$. For rational functions f, continuous extensions are usually found by canceling common factors.

EXAMPLE 9   A Continuous Extension

Show that

$$f(x) = \frac{x^2 + x - 6}{x^2 - 4}$$

has a continuous extension to $x = 2$, and find that extension.

Solution   Although $f(2)$ is not defined, if $x \neq 2$ we have

$$f(x) = \frac{x^2 + x - 6}{x^2 - 4} = \frac{(x - 2)(x + 3)}{(x - 2)(x + 2)} = \frac{x + 3}{x + 2}.$$

The new function

$$F(x) = \frac{x + 3}{x + 2}$$

is equal to $f(x)$ for $x \neq 2$, but is continuous at $x = 2$, having there the value of $5/4$. Thus F is the continuous extension of f to $x = 2$, and

$$\lim_{x \to 2} \frac{x^2 + x - 6}{x^2 - 4} = \lim_{x \to 2} f(x) = \frac{5}{4}.$$

The graph of f is shown in Figure 2.60. The continuous extension F has the same graph except with no hole at $(2, 5/4)$. Effectively, F is the function f with its point of discontinuity at $x = 2$ removed. ∎

FIGURE 2.60   (a) The graph of $f(x)$ and (b) the graph of its continuous extension $F(x)$ (Example 9).

Intermediate Value Theorem for Continuous Functions

Functions that are continuous on intervals have properties that make them particularly useful in mathematics and its applications. One of these is the *Intermediate Value Property*. A function is said to have the **Intermediate Value Property** if whenever it takes on two values, it also takes on all the values in between.

THEOREM 11   **The Intermediate Value Theorem for Continuous Functions**

A function $y = f(x)$ that is continuous on a closed interval $[a, b]$ takes on every value between $f(a)$ and $f(b)$. In other words, if y_0 is any value between $f(a)$ and $f(b)$, then $y_0 = f(c)$ for some c in $[a, b]$.

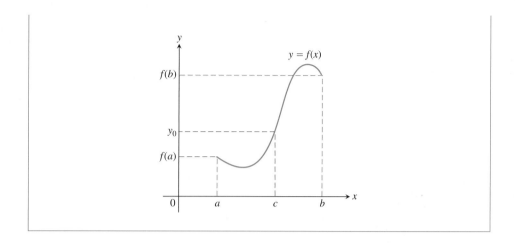

Geometrically, the Intermediate Value Theorem says that any horizontal line $y = y_0$ crossing the y-axis between the numbers $f(a)$ and $f(b)$ will cross the curve $y = f(x)$ at least once over the interval $[a, b]$.

The proof of the Intermediate Value Theorem depends on the completeness property of the real number system and can be found in more advanced texts.

The continuity of f on the interval is essential to Theorem 11. If f is discontinuous at even one point of the interval, the theorem's conclusion may fail, as it does for the function graphed in Figure 2.61.

A Consequence for Graphing: Connectivity   Theorem 11 is the reason the graph of a function continuous on an interval cannot have any breaks over the interval. It will be **connected**, a single, unbroken curve, like the graph of sin x. It will not have jumps like the graph of the greatest integer function (Figure 2.54) or separate branches like the graph of $1/x$ (Figure 2.56).

A Consequence for Root Finding   We call a solution of the equation $f(x) = 0$ a **root** of the equation or **zero** of the function f. The Intermediate Value Theorem tells us that if f is continuous, then any interval on which f changes sign contains a zero of the function.

In practical terms, when we see the graph of a continuous function cross the horizontal axis on a computer screen, we know it is not stepping across. There really is a point where the function's value is zero. This consequence leads to a procedure for estimating the zeros of any continuous function we can graph:

1.   Graph the function over a large interval to see roughly where the zeros are.

2.   Zoom in on each zero to estimate its x-coordinate value.

You can practice this procedure on your graphing calculator or computer in some of the exercises. Figure 2.62 shows a typical sequence of steps in a graphical solution of the equation $x^3 - x - 1 = 0$.

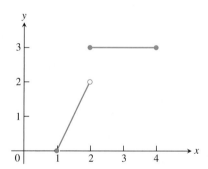

FIGURE 2.61   The function
$$f(x) = \begin{cases} 2x - 2, & 1 \le x < 2 \\ 3, & 2 \le x \le 4 \end{cases}$$
does not take on all values between $f(1) = 0$ and $f(4) = 3$; it misses all the values between 2 and 3.

(a)

(b)

(c)

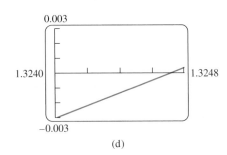

(d)

FIGURE 2.62 Zooming in on a zero of the function $f(x) = x^3 - x - 1$. The zero is near $x = 1.3247$.

EXERCISES 2.6

Continuity from Graphs

In Exercises 1–4, say whether the function graphed is continuous on $[-1, 3]$. If not, where does it fail to be continuous and why?

1.

2.

3.

4.

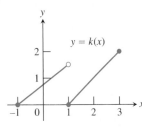

Exercises 5–10 are about the function

$$f(x) = \begin{cases} x^2 - 1, & -1 \le x < 0 \\ 2x, & 0 < x < 1 \\ 1, & x = 1 \\ -2x + 4, & 1 < x < 2 \\ 0, & 2 < x < 3 \end{cases}$$

graphed in the accompanying figure.

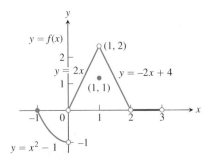

The graph for Exercises 5–10.

5. a. Does $f(-1)$ exist?

    b. Does $\lim_{x \to -1^+} f(x)$ exist?

    c. Does $\lim_{x \to -1^+} f(x) = f(-1)$?

    d. Is f continuous at $x = -1$?

6. a. Does $f(1)$ exist?

    b. Does $\lim_{x \to 1} f(x)$ exist?

    c. Does $\lim_{x \to 1} f(x) = f(1)$?

    d. Is f continuous at $x = 1$?

7. a. Is f defined at $x = 2$? (Look at the definition of f.)

    b. Is f continuous at $x = 2$?

8. At what values of x is f continuous?

9. What value should be assigned to $f(2)$ to make the extended function continuous at $x = 2$?

10. To what new value should $f(1)$ be changed to remove the discontinuity?

Applying the Continuity Test

At which points do the functions in Exercises 11 and 12 fail to be continuous? At which points, if any, are the discontinuities removable? Not removable? Give reasons for your answers.

11. Exercise 1, Section 2.4   **12.** Exercise 2, Section 2.4

At what points are the functions in Exercises 13–28 continuous?

13. $y = \dfrac{1}{x - 2} - 3x$ **14.** $y = \dfrac{1}{(x + 2)^2} + 4$

15. $y = \dfrac{x + 1}{x^2 - 4x + 3}$ **16.** $y = \dfrac{x + 3}{x^2 - 3x - 10}$

17. $y = |x - 1| + \sin x$ **18.** $y = \dfrac{1}{|x| + 1} - \dfrac{x^2}{2}$

19. $y = \dfrac{\cos x}{x}$ **20.** $y = \dfrac{x + 2}{\cos x}$

21. $y = \csc 2x$ **22.** $y = \tan \dfrac{\pi x}{2}$

23. $y = \dfrac{x \tan x}{x^2 + 1}$ **24.** $y = \dfrac{\sqrt{x^4 + 1}}{1 + \sin^2 x}$

25. $y = \sqrt{2x + 3}$ **26.** $y = \sqrt[4]{3x - 1}$

27. $y = (2x - 1)^{1/3}$ **28.** $y = (2 - x)^{1/5}$

Composite Functions

Find the limits in Exercises 29–34. Are the functions continuous at the point being approached?

29. $\lim_{x \to \pi} \sin (x - \sin x)$

30. $\lim_{t \to 0} \sin \left(\dfrac{\pi}{2} \cos (\tan t) \right)$

31. $\lim_{y \to 1} \sec (y \sec^2 y - \tan^2 y - 1)$

32. $\lim_{x \to 0} \tan \left(\dfrac{\pi}{4} \cos (\sin x^{1/3}) \right)$

33. $\lim_{t \to 0} \cos \left(\dfrac{\pi}{\sqrt{19 - 3 \sec 2t}} \right)$

34. $\lim_{x \to \pi/6} \sqrt{\csc^2 x + 5\sqrt{3} \tan x}$

Continuous Extensions

35. Define $g(3)$ in a way that extends $g(x) = (x^2 - 9)/(x - 3)$ to be continuous at $x = 3$.

36. Define $h(2)$ in a way that extends $h(t) = (t^2 + 3t - 10)/(t - 2)$ to be continuous at $t = 2$.

37. Define $f(1)$ in a way that extends $f(s) = (s^3 - 1)/(s^2 - 1)$ to be continuous at $s = 1$.

38. Define $g(4)$ in a way that extends $g(x) = (x^2 - 16)/(x^2 - 3x - 4)$ to be continuous at $x = 4$.

39. For what value of a is

$$f(x) = \begin{cases} x^2 - 1, & x < 3 \\ 2ax, & x \ge 3 \end{cases}$$

continuous at every x?

40. For what value of b is

$$g(x) = \begin{cases} x, & x < -2 \\ bx^2, & x \ge -2 \end{cases}$$

continuous at every x?

T In Exercises 41–44, graph the function f to see whether it appears to have a continuous extension to the origin. If it does, use Trace and Zoom to find a good candidate for the extended function's value at $x = 0$. If the function does not appear to have a continuous extension, can it be extended to be continuous at the origin from the right or from the left? If so, what do you think the extended function's value(s) should be?

41. $f(x) = \dfrac{10^x - 1}{x}$ **42.** $f(x) = \dfrac{10^{|x|} - 1}{x}$

43. $f(x) = \dfrac{\sin x}{|x|}$ **44.** $f(x) = (1 + 2x)^{1/x}$

Theory and Examples

45. A continuous function $y = f(x)$ is known to be negative at $x = 0$ and positive at $x = 1$. Why does the equation $f(x) = 0$ have at least one solution between $x = 0$ and $x = 1$? Illustrate with a sketch.

46. Explain why the equation $\cos x = x$ has at least one solution.

47. Roots of a cubic Show that the equation $x^3 - 15x + 1 = 0$ has three solutions in the interval $[-4, 4]$.

48. A function value Show that the function $F(x) = (x - a)^2 \cdot (x - b)^2 + x$ takes on the value $(a + b)/2$ for some value of x.

49. Solving an equation If $f(x) = x^3 - 8x + 10$, show that there are values c for which $f(c)$ equals (a) π; (b) $-\sqrt{3}$; (c) $5,000,000$.

50. Explain why the following five statements ask for the same information.

a. Find the roots of $f(x) = x^3 - 3x - 1$.

b. Find the x-coordinates of the points where the curve $y = x^3$ crosses the line $y = 3x + 1$.

c. Find all the values of x for which $x^3 - 3x = 1$.

d. Find the x-coordinates of the points where the cubic curve $y = x^3 - 3x$ crosses the line $y = 1$.

e. Solve the equation $x^3 - 3x - 1 = 0$.

51. Removable discontinuity Give an example of a function $f(x)$ that is continuous for all values of x except $x = 2$, where it has a removable discontinuity. Explain how you know that f is discontinuous at $x = 2$, and how you know the discontinuity is removable.

52. Nonremovable discontinuity Give an example of a function $g(x)$ that is continuous for all values of x except $x = -1$, where it has a nonremovable discontinuity. Explain how you know that g is discontinuous there and why the discontinuity is not removable.

53. A function discontinuous at every point

a. Use the fact that every nonempty interval of real numbers contains both rational and irrational numbers to show that the function

$$f(x) = \begin{cases} 1, & \text{if } x \text{ is rational} \\ 0, & \text{if } x \text{ is irrational} \end{cases}$$

is discontinuous at every point.

b. Is f right-continuous or left-continuous at any point?

54. If functions $f(x)$ and $g(x)$ are continuous for $0 \le x \le 1$, could $f(x)/g(x)$ possibly be discontinuous at a point of $[0, 1]$? Give reasons for your answer.

55. If the product function $h(x) = f(x) \cdot g(x)$ is continuous at $x = 0$, must $f(x)$ and $g(x)$ be continuous at $x = 0$? Give reasons for your answer.

56. Discontinuous composite of continuous functions Give an example of functions f and g, both continuous at $x = 0$, for which the composite $f \circ g$ is discontinuous at $x = 0$. Does this contradict Theorem 10? Give reasons for your answer.

57. Never-zero continuous functions Is it true that a continuous function that is never zero on an interval never changes sign on that interval? Give reasons for your answer.

58. Stretching a rubber band Is it true that if you stretch a rubber band by moving one end to the right and the other to the left, some point of the band will end up in its original position? Give reasons for your answer.

59. A fixed point theorem Suppose that a function f is continuous on the closed interval $[0, 1]$ and that $0 \le f(x) \le 1$ for every x in $[0, 1]$. Show that there must exist a number c in $[0, 1]$ such that $f(c) = c$ (c is called a **fixed point** of f).

60. The sign-preserving property of continuous functions Let f be defined on an interval (a, b) and suppose that $f(c) \neq 0$ at some c where f is continuous. Show that there is an interval $(c - \delta, c + \delta)$ about c where f has the same sign as $f(c)$. Notice how remarkable this conclusion is. Although f is defined throughout (a, b), it is not required to be continuous at any point except c. That and the condition $f(c) \neq 0$ are enough to make f different from zero (positive or negative) throughout an entire interval.

61. Prove that f is continuous at c if and only if

$$\lim_{h \to 0} f(c + h) = f(c).$$

62. Use Exercise 61 together with the identities

$$\sin(h + c) = \sin h \cos c + \cos h \sin c,$$
$$\cos(h + c) = \cos h \cos c - \sin h \sin c$$

to prove that $f(x) = \sin x$ and $g(x) = \cos x$ are continuous at every point $x = c$.

Solving Equations Graphically

[T] Use a graphing calculator or computer grapher to solve the equations in Exercises 63–70.

63. $x^3 - 3x - 1 = 0$

64. $2x^3 - 2x^2 - 2x + 1 = 0$

65. $x(x - 1)^2 = 1$ (one root)

66. $x^x = 2$

67. $\sqrt{x} + \sqrt{1 + x} = 4$

68. $x^3 - 15x + 1 = 0$ (three roots)

69. $\cos x = x$ (one root). Make sure you are using radian mode.

70. $2 \sin x = x$ (three roots). Make sure you are using radian mode.

2.7 Tangents and Derivatives

This section continues the discussion of secants and tangents begun in Section 2.1. We calculate limits of secant slopes to find tangents to curves.

What *Is* a Tangent to a Curve?

For circles, tangency is straightforward. A line L is tangent to a circle at a point P if L passes through P perpendicular to the radius at P (Figure 2.63). Such a line just *touches*

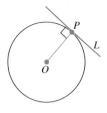

FIGURE 2.63 L is tangent to the circle at P if it passes through P perpendicular to radius OP.

the circle. But what does it mean to say that a line L is tangent to some other curve C at a point P? Generalizing from the geometry of the circle, we might say that it means one of the following:

1. L passes through P perpendicular to the line from P to the center of C.

2. L passes through only one point of C, namely P.

3. L passes through P and lies on one side of C only.

Although these statements are valid if C is a circle, none of them works consistently for more general curves. Most curves do not have centers, and a line we may want to call tangent may intersect C at other points or cross C at the point of tangency (Figure 2.64).

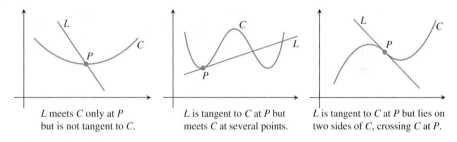

| L meets C only at P but is not tangent to C. | L is tangent to C at P but meets C at several points. | L is tangent to C at P but lies on two sides of C, crossing C at P. |

FIGURE 2.64 Exploding myths about tangent lines.

HISTORICAL BIOGRAPHY

Pierre de Fermat
(1601–1665)

To define tangency for general curves, we need a *dynamic* approach that takes into account the behavior of the secants through P and nearby points Q as Q moves toward P along the curve (Figure 2.65). It goes like this:

1. We start with what we *can* calculate, namely the slope of the secant PQ.

2. Investigate the limit of the secant slope as Q approaches P along the curve.

3. If the limit exists, take it to be the slope of the curve at P and define the tangent to the curve at P to be the line through P with this slope.

This approach is what we were doing in the falling-rock and fruit fly examples in Section 2.1.

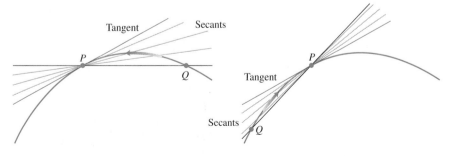

FIGURE 2.65 The dynamic approach to tangency. The tangent to the curve at P is the line through P whose slope is the limit of the secant slopes as $Q \to P$ from either side.

EXAMPLE 1 Tangent Line to a Parabola

Find the slope of the parabola $y = x^2$ at the point $P(2, 4)$. Write an equation for the tangent to the parabola at this point.

Solution We begin with a secant line through $P(2, 4)$ and $Q(2 + h, (2 + h)^2)$ nearby. We then write an expression for the slope of the secant PQ and investigate what happens to the slope as Q approaches P along the curve:

$$\text{Secant slope} = \frac{\Delta y}{\Delta x} = \frac{(2 + h)^2 - 2^2}{h} = \frac{h^2 + 4h + 4 - 4}{h}$$

$$= \frac{h^2 + 4h}{h} = h + 4.$$

If $h > 0$, then Q lies above and to the right of P, as in Figure 2.66. If $h < 0$, then Q lies to the left of P (not shown). In either case, as Q approaches P along the curve, h approaches zero and the secant slope approaches 4:

$$\lim_{h \to 0} (h + 4) = 4.$$

We take 4 to be the parabola's slope at P.

The tangent to the parabola at P is the line through P with slope 4:

$$y = 4 + 4(x - 2) \qquad \text{Point-slope equation}$$

$$y = 4x - 4.$$ ∎

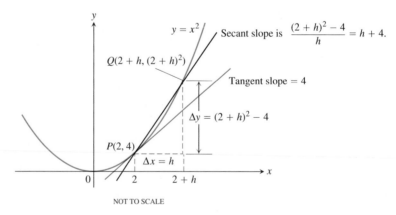

FIGURE 2.66 Finding the slope of the parabola $y = x^2$ at the point $P(2, 4)$ (Example 1).

Finding a Tangent to the Graph of a Function

The problem of finding a tangent to a curve was the dominant mathematical problem of the early seventeenth century. In optics, the tangent determined the angle at which a ray of light entered a curved lens. In mechanics, the tangent determined the direction of a body's motion at every point along its path. In geometry, the tangents to two curves at a point of intersection determined the angles at which they intersected. To find a tangent to an arbitrary curve $y = f(x)$ at a point $P(x_0, f(x_0))$, we use the same dynamic procedure. We calculate the slope of the secant through P and a point $Q(x_0 + h, f(x_0 + h))$. We then investigate the limit of the slope as $h \to 0$ (Figure 2.67). If the limit exists, we call it the slope of the curve at P and define the tangent at P to be the line through P having this slope.

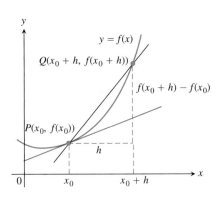

FIGURE 2.67 The slope of the tangent line at P is $\lim\limits_{h \to 0} \dfrac{f(x_0 + h) - f(x_0)}{h}$.

> **DEFINITIONS** Slope, Tangent Line
>
> The **slope of the curve** $y = f(x)$ at the point $P(x_0, f(x_0))$ is the number
>
> $$m = \lim_{h \to 0} \frac{f(x_0 + h) - f(x_0)}{h} \qquad \text{(provided the limit exists).}$$
>
> The **tangent line** to the curve at P is the line through P with this slope.

Whenever we make a new definition, we try it on familiar objects to be sure it is consistent with results we expect in familiar cases. Example 2 shows that the new definition of slope agrees with the old definition from Section 1.2 when we apply it to nonvertical lines.

EXAMPLE 2 Testing the Definition

Show that the line $y = mx + b$ is its own tangent at any point $(x_0, mx_0 + b)$.

Solution We let $f(x) = mx + b$ and organize the work into three steps.

1. *Find $f(x_0)$ and $f(x_0 + h)$.*

$$f(x_0) = mx_0 + b$$
$$f(x_0 + h) = m(x_0 + h) + b = mx_0 + mh + b$$

2. *Find the slope* $\lim\limits_{h \to 0}(f(x_0 + h) - f(x_0))/h$.

$$\lim_{h \to 0} \frac{f(x_0 + h) - f(x_0)}{h} = \lim_{h \to 0} \frac{(mx_0 + mh + b) - (mx_0 + b)}{h}$$
$$= \lim_{h \to 0} \frac{mh}{h} = m$$

3. *Find the tangent line using the point-slope equation.* The tangent line at the point $(x_0, mx_0 + b)$ is

$$y = (mx_0 + b) + m(x - x_0)$$
$$y = mx_0 + b + mx - mx_0$$
$$y = mx + b.$$

Let's summarize the steps in Example 2.

> **Finding the Tangent to the Curve $y = f(x)$ at (x_0, y_0)**
> 1. Calculate $f(x_0)$ and $f(x_0 + h)$.
> 2. Calculate the slope
> $$m = \lim_{h \to 0} \frac{f(x_0 + h) - f(x_0)}{h}.$$
> 3. If the limit exists, find the tangent line as
> $$y = y_0 + m(x - x_0).$$

EXAMPLE 3   Slope and Tangent to $y = 1/x$, $x \neq 0$

(a) Find the slope of the curve $y = 1/x$ at $x = a \neq 0$.

(b) Where does the slope equal $-1/4$?

(c) What happens to the tangent to the curve at the point $(a, 1/a)$ as a changes?

Solution

(a) Here $f(x) = 1/x$. The slope at $(a, 1/a)$ is

$$\lim_{h \to 0} \frac{f(a + h) - f(a)}{h} = \lim_{h \to 0} \frac{\dfrac{1}{a + h} - \dfrac{1}{a}}{h}$$

$$= \lim_{h \to 0} \frac{1}{h} \frac{a - (a + h)}{a(a + h)}$$

$$= \lim_{h \to 0} \frac{-h}{ha(a + h)}$$

$$= \lim_{h \to 0} \frac{-1}{a(a + h)} = -\frac{1}{a^2}.$$

Notice how we had to keep writing "$\lim_{h \to 0}$" before each fraction until the stage where we could evaluate the limit by substituting $h = 0$. The number a may be positive or negative, but not 0.

(b) The slope of $y = 1/x$ at the point where $x = a$ is $-1/a^2$. It will be $-1/4$ provided that

$$-\frac{1}{a^2} = -\frac{1}{4}.$$

This equation is equivalent to $a^2 = 4$, so $a = 2$ or $a = -2$. The curve has slope $-1/4$ at the two points $(2, 1/2)$ and $(-2, -1/2)$ (Figure 2.68).

(c) Notice that the slope $-1/a^2$ is always negative if $a \neq 0$. As $a \to 0^+$, the slope approaches $-\infty$ and the tangent becomes increasingly steep (Figure 2.69). We see this situation again as $a \to 0^-$. As a moves away from the origin in either direction, the slope approaches 0^- and the tangent levels off.   ∎

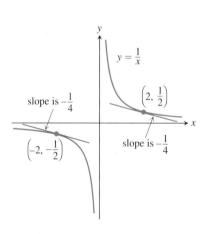

FIGURE 2.68   The two tangent lines to $y = 1/x$ having slope $-1/4$ (Example 3).

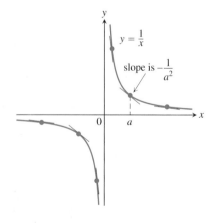

FIGURE 2.69   The tangent slopes, steep near the origin, become more gradual as the point of tangency moves away.

Rates of Change: Derivative at a Point

The expression

$$\frac{f(x_0 + h) - f(x_0)}{h}$$

is called the **difference quotient of f at x_0 with increment h**. If the difference quotient has a limit as h approaches zero, that limit is called the **derivative of f at x_0**. If we interpret the difference quotient as a secant slope, the derivative gives the slope of the curve and tangent at the point where $x = x_0$. If we interpret the difference quotient as an average rate of change, as we did in Section 2.1, the derivative gives the function's rate of change with respect to x at the point $x = x_0$. The derivative is one of the two most important mathematical objects considered in calculus. We begin a thorough study of it in Chapter 3. The other important object is the integral, and we initiate its study in Chapter 5.

EXAMPLE 4   Instantaneous Speed (Continuation of Section 2.1, Examples 1 and 2)

In Examples 1 and 2 in Section 2.1, we studied the speed of a rock falling freely from rest near the surface of the earth. We knew that the rock fell $y = 16t^2$ feet during the first t sec, and we used a sequence of average rates over increasingly short intervals to estimate the rock's speed at the instant $t = 1$. Exactly what *was* the rock's speed at this time?

Solution   We let $f(t) = 16t^2$. The average speed of the rock over the interval between $t = 1$ and $t = 1 + h$ seconds was

$$\frac{f(1 + h) - f(1)}{h} = \frac{16(1 + h)^2 - 16(1)^2}{h} = \frac{16(h^2 + 2h)}{h} = 16(h + 2).$$

The rock's speed at the instant $t = 1$ was

$$\lim_{h \to 0} 16(h + 2) = 16(0 + 2) = 32 \text{ ft/sec}.$$

Our original estimate of 32 ft/sec was right.   ∎

Summary

We have been discussing slopes of curves, lines tangent to a curve, the rate of change of a function, the limit of the difference quotient, and the derivative of a function at a point. All of these ideas refer to the same thing, summarized here:

---

1.   The slope of $y = f(x)$ at $x = x_0$
2.   The slope of the tangent to the curve $y = f(x)$ at $x = x_0$
3.   The rate of change of $f(x)$ with respect to x at $x = x_0$
4.   The derivative of f at $x = x_0$
5.   The limit of the difference quotient, $\displaystyle\lim_{h \to 0} \frac{f(x_0 + h) - f(x_0)}{h}$

EXERCISES 2.7

Slopes and Tangent Lines

In Exercises 1–4, use the grid and a straight edge to make a rough estimate of the slope of the curve (in y-units per x-unit) at the points P_1 and P_2. Graphs can shift during a press run, so your estimates may be somewhat different from those in the back of the book.

1.

2.

3.

4.

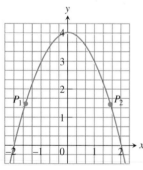

In Exercises 5–10, find an equation for the tangent to the curve at the given point. Then sketch the curve and tangent together.

5. $y = 4 - x^2$, $(-1, 3)$ **6.** $y = (x - 1)^2 + 1$, $(1, 1)$

7. $y = 2\sqrt{x}$, $(1, 2)$ **8.** $y = \dfrac{1}{x^2}$, $(-1, 1)$

9. $y = x^3$, $(-2, -8)$ **10.** $y = \dfrac{1}{x^3}$, $\left(-2, -\dfrac{1}{8}\right)$

In Exercises 11–18, find the slope of the function's graph at the given point. Then find an equation for the line tangent to the graph there.

11. $f(x) = x^2 + 1$, $(2, 5)$ **12.** $f(x) = x - 2x^2$, $(1, -1)$

13. $g(x) = \dfrac{x}{x - 2}$, $(3, 3)$ **14.** $g(x) = \dfrac{8}{x^2}$, $(2, 2)$

15. $h(t) = t^3$, $(2, 8)$ **16.** $h(t) = t^3 + 3t$, $(1, 4)$

17. $f(x) = \sqrt{x}$, $(4, 2)$ **18.** $f(x) = \sqrt{x + 1}$, $(8, 3)$

In Exercises 19–22, find the slope of the curve at the point indicated.

19. $y = 5x^2$, $x = -1$ **20.** $y = 1 - x^2$, $x = 2$

21. $y = \dfrac{1}{x - 1}$, $x = 3$ **22.** $y = \dfrac{x - 1}{x + 1}$, $x = 0$

Tangent Lines with Specified Slopes

At what points do the graphs of the functions in Exercises 23 and 24 have horizontal tangents?

23. $f(x) = x^2 + 4x - 1$ **24.** $g(x) = x^3 - 3x$

25. Find equations of all lines having slope -1 that are tangent to the curve $y = 1/(x - 1)$.

26. Find an equation of the straight line having slope $1/4$ that is tangent to the curve $y = \sqrt{x}$.

Rates of Change

27. Object dropped from a tower An object is dropped from the top of a 100-m-high tower. Its height above ground after t sec is $100 - 4.9t^2$ m. How fast is it falling 2 sec after it is dropped?

28. Speed of a rocket At t sec after liftoff, the height of a rocket is $3t^2$ ft. How fast is the rocket climbing 10 sec after liftoff?

29. Circle's changing area What is the rate of change of the area of a circle ($A = \pi r^2$) with respect to the radius when the radius is $r = 3$?

30. Ball's changing volume What is the rate of change of the volume of a ball ($V = (4/3)\pi r^3$) with respect to the radius when the radius is $r = 2$?

Testing for Tangents

31. Does the graph of

$$f(x) = \begin{cases} x^2 \sin (1/x), & x \neq 0 \\ 0, & x = 0 \end{cases}$$

have a tangent at the origin? Give reasons for your answer.

32. Does the graph of

$$g(x) = \begin{cases} x \sin (1/x), & x \neq 0 \\ 0, & x = 0 \end{cases}$$

have a tangent at the origin? Give reasons for your answer.

Vertical Tangents

We say that the curve $y = f(x)$ has a **vertical tangent** at the point where $x = x_0$ if $\lim_{h \to 0} (f(x_0 + h) - f(x_0))/h = \infty$ or $-\infty$.

Vertical tangent at $x = 0$ (see accompanying figure):

$$\lim_{h \to 0} \frac{f(0 + h) - f(0)}{h} = \lim_{h \to 0} \frac{h^{1/3} - 0}{h}$$

$$= \lim_{h \to 0} \frac{1}{h^{2/3}} = \infty$$

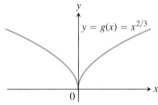

VERTICAL TANGENT AT ORIGIN

No vertical tangent at $x = 0$ (see next figure):

$$\lim_{h \to 0} \frac{g(0 + h) - g(0)}{h} = \lim_{h \to 0} \frac{h^{2/3} - 0}{h}$$

$$= \lim_{h \to 0} \frac{1}{h^{1/3}}$$

does not exist, because the limit is ∞ from the right and $-\infty$ from the left.

NO VERTICAL TANGENT AT ORIGIN

33. Does the graph of

$$f(x) = \begin{cases} -1, & x < 0 \\ 0, & x = 0 \\ 1, & x > 0 \end{cases}$$

have a vertical tangent at the origin? Give reasons for your answer.

34. Does the graph of

$$U(x) = \begin{cases} 0, & x < 0 \\ 1, & x \geq 0 \end{cases}$$

have a vertical tangent at the point $(0, 1)$? Give reasons for your answer.

T **a.** Graph the curves in Exercises 35–44. Where do the graphs appear to have vertical tangents?

  b. Confirm your findings in part (a) with limit calculations. But before you do, read the introduction to Exercises 33 and 34.

35. $y = x^{2/5}$

36. $y = x^{4/5}$

37. $y = x^{1/5}$

38. $y = x^{3/5}$

39. $y = 4x^{2/5} - 2x$

40. $y = x^{5/3} - 5x^{2/3}$

41. $y = x^{2/3} - (x - 1)^{1/3}$

42. $y = x^{1/3} + (x - 1)^{1/3}$

43. $y = \begin{cases} -\sqrt{|x|}, & x \leq 0 \\ \sqrt{x}, & x > 0 \end{cases}$

44. $y = \sqrt{|4 - x|}$

COMPUTER EXPLORATIONS

Graphing Secant and Tangent Lines

Use a CAS to perform the following steps for the functions in Exercises 45–48.

  a. Plot $y = f(x)$ over the interval $(x_0 - 1/2) \leq x \leq (x_0 + 3)$.

  b. Holding x_0 fixed, the difference quotient

$$q(h) = \frac{f(x_0 + h) - f(x_0)}{h}$$

at x_0 becomes a function of the step size h. Enter this function into your CAS workspace.

  c. Find the limit of q as $h \to 0$.

  d. Define the secant lines $y = f(x_0) + q \cdot (x - x_0)$ for $h = 3, 2$, and 1. Graph them together with f and the tangent line over the interval in part (a).

45. $f(x) = x^3 + 2x$, $x_0 = 0$ **46.** $f(x) = x + \dfrac{5}{x}$, $x_0 = 1$

47. $f(x) = x + \sin(2x)$, $x_0 = \pi/2$

48. $f(x) = \cos x + 4 \sin(2x)$, $x_0 = \pi$

Chapter 2 Questions to Guide Your Review

1. What is the average rate of change of the function $g(t)$ over the interval from $t = a$ to $t = b$? How is it related to a secant line?

2. What limit must be calculated to find the rate of change of a function $g(t)$ at $t = t_0$?

3. What is an informal or intuitive definition of the limit

$$\lim_{x \to x_0} f(x) = L?$$

Why is the definition "informal"? Give examples.

4. Does the existence and value of the limit of a function $f(x)$ as x approaches x_0 ever depend on what happens at $x = x_0$? Explain and give examples.

5. What function behaviors might occur for which the limit may fail to exist? Give examples.

6. What theorems are available for calculating limits? Give examples of how the theorems are used.

7. How are one-sided limits related to limits? How can this relationship sometimes be used to calculate a limit or prove it does not exist? Give examples.

8. What is the value of $\lim_{\theta \to 0} ((\sin \theta)/\theta)$? Does it matter whether θ is measured in degrees or radians? Explain.

9. What exactly does $\lim_{x \to x_0} f(x) = L$ mean? Give an example in which you find a $\delta > 0$ for a given f, L, x_0, and $\epsilon > 0$ in the precise definition of limit.

10. Give precise definitions of the following statements.
   a. $\lim_{x \to 2^-} f(x) = 5$ b. $\lim_{x \to 2^+} f(x) = 5$
   c. $\lim_{x \to 2} f(x) = \infty$ d. $\lim_{x \to 2} f(x) = -\infty$

11. What exactly do $\lim_{x \to \infty} f(x) = L$ and $\lim_{x \to -\infty} f(x) = L$ mean? Give examples.

12. What are $\lim_{x \to \pm\infty} k$ (k a constant) and $\lim_{x \to \pm\infty} (1/x)$? How do you extend these results to other functions? Give examples.

13. How do you find the limit of a rational function as $x \to \pm\infty$? Give examples.

14. What are horizontal, vertical, and oblique asymptotes? Give examples.

15. What conditions must be satisfied by a function if it is to be continuous at an interior point of its domain? At an endpoint?

16. How can looking at the graph of a function help you tell where the function is continuous?

17. What does it mean for a function to be right-continuous at a point? Left-continuous? How are continuity and one-sided continuity related?

18. What can be said about the continuity of polynomials? Of rational functions? Of trigonometric functions? Of rational powers and algebraic combinations of functions? Of composites of functions? Of absolute values of functions?

19. Under what circumstances can you extend a function $f(x)$ to be continuous at a point $x = c$? Give an example.

20. What does it mean for a function to be continuous on an interval?

21. What does it mean for a function to be continuous? Give examples to illustrate the fact that a function that is not continuous on its entire domain may still be continuous on selected intervals within the domain.

22. What are the basic types of discontinuity? Give an example of each. What is a removable discontinuity? Give an example.

23. What does it mean for a function to have the Intermediate Value Property? What conditions guarantee that a function has this property over an interval? What are the consequences for graphing and solving the equation $f(x) = 0$?

24. It is often said that a function is continuous if you can draw its graph without having to lift your pen from the paper. Why is that?

25. What does it mean for a line to be tangent to a curve C at a point P?

26. What is the significance of the formula

$$\lim_{h \to 0} \frac{f(x + h) - f(x)}{h} ?$$

Interpret the formula geometrically and physically.

27. How do you find the tangent to the curve $y = f(x)$ at a point (x_0, y_0) on the curve?

28. How does the slope of the curve $y = f(x)$ at $x = x_0$ relate to the function's rate of change with respect to x at $x = x_0$? To the derivative of f at x_0?

Chapter 2   Practice Exercises

Limits and Continuity

1. Graph the function

$$f(x) = \begin{cases} 1, & x \le -1 \\ -x, & -1 < x < 0 \\ 1, & x = 0 \\ -x, & 0 < x < 1 \\ 1, & x \ge 1. \end{cases}$$

Then discuss, in detail, limits, one-sided limits, continuity, and one-sided continuity of f at $x = -1, 0$, and 1. Are any of the discontinuities removable? Explain.

2. Repeat the instructions of Exercise 1 for

$$f(x) = \begin{cases} 0, & x \le -1 \\ 1/x, & 0 < |x| < 1 \\ 0, & x = 1 \\ 1, & x > 1. \end{cases}$$

3. Suppose that $f(t)$ and $g(t)$ are defined for all t and that $\lim_{t \to t_0} f(t) = -7$ and $\lim_{t \to t_0} g(t) = 0$. Find the limit as $t \to t_0$ of the following functions.
   a. $3f(t)$ b. $(f(t))^2$
   c. $f(t) \cdot g(t)$ d. $\dfrac{f(t)}{g(t) - 7}$
   e. $\cos (g(t))$ f. $|f(t)|$
   g. $f(t) + g(t)$ h. $1/f(t)$

4. Suppose that $f(x)$ and $g(x)$ are defined for all x and that $\lim_{x\to0} f(x) = 1/2$ and $\lim_{x\to0} g(x) = \sqrt{2}$. Find the limits as $x \to 0$ of the following functions.

a. $-g(x)$

b. $g(x) \cdot f(x)$

c. $f(x) + g(x)$

d. $1/f(x)$

e. $x + f(x)$

f. $\dfrac{f(x) \cdot \cos x}{x - 1}$

In Exercises 5 and 6, find the value that $\lim_{x\to0} g(x)$ must have if the given limit statements hold.

5. $\lim_{x\to0}\left(\dfrac{4 - g(x)}{x}\right) = 1$

6. $\lim_{x\to-4}\left(x \lim_{x\to0} g(x)\right) = 2$

7. On what intervals are the following functions continuous?

a. $f(x) = x^{1/3}$

b. $g(x) = x^{3/4}$

c. $h(x) = x^{-2/3}$

d. $k(x) = x^{-1/6}$

8. On what intervals are the following functions continuous?

a. $f(x) = \tan x$

b. $g(x) = \csc x$

c. $h(x) = \dfrac{\cos x}{x - \pi}$

d. $k(x) = \dfrac{\sin x}{x}$

Finding Limits

In Exercises 9–16, find the limit or explain why it does not exist.

9. $\lim \dfrac{x^2 - 4x + 4}{x^3 + 5x^2 - 14x}$

a. as $x \to 0$

b. as $x \to 2$

10. $\lim \dfrac{x^2 + x}{x^5 + 2x^4 + x^3}$

a. as $x \to 0$

b. as $x \to -1$

11. $\lim_{x\to1} \dfrac{1 - \sqrt{x}}{1 - x}$

12. $\lim_{x\to a} \dfrac{x^2 - a^2}{x^4 - a^4}$

13. $\lim_{h\to0} \dfrac{(x + h)^2 - x^2}{h}$

14. $\lim_{x\to0} \dfrac{(x + h)^2 - x^2}{h}$

15. $\lim_{x\to0} \dfrac{\dfrac{1}{2 + x} - \dfrac{1}{2}}{x}$

16. $\lim_{x\to0} \dfrac{(2 + x)^3 - 8}{x}$

In Exercises 17–20, find the limit of $g(x)$ as x approaches the indicated value.

17. $\lim_{x\to0^+} (4g(x))^{1/3} = 2$

18. $\lim_{x\to\sqrt{5}} \dfrac{1}{x + g(x)} = 2$

19. $\lim_{x\to1} \dfrac{3x^2 + 1}{g(x)} = \infty$

20. $\lim_{x\to-2} \dfrac{5 - x^2}{\sqrt{g(x)}} = 0$

Limits at Infinity

Find the limits in Exercises 21–30.

21. $\lim_{x\to\infty} \dfrac{2x + 3}{5x + 7}$

22. $\lim_{x\to-\infty} \dfrac{2x^2 + 3}{5x^2 + 7}$

23. $\lim_{x\to-\infty} \dfrac{x^2 - 4x + 8}{3x^3}$

24. $\lim_{x\to\infty} \dfrac{1}{x^2 - 7x + 1}$

25. $\lim_{x\to-\infty} \dfrac{x^2 - 7x}{x + 1}$

26. $\lim_{x\to\infty} \dfrac{x^4 + x^3}{12x^3 + 128}$

27. $\lim_{x\to\infty} \dfrac{\sin x}{\lfloor x \rfloor}$ (If you have a grapher, try graphing the function for $-5 \le x \le 5$.)

28. $\lim_{\theta\to\infty} \dfrac{\cos\theta - 1}{\theta}$

(If you have a grapher, try graphing $f(x) = x(\cos(1/x) - 1)$ near the origin to "see" the limit at infinity.)

29. $\lim_{x\to\infty} \dfrac{x + \sin x + 2\sqrt{x}}{x + \sin x}$

30. $\lim_{x\to\infty} \dfrac{x^{2/3} + x^{-1}}{x^{2/3} + \cos^2 x}$

Continuous Extension

31. Can $f(x) = x(x^2 - 1)/|x^2 - 1|$ be extended to be continuous at $x = 1$ or -1? Give reasons for your answers. (Graph the function—you will find the graph interesting.)

32. Explain why the function $f(x) = \sin(1/x)$ has no continuous extension to $x = 0$.

T In Exercises 33–36, graph the function to see whether it appears to have a continuous extension to the given point a. If it does, use Trace and Zoom to find a good candidate for the extended function's value at a. If the function does not appear to have a continuous extension, can it be extended to be continuous from the right or left? If so, what do you think the extended function's value should be?

33. $f(x) = \dfrac{x - 1}{x - \sqrt[4]{x}}$, $\quad a = 1$

34. $g(\theta) = \dfrac{5\cos\theta}{4\theta - 2\pi}$, $\quad a = \pi/2$

35. $h(t) = (1 + |t|)^{1/t}$, $\quad a = 0$

36. $k(x) = \dfrac{x}{1 - 2^{|x|}}$, $\quad a = 0$

Roots

T **37.** Let $f(x) = x^3 - x - 1$.

a. Show that f has a zero between -1 and 2.

b. Solve the equation $f(x) = 0$ graphically with an error of magnitude at most 10^{-8}.

c. It can be shown that the exact value of the solution in part (b) is

$$\left(\dfrac{1}{2} + \dfrac{\sqrt{69}}{18}\right)^{1/3} + \left(\dfrac{1}{2} - \dfrac{\sqrt{69}}{18}\right)^{1/3}$$

Evaluate this exact answer and compare it with the value you found in part (b).

T **38.** Let $f(\theta) = \theta^3 - 2\theta + 2$.

a. Show that f has a zero between -2 and 0.

b. Solve the equation $f(\theta) = 0$ graphically with an error of magnitude at most 10^{-4}.

c. It can be shown that the exact value of the solution in part (b) is

$$\left(\sqrt{\dfrac{19}{27}} - 1\right)^{1/3} - \left(\sqrt{\dfrac{19}{27}} + 1\right)^{1/3}$$

Evaluate this exact answer and compare it with the value you found in part (b).

Chapter 2   Additional and Advanced Exercises

Exit rate y ft³/min

T 1. **Assigning a value to 0^0** The rules of exponents (see Appendix 9) tell us that $a^0 = 1$ if a is any number different from zero. They also tell us that $0^n = 0$ if n is any positive number.

   If we tried to extend these rules to include the case 0^0, we would get conflicting results. The first rule would say $0^0 = 1$, whereas the second would say $0^0 = 0$.

   We are not dealing with a question of right or wrong here. Neither rule applies as it stands, so there is no contradiction. We could, in fact, define 0^0 to have any value we wanted as long as we could persuade others to agree.

   What value would you like 0^0 to have? Here is an example that might help you to decide. (See Exercise 2 below for another example.)

   a. Calculate x^x for $x = 0.1, 0.01, 0.001$, and so on as far as your calculator can go. Record the values you get. What pattern do you see?

   b. Graph the function $y = x^x$ for $0 < x \le 1$. Even though the function is not defined for $x \le 0$, the graph will approach the y-axis from the right. Toward what y-value does it seem to be headed? Zoom in to further support your idea.

T 2. **A reason you might want 0^0 to be something other than 0 or 1** As the number x increases through positive values, the numbers $1/x$ and $1/(\ln x)$ both approach zero. What happens to the number

$$f(x) = \left(\frac{1}{x}\right)^{1/(\ln x)}$$

as x increases? Here are two ways to find out.

   a. Evaluate f for $x = 10, 100, 1000$, and so on as far as your calculator can reasonably go. What pattern do you see?

   b. Graph f in a variety of graphing windows, including windows that contain the origin. What do you see? Trace the y-values along the graph. What do you find?

3. **Lorentz contraction** In relativity theory, the length of an object, say a rocket, appears to an observer to depend on the speed at which the object is traveling with respect to the observer. If the observer measures the rocket's length as L_0 at rest, then at speed v the length will appear to be

$$L = L_0\sqrt{1 - \frac{v^2}{c^2}}.$$

This equation is the Lorentz contraction formula. Here, c is the speed of light in a vacuum, about 3×10^8 m/sec. What happens to L as v increases? Find $\lim_{v \to c^-} L$. Why was the left-hand limit needed?

4. **Controlling the flow from a draining tank** Torricelli's law says that if you drain a tank like the one in the figure shown, the rate y at which water runs out is a constant times the square root of the water's depth x. The constant depends on the size and shape of the exit valve.

   Suppose that $y = \sqrt{x}/2$ for a certain tank. You are trying to maintain a fairly constant exit rate by adding water to the tank with a hose from time to time. How deep must you keep the water if you want to maintain the exit rate

   a. within 0.2 ft³/min of the rate $y_0 = 1$ ft³/min?

   b. within 0.1 ft³/min of the rate $y_0 = 1$ ft³/min?

5. **Thermal expansion in precise equipment** As you may know, most metals expand when heated and contract when cooled. The dimensions of a piece of laboratory equipment are sometimes so critical that the shop where the equipment is made must be held at the same temperature as the laboratory where the equipment is to be used. A typical aluminum bar that is 10 cm wide at 70°F will be

$$y = 10 + (t - 70) \times 10^{-4}$$

centimeters wide at a nearby temperature t. Suppose that you are using a bar like this in a gravity wave detector, where its width must stay within 0.0005 cm of the ideal 10 cm. How close to $t_0 = 70$°F must you maintain the temperature to ensure that this tolerance is not exceeded?

6. **Stripes on a measuring cup** The interior of a typical 1-L measuring cup is a right circular cylinder of radius 6 cm (see accompanying figure). The volume of water we put in the cup is therefore a function of the level h to which the cup is filled, the formula being

$$V = \pi 6^2 h = 36\pi h.$$

How closely must we measure h to measure out 1 L of water (1000 cm³) with an error of no more than 1% (10 cm³)?

Stripes about 1 mm wide

(a)

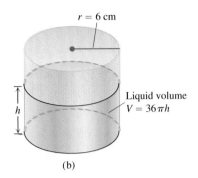

r = 6 cm

Liquid volume
V = 36πh

h

(b)

A 1-L measuring cup (a), modeled as a right circular cylinder (b) of radius $r = 6$ cm

Precise Definition of Limit

In Exercises 7–10, use the formal definition of limit to prove that the function is continuous at x_0.

7. $f(x) = x^2 - 7$, $x_0 = 1$ **8.** $g(x) = 1/(2x)$, $x_0 = 1/4$

9. $h(x) = \sqrt{2x - 3}$, $x_0 = 2$ **10.** $F(x) = \sqrt{9 - x}$, $x_0 = 5$

11. Uniqueness of limits Show that a function cannot have two different limits at the same point. That is, if $\lim_{x \to x_0} f(x) = L_1$ and $\lim_{x \to x_0} f(x) = L_2$, then $L_1 = L_2$.

12. Prove the limit Constant Multiple Rule:
$$\lim_{x \to c} kf(x) = k \lim_{x \to c} f(x) \qquad \text{for any constant } k.$$

13. One-sided limits If $\lim_{x \to 0^+} f(x) = A$ and $\lim_{x \to 0^-} f(x) = B$, find

a. $\lim_{x \to 0^+} f(x^3 - x)$ **b.** $\lim_{x \to 0^-} f(x^3 - x)$

c. $\lim_{x \to 0^+} f(x^2 - x^4)$ **d.** $\lim_{x \to 0^-} f(x^2 - x^4)$

14. Limits and continuity Which of the following statements are true, and which are false? If true, say why; if false, give a counterexample (that is, an example confirming the falsehood).

a. If $\lim_{x \to a} f(x)$ exists but $\lim_{x \to a} g(x)$ does not exist, then $\lim_{x \to a} (f(x) + g(x))$ does not exist.

b. If neither $\lim_{x \to a} f(x)$ nor $\lim_{x \to a} g(x)$ exists, then $\lim_{x \to a} (f(x) + g(x))$ does not exist.

c. If f is continuous at x, then so is $|f|$.

d. If $|f|$ is continuous at a, then so is f.

In Exercises 15 and 16, use the formal definition of limit to prove that the function has a continuous extension to the given value of x.

15. $f(x) = \dfrac{x^2 - 1}{x + 1}$, $x = -1$ **16.** $g(x) = \dfrac{x^2 - 2x - 3}{2x - 6}$, $x = 3$

17. A function continuous at only one point Let
$$f(x) = \begin{cases} x, & \text{if } x \text{ is rational} \\ 0, & \text{if } x \text{ is irrational.} \end{cases}$$

a. Show that f is continuous at $x = 0$.

b. Use the fact that every nonempty open interval of real numbers contains both rational and irrational numbers to show that f is not continuous at any nonzero value of x.

18. The Dirichlet ruler function If x is a rational number, then x can be written in a unique way as a quotient of integers m/n where $n > 0$ and m and n have no common factors greater than 1. (We say that such a fraction is in *lowest terms*. For example, 6/4 written in lowest terms is 3/2.) Let $f(x)$ be defined for all x in the interval $[0, 1]$ by
$$f(x) = \begin{cases} 1/n, & \text{if } x = m/n \text{ is a rational number in lowest terms} \\ 0, & \text{if } x \text{ is irrational.} \end{cases}$$

For instance, $f(0) = f(1) = 1$, $f(1/2) = 1/2$, $f(1/3) = f(2/3) = 1/3$, $f(1/4) = f(3/4) = 1/4$, and so on.

a. Show that f is discontinuous at every rational number in $[0, 1]$.

b. Show that f is continuous at every irrational number in $[0, 1]$. (*Hint:* If ϵ is a given positive number, show that there are only finitely many rational numbers r in $[0, 1]$ such that $f(r) \geq \epsilon$.)

c. Sketch the graph of f. Why do you think f is called the "ruler function"?

19. Antipodal points Is there any reason to believe that there is always a pair of antipodal (diametrically opposite) points on Earth's equator where the temperatures are the same? Explain.

20. If $\lim_{x \to c} (f(x) + g(x)) = 3$ and $\lim_{x \to c} (f(x) - g(x)) = -1$, find $\lim_{x \to c} f(x)g(x)$.

21. Roots of a quadratic equation that is almost linear The equation $ax^2 + 2x - 1 = 0$, where a is a constant, has two roots if $a > -1$ and $a \neq 0$, one positive and one negative:
$$r_+(a) = \frac{-1 + \sqrt{1 + a}}{a}, \qquad r_-(a) = \frac{-1 - \sqrt{1 + a}}{a}.$$

a. What happens to $r_+(a)$ as $a \to 0$? As $a \to -1^+$?

b. What happens to $r_-(a)$ as $a \to 0$? As $a \to -1^+$?

c. Support your conclusions by graphing $r_+(a)$ and $r_-(a)$ as functions of a. Describe what you see.

d. For added support, graph $f(x) = ax^2 + 2x - 1$ simultaneously for $a = 1, 0.5, 0.2, 0.1$, and 0.05.

22. Root of an equation Show that the equation $x + 2\cos x = 0$ has at least one solution.

23. Bounded functions A real-valued function f is **bounded from above** on a set D if there exists a number N such that $f(x) \leq N$ for all x in D. We call N, when it exists, an **upper bound** for f on D and say that f is bounded from above by N. In a similar manner, we say that f is **bounded from below** on D if there exists a number M such that $f(x) \geq M$ for all x in D. We call M, when it exists, a **lower bound** for f on D and say that f is bounded from below by M. We say that f is **bounded** on D if it is bounded from both above and below.

a. Show that f is bounded on D if and only if there exists a number B such that $|f(x)| \leq B$ for all x in D.

b. Suppose that f is bounded from above by N. Show that if $\lim_{x \to x_0} f(x) = L$, then $L \leq N$.

c. Suppose that f is bounded from below by M. Show that if $\lim_{x \to x_0} f(x) = L$, then $L \geq M$.

24. Max $\{a, b\}$ and min $\{a, b\}$

a. Show that the expression

$$\max \{a, b\} = \frac{a + b}{2} + \frac{|a - b|}{2}$$

equals a if $a \geq b$ and equals b if $b \geq a$. In other words, max $\{a, b\}$ gives the larger of the two numbers a and b.

b. Find a similar expression for min $\{a, b\}$, the smaller of a and b.

Generalized Limits Involving $\dfrac{\sin \theta}{\theta}$

The formula $\lim_{\theta \to 0} (\sin \theta)/\theta = 1$ can be generalized. If $\lim_{x \to c} f(x) = 0$ and $f(x)$ is never zero in an open interval containing the point $x = c$, except possibly c itself, then

$$\lim_{x \to c} \frac{\sin f(x)}{f(x)} = 1.$$

Here are several examples.

a. $\lim_{x \to 0} \dfrac{\sin x^2}{x^2} = 1.$

b. $\lim_{x \to 0} \dfrac{\sin x^2}{x} = \lim_{x \to 0} \dfrac{\sin x^2}{x^2} \lim_{x \to 0} \dfrac{x^2}{x} = 1 \cdot 0 = 0.$

c. $\lim_{x \to -1} \dfrac{\sin (x^2 - x - 2)}{x + 1} = \lim_{x \to -1} \dfrac{\sin (x^2 - x - 2)}{(x^2 - x - 2)} \cdot$

$\lim_{x \to -1} \dfrac{(x^2 - x - 2)}{x + 1} = 1 \cdot \lim_{x \to -1} \dfrac{(x + 1)(x - 2)}{x + 1} = -3.$

d. $\lim_{x \to 1} \dfrac{\sin \left(1 - \sqrt{x}\right)}{x - 1} = \lim_{x \to 1} \dfrac{\sin \left(1 - \sqrt{x}\right)}{1 - \sqrt{x}} \dfrac{1 - \sqrt{x}}{x - 1} =$

$1 \cdot \lim_{x \to 1} \dfrac{\left(1 - \sqrt{x}\right)\left(1 + \sqrt{x}\right)}{(x - 1)\left(1 + \sqrt{x}\right)} = \lim_{x \to 1} \dfrac{1 - x}{(x - 1)\left(1 + \sqrt{x}\right)} = -\dfrac{1}{2}.$

Find the limits in Exercises 25–30.

25. $\lim_{x \to 0} \dfrac{\sin (1 - \cos x)}{x}$

26. $\lim_{x \to 0^+} \dfrac{\sin x}{\sin \sqrt{x}}$

27. $\lim_{x \to 0} \dfrac{\sin (\sin x)}{x}$

28. $\lim_{x \to 0} \dfrac{\sin (x^2 + x)}{x}$

29. $\lim_{x \to 2} \dfrac{\sin (x^2 - 4)}{x - 2}$

30. $\lim_{x \to 9} \dfrac{\sin \left(\sqrt{x} - 3\right)}{x - 9}$

Chapter 2   Technology Application Projects

Mathematica-Maple Module
Take It to the Limit
Part I
Part II (Zero Raised to the Power Zero: What Does it Mean?)
Part III (One-Sided Limits)
Visualize and interpret the limit concept through graphical and numerical explorations.
Part IV (What a Difference a Power Makes)
See how sensitive limits can be with various powers of x.

Mathematica-Maple Module
Going to Infinity
Part I (Exploring Function Behavior as $x \to \infty$ or $x \to -\infty$)
This module provides four examples to explore the behavior of a function as $x \to \infty$ or $x \to -\infty$.
Part II (Rates of Growth)
Observe graphs that *appear* to be continuous, yet the function is not continuous. Several issues of continuity are explored to obtain results that you may find surprising.

Chapter

3

DIFFERENTIATION

OVERVIEW In Chapter 2, we defined the slope of a curve at a point as the limit of secant slopes. This limit, called a derivative, measures the rate at which a function changes, and it is one of the most important ideas in calculus. Derivatives are used to calculate velocity and acceleration, to estimate the rate of spread of a disease, to set levels of production so as to maximize efficiency, to find the best dimensions of a cylindrical can, to find the age of a prehistoric artifact, and for many other applications. In this chapter, we develop techniques to calculate derivatives easily and learn how to use derivatives to approximate complicated functions.

3.1 The Derivative as a Function

HISTORICAL ESSAY

The Derivative

At the end of Chapter 2, we defined the slope of a curve $y = f(x)$ at the point where $x = x_0$ to be

$$\lim_{h \to 0} \frac{f(x_0 + h) - f(x_0)}{h}.$$

We called this limit, when it existed, the derivative of f at x_0. We now investigate the derivative as a *function* derived from f by considering the limit at each point of the domain of f.

DEFINITION   Derivative Function

The **derivative** of the function $f(x)$ with respect to the variable x is the function f' whose value at x is

$$f'(x) = \lim_{h \to 0} \frac{f(x + h) - f(x)}{h},$$

provided the limit exists.

147

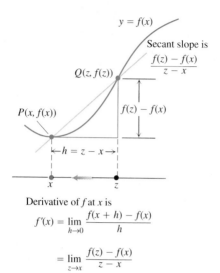

$y = f(x)$

Secant slope is
$$\frac{f(z) - f(x)}{z - x}$$

$Q(z, f(z))$

$f(z) - f(x)$

$P(x, f(x))$

$\leftarrow h = z - x \rightarrow$

x z

Derivative of f at x is

$$f'(x) = \lim_{h \to 0} \frac{f(x + h) - f(x)}{h}$$

$$= \lim_{z \to x} \frac{f(z) - f(x)}{z - x}$$

FIGURE 3.1 The way we write the difference quotient for the derivative of a function f depends on how we label the points involved.

We use the notation $f(x)$ rather than simply f in the definition to emphasize the independent variable x, which we are differentiating with respect to. The domain of f' is the set of points in the domain of f for which the limit exists, and the domain may be the same or smaller than the domain of f. If f' exists at a particular x, we say that f is **differentiable (has a derivative)** at x. If f' exists at every point in the domain of f, we call f **differentiable**.

If we write $z = x + h$, then $h = z - x$ and h approaches 0 if and only if z approaches x. Therefore, an equivalent definition of the derivative is as follows (see Figure 3.1).

Alternative Formula for the Derivative

$$f'(x) = \lim_{z \to x} \frac{f(z) - f(x)}{z - x}.$$

Calculating Derivatives from the Definition

The process of calculating a derivative is called **differentiation**. To emphasize the idea that differentiation is an operation performed on a function $y = f(x)$, we use the notation

$$\frac{d}{dx} f(x)$$

as another way to denote the derivative $f'(x)$. Examples 2 and 3 of Section 2.7 illustrate the differentiation process for the functions $y = mx + b$ and $y = 1/x$. Example 2 shows that

$$\frac{d}{dx}(mx + b) = m.$$

For instance,

$$\frac{d}{dx}\left(\frac{3}{2}x - 4\right) = \frac{3}{2}.$$

In Example 3, we see that

$$\frac{d}{dx}\left(\frac{1}{x}\right) = -\frac{1}{x^2}.$$

Here are two more examples.

EXAMPLE 1   Applying the Definition

Differentiate $f(x) = \dfrac{x}{x - 1}$.

Solution   Here we have $f(x) = \dfrac{x}{x - 1}$

and

$$f(x + h) = \frac{(x + h)}{(x + h) - 1}, \text{ so}$$

$$f'(x) = \lim_{h \to 0} \frac{f(x + h) - f(x)}{h}$$

$$= \lim_{h \to 0} \frac{\dfrac{x + h}{x + h - 1} - \dfrac{x}{x - 1}}{h}$$

$$= \lim_{h \to 0} \frac{1}{h} \cdot \frac{(x + h)(x - 1) - x(x + h - 1)}{(x + h - 1)(x - 1)} \qquad \frac{a}{b} - \frac{c}{d} = \frac{ad - cb}{bd}$$

$$= \lim_{h \to 0} \frac{1}{h} \cdot \frac{-h}{(x + h - 1)(x - 1)}$$

$$= \lim_{h \to 0} \frac{-1}{(x + h - 1)(x - 1)} = \frac{-1}{(x - 1)^2}.$$ ∎

EXAMPLE 2   Derivative of the Square Root Function

(a) Find the derivative of $y = \sqrt{x}$ for $x > 0$.

(b) Find the tangent line to the curve $y = \sqrt{x}$ at $x = 4$.

You will often need to know the derivative of $\sqrt{x}$ for $x > 0$:

$$\frac{d}{dx}\sqrt{x} = \frac{1}{2\sqrt{x}}.$$

Solution

(a) We use the equivalent form to calculate f':

$$f'(x) = \lim_{z \to x} \frac{f(z) - f(x)}{z - x}$$

$$= \lim_{z \to x} \frac{\sqrt{z} - \sqrt{x}}{z - x}$$

$$= \lim_{z \to x} \frac{\sqrt{z} - \sqrt{x}}{\left(\sqrt{z} - \sqrt{x}\right)\left(\sqrt{z} + \sqrt{x}\right)}$$

$$= \lim_{z \to x} \frac{1}{\sqrt{z} + \sqrt{x}} = \frac{1}{2\sqrt{x}}.$$

(b) The slope of the curve at $x = 4$ is

$$f'(4) = \frac{1}{2\sqrt{4}} = \frac{1}{4}.$$

The tangent is the line through the point $(4, 2)$ with slope $1/4$ (Figure 3.2):

$$y = 2 + \frac{1}{4}(x - 4)$$

$$y = \frac{1}{4}x + 1.$$ ∎

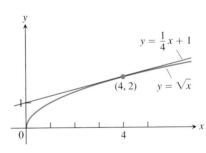

FIGURE 3.2   The curve $y = \sqrt{x}$ and its tangent at $(4, 2)$. The tangent's slope is found by evaluating the derivative at $x = 4$ (Example 2).

We consider the derivative of $y = \sqrt{x}$ when $x = 0$ in Example 6.

Notations

There are many ways to denote the derivative of a function $y = f(x)$, where the independent variable is x and the dependent variable is y. Some common alternative notations for the derivative are

$$f'(x) = y' = \frac{dy}{dx} = \frac{df}{dx} = \frac{d}{dx} f(x) = D(f)(x) = D_x f(x).$$

The symbols d/dx and D indicate the operation of differentiation and are called **differentiation operators**. We read dy/dx as "the derivative of y with respect to x," and df/dx and $(d/dx)f(x)$ as "the derivative of f with respect to x." The "prime" notations y' and f' come from notations that Newton used for derivatives. The d/dx notations are similar to those used by Leibniz. The symbol dy/dx should not be regarded as a ratio (until we introduce the idea of "differentials" in Section 3.8).

Be careful not to confuse the notation $D(f)$ as meaning the domain of the function f instead of the derivative function f'. The distinction should be clear from the context.

To indicate the value of a derivative at a specified number $x = a$, we use the notation

$$f'(a) = \left.\frac{dy}{dx}\right|_{x=a} = \left.\frac{df}{dx}\right|_{x=a} = \left.\frac{d}{dx} f(x)\right|_{x=a}.$$

For instance, in Example 2b we could write

$$f'(4) = \left.\frac{d}{dx} \sqrt{x}\right|_{x=4} = \left.\frac{1}{2\sqrt{x}}\right|_{x=4} = \frac{1}{2\sqrt{4}} = \frac{1}{4}.$$

To evaluate an expression, we sometimes use the right bracket] in place of the vertical bar | .

Graphing the Derivative

We can often make a reasonable plot of the derivative of $y = f(x)$ by estimating the slopes on the graph of f. That is, we plot the points $(x, f'(x))$ in the xy-plane and connect them with a smooth curve, which represents $y = f'(x)$.

EXAMPLE 3   Graphing a Derivative

Graph the derivative of the function $y = f(x)$ in Figure 3.3a.

Solution   We sketch the tangents to the graph of f at frequent intervals and use their slopes to estimate the values of $f'(x)$ at these points. We plot the corresponding $(x, f'(x))$ pairs and connect them with a smooth curve as sketched in Figure 3.3b.   ■

What can we learn from the graph of $y = f'(x)$? At a glance we can see

1. where the rate of change of f is positive, negative, or zero;

2. the rough size of the growth rate at any x and its size in relation to the size of $f(x)$;

3. where the rate of change itself is increasing or decreasing.

Here's another example.

EXAMPLE 4   Concentration of Blood Sugar

On April 23, 1988, the human-powered airplane *Daedalus* flew a record-breaking 119 km from Crete to the island of Santorini in the Aegean Sea, southeast of mainland Greece. Dur-

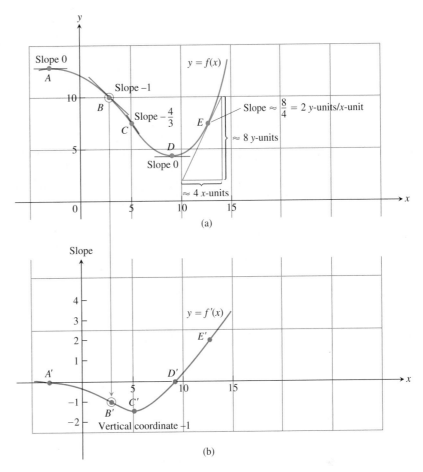

FIGURE 3.3   We made the graph of $y = f'(x)$ in (b) by plotting slopes from the graph of $y = f(x)$ in (a). The vertical coordinate of B' is the slope at B and so on. The graph of f' is a visual record of how the slope of f changes with x.

ing the 6-hour endurance tests before the flight, researchers monitored the prospective pilots' blood-sugar concentrations. The concentration graph for one of the athlete-pilots is shown in Figure 3.4a, where the concentration in milligrams/deciliter is plotted against time in hours.

The graph consists of line segments connecting data points. The constant slope of each segment gives an estimate of the derivative of the concentration between measurements. We calculated the slope of each segment from the coordinate grid and plotted the derivative as a step function in Figure 3.4b. To make the plot for the first hour, for instance, we observed that the concentration increased from about 79 mg/dL to 93 mg/dL. The net increase was $\Delta y = 93 - 79 = 14$ mg/dL. Dividing this by $\Delta t = 1$ hour gave the rate of change as

$$\frac{\Delta y}{\Delta t} = \frac{14}{1} = 14 \text{ mg/dL per hour}.$$

Notice that we can make no estimate of the concentration's rate of change at times $t = 1, 2, \ldots, 5$, where the graph we have drawn for the concentration has a corner and no slope. The derivative step function is not defined at these times. ∎

(a)

Time (h)

(b)

Daedalus's flight path on April 23, 1988

◀**FIGURE 3.4** (a) Graph of the sugar concentration in the blood of a *Daedalus* pilot during a 6-hour preflight endurance test. (b) The derivative of the pilot's blood-sugar concentration shows how rapidly the concentration rose and fell during various portions of the test.

Differentiable on an Interval; One-Sided Derivatives

A function $y = f(x)$ is **differentiable** on an open interval (finite or infinite) if it has a derivative at each point of the interval. It is differentiable on a closed interval $[a, b]$ if it is differentiable on the interior (a, b) and if the limits

$$\lim_{h \to 0^+} \frac{f(a + h) - f(a)}{h} \qquad \textbf{Right-hand derivative at } a$$

$$\lim_{h \to 0^-} \frac{f(b + h) - f(b)}{h} \qquad \textbf{Left-hand derivative at } b$$

exist at the endpoints (Figure 3.5).

Right-hand and left-hand derivatives may be defined at any point of a function's domain. The usual relation between one-sided and two-sided limits holds for these derivatives. Because of Theorem 6, Section 2.4, a function has a derivative at a point if and only if it has left-hand and right-hand derivatives there, and these one-sided derivatives are equal.

EXAMPLE 5 $y = |x|$ Is Not Differentiable at the Origin

Show that the function $y = |x|$ is differentiable on $(-\infty, 0)$ and $(0, \infty)$ but has no derivative at $x = 0$.

Solution To the right of the origin,

$$\frac{d}{dx}(|x|) = \frac{d}{dx}(x) = \frac{d}{dx}(1 \cdot x) = 1. \qquad \frac{d}{dx}(mx + b) = m, |x| = x$$

To the left,

$$\frac{d}{dx}(|x|) = \frac{d}{dx}(-x) = \frac{d}{dx}(-1 \cdot x) = -1 \qquad |x| = -x$$

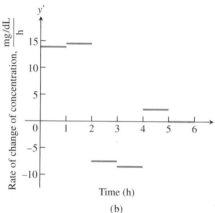

FIGURE 3.5 Derivatives at endpoints are one-sided limits.

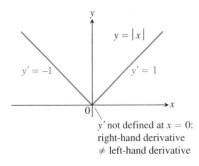

FIGURE 3.6 The function $y = |x|$ is not differentiable at the origin where the graph has a "corner."

(Figure 3.6). There can be no derivative at the origin because the one-sided derivatives differ there:

$$\text{Right-hand derivative of } |x| \text{ at zero} = \lim_{h \to 0^+} \frac{|0 + h| - |0|}{h} = \lim_{h \to 0^+} \frac{|h|}{h}$$

$$= \lim_{h \to 0^+} \frac{h}{h} \qquad |h| = h \text{ when } h > 0.$$

$$= \lim_{h \to 0^+} 1 = 1$$

$$\text{Left-hand derivative of } |x| \text{ at zero} = \lim_{h \to 0^-} \frac{|0 + h| - |0|}{h} = \lim_{h \to 0^-} \frac{|h|}{h}$$

$$= \lim_{h \to 0^-} \frac{-h}{h} \qquad |h| = -h \text{ when } h < 0.$$

$$= \lim_{h \to 0^-} - 1 = -1. \qquad \blacksquare$$

EXAMPLE 6 $y = \sqrt{x}$ Is Not Differentiable at $x = 0$

In Example 2 we found that for $x > 0$,

$$\frac{d}{dx} \sqrt{x} = \frac{1}{2\sqrt{x}}.$$

We apply the definition to examine if the derivative exists at $x = 0$:

$$\lim_{h \to 0^+} \frac{\sqrt{0 + h} - \sqrt{0}}{h} = \lim_{h \to 0^+} \frac{1}{\sqrt{h}} = \infty.$$

Since the (right-hand) limit is not finite, there is no derivative at $x = 0$. Since the slopes of the secant lines joining the origin to the points $\left(h, \sqrt{h}\right)$ on a graph of $y = \sqrt{x}$ approach ∞, the graph has a *vertical tangent* at the origin. $\qquad \blacksquare$

When Does a Function *Not* Have a Derivative at a Point?

A function has a derivative at a point x_0 if the slopes of the secant lines through $P(x_0, f(x_0))$ and a nearby point Q on the graph approach a limit as Q approaches P. Whenever the secants fail to take up a limiting position or become vertical as Q approaches P, the derivative does not exist. Thus differentiability is a "smoothness" condition on the graph of f. A function whose graph is otherwise smooth will fail to have a derivative at a point for several reasons, such as at points where the graph has

1. a *corner*, where the one-sided derivatives differ.

2. a *cusp*, where the slope of PQ approaches ∞ from one side and $-\infty$ from the other.

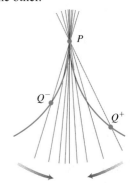

3. a *vertical tangent*, where the slope of PQ approaches ∞ from both sides or approaches $-\infty$ from both sides (here, $-\infty$).

4. a *discontinuity*.

 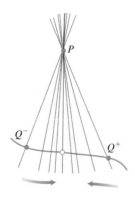

Differentiable Functions Are Continuous

A function is continuous at every point where it has a derivative.

THEOREM 1   Differentiability Implies Continuity

If f has a derivative at $x = c$, then f is continuous at $x = c$.

Proof   Given that $f'(c)$ exists, we must show that $\lim_{x \to c} f(x) = f(c)$, or equivalently, that $\lim_{h \to 0} f(c + h) = f(c)$. If $h \neq 0$, then

$$f(c + h) = f(c) + (f(c + h) - f(c))$$
$$= f(c) + \frac{f(c + h) - f(c)}{h} \cdot h.$$

Now take limits as $h \to 0$. By Theorem 1 of Section 2.2,

$$\lim_{h \to 0} f(c + h) = \lim_{h \to 0} f(c) + \lim_{h \to 0} \frac{f(c + h) - f(c)}{h} \cdot \lim_{h \to 0} h$$
$$= f(c) + f'(c) \cdot 0$$
$$= f(c) + 0$$
$$= f(c).$$ ∎

Similar arguments with one-sided limits show that if f has a derivative from one side (right or left) at $x = c$ then f is continuous from that side at $x = c$.

Theorem 1 on page 154 says that if a function has a discontinuity at a point (for instance, a jump discontinuity), then it cannot be differentiable there. The greatest integer function $y = \lfloor x \rfloor = \text{int } x$ fails to be differentiable at every integer $x = n$ (Example 4, Section 2.6).

CAUTION The converse of Theorem 1 is false. A function need not have a derivative at a point where it is continuous, as we saw in Example 5.

The Intermediate Value Property of Derivatives

Not every function can be some function's derivative, as we see from the following theorem, first proved in 1875 by the French mathematician Jean Gaston Darboux (1842–1917).

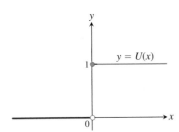

FIGURE 3.7 The unit step function does not have the Intermediate Value Property and cannot be the derivative of a function on the real line.

> **THEOREM 2** Darboux's Theorem
>
> If a and b are any two points in an interval on which f is differentiable, then f' takes on every value between $f'(a)$ and $f'(b)$.

Theorem 2 (which we will not prove) says that a function cannot *be* a derivative on an interval unless it has the Intermediate Value Property there. For example, the unit step function in Figure 3.7 cannot be the derivative of any real-valued function on the real line. In Chapter 5 we will see that every continuous function is a derivative of some function.

In Section 4.4, we invoke Theorem 2 to analyze what happens at a point on the graph of a twice-differentiable function where it changes its "bending" behavior.

EXERCISES 3.1

Finding Derivative Functions and Values

Using the definition, calculate the derivatives of the functions in Exercises 1–6. Then find the values of the derivatives as specified.

1. $f(x) = 4 - x^2$; $\quad f'(-3), f'(0), f'(1)$

2. $F(x) = (x - 1)^2 + 1$; $\quad F'(-1), F'(0), F'(2)$

3. $g(t) = \dfrac{1}{t^2}$; $\quad g'(-1), g'(2), g'\big(\sqrt{3}\big)$

4. $k(z) = \dfrac{1 - z}{2z}$; $\quad k'(-1), k'(1), k'\big(\sqrt{2}\big)$

5. $p(\theta) = \sqrt{3\theta}$; $\quad p'(1), p'(3), p'(2/3)$

6. $r(s) = \sqrt{2s + 1}$; $\quad r'(0), r'(1), r'(1/2)$

In Exercises 7–12, find the indicated derivatives.

7. $\dfrac{dy}{dx}$ if $y = 2x^3$

8. $\dfrac{dr}{ds}$ if $r = \dfrac{s^3}{2} + 1$

9. $\dfrac{ds}{dt}$ if $s = \dfrac{t}{2t + 1}$

10. $\dfrac{dv}{dt}$ if $v = t - \dfrac{1}{t}$

11. $\dfrac{dp}{dq}$ if $p = \dfrac{1}{\sqrt{q + 1}}$

12. $\dfrac{dz}{dw}$ if $z = \dfrac{1}{\sqrt{3w - 2}}$

Slopes and Tangent Lines

In Exercises 13–16, differentiate the functions and find the slope of the tangent line at the given value of the independent variable.

13. $f(x) = x + \dfrac{9}{x}, \quad x = -3$

14. $k(x) = \dfrac{1}{2 + x}, \quad x = 2$

15. $s = t^3 - t^2, \quad t = -1$

16. $y = (x + 1)^3, \quad x = -2$

In Exercises 17–18, differentiate the functions. Then find an equation of the tangent line at the indicated point on the graph of the function.

17. $y = f(x) = \dfrac{8}{\sqrt{x - 2}}, \quad (x, y) = (6, 4)$

18. $w = g(z) = 1 + \sqrt{4 - z}, \quad (z, w) = (3, 2)$

In Exercises 19–22, find the values of the derivatives.

19. $\dfrac{ds}{dt}\Big|_{t=-1}$ if $s = 1 - 3t^2$

20. $\dfrac{dy}{dx}\Big|_{x=\sqrt{3}}$ if $y = 1 - \dfrac{1}{x}$

21. $\dfrac{dr}{d\theta}\Big|_{\theta=0}$ if $r = \dfrac{2}{\sqrt{4 - \theta}}$

22. $\dfrac{dw}{dz}\Big|_{z=4}$ if $w = z + \sqrt{z}$

Using the Alternative Formula for Derivatives

Use the formula

$$f'(x) = \lim_{z \to x} \frac{f(z) - f(x)}{z - x}$$

to find the derivative of the functions in Exercises 23–26.

23. $f(x) = \dfrac{1}{x + 2}$

24. $f(x) = \dfrac{1}{(x - 1)^2}$

25. $g(x) = \dfrac{x}{x - 1}$

26. $g(x) = 1 + \sqrt{x}$

Graphs

Match the functions graphed in Exercises 27–30 with the derivatives graphed in the accompanying figures (a)–(d).

(a)

(b)

(c)

(d)

27.

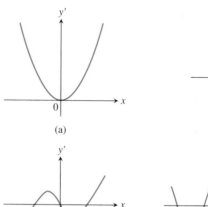

$y = f_1(x)$

28.

$y = f_2(x)$

29.

$y = f_3(x)$

30.

$y = f_4(x)$

31. a. The graph in the accompanying figure is made of line segments joined end to end. At which points of the interval $[-4, 6]$ is f' not defined? Give reasons for your answer.

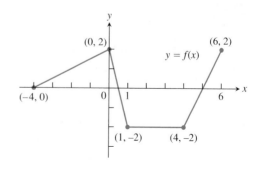

$(0, 2)$ $(6, 2)$

$y = f(x)$

$(-4, 0)$ 0 1 6

$(1, -2)$ $(4, -2)$

b. Graph the derivative of f.
   The graph should show a step function.

32. Recovering a function from its derivative

  a. Use the following information to graph the function f over the closed interval $[-2, 5]$.

   i) The graph of f is made of closed line segments joined end to end.

   ii) The graph starts at the point $(-2, 3)$.

   iii) The derivative of f is the step function in the figure shown here.

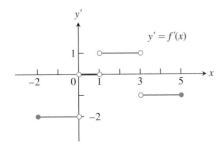

  b. Repeat part (a) assuming that the graph starts at $(-2, 0)$ instead of $(-2, 3)$.

33. Growth in the economy   The graph in the accompanying figure shows the average annual percentage change $y = f(t)$ in the U.S. gross national product (GNP) for the years 1983–1988. Graph dy/dt (where defined). (*Source: Statistical Abstracts of the United States*, 110th Edition, U.S. Department of Commerce, p. 427.)

34. Fruit flies   (*Continuation of Example 3, Section 2.1.*) Populations starting out in closed environments grow slowly at first, when there are relatively few members, then more rapidly as the number of reproducing individuals increases and resources are still abundant, then slowly again as the population reaches the carrying capacity of the environment.

  a. Use the graphical technique of Example 3 to graph the derivative of the fruit fly population introduced in Section 2.1. The graph of the population is reproduced here.

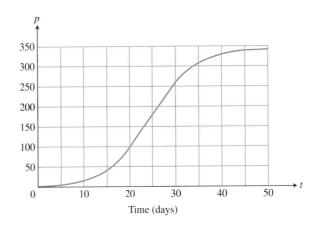

  b. During what days does the population seem to be increasing fastest? Slowest?

One-Sided Derivatives

Compare the right-hand and left-hand derivatives to show that the functions in Exercises 35–38 are not differentiable at the point P.

35.

36.

37.

38.

Differentiability and Continuity on an Interval

Each figure in Exercises 39–44 shows the graph of a function over a closed interval D. At what domain points does the function appear to be

  a. differentiable?

  b. continuous but not differentiable?

  c. neither continuous nor differentiable?

Give reasons for your answers.

39.

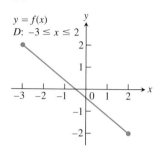

$y = f(x)$
$D: -3 \le x \le 2$

40.

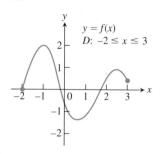

$y = f(x)$
$D: -2 \le x \le 3$

41.

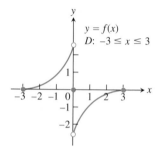

$y = f(x)$
$D: -3 \le x \le 3$

42.

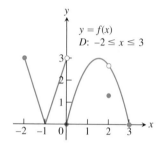

$y = f(x)$
$D: -2 \le x \le 3$

43.

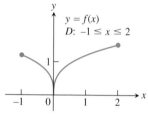

$y = f(x)$
$D: -1 \le x \le 2$

44.

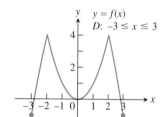

$y = f(x)$
$D: -3 \le x \le 3$

Theory and Examples

In Exercises 45–48,

a. Find the derivative $f'(x)$ of the given function $y = f(x)$.

b. Graph $y = f(x)$ and $y = f'(x)$ side by side using separate sets of coordinate axes, and answer the following questions.

c. For what values of x, if any, is f' positive? Zero? Negative?

d. Over what intervals of x-values, if any, does the function $y = f(x)$ increase as x increases? Decrease as x increases? How is this related to what you found in part (c)? (We will say more about this relationship in Chapter 4.)

45. $y = -x^2$ **46.** $y = -1/x$

47. $y = x^3/3$ **48.** $y = x^4/4$

49. Does the curve $y = x^3$ ever have a negative slope? If so, where? Give reasons for your answer.

50. Does the curve $y = 2\sqrt{x}$ have any horizontal tangents? If so, where? Give reasons for your answer.

51. Tangent to a parabola   Does the parabola $y = 2x^2 - 13x + 5$ have a tangent whose slope is -1? If so, find an equation for the line and the point of tangency. If not, why not?

52. Tangent to $y = \sqrt{x}$ Does any tangent to the curve $y = \sqrt{x}$ cross the x-axis at $x = -1$? If so, find an equation for the line and the point of tangency. If not, why not?

53. Greatest integer in x   Does any function differentiable on $(-\infty, \infty)$ have $y = \text{int } x$, the greatest integer in x (see Figure 2.55), as its derivative? Give reasons for your answer.

54. Derivative of $y = |x|$ Graph the derivative of $f(x) = |x|$. Then graph $y = (|x| - 0)/(x - 0) = |x|/x$. What can you conclude?

55. Derivative of $-f$ Does knowing that a function $f(x)$ is differentiable at $x = x_0$ tell you anything about the differentiability of the function $-f$ at $x = x_0$? Give reasons for your answer.

56. Derivative of multiples   Does knowing that a function $g(t)$ is differentiable at $t = 7$ tell you anything about the differentiability of the function $3g$ at $t = 7$? Give reasons for your answer.

57. Limit of a quotient   Suppose that functions $g(t)$ and $h(t)$ are defined for all values of t and $g(0) = h(0) = 0$. Can $\lim_{t \to 0} (g(t))/(h(t))$ exist? If it does exist, must it equal zero? Give reasons for your answers.

58. a. Let $f(x)$ be a function satisfying $|f(x)| \le x^2$ for $-1 \le x \le 1$. Show that f is differentiable at $x = 0$ and find $f'(0)$.

b. Show that

$$f(x) = \begin{cases} x^2 \sin\dfrac{1}{x}, & x \ne 0 \\ 0, & x = 0 \end{cases}$$

is differentiable at $x = 0$ and find $f'(0)$.

T **59.** Graph $y = 1/(2\sqrt{x})$ in a window that has $0 \le x \le 2$. Then, on the same screen, graph

$$y = \frac{\sqrt{x + h} - \sqrt{x}}{h}$$

for $h = 1, 0.5, 0.1$. Then try $h = -1, -0.5, -0.1$. Explain what is going on.

T **60.** Graph $y = 3x^2$ in a window that has $-2 \le x \le 2, 0 \le y \le 3$. Then, on the same screen, graph

$$y = \frac{(x + h)^3 - x^3}{h}$$

for $h = 2, 1, 0.2$. Then try $h = -2, -1, -0.2$. Explain what is going on.

T **61. Weierstrass's nowhere differentiable continuous function**   The sum of the first eight terms of the Weierstrass function $f(x) = \sum_{n=0}^{\infty} (2/3)^n \cos(9^n \pi x)$ is

$$g(x) = \cos(\pi x) + (2/3)^1 \cos(9\pi x) + (2/3)^2 \cos(9^2 \pi x)$$
$$+ (2/3)^3 \cos(9^3 \pi x) + \cdots + (2/3)^7 \cos(9^7 \pi x).$$

Graph this sum. Zoom in several times. How wiggly and bumpy is this graph? Specify a viewing window in which the displayed portion of the graph is smooth.

COMPUTER EXPLORATIONS

Use a CAS to perform the following steps for the functions in Exercises 62–67.

a. Plot $y = f(x)$ to see that function's global behavior.

b. Define the difference quotient q at a general point x, with general step size h.

c. Take the limit as $h \to 0$. What formula does this give?

d. Substitute the value $x = x_0$ and plot the function $y = f(x)$ together with its tangent line at that point.

e. Substitute various values for x larger and smaller than x_0 into the formula obtained in part (c). Do the numbers make sense with your picture?

f. Graph the formula obtained in part (c). What does it mean when its values are negative? Zero? Positive? Does this make sense with your plot from part (a)? Give reasons for your answer.

62. $f(x) = x^3 + x^2 - x, \quad x_0 = 1$

63. $f(x) = x^{1/3} + x^{2/3}, \quad x_0 = 1$

64. $f(x) = \dfrac{4x}{x^2 + 1}, \quad x_0 = 2$ **65.** $f(x) = \dfrac{x - 1}{3x^2 + 1}, \quad x_0 = -1$

66. $f(x) = \sin 2x, \quad x_0 = \pi/2$ **67.** $f(x) = x^2 \cos x, \quad x_0 = \pi/4$

3.2 Differentiation Rules

This section introduces a few rules that allow us to differentiate a great variety of functions. By proving these rules here, we can differentiate functions without having to apply the definition of the derivative each time.

Powers, Multiples, Sums, and Differences

The first rule of differentiation is that the derivative of every constant function is zero.

RULE 1   **Derivative of a Constant Function**

If f has the constant value $f(x) = c$, then

$$\frac{df}{dx} = \frac{d}{dx}(c) = 0.$$

EXAMPLE 1

If f has the constant value $f(x) = 8$, then

$$\frac{df}{dx} = \frac{d}{dx}(8) = 0.$$

Similarly,

$$\frac{d}{dx}\left(-\frac{\pi}{2}\right) = 0 \quad \text{and} \quad \frac{d}{dx}\left(\sqrt{3}\right) = 0. \qquad \blacksquare$$

FIGURE 3.8 The rule $(d/dx)(c) = 0$ is another way to say that the values of constant functions never change and that the slope of a horizontal line is zero at every point.

Proof of Rule 1 We apply the definition of derivative to $f(x) = c$, the function whose outputs have the constant value c (Figure 3.8). At every value of x, we find that

$$f'(x) = \lim_{h \to 0} \frac{f(x + h) - f(x)}{h} = \lim_{h \to 0} \frac{c - c}{h} = \lim_{h \to 0} 0 = 0. \qquad \blacksquare$$

The second rule tells how to differentiate x^n if n is a positive integer.

RULE 2 **Power Rule for Positive Integers**

If n is a positive integer, then

$$\frac{d}{dx}x^n = nx^{n-1}.$$

To apply the Power Rule, we subtract 1 from the original exponent (n) and multiply the result by n.

EXAMPLE 2 **Interpreting Rule 2**

f	x	x^2	x^3	x^4	$\cdots$
f'	1	$2x$	$3x^2$	$4x^3$	$\cdots$

■

First Proof of Rule 2 The formula

$$z^n - x^n = (z - x)(z^{n-1} + z^{n-2}x + \cdots + zx^{n-2} + x^{n-1})$$

can be verified by multiplying out the right-hand side. Then from the alternative form for the definition of the derivative,

$$f'(x) = \lim_{z \to x} \frac{f(z) - f(x)}{z - x} = \lim_{z \to x} \frac{z^n - x^n}{z - x}$$

$$= \lim_{z \to x}(z^{n-1} + z^{n-2}x + \cdots + zx^{n-2} + x^{n-1})$$

$$= nx^{n-1}$$

Second Proof of Rule 2 If $f(x) = x^n$, then $f(x + h) = (x + h)^n$. Since n is a positive integer, we can expand $(x + h)^n$ by the Binomial Theorem to get

$$f'(x) = \lim_{h \to 0} \frac{f(x + h) - f(x)}{h} = \lim_{h \to 0} \frac{(x + h)^n - x^n}{h}$$

$$= \lim_{h \to 0} \frac{\left[x^n + nx^{n-1}h + \dfrac{n(n - 1)}{2}x^{n-2}h^2 + \cdots + nxh^{n-1} + h^n\right] - x^n}{h}$$

$$= \lim_{h \to 0} \frac{nx^{n-1}h + \dfrac{n(n - 1)}{2}x^{n-2}h^2 + \cdots + nxh^{n-1} + h^n}{h}$$

$$= \lim_{h \to 0} \left[nx^{n-1} + \frac{n(n - 1)}{2}x^{n-2}h + \cdots + nxh^{n-2} + h^{n-1}\right]$$

$$= nx^{n-1}$$

■

The third rule says that when a differentiable function is multiplied by a constant, its derivative is multiplied by the same constant.

RULE 3   Constant Multiple Rule

If u is a differentiable function of x, and c is a constant, then

$$\frac{d}{dx}(cu) = c\frac{du}{dx}.$$

In particular, if n is a positive integer, then

$$\frac{d}{dx}(cx^n) = cnx^{n-1}.$$

EXAMPLE 3

(a) The derivative formula

$$\frac{d}{dx}(3x^2) = 3 \cdot 2x = 6x$$

says that if we rescale the graph of $y = x^2$ by multiplying each y-coordinate by 3, then we multiply the slope at each point by 3 (Figure 3.9).

(b) A useful special case

The derivative of the negative of a differentiable function u is the negative of the function's derivative. Rule 3 with $c = -1$ gives

$$\frac{d}{dx}(-u) = \frac{d}{dx}(-1 \cdot u) = -1 \cdot \frac{d}{dx}(u) = -\frac{du}{dx}. \quad \blacksquare$$

FIGURE 3.9 The graphs of $y = x^2$ and $y = 3x^2$. Tripling the y-coordinates triples the slope (Example 3).

Proof of Rule 3

$$
\begin{aligned}
\frac{d}{dx}cu &= \lim_{h \to 0} \frac{cu(x+h) - cu(x)}{h} && \text{Derivative definition} \\
&&& \text{with } f(x) = cu(x) \\
&= c\lim_{h \to 0} \frac{u(x+h) - u(x)}{h} && \text{Limit property} \\
&= c\frac{du}{dx} && u \text{ is differentiable.} \quad \blacksquare
\end{aligned}
$$

The next rule says that the derivative of the sum of two differentiable functions is the sum of their derivatives.

Denoting Functions by u and v
The functions we are working with when we need a differentiation formula are likely to be denoted by letters like f and g. When we apply the formula, we do not want to find it using these same letters in some other way. To guard against this problem, we denote the functions in differentiation rules by letters like u and v that are not likely to be already in use.

RULE 4   Derivative Sum Rule

If u and v are differentiable functions of x, then their sum $u + v$ is differentiable at every point where u and v are both differentiable. At such points,

$$\frac{d}{dx}(u + v) = \frac{du}{dx} + \frac{dv}{dx}.$$

EXAMPLE 4 Derivative of a Sum

$$y = x^4 + 12x$$

$$\frac{dy}{dx} = \frac{d}{dx}(x^4) + \frac{d}{dx}(12x)$$

$$= 4x^3 + 12 \qquad \blacksquare$$

Proof of Rule 4 We apply the definition of derivative to $f(x) = u(x) + v(x)$:

$$\frac{d}{dx}[u(x) + v(x)] = \lim_{h \to 0} \frac{[u(x + h) + v(x + h)] - [u(x) + v(x)]}{h}$$

$$= \lim_{h \to 0} \left[\frac{u(x + h) - u(x)}{h} + \frac{v(x + h) - v(x)}{h} \right]$$

$$= \lim_{h \to 0} \frac{u(x + h) - u(x)}{h} + \lim_{h \to 0} \frac{v(x + h) - v(x)}{h} = \frac{du}{dx} + \frac{dv}{dx}. \qquad \blacksquare$$

Combining the Sum Rule with the Constant Multiple Rule gives the **Difference Rule,** which says that the derivative of a *difference* of differentiable functions is the difference of their derivatives.

$$\frac{d}{dx}(u - v) = \frac{d}{dx}[u + (-1)v] = \frac{du}{dx} + (-1)\frac{dv}{dx} = \frac{du}{dx} - \frac{dv}{dx}$$

The Sum Rule also extends to sums of more than two functions, as long as there are only finitely many functions in the sum. If $u_1, u_2, \ldots, u_n$ are differentiable at x, then so is $u_1 + u_2 + \cdots + u_n$, and

$$\frac{d}{dx}(u_1 + u_2 + \cdots + u_n) = \frac{du_1}{dx} + \frac{du_2}{dx} + \cdots + \frac{du_n}{dx}.$$

EXAMPLE 5 Derivative of a Polynomial

$$y = x^3 + \frac{4}{3}x^2 - 5x + 1$$

$$\frac{dy}{dx} = \frac{d}{dx}x^3 + \frac{d}{dx}\left(\frac{4}{3}x^2\right) - \frac{d}{dx}(5x) + \frac{d}{dx}(1)$$

$$= 3x^2 + \frac{4}{3} \cdot 2x - 5 + 0$$

$$= 3x^2 + \frac{8}{3}x - 5 \qquad \blacksquare$$

Notice that we can differentiate any polynomial term by term, the way we differentiated the polynomial in Example 5. All polynomials are differentiable everywhere.

Proof of the Sum Rule for Sums of More Than Two Functions We prove the statement

$$\frac{d}{dx}(u_1 + u_2 + \cdots + u_n) = \frac{du_1}{dx} + \frac{du_2}{dx} + \cdots + \frac{du_n}{dx}$$

by mathematical induction (see Appendix 1). The statement is true for $n = 2$, as was just proved. This is Step 1 of the induction proof.

Step 2 is to show that if the statement is true for any positive integer $n = k$, where $k \geq n_0 = 2$, then it is also true for $n = k + 1$. So suppose that

$$\frac{d}{dx}(u_1 + u_2 + \cdots + u_k) = \frac{du_1}{dx} + \frac{du_2}{dx} + \cdots + \frac{du_k}{dx}. \qquad (1)$$

Then

$$\frac{d}{dx}\underbrace{(u_1 + u_2 + \cdots + u_k}_{\substack{\text{Call the function} \\ \text{defined by this sum } u.}} + \overbrace{u_{k+1}}^{\substack{\text{Call this} \\ \text{function } v.}})$$

$$= \frac{d}{dx}(u_1 + u_2 + \cdots + u_k) + \frac{du_{k+1}}{dx} \qquad \text{Rule 4 for } \frac{d}{dx}(u + v)$$

$$= \frac{du_1}{dx} + \frac{du_2}{dx} + \cdots + \frac{du_k}{dx} + \frac{du_{k+1}}{dx}. \qquad \text{Eq. (1)}$$

With these steps verified, the mathematical induction principle now guarantees the Sum Rule for every integer $n \geq 2$. ∎

EXAMPLE 6 Finding Horizontal Tangents

Does the curve $y = x^4 - 2x^2 + 2$ have any horizontal tangents? If so, where?

Solution   The horizontal tangents, if any, occur where the slope dy/dx is zero. We have,

$$\frac{dy}{dx} = \frac{d}{dx}(x^4 - 2x^2 + 2) = 4x^3 - 4x.$$

Now solve the equation $\dfrac{dy}{dx} = 0$ for x:

$$4x^3 - 4x = 0$$
$$4x(x^2 - 1) = 0$$
$$x = 0, 1, -1.$$

The curve $y = x^4 - 2x^2 + 2$ has horizontal tangents at $x = 0, 1$, and -1. The corresponding points on the curve are $(0, 2)$, $(1, 1)$ and $(-1, 1)$. See Figure 3.10. ∎

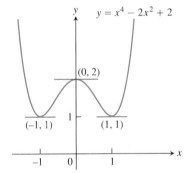

FIGURE 3.10   The curve $y = x^4 - 2x^2 + 2$ and its horizontal tangents (Example 6).

Products and Quotients

While the derivative of the sum of two functions is the sum of their derivatives, the derivative of the product of two functions is *not* the product of their derivatives. For instance,

$$\frac{d}{dx}(x \cdot x) = \frac{d}{dx}(x^2) = 2x, \qquad \text{while} \qquad \frac{d}{dx}(x) \cdot \frac{d}{dx}(x) = 1 \cdot 1 = 1.$$

The derivative of a product of two functions is the sum of *two* products, as we now explain.

RULE 5   Derivative Product Rule

If u and v are differentiable at x, then so is their product uv, and

$$\frac{d}{dx}(uv) = u\frac{dv}{dx} + v\frac{du}{dx}.$$

Picturing the Product Rule

If $u(x)$ and $v(x)$ are positive and increase when x increases, and if $h > 0$,

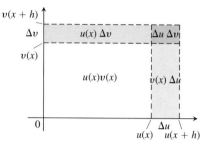

then the total shaded area in the picture is

$$u(x + h)v(x + h) - u(x)v(x)$$
$$= u(x + h)\,\Delta v + v(x + h)$$
$$\Delta u - \Delta u \Delta v.$$

Dividing both sides of this equation by h gives

$$\frac{u(x + h)v(x + h) - u(x)v(x)}{h}$$

$$= u(x + h)\frac{\Delta v}{h} + v(x + h)\frac{\Delta u}{h}$$

$$- \Delta u \frac{\Delta v}{h}.$$

As $h \to 0^+$,

$$\Delta u \cdot \frac{\Delta v}{h} \to 0 \cdot \frac{dv}{dx} = 0,$$

leaving

$$\frac{d}{dx}(uv) = u\frac{dv}{dx} + v\frac{du}{dx}.$$

The derivative of the product uv is u times the derivative of v plus v times the derivative of u. In *prime notation*, $(uv)' = uv' + vu'$. In function notation,

$$\frac{d}{dx}[f(x)g(x)] = f(x)g'(x) + g(x)f'(x).$$

EXAMPLE 7   Using the Product Rule

Find the derivative of

$$y = \frac{1}{x}\left(x^2 + \frac{1}{x}\right).$$

Solution   We apply the Product Rule with $u = 1/x$ and $v = x^2 + (1/x)$:

$$\frac{d}{dx}\left[\frac{1}{x}\left(x^2 + \frac{1}{x}\right)\right] = \frac{1}{x}\left(2x - \frac{1}{x^2}\right) + \left(x^2 + \frac{1}{x}\right)\left(-\frac{1}{x^2}\right)$$

$$\frac{d}{dx}(uv) = u\frac{dv}{dx} + v\frac{du}{dx}, \text{ and}$$
$$\frac{d}{dx}\left(\frac{1}{x}\right) = -\frac{1}{x^2} \text{ by}$$
Example 3, Section 2.7.

$$= 2 - \frac{1}{x^3} - 1 - \frac{1}{x^3}$$

$$= 1 - \frac{2}{x^3}.$$

Proof of Rule 5

$$\frac{d}{dx}(uv) = \lim_{h \to 0} \frac{u(x + h)v(x + h) - u(x)v(x)}{h}$$

To change this fraction into an equivalent one that contains difference quotients for the derivatives of u and v, we subtract and add $u(x + h)v(x)$ in the numerator:

$$\frac{d}{dx}(uv) = \lim_{h \to 0} \frac{u(x + h)v(x + h) - u(x + h)v(x) + u(x + h)v(x) - u(x)v(x)}{h}$$

$$= \lim_{h \to 0}\left[u(x + h)\frac{v(x + h) - v(x)}{h} + v(x)\frac{u(x + h) - u(x)}{h}\right]$$

$$= \lim_{h \to 0} u(x + h) \cdot \lim_{h \to 0}\frac{v(x + h) - v(x)}{h} + v(x) \cdot \lim_{h \to 0}\frac{u(x + h) - u(x)}{h}.$$

As h approaches zero, $u(x + h)$ approaches $u(x)$ because u, being differentiable at x, is continuous at x. The two fractions approach the values of dv/dx at x and du/dx at x. In short,

$$\frac{d}{dx}(uv) = u\frac{dv}{dx} + v\frac{du}{dx}.$$

In the following example, we have only numerical values with which to work.

EXAMPLE 8   Derivative from Numerical Values

Let $y = uv$ be the product of the functions u and v. Find $y'(2)$ if

$$u(2) = 3, \quad u'(2) = -4, \quad v(2) = 1, \quad \text{and} \quad v'(2) = 2.$$

Solution   From the Product Rule, in the form

$$y' = (uv)' = uv' + vu',$$

we have

$$y'(2) = u(2)v'(2) + v(2)u'(2)$$
$$= (3)(2) + (1)(-4) = 6 - 4 = 2.$$ ∎

EXAMPLE 9 Differentiating a Product in Two Ways

Find the derivative of $y = (x^2 + 1)(x^3 + 3)$.

Solution

(a) From the Product Rule with $u = x^2 + 1$ and $v = x^3 + 3$, we find

$$\frac{d}{dx}\left[\left(x^2 + 1\right)\left(x^3 + 3\right)\right] = (x^2 + 1)(3x^2) + (x^3 + 3)(2x)$$
$$= 3x^4 + 3x^2 + 2x^4 + 6x$$
$$= 5x^4 + 3x^2 + 6x.$$

(b) This particular product can be differentiated as well (perhaps better) by multiplying out the original expression for y and differentiating the resulting polynomial:

$$y = (x^2 + 1)(x^3 + 3) = x^5 + x^3 + 3x^2 + 3$$
$$\frac{dy}{dx} = 5x^4 + 3x^2 + 6x.$$

This is in agreement with our first calculation. ∎

Just as the derivative of the product of two differentiable functions is not the product of their derivatives, the derivative of the quotient of two functions is not the quotient of their derivatives. What happens instead is the Quotient Rule.

RULE 6 Derivative Quotient Rule

If u and v are differentiable at x and if $v(x) \neq 0$, then the quotient u/v is differentiable at x, and

$$\frac{d}{dx}\left(\frac{u}{v}\right) = \frac{v\dfrac{du}{dx} - u\dfrac{dv}{dx}}{v^2}.$$

In function notation,

$$\frac{d}{dx}\left[\frac{f(x)}{g(x)}\right] = \frac{g(x)f'(x) - f(x)g'(x)}{g^2(x)}.$$

EXAMPLE 10 Using the Quotient Rule

Find the derivative of

$$y = \frac{t^2 - 1}{t^2 + 1}.$$

Solution

We apply the Quotient Rule with $u = t^2 - 1$ and $v = t^2 + 1$:

$$\frac{dy}{dt} = \frac{(t^2 + 1) \cdot 2t - (t^2 - 1) \cdot 2t}{(t^2 + 1)^2} \qquad \frac{d}{dt}\left(\frac{u}{v}\right) = \frac{v(du/dt) - u(dv/dt)}{v^2}$$

$$= \frac{2t^3 + 2t - 2t^3 + 2t}{(t^2 + 1)^2}$$

$$= \frac{4t}{(t^2 + 1)^2}.$$ ∎

Proof of Rule 6

$$\frac{d}{dx}\left(\frac{u}{v}\right) = \lim_{h \to 0} \frac{\dfrac{u(x + h)}{v(x + h)} - \dfrac{u(x)}{v(x)}}{h}$$

$$= \lim_{h \to 0} \frac{v(x)u(x + h) - u(x)v(x + h)}{hv(x + h)v(x)}$$

To change the last fraction into an equivalent one that contains the difference quotients for the derivatives of u and v, we subtract and add $v(x)u(x)$ in the numerator. We then get

$$\frac{d}{dx}\left(\frac{u}{v}\right) = \lim_{h \to 0} \frac{v(x)u(x + h) - v(x)u(x) + v(x)u(x) - u(x)v(x + h)}{hv(x + h)v(x)}$$

$$= \lim_{h \to 0} \frac{v(x)\dfrac{u(x + h) - u(x)}{h} - u(x)\dfrac{v(x + h) - v(x)}{h}}{v(x + h)v(x)}.$$

Taking the limit in the numerator and denominator now gives the Quotient Rule. ∎

Negative Integer Powers of x

The Power Rule for negative integers is the same as the rule for positive integers.

RULE 7   Power Rule for Negative Integers

If n is a negative integer and $x \neq 0$, then

$$\frac{d}{dx}(x^n) = nx^{n-1}.$$

EXAMPLE 11

(a) $\dfrac{d}{dx}\left(\dfrac{1}{x}\right) = \dfrac{d}{dx}(x^{-1}) = (-1)x^{-2} = -\dfrac{1}{x^2}$ \qquad Agrees with Example 3, Section 2.7

(b) $\dfrac{d}{dx}\left(\dfrac{4}{x^3}\right) = 4\dfrac{d}{dx}(x^{-3}) = 4(-3)x^{-4} = -\dfrac{12}{x^4}$ ∎

Proof of Rule 7 The proof uses the Quotient Rule. If n is a negative integer, then $n = -m$, where m is a positive integer. Hence, $x^n = x^{-m} = 1/x^m$, and

$$\frac{d}{dx}(x^n) = \frac{d}{dx}\left(\frac{1}{x^m}\right)$$

$$= \frac{x^m \cdot \frac{d}{dx}(1) - 1 \cdot \frac{d}{dx}(x^m)}{(x^m)^2} \qquad \text{Quotient Rule with } u = 1 \text{ and } v = x^m$$

$$= \frac{0 - mx^{m-1}}{x^{2m}} \qquad \text{Since } m > 0, \frac{d}{dx}(x^m) = mx^{m-1}$$

$$= -mx^{-m-1}$$

$$= nx^{n-1}. \qquad \text{Since } -m = n \qquad \blacksquare$$

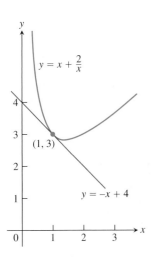

FIGURE 3.11 The tangent to the curve $y = x + (2/x)$ at $(1, 3)$ in Example 12. The curve has a third-quadrant portion not shown here. We see how to graph functions like this one in Chapter 4.

EXAMPLE 12 Tangent to a Curve

Find an equation for the tangent to the curve

$$y = x + \frac{2}{x}$$

at the point $(1, 3)$ (Figure 3.11).

Solution The slope of the curve is

$$\frac{dy}{dx} = \frac{d}{dx}(x) + 2\frac{d}{dx}\left(\frac{1}{x}\right) = 1 + 2\left(-\frac{1}{x^2}\right) = 1 - \frac{2}{x^2}.$$

The slope at $x = 1$ is

$$\frac{dy}{dx}\bigg|_{x=1} = \left[1 - \frac{2}{x^2}\right]_{x=1} = 1 - 2 = -1.$$

The line through $(1, 3)$ with slope $m = -1$ is

$$y - 3 = (-1)(x - 1) \qquad \text{Point-slope equation}$$

$$y = -x + 1 + 3$$

$$y = -x + 4. \qquad \blacksquare$$

The choice of which rules to use in solving a differentiation problem can make a difference in how much work you have to do. Here is an example.

EXAMPLE 13 Choosing Which Rule to Use

Rather than using the Quotient Rule to find the derivative of

$$y = \frac{(x - 1)(x^2 - 2x)}{x^4},$$

expand the numerator and divide by x^4:

$$y = \frac{(x - 1)(x^2 - 2x)}{x^4} = \frac{x^3 - 3x^2 + 2x}{x^4} = x^{-1} - 3x^{-2} + 2x^{-3}.$$

Then use the Sum and Power Rules:

$$\frac{dy}{dx} = -x^{-2} - 3(-2)x^{-3} + 2(-3)x^{-4}$$

$$= -\frac{1}{x^2} + \frac{6}{x^3} - \frac{6}{x^4}.$$ ∎

Second- and Higher-Order Derivatives

If $y = f(x)$ is a differentiable function, then its derivative $f'(x)$ is also a function. If f' is also differentiable, then we can differentiate f' to get a new function of x denoted by f''. So $f'' = (f')'$. The function f'' is called the **second derivative** of f because it is the derivative of the first derivative. Notationally,

$$f''(x) = \frac{d^2y}{dx^2} = \frac{d}{dx}\left(\frac{dy}{dx}\right) = \frac{dy'}{dx} = y'' = D^2(f)(x) = D_x^2 f(x).$$

The symbol D^2 means the operation of differentiation is performed twice.

If $y = x^6$, then $y' = 6x^5$ and we have

$$y'' = \frac{dy'}{dx} = \frac{d}{dx}\left(6x^5\right) = 30x^4.$$

Thus $D^2(x^6) = 30x^4$.

If y'' is differentiable, its derivative, $y''' = dy''/dx = d^3y/dx^3$ is the **third derivative** of y with respect to x. The names continue as you imagine, with

$$y^{(n)} = \frac{d}{dx}y^{(n-1)} = \frac{d^ny}{dx^n} = D^ny$$

denoting the **nth derivative** of y with respect to x for any positive integer n.

We can interpret the second derivative as the rate of change of the slope of the tangent to the graph of $y = f(x)$ at each point. You will see in the next chapter that the second derivative reveals whether the graph bends upward or downward from the tangent line as we move off the point of tangency. In the next section, we interpret both the second and third derivatives in terms of motion along a straight line.

> **How to Read the Symbols for Derivatives**
>
> y' "y prime"
> y'' "y double prime"
> $\dfrac{d^2y}{dx^2}$ "d squared y dx squared"
> y''' "y triple prime"
> $y^{(n)}$ "y super n"
> $\dfrac{d^ny}{dx^n}$ "d to the n of y by dx to the n"
> D^n "D to the n"

EXAMPLE 14   Finding Higher Derivatives

The first four derivatives of $y = x^3 - 3x^2 + 2$ are

First derivative: $y' = 3x^2 - 6x$
Second derivative: $y'' = 6x - 6$
Third derivative: $y''' = 6$
Fourth derivative: $y^{(4)} = 0.$

The function has derivatives of all orders, the fifth and later derivatives all being zero. ∎

EXERCISES 3.2

Derivative Calculations

In Exercises 1–12, find the first and second derivatives.

1. $y = -x^2 + 3$

2. $y = x^2 + x + 8$

3. $s = 5t^3 - 3t^5$

4. $w = 3z^7 - 7z^3 + 21z^2$

5. $y = \dfrac{4x^3}{3} - x$

6. $y = \dfrac{x^3}{3} + \dfrac{x^2}{2} + \dfrac{x}{4}$

7. $w = 3z^{-2} - \dfrac{1}{z}$

8. $s = -2t^{-1} + \dfrac{4}{t^2}$

9. $y = 6x^2 - 10x - 5x^{-2}$

10. $y = 4 - 2x - x^{-3}$

11. $r = \dfrac{1}{3s^2} - \dfrac{5}{2s}$

12. $r = \dfrac{12}{\theta} - \dfrac{4}{\theta^3} + \dfrac{1}{\theta^4}$

In Exercises 13–16, find y' **(a)** by applying the Product Rule and **(b)** by multiplying the factors to produce a sum of simpler terms to differentiate.

13. $y = (3 - x^2)(x^3 - x + 1)$ **14.** $y = (x - 1)(x^2 + x + 1)$

15. $y = (x^2 + 1)\left(x + 5 + \dfrac{1}{x}\right)$ **16.** $y = \left(x + \dfrac{1}{x}\right)\left(x - \dfrac{1}{x} + 1\right)$

Find the derivatives of the functions in Exercises 17–28.

17. $y = \dfrac{2x + 5}{3x - 2}$

18. $z = \dfrac{2x + 1}{x^2 - 1}$

19. $g(x) = \dfrac{x^2 - 4}{x + 0.5}$

20. $f(t) = \dfrac{t^2 - 1}{t^2 + t - 2}$

21. $v = (1 - t)(1 + t^2)^{-1}$

22. $w = (2x - 7)^{-1}(x + 5)$

23. $f(s) = \dfrac{\sqrt{s} - 1}{\sqrt{s} + 1}$

24. $u = \dfrac{5x + 1}{2\sqrt{x}}$

25. $v = \dfrac{1 + x - 4\sqrt{x}}{x}$

26. $r = 2\left(\dfrac{1}{\sqrt{\theta}} + \sqrt{\theta}\right)$

27. $y = \dfrac{1}{(x^2 - 1)(x^2 + x + 1)}$

28. $y = \dfrac{(x + 1)(x + 2)}{(x - 1)(x - 2)}$

Find the derivatives of all orders of the functions in Exercises 29 and 30.

29. $y = \dfrac{x^4}{2} - \dfrac{3}{2}x^2 - x$

30. $y = \dfrac{x^5}{120}$

Find the first and second derivatives of the functions in Exercises 31–38.

31. $y = \dfrac{x^3 + 7}{x}$

32. $s = \dfrac{t^2 + 5t - 1}{t^2}$

33. $r = \dfrac{(\theta - 1)(\theta^2 + \theta + 1)}{\theta^3}$

34. $u = \dfrac{(x^2 + x)(x^2 - x + 1)}{x^4}$

35. $w = \left(\dfrac{1 + 3z}{3z}\right)(3 - z)$

36. $w = (z + 1)(z - 1)(z^2 + 1)$

37. $p = \left(\dfrac{q^2 + 3}{12q}\right)\left(\dfrac{q^4 - 1}{q^3}\right)$ **38.** $p = \dfrac{q^2 + 3}{(q - 1)^3 + (q + 1)^3}$

Using Numerical Values

39. Suppose u and v are functions of x that are differentiable at $x = 0$ and that

$$u(0) = 5, \quad u'(0) = -3, \quad v(0) = -1, \quad v'(0) = 2.$$

Find the values of the following derivatives at $x = 0$.

a. $\dfrac{d}{dx}(uv)$ **b.** $\dfrac{d}{dx}\left(\dfrac{u}{v}\right)$ **c.** $\dfrac{d}{dx}\left(\dfrac{v}{u}\right)$ **d.** $\dfrac{d}{dx}(7v - 2u)$

40. Suppose u and v are differentiable functions of x and that

$$u(1) = 2, \quad u'(1) = 0, \quad v(1) = 5, \quad v'(1) = -1.$$

Find the values of the following derivatives at $x = 1$.

a. $\dfrac{d}{dx}(uv)$ **b.** $\dfrac{d}{dx}\left(\dfrac{u}{v}\right)$ **c.** $\dfrac{d}{dx}\left(\dfrac{v}{u}\right)$ **d.** $\dfrac{d}{dx}(7v - 2u)$

Slopes and Tangents

41. a. Normal to a curve Find an equation for the line perpendicular to the tangent to the curve $y = x^3 - 4x + 1$ at the point $(2, 1)$.

   b. Smallest slope What is the smallest slope on the curve? At what point on the curve does the curve have this slope?

   c. Tangents having specified slope Find equations for the tangents to the curve at the points where the slope of the curve is 8.

42. a. Horizontal tangents Find equations for the horizontal tangents to the curve $y = x^3 - 3x - 2$. Also find equations for the lines that are perpendicular to these tangents at the points of tangency.

   b. Smallest slope What is the smallest slope on the curve? At what point on the curve does the curve have this slope? Find an equation for the line that is perpendicular to the curve's tangent at this point.

43. Find the tangents to *Newton's serpentine* (graphed here) at the origin and the point $(1, 2)$.

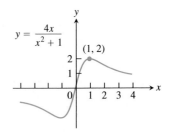

44. Find the tangent to the *Witch of Agnesi* (graphed here) at the point (2, 1).

45. Quadratic tangent to identity function The curve $y = ax^2 + bx + c$ passes through the point (1, 2) and is tangent to the line $y = x$ at the origin. Find a, b, and c.

46. Quadratics having a common tangent The curves $y = x^2 + ax + b$ and $y = cx - x^2$ have a common tangent line at the point (1, 0). Find a, b, and c.

47. a. Find an equation for the line that is tangent to the curve $y = x^3 - x$ at the point $(-1, 0)$.

T b. Graph the curve and tangent line together. The tangent intersects the curve at another point. Use Zoom and Trace to estimate the point's coordinates.

T c. Confirm your estimates of the coordinates of the second intersection point by solving the equations for the curve and tangent simultaneously (Solver key).

48. a. Find an equation for the line that is tangent to the curve $y = x^3 - 6x^2 + 5x$ at the origin.

T b. Graph the curve and tangent together. The tangent intersects the curve at another point. Use Zoom and Trace to estimate the point's coordinates.

T c. Confirm your estimates of the coordinates of the second intersection point by solving the equations for the curve and tangent simultaneously (Solver key).

Theory and Examples

49. The general polynomial of degree n has the form

$$P(x) = a_n x^n + a_{n-1} x^{n-1} + \cdots + a_2 x^2 + a_1 x + a_0$$

where $a_n \neq 0$. Find $P'(x)$.

50. The body's reaction to medicine The reaction of the body to a dose of medicine can sometimes be represented by an equation of the form

$$R = M^2 \left(\frac{C}{2} - \frac{M}{3} \right),$$

where C is a positive constant and M is the amount of medicine absorbed in the blood. If the reaction is a change in blood pressure, R is measured in millimeters of mercury. If the reaction is a change in temperature, R is measured in degrees, and so on.

Find dR/dM. This derivative, as a function of M, is called the sensitivity of the body to the medicine. In Section 4.5, we will see

how to find the amount of medicine to which the body is most sensitive.

51. Suppose that the function v in the Product Rule has a constant value c. What does the Product Rule then say? What does this say about the Constant Multiple Rule?

52. The Reciprocal Rule

a. The *Reciprocal Rule* says that at any point where the function $v(x)$ is differentiable and different from zero,

$$\frac{d}{dx} \left(\frac{1}{v} \right) = -\frac{1}{v^2} \frac{dv}{dx}.$$

Show that the Reciprocal Rule is a special case of the Quotient Rule.

b. Show that the Reciprocal Rule and the Product Rule together imply the Quotient Rule.

53. Generalizing the Product Rule The Product Rule gives the formula

$$\frac{d}{dx} (uv) = u \frac{dv}{dx} + v \frac{du}{dx}$$

for the derivative of the product uv of two differentiable functions of x.

a. What is the analogous formula for the derivative of the product uvw of *three* differentiable functions of x?

b. What is the formula for the derivative of the product $u_1 u_2 u_3 u_4$ of *four* differentiable functions of x?

c. What is the formula for the derivative of a product $u_1 u_2 u_3 \ldots u_n$ of a finite number n of differentiable functions of x?

54. Rational Powers

a. Find $\frac{d}{dx} \left(x^{3/2} \right)$ by writing $x^{3/2}$ as $x \cdot x^{1/2}$ and using the Product Rule. Express your answer as a rational number times a rational power of x. Work parts (b) and (c) by a similar method.

b. Find $\frac{d}{dx} (x^{5/2})$.

c. Find $\frac{d}{dx} (x^{7/2})$.

d. What patterns do you see in your answers to parts (a), (b), and (c)? Rational powers are one of the topics in Section 3.6.

55. Cylinder pressure If gas in a cylinder is maintained at a constant temperature T, the pressure P is related to the volume V by a formula of the form

$$P = \frac{nRT}{V - nb} - \frac{an^2}{V^2},$$

in which a, b, n, and R are constants. Find dP/dV. (See accompanying figure.)

56. The best quantity to order One of the formulas for inventory management says that the average weekly cost of ordering, paying for, and holding merchandise is

$$A(q) = \frac{km}{q} + cm + \frac{hq}{2},$$

where q is the quantity you order when things run low (shoes, radios, brooms, or whatever the item might be); k is the cost of placing an order (the same, no matter how often you order); c is the cost of one item (a constant); m is the number of items sold each week (a constant); and h is the weekly holding cost per item (a constant that takes into account things such as space, utilities, insurance, and security). Find dA/dq and d^2A/dq^2.

3.3 The Derivative as a Rate of Change

In Section 2.1, we initiated the study of average and instantaneous rates of change. In this section, we continue our investigations of applications in which derivatives are used to model the rates at which things change in the world around us. We revisit the study of motion along a line and examine other applications.

It is natural to think of change as change with respect to time, but other variables can be treated in the same way. For example, a physician may want to know how change in dosage affects the body's response to a drug. An economist may want to study how the cost of producing steel varies with the number of tons produced.

Instantaneous Rates of Change

If we interpret the difference quotient $(f(x + h) - f(x))/h$ as the average rate of change in f over the interval from x to $x + h$, we can interpret its limit as $h \to 0$ as the rate at which f is changing at the point x.

DEFINITION Instantaneous Rate of Change

The **instantaneous rate of change** of f with respect to x at x_0 is the derivative

$$f'(x_0) = \lim_{h \to 0} \frac{f(x_0 + h) - f(x_0)}{h},$$

provided the limit exists.

Thus, instantaneous rates are limits of average rates.

It is conventional to use the word *instantaneous* even when x does not represent time. The word is, however, frequently omitted. When we say *rate of change*, we mean *instantaneous rate of change*.

EXAMPLE 1 How a Circle's Area Changes with Its Diameter

The area A of a circle is related to its diameter by the equation

$$A = \frac{\pi}{4} D^2.$$

How fast does the area change with respect to the diameter when the diameter is 10 m?

Solution The rate of change of the area with respect to the diameter is

$$\frac{dA}{dD} = \frac{\pi}{4} \cdot 2D = \frac{\pi D}{2}.$$

When $D = 10$ m, the area is changing at rate $(\pi/2)10 = 5\pi$ m^2/m. ∎

Motion Along a Line: Displacement, Velocity, Speed, Acceleration, and Jerk

Position at time t … and at time $t + \Delta t$

FIGURE 3.12 The positions of a body moving along a coordinate line at time t and shortly later at time $t + \Delta t$.

Suppose that an object is moving along a coordinate line (say an s-axis) so that we know its position s on that line as a function of time t:

$$s = f(t).$$

The **displacement** of the object over the time interval from t to $t + \Delta t$ (Figure 3.12) is

$$\Delta s = f(t + \Delta t) - f(t),$$

and the **average velocity** of the object over that time interval is

$$v_{av} = \frac{\text{displacement}}{\text{travel time}} = \frac{\Delta s}{\Delta t} = \frac{f(t + \Delta t) - f(t)}{\Delta t}.$$

To find the body's velocity at the exact instant t, we take the limit of the average velocity over the interval from t to $t + \Delta t$ as Δt shrinks to zero. This limit is the derivative of f with respect to t.

DEFINITION Velocity

Velocity (instantaneous velocity) is the derivative of position with respect to time. If a body's position at time t is $s = f(t)$, then the body's velocity at time t is

$$v(t) = \frac{ds}{dt} = \lim_{\Delta t \to 0} \frac{f(t + \Delta t) - f(t)}{\Delta t}.$$

EXAMPLE 2 Finding the Velocity of a Race Car

Figure 3.13 shows the time-to-distance graph of a 1996 Riley & Scott Mk III-Olds WSC race car. The slope of the secant PQ is the average velocity for the 3-sec interval from $t = 2$ to $t = 5$ sec; in this case, it is about 100 ft/sec or 68 mph.

The slope of the tangent at P is the speedometer reading at $t = 2$ sec, about 57 ft/sec or 39 mph. The acceleration for the period shown is a nearly constant 28.5 ft/sec^2 during

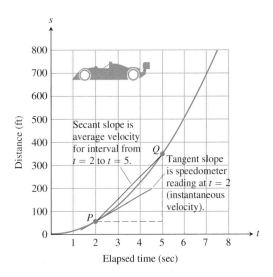

FIGURE 3.13 The time-to-distance graph for Example 2. The slope of the tangent line at P is the instantaneous velocity at $t = 2$ sec.

each second, which is about $0.89g$, where g is the acceleration due to gravity. The race car's top speed is an estimated 190 mph. (*Source: Road and Track*, March 1997.) ∎

Besides telling how fast an object is moving, its velocity tells the direction of motion. When the object is moving forward (s increasing), the velocity is positive; when the body is moving backward (s decreasing), the velocity is negative (Figure 3.14).

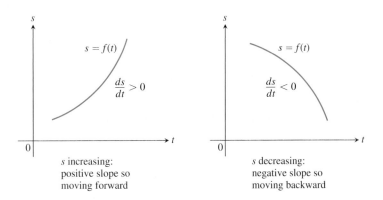

FIGURE 3.14 For motion $s = f(t)$ along a straight line, $v = ds/dt$ is positive when s increases and negative when s decreases.

If we drive to a friend's house and back at 30 mph, say, the speedometer will show 30 on the way over but it will not show -30 on the way back, even though our distance from home is decreasing. The speedometer always shows *speed*, which is the absolute value of velocity. Speed measures the rate of progress regardless of direction.

DEFINITION Speed

Speed is the absolute value of velocity.

$$\text{Speed} = |v(t)| = \left|\frac{ds}{dt}\right|$$

EXAMPLE 3 Horizontal Motion

Figure 3.15 shows the velocity $v = f'(t)$ of a particle moving on a coordinate line. The particle moves forward for the first 3 sec, moves backward for the next 2 sec, stands still for a second, and moves forward again. The particle achieves its greatest speed at time $t = 4$, while moving backward. ∎

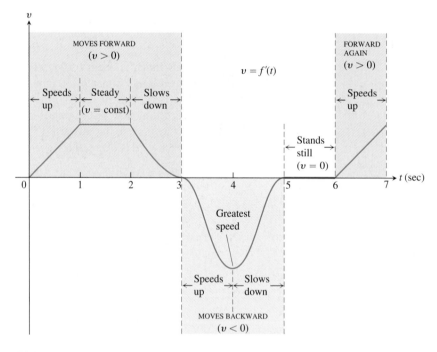

FIGURE 3.15 The velocity graph for Example 3.

HISTORICAL BIOGRAPHY

Bernard Bolzano
(1781–1848)

The rate at which a body's velocity changes is the body's *acceleration*. The acceleration measures how quickly the body picks up or loses speed.

A sudden change in acceleration is called a *jerk*. When a ride in a car or a bus is jerky, it is not that the accelerations involved are necessarily large but that the changes in acceleration are abrupt.

> **DEFINITIONS**   Acceleration, Jerk
>
> **Acceleration** is the derivative of velocity with respect to time. If a body's position at time t is $s = f(t)$, then the body's acceleration at time t is
>
> $$a(t) = \frac{dv}{dt} = \frac{d^2s}{dt^2}.$$
>
> **Jerk** is the derivative of acceleration with respect to time:
>
> $$j(t) = \frac{da}{dt} = \frac{d^3s}{dt^3}.$$

Near the surface of the Earth all bodies fall with the same constant acceleration. Galileo's experiments with free fall (Example 1, Section 2.1) lead to the equation

$$s = \frac{1}{2}gt^2,$$

where s is distance and g is the acceleration due to Earth's gravity. This equation holds in a vacuum, where there is no air resistance, and closely models the fall of dense, heavy objects, such as rocks or steel tools, for the first few seconds of their fall, before air resistance starts to slow them down.

The value of g in the equation $s = (1/2)gt^2$ depends on the units used to measure t and s. With t in seconds (the usual unit), the value of g determined by measurement at sea level is approximately 32 ft/sec^2 (feet per second squared) in English units, and $g = 9.8 \text{ m/sec}^2$ (meters per second squared) in metric units. (These gravitational constants depend on the distance from Earth's center of mass, and are slightly lower on top of Mt. Everest, for example.)

The jerk of the constant acceleration of gravity ($g = 32 \text{ ft/sec}^2$) is zero:

$$j = \frac{d}{dt}(g) = 0.$$

An object does not exhibit jerkiness during free fall.

EXAMPLE 4   Modeling Free Fall

Figure 3.16 shows the free fall of a heavy ball bearing released from rest at time $t = 0 \text{ sec}$.

(a) How many meters does the ball fall in the first 2 sec?

(b) What is its velocity, speed, and acceleration then?

Solution

(a) The metric free-fall equation is $s = 4.9t^2$. During the first 2 sec, the ball falls

$$s(2) = 4.9(2)^2 = 19.6 \text{ m}.$$

(b) At any time t, *velocity* is the derivative of position:

$$v(t) = s'(t) = \frac{d}{dt}(4.9t^2) = 9.8t.$$

t (seconds) s (meters)

$t = 0$ 0
$t = 1$ 5
           10
           15
$t = 2$ 20
           25
           30
           35
           40
$t = 3$ 45

FIGURE 3.16   A ball bearing falling from rest (Example 4).

(a)

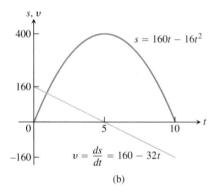

(b)

FIGURE 3.17 (a) The rock in Example 5. (b) The graphs of s and v as functions of time; s is largest when $v = ds/dt = 0$. The graph of s is *not* the path of the rock: It is a plot of height versus time. The slope of the plot is the rock's velocity, graphed here as a straight line.

At $t = 2$, the velocity is

$$v(2) = 19.6 \text{ m/sec}$$

in the downward (increasing s) direction. The *speed* at $t = 2$ is

$$\text{Speed} = |v(2)| = 19.6 \text{ m/sec}.$$

The *acceleration* at any time t is

$$a(t) = v'(t) = s''(t) = 9.8 \text{ m/sec}^2.$$

At $t = 2$, the acceleration is 9.8 m/sec^2. ∎

EXAMPLE 5   Modeling Vertical Motion

A dynamite blast blows a heavy rock straight up with a launch velocity of 160 ft/sec (about 109 mph) (Figure 3.17a). It reaches a height of $s = 160t - 16t^2$ ft after t sec.

(a) How high does the rock go?

(b) What are the velocity and speed of the rock when it is 256 ft above the ground on the way up? On the way down?

(c) What is the acceleration of the rock at any time t during its flight (after the blast)?

(d) When does the rock hit the ground again?

Solution

(a) In the coordinate system we have chosen, s measures height from the ground up, so the velocity is positive on the way up and negative on the way down. The instant the rock is at its highest point is the one instant during the flight when the velocity is 0. To find the maximum height, all we need to do is to find when $v = 0$ and evaluate s at this time.

At any time t, the velocity is

$$v = \frac{ds}{dt} = \frac{d}{dt}(160t - 16t^2) = 160 - 32t \text{ ft/sec}.$$

The velocity is zero when

$$160 - 32t = 0 \qquad \text{or} \qquad t = 5 \text{ sec}.$$

The rock's height at $t = 5$ sec is

$$s_{max} = s(5) = 160(5) - 16(5)^2 = 800 - 400 = 400 \text{ ft}.$$

See Figure 3.17b.

(b) To find the rock's velocity at 256 ft on the way up and again on the way down, we first find the two values of t for which

$$s(t) = 160t - 16t^2 = 256.$$

To solve this equation, we write

$$16t^2 - 160t + 256 = 0$$
$$16(t^2 - 10t + 16) = 0$$
$$(t - 2)(t - 8) = 0$$
$$t = 2 \text{ sec}, t = 8 \text{ sec}.$$

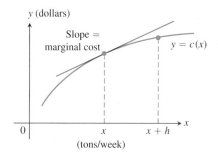

y (dollars)

Slope = marginal cost

$y = c(x)$

0   x $x + h$ x

(tons/week)

FIGURE 3.18 Weekly steel production: $c(x)$ is the cost of producing x tons per week. The cost of producing an additional h tons is $c(x + h) - c(x)$.

The rock is 256 ft above the ground 2 sec after the explosion and again 8 sec after the explosion. The rock's velocities at these times are

$$v(2) = 160 - 32(2) = 160 - 64 = 96 \text{ ft/sec}.$$
$$v(8) = 160 - 32(8) = 160 - 256 = -96 \text{ ft/sec}.$$

At both instants, the rock's speed is 96 ft/sec. Since $v(2) > 0$, the rock is moving upward (s is increasing) at $t = 2$ sec; it is moving downward (s is decreasing) at $t = 8$ because $v(8) < 0$.

(c) At any time during its flight following the explosion, the rock's acceleration is a constant

$$a = \frac{dv}{dt} = \frac{d}{dt}(160 - 32t) = -32 \text{ ft/sec}^2.$$

The acceleration is always downward. As the rock rises, it slows down; as it falls, it speeds up.

(d) The rock hits the ground at the positive time t for which $s = 0$. The equation $160t - 16t^2 = 0$ factors to give $16t(10 - t) = 0$, so it has solutions $t = 0$ and $t = 10$. At $t = 0$, the blast occurred and the rock was thrown upward. It returned to the ground 10 sec later. ∎

Derivatives in Economics

Engineers use the terms *velocity* and *acceleration* to refer to the derivatives of functions describing motion. Economists, too, have a specialized vocabulary for rates of change and derivatives. They call them *marginals*.

In a manufacturing operation, the *cost of production* $c(x)$ is a function of x, the number of units produced. The **marginal cost of production** is the rate of change of cost with respect to level of production, so it is dc/dx.

Suppose that $c(x)$ represents the dollars needed to produce x tons of steel in one week. It costs more to produce $x + h$ units per week, and the cost difference, divided by h, is the average cost of producing each additional ton:

$$\frac{c(x + h) - c(x)}{h} = \begin{array}{l} \text{average cost of each of the additional} \\ h \text{ tons of steel produced.} \end{array}$$

The limit of this ratio as $h \to 0$ is the *marginal cost* of producing more steel per week when the current weekly production is x tons (Figure 3.18).

$$\frac{dc}{dx} = \lim_{h \to 0} \frac{c(x + h) - c(x)}{h} = \text{marginal cost of production}.$$

Sometimes the marginal cost of production is loosely defined to be the extra cost of producing one unit:

$$\frac{\Delta c}{\Delta x} = \frac{c(x + 1) - c(x)}{1},$$

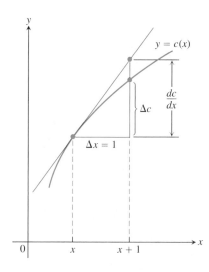

y

$y = c(x)$

$\frac{dc}{dx}$

Δc

$\Delta x = 1$

0   x $x + 1$ x

FIGURE 3.19 The marginal cost dc/dx is approximately the extra cost Δc of producing $\Delta x = 1$ more unit.

which is approximated by the value of dc/dx at x. This approximation is acceptable if the slope of the graph of c does not change quickly near x. Then the difference quotient will be close to its limit dc/dx, which is the rise in the tangent line if $\Delta x = 1$ (Figure 3.19). The approximation works best for large values of x.

Economists often represent a total cost function by a cubic polynomial

$$c(x) = \alpha x^3 + \beta x^2 + \gamma x + \delta$$

where δ represents *fixed costs* such as rent, heat, equipment capitalization, and management costs. The other terms represent *variable costs* such as the costs of raw materials, taxes, and labor. Fixed costs are independent of the number of units produced, whereas variable costs depend on the quantity produced. A cubic polynomial is usually complicated enough to capture the cost behavior on a relevant quantity interval.

EXAMPLE 6   Marginal Cost and Marginal Revenue

Suppose that it costs

$$c(x) = x^3 - 6x^2 + 15x$$

dollars to produce x radiators when 8 to 30 radiators are produced and that

$$r(x) = x^3 - 3x^2 + 12x$$

gives the dollar revenue from selling x radiators. Your shop currently produces 10 radiators a day. About how much extra will it cost to produce one more radiator a day, and what is your estimated increase in revenue for selling 11 radiators a day?

Solution   The cost of producing one more radiator a day when 10 are produced is about $c'(10)$:

$$c'(x) = \frac{d}{dx}\left(x^3 - 6x^2 + 15x\right) = 3x^2 - 12x + 15$$

$$c'(10) = 3(100) - 12(10) + 15 = 195.$$

The additional cost will be about \$195. The marginal revenue is

$$r'(x) = \frac{d}{dx}\left(x^3 - 3x^2 + 12x\right) = 3x^2 - 6x + 12.$$

The marginal revenue function estimates the increase in revenue that will result from selling one additional unit. If you currently sell 10 radiators a day, you can expect your revenue to increase by about

$$r'(10) = 3(100) - 6(10) + 12 = \$252$$

if you increase sales to 11 radiators a day.   ∎

EXAMPLE 7   Marginal Tax Rate

To get some feel for the language of marginal rates, consider marginal tax rates. If your marginal income tax rate is 28% and your income increases by \$1000, you can expect to pay an extra \$280 in taxes. This does not mean that you pay 28% of your entire income in taxes. It just means that at your current income level I, the rate of increase of taxes T with respect to income is $dT/dI = 0.28$. You will pay \$0.28 out of every extra dollar you earn in taxes. Of course, if you earn a lot more, you may land in a higher tax bracket and your marginal rate will increase.   ∎

Sensitivity to Change

When a small change in x produces a large change in the value of a function $f(x)$, we say that the function is relatively **sensitive** to changes in x. The derivative $f'(x)$ is a measure of this sensitivity.

EXAMPLE 8   Genetic Data and Sensitivity to Change

The Austrian monk Gregor Johann Mendel (1822–1884), working with garden peas and other plants, provided the first scientific explanation of hybridization.

His careful records showed that if p (a number between 0 and 1) is the frequency of the gene for smooth skin in peas (dominant) and $(1 - p)$ is the frequency of the gene for wrinkled skin in peas, then the proportion of smooth-skinned peas in the next generation will be

$$y = 2p(1 - p) + p^2 = 2p - p^2.$$

The graph of y versus p in Figure 3.20a suggests that the value of y is more sensitive to a change in p when p is small than when p is large. Indeed, this fact is borne out by the derivative graph in Figure 3.20b, which shows that dy/dp is close to 2 when p is near 0 and close to 0 when p is near 1.

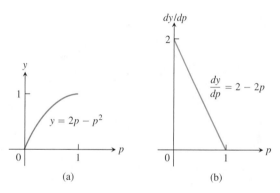

FIGURE 3.20   (a) The graph of $y = 2p - p^2$, describing the proportion of smooth-skinned peas. (b) The graph of dy/dp (Example 8).

The implication for genetics is that introducing a few more dominant genes into a highly recessive population (where the frequency of wrinkled skin peas is small) will have a more dramatic effect on later generations than will a similar increase in a highly dominant population.   ■

EXERCISES 3.3

Motion Along a Coordinate Line

Exercises 1–6 give the positions $s = f(t)$ of a body moving on a coordinate line, with s in meters and t in seconds.

a. Find the body's displacement and average velocity for the given time interval.

b. Find the body's speed and acceleration at the endpoints of the interval.

c. When, if ever, during the interval does the body change direction?

1. $s = t^2 - 3t + 2, \quad 0 \le t \le 2$

2. $s = 6t - t^2, \quad 0 \le t \le 6$

3. $s = -t^3 + 3t^2 - 3t, \quad 0 \le t \le 3$

4. $s = (t^4/4) - t^3 + t^2, \quad 0 \le t \le 3$

5. $s = \dfrac{25}{t^2} - \dfrac{5}{t}, \quad 1 \le t \le 5$

6. $s = \dfrac{25}{t + 5}, \quad -4 \le t \le 0$

7. Particle motion   At time t, the position of a body moving along the s-axis is $s = t^3 - 6t^2 + 9t$ m.

  a. Find the body's acceleration each time the velocity is zero.

  b. Find the body's speed each time the acceleration is zero.

  c. Find the total distance traveled by the body from $t = 0$ to $t = 2$.

8. Particle motion   At time $t \ge 0$, the velocity of a body moving along the s-axis is $v = t^2 - 4t + 3$.

  a. Find the body's acceleration each time the velocity is zero.

  b. When is the body moving forward? Backward?

  c. When is the body's velocity increasing? Decreasing?

Free-Fall Applications

9. Free fall on Mars and Jupiter   The equations for free fall at the surfaces of Mars and Jupiter (s in meters, t in seconds) are $s = 1.86t^2$ on Mars and $s = 11.44t^2$ on Jupiter. How long does it take a rock falling from rest to reach a velocity of 27.8 m/sec (about 100 km/h) on each planet?

10. Lunar projectile motion   A rock thrown vertically upward from the surface of the moon at a velocity of 24 m/sec (about 86 km/h) reaches a height of $s = 24t - 0.8t^2$ meters in t sec.

  a. Find the rock's velocity and acceleration at time t. (The acceleration in this case is the acceleration of gravity on the moon.)

  b. How long does it take the rock to reach its highest point?

  c. How high does the rock go?

  d. How long does it take the rock to reach half its maximum height?

  e. How long is the rock aloft?

11. Finding g on a small airless planet   Explorers on a small airless planet used a spring gun to launch a ball bearing vertically upward from the surface at a launch velocity of 15 m/sec. Because the acceleration of gravity at the planet's surface was g_s m/sec^2, the explorers expected the ball bearing to reach a height of $s = 15t - (1/2)g_s t^2$ meters t sec later. The ball bearing reached its maximum height 20 sec after being launched. What was the value of g_s?

12. Speeding bullet   A 45-caliber bullet fired straight up from the surface of the moon would reach a height of $s = 832t - 2.6t^2$ feet after t sec. On Earth, in the absence of air, its height would be $s = 832t - 16t^2$ ft after t sec. How long will the bullet be aloft in each case? How high will the bullet go?

13. Free fall from the Tower of Pisa   Had Galileo dropped a cannonball from the Tower of Pisa, 179 ft above the ground, the ball's

height above ground t sec into the fall would have been $s = 179 - 16t^2$.

  a. What would have been the ball's velocity, speed, and acceleration at time t?

  b. About how long would it have taken the ball to hit the ground?

  c. What would have been the ball's velocity at the moment of impact?

14. Galileo's free-fall formula   Galileo developed a formula for a body's velocity during free fall by rolling balls from rest down increasingly steep inclined planks and looking for a limiting formula that would predict a ball's behavior when the plank was vertical and the ball fell freely; see part (a) of the accompanying figure. He found that, for any given angle of the plank, the ball's velocity t sec into motion was a constant multiple of t. That is, the velocity was given by a formula of the form $v = kt$. The value of the constant k depended on the inclination of the plank.

In modern notation—part (b) of the figure—with distance in meters and time in seconds, what Galileo determined by experiment was that, for any given angle θ, the ball's velocity t sec into the roll was

$$v = 9.8(\sin \theta)t \text{ m/sec}.$$

(a)   (b)

  a. What is the equation for the ball's velocity during free fall?

  b. Building on your work in part (a), what constant acceleration does a freely falling body experience near the surface of Earth?

Conclusions About Motion from Graphs

15. The accompanying figure shows the velocity $v = ds/dt = f(t)$ (m/sec) of a body moving along a coordinate line.

  a. When does the body reverse direction?

  b. When (approximately) is the body moving at a constant speed?

  c. Graph the body's speed for $0 \le t \le 10$.

  d. Graph the acceleration, where defined.

16. A particle P moves on the number line shown in part (a) of the accompanying figure. Part (b) shows the position of P as a function of time t.

(a)

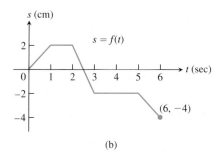

(b)

a. When is P moving to the left? Moving to the right? Standing still?

b. Graph the particle's velocity and speed (where defined).

17. Launching a rocket When a model rocket is launched, the propellant burns for a few seconds, accelerating the rocket upward. After burnout, the rocket coasts upward for a while and then begins to fall. A small explosive charge pops out a parachute shortly after the rocket starts down. The parachute slows the rocket to keep it from breaking when it lands.

The figure here shows velocity data from the flight of the model rocket. Use the data to answer the following.

a. How fast was the rocket climbing when the engine stopped?

b. For how many seconds did the engine burn?

c. When did the rocket reach its highest point? What was its velocity then?

d. When did the parachute pop out? How fast was the rocket falling then?

e. How long did the rocket fall before the parachute opened?

f. When was the rocket's acceleration greatest?

g. When was the acceleration constant? What was its value then (to the nearest integer)?

18. The accompanying figure shows the velocity $v = f(t)$ of a particle moving on a coordinate line.

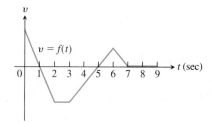

a. When does the particle move forward? Move backward? Speed up? Slow down?

b. When is the particle's acceleration positive? Negative? Zero?

c. When does the particle move at its greatest speed?

d. When does the particle stand still for more than an instant?

19. Two falling balls The multiflash photograph in the accompanying figure shows two balls falling from rest. The vertical rulers are marked in centimeters. Use the equation $s = 490t^2$ (the free-fall equation for s in centimeters and t in seconds) to answer the following questions.

a. How long did it take the balls to fall the first 160 cm? What was their average velocity for the period?

b. How fast were the balls falling when they reached the 160-cm mark? What was their acceleration then?

c. About how fast was the light flashing (flashes per second)?

20. A traveling truck The accompanying graph shows the position s of a truck traveling on a highway. The truck starts at $t = 0$ and returns 15 h later at $t = 15$.

a. Use the technique described in Section 3.1, Example 3, to graph the truck's velocity $v = ds/dt$ for $0 \le t \le 15$. Then repeat the process, with the velocity curve, to graph the truck's acceleration dv/dt.

b. Suppose that $s = 15t^2 - t^3$. Graph ds/dt and d^2s/dt^2 and compare your graphs with those in part (a).

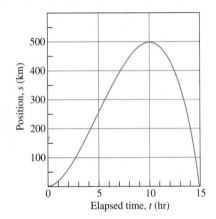

21. The graphs in Figure 3.21 show the position s, velocity $v = ds/dt$, and acceleration $a = d^2s/dt^2$ of a body moving along a coordinate line as functions of time t. Which graph is which? Give reasons for your answers.

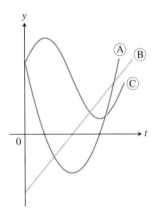

FIGURE 3.21 The graphs for Exercise 21.

22. The graphs in Figure 3.22 show the position s, the velocity $v = ds/dt$, and the acceleration $a = d^2s/dt^2$ of a body moving along the coordinate line as functions of time t. Which graph is which? Give reasons for your answers.

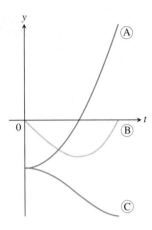

FIGURE 3.22 The graphs for Exercise 22.

Economics

23. Marginal cost Suppose that the dollar cost of producing x washing machines is $c(x) = 2000 + 100x - 0.1x^2$.

a. Find the average cost per machine of producing the first 100 washing machines.

b. Find the marginal cost when 100 washing machines are produced.

c. Show that the marginal cost when 100 washing machines are produced is approximately the cost of producing one more washing machine after the first 100 have been made, by calculating the latter cost directly.

24. Marginal revenue Suppose that the revenue from selling x washing machines is

$$r(x) = 20{,}000 \left(1 - \frac{1}{x} \right)$$

dollars.

a. Find the marginal revenue when 100 machines are produced.

b. Use the function $r'(x)$ to estimate the increase in revenue that will result from increasing production from 100 machines a week to 101 machines a week.

c. Find the limit of $r'(x)$ as $x \to \infty$. How would you interpret this number?

Additional Applications

25. Bacterium population When a bactericide was added to a nutrient broth in which bacteria were growing, the bacterium population continued to grow for a while, but then stopped growing and began to decline. The size of the population at time t (hours) was $b = 10^6 + 10^4 t - 10^3 t^2$. Find the growth rates at

a. $t = 0$ hours.

b. $t = 5$ hours.

c. $t = 10$ hours.

26. **Draining a tank** The number of gallons of water in a tank t minutes after the tank has started to drain is $Q(t) = 200(30 - t)^2$. How fast is the water running out at the end of 10 min? What is the average rate at which the water flows out during the first 10 min?

T 27. **Draining a tank** It takes 12 hours to drain a storage tank by opening the valve at the bottom. The depth y of fluid in the tank t hours after the valve is opened is given by the formula

$$y = 6\left(1 - \frac{t}{12}\right)^2 \text{ m.}$$

a. Find the rate dy/dt (m/h) at which the tank is draining at time t.

b. When is the fluid level in the tank falling fastest? Slowest? What are the values of dy/dt at these times?

c. Graph y and dy/dt together and discuss the behavior of y in relation to the signs and values of dy/dt.

28. **Inflating a balloon** The volume $V = (4/3)\pi r^3$ of a spherical balloon changes with the radius.

a. At what rate (ft^3/ft) does the volume change with respect to the radius when $r = 2$ ft?

b. By approximately how much does the volume increase when the radius changes from 2 to 2.2 ft?

29. **Airplane takeoff** Suppose that the distance an aircraft travels along a runway before takeoff is given by $D = (10/9)t^2$, where D is measured in meters from the starting point and t is measured in seconds from the time the brakes are released. The aircraft will become airborne when its speed reaches 200 km/h. How long will it take to become airborne, and what distance will it travel in that time?

30. **Volcanic lava fountains** Although the November 1959 Kilauea Iki eruption on the island of Hawaii began with a line of fountains along the wall of the crater, activity was later confined to a single vent in the crater's floor, which at one point shot lava 1900 ft straight into the air (a world record). What was the lava's exit velocity in feet per second? In miles per hour? (*Hint:* If v_0 is the exit velocity of a particle of lava, its height t sec later will be $s = v_0 t - 16t^2$ ft. Begin by finding the time at which $ds/dt = 0$. Neglect air resistance.)

T Exercises 31–34 give the position function $s = f(t)$ of a body moving along the s-axis as a function of time t. Graph f together with the velocity function $v(t) = ds/dt = f'(t)$ and the acceleration function $a(t) = d^2s/dt^2 = f''(t)$. Comment on the body's behavior in relation to the signs and values of v and a. Include in your commentary such topics as the following:

a. When is the body momentarily at rest?

b. When does it move to the left (down) or to the right (up)?

c. When does it change direction?

d. When does it speed up and slow down?

e. When is it moving fastest (highest speed)? Slowest?

f. When is it farthest from the axis origin?

31. $s = 200t - 16t^2$, $0 \le t \le 12.5$ (a heavy object fired straight up from Earth's surface at 200 ft/sec)

32. $s = t^2 - 3t + 2$, $0 \le t \le 5$

33. $s = t^3 - 6t^2 + 7t$, $0 \le t \le 4$

34. $s = 4 - 7t + 6t^2 - t^3$, $0 \le t \le 4$

35. **Thoroughbred racing** A racehorse is running a 10-furlong race. (A furlong is 220 yards, although we will use furlongs and seconds as our units in this exercise.) As the horse passes each furlong marker (F), a steward records the time elapsed (t) since the beginning of the race, as shown in the table:

F	0	1	2	3	4	5	6	7	8	9	10
t	0	20	33	46	59	73	86	100	112	124	135

a. How long does it take the horse to finish the race?

b. What is the average speed of the horse over the first 5 furlongs?

c. What is the approximate speed of the horse as it passes the 3-furlong marker?

d. During which portion of the race is the horse running the fastest?

e. During which portion of the race is the horse accelerating the fastest?

3.4 Derivatives of Trigonometric Functions

Many of the phenomena we want information about are approximately periodic (electromagnetic fields, heart rhythms, tides, weather). The derivatives of sines and cosines play a key role in describing periodic changes. This section shows how to differentiate the six basic trigonometric functions.

Derivative of the Sine Function

To calculate the derivative of $f(x) = \sin x$, for x measured in radians, we combine the limits in Example 5a and Theorem 7 in Section 2.4 with the angle sum identity for the sine:

$$\sin (x + h) = \sin x \cos h + \cos x \sin h.$$

If $f(x) = \sin x$, then

$$
\begin{aligned}
f'(x) &= \lim_{h \to 0} \frac{f(x + h) - f(x)}{h} \\[2mm]
&= \lim_{h \to 0} \frac{\sin(x + h) - \sin x}{h} \qquad \text{Derivative definition} \\[2mm]
&= \lim_{h \to 0} \frac{(\sin x \cos h + \cos x \sin h) - \sin x}{h} \qquad \text{Sine angle sum identity} \\[2mm]
&= \lim_{h \to 0} \frac{\sin x (\cos h - 1) + \cos x \sin h}{h} \\[2mm]
&= \lim_{h \to 0} \left(\sin x \cdot \frac{\cos h - 1}{h} \right) + \lim_{h \to 0} \left(\cos x \cdot \frac{\sin h}{h} \right) \\[2mm]
&= \sin x \cdot \lim_{h \to 0} \frac{\cos h - 1}{h} + \cos x \cdot \lim_{h \to 0} \frac{\sin h}{h} \\[2mm]
&= \sin x \cdot 0 + \cos x \cdot 1 \qquad \text{Example 5(a) and} \\
&= \cos x. \qquad\qquad\qquad\quad \text{Theorem 7, Section 2.4}
\end{aligned}
$$

The derivative of the sine function is the cosine function:

$$
\frac{d}{dx} (\sin x) = \cos x.
$$

EXAMPLE 1 Derivatives Involving the Sine

(a) $y = x^2 - \sin x$:

$$
\begin{aligned}
\frac{dy}{dx} &= 2x - \frac{d}{dx} (\sin x) \qquad \text{Difference Rule} \\[2mm]
&= 2x - \cos x.
\end{aligned}
$$

(b) $y = x^2 \sin x$:

$$
\begin{aligned}
\frac{dy}{dx} &= x^2 \frac{d}{dx} (\sin x) + 2x \sin x \qquad \text{Product Rule} \\[2mm]
&= x^2 \cos x + 2x \sin x.
\end{aligned}
$$

(c) $y = \dfrac{\sin x}{x}$:

$$
\begin{aligned}
\frac{dy}{dx} &= \frac{x \cdot \frac{d}{dx} (\sin x) - \sin x \cdot 1}{x^2} \qquad \text{Quotient Rule} \\[2mm]
&= \frac{x \cos x - \sin x}{x^2}.
\end{aligned}
$$

■

Derivative of the Cosine Function

With the help of the angle sum formula for the cosine,

$$
\cos(x + h) = \cos x \cos h - \sin x \sin h,
$$

we have

$$\frac{d}{dx}(\cos x) = \lim_{h \to 0} \frac{\cos(x + h) - \cos x}{h}$$ Derivative definition

$$= \lim_{h \to 0} \frac{(\cos x \cos h - \sin x \sin h) - \cos x}{h}$$ Cosine angle sum identity

$$= \lim_{h \to 0} \frac{\cos x(\cos h - 1) - \sin x \sin h}{h}$$

$$= \lim_{h \to 0} \cos x \cdot \frac{\cos h - 1}{h} - \lim_{h \to 0} \sin x \cdot \frac{\sin h}{h}$$

$$= \cos x \cdot \lim_{h \to 0} \frac{\cos h - 1}{h} - \sin x \cdot \lim_{h \to 0} \frac{\sin h}{h}$$

$$= \cos x \cdot 0 - \sin x \cdot 1$$ Example 5(a) and Theorem 7, Section 2.4

$$= -\sin x.$$

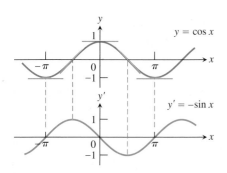

FIGURE 3.23 The curve $y' = -\sin x$ as the graph of the slopes of the tangents to the curve $y = \cos x$.

The derivative of the cosine function is the negative of the sine function:

$$\frac{d}{dx}(\cos x) = -\sin x$$

Figure 3.23 shows a way to visualize this result.

EXAMPLE 2   Derivatives Involving the Cosine

(a) $y = 5x + \cos x$:

$$\frac{dy}{dx} = \frac{d}{dx}(5x) + \frac{d}{dx}(\cos x)$$ Sum Rule

$$= 5 - \sin x.$$

(b) $y = \sin x \cos x$:

$$\frac{dy}{dx} = \sin x \frac{d}{dx}(\cos x) + \cos x \frac{d}{dx}(\sin x)$$ Product Rule

$$= \sin x(-\sin x) + \cos x(\cos x)$$

$$= \cos^2 x - \sin^2 x.$$

(c) $y = \dfrac{\cos x}{1 - \sin x}$:

$$\frac{dy}{dx} = \frac{(1 - \sin x)\dfrac{d}{dx}(\cos x) - \cos x \dfrac{d}{dx}(1 - \sin x)}{(1 - \sin x)^2}$$ Quotient Rule

$$= \frac{(1 - \sin x)(-\sin x) - \cos x(0 - \cos x)}{(1 - \sin x)^2}$$

$$= \frac{1 - \sin x}{(1 - \sin x)^2}$$ $\sin^2 x + \cos^2 x = 1$

$$= \frac{1}{1 - \sin x}.$$

FIGURE 3.24 A body hanging from a vertical spring and then displaced oscillates above and below its rest position. Its motion is described by trigonometric functions (Example 3).

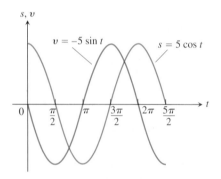

FIGURE 3.25 The graphs of the position and velocity of the body in Example 3.

Simple Harmonic Motion

The motion of a body bobbing freely up and down on the end of a spring or bungee cord is an example of *simple harmonic motion*. The next example describes a case in which there are no opposing forces such as friction or buoyancy to slow the motion down.

EXAMPLE 3 Motion on a Spring

A body hanging from a spring (Figure 3.24) is stretched 5 units beyond its rest position and released at time $t = 0$ to bob up and down. Its position at any later time t is

$$s = 5 \cos t.$$

What are its velocity and acceleration at time t?

Solution   We have

Position: $s = 5 \cos t$

Velocity: $v = \dfrac{ds}{dt} = \dfrac{d}{dt}(5 \cos t) = -5 \sin t$

Acceleration: $a = \dfrac{dv}{dt} = \dfrac{d}{dt}(-5 \sin t) = -5 \cos t.$

Notice how much we can learn from these equations:

1. As time passes, the weight moves down and up between $s = -5$ and $s = 5$ on the s-axis. The amplitude of the motion is 5. The period of the motion is 2π.

2. The velocity $v = -5 \sin t$ attains its greatest magnitude, 5, when $\cos t = 0$, as the graphs show in Figure 3.25. Hence, the speed of the weight, $|v| = 5|\sin t|$, is greatest when $\cos t = 0$, that is, when $s = 0$ (the rest position). The speed of the weight is zero when $\sin t = 0$. This occurs when $s = 5 \cos t = \pm 5$, at the endpoints of the interval of motion.

3. The acceleration value is always the exact opposite of the position value. When the weight is above the rest position, gravity is pulling it back down; when the weight is below the rest position, the spring is pulling it back up.

4. The acceleration, $a = -5 \cos t$, is zero only at the rest position, where $\cos t = 0$ and the force of gravity and the force from the spring offset each other. When the weight is anywhere else, the two forces are unequal and acceleration is nonzero. The acceleration is greatest in magnitude at the points farthest from the rest position, where $\cos t = \pm 1$.   ■

EXAMPLE 4 Jerk

The jerk of the simple harmonic motion in Example 3 is

$$j = \frac{da}{dt} = \frac{d}{dt}(-5 \cos t) = 5 \sin t.$$

It has its greatest magnitude when $\sin t = \pm 1$, not at the extremes of the displacement but at the rest position, where the acceleration changes direction and sign.   ■

Derivatives of the Other Basic Trigonometric Functions

Because $\sin x$ and $\cos x$ are differentiable functions of x, the related functions

$$\tan x = \frac{\sin x}{\cos x}, \qquad \cot x = \frac{\cos x}{\sin x}, \qquad \sec x = \frac{1}{\cos x}, \qquad \text{and} \qquad \csc x = \frac{1}{\sin x}$$

are differentiable at every value of x at which they are defined. Their derivatives, calculated from the Quotient Rule, are given by the following formulas. Notice the negative signs in the derivative formulas for the cofunctions.

Derivatives of the Other Trigonometric Functions

$$\frac{d}{dx}(\tan x) = \sec^2 x$$

$$\frac{d}{dx}(\sec x) = \sec x \tan x$$

$$\frac{d}{dx}(\cot x) = -\csc^2 x$$

$$\frac{d}{dx}(\csc x) = -\csc x \cot x$$

To show a typical calculation, we derive the derivative of the tangent function. The other derivations are left to Exercise 50.

EXAMPLE 5

Find $d(\tan x)/dx$.

Solution

$$\frac{d}{dx}\left(\tan x\right) = \frac{d}{dx}\left(\frac{\sin x}{\cos x}\right) = \frac{\cos x \frac{d}{dx}\left(\sin x\right) - \sin x \frac{d}{dx}\left(\cos x\right)}{\cos^2 x} \qquad \text{Quotient Rule}$$

$$= \frac{\cos x \cos x - \sin x\,(-\sin x)}{\cos^2 x}$$

$$= \frac{\cos^2 x + \sin^2 x}{\cos^2 x}$$

$$= \frac{1}{\cos^2 x} = \sec^2 x \qquad\blacksquare$$

EXAMPLE 6

Find y'' if $y = \sec x$.

Solution

$$y = \sec x$$

$$y' = \sec x \tan x$$

$$y'' = \frac{d}{dx}(\sec x \tan x)$$

$$= \sec x \frac{d}{dx}\left(\tan x\right) + \tan x \frac{d}{dx}\left(\sec x\right) \qquad \text{Product Rule}$$

$$= \sec x(\sec^2 x) + \tan x(\sec x \tan x)$$

$$= \sec^3 x + \sec x \tan^2 x \qquad\blacksquare$$

The differentiability of the trigonometric functions throughout their domains gives another proof of their continuity at every point in their domains (Theorem 1, Section 3.1). So we can calculate limits of algebraic combinations and composites of trigonometric functions by direct substitution.

EXAMPLE 7   Finding a Trigonometric Limit

$$\lim_{x \to 0} \frac{\sqrt{2 + \sec x}}{\cos(\pi - \tan x)} = \frac{\sqrt{2 + \sec 0}}{\cos(\pi - \tan 0)} = \frac{\sqrt{2 + 1}}{\cos(\pi - 0)} = \frac{\sqrt{3}}{-1} = -\sqrt{3} \quad \blacksquare$$

EXERCISES 3.4

Derivatives

In Exercises 1–12, find dy/dx.

1. $y = -10x + 3\cos x$

2. $y = \frac{3}{x} + 5\sin x$

3. $y = \csc x - 4\sqrt{x} + 7$

4. $y = x^2 \cot x - \frac{1}{x^2}$

5. $y = (\sec x + \tan x)(\sec x - \tan x)$

6. $y = (\sin x + \cos x)\sec x$

7. $y = \frac{\cot x}{1 + \cot x}$

8. $y = \frac{\cos x}{1 + \sin x}$

9. $y = \frac{4}{\cos x} + \frac{1}{\tan x}$

10. $y = \frac{\cos x}{x} + \frac{x}{\cos x}$

11. $y = x^2 \sin x + 2x \cos x - 2\sin x$

12. $y = x^2 \cos x - 2x \sin x - 2\cos x$

In Exercises 13–16, find ds/dt.

13. $s = \tan t - t$

14. $s = t^2 - \sec t + 1$

15. $s = \frac{1 + \csc t}{1 - \csc t}$

16. $s = \frac{\sin t}{1 - \cos t}$

In Exercises 17–20, find $dr/d\theta$.

17. $r = 4 - \theta^2 \sin \theta$

18. $r = \theta \sin \theta + \cos \theta$

19. $r = \sec \theta \csc \theta$

20. $r = (1 + \sec \theta)\sin \theta$

In Exercises 21–24, find dp/dq.

21. $p = 5 + \frac{1}{\cot q}$

22. $p = (1 + \csc q)\cos q$

23. $p = \frac{\sin q + \cos q}{\cos q}$

24. $p = \frac{\tan q}{1 + \tan q}$

25. Find y'' if

a. $y = \csc x$.

b. $y = \sec x$.

26. Find $y^{(4)} = d^4 y/dx^4$ if

a. $y = -2\sin x$.

b. $y = 9\cos x$.

Tangent Lines

In Exercises 27–30, graph the curves over the given intervals, together with their tangents at the given values of x. Label each curve and tangent with its equation.

27. $y = \sin x$, $-3\pi/2 \le x \le 2\pi$

$x = -\pi, 0, 3\pi/2$

28. $y = \tan x$, $-\pi/2 < x < \pi/2$

$x = -\pi/3, 0, \pi/3$

29. $y = \sec x$, $-\pi/2 < x < \pi/2$

$x = -\pi/3, \pi/4$

30. $y = 1 + \cos x$, $-3\pi/2 \le x \le 2\pi$

$x = -\pi/3, 3\pi/2$

T Do the graphs of the functions in Exercises 31–34 have any horizontal tangents in the interval $0 \le x \le 2\pi$? If so, where? If not, why not? Visualize your findings by graphing the functions with a grapher.

31. $y = x + \sin x$

32. $y = 2x + \sin x$

33. $y = x - \cot x$

34. $y = x + 2\cos x$

35. Find all points on the curve $y = \tan x$, $-\pi/2 < x < \pi/2$, where the tangent line is parallel to the line $y = 2x$. Sketch the curve and tangent(s) together, labeling each with its equation.

36. Find all points on the curve $y = \cot x$, $0 < x < \pi$, where the tangent line is parallel to the line $y = -x$. Sketch the curve and tangent(s) together, labeling each with its equation.

In Exercises 37 and 38, find an equation for **(a)** the tangent to the curve at P and **(b)** the horizontal tangent to the curve at Q.

37.

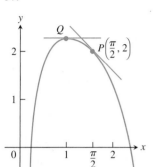

$y = 4 + \cot x - 2\csc x$

38.

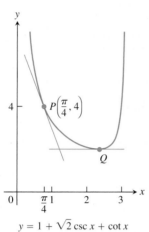

$y = 1 + \sqrt{2}\csc x + \cot x$

Trigonometric Limits

Find the limits in Exercises 39–44.

39. $\displaystyle\lim_{x \to 2} \sin\left(\frac{1}{x} - \frac{1}{2}\right)$

40. $\displaystyle\lim_{x \to -\pi/6} \sqrt{1 + \cos(\pi \csc x)}$

41. $\displaystyle\lim_{x \to 0} \sec\left[\cos x + \pi \tan\left(\frac{\pi}{4 \sec x}\right) - 1\right]$

42. $\displaystyle\lim_{x \to 0} \sin\left(\frac{\pi + \tan x}{\tan x - 2 \sec x}\right)$

43. $\displaystyle\lim_{t \to 0} \tan\left(1 - \frac{\sin t}{t}\right)$

44. $\displaystyle\lim_{\theta \to 0} \cos\left(\frac{\pi \theta}{\sin \theta}\right)$

Simple Harmonic Motion

The equations in Exercises 45 and 46 give the position $s = f(t)$ of a body moving on a coordinate line (s in meters, t in seconds). Find the body's velocity, speed, acceleration, and jerk at time $t = \pi/4$ sec.

45. $s = 2 - 2 \sin t$ **46.** $s = \sin t + \cos t$

Theory and Examples

47. Is there a value of c that will make

$$f(x) = \begin{cases} \dfrac{\sin^2 3x}{x^2}, & x \neq 0 \\ c, & x = 0 \end{cases}$$

continuous at $x = 0$? Give reasons for your answer.

48. Is there a value of b that will make

$$g(x) = \begin{cases} x + b, & x < 0 \\ \cos x, & x \geq 0 \end{cases}$$

continuous at $x = 0$? Differentiable at $x = 0$? Give reasons for your answers.

49. Find $d^{999}/dx^{999} (\cos x)$.

50. Derive the formula for the derivative with respect to x of

  a. $\sec x$.   **b.** $\csc x$.   **c.** $\cot x$.

T 51. Graph $y = \cos x$ for $-\pi \leq x \leq 2\pi$. On the same screen, graph

$$y = \frac{\sin(x + h) - \sin x}{h}$$

for $h = 1, 0.5, 0.3$, and 0.1. Then, in a new window, try $h = -1, -0.5$, and -0.3. What happens as $h \to 0^+$? As $h \to 0^-$? What phenomenon is being illustrated here?

T 52. Graph $y = -\sin x$ for $-\pi \leq x \leq 2\pi$. On the same screen, graph

$$y = \frac{\cos(x + h) - \cos x}{h}$$

for $h = 1, 0.5, 0.3$, and 0.1. Then, in a new window, try $h = -1, -0.5$, and -0.3. What happens as $h \to 0^+$? As $h \to 0^-$? What phenomenon is being illustrated here?

T 53. Centered difference quotients The *centered difference quotient*

$$\frac{f(x + h) - f(x - h)}{2h}$$

is used to approximate $f'(x)$ in numerical work because (1) its limit as $h \to 0$ equals $f'(x)$ when $f'(x)$ exists, and (2) it usually gives a better approximation of $f'(x)$ for a given value of h than Fermat's difference quotient

$$\frac{f(x + h) - f(x)}{h}.$$

See the accompanying figure.

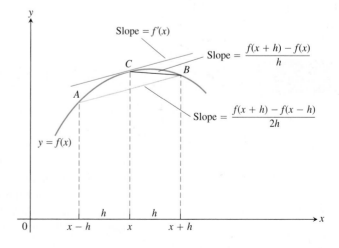

a. To see how rapidly the centered difference quotient for $f(x) = \sin x$ converges to $f'(x) = \cos x$, graph $y = \cos x$ together with

$$y = \frac{\sin(x + h) - \sin(x - h)}{2h}$$

over the interval $[-\pi, 2\pi]$ for $h = 1, 0.5$, and 0.3. Compare the results with those obtained in Exercise 51 for the same values of h.

b. To see how rapidly the centered difference quotient for $f(x) = \cos x$ converges to $f'(x) = -\sin x$, graph $y = -\sin x$ together with

$$y = \frac{\cos(x + h) - \cos(x - h)}{2h}$$

over the interval $[-\pi, 2\pi]$ for $h = 1, 0.5$, and 0.3. Compare the results with those obtained in Exercise 52 for the same values of h.

54. A caution about centered difference quotients (*Continuation of Exercise 53.*) The quotient

$$\frac{f(x + h) - f(x - h)}{2h}$$

may have a limit as $h \to 0$ when f has no derivative at x. As a case in point, take $f(x) = |x|$ and calculate

$$\lim_{h \to 0} \frac{|0 + h| - |0 - h|}{2h}.$$

As you will see, the limit exists even though $f(x) = |x|$ has no derivative at $x = 0$. *Moral:* Before using a centered difference quotient, be sure the derivative exists.

T **55. Slopes on the graph of the tangent function** Graph $y = \tan x$ and its derivative together on $(-\pi/2, \pi/2)$. Does the graph of the tangent function appear to have a smallest slope? a largest slope? Is the slope ever negative? Give reasons for your answers.

T **56. Slopes on the graph of the cotangent function** Graph $y = \cot x$ and its derivative together for $0 < x < \pi$. Does the graph of the cotangent function appear to have a smallest slope? A largest slope? Is the slope ever positive? Give reasons for your answers.

T **57. Exploring $(\sin kx)/x$** Graph $y = (\sin x)/x$, $y = (\sin 2x)/x$, and $y = (\sin 4x)/x$ together over the interval $-2 \le x \le 2$. Where does each graph appear to cross the y-axis? Do the graphs really intersect the axis? What would you expect the graphs of $y = (\sin 5x)/x$ and $y = (\sin(-3x))/x$ to do as $x \to 0$? Why? What about the graph of $y = (\sin kx)/x$ for other values of k? Give reasons for your answers.

T **58. Radians versus degrees: degree mode derivatives** What happens to the derivatives of $\sin x$ and $\cos x$ if x is measured in degrees instead of radians? To find out, take the following steps.

a. With your graphing calculator or computer grapher in *degree mode*, graph

$$f(h) = \frac{\sin h}{h}$$

and estimate $\lim_{h \to 0} f(h)$. Compare your estimate with $\pi/180$. Is there any reason to believe the limit *should* be $\pi/180$?

b. With your grapher still in degree mode, estimate

$$\lim_{h \to 0} \frac{\cos h - 1}{h}.$$

c. Now go back to the derivation of the formula for the derivative of $\sin x$ in the text and carry out the steps of the derivation using degree-mode limits. What formula do you obtain for the derivative?

d. Work through the derivation of the formula for the derivative of $\cos x$ using degree-mode limits. What formula do you obtain for the derivative?

e. The disadvantages of the degree-mode formulas become apparent as you start taking derivatives of higher order. Try it. What are the second and third degree-mode derivatives of $\sin x$ and $\cos x$?

3.5 The Chain Rule and Parametric Equations

We know how to differentiate $y = f(u) = \sin u$ and $u = g(x) = x^2 - 4$, but how do we differentiate a composite like $F(x) = f(g(x)) = \sin(x^2 - 4)$? The differentiation formulas we have studied so far do not tell us how to calculate $F'(x)$. So how do we find the derivative of $F = f \circ g$? The answer is, with the Chain Rule, which says that the derivative of the composite of two differentiable functions is the product of their derivatives evaluated at appropriate points. The Chain Rule is one of the most important and widely used rules of differentiation. This section describes the rule and how to use it. We then apply the rule to describe curves in the plane and their tangent lines in another way.

Derivative of a Composite Function

We begin with examples.

EXAMPLE 1   Relating Derivatives

The function $y = \dfrac{3}{2}x = \dfrac{1}{2}(3x)$ is the composite of the functions $y = \dfrac{1}{2}u$ and $u = 3x$. How are the derivatives of these functions related?

Solution   We have

$$\frac{dy}{dx} = \frac{3}{2}, \qquad \frac{dy}{du} = \frac{1}{2}, \qquad \text{and} \qquad \frac{du}{dx} = 3.$$

Since $\dfrac{3}{2} = \dfrac{1}{2} \cdot 3$, we see that

$$\frac{dy}{dx} = \frac{dy}{du} \cdot \frac{du}{dx}.$$

Is it an accident that

$$\frac{dy}{dx} = \frac{dy}{du} \cdot \frac{du}{dx}?$$

If we think of the derivative as a rate of change, our intuition allows us to see that this relationship is reasonable. If $y = f(u)$ changes half as fast as u and $u = g(x)$ changes three times as fast as x, then we expect y to change $3/2$ times as fast as x. This effect is much like that of a multiple gear train (Figure 3.26). ∎

FIGURE 3.26   When gear A makes x turns, gear B makes u turns and gear C makes y turns. By comparing circumferences or counting teeth, we see that $y = u/2$ (C turns one-half turn for each B turn) and $u = 3x$ (B turns three times for A's one), so $y = 3x/2$. Thus, $dy/dx = 3/2 = (1/2)(3) = (dy/du)(du/dx)$.

C: y turns   B: u turns   A: x turns

EXAMPLE 2

The function

$$y = 9x^4 + 6x^2 + 1 = (3x^2 + 1)^2$$

is the composite of $y = u^2$ and $u = 3x^2 + 1$. Calculating derivatives, we see that

$$\frac{dy}{du} \cdot \frac{du}{dx} = 2u \cdot 6x$$

$$= 2(3x^2 + 1) \cdot 6x$$

$$= 36x^3 + 12x.$$

Calculating the derivative from the expanded formula, we get

$$\frac{dy}{dx} = \frac{d}{dx}\left(9x^4 + 6x^2 + 1\right)$$

$$= 36x^3 + 12x.$$

Once again,

$$\frac{dy}{du} \cdot \frac{du}{dx} = \frac{dy}{dx}.$$
∎

The derivative of the composite function $f(g(x))$ at x is the derivative of f at $g(x)$ times the derivative of g at x. This is known as the Chain Rule (Figure 3.27).

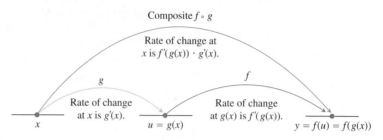

FIGURE 3.27 Rates of change multiply: The derivative of $f \circ g$ at x is the derivative of f at $g(x)$ times the derivative of g at x.

THEOREM 3   The Chain Rule

If $f(u)$ is differentiable at the point $u = g(x)$ and $g(x)$ is differentiable at x, then the composite function $(f \circ g)(x) = f(g(x))$ is differentiable at x, and

$$(f \circ g)'(x) = f'(g(x)) \cdot g'(x).$$

In Leibniz's notation, if $y = f(u)$ and $u = g(x)$, then

$$\frac{dy}{dx} = \frac{dy}{du} \cdot \frac{du}{dx},$$

where dy/du is evaluated at $u = g(x)$.

Intuitive "Proof" of the Chain Rule:

Let Δu be the change in u corresponding to a change of Δx in x, that is

$$\Delta u = g(x + \Delta x) - g(x)$$

Then the corresponding change in y is

$$\Delta y = f(u + \Delta u) - f(u).$$

It would be tempting to write

$$\frac{\Delta y}{\Delta x} = \frac{\Delta y}{\Delta u} \cdot \frac{\Delta u}{\Delta x} \tag{1}$$

and take the limit as $\Delta x \to 0$:

$$
\begin{aligned}
\frac{dy}{dx} &= \lim_{\Delta x \to 0} \frac{\Delta y}{\Delta x} \\[6pt]
&= \lim_{\Delta x \to 0} \frac{\Delta y}{\Delta u} \cdot \frac{\Delta u}{\Delta x} \\[6pt]
&= \lim_{\Delta x \to 0} \frac{\Delta y}{\Delta u} \cdot \lim_{\Delta x \to 0} \frac{\Delta u}{\Delta x} \\[6pt]
&= \lim_{\Delta u \to 0} \frac{\Delta y}{\Delta u} \cdot \lim_{\Delta x \to 0} \frac{\Delta u}{\Delta x} \qquad \text{(Note that } \Delta u \to 0 \text{ as } \Delta x \to 0 \\
&\qquad\qquad\qquad\qquad\qquad\qquad \text{since } g \text{ is continuous.)} \\[6pt]
&= \frac{dy}{du} \frac{du}{dx}.
\end{aligned}
$$

The only flaw in this reasoning is that in Equation (1) it might happen that $\Delta u = 0$ (even when $\Delta x \neq 0$) and, of course, we can't divide by 0. The proof requires a different approach to overcome this flaw, and we give a precise proof in Section 3.8.   ∎

EXAMPLE 3   Applying the Chain Rule

An object moves along the x-axis so that its position at any time $t \geq 0$ is given by $x(t) = \cos(t^2 + 1)$. Find the velocity of the object as a function of t.

Solution   We know that the velocity is dx/dt. In this instance, x is a composite function: $x = \cos(u)$ and $u = t^2 + 1$. We have

$$\frac{dx}{du} = -\sin(u) \qquad x = \cos(u)$$

$$\frac{du}{dt} = 2t. \qquad u = t^2 + 1$$

By the Chain Rule,

$$\frac{dx}{dt} = \frac{dx}{du} \cdot \frac{du}{dt}$$

$$= -\sin(u) \cdot 2t \qquad \frac{dx}{du} \text{ evaluated at } u$$

$$= -\sin(t^2 + 1) \cdot 2t$$

$$= -2t \sin(t^2 + 1).$$ ∎

As we see from Example 3, a difficulty with the Leibniz notation is that it doesn't state specifically where the derivatives are supposed to be evaluated.

"Outside-Inside" Rule

It sometimes helps to think about the Chain Rule this way: If $y = f(g(x))$, then

$$\frac{dy}{dx} = f'(g(x)) \cdot g'(x).$$

In words, differentiate the "outside" function f and evaluate it at the "inside" function $g(x)$ left alone; then multiply by the derivative of the "inside function."

EXAMPLE 4   Differentiating from the Outside In

Differentiate $\sin(x^2 + x)$ with respect to x.

Solution

$$\frac{d}{dx} \sin(\underbrace{x^2 + x}_{\text{inside}}) = \cos(\underbrace{x^2 + x}_{\substack{\text{inside} \\ \text{left alone}}}) \cdot \underbrace{(2x + 1)}_{\substack{\text{derivative of} \\ \text{the inside}}}$$ ∎

Repeated Use of the Chain Rule

We sometimes have to use the Chain Rule two or more times to find a derivative. Here is an example.

EXAMPLE 5   A Three-Link "Chain"

Find the derivative of $g(t) = \tan(5 - \sin 2t)$.

Solution   Notice here that the tangent is a function of $5 - \sin 2t$, whereas the sine is a function of $2t$, which is itself a function of t. Therefore, by the Chain Rule,

$$g'(t) = \frac{d}{dt}\left(\tan\left(5 - \sin 2t\right)\right)$$

$$= \sec^2\left(5 - \sin 2t\right) \cdot \frac{d}{dt}\left(5 - \sin 2t\right) \qquad \text{Derivative of } \tan u \text{ with } u = 5 - \sin 2t$$

$$= \sec^2\left(5 - \sin 2t\right) \cdot \left(0 - \cos 2t \cdot \frac{d}{dt}\left(2t\right)\right) \qquad \text{Derivative of } 5 - \sin u \text{ with } u = 2t$$

$$= \sec^2\left(5 - \sin 2t\right) \cdot (-\cos 2t) \cdot 2$$

$$= -2(\cos 2t)\sec^2\left(5 - \sin 2t\right). \qquad \blacksquare$$

The Chain Rule with Powers of a Function

If f is a differentiable function of u and if u is a differentiable function of x, then substituting $y = f(u)$ into the Chain Rule formula

$$\frac{dy}{dx} = \frac{dy}{du} \cdot \frac{du}{dx}$$

leads to the formula

$$\frac{d}{dx} f(u) = f'(u) \frac{du}{dx}.$$

Here's an example of how it works: If n is a positive or negative integer and $f(u) = u^n$, the Power Rules (Rules 2 and 7) tell us that $f'(u) = nu^{n-1}$. If u is a differentiable function of x, then we can use the Chain Rule to extend this to the **Power Chain Rule**:

$$\frac{d}{dx} u^n = nu^{n-1} \frac{du}{dx}. \qquad \frac{d}{du}\left(u^n\right) = nu^{n-1}$$

EXAMPLE 6   Applying the Power Chain Rule

(a) $\dfrac{d}{dx}(5x^3 - x^4)^7 = 7(5x^3 - x^4)^6 \dfrac{d}{dx}\left(5x^3 - x^4\right) \qquad$ Power Chain Rule with $u = 5x^3 - x^4, n = 7$

$$= 7(5x^3 - x^4)^6(5 \cdot 3x^2 - 4x^3)$$

$$= 7(5x^3 - x^4)^6(15x^2 - 4x^3)$$

(b) $\dfrac{d}{dx}\left(\dfrac{1}{3x - 2}\right) = \dfrac{d}{dx}(3x - 2)^{-1}$

$$= -1(3x - 2)^{-2}\dfrac{d}{dx}\left(3x - 2\right) \qquad \text{Power Chain Rule with } u = 3x - 2, n = -1$$

$$= -1(3x - 2)^{-2}(3)$$

$$= -\dfrac{3}{(3x - 2)^2}$$

In part (b) we could also have found the derivative with the Quotient Rule. $\qquad \blacksquare$

$\boxed{\sin^n x \text{ means } (\sin x)^n, n \neq -1.}$

EXAMPLE 7   Finding Tangent Slopes

(a) Find the slope of the line tangent to the curve $y = \sin^5 x$ at the point where $x = \pi/3$.

(b) Show that the slope of every line tangent to the curve $y = 1/(1 - 2x)^3$ is positive.

Solution

(a) $\dfrac{dy}{dx} = 5 \sin^4 x \cdot \dfrac{d}{dx} \sin x$ Power Chain Rule with $u = \sin x$, $n = 5$

$\qquad\quad = 5 \sin^4 x \cos x$

The tangent line has slope

$$\left.\frac{dy}{dx}\right|_{x=\pi/3} = 5\left(\frac{\sqrt{3}}{2}\right)^4\left(\frac{1}{2}\right) = \frac{45}{32}.$$

(b) $\dfrac{dy}{dx} = \dfrac{d}{dx}(1 - 2x)^{-3}$

$\qquad\quad = -3(1 - 2x)^{-4} \cdot \dfrac{d}{dx}(1 - 2x)$ Power Chain Rule with $u = (1 - 2x)$, $n = -3$

$\qquad\quad = -3(1 - 2x)^{-4} \cdot (-2)$

$\qquad\quad = \dfrac{6}{(1 - 2x)^4}$

At any point (x, y) on the curve, $x \neq 1/2$ and the slope of the tangent line is

$$\frac{dy}{dx} = \frac{6}{(1 - 2x)^4},$$

the quotient of two positive numbers. ∎

EXAMPLE 8   Radians Versus Degrees

It is important to remember that the formulas for the derivatives of both $\sin x$ and $\cos x$ were obtained under the assumption that x is measured in radians, *not* degrees. The Chain Rule gives us new insight into the difference between the two. Since $180° = \pi$ radians, $x° = \pi x/180$ radians where $x°$ means the angle x measured in degrees.

By the Chain Rule,

$$\frac{d}{dx}\sin(x°) = \frac{d}{dx}\sin\left(\frac{\pi x}{180}\right) = \frac{\pi}{180}\cos\left(\frac{\pi x}{180}\right) = \frac{\pi}{180}\cos(x°).$$

See Figure 3.28. Similarly, the derivative of $\cos(x°)$ is $-(\pi/180)\sin(x°)$.

The factor $\pi/180$, annoying in the first derivative, would compound with repeated differentiation. We see at a glance the compelling reason for the use of radian measure. ∎

Parametric Equations

Instead of describing a curve by expressing the y-coordinate of a point $P(x, y)$ on the curve as a function of x, it is sometimes more convenient to describe the curve by expressing *both* coordinates as functions of a third variable t. Figure 3.29 shows the path of a moving particle described by a pair of equations, $x = f(t)$ and $y = g(t)$. For studying motion,

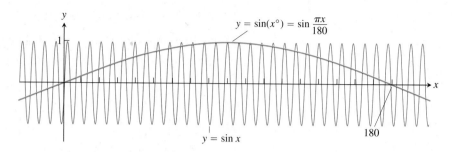

FIGURE 3.28   Sin $(x°)$ oscillates only $\pi/180$ times as often as $\sin x$ oscillates. Its maximum slope is $\pi/180$ at $x = 0$ (Example 8).

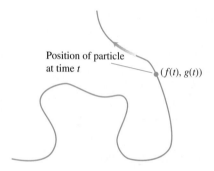

FIGURE 3.29   The path traced by a particle moving in the xy-plane is not always the graph of a function of x or a function of y.

t usually denotes time. Equations like these are better than a Cartesian formula because they tell us the particle's position $(x, y) = (f(t), g(t))$ at any time t.

DEFINITION   **Parametric Curve**

If x and y are given as functions

$$x = f(t), \qquad y = g(t)$$

over an interval of t-values, then the set of points $(x, y) = (f(t), g(t))$ defined by these equations is a **parametric curve**. The equations are **parametric equations** for the curve.

The variable t is a **parameter** for the curve, and its domain I is the **parameter interval**. If I is a closed interval, $a \leq t \leq b$, the point $(f(a), g(a))$ is the **initial point** of the curve. The point $(f(b), g(b))$ is the **terminal point**. When we give parametric equations and a parameter interval for a curve, we say that we have **parametrized** the curve. The equations and interval together constitute a **parametrization** of the curve.

EXAMPLE 9   Moving Counterclockwise on a Circle

Graph the parametric curves

(a) $x = \cos t, \qquad y = \sin t, \qquad 0 \leq t \leq 2\pi.$

(b) $x = a \cos t, \qquad y = a \sin t, \qquad 0 \leq t \leq 2\pi.$

Solution

(a) Since $x^2 + y^2 = \cos^2 t + \sin^2 t = 1$, the parametric curve lies along the unit circle $x^2 + y^2 = 1$. As t increases from 0 to 2π, the point $(x, y) = (\cos t, \sin t)$ starts at $(1, 0)$ and traces the entire circle once counterclockwise (Figure 3.30).

(b) For $x = a \cos t, y = a \sin t, 0 \leq t \leq 2\pi$, we have $x^2 + y^2 = a^2 \cos^2 t + a^2 \sin^2 t = a^2$. The parametrization describes a motion that begins at the point $(a, 0)$ and traverses the circle $x^2 + y^2 = a^2$ once counterclockwise, returning to $(a, 0)$ at $t = 2\pi$. ∎

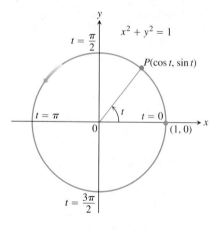

FIGURE 3.30   The equations $x = \cos t$ and $y = \sin t$ describe motion on the circle $x^2 + y^2 = 1$. The arrow shows the direction of increasing t (Example 9).

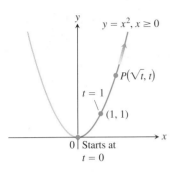

FIGURE 3.31 The equations $x = \sqrt{t}$ and $y = t$ and the interval $t \geq 0$ describe the motion of a particle that traces the right-hand half of the parabola $y = x^2$ (Example 10).

EXAMPLE 10   Moving Along a Parabola

The position $P(x, y)$ of a particle moving in the xy-plane is given by the equations and parameter interval

$$x = \sqrt{t}, \qquad y = t, \qquad t \geq 0.$$

Identify the path traced by the particle and describe the motion.

Solution   We try to identify the path by eliminating t between the equations $x = \sqrt{t}$ and $y = t$. With any luck, this will produce a recognizable algebraic relation between x and y. We find that

$$y = t = \left(\sqrt{t}\right)^2 = x^2.$$

Thus, the particle's position coordinates satisfy the equation $y = x^2$, so the particle moves along the parabola $y = x^2$.

It would be a mistake, however, to conclude that the particle's path is the entire parabola $y = x^2$; it is only half the parabola. The particle's x-coordinate is never negative. The particle starts at $(0, 0)$ when $t = 0$ and rises into the first quadrant as t increases (Figure 3.31). The parameter interval is $[0, \infty)$ and there is no terminal point. ∎

EXAMPLE 11   Parametrizing a Line Segment

Find a parametrization for the line segment with endpoints $(-2, 1)$ and $(3, 5)$.

Solution   Using $(-2, 1)$ we create the parametric equations

$$x = -2 + at, \qquad y = 1 + bt.$$

These represent a line, as we can see by solving each equation for t and equating to obtain

$$\frac{x + 2}{a} = \frac{y - 1}{b}.$$

This line goes through the point $(-2, 1)$ when $t = 0$. We determine a and b so that the line goes through $(3, 5)$ when $t = 1$.

$$3 = -2 + a \qquad \Rightarrow \qquad a = 5 \qquad \text{\small $x = 3$ when $t = 1$.}$$
$$5 = 1 + b \qquad \Rightarrow \qquad b = 4 \qquad \text{\small $y = 5$ when $t = 1$.}$$

Therefore,

$$x = -2 + 5t, \qquad y = 1 + 4t, \qquad 0 \leq t \leq 1$$

is a parametrization of the line segment with initial point $(-2, 1)$ and terminal point $(3, 5)$. ∎

Slopes of Parametrized Curves

A parametrized curve $x = f(t)$ and $y = g(t)$ is **differentiable** at t if f and g are differentiable at t. At a point on a differentiable parametrized curve where y is also a differentiable function of x, the derivatives dy/dt, dx/dt, and dy/dx are related by the Chain Rule:

$$\frac{dy}{dt} = \frac{dy}{dx} \cdot \frac{dx}{dt}.$$

If $dx/dt \neq 0$, we may divide both sides of this equation by dx/dt to solve for dy/dx.

Parametric Formula for dy/dx

If all three derivatives exist and $dx/dt \neq 0$,

$$\frac{dy}{dx} = \frac{dy/dt}{dx/dt}. \qquad (2)$$

EXAMPLE 12 Differentiating with a Parameter

If $x = 2t + 3$ and $y = t^2 - 1$, find the value of dy/dx at $t = 6$.

Solution Equation (2) gives dy/dx as a function of t:

$$\frac{dy}{dx} = \frac{dy/dt}{dx/dt} = \frac{2t}{2} = t = \frac{x-3}{2}.$$

When $t = 6$, $dy/dx = 6$. Notice that we are also able to find the derivative dy/dx as a function of x. ∎

EXAMPLE 13 Moving Along the Ellipse $x^2/a^2 + y^2/b^2 = 1$

Describe the motion of a particle whose position $P(x, y)$ at time t is given by

$$x = a \cos t, \qquad y = b \sin t, \qquad 0 \leq t \leq 2\pi.$$

Find the line tangent to the curve at the point $\left(a/\sqrt{2}, b/\sqrt{2} \right)$, where $t = \pi/4$. (The constants a and b are both positive.)

Solution We find a Cartesian equation for the particle's coordinates by eliminating t between the equations

$$\cos t = \frac{x}{a}, \qquad \sin t = \frac{y}{b}.$$

The identity $\cos^2 t + \sin^2 t = 1$, yields

$$\left(\frac{x}{a} \right)^2 + \left(\frac{y}{b} \right)^2 = 1, \qquad \text{or} \qquad \frac{x^2}{a^2} + \frac{y^2}{b^2} = 1.$$

The particle's coordinates (x, y) satisfy the equation $(x^2/a^2) + (y^2/b^2) = 1$, so the particle moves along this ellipse. When $t = 0$, the particle's coordinates are

$$x = a \cos(0) = a, \qquad y = b \sin(0) = 0,$$

so the motion starts at $(a, 0)$. As t increases, the particle rises and moves toward the left, moving counterclockwise. It traverses the ellipse once, returning to its starting position $(a, 0)$ at $t = 2\pi$.

The slope of the tangent line to the ellipse when $t = \pi/4$ is

$$\left. \frac{dy}{dx} \right|_{t=\pi/4} = \left. \frac{dy/dt}{dx/dt} \right|_{t=\pi/4} \qquad \text{Eq. (2)}$$

$$= \left. \frac{b \cos t}{-a \sin t} \right|_{t=\pi/4}$$

$$= \frac{b/\sqrt{2}}{-a/\sqrt{2}} = -\frac{b}{a}.$$

The tangent line is

$$y - \frac{b}{\sqrt{2}} = -\frac{b}{a}\left(x - \frac{a}{\sqrt{2}}\right)$$

$$y = \frac{b}{\sqrt{2}} - \frac{b}{a}\left(x - \frac{a}{\sqrt{2}}\right)$$

or

$$y = -\frac{b}{a}x + \sqrt{2}\,b.$$

∎

If parametric equations define y as a twice-differentiable function of x, we can apply Equation (2) to the function $dy/dx = y'$ to calculate d^2y/dx^2 as a function of t:

$$\frac{d^2y}{dx^2} = \frac{d}{dx}(y') = \frac{dy'/dt}{dx/dt}. \qquad \text{Eq. (2) with } y' \text{ in place of } y$$

Parametric Formula for d^2y/dx^2

If the equations $x = f(t), y = g(t)$ define y as a twice-differentiable function of x, then at any point where $dx/dt \neq 0$,

$$\frac{d^2y}{dx^2} = \frac{dy'/dt}{dx/dt}. \qquad\qquad (3)$$

EXAMPLE 14 Finding d^2y/dx^2 for a Parametrized Curve

Find d^2y/dx^2 as a function of t if $x = t - t^2$, $y = t - t^3$.

Finding d^2y/dx^2 in Terms of t
1. Express $y' = dy/dx$ in terms of t.
2. Find dy'/dt.
3. Divide dy'/dt by dx/dt.

Solution

1. Express $y' = dy/dx$ in terms of t.

$$y' = \frac{dy}{dx} = \frac{dy/dt}{dx/dt} = \frac{1 - 3t^2}{1 - 2t}$$

2. Differentiate y' with respect to t.

$$\frac{dy'}{dt} = \frac{d}{dt}\left(\frac{1 - 3t^2}{1 - 2t}\right) = \frac{2 - 6t + 6t^2}{(1 - 2t)^2} \qquad \text{Quotient Rule}$$

3. Divide dy'/dt by dx/dt.

$$\frac{d^2y}{dx^2} = \frac{dy'/dt}{dx/dt} = \frac{(2 - 6t + 6t^2)/(1 - 2t)^2}{1 - 2t} = \frac{2 - 6t + 6t^2}{(1 - 2t)^3} \qquad \text{Eq. (3)} \qquad ∎$$

EXAMPLE 15 Dropping Emergency Supplies

A Red Cross aircraft is dropping emergency food and medical supplies into a disaster area. If the aircraft releases the supplies immediately above the edge of an open field 700 ft long and if the cargo moves along the path

$$x = 120t \qquad \text{and} \qquad y = -16t^2 + 500, \qquad t \geq 0$$

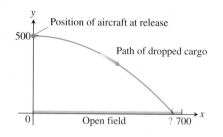

FIGURE 3.32 The path of the dropped cargo of supplies in Example 15.

does the cargo land in the field? The coordinates x and y are measured in feet, and the parameter t (time since release) in seconds. Find a Cartesian equation for the path of the falling cargo (Figure 3.32) and the cargo's rate of descent relative to its forward motion when it hits the ground.

Solution   The cargo hits the ground when $y = 0$, which occurs at time t when

$$-16t^2 + 500 = 0 \qquad\qquad \text{Set } y = 0.$$

$$t = \sqrt{\frac{500}{16}} = \frac{5\sqrt{5}}{2} \text{ sec}. \qquad t \geq 0$$

The x-coordinate at the time of the release is $x = 0$. At the time the cargo hits the ground, the x-coordinate is

$$x = 120t = 120\left(\frac{5\sqrt{5}}{2}\right) = 300\sqrt{5} \text{ ft}.$$

Since $300\sqrt{5} \approx 670.8 < 700$, the cargo does land in the field.

We find a Cartesian equation for the cargo's coordinates by eliminating t between the parametric equations:

$$y = -16t^2 + 500 \qquad\qquad \text{Parametric equation for } y$$

$$= -16\left(\frac{x}{120}\right)^2 + 500 \qquad \begin{array}{l}\text{Substitute for } t \text{ from the}\\ \text{equation } x = 120t.\end{array}$$

$$= -\frac{1}{900}x^2 + 500. \qquad\qquad \text{A parabola}$$

The rate of descent relative to its forward motion when the cargo hits the ground is

$$\left.\frac{dy}{dx}\right|_{t=5\sqrt{5}/2} = \left.\frac{dy/dt}{dx/dt}\right|_{t=5\sqrt{5}/2} \qquad\qquad \text{Eq. (2)}$$

$$= \left.\frac{-32t}{120}\right|_{t=5\sqrt{5}/2}$$

$$= -\frac{2\sqrt{5}}{3} \approx -1.49.$$

Thus, it is falling about 1.5 feet for every foot of forward motion when it hits the ground.   ∎

USING TECHNOLOGY   Simulation of Motion on a Vertical Line

The parametric equations

$$x(t) = c, \qquad y(t) = f(t)$$

will illuminate pixels along the vertical line $x = c$. If $f(t)$ denotes the height of a moving body at time t, graphing $(x(t), y(t)) = (c, f(t))$ will simulate the actual motion. Try it for the rock in Example 5, Section 3.3 with $x(t) = 2$, say, and $y(t) = 160t - 16t^2$, in dot mode with t Step $= 0.1$. Why does the spacing of the dots vary? Why does the grapher seem to stop after it reaches the top? (Try the plots for $0 \leq t \leq 5$ and $5 \leq t \leq 10$ separately.)

For a second experiment, plot the parametric equations

$$x(t) = t, \qquad y(t) = 160t - 16t^2$$

$$\begin{cases} x(t) = 2 \\ y(t) = 160t - 16t^2 \end{cases}$$

and

$$\begin{cases} x(t) = t \\ y(t) = 160t - 16t^2 \end{cases}$$

in dot mode

together with the vertical line simulation of the motion, again in dot mode. Use what you know about the behavior of the rock from the calculations of Example 5 to select a window size that will display all the interesting behavior.

Standard Parametrizations and Derivative Rules

CIRCLE $x^2 + y^2 = a^2$:

$$x = a \cos t$$
$$y = a \sin t$$
$$0 \le t \le 2\pi$$

ELLIPSE $\dfrac{x^2}{a^2} + \dfrac{y^2}{b^2} = 1$:

$$x = a \cos t$$
$$y = b \sin t$$
$$0 \le t \le 2\pi$$

FUNCTION $y = f(x)$:

$$x = t$$
$$y = f(t)$$

DERIVATIVES

$$y' = \frac{dy}{dx} = \frac{dy/dt}{dx/dt}, \qquad \frac{d^2y}{dx^2} = \frac{dy'/dt}{dx/dt}$$

EXERCISES 3.5

Derivative Calculations

In Exercises 1–8, given $y = f(u)$ and $u = g(x)$, find $dy/dx = f'(g(x))g'(x)$.

1. $y = 6u - 9, \quad u = (1/2)x^4$ **2.** $y = 2u^3, \quad u = 8x - 1$

3. $y = \sin u, \quad u = 3x + 1$ **4.** $y = \cos u, \quad u = -x/3$

5. $y = \cos u, \quad u = \sin x$ **6.** $y = \sin u, \quad u = x - \cos x$

7. $y = \tan u, \quad u = 10x - 5$ **8.** $y = -\sec u, \quad u = x^2 + 7x$

In Exercises 9–18, write the function in the form $y = f(u)$ and $u = g(x)$. Then find dy/dx as a function of x.

9. $y = (2x + 1)^5$ **10.** $y = (4 - 3x)^9$

11. $y = \left(1 - \dfrac{x}{7}\right)^{-7}$ **12.** $y = \left(\dfrac{x}{2} - 1\right)^{-10}$

13. $y = \left(\dfrac{x^2}{8} + x - \dfrac{1}{x}\right)^4$ **14.** $y = \left(\dfrac{x}{5} + \dfrac{1}{5x}\right)^5$

15. $y = \sec(\tan x)$ **16.** $y = \cot\left(\pi - \dfrac{1}{x}\right)$

17. $y = \sin^3 x$ **18.** $y = 5 \cos^{-4} x$

Find the derivatives of the functions in Exercises 19–38.

19. $p = \sqrt{3 - t}$ **20.** $q = \sqrt{2r - r^2}$

21. $s = \dfrac{4}{3\pi} \sin 3t + \dfrac{4}{5\pi} \cos 5t$

22. $s = \sin\left(\dfrac{3\pi t}{2}\right) + \cos\left(\dfrac{3\pi t}{2}\right)$

23. $r = (\csc \theta + \cot \theta)^{-1}$ **24.** $r = -(\sec \theta + \tan \theta)^{-1}$

25. $y = x^2 \sin^4 x + x \cos^{-2} x$ **26.** $y = \dfrac{1}{x} \sin^{-5} x - \dfrac{x}{3} \cos^3 x$

27. $y = \dfrac{1}{21}(3x - 2)^7 + \left(4 - \dfrac{1}{2x^2}\right)^{-1}$

28. $y = (5 - 2x)^{-3} + \dfrac{1}{8}\left(\dfrac{2}{x} + 1\right)^4$

29. $y = (4x + 3)^4(x + 1)^{-3}$ **30.** $y = (2x - 5)^{-1}(x^2 - 5x)^6$

31. $h(x) = x \tan\left(2\sqrt{x}\right) + 7$ **32.** $k(x) = x^2 \sec\left(\dfrac{1}{x}\right)$

33. $f(\theta) = \left(\dfrac{\sin \theta}{1 + \cos \theta}\right)^2$ **34.** $g(t) = \left(\dfrac{1 + \cos t}{\sin t}\right)^{-1}$

35. $r = \sin(\theta^2) \cos(2\theta)$ **36.** $r = \sec\sqrt{\theta} \tan\left(\dfrac{1}{\theta}\right)$

37. $q = \sin\left(\dfrac{t}{\sqrt{t + 1}}\right)$ **38.** $q = \cot\left(\dfrac{\sin t}{t}\right)$

In Exercises 39–48, find dy/dt.

39. $y = \sin^2(\pi t - 2)$ **40.** $y = \sec^2 \pi t$

41. $y = (1 + \cos 2t)^{-4}$ **42.** $y = (1 + \cot(t/2))^{-2}$

43. $y = \sin(\cos(2t - 5))$

44. $y = \cos\left(5 \sin\left(\dfrac{t}{3}\right)\right)$

45. $y = \left(1 + \tan^4\left(\dfrac{t}{12}\right)\right)^3$

46. $y = \dfrac{1}{6}\left(1 + \cos^2(7t)\right)^3$

47. $y = \sqrt{1 + \cos(t^2)}$

48. $y = 4 \sin\left(\sqrt{1 + \sqrt{t}}\right)$

Second Derivatives

Find y'' in Exercises 49–52.

49. $y = \left(1 + \dfrac{1}{x}\right)^3$

50. $y = \left(1 - \sqrt{x}\right)^{-1}$

51. $y = \dfrac{1}{9}\cot(3x - 1)$

52. $y = 9 \tan\left(\dfrac{x}{3}\right)$

Finding Numerical Values of Derivatives

In Exercises 53–58, find the value of $(f \circ g)'$ at the given value of x.

53. $f(u) = u^5 + 1, \quad u = g(x) = \sqrt{x}, \quad x = 1$

54. $f(u) = 1 - \dfrac{1}{u}, \quad u = g(x) = \dfrac{1}{1 - x}, \quad x = -1$

55. $f(u) = \cot\dfrac{\pi u}{10}, \quad u = g(x) = 5\sqrt{x}, \quad x = 1$

56. $f(u) = u + \dfrac{1}{\cos^2 u}, \quad u = g(x) = \pi x, \quad x = 1/4$

57. $f(u) = \dfrac{2u}{u^2 + 1}, \quad u = g(x) = 10x^2 + x + 1, \quad x = 0$

58. $f(u) = \left(\dfrac{u - 1}{u + 1}\right)^2, \quad u = g(x) = \dfrac{1}{x^2} - 1, \quad x = -1$

59. Suppose that functions f and g and their derivatives with respect to x have the following values at $x = 2$ and $x = 3$.

x	$f(x)$	$g(x)$	$f'(x)$	$g'(x)$
2	8	2	1/3	−3
3	3	−4	2π	5

Find the derivatives with respect to x of the following combinations at the given value of x.

a. $2f(x), \quad x = 2$

b. $f(x) + g(x), \quad x = 3$

c. $f(x) \cdot g(x), \quad x = 3$

d. $f(x)/g(x), \quad x = 2$

e. $f(g(x)), \quad x = 2$

f. $\sqrt{f(x)}, \quad x = 2$

g. $1/g^2(x), \quad x = 3$

h. $\sqrt{f^2(x) + g^2(x)}, \quad x = 2$

60. Suppose that the functions f and g and their derivatives with respect to x have the following values at $x = 0$ and $x = 1$.

x	$f(x)$	$g(x)$	$f'(x)$	$g'(x)$
0	1	1	5	1/3
1	3	−4	−1/3	−8/3

Find the derivatives with respect to x of the following combinations at the given value of x,

a. $5f(x) - g(x), \quad x = 1$

b. $f(x)g^3(x), \quad x = 0$

c. $\dfrac{f(x)}{g(x) + 1}, \quad x = 1$

d. $f(g(x)), \quad x = 0$

e. $g(f(x)), \quad x = 0$

f. $(x^{11} + f(x))^{-2}, \quad x = 1$

g. $f(x + g(x)), \quad x = 0$

61. Find ds/dt when $\theta = 3\pi/2$ if $s = \cos\theta$ and $d\theta/dt = 5$.

62. Find dy/dt when $x = 1$ if $y = x^2 + 7x - 5$ and $dx/dt = 1/3$.

Choices in Composition

What happens if you can write a function as a composite in different ways? Do you get the same derivative each time? The Chain Rule says you should. Try it with the functions in Exercises 63 and 64.

63. Find dy/dx if $y = x$ by using the Chain Rule with y as a composite of

a. $y = (u/5) + 7$ and $u = 5x - 35$

b. $y = 1 + (1/u)$ and $u = 1/(x - 1)$.

64. Find dy/dx if $y = x^{3/2}$ by using the Chain Rule with y as a composite of

a. $y = u^3$ and $u = \sqrt{x}$

b. $y = \sqrt{u}$ and $u = x^3$.

Tangents and Slopes

65. a. Find the tangent to the curve $y = 2\tan(\pi x/4)$ at $x = 1$.

b. Slopes on a tangent curve What is the smallest value the slope of the curve can ever have on the interval $-2 < x < 2$? Give reasons for your answer.

66. Slopes on sine curves

a. Find equations for the tangents to the curves $y = \sin 2x$ and $y = -\sin(x/2)$ at the origin. Is there anything special about how the tangents are related? Give reasons for your answer.

b. Can anything be said about the tangents to the curves $y = \sin mx$ and $y = -\sin(x/m)$ at the origin (m a constant $\neq 0$)? Give reasons for your answer.

c. For a given m, what are the largest values the slopes of the curves $y = \sin mx$ and $y = -\sin(x/m)$ can ever have? Give reasons for your answer.

d. The function $y = \sin x$ completes one period on the interval $[0, 2\pi]$, the function $y = \sin 2x$ completes two periods, the function $y = \sin(x/2)$ completes half a period, and so on. Is there any relation between the number of periods $y = \sin mx$ completes on $[0, 2\pi]$ and the slope of the curve $y = \sin mx$ at the origin? Give reasons for your answer.

Finding Cartesian Equations from Parametric Equations

Exercises 67–78 give parametric equations and parameter intervals for the motion of a particle in the xy-plane. Identify the particle's path by finding a Cartesian equation for it. Graph the Cartesian equation. (The graphs will vary with the equation used.) Indicate the portion of the graph traced by the particle and the direction of motion.

67. $x = \cos 2t, \quad y = \sin 2t, \quad 0 \le t \le \pi$

68. $x = \cos(\pi - t), \quad y = \sin(\pi - t), \quad 0 \le t \le \pi$

69. $x = 4 \cos t, \quad y = 2 \sin t, \quad 0 \le t \le 2\pi$

70. $x = 4 \sin t, \quad y = 5 \cos t, \quad 0 \le t \le 2\pi$

71. $x = 3t, \quad y = 9t^2, \quad -\infty < t < \infty$

72. $x = -\sqrt{t}, \quad y = t, \quad t \ge 0$

73. $x = 2t - 5, \quad y = 4t - 7, \quad -\infty < t < \infty$

74. $x = 3 - 3t, \quad y = 2t, \quad 0 \le t \le 1$

75. $x = t, \quad y = \sqrt{1 - t^2}, \quad -1 \le t \le 0$

76. $x = \sqrt{t + 1}, \quad y = \sqrt{t}, \quad t \ge 0$

77. $x = \sec^2 t - 1, \quad y = \tan t, \quad -\pi/2 < t < \pi/2$

78. $x = -\sec t, \quad y = \tan t, \quad -\pi/2 < t < \pi/2$

Determining Parametric Equations

79. Find parametric equations and a parameter interval for the motion of a particle that starts at $(a, 0)$ and traces the circle $x^2 + y^2 = a^2$

 a. once clockwise.   **b.** once counterclockwise.

 c. twice clockwise.   **d.** twice counterclockwise.

 (There are many ways to do these, so your answers may not be the same as the ones in the back of the book.)

80. Find parametric equations and a parameter interval for the motion of a particle that starts at $(a, 0)$ and traces the ellipse $(x^2/a^2) + (y^2/b^2) = 1$

 a. once clockwise.   **b.** once counterclockwise.

 c. twice clockwise.   **d.** twice counterclockwise.

 (As in Exercise 79, there are many correct answers.)

In Exercises 81–86, find a parametrization for the curve.

81. the line segment with endpoints $(-1, -3)$ and $(4, 1)$

82. the line segment with endpoints $(-1, 3)$ and $(3, -2)$

83. the lower half of the parabola $x - 1 = y^2$

84. the left half of the parabola $y = x^2 + 2x$

85. the ray (half line) with initial point $(2, 3)$ that passes through the point $(-1, -1)$

86. the ray (half line) with initial point $(-1, 2)$ that passes through the point $(0, 0)$

Tangents to Parametrized Curves

In Exercises 87–94, find an equation for the line tangent to the curve at the point defined by the given value of t. Also, find the value of d^2y/dx^2 at this point.

87. $x = 2 \cos t, \quad y = 2 \sin t, \quad t = \pi/4$

88. $x = \cos t, \quad y = \sqrt{3} \cos t, \quad t = 2\pi/3$

89. $x = t, \quad y = \sqrt{t}, \quad t = 1/4$

90. $x = -\sqrt{t + 1}, \quad y = \sqrt{3t}, \quad t = 3$

91. $x = 2t^2 + 3, \quad y = t^4, \quad t = -1$

92. $x = t - \sin t, \quad y = 1 - \cos t, \quad t = \pi/3$

93. $x = \cos t, \quad y = 1 + \sin t, \quad t = \pi/2$

94. $x = \sec^2 t - 1, \quad y = \tan t, \quad t = -\pi/4$

Theory, Examples, and Applications

95. Running machinery too fast Suppose that a piston is moving straight up and down and that its position at time t sec is

$$s = A \cos(2\pi bt),$$

with A and b positive. The value of A is the amplitude of the motion, and b is the frequency (number of times the piston moves up and down each second). What effect does doubling the frequency have on the piston's velocity, acceleration, and jerk? (Once you find out, you will know why machinery breaks when you run it too fast.)

96. Temperatures in Fairbanks, Alaska The graph in Figure 3.33 shows the average Fahrenheit temperature in Fairbanks, Alaska, during a typical 365-day year. The equation that approximates the temperature on day x is

$$y = 37 \sin\left[\frac{2\pi}{365}(x - 101)\right] + 25.$$

 a. On what day is the temperature increasing the fastest?

 b. About how many degrees per day is the temperature increasing when it is increasing at its fastest?

FIGURE 3.33 Normal mean air temperatures at Fairbanks, Alaska, plotted as data points, and the approximating sine function (Exercise 96).

97. Particle motion The position of a particle moving along a coordinate line is $s = \sqrt{1 + 4t}$, with s in meters and t in seconds. Find the particle's velocity and acceleration at $t = 6$ sec.

98. Constant acceleration Suppose that the velocity of a falling body is $v = k\sqrt{s}$ m/sec (k a constant) at the instant the body has fallen s m from its starting point. Show that the body's acceleration is constant.

99. Falling meteorite The velocity of a heavy meteorite entering Earth's atmosphere is inversely proportional to $\sqrt{s}$ when it is s km from Earth's center. Show that the meteorite's acceleration is inversely proportional to s^2.

100. Particle acceleration A particle moves along the x-axis with velocity $dx/dt = f(x)$. Show that the particle's acceleration is $f(x)f'(x)$.

101. Temperature and the period of a pendulum For oscillations of small amplitude (short swings), we may safely model the relationship between the period T and the length L of a simple pendulum with the equation

$$T = 2\pi\sqrt{\frac{L}{g}},$$

where g is the constant acceleration of gravity at the pendulum's location. If we measure g in centimeters per second squared, we measure L in centimeters and T in seconds. If the pendulum is made of metal, its length will vary with temperature, either increasing or decreasing at a rate that is roughly proportional to L. In symbols, with u being temperature and k the proportionality constant,

$$\frac{dL}{du} = kL.$$

Assuming this to be the case, show that the rate at which the period changes with respect to temperature is $kT/2$.

102. Chain Rule Suppose that $f(x) = x^2$ and $g(x) = |x|$. Then the composites

$$(f \circ g)(x) = |x|^2 = x^2 \quad \text{and} \quad (g \circ f)(x) = |x^2| = x^2$$

are both differentiable at $x = 0$ even though g itself is not differentiable at $x = 0$. Does this contradict the Chain Rule? Explain.

103. Tangents Suppose that $u = g(x)$ is differentiable at $x = 1$ and that $y = f(u)$ is differentiable at $u = g(1)$. If the graph of $y = f(g(x))$ has a horizontal tangent at $x = 1$, can we conclude anything about the tangent to the graph of g at $x = 1$ or the tangent to the graph of f at $u = g(1)$? Give reasons for your answer.

104. Suppose that $u = g(x)$ is differentiable at $x = -5$, $y = f(u)$ is differentiable at $u = g(-5)$, and $(f \circ g)'(-5)$ is negative. What, if anything, can be said about the values of $g'(-5)$ and $f'(g(-5))$?

T **105. The derivative of sin 2x** Graph the function $y = 2\cos 2x$ for $-2 \le x \le 3.5$. Then, on the same screen, graph

$$y = \frac{\sin 2(x + h) - \sin 2x}{h}$$

for $h = 1.0, 0.5$, and 0.2. Experiment with other values of h, including negative values. What do you see happening as $h \to 0$? Explain this behavior.

T **106. The derivative of cos (x^2)** Graph $y = -2x\sin(x^2)$ for $-2 \le x \le 3$. Then, on the same screen, graph

$$y = \frac{\cos((x + h)^2) - \cos(x^2)}{h}$$

for $h = 1.0, 0.7$, and 0.3. Experiment with other values of h. What do you see happening as $h \to 0$? Explain this behavior.

T The curves in Exercises 107 and 108 are called *Bowditch curves* or *Lissajous figures*. In each case, find the point in the interior of the first quadrant where the tangent to the curve is horizontal, and find the equations of the two tangents at the origin.

107.
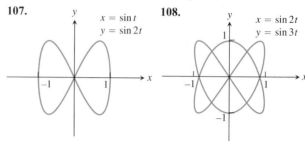
$$x = \sin t$$
$$y = \sin 2t$$

108.
$$x = \sin 2t$$
$$y = \sin 3t$$

Using the Chain Rule, show that the power rule $(d/dx)x^n = nx^{n-1}$ holds for the functions x^n in Exercises 109 and 110.

109. $x^{1/4} = \sqrt{\sqrt{x}}$

110. $x^{3/4} = \sqrt{x\sqrt{x}}$

COMPUTER EXPLORATIONS

Trigonometric Polynomials

111. As Figure 3.34 shows, the trigonometric "polynomial"

$$s = f(t) = 0.78540 - 0.63662\cos 2t - 0.07074\cos 6t$$
$$-0.02546\cos 10t - 0.01299\cos 14t$$

gives a good approximation of the sawtooth function $s = g(t)$ on the interval $[-\pi, \pi]$. How well does the derivative of f approximate the derivative of g at the points where dg/dt is defined? To find out, carry out the following steps.

a. Graph dg/dt (where defined) over $[-\pi, \pi]$.

b. Find df/dt.

c. Graph df/dt. Where does the approximation of dg/dt by df/dt seem to be best? Least good? Approximations by trigonometric polynomials are important in the theories of heat and oscillation, but we must not expect too much of them, as we see in the next exercise.

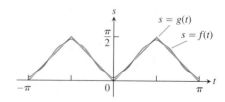

FIGURE 3.34 The approximation of a sawtooth function by a trigonometric "polynomial" (Exercise 111).

112. (*Continuation of Exercise 111.*) In Exercise 111, the trigonometric polynomial $f(t)$ that approximated the sawtooth function $g(t)$ on $[-\pi, \pi]$ had a derivative that approximated the derivative of the sawtooth function. It is possible, however, for a trigonometric polynomial to approximate a function in a reasonable way without its derivative approximating the function's derivative at all well. As a case in point, the "polynomial"

$$s = h(t) = 1.2732 \sin 2t + 0.4244 \sin 6t + 0.25465 \sin 10t$$
$$+ 0.18189 \sin 14t + 0.14147 \sin 18t$$

graphed in Figure 3.35 approximates the step function $s = k(t)$ shown there. Yet the derivative of h is nothing like the derivative of k.

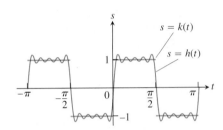

FIGURE 3.35 The approximation of a step function by a trigonometric "polynomial" (Exercise 112).

a. Graph dk/dt (where defined) over $[-\pi, \pi]$.

b. Find dh/dt.

c. Graph dh/dt to see how badly the graph fits the graph of dk/dt. Comment on what you see.

Parametrized Curves

Use a CAS to perform the following steps on the parametrized curves in Exercises 113–116.

a. Plot the curve for the given interval of t values.

b. Find dy/dx and d^2y/dx^2 at the point t_0.

c. Find an equation for the tangent line to the curve at the point defined by the given value t_0. Plot the curve together with the tangent line on a single graph.

113. $x = \dfrac{1}{3}t^3, \quad y = \dfrac{1}{2}t^2, \quad 0 \le t \le 1, \quad t_0 = 1/2$

114. $x = 2t^3 - 16t^2 + 25t + 5, \quad y = t^2 + t - 3, \quad 0 \le t \le 6, \quad t_0 = 3/2$

115. $x = t - \cos t, \quad y = 1 + \sin t, \quad -\pi \le t \le \pi, \quad t_0 = \pi/4$

116. $x = e^t \cos t, \quad y = e^t \sin t, \quad 0 \le t \le \pi, \quad t_0 = \pi/2$

3.6 Implicit Differentiation

Most of the functions we have dealt with so far have been described by an equation of the form $y = f(x)$ that expresses y explicitly in terms of the variable x. We have learned rules for differentiating functions defined in this way. In Section 3.5 we also learned how to find the derivative dy/dx when a curve is defined parametrically by equations $x = x(t)$ and $y = y(t)$. A third situation occurs when we encounter equations like

$$x^2 + y^2 - 25 = 0, \qquad y^2 - x = 0, \qquad \text{or} \quad x^3 + y^3 - 9xy = 0.$$

(See Figures 3.36, 3.37, and 3.38.) These equations define an *implicit* relation between the variables x and y. In some cases we may be able to solve such an equation for y as an explicit function (or even several functions) of x. When we cannot put an equation $F(x, y) = 0$ in the form $y = f(x)$ to differentiate it in the usual way, we may still be able to find dy/dx by *implicit differentiation*. This consists of differentiating both sides of the equation with respect to x and then solving the resulting equation for y'. This section describes the technique and uses it to extend the Power Rule for differentiation to include rational exponents. In the examples and exercises of this section it is always assumed that the given equation determines y implicitly as a differentiable function of x.

FIGURE 3.36 The circle combines the graphs of two functions. The graph of y_2 is the lower semicircle and passes through $(3, -4)$.

Implicitly Defined Functions

We begin with an example.

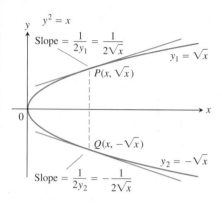

FIGURE 3.37 The equation $y^2 - x = 0$, or $y^2 = x$ as it is usually written, defines two differentiable functions of x on the interval $x \geq 0$. Example 1 shows how to find the derivatives of these functions without solving the equation $y^2 = x$ for y.

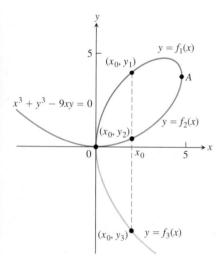

FIGURE 3.38 The curve $x^3 + y^3 - 9xy = 0$ is not the graph of any one function of x. The curve can, however, be divided into separate arcs that *are* the graphs of functions of x. This particular curve, called a *folium*, dates to Descartes in 1638.

EXAMPLE 1   Differentiating Implicitly

Find dy/dx if $y^2 = x$.

Solution   The equation $y^2 = x$ defines two differentiable functions of x that we can actually find, namely $y_1 = \sqrt{x}$ and $y_2 = -\sqrt{x}$ (Figure 3.37). We know how to calculate the derivative of each of these for $x > 0$:

$$\frac{dy_1}{dx} = \frac{1}{2\sqrt{x}} \quad \text{and} \quad \frac{dy_2}{dx} = -\frac{1}{2\sqrt{x}}.$$

But suppose that we knew only that the equation $y^2 = x$ defined y as one or more differentiable functions of x for $x > 0$ without knowing exactly what these functions were. Could we still find dy/dx?

The answer is yes. To find dy/dx, we simply differentiate both sides of the equation $y^2 = x$ with respect to x, treating $y = f(x)$ as a differentiable function of x:

$$y^2 = x$$
$$2y \frac{dy}{dx} = 1 \qquad \text{The Chain Rule gives } \frac{d}{dx}\left(y^2\right) =$$
$$\frac{dy}{dx} = \frac{1}{2y}. \qquad \frac{d}{dx}\left[f(x)\right]^2 = 2f(x)f'(x) = 2y\frac{dy}{dx}.$$

This one formula gives the derivatives we calculated for *both* explicit solutions $y_1 = \sqrt{x}$ and $y_2 = -\sqrt{x}$:

$$\frac{dy_1}{dx} = \frac{1}{2y_1} = \frac{1}{2\sqrt{x}} \quad \text{and} \quad \frac{dy_2}{dx} = \frac{1}{2y_2} = \frac{1}{2\left(-\sqrt{x}\right)} = -\frac{1}{2\sqrt{x}}. \qquad \blacksquare$$

EXAMPLE 2   Slope of a Circle at a Point

Find the slope of circle $x^2 + y^2 = 25$ at the point $(3, -4)$.

Solution   The circle is not the graph of a single function of x. Rather it is the combined graphs of two differentiable functions, $y_1 = \sqrt{25 - x^2}$ and $y_2 = -\sqrt{25 - x^2}$ (Figure 3.36). The point $(3, -4)$ lies on the graph of y_2, so we can find the slope by calculating explicitly:

$$\left.\frac{dy_2}{dx}\right|_{x=3} = -\left.\frac{-2x}{2\sqrt{25 - x^2}}\right|_{x=3} = -\frac{-6}{2\sqrt{25 - 9}} = \frac{3}{4}.$$

But we can also solve the problem more easily by differentiating the given equation of the circle implicitly with respect to x:

$$\frac{d}{dx}\left(x^2\right) + \frac{d}{dx}\left(y^2\right) = \frac{d}{dx}\left(25\right)$$
$$2x + 2y\frac{dy}{dx} = 0$$
$$\frac{dy}{dx} = -\frac{x}{y}.$$

The slope at $(3, -4)$ is $-\left.\frac{x}{y}\right|_{(3, -4)} = -\frac{3}{-4} = \frac{3}{4}.$

Notice that unlike the slope formula for dy_2/dx, which applies only to points below the x-axis, the formula $dy/dx = -x/y$ applies everywhere the circle has a slope. Notice also that the derivative involves *both* variables x and y, not just the independent variable x. ∎

To calculate the derivatives of other implicitly defined functions, we proceed as in Examples 1 and 2: We treat y as a differentiable implicit function of x and apply the usual rules to differentiate both sides of the defining equation.

EXAMPLE 3   Differentiating Implicitly

Find dy/dx if $y^2 = x^2 + \sin xy$ (Figure 3.39).

Solution

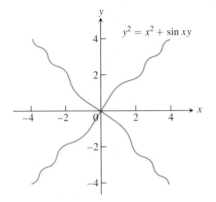

$$y^2 = x^2 + \sin xy$$

$$\frac{d}{dx}\left(y^2\right) = \frac{d}{dx}\left(x^2\right) + \frac{d}{dx}\left(\sin xy\right) \qquad \text{Differentiate both sides with respect to } x \ldots$$

$$2y\frac{dy}{dx} = 2x + (\cos xy)\frac{d}{dx}(xy) \qquad \ldots \text{ treating } y \text{ as a function of } x \text{ and using the Chain Rule.}$$

$$2y\frac{dy}{dx} = 2x + (\cos xy)\left(y + x\frac{dy}{dx}\right) \qquad \text{Treat } xy \text{ as a product.}$$

$$2y\frac{dy}{dx} - (\cos xy)\left(x\frac{dy}{dx}\right) = 2x + (\cos xy)y \qquad \text{Collect terms with } dy/dx \ldots$$

$$(2y - x\cos xy)\frac{dy}{dx} = 2x + y\cos xy \qquad \ldots \text{ and factor out } dy/dx.$$

$$\frac{dy}{dx} = \frac{2x + y\cos xy}{2y - x\cos xy} \qquad \text{Solve for } dy/dx \text{ by dividing.}$$

Notice that the formula for dy/dx applies everywhere that the implicitly defined curve has a slope. Notice again that the derivative involves *both* variables x and y, not just the independent variable x. ∎

FIGURE 3.39 The graph of $y^2 = x^2 + \sin xy$ in Example 3. The example shows how to find slopes on this implicitly defined curve.

Implicit Differentiation

1. Differentiate both sides of the equation with respect to x, treating y as a differentiable function of x.

2. Collect the terms with dy/dx on one side of the equation.

3. Solve for dy/dx.

Lenses, Tangents, and Normal Lines

In the law that describes how light changes direction as it enters a lens, the important angles are the angles the light makes with the line perpendicular to the surface of the lens at the point of entry (angles A and B in Figure 3.40). This line is called the *normal* to the surface at the point of entry. In a profile view of a lens like the one in Figure 3.40, the **normal** is the line perpendicular to the tangent to the profile curve at the point of entry.

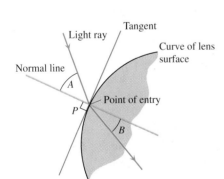

FIGURE 3.40 The profile of a lens, showing the bending (refraction) of a ray of light as it passes through the lens surface.

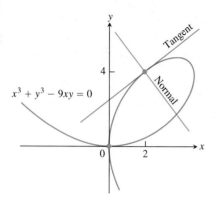

FIGURE 3.41   Example 4 shows how to find equations for the tangent and normal to the folium of Descartes at (2, 4).

EXAMPLE 4   Tangent and Normal to the Folium of Descartes

Show that the point (2, 4) lies on the curve $x^3 + y^3 - 9xy = 0$. Then find the tangent and normal to the curve there (Figure 3.41).

Solution   The point (2, 4) lies on the curve because its coordinates satisfy the equation given for the curve: $2^3 + 4^3 - 9(2)(4) = 8 + 64 - 72 = 0$.

To find the slope of the curve at (2, 4), we first use implicit differentiation to find a formula for dy/dx:

$$x^3 + y^3 - 9xy = 0$$

$$\frac{d}{dx}\left(x^3\right) + \frac{d}{dx}\left(y^3\right) - \frac{d}{dx}\left(9xy\right) = \frac{d}{dx}\left(0\right) \qquad \text{Differentiate both sides with respect to } x.$$

$$3x^2 + 3y^2\frac{dy}{dx} - 9\left(x\frac{dy}{dx} + y\frac{dx}{dx}\right) = 0 \qquad \text{Treat } xy \text{ as a product and } y \text{ as a function of } x.$$

$$(3y^2 - 9x)\frac{dy}{dx} + 3x^2 - 9y = 0$$

$$3(y^2 - 3x)\frac{dy}{dx} = 9y - 3x^2$$

$$\frac{dy}{dx} = \frac{3y - x^2}{y^2 - 3x}. \qquad \text{Solve for } dy/dx.$$

We then evaluate the derivative at $(x, y) = (2, 4)$:

$$\left.\frac{dy}{dx}\right|_{(2,4)} = \left.\frac{3y - x^2}{y^2 - 3x}\right|_{(2,4)} = \frac{3(4) - 2^2}{4^2 - 3(2)} = \frac{8}{10} = \frac{4}{5}.$$

The tangent at (2, 4) is the line through (2, 4) with slope 4/5:

$$y = 4 + \frac{4}{5}(x - 2)$$

$$y = \frac{4}{5}x + \frac{12}{5}.$$

The normal to the curve at (2, 4) is the line perpendicular to the tangent there, the line through (2, 4) with slope $-5/4$:

$$y = 4 - \frac{5}{4}(x - 2)$$

$$y = -\frac{5}{4}x + \frac{13}{2}. \qquad \blacksquare$$

The quadratic formula enables us to solve a second-degree equation like $y^2 - 2xy + 3x^2 = 0$ for y in terms of x. There is a formula for the three roots of a cubic equation that is like the quadratic formula but much more complicated. If this formula is used to solve the equation $x^3 + y^3 = 9xy$ for y in terms of x, then three functions determined by the equation are

$$y = f(x) = \sqrt[3]{-\frac{x^3}{2} + \sqrt{\frac{x^6}{4} - 27x^3}} + \sqrt[3]{-\frac{x^3}{2} - \sqrt{\frac{x^6}{4} - 27x^3}}$$

and

$$y = \frac{1}{2}\left[-f(x) \pm \sqrt{-3}\left(\sqrt[3]{-\frac{x^3}{2} + \sqrt{\frac{x^6}{4} - 27x^3}} - \sqrt[3]{-\frac{x^3}{2} - \sqrt{\frac{x^6}{4} - 27x^3}}\right)\right].$$

Using implicit differentiation in Example 4 was much simpler than calculating dy/dx directly from any of the above formulas. Finding slopes on curves defined by higher-degree equations usually requires implicit differentiation.

Derivatives of Higher Order

Implicit differentiation can also be used to find higher derivatives. Here is an example.

EXAMPLE 5   Finding a Second Derivative Implicitly

Find d^2y/dx^2 if $2x^3 - 3y^2 = 8$.

Solution   To start, we differentiate both sides of the equation with respect to x in order to find $y' = dy/dx$.

$$\frac{d}{dx}\left(2x^3 - 3y^2\right) = \frac{d}{dx}(8)$$

$$6x^2 - 6yy' = 0 \qquad\qquad \text{Treat } y \text{ as a function of } x.$$

$$x^2 - yy' = 0$$

$$y' = \frac{x^2}{y}, \qquad \text{when } y \neq 0 \qquad \text{Solve for } y'.$$

We now apply the Quotient Rule to find y''.

$$y'' = \frac{d}{dx}\left(\frac{x^2}{y}\right) = \frac{2xy - x^2y'}{y^2} = \frac{2x}{y} - \frac{x^2}{y^2}\cdot y'$$

Finally, we substitute $y' = x^2/y$ to express y'' in terms of x and y.

$$y'' = \frac{2x}{y} - \frac{x^2}{y^2}\left(\frac{x^2}{y}\right) = \frac{2x}{y} - \frac{x^4}{y^3}, \qquad \text{when } y \neq 0 \qquad\blacksquare$$

Rational Powers of Differentiable Functions

We know that the rule

$$\frac{d}{dx}x^n = nx^{n-1}$$

holds when n is an integer. Using implicit differentiation we can show that it holds when n is any rational number.

THEOREM 4   Power Rule for Rational Powers

If p/q is a rational number, then $x^{p/q}$ is differentiable at every interior point of the domain of $x^{(p/q)-1}$, and

$$\frac{d}{dx}x^{p/q} = \frac{p}{q}x^{(p/q)-1}.$$

EXAMPLE 6   Using the Rational Power Rule

(a) $\dfrac{d}{dx}\left(x^{1/2}\right) = \dfrac{1}{2}x^{-1/2} = \dfrac{1}{2\sqrt{x}}$ for $x > 0$

(b) $\dfrac{d}{dx}\left(x^{2/3}\right) = \dfrac{2}{3}x^{-1/3}$ for $x \neq 0$

(c) $\dfrac{d}{dx}\left(x^{-4/3}\right) = -\dfrac{4}{3}x^{-7/3}$ for $x \neq 0$ ∎

Proof of Theorem 4   Let p and q be integers with $q > 0$ and suppose that $y = \sqrt[q]{x^p} = x^{p/q}$. Then

$$y^q = x^p.$$

Since p and q are integers (for which we already have the Power Rule), and assuming that y is a differentiable function of x, we can differentiate both sides of the equation with respect to x and get

$$qy^{q-1}\frac{dy}{dx} = px^{p-1}.$$

If $y \neq 0$, we can divide both sides of the equation by qy^{q-1} to solve for dy/dx, obtaining

$$\frac{dy}{dx} = \frac{px^{p-1}}{qy^{q-1}}$$

$$= \frac{p}{q} \cdot \frac{x^{p-1}}{(x^{p/q})^{q-1}} \qquad\qquad y = x^{p/q}$$

$$= \frac{p}{q} \cdot \frac{x^{p-1}}{x^{p-p/q}} \qquad\qquad \frac{p}{q}(q-1) = p - \frac{p}{q}$$

$$= \frac{p}{q} \cdot x^{(p-1)-(p-p/q)} \qquad\qquad \text{A law of exponents}$$

$$= \frac{p}{q} \cdot x^{(p/q)-1},$$

which proves the rule.   ∎

We will drop the assumption of differentiability used in the proof of Theorem 4 in Chapter 7, where we prove the Power Rule for any nonzero real exponent. (See Section 7.3.)

By combining the result of Theorem 4 with the Chain Rule, we get an extension of the Power Chain Rule to rational powers of u: If p/q is a rational number and u is a differentiable function of x, then $u^{p/q}$ is a differentiable function of x and

$$\frac{d}{dx}u^{p/q} = \frac{p}{q}u^{(p/q)-1}\frac{du}{dx},$$

provided that $u \neq 0$ if $(p/q) < 1$. This restriction is necessary because 0 might be in the domain of $u^{p/q}$ but not in the domain of $u^{(p/q)-1}$, as we see in the next example.

EXAMPLE 7 Using the Rational Power and Chain Rules

(a) $\overbrace{\dfrac{d}{dx}\left(1 - x^2\right)^{1/4}}^{\text{function defined on }[-1, 1]} = \dfrac{1}{4}\left(1 - x^2\right)^{-3/4}(-2x)$ Power Chain Rule with $u = 1 - x^2$

$$= \underbrace{\dfrac{-x}{2\left(1 - x^2\right)^{3/4}}}_{\text{derivative defined only on }(-1, 1)}$$

(b) $\dfrac{d}{dx}(\cos x)^{-1/5} = -\dfrac{1}{5}(\cos x)^{-6/5}\dfrac{d}{dx}(\cos x)$

$$= -\dfrac{1}{5}(\cos x)^{-6/5}(-\sin x)$$

$$= \dfrac{1}{5}(\sin x)(\cos x)^{-6/5}$$ ∎

EXERCISES 3.6

Derivatives of Rational Powers

Find dy/dx in Exercises 1-10.

1. $y = x^{9/4}$ **2.** $y = x^{-3/5}$

3. $y = \sqrt[3]{2x}$ **4.** $y = \sqrt[4]{5x}$

5. $y = 7\sqrt{x + 6}$ **6.** $y = -2\sqrt{x - 1}$

7. $y = (2x + 5)^{-1/2}$ **8.** $y = (1 - 6x)^{2/3}$

9. $y = x(x^2 + 1)^{1/2}$ **10.** $y = x(x^2 + 1)^{-1/2}$

Find the first derivatives of the functions in Exercises 11-18.

11. $s = \sqrt{t^2}$ **12.** $r = \sqrt[4]{\theta^{-3}}$

13. $y = \sin[(2t + 5)^{-2/3}]$ **14.** $z = \cos[(1 - 6t)^{2/3}]$

15. $f(x) = \sqrt{1 - \sqrt{x}}$ **16.** $g(x) = 2(2x^{-1/2} + 1)^{-1/3}$

17. $h(\theta) = \sqrt[3]{1 + \cos(2\theta)}$ **18.** $k(\theta) = (\sin(\theta + 5))^{5/4}$

Differentiating Implicitly

Use implicit differentiation to find dy/dx in Exercises 19-32.

19. $x^2y + xy^2 = 6$ **20.** $x^3 + y^3 = 18xy$

21. $2xy + y^2 = x + y$ **22.** $x^3 - xy + y^3 = 1$

23. $x^2(x - y)^2 = x^2 - y^2$ **24.** $(3xy + 7)^2 = 6y$

25. $y^2 = \dfrac{x - 1}{x + 1}$ **26.** $x^2 = \dfrac{x - y}{x + y}$

27. $x = \tan y$ **28.** $xy = \cot(xy)$

29. $x + \tan(xy) = 0$ **30.** $x + \sin y = xy$

31. $y \sin\left(\dfrac{1}{y}\right) = 1 - xy$ **32.** $y^2 \cos\left(\dfrac{1}{y}\right) = 2x + 2y$

Find $dr/d\theta$ in Exercises 33-36.

33. $\theta^{1/2} + r^{1/2} = 1$ **34.** $r - 2\sqrt{\theta} = \dfrac{3}{2}\theta^{2/3} + \dfrac{4}{3}\theta^{3/4}$

35. $\sin(r\theta) = \dfrac{1}{2}$ **36.** $\cos r + \cot \theta = r\theta$

Second Derivatives

In Exercises 37-42, use implicit differentiation to find dy/dx and then d^2y/dx^2.

37. $x^2 + y^2 = 1$ **38.** $x^{2/3} + y^{2/3} = 1$

39. $y^2 = x^2 + 2x$ **40.** $y^2 - 2x = 1 - 2y$

41. $2\sqrt{y} = x - y$ **42.** $xy + y^2 = 1$

43. If $x^3 + y^3 = 16$, find the value of d^2y/dx^2 at the point $(2, 2)$.

44. If $xy + y^2 = 1$, find the value of d^2y/dx^2 at the point $(0, -1)$.

Slopes, Tangents, and Normals

In Exercises 45 and 46, find the slope of the curve at the given points.

45. $y^2 + x^2 = y^4 - 2x$ at $(-2, 1)$ and $(-2, -1)$

46. $(x^2 + y^2)^2 = (x - y)^2$ at $(1, 0)$ and $(1, -1)$

In Exercises 47-56, verify that the given point is on the curve and find the lines that are **(a)** tangent and **(b)** normal to the curve at the given point.

47. $x^2 + xy - y^2 = 1$, $(2, 3)$

48. $x^2 + y^2 = 25$, $(3, -4)$

49. $x^2y^2 = 9$, $(-1, 3)$

50. $y^2 - 2x - 4y - 1 = 0$, $(-2, 1)$

51. $6x^2 + 3xy + 2y^2 + 17y - 6 = 0$, $(-1, 0)$

52. $x^2 - \sqrt{3}xy + 2y^2 = 5$, $(\sqrt{3}, 2)$

53. $2xy + \pi \sin y = 2\pi$, $(1, \pi/2)$

54. $x \sin 2y = y \cos 2x$, $(\pi/4, \pi/2)$

55. $y = 2 \sin(\pi x - y)$, $(1, 0)$

56. $x^2 \cos^2 y - \sin y = 0$, $(0, \pi)$

57. Parallel tangents Find the two points where the curve $x^2 + xy + y^2 = 7$ crosses the x-axis, and show that the tangents to the curve at these points are parallel. What is the common slope of these tangents?

58. Tangents parallel to the coordinate axes Find points on the curve $x^2 + xy + y^2 = 7$ **(a)** where the tangent is parallel to the x-axis and **(b)** where the tangent is parallel to the y-axis. In the latter case, dy/dx is not defined, but dx/dy is. What value does dx/dy have at these points?

59. The eight curve Find the slopes of the curve $y^4 = y^2 - x^2$ at the two points shown here.

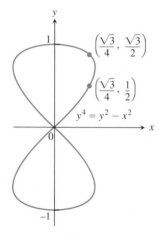

60. The cissoid of Diocles (from about 200 B.C.) Find equations for the tangent and normal to the cissoid of Diocles $y^2(2 - x) = x^3$ at $(1, 1)$.

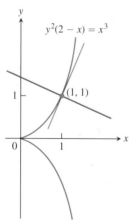

61. The devil's curve (Gabriel Cramer [the Cramer of Cramer's rule], 1750) Find the slopes of the devil's curve $y^4 - 4y^2 = x^4 - 9x^2$ at the four indicated points.

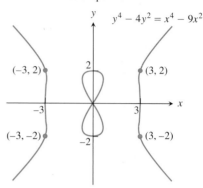

62. The folium of Descartes (See Figure 3.38)

a. Find the slope of the folium of Descartes, $x^3 + y^3 - 9xy = 0$ at the points $(4, 2)$ and $(2, 4)$.

b. At what point other than the origin does the folium have a horizontal tangent?

c. Find the coordinates of the point A in Figure 3.38, where the folium has a vertical tangent.

Implicitly Defined Parametrizations

Assuming that the equations in Exercises 63–66 define x and y implicitly as differentiable functions $x = f(t), y = g(t)$, find the slope of the curve $x = f(t), y = g(t)$ at the given value of t.

63. $x^2 - 2tx + 2t^2 = 4$, $2y^3 - 3t^2 = 4$, $t = 2$

64. $x = \sqrt{5 - \sqrt{t}}$, $y(t - 1) = \sqrt{t}$, $t = 4$

65. $x + 2x^{3/2} = t^2 + t$, $y\sqrt{t + 1} + 2t\sqrt{y} = 4$, $t = 0$

66. $x \sin t + 2x = t$, $t \sin t - 2t = y$, $t = \pi$

Theory and Examples

67. Which of the following could be true if $f''(x) = x^{-1/3}$?

a. $f(x) = \dfrac{3}{2}x^{2/3} - 3$ **b.** $f(x) = \dfrac{9}{10}x^{5/3} - 7$

c. $f'''(x) = -\dfrac{1}{3}x^{-4/3}$ **d.** $f'(x) = \dfrac{3}{2}x^{2/3} + 6$

68. Is there anything special about the tangents to the curves $y^2 = x^3$ and $2x^2 + 3y^2 = 5$ at the points $(1, \pm1)$? Give reasons for your answer.

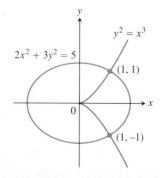

69. **Intersecting normal** The line that is normal to the curve $x^2 + 2xy - 3y^2 = 0$ at $(1, 1)$ intersects the curve at what other point?

70. **Normals parallel to a line** Find the normals to the curve $xy + 2x - y = 0$ that are parallel to the line $2x + y = 0$.

71. **Normals to a parabola** Show that if it is possible to draw three normals from the point $(a, 0)$ to the parabola $x = y^2$ shown here, then a must be greater than $1/2$. One of the normals is the x-axis. For what value of a are the other two normals perpendicular?

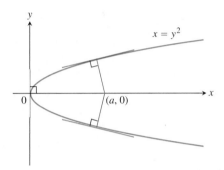

72. What is the geometry behind the restrictions on the domains of the derivatives in Example 6(b) and Example 7(a)?

T In Exercises 73 and 74, find both dy/dx (treating y as a differentiable function of x) and dx/dy (treating x as a differentiable function of y). How do dy/dx and dx/dy seem to be related? Explain the relationship geometrically in terms of the graphs.

73. $xy^3 + x^2y = 6$ 74. $x^3 + y^2 = \sin^2 y$

COMPUTER EXPLORATIONS

75. **a.** Given that $x^4 + 4y^2 = 1$, find dy/dx two ways: (1) by solving for y and differentiating the resulting functions in the usual way and (2) by implicit differentiation. Do you get the same result each way?

    b. Solve the equation $x^4 + 4y^2 = 1$ for y and graph the resulting functions together to produce a complete graph of the equation $x^4 + 4y^2 = 1$. Then add the graphs of the first derivatives of these functions to your display. Could you have

predicted the general behavior of the derivative graphs from looking at the graph of $x^4 + 4y^2 = 1$? Could you have predicted the general behavior of the graph of $x^4 + 4y^2 = 1$ by looking at the derivative graphs? Give reasons for your answers.

76. **a.** Given that $(x - 2)^2 + y^2 = 4$ find dy/dx two ways: (1) by solving for y and differentiating the resulting functions with respect to x and (2) by implicit differentiation. Do you get the same result each way?

    b. Solve the equation $(x - 2)^2 + y^2 = 4$ for y and graph the resulting functions together to produce a complete graph of the equation $(x - 2)^2 + y^2 = 4$. Then add the graphs of the functions' first derivatives to your picture. Could you have predicted the general behavior of the derivative graphs from looking at the graph of $(x - 2)^2 + y^2 = 4$? Could you have predicted the general behavior of the graph of $(x - 2)^2 + y^2 = 4$ by looking at the derivative graphs? Give reasons for your answers.

Use a CAS to perform the following steps in Exercises 77–84.

    a. Plot the equation with the implicit plotter of a CAS. Check to see that the given point P satisfies the equation.

    b. Using implicit differentiation, find a formula for the derivative dy/dx and evaluate it at the given point P.

    c. Use the slope found in part (b) to find an equation for the tangent line to the curve at P. Then plot the implicit curve and tangent line together on a single graph.

77. $x^3 - xy + y^3 = 7$, $P(2, 1)$

78. $x^5 + y^3x + yx^2 + y^4 = 4$, $P(1, 1)$

79. $y^2 + y = \dfrac{2 + x}{1 - x}$, $P(0, 1)$

80. $y^3 + \cos xy = x^2$, $P(1, 0)$

81. $x + \tan\left(\dfrac{y}{x}\right) = 2$, $P\left(1, \dfrac{\pi}{4}\right)$

82. $xy^3 + \tan(x + y) = 1$, $P\left(\dfrac{\pi}{4}, 0\right)$

83. $2y^2 + (xy)^{1/3} = x^2 + 2$, $P(1, 1)$

84. $x\sqrt{1 + 2y} + y = x^2$, $P(1, 0)$

3.7 Related Rates

In this section we look at problems that ask for the rate at which some variable changes. In each case the rate is a derivative that has to be computed from the rate at which some other variable (or perhaps several variables) is known to change. To find it, we write an equation that relates the variables involved and differentiate it to get an equation that relates the rate we seek to the rates we know. The problem of finding a rate you cannot measure easily from some other rates that you can is called a *related rates problem*.

Related Rates Equations

Suppose we are pumping air into a spherical balloon. Both the volume and radius of the balloon are increasing over time. If V is the volume and r is the radius of the balloon at an instant of time, then

$$V = \frac{4}{3}\pi r^3.$$

Using the Chain Rule, we differentiate to find the related rates equation

$$\frac{dV}{dt} = \frac{dV}{dr}\frac{dr}{dt} = 4\pi r^2 \frac{dr}{dt}.$$

So if we know the radius r of the balloon and the rate dV/dt at which the volume is increasing at a given instant of time, then we can solve this last equation for dr/dt to find how fast the radius is increasing at that instant. Note that it is easier to measure directly the rate of increase of the volume than it is to measure the increase in the radius. The related rates equation allows us to calculate dr/dt from dV/dt.

Very often the key to relating the variables in a related rates problem is drawing a picture that shows the geometric relations between them, as illustrated in the following example.

EXAMPLE 1   Pumping Out a Tank

How rapidly will the fluid level inside a vertical cylindrical tank drop if we pump the fluid out at the rate of 3000 L/min?

Solution   We draw a picture of a partially filled vertical cylindrical tank, calling its radius r and the height of the fluid h (Figure 3.42). Call the volume of the fluid V.

As time passes, the radius remains constant, but V and h change. We think of V and h as differentiable functions of time and use t to represent time. We are told that

$$\frac{dV}{dt} = -3000.$$

We pump out at the rate of 3000 L/min. The rate is negative because the volume is decreasing.

We are asked to find

$$\frac{dh}{dt}.$$

How fast will the fluid level drop?

To find dh/dt, we first write an equation that relates h to V. The equation depends on the units chosen for V, r, and h. With V in liters and r and h in meters, the appropriate equation for the cylinder's volume is

$$V = 1000\pi r^2 h$$

because a cubic meter contains 1000 L.

Since V and h are differentiable functions of t, we can differentiate both sides of the equation $V = 1000\pi r^2 h$ with respect to t to get an equation that relates dh/dt to dV/dt:

$$\frac{dV}{dt} = 1000\pi r^2 \frac{dh}{dt}.$$ r is a constant.

We substitute the known value $dV/dt = -3000$ and solve for dh/dt:

$$\frac{dh}{dt} = \frac{-3000}{1000\pi r^2} = -\frac{3}{\pi r^2}.$$

$$\frac{dh}{dt} = \,?$$

$$\frac{dV}{dt} = -3000 \text{ L/min}$$

FIGURE 3.42   The rate of change of fluid volume in a cylindrical tank is related to the rate of change of fluid level in the tank (Example 1).

The fluid level will drop at the rate of $3/(\pi r^2)$ m/min.

The equation $dh/dt = -3/\pi r^2$ shows how the rate at which the fluid level drops depends on the tank's radius. If r is small, dh/dt will be large; if r is large, dh/dt will be small.

$$\text{If } r = 1 \text{ m:} \qquad \frac{dh}{dt} = -\frac{3}{\pi} \approx -0.95 \text{ m/min} = -95 \text{ cm/min}.$$

$$\text{If } r = 10 \text{ m:} \qquad \frac{dh}{dt} = -\frac{3}{100\pi} \approx -0.0095 \text{ m/min} = -0.95 \text{ cm/min.} \qquad \blacksquare$$

Related Rates Problem Strategy

1. *Draw a picture and name the variables and constants.* Use t for time. Assume that all variables are differentiable functions of t.

2. *Write down the numerical information* (in terms of the symbols you have chosen).

3. *Write down what you are asked to find* (usually a rate, expressed as a derivative).

4. *Write an equation that relates the variables.* You may have to combine two or more equations to get a single equation that relates the variable whose rate you want to the variables whose rates you know.

5. *Differentiate with respect to t.* Then express the rate you want in terms of the rate and variables whose values you know.

6. *Evaluate.* Use known values to find the unknown rate.

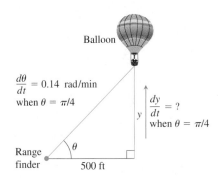

$\frac{d\theta}{dt} = 0.14$ rad/min
when $\theta = \pi/4$

y $\quad \frac{dy}{dt} = ?$
when $\theta = \pi/4$

Range finder

θ

500 ft

Balloon

FIGURE 3.43 The rate of change of the balloon's height is related to the rate of change of the angle the range finder makes with the ground (Example 2).

EXAMPLE 2   A Rising Balloon

A hot air balloon rising straight up from a level field is tracked by a range finder 500 ft from the liftoff point. At the moment the range finder's elevation angle is $\pi/4$, the angle is increasing at the rate of 0.14 rad/min. How fast is the balloon rising at that moment?

Solution   We answer the question in six steps.

1. *Draw a picture and name the variables and constants* (Figure 3.43). The variables in the picture are

   $\theta = $ the angle in radians the range finder makes with the ground.

   $y = $ the height in feet of the balloon.

   We let t represent time in minutes and assume that θ and y are differentiable functions of t.

   The one constant in the picture is the distance from the range finder to the liftoff point (500 ft). There is no need to give it a special symbol.

2. *Write down the additional numerical information.*

   $$\frac{d\theta}{dt} = 0.14 \text{ rad/min} \qquad \text{when} \qquad \theta = \frac{\pi}{4}$$

3. *Write down what we are to find.* We want dy/dt when $\theta = \pi/4$.

4. *Write an equation that relates the variables y and θ.*

$$\frac{y}{500} = \tan\theta \qquad \text{or} \qquad y = 500\tan\theta$$

5. *Differentiate with respect to t using the Chain Rule.* The result tells how dy/dt (which we want) is related to $d\theta/dt$ (which we know).

$$\frac{dy}{dt} = 500\,(\sec^2\theta)\,\frac{d\theta}{dt}$$

6. *Evaluate with* $\theta = \pi/4$ *and* $d\theta/dt = 0.14$ *to find* dy/dt.

$$\frac{dy}{dt} = 500\big(\sqrt{2}\big)^2(0.14) = 140 \qquad \sec\frac{\pi}{4} = \sqrt{2}$$

At the moment in question, the balloon is rising at the rate of 140 ft/min. ∎

EXAMPLE 3   A Highway Chase

A police cruiser, approaching a right-angled intersection from the north, is chasing a speeding car that has turned the corner and is now moving straight east. When the cruiser is 0.6 mi north of the intersection and the car is 0.8 mi to the east, the police determine with radar that the distance between them and the car is increasing at 20 mph. If the cruiser is moving at 60 mph at the instant of measurement, what is the speed of the car?

Solution   We picture the car and cruiser in the coordinate plane, using the positive x-axis as the eastbound highway and the positive y-axis as the southbound highway (Figure 3.44). We let t represent time and set

$$x = \text{position of car at time } t$$
$$y = \text{position of cruiser at time } t$$
$$s = \text{distance between car and cruiser at time } t.$$

We assume that x, y, and s are differentiable functions of t.
    We want to find dx/dt when

$$x = 0.8\text{ mi}, \qquad y = 0.6\text{ mi}, \qquad \frac{dy}{dt} = -60\text{ mph}, \qquad \frac{ds}{dt} = 20\text{ mph}.$$

Note that dy/dt is negative because y is decreasing.
    We differentiate the distance equation

$$s^2 = x^2 + y^2$$

(we could also use $s = \sqrt{x^2 + y^2}$), and obtain

$$2s\,\frac{ds}{dt} = 2x\frac{dx}{dt} + 2y\frac{dy}{dt}$$

$$\frac{ds}{dt} = \frac{1}{s}\left(x\frac{dx}{dt} + y\frac{dy}{dt} \right)$$

$$= \frac{1}{\sqrt{x^2 + y^2}}\left(x\frac{dx}{dt} + y\frac{dy}{dt} \right).$$

FIGURE 3.44   The speed of the car is related to the speed of the police cruiser and the rate of change of the distance between them (Example 3).

Finally, use $x = 0.8$, $y = 0.6$, $dy/dt = -60$, $ds/dt = 20$, and solve for dx/dt.

$$20 = \frac{1}{\sqrt{(0.8)^2 + (0.6)^2}}\left(0.8\frac{dx}{dt} + (0.6)(-60)\right)$$

$$\frac{dx}{dt} = \frac{20\sqrt{(0.8)^2 + (0.6)^2} + (0.6)(60)}{0.8} = 70$$

At the moment in question, the car's speed is 70 mph. ∎

EXAMPLE 4 Filling a Conical Tank

Water runs into a conical tank at the rate of 9 ft^3/min. The tank stands point down and has a height of 10 ft and a base radius of 5 ft. How fast is the water level rising when the water is 6 ft deep?

$\frac{dV}{dt} = 9\ \text{ft}^3/\text{min}$

5 ft

x

10 ft

$\frac{dy}{dt} = ?$
when $y = 6$ ft

y

FIGURE 3.45 The geometry of the conical tank and the rate at which water fills the tank determine how fast the water level rises (Example 4).

Solution Figure 3.45 shows a partially filled conical tank. The variables in the problem are

$V = $ volume (ft^3) of the water in the tank at time t (min)

$x = $ radius (ft) of the surface of the water at time t

$y = $ depth (ft) of water in tank at time t.

We assume that V, x, and y are differentiable functions of t. The constants are the dimensions of the tank. We are asked for dy/dt when

$$y = 6\ \text{ft} \qquad \text{and} \qquad \frac{dV}{dt} = 9\ \text{ft}^3/\text{min}.$$

The water forms a cone with volume

$$V = \frac{1}{3}\pi x^2 y.$$

This equation involves x as well as V and y. Because no information is given about x and dx/dt at the time in question, we need to eliminate x. The similar triangles in Figure 3.45 give us a way to express x in terms of y:

$$\frac{x}{y} = \frac{5}{10} \qquad \text{or} \qquad x = \frac{y}{2}.$$

Therefore,

$$V = \frac{1}{3}\pi\left(\frac{y}{2}\right)^2 y = \frac{\pi}{12}y^3$$

to give the derivative

$$\frac{dV}{dt} = \frac{\pi}{12}\cdot 3y^2\frac{dy}{dt} = \frac{\pi}{4}y^2\frac{dy}{dt}.$$

Finally, use $y = 6$ and $dV/dt = 9$ to solve for dy/dt.

$$9 = \frac{\pi}{4}(6)^2\frac{dy}{dt}$$

$$\frac{dy}{dt} = \frac{1}{\pi} \approx 0.32$$

At the moment in question, the water level is rising at about 0.32 ft/min. ∎

EXERCISES 3.7

1. **Area**   Suppose that the radius r and area $A = \pi r^2$ of a circle are differentiable functions of t. Write an equation that relates dA/dt to dr/dt.

2. **Surface area**   Suppose that the radius r and surface area $S = 4\pi r^2$ of a sphere are differentiable functions of t. Write an equation that relates dS/dt to dr/dt.

3. **Volume**   The radius r and height h of a right circular cylinder are related to the cylinder's volume V by the formula $V = \pi r^2 h$.

   a. How is dV/dt related to dh/dt if r is constant?

   b. How is dV/dt related to dr/dt if h is constant?

   c. How is dV/dt related to dr/dt and dh/dt if neither r nor h is constant?

4. **Volume**   The radius r and height h of a right circular cone are related to the cone's volume V by the equation $V = (1/3)\pi r^2 h$.

   a. How is dV/dt related to dh/dt if r is constant?

   b. How is dV/dt related to dr/dt if h is constant?

   c. How is dV/dt related to dr/dt and dh/dt if neither r nor h is constant?

5. **Changing voltage**   The voltage V (volts), current I (amperes), and resistance R (ohms) of an electric circuit like the one shown here are related by the equation $V = IR$. Suppose that V is increasing at the rate of 1 volt/sec while I is decreasing at the rate of 1/3 amp/sec. Let t denote time in seconds.

   a. What is the value of dV/dt?

   b. What is the value of dI/dt?

   c. What equation relates dR/dt to dV/dt and dI/dt?

   d. Find the rate at which R is changing when $V = 12$ volts and $I = 2$ amp. Is R increasing, or decreasing?

6. **Electrical power**   The power P (watts) of an electric circuit is related to the circuit's resistance R (ohms) and current I (amperes) by the equation $P = RI^2$.

   a. How are dP/dt, dR/dt, and dI/dt related if none of P, R, and I are constant?

   b. How is dR/dt related to dI/dt if P is constant?

7. **Distance**   Let x and y be differentiable functions of t and let $s = \sqrt{x^2 + y^2}$ be the distance between the points $(x, 0)$ and $(0, y)$ in the xy-plane.

   a. How is ds/dt related to dx/dt if y is constant?

   b. How is ds/dt related to dx/dt and dy/dt if neither x nor y is constant?

   c. How is dx/dt related to dy/dt if s is constant?

8. **Diagonals**   If x, y, and z are lengths of the edges of a rectangular box, the common length of the box's diagonals is $s = \sqrt{x^2 + y^2 + z^2}$.

   a. Assuming that x, y, and z are differentiable functions of t, how is ds/dt related to dx/dt, dy/dt, and dz/dt?

   b. How is ds/dt related to dy/dt and dz/dt if x is constant?

   c. How are dx/dt, dy/dt, and dz/dt related if s is constant?

9. **Area**   The area A of a triangle with sides of lengths a and b enclosing an angle of measure θ is

$$A = \frac{1}{2} ab \sin \theta.$$

   a. How is dA/dt related to $d\theta/dt$ if a and b are constant?

   b. How is dA/dt related to $d\theta/dt$ and da/dt if only b is constant?

   c. How is dA/dt related to $d\theta/dt$, da/dt, and db/dt if none of a, b, and θ are constant?

10. **Heating a plate**   When a circular plate of metal is heated in an oven, its radius increases at the rate of 0.01 cm/min. At what rate is the plate's area increasing when the radius is 50 cm?

11. **Changing dimensions in a rectangle**   The length l of a rectangle is decreasing at the rate of 2 cm/sec while the width w is increasing at the rate of 2 cm/sec. When $l = 12$ cm and $w = 5$ cm, find the rates of change of (a) the area, (b) the perimeter, and (c) the lengths of the diagonals of the rectangle. Which of these quantities are decreasing, and which are increasing?

12. **Changing dimensions in a rectangular box**   Suppose that the edge lengths x, y, and z of a closed rectangular box are changing at the following rates:

$$\frac{dx}{dt} = 1 \text{ m/sec}, \quad \frac{dy}{dt} = -2 \text{ m/sec}, \quad \frac{dz}{dt} = 1 \text{ m/sec}.$$

   Find the rates at which the box's (a) volume, (b) surface area, and (c) diagonal length $s = \sqrt{x^2 + y^2 + z^2}$ are changing at the instant when $x = 4$, $y = 3$, and $z = 2$.

13. **A sliding ladder**   A 13-ft ladder is leaning against a house when its base starts to slide away. By the time the base is 12 ft from the house, the base is moving at the rate of 5 ft/sec.

   a. How fast is the top of the ladder sliding down the wall then?

   b. At what rate is the area of the triangle formed by the ladder, wall, and ground changing then?

   c. At what rate is the angle θ between the ladder and the ground changing then?

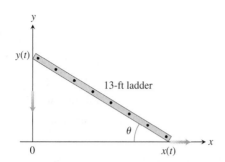

y(t)

13-ft ladder

θ

0   x(t)

14. **Commercial air traffic**   Two commercial airplanes are flying at 40,000 ft along straight-line courses that intersect at right angles. Plane A is approaching the intersection point at a speed of 442 knots (nautical miles per hour; a nautical mile is 2000 yd). Plane B is approaching the intersection at 481 knots. At what rate is the distance between the planes changing when A is 5 nautical miles from the intersection point and B is 12 nautical miles from the intersection point?

15. **Flying a kite**   A girl flies a kite at a height of 300 ft, the wind carrying the kite horizontally away from her at a rate of 25 ft/sec. How fast must she let out the string when the kite is 500 ft away from her?

16. **Boring a cylinder**   The mechanics at Lincoln Automotive are reboring a 6-in.-deep cylinder to fit a new piston. The machine they are using increases the cylinder's radius one-thousandth of an inch every 3 min. How rapidly is the cylinder volume increasing when the bore (diameter) is 3.800 in.?

17. **A growing sand pile**   Sand falls from a conveyor belt at the rate of 10 m³/min onto the top of a conical pile. The height of the pile is always three-eighths of the base diameter. How fast are the **(a)** height and **(b)** radius changing when the pile is 4 m high? Answer in centimeters per minute.

18. **A draining conical reservoir**   Water is flowing at the rate of 50 m³/min from a shallow concrete conical reservoir (vertex down) of base radius 45 m and height 6 m.

   a. How fast (centimeters per minute) is the water level falling when the water is 5 m deep?

   b. How fast is the radius of the water's surface changing then? Answer in centimeters per minute.

19. **A draining hemispherical reservoir**   Water is flowing at the rate of 6 m³/min from a reservoir shaped like a hemispherical bowl of radius 13 m, shown here in profile. Answer the following questions, given that the volume of water in a hemispherical bowl of radius R is $V = (\pi/3)y^2(3R - y)$ when the water is y meters deep.

Center of sphere

Water level

13

r

y

a. At what rate is the water level changing when the water is 8 m deep?

b. What is the radius r of the water's surface when the water is y m deep?

c. At what rate is the radius r changing when the water is 8 m deep?

20. **A growing raindrop**   Suppose that a drop of mist is a perfect sphere and that, through condensation, the drop picks up moisture at a rate proportional to its surface area. Show that under these circumstances the drop's radius increases at a constant rate.

21. **The radius of an inflating balloon**   A spherical balloon is inflated with helium at the rate of 100π ft³/min. How fast is the balloon's radius increasing at the instant the radius is 5 ft? How fast is the surface area increasing?

22. **Hauling in a dinghy**   A dinghy is pulled toward a dock by a rope from the bow through a ring on the dock 6 ft above the bow. The rope is hauled in at the rate of 2 ft/sec.

   a. How fast is the boat approaching the dock when 10 ft of rope are out?

   b. At what rate is the angle θ changing then (see the figure)?

Ring at edge of dock

θ

6'

23. **A balloon and a bicycle**   A balloon is rising vertically above a level, straight road at a constant rate of 1 ft/sec. Just when the balloon is 65 ft above the ground, a bicycle moving at a constant rate of 17 ft/sec passes under it. How fast is the distance $s(t)$ between the bicycle and balloon increasing 3 sec later?

y

y(t)

s(t)

0   x(t)   x

24. Making coffee Coffee is draining from a conical filter into a cylindrical coffeepot at the rate of $10 \text{ in}^3/\text{min}$.

a. How fast is the level in the pot rising when the coffee in the cone is 5 in. deep?

b. How fast is the level in the cone falling then?

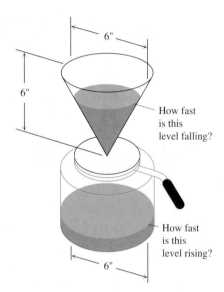

How fast is this level falling?

How fast is this level rising?

25. Cardiac output In the late 1860s, Adolf Fick, a professor of physiology in the Faculty of Medicine in Würzberg, Germany, developed one of the methods we use today for measuring how much blood your heart pumps in a minute. Your cardiac output as you read this sentence is probably about 7 L/min. At rest it is likely to be a bit under 6 L/min. If you are a trained marathon runner running a marathon, your cardiac output can be as high as 30 L/min.

Your cardiac output can be calculated with the formula

$$y = \frac{Q}{D},$$

where Q is the number of milliliters of CO_2 you exhale in a minute and D is the difference between the CO_2 concentration (ml/L) in the blood pumped to the lungs and the CO_2 concentration in the blood returning from the lungs. With $Q = 233 \text{ ml/min}$ and $D = 97 - 56 = 41 \text{ ml/L}$,

$$y = \frac{233 \text{ ml/min}}{41 \text{ ml/L}} \approx 5.68 \text{ L/min},$$

fairly close to the 6 L/min that most people have at basal (resting) conditions. (Data courtesy of J. Kenneth Herd, M.D., Quillan College of Medicine, East Tennessee State University.)

Suppose that when $Q = 233$ and $D = 41$, we also know that D is decreasing at the rate of 2 units a minute but that Q remains unchanged. What is happening to the cardiac output?

26. Cost, revenue, and profit A company can manufacture x items at a cost of $c(x)$ thousand dollars, a sales revenue of $r(x)$ thousand dollars, and a profit of $p(x) = r(x) - c(x)$ thousand dollars. Find dc/dt, dr/dt, and dp/dt for the following values of x and dx/dt.

a. $r(x) = 9x$, $c(x) = x^3 - 6x^2 + 15x$, and $dx/dt = 0.1$ when $x = 2$

b. $r(x) = 70x$, $c(x) = x^3 - 6x^2 + 45/x$, and $dx/dt = 0.05$ when $x = 1.5$

27. Moving along a parabola A particle moves along the parabola $y = x^2$ in the first quadrant in such a way that its x-coordinate (measured in meters) increases at a steady 10 m/sec. How fast is the angle of inclination θ of the line joining the particle to the origin changing when $x = 3$ m?

28. Moving along another parabola A particle moves from right to left along the parabolic curve $y = \sqrt{-x}$ in such a way that its x-coordinate (measured in meters) decreases at the rate of 8 m/sec. How fast is the angle of inclination θ of the line joining the particle to the origin changing when $x = -4$?

29. Motion in the plane The coordinates of a particle in the metric xy-plane are differentiable functions of time t with $dx/dt = -1$ m/sec and $dy/dt = -5$ m/sec. How fast is the particle's distance from the origin changing as it passes through the point $(5, 12)$?

30. A moving shadow A man 6 ft tall walks at the rate of 5 ft/sec toward a streetlight that is 16 ft above the ground. At what rate is the tip of his shadow moving? At what rate is the length of his shadow changing when he is 10 ft from the base of the light?

31. Another moving shadow A light shines from the top of a pole 50 ft high. A ball is dropped from the same height from a point 30 ft away from the light. (See accompanying figure.) How fast is the shadow of the ball moving along the ground 1/2 sec later? (Assume the ball falls a distance $s = 16t^2$ ft in t sec.)

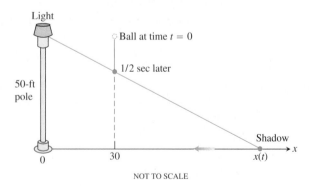

Light

Ball at time $t = 0$

1/2 sec later

50-ft pole

Shadow

x

$x(t)$

0   30

NOT TO SCALE

32. Videotaping a moving car You are videotaping a race from a stand 132 ft from the track, following a car that is moving at 180 mi/h (264 ft/sec). How fast will your camera angle θ be changing when the car is right in front of you? A half second later?

Camera

θ

132'

Car

33. A melting ice layer A spherical iron ball 8 in. in diameter is coated with a layer of ice of uniform thickness. If the ice melts at the rate of 10 in³/min, how fast is the thickness of the ice decreasing when it is 2 in. thick? How fast is the outer surface area of ice decreasing?

34. Highway patrol A highway patrol plane flies 3 mi above a level, straight road at a steady 120 mi/h. The pilot sees an oncoming car and with radar determines that at the instant the line-of-sight distance from plane to car is 5 mi, the line-of-sight distance is decreasing at the rate of 160 mi/h. Find the car's speed along the highway.

35. A building's shadow On a morning of a day when the sun will pass directly overhead, the shadow of an 80-ft building on level ground is 60 ft long. At the moment in question, the angle θ the sun makes with the ground is increasing at the rate of 0.27°/min. At what rate is the shadow decreasing? (Remember to use radians. Express your answer in inches per minute, to the nearest tenth.)

80'

θ

36. Walkers A and B are walking on straight streets that meet at right angles. A approaches the intersection at 2 m/sec; B moves away from the intersection 1 m/sec. At what rate is the angle θ changing when A is 10 m from the intersection and B is 20 m from the intersection? Express your answer in degrees per second to the nearest degree.

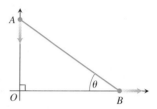

A

θ

O

B

37. Baseball players A baseball diamond is a square 90 ft on a side. A player runs from first base to second at a rate of 16 ft/sec.

  a. At what rate is the player's distance from third base changing when the player is 30 ft from first base?

  b. At what rates are angles θ_1 and θ_2 (see the figure) changing at that time?

  c. The player slides into second base at the rate of 15 ft/sec. At what rates are angles θ_1 and θ_2 changing as the player touches base?

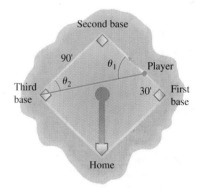

Second base

90'

θ_1

Player

θ_2

Third base

30'

First base

Home

38. Ships Two ships are steaming straight away from a point O along routes that make a 120° angle. Ship A moves at 14 knots (nautical miles per hour; a nautical mile is 2000 yd). Ship B moves at 21 knots. How fast are the ships moving apart when $OA = 5$ and $OB = 3$ nautical miles?

| **3.8** | **Linearization and Differentials** |

Sometimes we can approximate complicated functions with simpler ones that give the accuracy we want for specific applications and are easier to work with. The approximating functions discussed in this section are called *linearizations*, and they are based on tangent lines. Other approximating functions, such as polynomials, are discussed in Chapter 11.

We introduce new variables dx and dy, called *differentials*, and define them in a way that makes Leibniz's notation for the derivative dy/dx a true ratio. We use dy to estimate error in measurement and sensitivity of a function to change. Application of these ideas then provides for a precise proof of the Chain Rule (Section 3.5).

Linearization

As you can see in Figure 3.46, the tangent to the curve $y = x^2$ lies close to the curve near the point of tangency. For a brief interval to either side, the y-values along the tangent line give good approximations to the y-values on the curve. We observe this phenomenon by zooming in on the two graphs at the point of tangency or by looking at tables of values for the difference between $f(x)$ and its tangent line near the x-coordinate of the point of tangency. Locally, every differentiable curve behaves like a straight line.

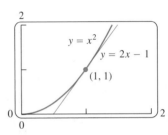

$y = x^2$ and its tangent $y = 2x - 1$ at $(1, 1)$.

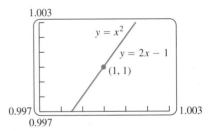

Tangent and curve very close near $(1, 1)$.

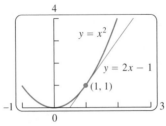

Tangent and curve very close throughout entire x-interval shown.

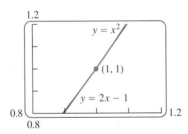

Tangent and curve closer still. Computer screen cannot distinguish tangent from curve on this x-interval.

FIGURE 3.46 The more we magnify the graph of a function near a point where the function is differentiable, the flatter the graph becomes and the more it resembles its tangent.

FIGURE 3.47 The tangent to the curve $y = f(x)$ at $x = a$ is the line $L(x) = f(a) + f'(a)(x - a)$.

In general, the tangent to $y = f(x)$ at a point $x = a$, where f is differentiable (Figure 3.47), passes through the point $(a, f(a))$, so its point-slope equation is

$$y = f(a) + f'(a)(x - a).$$

Thus, this tangent line is the graph of the linear function

$$L(x) = f(a) + f'(a)(x - a).$$

For as long as this line remains close to the graph of f, $L(x)$ gives a good approximation to $f(x)$.

DEFINITIONS   Linearization, Standard Linear Approximation

If f is differentiable at $x = a$, then the approximating function

$$L(x) = f(a) + f'(a)(x - a)$$

is the **linearization** of f at a. The approximation

$$f(x) \approx L(x)$$

of f by L is the **standard linear approximation** of f at a. The point $x = a$ is the **center** of the approximation.

EXAMPLE 1   Finding a Linearization

Find the linearization of $f(x) = \sqrt{1 + x}$ at $x = 0$ (Figure 3.48).

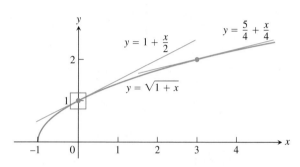

FIGURE 3.48   The graph of $y = \sqrt{1 + x}$ and its linearizations at $x = 0$ and $x = 3$. Figure 3.49 shows a magnified view of the small window about 1 on the y-axis.

Solution   Since

$$f'(x) = \frac{1}{2}\left(1 + x\right)^{-1/2},$$

we have $f(0) = 1$ and $f'(0) = 1/2$, giving the linearization

$$L(x) = f(a) + f'(a)(x - a) = 1 + \frac{1}{2}\left(x - 0\right) = 1 + \frac{x}{2}.$$

See Figure 3.49.   ∎

Look at how accurate the approximation $\sqrt{1 + x} \approx 1 + (x/2)$ from Example 1 is for values of x near 0.

As we move away from zero, we lose accuracy. For example, for $x = 2$, the linearization gives 2 as the approximation for $\sqrt{3}$, which is not even accurate to one decimal place.

Do not be misled by the preceding calculations into thinking that whatever we do with a linearization is better done with a calculator. In practice, we would never use a linearization to find a particular square root. The utility of a linearization is its ability to replace a complicated formula by a simpler one over an entire interval of values. If we have to work with $\sqrt{1 + x}$ for x close to 0 and can tolerate the small amount of error involved, we can

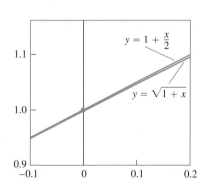

FIGURE 3.49   Magnified view of the window in Figure 3.48.

Approximation	True value	$\lvert$ True value $-$ approximation $\rvert$
$\sqrt{1.2} \approx 1 + \dfrac{0.2}{2} = 1.10$	1.095445	$<10^{-2}$
$\sqrt{1.05} \approx 1 + \dfrac{0.05}{2} = 1.025$	1.024695	$<10^{-3}$
$\sqrt{1.005} \approx 1 + \dfrac{0.005}{2} = 1.00250$	1.002497	$<10^{-5}$

work with $1 + (x/2)$ instead. Of course, we then need to know how much error there is. We have more to say on the estimation of error in Chapter 11.

A linear approximation normally loses accuracy away from its center. As Figure 3.48 suggests, the approximation $\sqrt{1 + x} \approx 1 + (x/2)$ will probably be too crude to be useful near $x = 3$. There, we need the linearization at $x = 3$.

EXAMPLE 2   Finding a Linearization at Another Point

Find the linearization of $f(x) = \sqrt{1 + x}$ at $x = 3$.

Solution   We evaluate the equation defining $L(x)$ at $a = 3$. With

$$f(3) = 2, \qquad f'(3) = \frac{1}{2}\left(1 + x\right)^{-1/2}\bigg|_{x=3} = \frac{1}{4},$$

we have

$$L(x) = 2 + \frac{1}{4}\left(x - 3\right) = \frac{5}{4} + \frac{x}{4}. \qquad \blacksquare$$

At $x = 3.2$, the linearization in Example 2 gives

$$\sqrt{1 + x} = \sqrt{1 + 3.2} \approx \frac{5}{4} + \frac{3.2}{4} = 1.250 + 0.800 = 2.050,$$

which differs from the true value $\sqrt{4.2} \approx 2.04939$ by less than one one-thousandth. The linearization in Example 1 gives

$$\sqrt{1 + x} = \sqrt{1 + 3.2} \approx 1 + \frac{3.2}{2} = 1 + 1.6 = 2.6,$$

a result that is off by more than 25%.

EXAMPLE 3   Finding a Linearization for the Cosine Function

Find the linearization of $f(x) = \cos x$ at $x = \pi/2$ (Figure 3.50).

Solution   Since $f(\pi/2) = \cos(\pi/2) = 0$, $f'(x) = -\sin x$, and $f'(\pi/2) = -\sin(\pi/2) = -1$, we have

$$L(x) = f(a) + f'(a)(x - a)$$

$$= 0 + (-1)\left(x - \frac{\pi}{2}\right)$$

$$= -x + \frac{\pi}{2}. \qquad \blacksquare$$

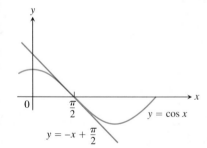

FIGURE 3.50 The graph of $f(x) = \cos x$ and its linearization at $x = \pi/2$. Near $x = \pi/2$, $\cos x \approx -x + (\pi/2)$ (Example 3).

An important linear approximation for roots and powers is

$$(1 + x)^k \approx 1 + kx \qquad (x \text{ near } 0; \text{ any number } k)$$

(Exercise 15). This approximation, good for values of x sufficiently close to zero, has broad application. For example, when x is small,

$$\sqrt{1 + x} \approx 1 + \frac{1}{2}x \qquad\qquad\qquad k = 1/2$$

$$\frac{1}{1 - x} = (1 - x)^{-1} \approx 1 + (-1)(-x) = 1 + x \qquad k = -1; \text{ replace } x \text{ by } -x.$$

$$\sqrt[3]{1 + 5x^4} = (1 + 5x^4)^{1/3} \approx 1 + \frac{1}{3}\left(5x^4\right) = 1 + \frac{5}{3}x^4 \qquad k = 1/3; \text{ replace } x \text{ by } 5x^4.$$

$$\frac{1}{\sqrt{1 - x^2}} = (1 - x^2)^{-1/2} \approx 1 + \left(-\frac{1}{2}\right)(-x^2) = 1 + \frac{1}{2}x^2 \qquad \begin{array}{l} k = -1/2; \\ \text{replace } x \text{ by } -x^2. \end{array}$$

Differentials

We sometimes use the Leibniz notation dy/dx to represent the derivative of y with respect to x. Contrary to its appearance, it is not a ratio. We now introduce two new variables dx and dy with the property that if their ratio exists, it will be equal to the derivative.

DEFINITION   **Differential**

Let $y = f(x)$ be a differentiable function. The **differential dx** is an independent variable. The **differential dy** is

$$dy = f'(x)\, dx.$$

Unlike the independent variable dx, the variable dy is always a dependent variable. It depends on both x and dx. If dx is given a specific value and x is a particular number in the domain of the function f, then the numerical value of dy is determined.

EXAMPLE 4   Finding the Differential dy

(a) Find dy if $y = x^5 + 37x$.

(b) Find the value of dy when $x = 1$ and $dx = 0.2$.

Solution

(a) $dy = (5x^4 + 37)\, dx$

(b) Substituting $x = 1$ and $dx = 0.2$ in the expression for dy, we have

$$dy = (5 \cdot 1^4 + 37)0.2 = 8.4. \qquad\blacksquare$$

The geometric meaning of differentials is shown in Figure 3.51. Let $x = a$ and set $dx = \Delta x$. The corresponding change in $y = f(x)$ is

$$\Delta y = f(a + dx) - f(a).$$

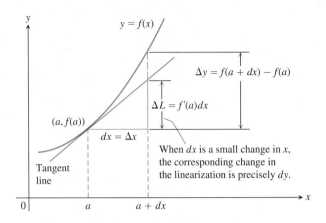

FIGURE 3.51 Geometrically, the differential dy is the change ΔL in the linearization of f when $x = a$ changes by an amount $dx = \Delta x$.

The corresponding change in the tangent line L is

$$\Delta L = L(a + dx) - L(a)$$

$$= \underbrace{f(a) + f'(a)[(a + dx) - a]}_{L(a + dx)} - \underbrace{f(a)}_{L(a)}$$

$$= f'(a)\, dx.$$

That is, the change in the linearization of f is precisely the value of the differential dy when $x = a$ and $dx = \Delta x$. Therefore, dy represents the amount the tangent line rises or falls when x changes by an amount $dx = \Delta x$.

If $dx \neq 0$, then the quotient of the differential dy by the differential dx is equal to the derivative $f'(x)$ because

$$dy \div dx = \frac{f'(x)\, dx}{dx} = f'(x) = \frac{dy}{dx}.$$

We sometimes write

$$df = f'(x)\, dx$$

in place of $dy = f'(x)\, dx$, calling df the **differential of f**. For instance, if $f(x) = 3x^2 - 6$, then

$$df = d(3x^2 - 6) = 6x\, dx.$$

Every differentiation formula like

$$\frac{d(u + v)}{dx} = \frac{du}{dx} + \frac{dv}{dx} \qquad \text{or} \qquad \frac{d(\sin u)}{dx} = \cos u \, \frac{du}{dx}$$

has a corresponding differential form like

$$d(u + v) = du + dv \qquad \text{or} \qquad d(\sin u) = \cos u \, du.$$

EXAMPLE 5   Finding Differentials of Functions

(a) $d(\tan 2x) = \sec^2(2x)\, d(2x) = 2 \sec^2 2x\, dx$

(b) $d\left(\dfrac{x}{x+1}\right) = \dfrac{(x+1)\, dx - x\, d(x+1)}{(x+1)^2} = \dfrac{x\, dx + dx - x\, dx}{(x+1)^2} = \dfrac{dx}{(x+1)^2}$ ∎

Estimating with Differentials

Suppose we know the value of a differentiable function $f(x)$ at a point a and want to predict how much this value will change if we move to a nearby point $a + dx$. If dx is small, then we can see from Figure 3.51 that Δy is approximately equal to the differential dy. Since

$$f(a + dx) = f(a) + \Delta y,$$

the differential approximation gives

$$f(a + dx) \approx f(a) + dy$$

where $dx = \Delta x$. Thus the approximation $\Delta y \approx dy$ can be used to calculate $f(a + dx)$ when $f(a)$ is known and dx is small.

EXAMPLE 6   Estimating with Differentials

The radius r of a circle increases from $a = 10$ m to 10.1 m (Figure 3.52). Use dA to estimate the increase in the circle's area A. Estimate the area of the enlarged circle and compare your estimate to the true area.

Solution   Since $A = \pi r^2$, the estimated increase is

$$dA = A'(a)\, dr = 2\pi a\, dr = 2\pi(10)(0.1) = 2\pi \text{ m}^2.$$

Thus,

$$A(10 + 0.1) \approx A(10) + 2\pi$$
$$= \pi(10)^2 + 2\pi = 102\pi.$$

The area of a circle of radius 10.1 m is approximately 102π m^2.

The true area is

$$A(10.1) = \pi(10.1)^2$$
$$= 102.01\pi \text{ m}^2.$$

The error in our estimate is 0.01π m^2, which is the difference $\Delta A - dA$.   ∎

Error in Differential Approximation

Let $f(x)$ be differentiable at $x = a$ and suppose that $dx = \Delta x$ is an increment of x. We have two ways to describe the change in f as x changes from a to $a + \Delta x$:

The true change: $\Delta f = f(a + \Delta x) - f(a)$

The differential estimate: $df = f'(a)\, \Delta x.$

How well does df approximate Δf?

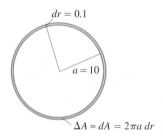

FIGURE 3.52   When dr is small compared with a, as it is when $dr = 0.1$ and $a = 10$, the differential $dA = 2\pi a\, dr$ gives a way to estimate the area of the circle with radius $r = a + dr$ (Example 6).

We measure the approximation error by subtracting df from Δf:

$$
\begin{aligned}
\text{Approximation error} &= \Delta f - df \\
&= \Delta f - f'(a)\Delta x \\
&= \underbrace{f(a + \Delta x) - f(a)}_{\Delta f} - f'(a)\Delta x \\
&= \underbrace{\left(\frac{f(a + \Delta x) - f(a)}{\Delta x} - f'(a) \right)}_{\text{Call this part } \epsilon} \cdot \Delta x \\
&= \epsilon \cdot \Delta x .
\end{aligned}
$$

As $\Delta x \to 0$, the difference quotient

$$
\frac{f(a + \Delta x) - f(a)}{\Delta x}
$$

approaches $f'(a)$ (remember the definition of $f'(a)$), so the quantity in parentheses becomes a very small number (which is why we called it ϵ). In fact, $\epsilon \to 0$ as $\Delta x \to 0$. When Δx is small, the approximation error $\epsilon \, \Delta x$ is smaller still.

$$
\underbrace{\Delta f}_{\substack{\text{true} \\ \text{change}}} = \underbrace{f'(a)\Delta x}_{\substack{\text{estimated} \\ \text{change}}} + \underbrace{\epsilon \, \Delta x}_{\text{error}}
$$

Although we do not know exactly how small the error is and will not be able to make much progress on this front until Chapter 11, there is something worth noting here, namely the *form* taken by the equation.

Change in $y = f(x)$ near $x = a$

If $y = f(x)$ is differentiable at $x = a$ and x changes from a to $a + \Delta x$, the change Δy in f is given by an equation of the form

$$
\Delta y = f'(a) \, \Delta x + \epsilon \, \Delta x \qquad (1)
$$

in which $\epsilon \to 0$ as $\Delta x \to 0$.

In Example 6 we found that

$$
\Delta A = \pi(10.1)^2 - \pi(10)^2 = (102.01 - 100)\pi = \underbrace{(2\pi}_{dA} + \underbrace{0.01\pi)}_{\text{error}} \, \text{m}^2
$$

so the approximation error is $\Delta A - dA = \epsilon \, \Delta r = 0.01\pi$ and $\epsilon = 0.01\pi / \Delta r = 0.01\pi / 0.1 = 0.1\pi$ m.

Equation (1) enables us to bring the proof of the Chain Rule to a successful conclusion.

Proof of the Chain Rule

Our goal is to show that if $f(u)$ is a differentiable function of u and $u = g(x)$ is a differentiable function of x, then the composite $y = f(g(x))$ is a differentiable function of x.

More precisely, if g is differentiable at x_0 and f is differentiable at $g(x_0)$, then the composite is differentiable at x_0 and

$$\frac{dy}{dx}\bigg|_{x=x_0} = f'(g(x_0)) \cdot g'(x_0).$$

Let Δx be an increment in x and let Δu and Δy be the corresponding increments in u and y. Applying Equation (1) we have,

$$\Delta u = g'(x_0)\Delta x + \epsilon_1 \Delta x = (g'(x_0) + \epsilon_1)\Delta x,$$

where $\epsilon_1 \to 0$ as $\Delta x \to 0$. Similarly,

$$\Delta y = f'(u_0)\Delta u + \epsilon_2 \Delta u = (f'(u_0) + \epsilon_2)\Delta u,$$

where $\epsilon_2 \to 0$ as $\Delta u \to 0$. Notice also that $\Delta u \to 0$ as $\Delta x \to 0$. Combining the equations for Δu and Δy gives

$$\Delta y = (f'(u_0) + \epsilon_2)(g'(x_0) + \epsilon_1)\Delta x,$$

so

$$\frac{\Delta y}{\Delta x} = f'(u_0)g'(x_0) + \epsilon_2\, g'(x_0) + f'(u_0)\epsilon_1 + \epsilon_2\epsilon_1.$$

Since ϵ_1 and ϵ_2 go to zero as Δx goes to zero, three of the four terms on the right vanish in the limit, leaving

$$\frac{dy}{dx}\bigg|_{x=x_0} = \lim_{\Delta x \to 0} \frac{\Delta y}{\Delta x} = f'(u_0)g'(x_0) = f'(g(x_0)) \cdot g'(x_0).$$

This concludes the proof. ∎

Sensitivity to Change

The equation $df = f'(x)\, dx$ tells how *sensitive* the output of f is to a change in input at different values of x. The larger the value of f' at x, the greater the effect of a given change dx. As we move from a to a nearby point $a + dx$, we can describe the change in f in three ways:

	True	Estimated
Absolute change	$\Delta f = f(a + dx) - f(a)$	$df = f'(a)\, dx$
Relative change	$\dfrac{\Delta f}{f(a)}$	$\dfrac{df}{f(a)}$
Percentage change	$\dfrac{\Delta f}{f(a)} \times 100$	$\dfrac{df}{f(a)} \times 100$

EXAMPLE 7   Finding the Depth of a Well

You want to calculate the depth of a well from the equation $s = 16t^2$ by timing how long it takes a heavy stone you drop to splash into the water below. How sensitive will your calculations be to a 0.1-sec error in measuring the time?

Solution   The size of ds in the equation

$$ds = 32t\, dt$$

depends on how big t is. If $t = 2$ sec, the change caused by $dt = 0.1$ is about

$$ds = 32(2)(0.1) = 6.4 \text{ ft.}$$

Three seconds later at $t = 5$ sec, the change caused by the same dt is

$$ds = 32(5)(0.1) = 16 \text{ ft.}$$

The estimated depth of the well differs from its true depth by a greater distance the longer the time it takes the stone to splash into the water below, for a given error in measuring the time. ∎

EXAMPLE 8   Unclogging Arteries

Angiography

An opaque dye is injected into a partially blocked artery to make the inside visible under X-rays. This reveals the location and severity of the blockage.

In the late 1830s, French physiologist Jean Poiseuille ("pwa-ZOY") discovered the formula we use today to predict how much the radius of a partially clogged artery has to be expanded to restore normal flow. His formula,

$$V = kr^4,$$

says that the volume V of fluid flowing through a small pipe or tube in a unit of time at a fixed pressure is a constant times the fourth power of the tube's radius r. How will a 10% increase in r affect V?

Solution   The differentials of r and V are related by the equation

$$dV = \frac{dV}{dr} \, dr = 4kr^3 \, dr.$$

The relative change in V is

$$\frac{dV}{V} = \frac{4kr^3 \, dr}{kr^4} = 4 \frac{dr}{r}.$$

Angioplasty

A balloon-tipped catheter is inflated inside the artery to widen it at the blockage site.

The relative change in V is 4 times the relative change in r, so a 10% increase in r will produce a 40% increase in the flow. ∎

EXAMPLE 9   Converting Mass to Energy

Newton's second law,

$$F = \frac{d}{dt}(mv) = m \frac{dv}{dt} = ma,$$

is stated with the assumption that mass is constant, but we know this is not strictly true because the mass of a body increases with velocity. In Einstein's corrected formula, mass has the value

$$m = \frac{m_0}{\sqrt{1 - v^2/c^2}},$$

where the "rest mass" m_0 represents the mass of a body that is not moving and c is the speed of light, which is about 300,000 km/sec. Use the approximation

$$\frac{1}{\sqrt{1 - x^2}} \approx 1 + \frac{1}{2}x^2 \qquad (2)$$

to estimate the increase Δm in mass resulting from the added velocity v.

Solution When v is very small compared with c, v^2/c^2 is close to zero and it is safe to use the approximation

$$\frac{1}{\sqrt{1 - v^2/c^2}} \approx 1 + \frac{1}{2}\left(\frac{v^2}{c^2}\right) \qquad \text{Eq. (2) with } x = \frac{v}{c}$$

to obtain

$$m = \frac{m_0}{\sqrt{1 - v^2/c^2}} \approx m_0\left[1 + \frac{1}{2}\left(\frac{v^2}{c^2}\right)\right] = m_0 + \frac{1}{2}m_0 v^2\left(\frac{1}{c^2}\right),$$

or

$$m \approx m_0 + \frac{1}{2}m_0 v^2\left(\frac{1}{c^2}\right). \tag{3}$$

Equation (3) expresses the increase in mass that results from the added velocity v.

Energy Interpretation

In Newtonian physics, $(1/2)m_0 v^2$ is the kinetic energy (KE) of the body, and if we rewrite Equation (3) in the form

$$(m - m_0)c^2 \approx \frac{1}{2}m_0 v^2,$$

we see that

$$(m - m_0)c^2 \approx \frac{1}{2}m_0 v^2 = \frac{1}{2}m_0 v^2 - \frac{1}{2}m_0(0)^2 = \Delta(\text{KE}),$$

or

$$(\Delta m)c^2 \approx \Delta(\text{KE}).$$

So the change in kinetic energy $\Delta(\text{KE})$ in going from velocity 0 to velocity v is approximately equal to $(\Delta m)c^2$, the change in mass times the square of the speed of light. Using $c \approx 3 \times 10^8$ m/sec, we see that a small change in mass can create a large change in energy. ∎

EXERCISES 3.8

Finding Linearizations

In Exercises 1–4, find the linearization $L(x)$ of $f(x)$ at $x = a$.

1. $f(x) = x^3 - 2x + 3$, $a = 2$
2. $f(x) = \sqrt{x^2 + 9}$, $a = -4$
3. $f(x) = x + \frac{1}{x}$, $a = 1$
4. $f(x) = \sqrt[3]{x}$, $a = -8$

Linearization for Approximation

You want linearizations that will replace the functions in Exercises 5–10 over intervals that include the given points x_0. To make your subsequent work as simple as possible, you want to center each linearization not at x_0 but at a nearby integer $x = a$ at which the given function and its derivative are easy to evaluate. What linearization do you use in each case?

5. $f(x) = x^2 + 2x$, $x_0 = 0.1$
6. $f(x) = x^{-1}$, $x_0 = 0.9$
7. $f(x) = 2x^2 + 4x - 3$, $x_0 = -0.9$
8. $f(x) = 1 + x$, $x_0 = 8.1$
9. $f(x) = \sqrt[3]{x}$, $x_0 = 8.5$
10. $f(x) = \frac{x}{x + 1}$, $x_0 = 1.3$

Linearizing Trigonometric Functions

In Exercises 11–14, find the linearization of f at $x = a$. Then graph the linearization and f together.

11. $f(x) = \sin x$ at (a) $x = 0$, (b) $x = \pi$

12. $f(x) = \cos x$ at (a) $x = 0$, (b) $x = -\pi/2$

13. $f(x) = \sec x$ at (a) $x = 0$, (b) $x = -\pi/3$

14. $f(x) = \tan x$ at (a) $x = 0$, (b) $x = \pi/4$

The Approximation $(1 + x)^k \approx 1 + kx$

15. Show that the linearization of $f(x) = (1 + x)^k$ at $x = 0$ is $L(x) = 1 + kx$.

16. Use the linear approximation $(1 + x)^k \approx 1 + kx$ to find an approximation for the function $f(x)$ for values of x near zero.

  a. $f(x) = (1 - x)^6$ **b.** $f(x) = \dfrac{2}{1 - x}$

  c. $f(x) = \dfrac{1}{\sqrt{1 + x}}$ **d.** $f(x) = \sqrt{2 + x^2}$

  e. $f(x) = (4 + 3x)^{1/3}$ **f.** $f(x) = \sqrt[3]{\left(1 - \dfrac{1}{2 + x}\right)^2}$

17. Faster than a calculator Use the approximation $(1 + x)^k \approx 1 + kx$ to estimate the following.

  a. $(1.0002)^{50}$ **b.** $\sqrt[3]{1.009}$

18. Find the linearization of $f(x) = \sqrt{x + 1} + \sin x$ at $x = 0$. How is it related to the individual linearizations of $\sqrt{x + 1}$ and $\sin x$ at $x = 0$?

Derivatives in Differential Form

In Exercises 19–30, find dy.

19. $y = x^3 - 3\sqrt{x}$ **20.** $y = x\sqrt{1 - x^2}$

21. $y = \dfrac{2x}{1 + x^2}$ **22.** $y = \dfrac{2\sqrt{x}}{3(1 + \sqrt{x})}$

23. $2y^{3/2} + xy - x = 0$ **24.** $xy^2 - 4x^{3/2} - y = 0$

25. $y = \sin(5\sqrt{x})$ **26.** $y = \cos(x^2)$

27. $y = 4\tan(x^3/3)$ **28.** $y = \sec(x^2 - 1)$

29. $y = 3\csc(1 - 2\sqrt{x})$ **30.** $y = 2\cot\left(\dfrac{1}{\sqrt{x}}\right)$

Approximation Error

In Exercises 31–36, each function $f(x)$ changes value when x changes from x_0 to $x_0 + dx$. Find

  a. the change $\Delta f = f(x_0 + dx) - f(x_0)$;

  b. the value of the estimate $df = f'(x_0)\, dx$; and

  c. the approximation error $|\Delta f - df|$.

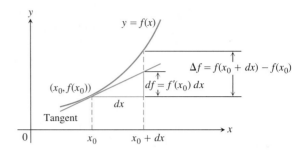

31. $f(x) = x^2 + 2x$, $x_0 = 1$, $dx = 0.1$

32. $f(x) = 2x^2 + 4x - 3$, $x_0 = -1$, $dx = 0.1$

33. $f(x) = x^3 - x$, $x_0 = 1$, $dx = 0.1$

34. $f(x) = x^4$, $x_0 = 1$, $dx = 0.1$

35. $f(x) = x^{-1}$, $x_0 = 0.5$, $dx = 0.1$

36. $f(x) = x^3 - 2x + 3$, $x_0 = 2$, $dx = 0.1$

Differential Estimates of Change

In Exercises 37–42, write a differential formula that estimates the given change in volume or surface area.

37. The change in the volume $V = (4/3)\pi r^3$ of a sphere when the radius changes from r_0 to $r_0 + dr$

38. The change in the volume $V = x^3$ of a cube when the edge lengths change from x_0 to $x_0 + dx$

39. The change in the surface area $S = 6x^2$ of a cube when the edge lengths change from x_0 to $x_0 + dx$

40. The change in the lateral surface area $S = \pi r \sqrt{r^2 + h^2}$ of a right circular cone when the radius changes from r_0 to $r_0 + dr$ and the height does not change

41. The change in the volume $V = \pi r^2 h$ of a right circular cylinder when the radius changes from r_0 to $r_0 + dr$ and the height does not change

42. The change in the lateral surface area $S = 2\pi r h$ of a right circular cylinder when the height changes from h_0 to $h_0 + dh$ and the radius does not change

Applications

43. The radius of a circle is increased from 2.00 to 2.02 m.

  a. Estimate the resulting change in area.

  b. Express the estimate as a percentage of the circle's original area.

44. The diameter of a tree was 10 in. During the following year, the circumference increased 2 in. About how much did the tree's diameter increase? The tree's cross-section area?

45. Estimating volume Estimate the volume of material in a cylindrical shell with height 30 in., radius 6 in., and shell thickness 0.5 in.

0.5 in.

30 in.

6 in.

46. Estimating height of a building A surveyor, standing 30 ft from the base of a building, measures the angle of elevation to the top of the building to be 75°. How accurately must the angle be measured for the percentage error in estimating the height of the building to be less than 4%?

47. Tolerance The height and radius of a right circular cylinder are equal, so the cylinder's volume is $V = \pi h^3$. The volume is to be calculated with an error of no more than 1% of the true value. Find approximately the greatest error that can be tolerated in the measurement of h, expressed as a percentage of h.

48. Tolerance

a. About how accurately must the interior diameter of a 10-m-high cylindrical storage tank be measured to calculate the tank's volume to within 1% of its true value?

b. About how accurately must the tank's exterior diameter be measured to calculate the amount of paint it will take to paint the side of the tank to within 5% of the true amount?

49. Minting coins A manufacturer contracts to mint coins for the federal government. How much variation dr in the radius of the coins can be tolerated if the coins are to weigh within 1/1000 of their ideal weight? Assume that the thickness does not vary.

50. Sketching the change in a cube's volume The volume $V = x^3$ of a cube with edges of length x increases by an amount ΔV when x increases by an amount Δx. Show with a sketch how to represent ΔV geometrically as the sum of the volumes of

a. three slabs of dimensions x by x by Δx

b. three bars of dimensions x by Δx by Δx

c. one cube of dimensions Δx by Δx by Δx.

The differential formula $dV = 3x^2\,dx$ estimates the change in V with the three slabs.

51. The effect of flight maneuvers on the heart The amount of work done by the heart's main pumping chamber, the left ventricle, is given by the equation

$$W = PV + \frac{V\delta v^2}{2g},$$

where W is the work per unit time, P is the average blood pressure, V is the volume of blood pumped out during the unit of time,

δ ("delta") is the weight density of the blood, v is the average velocity of the exiting blood, and g is the acceleration of gravity.

When P, V, δ, and v remain constant, W becomes a function of g, and the equation takes the simplified form

$$W = a + \frac{b}{g} \quad (a, b \text{ constant}).$$

As a member of NASA's medical team, you want to know how sensitive W is to apparent changes in g caused by flight maneuvers, and this depends on the initial value of g. As part of your investigation, you decide to compare the effect on W of a given change dg on the moon, where $g = 5.2$ ft/sec^2, with the effect the same change dg would have on Earth, where $g = 32$ ft/sec^2. Use the simplified equation above to find the ratio of dW_{moon} to dW_{Earth}.

52. Measuring acceleration of gravity When the length L of a clock pendulum is held constant by controlling its temperature, the pendulum's period T depends on the acceleration of gravity g. The period will therefore vary slightly as the clock is moved from place to place on the earth's surface, depending on the change in g. By keeping track of ΔT, we can estimate the variation in g from the equation $T = 2\pi(L/g)^{1/2}$ that relates T, g, and L.

a. With L held constant and g as the independent variable, calculate dT and use it to answer parts (b) and (c).

b. If g increases, will T increase or decrease? Will a pendulum clock speed up or slow down? Explain.

c. A clock with a 100-cm pendulum is moved from a location where $g = 980$ cm/sec^2 to a new location. This increases the period by $dT = 0.001$ sec. Find dg and estimate the value of g at the new location.

53. The edge of a cube is measured as 10 cm with an error of 1%. The cube's volume is to be calculated from this measurement. Estimate the percentage error in the volume calculation.

54. About how accurately should you measure the side of a square to be sure of calculating the area within 2% of its true value?

55. The diameter of a sphere is measured as 100 ± 1 cm and the volume is calculated from this measurement. Estimate the percentage error in the volume calculation.

56. Estimate the allowable percentage error in measuring the diameter D of a sphere if the volume is to be calculated correctly to within 3%.

57. (*Continuation of Example 7.*) Show that a 5% error in measuring t will cause about a 10% error in calculating s from the equation $s = 16t^2$.

58. (*Continuation of Example 8.*) By what percentage should r be increased to increase V by 50%?

Theory and Examples

59. Show that the approximation of $\sqrt{1 + x}$ by its linearization at the origin must improve as $x \to 0$ by showing that

$$\lim_{x \to 0} \frac{\sqrt{1 + x}}{1 + (x/2)} = 1.$$

60. Show that the approximation of $\tan x$ by its linearization at the origin must improve as $x \to 0$ by showing that

$$\lim_{x \to 0} \frac{\tan x}{x} = 1.$$

61. The linearization is the best linear approximation (This is why we use the linearization.) Suppose that $y = f(x)$ is differentiable at $x = a$ and that $g(x) = m(x - a) + c$ is a linear function in which m and c are constants. If the error $E(x) = f(x) - g(x)$ were small enough near $x = a$, we might think of using g as a linear approximation of f instead of the linearization $L(x) = f(a) + f'(a)(x - a)$. Show that if we impose on g the conditions

1. $E(a) = 0$ — The approximation error is zero at $x = a$.

2. $\lim_{x \to a} \dfrac{E(x)}{x - a} = 0$ — The error is negligible when compared with $x - a$.

then $g(x) = f(a) + f'(a)(x - a)$. Thus, the linearization $L(x)$ gives the only linear approximation whose error is both zero at $x = a$ and negligible in comparison with $x - a$.

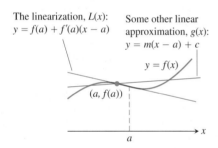

The linearization, $L(x)$:
$y = f(a) + f'(a)(x - a)$

Some other linear approximation, $g(x)$:
$y = m(x - a) + c$

$y = f(x)$

$(a, f(a))$

62. Quadratic approximations

a. Let $Q(x) = b_0 + b_1(x - a) + b_2(x - a)^2$ be a quadratic approximation to $f(x)$ at $x = a$ with the properties:

i. $Q(a) = f(a)$

ii. $Q'(a) = f'(a)$

iii. $Q''(a) = f''(a)$

Determine the coefficients b_0, b_1, and b_2.

b. Find the quadratic approximation to $f(x) = 1/(1 - x)$ at $x = 0$.

T c. Graph $f(x) = 1/(1 - x)$ and its quadratic approximation at $x = 0$. Then zoom in on the two graphs at the point $(0, 1)$. Comment on what you see.

T d. Find the quadratic approximation to $g(x) = 1/x$ at $x = 1$. Graph g and its quadratic approximation together. Comment on what you see.

T e. Find the quadratic approximation to $h(x) = \sqrt{1 + x}$ at $x = 0$. Graph h and its quadratic approximation together. Comment on what you see.

f. What are the linearizations of f, g, and h at the respective points in parts (b), (d), and (e)?

T **63. Reading derivatives from graphs** The idea that differentiable curves flatten out when magnified can be used to estimate the values of the derivatives of functions at particular points. We magnify the curve until the portion we see looks like a straight line through the point in question, and then we use the screen's coordinate grid to read the slope of the curve as the slope of the line it resembles.

a. To see how the process works, try it first with the function $y = x^2$ at $x = 1$. The slope you read should be 2.

b. Then try it with the curve $y = e^x$ at $x = 1$, $x = 0$, and $x = -1$. In each case, compare your estimate of the derivative with the value of e^x at the point. What pattern do you see? Test it with other values of x. Chapter 7 will explain what is going on.

64. Suppose that the graph of a differentiable function $f(x)$ has a horizontal tangent at $x = a$. Can anything be said about the linearization of f at $x = a$? Give reasons for your answer.

65. To what relative speed should a body at rest be accelerated to increase its mass by 1%?

T **66. Repeated root-taking**

a. Enter 2 in your calculator and take successive square roots by pressing the square root key repeatedly (or raising the displayed number repeatedly to the 0.5 power). What pattern do you see emerging? Explain what is going on. What happens if you take successive tenth roots instead?

b. Repeat the procedure with 0.5 in place of 2 as the original entry. What happens now? Can you use any positive number x in place of 2? Explain what is going on.

COMPUTER EXPLORATIONS

Comparing Functions with Their Linearizations

In Exercises 67–70, use a CAS to estimate the magnitude of the error in using the linearization in place of the function over a specified interval I. Perform the following steps:

a. Plot the function f over I.

b. Find the linearization L of the function at the point a.

c. Plot f and L together on a single graph.

d. Plot the absolute error $|f(x) - L(x)|$ over I and find its maximum value.

e. From your graph in part (d), estimate as large a $\delta > 0$ as you can, satisfying

$$|x - a| < \delta \quad \Rightarrow \quad |f(x) - L(x)| < \epsilon$$

for $\epsilon = 0.5, 0.1,$ and 0.01. Then check graphically to see if your δ-estimate holds true.

67. $f(x) = x^3 + x^2 - 2x, \quad [-1, 2], \quad a = 1$

68. $f(x) = \dfrac{x - 1}{4x^2 + 1}, \quad \left[-\dfrac{3}{4}, 1\right], \quad a = \dfrac{1}{2}$

69. $f(x) = x^{2/3}(x - 2), \quad [-2, 3], \quad a = 2$

70. $f(x) = \sqrt{x} - \sin x, \quad [0, 2\pi], \quad a = 2$

1. What is the derivative of a function f? How is its domain related to the domain of f? Give examples.

2. What role does the derivative play in defining slopes, tangents, and rates of change?

3. How can you sometimes graph the derivative of a function when all you have is a table of the function's values?

4. What does it mean for a function to be differentiable on an open interval? On a closed interval?

5. How are derivatives and one-sided derivatives related?

6. Describe geometrically when a function typically does *not* have a derivative at a point.

7. How is a function's differentiability at a point related to its continuity there, if at all?

8. Could the unit step function

$$U(x) = \begin{cases} 0, & x < 0 \\ 1, & x \geq 0 \end{cases}$$

possibly be the derivative of some other function on $[-1, 1]$? Explain.

9. What rules do you know for calculating derivatives? Give some examples.

10. Explain how the three formulas

a. $\dfrac{d}{dx}(x^n) = nx^{n-1}$

b. $\dfrac{d}{dx}(cu) = c\dfrac{du}{dx}$

c. $\dfrac{d}{dx}(u_1 + u_2 + \cdots + u_n) = \dfrac{du_1}{dx} + \dfrac{du_2}{dx} + \cdots + \dfrac{du_n}{dx}$

enable us to differentiate any polynomial.

11. What formula do we need, in addition to the three listed in Question 10, to differentiate rational functions?

12. What is a second derivative? A third derivative? How many derivatives do the functions you know have? Give examples.

13. What is the relationship between a function's average and instantaneous rates of change? Give an example.

14. How do derivatives arise in the study of motion? What can you learn about a body's motion along a line by examining the derivatives of the body's position function? Give examples.

15. How can derivatives arise in economics?

16. Give examples of still other applications of derivatives.

17. What do the limits $\lim_{h\to 0}((\sin h)/h)$ and $\lim_{h\to 0}((\cos h - 1)/h)$ have to do with the derivatives of the sine and cosine functions? What *are* the derivatives of these functions?

18. Once you know the derivatives of $\sin x$ and $\cos x$, how can you find the derivatives of $\tan x$, $\cot x$, $\sec x$, and $\csc x$? What *are* the derivatives of these functions?

19. At what points are the six basic trigonometric functions continuous? How do you know?

20. What is the rule for calculating the derivative of a composite of two differentiable functions? How is such a derivative evaluated? Give examples.

21. What is the formula for the slope dy/dx of a parametrized curve $x = f(t), y = g(t)$? When does the formula apply? When can you expect to be able to find d^2y/dx^2 as well? Give examples.

22. If u is a differentiable function of x, how do you find $(d/dx)(u^n)$ if n is an integer? If n is a rational number? Give examples.

23. What is implicit differentiation? When do you need it? Give examples.

24. How do related rates problems arise? Give examples.

25. Outline a strategy for solving related rates problems. Illustrate with an example.

26. What is the linearization $L(x)$ of a function $f(x)$ at a point $x = a$? What is required of f at a for the linearization to exist? How are linearizations used? Give examples.

27. If x moves from a to a nearby value $a + dx$, how do you estimate the corresponding change in the value of a differentiable function $f(x)$? How do you estimate the relative change? The percentage change? Give an example.

Derivatives of Functions

Find the derivatives of the functions in Exercises 1–40.

1. $y = x^5 - 0.125x^2 + 0.25x$ **2.** $y = 3 - 0.7x^3 + 0.3x^7$

3. $y = x^3 - 3(x^2 + \pi^2)$ **4.** $y = x^7 + \sqrt{7}x - \dfrac{1}{\pi + 1}$

5. $y = (x + 1)^2(x^2 + 2x)$

6. $y = (2x - 5)(4 - x)^{-1}$

7. $y = (\theta^2 + \sec\theta + 1)^3$

8. $y = \left(-1 - \dfrac{\csc\theta}{2} - \dfrac{\theta^2}{4}\right)^2$

9. $s = \dfrac{\sqrt{t}}{1 + \sqrt{t}}$

10. $s = \dfrac{1}{\sqrt{t} - 1}$

11. $y = 2\tan^2 x - \sec^2 x$

12. $y = \dfrac{1}{\sin^2 x} - \dfrac{2}{\sin x}$

13. $s = \cos^4(1 - 2t)$

14. $s = \cot^3\left(\dfrac{2}{t}\right)$

15. $s = (\sec t + \tan t)^5$

16. $s = \csc^5(1 - t + 3t^2)$

17. $r = \sqrt{2\theta\sin\theta}$

18. $r = 2\theta\sqrt{\cos\theta}$

19. $r = \sin\sqrt{2\theta}$

20. $r = \sin\left(\theta + \sqrt{\theta + 1}\right)$

21. $y = \dfrac{1}{2}x^2\csc\dfrac{2}{x}$

22. $y = 2\sqrt{x}\sin\sqrt{x}$

23. $y = x^{-1/2}\sec(2x)^2$

24. $y = \sqrt{x}\csc(x + 1)^3$

25. $y = 5\cot x^2$

26. $y = x^2\cot 5x$

27. $y = x^2\sin^2(2x^2)$

28. $y = x^{-2}\sin^2(x^3)$

29. $s = \left(\dfrac{4t}{t + 1}\right)^{-2}$

30. $s = \dfrac{-1}{15(15t - 1)^3}$

31. $y = \left(\dfrac{\sqrt{x}}{1 + x}\right)^2$

32. $y = \left(\dfrac{2\sqrt{x}}{2\sqrt{x} + 1}\right)^2$

33. $y = \sqrt{\dfrac{x^2 + x}{x^2}}$

34. $y = 4x\sqrt{x} + \sqrt{x}$

35. $r = \left(\dfrac{\sin\theta}{\cos\theta - 1}\right)^2$

36. $r = \left(\dfrac{1 + \sin\theta}{1 - \cos\theta}\right)^2$

37. $y = (2x + 1)\sqrt{2x + 1}$

38. $y = 20(3x - 4)^{1/4}(3x - 4)^{-1/5}$

39. $y = \dfrac{3}{(5x^2 + \sin 2x)^{3/2}}$

40. $y = (3 + \cos^3 3x)^{-1/3}$

Implicit Differentiation

In Exercises 41–48, find dy/dx.

41. $xy + 2x + 3y = 1$

42. $x^2 + xy + y^2 - 5x = 2$

43. $x^3 + 4xy - 3y^{4/3} = 2x$

44. $5x^{4/5} + 10y^{6/5} = 15$

45. $\sqrt{xy} = 1$

46. $x^2y^2 = 1$

47. $y^2 = \dfrac{x}{x + 1}$

48. $y^2 = \sqrt{\dfrac{1 + x}{1 - x}}$

In Exercises 49 and 50, find dp/dq.

49. $p^3 + 4pq - 3q^2 = 2$

50. $q = (5p^2 + 2p)^{-3/2}$

In Exercises 51 and 52, find dr/ds.

51. $r\cos 2s + \sin^2 s = \pi$

52. $2rs - r - s + s^2 = -3$

53. Find d^2y/dx^2 by implicit differentiation:

  a. $x^3 + y^3 = 1$

  b. $y^2 = 1 - \dfrac{2}{x}$

54. a. By differentiating $x^2 - y^2 = 1$ implicitly, show that $dy/dx = x/y$.

  b. Then show that $d^2y/dx^2 = -1/y^3$.

Numerical Values of Derivatives

55. Suppose that functions $f(x)$ and $g(x)$ and their first derivatives have the following values at $x = 0$ and $x = 1$.

x	$f(x)$	$g(x)$	$f'(x)$	$g'(x)$
0	1	1	-3	$1/2$
1	3	5	$1/2$	-4

Find the first derivatives of the following combinations at the given value of x.

  a. $6f(x) - g(x)$, $\quad x = 1$

  b. $f(x)g^2(x)$, $\quad x = 0$

  c. $\dfrac{f(x)}{g(x) + 1}$, $\quad x = 1$

  d. $f(g(x))$, $\quad x = 0$

  e. $g(f(x))$, $\quad x = 0$

  f. $(x + f(x))^{3/2}$, $\quad x = 1$

  g. $f(x + g(x))$, $\quad x = 0$

56. Suppose that the function $f(x)$ and its first derivative have the following values at $x = 0$ and $x = 1$.

x	$f(x)$	$f'(x)$
0	9	-2
1	-3	$1/5$

Find the first derivatives of the following combinations at the given value of x.

  a. $\sqrt{x}\,f(x)$, $\quad x = 1$

  b. $\sqrt{f(x)}$, $\quad x = 0$

  c. $f(\sqrt{x})$, $\quad x = 1$

  d. $f(1 - 5\tan x)$, $\quad x = 0$

  e. $\dfrac{f(x)}{2 + \cos x}$, $\quad x = 0$

  f. $10\sin\left(\dfrac{\pi x}{2}\right)f^2(x)$, $\quad x = 1$

57. Find the value of dy/dt at $t = 0$ if $y = 3\sin 2x$ and $x = t^2 + \pi$.

58. Find the value of ds/du at $u = 2$ if $s = t^2 + 5t$ and $t = (u^2 + 2u)^{1/3}$.

59. Find the value of dw/ds at $s = 0$ if $w = \sin\left(\sqrt{r} - 2\right)$ and $r = 8\sin(s + \pi/6)$.

60. Find the value of dr/dt at $t = 0$ if $r = (\theta^2 + 7)^{1/3}$ and $\theta^2 t + \theta = 1$.

61. If $y^3 + y = 2\cos x$, find the value of d^2y/dx^2 at the point $(0, 1)$.

62. If $x^{1/3} + y^{1/3} = 4$, find d^2y/dx^2 at the point $(8, 8)$.

Derivative Definition

In Exercises 63 and 64, find the derivative using the definition.

63. $f(t) = \dfrac{1}{2t + 1}$

64. $g(x) = 2x^2 + 1$

65. a. Graph the function

$$f(x) = \begin{cases} x^2, & -1 \le x < 0 \\ -x^2, & 0 \le x \le 1. \end{cases}$$

  b. Is f continuous at $x = 0$?

  c. Is f differentiable at $x = 0$?

Give reasons for your answers.

66. a. Graph the function

$$f(x) = \begin{cases} x, & -1 \le x < 0 \\ \tan x, & 0 \le x \le \pi/4. \end{cases}$$

b. Is f continuous at $x = 0$?

c. Is f differentiable at $x = 0$?

Give reasons for your answers.

67. a. Graph the function

$$f(x) = \begin{cases} x, & 0 \le x \le 1 \\ 2 - x, & 1 < x \le 2. \end{cases}$$

b. Is f continuous at $x = 1$?

c. Is f differentiable at $x = 1$?

Give reasons for your answers.

68. For what value or values of the constant m, if any, is

$$f(x) = \begin{cases} \sin 2x, & x \le 0 \\ mx, & x > 0 \end{cases}$$

a. continuous at $x = 0$?

b. differentiable at $x = 0$?

Give reasons for your answers.

Slopes, Tangents, and Normals

69. Tangents with specified slope   Are there any points on the curve $y = (x/2) + 1/(2x - 4)$ where the slope is $-3/2$? If so, find them.

70. Tangents with specified slope   Are there any points on the curve $y = x - 1/(2x)$ where the slope is 3? If so, find them.

71. Horizontal tangents   Find the points on the curve $y = 2x^3 - 3x^2 - 12x + 20$ where the tangent is parallel to the x-axis.

72. Tangent intercepts   Find the x- and y-intercepts of the line that is tangent to the curve $y = x^3$ at the point $(-2, -8)$.

73. Tangents perpendicular or parallel to lines   Find the points on the curve $y = 2x^3 - 3x^2 - 12x + 20$ where the tangent is

a. perpendicular to the line $y = 1 - (x/24)$.

b. parallel to the line $y = \sqrt{2} - 12x$.

74. Intersecting tangents   Show that the tangents to the curve $y = (\pi \sin x)/x$ at $x = \pi$ and $x = -\pi$ intersect at right angles.

75. Normals parallel to a line   Find the points on the curve $y = \tan x$, $-\pi/2 < x < \pi/2$, where the normal is parallel to the line $y = -x/2$. Sketch the curve and normals together, labeling each with its equation.

76. Tangent and normal lines   Find equations for the tangent and normal to the curve $y = 1 + \cos x$ at the point $(\pi/2, 1)$. Sketch the curve, tangent, and normal together, labeling each with its equation.

77. Tangent parabola   The parabola $y = x^2 + C$ is to be tangent to the line $y = x$. Find C.

78. Slope of tangent   Show that the tangent to the curve $y = x^3$ at any point (a, a^3) meets the curve again at a point where the slope is four times the slope at (a, a^3).

79. Tangent curve   For what value of c is the curve $y = c/(x + 1)$ tangent to the line through the points $(0, 3)$ and $(5, -2)$?

80. Normal to a circle   Show that the normal line at any point of the circle $x^2 + y^2 = a^2$ passes through the origin.

Tangents and Normals to Implicitly Defined Curves

In Exercises 81–86, find equations for the lines that are tangent and normal to the curve at the given point.

81. $x^2 + 2y^2 = 9$, $(1, 2)$

82. $x^3 + y^2 = 2$, $(1, 1)$

83. $xy + 2x - 5y = 2$, $(3, 2)$

84. $(y - x)^2 = 2x + 4$, $(6, 2)$

85. $x + \sqrt{xy} = 6$, $(4, 1)$

86. $x^{3/2} + 2y^{3/2} = 17$, $(1, 4)$

87. Find the slope of the curve $x^3y^3 + y^2 = x + y$ at the points $(1, 1)$ and $(1, -1)$.

88. The graph shown suggests that the curve $y = \sin(x - \sin x)$ might have horizontal tangents at the x-axis. Does it? Give reasons for your answer.

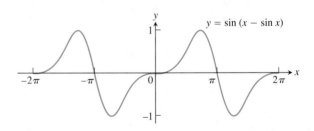

Tangents to Parametrized Curves

In Exercises 89 and 90, find an equation for the line in the xy-plane that is tangent to the curve at the point corresponding to the given value of t. Also, find the value of d^2y/dx^2 at this point.

89. $x = (1/2)\tan t$, $y = (1/2)\sec t$, $t = \pi/3$

90. $x = 1 + 1/t^2$, $y = 1 - 3/t$, $t = 2$

Analyzing Graphs

Each of the figures in Exercises 91 and 92 shows two graphs, the graph of a function $y = f(x)$ together with the graph of its derivative $f'(x)$. Which graph is which? How do you know?

91.

92.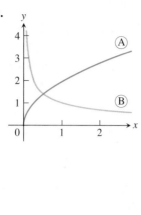

93. Use the following information to graph the function $y = f(x)$ for $-1 \le x \le 6$.

  i. The graph of f is made of line segments joined end to end.

  ii. The graph starts at the point $(-1, 2)$.

  iii. The derivative of f, where defined, agrees with the step function shown here.

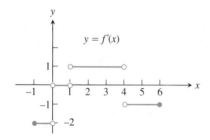

94. Repeat Exercise 93, supposing that the graph starts at $(-1, 0)$ instead of $(-1, 2)$.

Exercises 95 and 96 are about the graphs in Figure 3.53 (right-hand column). The graphs in part (a) show the numbers of rabbits and foxes in a small arctic population. They are plotted as functions of time for 200 days. The number of rabbits increases at first, as the rabbits reproduce. But the foxes prey on rabbits and, as the number of foxes increases, the rabbit population levels off and then drops. Figure 3.53b shows the graph of the derivative of the rabbit population. We made it by plotting slopes.

95. a. What is the value of the derivative of the rabbit population in Figure 3.53 when the number of rabbits is largest? Smallest?

  b. What is the size of the rabbit population in Figure 3.53 when its derivative is largest? Smallest (negative value)?

96. In what units should the slopes of the rabbit and fox population curves be measured?

Trigonometric Limits

97. $\displaystyle\lim_{x \to 0} \frac{\sin x}{2x^2 - x}$

98. $\displaystyle\lim_{x \to 0} \frac{3x - \tan 7x}{2x}$

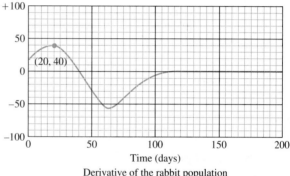

FIGURE 3.53 Rabbits and foxes in an arctic predator-prey food chain.

99. $\displaystyle\lim_{r \to 0} \frac{\sin r}{\tan 2r}$

100. $\displaystyle\lim_{\theta \to 0} \frac{\sin (\sin \theta)}{\theta}$

101. $\displaystyle\lim_{\theta \to (\pi/2)^-} \frac{4 \tan^2 \theta + \tan \theta + 1}{\tan^2 \theta + 5}$

102. $\displaystyle\lim_{\theta \to 0^+} \frac{1 - 2 \cot^2 \theta}{5 \cot^2 \theta - 7 \cot \theta - 8}$

103. $\displaystyle\lim_{x \to 0} \frac{x \sin x}{2 - 2 \cos x}$

104. $\displaystyle\lim_{\theta \to 0} \frac{1 - \cos \theta}{\theta^2}$

Show how to extend the functions in Exercises 105 and 106 to be continuous at the origin.

105. $g(x) = \dfrac{\tan (\tan x)}{\tan x}$

106. $f(x) = \dfrac{\tan (\tan x)}{\sin (\sin x)}$

Related Rates

107. Right circular cylinder The total surface area S of a right circular cylinder is related to the base radius r and height h by the equation $S = 2\pi r^2 + 2\pi rh$.

  a. How is dS/dt related to dr/dt if h is constant?

  b. How is dS/dt related to dh/dt if r is constant?

c. How is dS/dt related to dr/dt and dh/dt if neither r nor h is constant?

d. How is dr/dt related to dh/dt if S is constant?

108. Right circular cone The lateral surface area S of a right circular cone is related to the base radius r and height h by the equation $S = \pi r \sqrt{r^2 + h^2}$.

a. How is dS/dt related to dr/dt if h is constant?

b. How is dS/dt related to dh/dt if r is constant?

c. How is dS/dt related to dr/dt and dh/dt if neither r nor h is constant?

109. Circle's changing area The radius of a circle is changing at the rate of $-2/\pi$ m/sec. At what rate is the circle's area changing when $r = 10$ m?

110. Cube's changing edges The volume of a cube is increasing at the rate of 1200 cm^3/min at the instant its edges are 20 cm long. At what rate are the lengths of the edges changing at that instant?

111. Resistors connected in parallel If two resistors of R_1 and R_2 ohms are connected in parallel in an electric circuit to make an R-ohm resistor, the value of R can be found from the equation

$$\frac{1}{R} = \frac{1}{R_1} + \frac{1}{R_2}.$$

If R_1 is decreasing at the rate of 1 ohm/sec and R_2 is increasing at the rate of 0.5 ohm/sec, at what rate is R changing when $R_1 = 75$ ohms and $R_2 = 50$ ohms?

112. Impedance in a series circuit The impedance Z (ohms) in a series circuit is related to the resistance R (ohms) and reactance X (ohms) by the equation $Z = \sqrt{R^2 + X^2}$. If R is increasing at 3 ohms/sec and X is decreasing at 2 ohms/sec, at what rate is Z changing when $R = 10$ ohms and $X = 20$ ohms?

113. Speed of moving particle The coordinates of a particle moving in the metric xy-plane are differentiable functions of time t with $dx/dt = 10$ m/sec and $dy/dt = 5$ m/sec. How fast is the particle moving away from the origin as it passes through the point $(3, -4)$?

114. Motion of a particle A particle moves along the curve $y = x^{3/2}$ in the first quadrant in such a way that its distance from the origin increases at the rate of 11 units per second. Find dx/dt when $x = 3$.

115. Draining a tank Water drains from the conical tank shown in the accompanying figure at the rate of 5 ft^3/min.

a. What is the relation between the variables h and r in the figure?

b. How fast is the water level dropping when $h = 6$ ft?

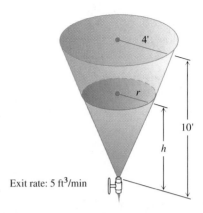

Exit rate: 5 ft^3/min

116. Rotating spool As television cable is pulled from a large spool to be strung from the telephone poles along a street, it unwinds from the spool in layers of constant radius (see accompanying figure). If the truck pulling the cable moves at a steady 6 ft/sec (a touch over 4 mph), use the equation $s = r\theta$ to find how fast (radians per second) the spool is turning when the layer of radius 1.2 ft is being unwound.

117. Moving searchlight beam The figure shows a boat 1 km offshore, sweeping the shore with a searchlight. The light turns at a constant rate, $d\theta/dt = -0.6$ rad/sec.

a. How fast is the light moving along the shore when it reaches point A?

b. How many revolutions per minute is 0.6 rad/sec?

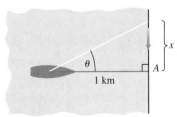

118. Points moving on coordinate axes Points A and B move along the x- and y-axes, respectively, in such a way that the distance r (meters) along the perpendicular from the origin to the line AB remains constant. How fast is OA changing, and is it increasing, or decreasing, when $OB = 2r$ and B is moving toward O at the rate of $0.3r$ m/sec?

Linearization

119. Find the linearizations of

    a. $\tan x$ at $x = -\pi/4$ **b.** $\sec x$ at $x = -\pi/4$.

Graph the curves and linearizations together.

120. We can obtain a useful linear approximation of the function $f(x) = 1/(1 + \tan x)$ at $x = 0$ by combining the approximations

$$\frac{1}{1 + x} \approx 1 - x \quad \text{and} \quad \tan x \approx x$$

to get

$$\frac{1}{1 + \tan x} \approx 1 - x.$$

Show that this result is the standard linear approximation of $1/(1 + \tan x)$ at $x = 0$.

121. Find the linearization of $f(x) = \sqrt{1 + x} + \sin x - 0.5$ at $x = 0$.

122. Find the linearization of $f(x) = 2/(1 - x) + \sqrt{1 + x} - 3.1$ at $x = 0$.

Differential Estimates of Change

123. Surface area of a cone Write a formula that estimates the change that occurs in the lateral surface area of a right circular cone when the height changes from h_0 to $h_0 + dh$ and the radius does not change.

$$V = \frac{1}{3}\pi r^2 h$$
$$S = \pi r \sqrt{r^2 + h^2}$$
(Lateral surface area)

124. Controlling error

    a. How accurately should you measure the edge of a cube to be reasonably sure of calculating the cube's surface area with an error of no more than 2%?

    b. Suppose that the edge is measured with the accuracy required in part (a). About how accurately can the cube's volume be calculated from the edge measurement? To find out, estimate the percentage error in the volume calculation that might result from using the edge measurement.

125. Compounding error The circumference of the equator of a sphere is measured as 10 cm with a possible error of 0.4 cm. This measurement is then used to calculate the radius. The radius is then used to calculate the surface area and volume of the sphere. Estimate the percentage errors in the calculated values of

    a. the radius.

    b. the surface area.

    c. the volume.

126. Finding height To find the height of a lamppost (see accompanying figure), you stand a 6 ft pole 20 ft from the lamp and measure the length a of its shadow, finding it to be 15 ft, give or take an inch. Calculate the height of the lamppost using the value $a = 15$ and estimate the possible error in the result.

---

1. An equation like $\sin^2 \theta + \cos^2 \theta = 1$ is called an **identity** because it holds for all values of θ. An equation like $\sin \theta = 0.5$ is not an identity because it holds only for selected values of θ, not all. If you differentiate both sides of a trigonometric identity in θ with respect to θ, the resulting new equation will also be an identity.

    Differentiate the following to show that the resulting equations hold for all θ.

    a. $\sin 2\theta = 2 \sin \theta \cos \theta$

    b. $\cos 2\theta = \cos^2 \theta - \sin^2 \theta$

2. If the identity $\sin(x + a) = \sin x \cos a + \cos x \sin a$ is differentiated with respect to x, is the resulting equation also an identity? Does this principle apply to the equation $x^2 - 2x - 8 = 0$? Explain.

3. a. Find values for the constants a, b, and c that will make

$$f(x) = \cos x \quad \text{and} \quad g(x) = a + bx + cx^2$$

satisfy the conditions

$$f(0) = g(0), \quad f'(0) = g'(0), \quad \text{and} \quad f''(0) = g''(0).$$

b. Find values for b and c that will make

$$f(x) = \sin(x + a) \quad \text{and} \quad g(x) = b \sin x + c \cos x$$

satisfy the conditions

$$f(0) = g(0) \quad \text{and} \quad f'(0) = g'(0).$$

c. For the determined values of a, b, and c, what happens for the third and fourth derivatives of f and g in each of parts (a) and (b)?

4. Solutions to differential equations

a. Show that $y = \sin x$, $y = \cos x$, and $y = a \cos x + b \sin x$ (a and b constants) all satisfy the equation

$$y'' + y = 0.$$

b. How would you modify the functions in part (a) to satisfy the equation

$$y'' + 4y = 0?$$

Generalize this result.

5. An osculating circle Find the values of h, k, and a that make the circle $(x - h)^2 + (y - k)^2 = a^2$ tangent to the parabola $y = x^2 + 1$ at the point $(1, 2)$ and that also make the second derivatives d^2y/dx^2 have the same value on both curves there. Circles like this one that are tangent to a curve and have the same second derivative as the curve at the point of tangency are called *osculating circles* (from the Latin *osculari*, meaning "to kiss"). We encounter them again in Chapter 13.

6. Marginal revenue A bus will hold 60 people. The number x of people per trip who use the bus is related to the fare charged (p dollars) by the law $p = [3 - (x/40)]^2$. Write an expression for the total revenue $r(x)$ per trip received by the bus company. What number of people per trip will make the marginal revenue dr/dx equal to zero? What is the corresponding fare? (This fare is the one that maximizes the revenue, so the bus company should probably rethink its fare policy.)

7. Industrial production

a. Economists often use the expression "rate of growth" in relative rather than absolute terms. For example, let $u = f(t)$ be the number of people in the labor force at time t in a given industry. (We treat this function as though it were differentiable even though it is an integer-valued step function.)

   Let $v = g(t)$ be the average production per person in the labor force at time t. The total production is then $y = uv$. If the labor force is growing at the rate of 4% per year ($du/dt = 0.04u$) and the production per worker is growing at the rate of 5% per year ($dv/dt = 0.05v$), find the rate of growth of the total production, y.

b. Suppose that the labor force in part (a) is decreasing at the rate of 2% per year while the production per person is increasing at the rate of 3% per year. Is the total production increasing, or is it decreasing, and at what rate?

8. Designing a gondola The designer of a 30-ft-diameter spherical hot air balloon wants to suspend the gondola 8 ft below the bottom of the balloon with cables tangent to the surface of the balloon, as shown. Two of the cables are shown running from the top edges of the gondola to their points of tangency, $(-12, -9)$ and $(12, -9)$. How wide should the gondola be?

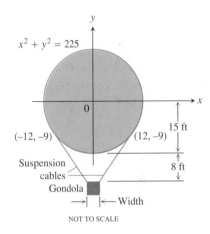

NOT TO SCALE

9. Pisa by parachute The photograph shows Mike McCarthy parachuting from the top of the Tower of Pisa on August 5, 1988. Make a rough sketch to show the shape of the graph of his speed during the jump.

Mike McCarthy of London jumped from the Tower of Pisa and then opened his parachute in what he said was a world record low-level parachute jump of 179 ft. (*Source: Boston Globe*, Aug. 6, 1988.)

10. **Motion of a particle**   The position at time $t \geq 0$ of a particle moving along a coordinate line is

$$s = 10 \cos(t + \pi/4).$$

   a. What is the particle's starting position $(t = 0)$?

   b. What are the points farthest to the left and right of the origin reached by the particle?

   c. Find the particle's velocity and acceleration at the points in part (b).

   d. When does the particle first reach the origin? What are its velocity, speed, and acceleration then?

11. **Shooting a paper clip**   On Earth, you can easily shoot a paper clip 64 ft straight up into the air with a rubber band. In t sec after firing, the paper clip is $s = 64t - 16t^2$ ft above your hand.

   a. How long does it take the paper clip to reach its maximum height? With what velocity does it leave your hand?

   b. On the moon, the same acceleration will send the paper clip to a height of $s = 64t - 2.6t^2$ ft in t sec. About how long will it take the paper clip to reach its maximum height, and how high will it go?

12. **Velocities of two particles**   At time t sec, the positions of two particles on a coordinate line are $s_1 = 3t^3 - 12t^2 + 18t + 5$ m and $s_2 = -t^3 + 9t^2 - 12t$ m. When do the particles have the same velocities?

13. **Velocity of a particle**   A particle of constant mass m moves along the x-axis. Its velocity v and position x satisfy the equation

$$\frac{1}{2} m(v^2 - v_0{}^2) = \frac{1}{2} k(x_0{}^2 - x^2),$$

   where k, v_0, and x_0 are constants. Show that whenever $v \neq 0$,

$$m \frac{dv}{dt} = -kx.$$

14. **Average and instantaneous velocity**

   a. Show that if the position x of a moving point is given by a quadratic function of t, $x = At^2 + Bt + C$, then the average velocity over any time interval $[t_1, t_2]$ is equal to the instantaneous velocity at the midpoint of the time interval.

   b. What is the geometric significance of the result in part (a)?

15. Find all values of the constants m and b for which the function

$$y = \begin{cases} \sin x, & x < \pi \\ mx + b, & x \geq \pi \end{cases}$$

   is

   a. continuous at $x = \pi$.

   b. differentiable at $x = \pi$.

16. Does the function

$$f(x) = \begin{cases} \dfrac{1 - \cos x}{x}, & x \neq 0 \\ 0, & x = 0 \end{cases}$$

have a derivative at $x = 0$? Explain.

17. **a.** For what values of a and b will

$$f(x) = \begin{cases} ax, & x < 2 \\ ax^2 - bx + 3, & x \geq 2 \end{cases}$$

   be differentiable for all values of x?

   b. Discuss the geometry of the resulting graph of f.

18. **a.** For what values of a and b will

$$g(x) = \begin{cases} ax + b, & x \leq -1 \\ ax^3 + x + 2b, & x > -1 \end{cases}$$

   be differentiable for all values of x?

   b. Discuss the geometry of the resulting graph of g.

19. **Odd differentiable functions**   Is there anything special about the derivative of an odd differentiable function of x? Give reasons for your answer.

20. **Even differentiable functions**   Is there anything special about the derivative of an even differentiable function of x? Give reasons for your answer.

21. Suppose that the functions f and g are defined throughout an open interval containing the point x_0, that f is differentiable at x_0, that $f(x_0) = 0$, and that g is continuous at x_0. Show that the product fg is differentiable at x_0. This process shows, for example, that although $|x|$ is not differentiable at $x = 0$, the product $x|x|$ is differentiable at $x = 0$.

22. *(Continuation of Exercise 21.)* Use the result of Exercise 21 to show that the following functions are differentiable at $x = 0$.

   a. $|x| \sin x$ **b.** $x^{2/3} \sin x$ **c.** $\sqrt[3]{x}(1 - \cos x)$

   d. $h(x) = \begin{cases} x^2 \sin(1/x), & x \neq 0 \\ 0, & x = 0 \end{cases}$

23. Is the derivative of

$$h(x) = \begin{cases} x^2 \sin(1/x), & x \neq 0 \\ 0, & x = 0 \end{cases}$$

   continuous at $x = 0$? How about the derivative of $k(x) = xh(x)$? Give reasons for your answers.

24. Suppose that a function f satisfies the following conditions for all real values of x and y:

   i. $f(x + y) = f(x) \cdot f(y)$.

   ii. $f(x) = 1 + xg(x)$, where $\lim_{x \to 0} g(x) = 1$.

   Show that the derivative $f'(x)$ exists at every value of x and that $f'(x) = f(x)$.

25. **The generalized product rule**   Use mathematical induction to prove that if $y = u_1 u_2 \cdots u_n$ is a finite product of differentiable functions, then y is differentiable on their common domain and

$$\frac{dy}{dx} = \frac{du_1}{dx} u_2 \cdots u_n + u_1 \frac{du_2}{dx} \cdots u_n + \cdots + u_1 u_2 \cdots u_{n-1} \frac{du_n}{dx}.$$

26. **Leibniz's rule for higher-order derivatives of products** Leibniz's rule for higher-order derivatives of products of differentiable functions says that

a. $\dfrac{d^2(uv)}{dx^2} = \dfrac{d^2u}{dx^2}v + 2\dfrac{du}{dx}\dfrac{dv}{dx} + u\dfrac{d^2v}{dx^2}$

b. $\dfrac{d^3(uv)}{dx^3} = \dfrac{d^3u}{dx^3}v + 3\dfrac{d^2u}{dx^2}\dfrac{dv}{dx} + 3\dfrac{du}{dx}\dfrac{d^2v}{dx^2} + u\dfrac{d^3v}{dx^3}$

c. $\dfrac{d^n(uv)}{dx^n} = \dfrac{d^nu}{dx^n}v + n\dfrac{d^{n-1}u}{dx^{n-1}}\dfrac{dv}{dx} + \cdots$

$$+ \frac{n(n-1)\cdots(n-k+1)}{k!}\frac{d^{n-k}u}{dx^{n-k}}\frac{d^kv}{dx^k}$$

$$+ \cdots + u\frac{d^nv}{dx^n}.$$

The equations in parts (a) and (b) are special cases of the equation in part (c). Derive the equation in part (c) by mathematical induction, using

$$\binom{m}{k} + \binom{m}{k+1} = \frac{m!}{k!(m-k)!} + \frac{m!}{(k+1)!(m-k-1)!}.$$

27. **The period of a clock pendulum** The period T of a clock pendulum (time for one full swing and back) is given by the formula $T^2 = 4\pi^2 L/g$, where T is measured in seconds, $g = 32.2 \text{ ft/sec}^2$, and L, the length of the pendulum, is measured in feet. Find approximately

a. the length of a clock pendulum whose period is $T = 1$ sec.

b. the change dT in T if the pendulum in part (a) is lengthened 0.01 ft.

c. the amount the clock gains or loses in a day as a result of the period's changing by the amount dT found in part (b).

28. **The melting ice cube** Assume an ice cube retains its cubical shape as it melts. If we call its edge length s, its volume is $V = s^3$ and its surface area is $6s^2$. We assume that V and s are differentiable functions of time t. We assume also that the cube's volume decreases at a rate that is proportional to its surface area. (This latter assumption seems reasonable enough when we think that the melting takes place at the surface: Changing the amount of surface changes the amount of ice exposed to melt.) In mathematical terms,

$$\frac{dV}{dt} = -k(6s^2), \qquad k > 0.$$

The minus sign indicates that the volume is decreasing. We assume that the proportionality factor k is constant. (It probably depends on many things, such as the relative humidity of the surrounding air, the air temperature, and the incidence or absence of sunlight, to name only a few.) Assume a particular set of conditions in which the cube lost 1/4 of its volume during the first hour, and that the volume is V_0 when $t = 0$. How long will it take the ice cube to melt?

Chapter 3 Technology Application Projects

Mathematica/Maple Module
Convergence of Secant Slopes to the Derivative Function
You will visualize the secant line between successive points on a curve and observe what happens as the distance between them becomes small. The function, sample points, and secant lines are plotted on a single graph, while a second graph compares the slopes of the secant lines with the derivative function.

Mathematica/Maple Module
Derivatives, Slopes, Tangent Lines, and Making Movies
Parts I–III. You will visualize the derivative at a point, the linearization of a function, and the derivative of a function. You learn how to plot the function and selected tangents on the same graph.
Part IV (Plotting Many Tangents)
Part V (Making Movies). Parts IV and V of the module can be used to animate tangent lines as one moves along the graph of a function.

Mathematica/Maple Module
Convergence of Secant Slopes to the Derivative Function
You will visualize right-hand and left-hand derivatives.

Mathematica/Maple Module
Motion Along a Straight Line: Position $\rightarrow$ Velocity $\rightarrow$ Acceleration
Observe dramatic animated visualizations of the derivative relations among the position, velocity, and acceleration functions. Figures in the text can be animated.

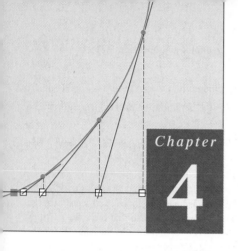

4

APPLICATIONS OF DERIVATIVES

OVERVIEW   This chapter studies some of the important applications of derivatives. We learn how derivatives are used to find extreme values of functions, to determine and analyze the shapes of graphs, to calculate limits of fractions whose numerators and denominators both approach zero or infinity, and to find numerically where a function equals zero. We also consider the process of recovering a function from its derivative. The key to many of these accomplishments is the Mean Value Theorem, a theorem whose corollaries provide the gateway to integral calculus in Chapter 5.

4.1   Extreme Values of Functions

This section shows how to locate and identify extreme values of a continuous function from its derivative. Once we can do this, we can solve a variety of *optimization problems* in which we find the optimal (best) way to do something in a given situation.

DEFINITIONS   Absolute Maximum, Absolute Minimum

Let f be a function with domain D. Then f has an **absolute maximum** value on D at a point c if

$$f(x) \leq f(c) \qquad \text{for all } x \text{ in } D$$

and an **absolute minimum** value on D at c if

$$f(x) \geq f(c) \qquad \text{for all } x \text{ in } D.$$

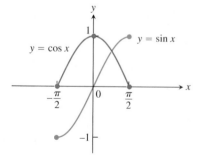

FIGURE 4.1   Absolute extrema for the sine and cosine functions on $[-\pi/2, \pi/2]$. These values can depend on the domain of a function.

Absolute maximum and minimum values are called absolute **extrema** (plural of the Latin *extremum*). Absolute extrema are also called **global** extrema, to distinguish them from *local extrema* defined below.

For example, on the closed interval $[-\pi/2, \pi/2]$ the function $f(x) = \cos x$ takes on an absolute maximum value of 1 (once) and an absolute minimum value of 0 (twice). On the same interval, the function $g(x) = \sin x$ takes on a maximum value of 1 and a minimum value of -1 (Figure 4.1).

Functions with the same defining rule can have different extrema, depending on the domain.

EXAMPLE 1   Exploring Absolute Extrema

The absolute extrema of the following functions on their domains can be seen in Figure 4.2.

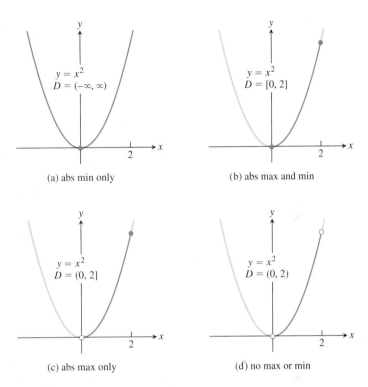

FIGURE 4.2   Graphs for Example 1.

Function rule	Domain D	Absolute extrema on D
(a) $y = x^2$	$(-\infty, \infty)$	No absolute maximum. Absolute minimum of 0 at $x = 0$.
(b) $y = x^2$	$[0, 2]$	Absolute maximum of 4 at $x = 2$. Absolute minimum of 0 at $x = 0$.
(c) $y = x^2$	$(0, 2]$	Absolute maximum of 4 at $x = 2$. No absolute minimum.
(d) $y = x^2$	$(0, 2)$	No absolute extrema.

HISTORICAL BIOGRAPHY

Daniel Bernoulli
(1700–1782)

The following theorem asserts that a function which is continuous at every point of a closed interval $[a, b]$ has an absolute maximum and an absolute minimum value on the interval. We always look for these values when we graph a function.

THEOREM 1   The Extreme Value Theorem

If f is continuous on a closed interval $[a, b]$, then f attains both an absolute maximum value M and an absolute minimum value m in $[a, b]$. That is, there are numbers x_1 and x_2 in $[a, b]$ with $f(x_1) = m$, $f(x_2) = M$, and $m \leq f(x) \leq M$ for every other x in $[a, b]$ (Figure 4.3).

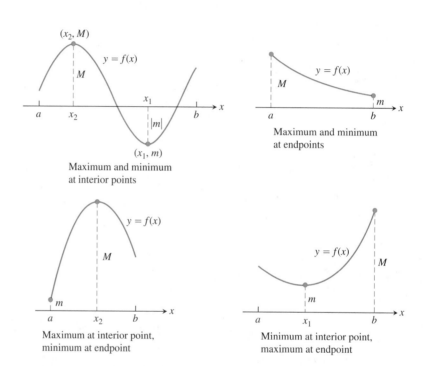

FIGURE 4.3 Some possibilities for a continuous function's maximum and minimum on a closed interval $[a, b]$.

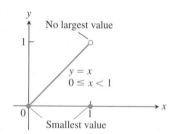

FIGURE 4.4 Even a single point of discontinuity can keep a function from having either a maximum or minimum value on a closed interval. The function

$$y = \begin{cases} x, & 0 \leq x < 1 \\ 0, & x = 1 \end{cases}$$

is continuous at every point of $[0, 1]$ except $x = 1$, yet its graph over $[0, 1]$ does not have a highest point.

The proof of The Extreme Value Theorem requires a detailed knowledge of the real number system (see Appendix 4) and we will not give it here. Figure 4.3 illustrates possible locations for the absolute extrema of a continuous function on a closed interval $[a, b]$. As we observed for the function $y = \cos x$, it is possible that an absolute minimum (or absolute maximum) may occur at two or more different points of the interval.

The requirements in Theorem 1 that the interval be closed and finite, and that the function be continuous, are key ingredients. Without them, the conclusion of the theorem need not hold. Example 1 shows that an absolute extreme value may not exist if the interval fails to be both closed and finite. Figure 4.4 shows that the continuity requirement cannot be omitted.

Local (Relative) Extreme Values

Figure 4.5 shows a graph with five points where a function has extreme values on its domain $[a, b]$. The function's absolute minimum occurs at a even though at e the function's value is

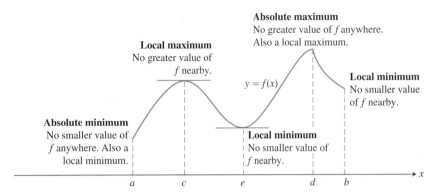

FIGURE 4.5 How to classify maxima and minima.

smaller than at any other point *nearby*. The curve rises to the left and falls to the right around *c*, making *f(c)* a maximum locally. The function attains its absolute maximum at *d*.

DEFINITIONS   Local Maximum, Local Minimum

A function *f* has a **local maximum** value at an interior point *c* of its domain if

$$f(x) \leq f(c) \qquad \text{for all } x \text{ in some open interval containing } c.$$

A function *f* has a **local minimum** value at an interior point *c* of its domain if

$$f(x) \geq f(c) \qquad \text{for all } x \text{ in some open interval containing } c.$$

We can extend the definitions of local extrema to the endpoints of intervals by defining *f* to have a **local maximum** or **local minimum** value *at an endpoint c* if the appropriate inequality holds for all *x* in some half-open interval in its domain containing *c*. In Figure 4.5, the function *f* has local maxima at *c* and *d* and local minima at *a*, *e*, and *b*. Local extrema are also called **relative extrema**.

An absolute maximum is also a local maximum. Being the largest value overall, it is also the largest value in its immediate neighborhood. Hence, *a list of all local maxima will automatically include the absolute maximum if there is one.* Similarly, *a list of all local minima will include the absolute minimum if there is one.*

Finding Extrema

The next theorem explains why we usually need to investigate only a few values to find a function's extrema.

THEOREM 2   The First Derivative Theorem for Local Extreme Values

If *f* has a local maximum or minimum value at an interior point *c* of its domain, and if *f'* is defined at *c*, then

$$f'(c) = 0.$$

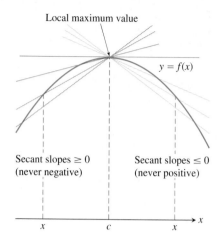

Local maximum value

$y = f(x)$

Secant slopes ≥ 0 (never negative)

Secant slopes ≤ 0 (never positive)

x

$x \quad c \quad x$

FIGURE 4.6 A curve with a local maximum value. The slope at c, simultaneously the limit of nonpositive numbers and nonnegative numbers, is zero.

Proof To prove that $f'(c)$ is zero at a local extremum, we show first that $f'(c)$ cannot be positive and second that $f'(c)$ cannot be negative. The only number that is neither positive nor negative is zero, so that is what $f'(c)$ must be.

To begin, suppose that f has a local maximum value at $x = c$ (Figure 4.6) so that $f(x) - f(c) \leq 0$ for all values of x near enough to c. Since c is an interior point of f's domain, $f'(c)$ is defined by the two-sided limit

$$\lim_{x \to c} \frac{f(x) - f(c)}{x - c}.$$

This means that the right-hand and left-hand limits both exist at $x = c$ and equal $f'(c)$. When we examine these limits separately, we find that

$$f'(c) = \lim_{x \to c^+} \frac{f(x) - f(c)}{x - c} \leq 0. \qquad \text{Because } (x - c) > 0 \text{ and } f(x) \leq f(c) \qquad (1)$$

Similarly,

$$f'(c) = \lim_{x \to c^-} \frac{f(x) - f(c)}{x - c} \geq 0. \qquad \text{Because } (x - c) < 0 \text{ and } f(x) \leq f(c) \qquad (2)$$

Together, Equations (1) and (2) imply $f'(c) = 0$.

This proves the theorem for local maximum values. To prove it for local minimum values, we simply use $f(x) \geq f(c)$, which reverses the inequalities in Equations (1) and (2). ∎

Theorem 2 says that a function's first derivative is always zero at an interior point where the function has a local extreme value and the derivative is defined. Hence the only places where a function f can possibly have an extreme value (local or global) are

1. interior points where $f' = 0$,

2. interior points where f' is undefined,

3. endpoints of the domain of f.

The following definition helps us to summarize.

DEFINITION Critical Point

An interior point of the domain of a function f where f' is zero or undefined is a **critical point** of f.

Thus the only domain points where a function can assume extreme values are critical points and endpoints.

Be careful not to misinterpret Theorem 2 because its converse is false. A differentiable function may have a critical point at $x = c$ without having a local extreme value there. For instance, the function $f(x) = x^3$ has a critical point at the origin and zero value there, but is positive to the right of the origin and negative to the left. So it cannot have a local extreme value at the origin. Instead, it has a *point of inflection* there. This idea is defined and discussed further in Section 4.4.

Most quests for extreme values call for finding the absolute extrema of a continuous function on a closed and finite interval. Theorem 1 assures us that such values exist; Theorem 2 tells us that they are taken on only at critical points and endpoints. Often we can simply list these points and calculate the corresponding function values to find what the largest and smallest values are, and where they are located.

> **How to Find the Absolute Extrema of a Continuous Function f on a Finite Closed Interval**
>
> **1.** Evaluate f at all critical points and endpoints.
> **2.** Take the largest and smallest of these values.

EXAMPLE 2   Finding Absolute Extrema

Find the absolute maximum and minimum values of $f(x) = x^2$ on $[-2, 1]$.

Solution   The function is differentiable over its entire domain, so the only critical point is where $f'(x) = 2x = 0$, namely $x = 0$. We need to check the function's values at $x = 0$ and at the endpoints $x = -2$ and $x = 1$:

Critical point value: $f(0) = 0$

Endpoint values: $f(-2) = 4$
$f(1) = 1$

The function has an absolute maximum value of 4 at $x = -2$ and an absolute minimum value of 0 at $x = 0$.   ∎

EXAMPLE 3   Absolute Extrema at Endpoints

Find the absolute extrema values of $g(t) = 8t - t^4$ on $[-2, 1]$.

Solution   The function is differentiable on its entire domain, so the only critical points occur where $g'(t) = 0$. Solving this equation gives

$$8 - 4t^3 = 0 \quad \text{or} \quad t = \sqrt[3]{2} > 1,$$

a point not in the given domain. The function's absolute extrema therefore occur at the endpoints, $g(-2) = -32$ (absolute minimum), and $g(1) = 7$ (absolute maximum). See Figure 4.7.   ∎

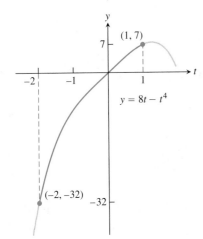

FIGURE 4.7   The extreme values of $g(t) = 8t - t^4$ on $[-2, 1]$ (Example 3).

EXAMPLE 4   Finding Absolute Extrema on a Closed Interval

Find the absolute maximum and minimum values of $f(x) = x^{2/3}$ on the interval $[-2, 3]$.

Solution   We evaluate the function at the critical points and endpoints and take the largest and smallest of the resulting values.

The first derivative

$$f'(x) = \frac{2}{3}x^{-1/3} = \frac{2}{3\sqrt[3]{x}}$$

has no zeros but is undefined at the interior point $x = 0$. The values of f at this one critical point and at the endpoints are

Critical point value: $f(0) = 0$

Endpoint values: $f(-2) = (-2)^{2/3} = \sqrt[3]{4}$
$f(3) = (3)^{2/3} = \sqrt[3]{9}.$

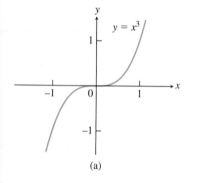

FIGURE 4.8 The extreme values of $f(x) = x^{2/3}$ on $[-2, 3]$ occur at $x = 0$ and $x = 3$ (Example 4).

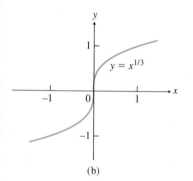

FIGURE 4.9 Critical points without extreme values. (a) $y' = 3x^2$ is 0 at $x = 0$, but $y = x^3$ has no extremum there. (b) $y' = (1/3)x^{-2/3}$ is undefined at $x = 0$, but $y = x^{1/3}$ has no extremum there.

We can see from this list that the function's absolute maximum value is $\sqrt[3]{9} \approx 2.08$, and it occurs at the right endpoint $x = 3$. The absolute minimum value is 0, and it occurs at the interior point $x = 0$. (Figure 4.8). ∎

While a function's extrema can occur only at critical points and endpoints, not every critical point or endpoint signals the presence of an extreme value. Figure 4.9 illustrates this for interior points.

We complete this section with an example illustrating how the concepts we studied are used to solve a real-world optimization problem.

EXAMPLE 5   Piping Oil from a Drilling Rig to a Refinery

A drilling rig 12 mi offshore is to be connected by pipe to a refinery onshore, 20 mi straight down the coast from the rig. If underwater pipe costs $500,000 per mile and land-based pipe costs $300,000 per mile, what combination of the two will give the least expensive connection?

Solution   We try a few possibilities to get a feel for the problem:

(a) *Smallest amount of underwater pipe*

Underwater pipe is more expensive, so we use as little as we can. We run straight to shore (12 mi) and use land pipe for 20 mi to the refinery.

$$\text{Dollar cost} = 12(500,000) + 20(300,000)$$
$$= 12,000,000$$

(b) *All pipe underwater (most direct route)*

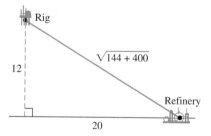

We go straight to the refinery underwater.

$$\text{Dollar cost} = \sqrt{544}\,(500,000)$$
$$\approx 11,661,900$$

This is less expensive than plan (a).

(c) *Something in between*

Now we introduce the length x of underwater pipe and the length y of land-based pipe as variables. The right angle opposite the rig is the key to expressing the relationship between x and y, for the Pythagorean theorem gives

$$x^2 = 12^2 + (20 - y)^2$$
$$x = \sqrt{144 + (20 - y)^2}. \tag{3}$$

Only the positive root has meaning in this model.

The dollar cost of the pipeline is

$$c = 500{,}000x + 300{,}000y.$$

To express c as a function of a single variable, we can substitute for x, using Equation (3):

$$c(y) = 500{,}000\sqrt{144 + (20 - y)^2} + 300{,}000y.$$

Our goal now is to find the minimum value of $c(y)$ on the interval $0 \le y \le 20$. The first derivative of $c(y)$ with respect to y according to the Chain Rule is

$$c'(y) = 500{,}000 \cdot \frac{1}{2} \cdot \frac{2(20 - y)(-1)}{\sqrt{144 + (20 - y)^2}} + 300{,}000$$

$$= -500{,}000 \frac{20 - y}{\sqrt{144 + (20 - y)^2}} + 300{,}000.$$

Setting c' equal to zero gives

$$500{,}000\,(20 - y) = 300{,}000\sqrt{144 + (20 - y)^2}$$

$$\frac{5}{3}\left(20 - y\right) = \sqrt{144 + (20 - y)^2}$$

$$\frac{25}{9}\left(20 - y\right)^2 = 144 + (20 - y)^2$$

$$\frac{16}{9}\left(20 - y\right)^2 = 144$$

$$(20 - y) = \pm\frac{3}{4} \cdot 12 = \pm 9$$

$$y = 20 \pm 9$$

$$y = 11 \quad \text{or} \quad y = 29.$$

Only $y = 11$ lies in the interval of interest. The values of c at this one critical point and at the endpoints are

$$c(11) = 10{,}800{,}000$$
$$c(0) = 11{,}661{,}900$$
$$c(20) = 12{,}000{,}000$$

The least expensive connection costs \$10,800,000, and we achieve it by running the line underwater to the point on shore 11 mi from the refinery. ∎

EXERCISES 4.1

Finding Extrema from Graphs

In Exercises 1–6, determine from the graph whether the function has any absolute extreme values on $[a, b]$. Then explain how your answer is consistent with Theorem 1.

1.

2.

3.

4.

5.

6.
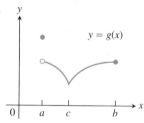

In Exercises 7–10, find the extreme values and where they occur.

7.

8.

9.

10.
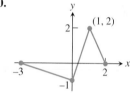

In Exercises 11-14, match the table with a graph.

11.

x	$f'(x)$
a	0
b	0
c	5

12.

x	$f'(x)$
a	0
b	0
c	-5

13.

x	$f'(x)$
a	does not exist
b	0
c	-2

14.

x	$f'(x)$
a	does not exist
b	does not exist
c	-1.7

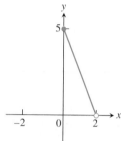

(a)

(b)

(c)

(d)

Absolute Extrema on Finite Closed Intervals

In Exercises 15–30, find the absolute maximum and minimum values of each function on the given interval. Then graph the function. Identify the points on the graph where the absolute extrema occur, and include their coordinates.

15. $f(x) = \frac{2}{3}x - 5, \quad -2 \le x \le 3$

16. $f(x) = -x - 4, \quad -4 \le x \le 1$

17. $f(x) = x^2 - 1, \quad -1 \le x \le 2$

18. $f(x) = 4 - x^2, \quad -3 \le x \le 1$

19. $F(x) = -\frac{1}{x^2}, \quad 0.5 \le x \le 2$

20. $F(x) = -\frac{1}{x}, \quad -2 \le x \le -1$

21. $h(x) = \sqrt[3]{x}, \quad -1 \le x \le 8$

22. $h(x) = -3x^{2/3}, \quad -1 \le x \le 1$

23. $g(x) = \sqrt{4 - x^2}, \quad -2 \le x \le 1$

24. $g(x) = -\sqrt{5 - x^2}, \quad -\sqrt{5} \le x \le 0$

25. $f(\theta) = \sin\theta, \quad -\frac{\pi}{2} \le \theta \le \frac{5\pi}{6}$

26. $f(\theta) = \tan\theta, \quad -\frac{\pi}{3} \le \theta \le \frac{\pi}{4}$

27. $g(x) = \csc x, \quad \frac{\pi}{3} \le x \le \frac{2\pi}{3}$

28. $g(x) = \sec x, \quad -\frac{\pi}{3} \le x \le \frac{\pi}{6}$

29. $f(t) = 2 - |t|, \quad -1 \le t \le 3$

30. $f(t) = |t - 5|, \quad 4 \le t \le 7$

In Exercises 31–34, find the function's absolute maximum and minimum values and say where they are assumed.

31. $f(x) = x^{4/3}, \quad -1 \le x \le 8$

32. $f(x) = x^{5/3}, \quad -1 \le x \le 8$

33. $g(\theta) = \theta^{3/5}, \quad -32 \le \theta \le 1$

34. $h(\theta) = 3\theta^{2/3}, \quad -27 \le \theta \le 8$

Finding Extreme Values

In Exercises 35–44, find the extreme values of the function and where they occur.

35. $y = 2x^2 - 8x + 9$

36. $y = x^3 - 2x + 4$

37. $y = x^3 + x^2 - 8x + 5$

38. $y = x^3 - 3x^2 + 3x - 2$

39. $y = \sqrt{x^2 - 1}$

40. $y = \dfrac{1}{\sqrt{1 - x^2}}$

41. $y = \dfrac{1}{\sqrt[3]{1 - x^2}}$

42. $y = \sqrt{3 + 2x - x^2}$

43. $y = \dfrac{x}{x^2 + 1}$

44. $y = \dfrac{x + 1}{x^2 + 2x + 2}$

Local Extrema and Critical Points

In Exercises 45–52, find the derivative at each critical point and determine the local extreme values.

45. $y = x^{2/3}(x + 2)$

46. $y = x^{2/3}(x^2 - 4)$

47. $y = x\sqrt{4 - x^2}$

48. $y = x^2\sqrt{3 - x}$

49. $y = \begin{cases} 4 - 2x, & x \le 1 \\ x + 1, & x > 1 \end{cases}$

50. $y = \begin{cases} 3 - x, & x < 0 \\ 3 + 2x - x^2, & x \ge 0 \end{cases}$

51. $y = \begin{cases} -x^2 - 2x + 4, & x \le 1 \\ -x^2 + 6x - 4, & x > 1 \end{cases}$

52. $y = \begin{cases} -\frac{1}{4}x^2 - \frac{1}{2}x + \frac{15}{4}, & x \le 1 \\ x^3 - 6x^2 + 8x, & x > 1 \end{cases}$

In Exercises 53 and 54, give reasons for your answers.

53. Let $f(x) = (x - 2)^{2/3}$.

a. Does $f'(2)$ exist?

b. Show that the only local extreme value of f occurs at $x = 2$.

c. Does the result in part (b) contradict the Extreme Value Theorem?

d. Repeat parts (a) and (b) for $f(x) = (x - a)^{2/3}$, replacing 2 by a.

54. Let $f(x) = |x^3 - 9x|$.

a. Does $f'(0)$ exist?

b. Does $f'(3)$ exist?

c. Does $f'(-3)$ exist?

d. Determine all extrema of f.

Optimization Applications

Whenever you are maximizing or minimizing a function of a single variable, we urge you to graph the function over the domain that is appropriate to the problem you are solving. The graph will provide insight before you begin to calculate and will furnish a visual context for understanding your answer.

55. Constructing a pipeline Supertankers off-load oil at a docking facility 4 mi offshore. The nearest refinery is 9 mi east of the shore point nearest the docking facility. A pipeline must be constructed connecting the docking facility with the refinery. The pipeline costs $300,000 per mile if constructed underwater and $200,000 per mile if overland.

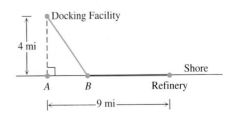

a. Locate Point B to minimize the cost of the construction.

b. The cost of underwater construction is expected to increase, whereas the cost of overland construction is expected to stay constant. At what cost does it become optimal to construct the pipeline directly to Point A?

56. Upgrading a highway   A highway must be constructed to connect Village A with Village B. There is a rudimentary roadway that can be upgraded 50 mi south of the line connecting the two villages. The cost of upgrading the existing roadway is $300,000 per mile, whereas the cost of constructing a new highway is $500,000 per mile. Find the combination of upgrading and new construction that minimizes the cost of connecting the two villages. Clearly define the location of the proposed highway.

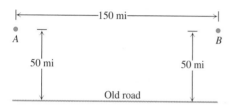

57. Locating a pumping station   Two towns lie on the south side of a river. A pumping station is to be located to serve the two towns. A pipeline will be constructed from the pumping station to each of the towns along the line connecting the town and the pumping station. Locate the pumping station to minimize the amount of pipeline that must be constructed.

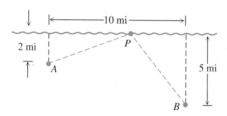

58. Length of a guy wire   One tower is 50 ft high and another tower is 30 ft high. The towers are 150 ft apart. A guy wire is to run from Point A to the top of each tower.

a. Locate Point A so that the total length of guy wire is minimal.

b. Show in general that regardless of the height of the towers, the length of guy wire is minimized if the angles at A are equal.

59. The function

$$V(x) = x(10 - 2x)(16 - 2x), \qquad 0 < x < 5,$$

models the volume of a box.

a. Find the extreme values of V.

b. Interpret any values found in part (a) in terms of volume of the box.

60. The function

$$P(x) = 2x + \frac{200}{x}, \qquad 0 < x < \infty,$$

models the perimeter of a rectangle of dimensions x by $100/x$.

a. Find any extreme values of P.

b. Give an interpretation in terms of perimeter of the rectangle for any values found in part (a).

61. Area of a right triangle   What is the largest possible area for a right triangle whose hypotenuse is 5 cm long?

62. Area of an athletic field   An athletic field is to be built in the shape of a rectangle x units long capped by semicircular regions of radius r at the two ends. The field is to be bounded by a 400-m racetrack.

a. Express the area of the rectangular portion of the field as a function of x alone or r alone (your choice).

b. What values of x and r give the rectangular portion the largest possible area?

63. Maximum height of a vertically moving body   The height of a body moving vertically is given by

$$s = -\frac{1}{2}gt^2 + v_0 t + s_0, \qquad g > 0,$$

with s in meters and t in seconds. Find the body's maximum height.

64. Peak alternating current   Suppose that at any given time t (in seconds) the current i (in amperes) in an alternating current circuit is $i = 2\cos t + 2\sin t$. What is the peak current for this circuit (largest magnitude)?

Theory and Examples

65. A minimum with no derivative   The function $f(x) = |x|$ has an absolute minimum value at $x = 0$ even though f is not differentiable at $x = 0$. Is this consistent with Theorem 2? Give reasons for your answer.

66. Even functions   If an even function $f(x)$ has a local maximum value at $x = c$, can anything be said about the value of f at $x = -c$? Give reasons for your answer.

67. Odd functions   If an odd function $g(x)$ has a local minimum value at $x = c$, can anything be said about the value of g at $x = -c$? Give reasons for your answer.

68. We know how to find the extreme values of a continuous function $f(x)$ by investigating its values at critical points and endpoints. But what if there *are* no critical points or endpoints? What happens then? Do such functions really exist? Give reasons for your answers.

69. Cubic functions   Consider the cubic function

$$f(x) = ax^3 + bx^2 + cx + d.$$

a. Show that f can have 0, 1, or 2 critical points. Give examples and graphs to support your argument.

b. How many local extreme values can f have?

T **70. Functions with no extreme values at endpoints**

a. Graph the function

$$f(x) = \begin{cases} \sin \dfrac{1}{x}, & x > 0 \\ 0, & x = 0. \end{cases}$$

Explain why $f(0) = 0$ is not a local extreme value of f.

b. Construct a function of your own that fails to have an extreme value at a domain endpoint.

T Graph the functions in Exercises 71–74. Then find the extreme values of the function on the interval and say where they occur.

71. $f(x) = |x - 2| + |x + 3|, \quad -5 \le x \le 5$

72. $g(x) = |x - 1| - |x - 5|, \quad -2 \le x \le 7$

73. $h(x) = |x + 2| - |x - 3|, \quad -\infty < x < \infty$

74. $k(x) = |x + 1| + |x - 3|, \quad -\infty < x < \infty$

COMPUTER EXPLORATIONS

In Exercises 75–80, you will use a CAS to help find the absolute extrema of the given function over the specified closed interval. Perform the following steps.

a. Plot the function over the interval to see its general behavior there.

b. Find the interior points where $f' = 0$. (In some exercises, you may have to use the numerical equation solver to approximate a solution.) You may want to plot f' as well.

c. Find the interior points where f' does not exist.

d. Evaluate the function at all points found in parts (b) and (c) and at the endpoints of the interval.

e. Find the function's absolute extreme values on the interval and identify where they occur.

75. $f(x) = x^4 - 8x^2 + 4x + 2, \quad [-20/25, 64/25]$

76. $f(x) = -x^4 + 4x^3 - 4x + 1, \quad [-3/4, 3]$

77. $f(x) = x^{2/3}(3 - x), \quad [-2, 2]$

78. $f(x) = 2 + 2x - 3x^{2/3}, \quad [-1, 10/3]$

79. $f(x) = \sqrt{x} + \cos x, \quad [0, 2\pi]$

80. $f(x) = x^{3/4} - \sin x + \dfrac{1}{2}, \quad [0, 2\pi]$

4.2 The Mean Value Theorem

We know that constant functions have zero derivatives, but could there be a complicated function, with many terms, the derivatives of which all cancel to give zero? What is the relationship between two functions that have identical derivatives over an interval? What we are really asking here is what functions can have a particular *kind* of derivative. These and many other questions we study in this chapter are answered by applying the Mean Value Theorem. To arrive at this theorem we first need Rolle's Theorem.

Rolle's Theorem

Drawing the graph of a function gives strong geometric evidence that between any two points where a differentiable function crosses a horizontal line there is at least one point on the curve where the tangent is horizontal (Figure 4.10). More precisely, we have the following theorem.

(a)

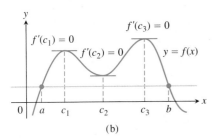

(b)

FIGURE 4.10 Rolle's Theorem says that a differentiable curve has at least one horizontal tangent between any two points where it crosses a horizontal line. It may have just one (a), or it may have more (b).

THEOREM 3 Rolle's Theorem

Suppose that $y = f(x)$ is continuous at every point of the closed interval $[a, b]$ and differentiable at every point of its interior (a, b). If

$$f(a) = f(b),$$

then there is at least one number c in (a, b) at which

$$f'(c) = 0.$$

Proof Being continuous, f assumes absolute maximum and minimum values on $[a, b]$. These can occur only

1. at interior points where f' is zero,

2. at interior points where f' does not exist,

3. at the endpoints of the function's domain, in this case a and b.

By hypothesis, f has a derivative at every interior point. That rules out possibility (2), leaving us with interior points where $f' = 0$ and with the two endpoints a and b.

If either the maximum or the minimum occurs at a point c between a and b, then $f'(c) = 0$ by Theorem 2 in Section 4.1, and we have found a point for Rolle's theorem.

If both the absolute maximum and the absolute minimum occur at the endpoints, then because $f(a) = f(b)$ it must be the case that f is a constant function with $f(x) = f(a) = f(b)$ for every $x \in [a, b]$. Therefore $f'(x) = 0$ and the point c can be taken anywhere in the interior (a, b). ∎

The hypotheses of Theorem 3 are essential. If they fail at even one point, the graph may not have a horizontal tangent (Figure 4.11).

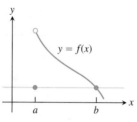
(a) Discontinuous at an endpoint of $[a, b]$

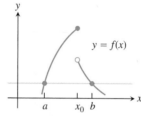
(b) Discontinuous at an interior point of $[a, b]$

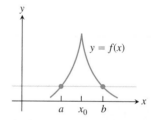
(c) Continuous on $[a, b]$ but not differentiable at an interior point

FIGURE 4.11 There may be no horizontal tangent if the hypotheses of Rolle's Theorem do not hold.

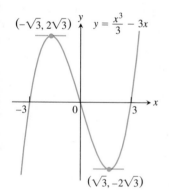

FIGURE 4.12 As predicted by Rolle's Theorem, this curve has horizontal tangents between the points where it crosses the x-axis (Example 1).

EXAMPLE 1 Horizontal Tangents of a Cubic Polynomial

The polynomial function

$$f(x) = \frac{x^3}{3} - 3x$$

graphed in Figure 4.12 is continuous at every point of $[-3, 3]$ and is differentiable at every point of $(-3, 3)$. Since $f(-3) = f(3) = 0$, Rolle's Theorem says that f' must be zero at least once in the open interval between $a = -3$ and $b = 3$. In fact, $f'(x) = x^2 - 3$ is zero twice in this interval, once at $x = -\sqrt{3}$ and again at $x = \sqrt{3}$. ∎

EXAMPLE 2 Solution of an Equation $f(x) = 0$

Show that the equation

$$x^3 + 3x + 1 = 0$$

has exactly one real solution.

Solution Let

$$y = f(x) = x^3 + 3x + 1.$$

Then the derivative

$$f'(x) = 3x^2 + 3$$

is never zero (because it is always positive). Now, if there were even two points $x = a$ and $x = b$ where $f(x)$ was zero, Rolle's Theorem would guarantee the existence of a point $x = c$ in between them where f' was zero. Therefore, f has no more than one zero. It does in fact have one zero, because the Intermediate Value Theorem tells us that the graph of $y = f(x)$ crosses the x-axis somewhere between $x = -1$ (where $y = -3$) and $x = 0$ (where $y = 1$). (See Figure 4.13.) ∎

Our main use of Rolle's Theorem is in proving the Mean Value Theorem.

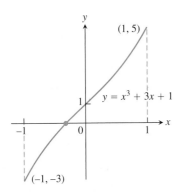

FIGURE 4.13 The only real zero of the polynomial $y = x^3 + 3x + 1$ is the one shown here where the curve crosses the x-axis between -1 and 0 (Example 2).

The Mean Value Theorem

The Mean Value Theorem, which was first stated by Joseph-Louis Lagrange, is a slanted version of Rolle's Theorem (Figure 4.14). There is a point where the tangent is parallel to chord AB.

THEOREM 4   The Mean Value Theorem

Suppose $y = f(x)$ is continuous on a closed interval $[a, b]$ and differentiable on the interval's interior (a, b). Then there is at least one point c in (a, b) at which

$$\frac{f(b) - f(a)}{b - a} = f'(c). \tag{1}$$

Proof   We picture the graph of f as a curve in the plane and draw a line through the points $A(a, f(a))$ and $B(b, f(b))$ (see Figure 4.15). The line is the graph of the function

$$g(x) = f(a) + \frac{f(b) - f(a)}{b - a}(x - a) \tag{2}$$

(point-slope equation). The vertical difference between the graphs of f and g at x is

$$h(x) = f(x) - g(x)$$
$$= f(x) - f(a) - \frac{f(b) - f(a)}{b - a}(x - a). \tag{3}$$

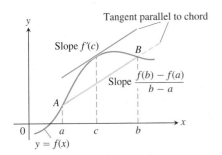

FIGURE 4.14 Geometrically, the Mean Value Theorem says that somewhere between A and B the curve has at least one tangent parallel to chord AB.

Figure 4.16 shows the graphs of f, g, and h together.

The function h satisfies the hypotheses of Rolle's Theorem on $[a, b]$. It is continuous on $[a, b]$ and differentiable on (a, b) because both f and g are. Also, $h(a) = h(b) = 0$ because the graphs of f and g both pass through A and B. Therefore $h'(c) = 0$ at some point $c \in (a, b)$. This is the point we want for Equation (1).

To verify Equation (1), we differentiate both sides of Equation (3) with respect to x and then set $x = c$:

$$h'(x) = f'(x) - \frac{f(b) - f(a)}{b - a} \qquad \text{Derivative of Eq. (3)} \dots$$

$$h'(c) = f'(c) - \frac{f(b) - f(a)}{b - a} \qquad \dots \text{with } x = c$$

$$0 = f'(c) - \frac{f(b) - f(a)}{b - a} \qquad h'(c) = 0$$

$$f'(c) = \frac{f(b) - f(a)}{b - a}, \qquad \text{Rearranged}$$

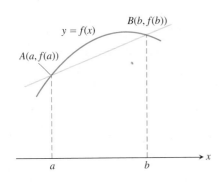

FIGURE 4.15 The graph of f and the chord AB over the interval $[a, b]$.

which is what we set out to prove. ∎

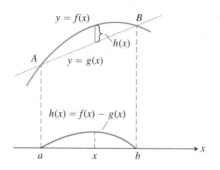

FIGURE 4.16 The chord AB is the graph of the function $g(x)$. The function $h(x) = f(x) - g(x)$ gives the vertical distance between the graphs of f and g at x.

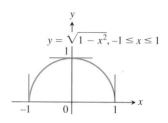

FIGURE 4.17 The function $f(x) = \sqrt{1 - x^2}$ satisfies the hypotheses (and conclusion) of the Mean Value Theorem on $[-1, 1]$ even though f is not differentiable at -1 and 1.

The hypotheses of the Mean Value Theorem do not require f to be differentiable at either a or b. Continuity at a and b is enough (Figure 4.17).

EXAMPLE 3 The function $f(x) = x^2$ (Figure 4.18) is continuous for $0 \le x \le 2$ and differentiable for $0 < x < 2$. Since $f(0) = 0$ and $f(2) = 4$, the Mean Value Theorem says that at some point c in the interval, the derivative $f'(x) = 2x$ must have the value $(4 - 0)/(2 - 0) = 2$. In this (exceptional) case we can identify c by solving the equation $2c = 2$ to get $c = 1$. ∎

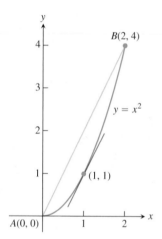

FIGURE 4.18 As we find in Example 3, $c = 1$ is where the tangent is parallel to the chord.

A Physical Interpretation

If we think of the number $(f(b) - f(a))/(b - a)$ as the average change in f over $[a, b]$ and $f'(c)$ as an instantaneous change, then the Mean Value Theorem says that at some interior point the instantaneous change must equal the average change over the entire interval.

EXAMPLE 4 If a car accelerating from zero takes 8 sec to go 352 ft, its average velocity for the 8-sec interval is $352/8 = 44$ ft/sec. At some point during the acceleration, the Mean Value Theorem says, the speedometer must read exactly 30 mph (44 ft/sec) (Figure 4.19). ∎

Mathematical Consequences

At the beginning of the section, we asked what kind of function has a zero derivative over an interval. The first corollary of the Mean Value Theorem provides the answer.

FIGURE 4.19 Distance versus elapsed time for the car in Example 4.

COROLLARY 1 Functions with Zero Derivatives Are Constant

If $f'(x) = 0$ at each point x of an open interval (a, b), then $f(x) = C$ for all $x \in (a, b)$, where C is a constant.

Proof   We want to show that f has a constant value on the interval (a, b). We do so by showing that if x_1 and x_2 are any two points in (a, b), then $f(x_1) = f(x_2)$. Numbering x_1 and x_2 from left to right, we have $x_1 < x_2$. Then f satisfies the hypotheses of the Mean Value Theorem on $[x_1, x_2]$: It is differentiable at every point of $[x_1, x_2]$ and hence continuous at every point as well. Therefore,

$$\frac{f(x_2) - f(x_1)}{x_2 - x_1} = f'(c)$$

at some point c between x_1 and x_2. Since $f' = 0$ throughout (a, b), this equation translates successively into

$$\frac{f(x_2) - f(x_1)}{x_2 - x_1} = 0, \qquad f(x_2) - f(x_1) = 0, \qquad \text{and} \qquad f(x_1) = f(x_2). \qquad \blacksquare$$

At the beginning of this section, we also asked about the relationship between two functions that have identical derivatives over an interval. The next corollary tells us that their values on the interval have a constant difference.

COROLLARY 2   Functions with the Same Derivative Differ by a Constant

If $f'(x) = g'(x)$ at each point x in an open interval (a, b), then there exists a constant C such that $f(x) = g(x) + C$ for all $x \in (a, b)$. That is, $f - g$ is a constant on (a, b).

Proof   At each point $x \in (a, b)$ the derivative of the difference function $h = f - g$ is

$$h'(x) = f'(x) - g'(x) = 0.$$

Thus, $h(x) = C$ on (a, b) by Corollary 1. That is, $f(x) - g(x) = C$ on (a, b), so $f(x) = g(x) + C$. $\qquad\blacksquare$

Corollaries 1 and 2 are also true if the open interval (a, b) fails to be finite. That is, they remain true if the interval is (a, ∞), $(-\infty, b)$, or $(-\infty, \infty)$.

Corollary 2 plays an important role when we discuss antiderivatives in Section 4.8. It tells us, for instance, that since the derivative of $f(x) = x^2$ on $(-\infty, \infty)$ is $2x$, any other function with derivative $2x$ on $(-\infty, \infty)$ must have the formula $x^2 + C$ for some value of C (Figure 4.20).

EXAMPLE 5   Find the function $f(x)$ whose derivative is $\sin x$ and whose graph passes through the point $(0, 2)$.

Solution   Since $f(x)$ has the same derivative as $g(x) = -\cos x$, we know that $f(x) = -\cos x + C$ for some constant C. The value of C can be determined from the condition that $f(0) = 2$ (the graph of f passes through $(0, 2)$):

$$f(0) = -\cos(0) + C = 2, \qquad \text{so} \qquad C = 3.$$

The function is $f(x) = -\cos x + 3$. $\qquad\blacksquare$

Finding Velocity and Position from Acceleration

Here is how to find the velocity and displacement functions of a body falling freely from rest with acceleration 9.8 m/sec^2.

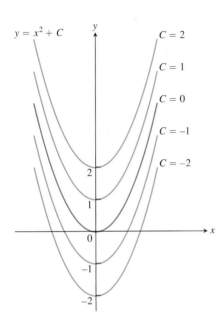

FIGURE 4.20   From a geometric point of view, Corollary 2 of the Mean Value Theorem says that the graphs of functions with identical derivatives on an interval can differ only by a vertical shift there. The graphs of the functions with derivative $2x$ are the parabolas $y = x^2 + C$, shown here for selected values of C.

We know that $v(t)$ is some function whose derivative is 9.8. We also know that the derivative of $g(t) = 9.8t$ is 9.8. By Corollary 2,

$$v(t) = 9.8t + C$$

for some constant C. Since the body falls from rest, $v(0) = 0$. Thus

$$9.8(0) + C = 0, \quad \text{and} \quad C = 0.$$

The velocity function must be $v(t) = 9.8t$. How about the position function $s(t)$?

We know that $s(t)$ is some function whose derivative is $9.8t$. We also know that the derivative of $f(t) = 4.9t^2$ is $9.8t$. By Corollary 2,

$$s(t) = 4.9t^2 + C$$

for some constant C. If the initial height is $s(0) = h$, measured positive downward from the rest position, then

$$4.9(0)^2 + C = h, \quad \text{and} \quad C = h.$$

The position function must be $s(t) = 4.9t^2 + h$.

The ability to find functions from their rates of change is one of the very powerful tools of calculus. As we will see, it lies at the heart of the mathematical developments in Chapter 5.

EXERCISES 4.2

Finding c in the Mean Value Theorem

Find the value or values of c that satisfy the equation

$$\frac{f(b) - f(a)}{b - a} = f'(c)$$

in the conclusion of the Mean Value Theorem for the functions and intervals in Exercises 1–4.

1. $f(x) = x^2 + 2x - 1, \quad [0, 1]$

2. $f(x) = x^{2/3}, \quad [0, 1]$

3. $f(x) = x + \dfrac{1}{x}, \quad \left[\dfrac{1}{2}, 2\right]$

4. $f(x) = \sqrt{x - 1}, \quad [1, 3]$

Checking and Using Hypotheses

Which of the functions in Exercises 5–8 satisfy the hypotheses of the Mean Value Theorem on the given interval, and which do not? Give reasons for your answers.

5. $f(x) = x^{2/3}, \quad [-1, 8]$

6. $f(x) = x^{4/5}, \quad [0, 1]$

7. $f(x) = \sqrt{x(1 - x)}, \quad [0, 1]$

8. $f(x) = \begin{cases} \dfrac{\sin x}{x}, & -\pi \le x < 0 \\ 0, & x = 0 \end{cases}$

9. The function

$$f(x) = \begin{cases} x, & 0 \le x < 1 \\ 0, & x = 1 \end{cases}$$

is zero at $x = 0$ and $x = 1$ and differentiable on $(0, 1)$, but its derivative on $(0, 1)$ is never zero. How can this be? Doesn't Rolle's Theorem say the derivative has to be zero somewhere in $(0, 1)$? Give reasons for your answer.

10. For what values of a, m and b does the function

$$f(x) = \begin{cases} 3, & x = 0 \\ -x^2 + 3x + a, & 0 < x < 1 \\ mx + b, & 1 \le x \le 2 \end{cases}$$

satisfy the hypotheses of the Mean Value Theorem on the interval $[0, 2]$?

Roots (Zeros)

11. **a.** Plot the zeros of each polynomial on a line together with the zeros of its first derivative.

   i) $y = x^2 - 4$

   ii) $y = x^2 + 8x + 15$

   iii) $y = x^3 - 3x^2 + 4 = (x + 1)(x - 2)^2$

   iv) $y = x^3 - 33x^2 + 216x = x(x - 9)(x - 24)$

b. Use Rolle's Theorem to prove that between every two zeros of $x^n + a_{n-1}x^{n-1} + \cdots + a_1 x + a_0$ there lies a zero of
$$nx^{n-1} + (n-1)a_{n-1}x^{n-2} + \cdots + a_1.$$

12. Suppose that f'' is continuous on $[a, b]$ and that f has three zeros in the interval. Show that f'' has at least one zero in (a, b). Generalize this result.

13. Show that if $f'' > 0$ throughout an interval $[a, b]$, then f' has at most one zero in $[a, b]$. What if $f'' < 0$ throughout $[a, b]$ instead?

14. Show that a cubic polynomial can have at most three real zeros.

Show that the functions in Exercises 15–22 have exactly one zero in the given interval.

15. $f(x) = x^4 + 3x + 1, \quad [-2, -1]$

16. $f(x) = x^3 + \dfrac{4}{x^2} + 7, \quad (-\infty, 0)$

17. $g(t) = \sqrt{t} + \sqrt{1 + t} - 4, \quad (0, \infty)$

18. $g(t) = \dfrac{1}{1 - t} + \sqrt{1 + t} - 3.1, \quad (-1, 1)$

19. $r(\theta) = \theta + \sin^2\left(\dfrac{\theta}{3}\right) - 8, \quad (-\infty, \infty)$

20. $r(\theta) = 2\theta - \cos^2\theta + \sqrt{2}, \quad (-\infty, \infty)$

21. $r(\theta) = \sec\theta - \dfrac{1}{\theta^3} + 5, \quad (0, \pi/2)$

22. $r(\theta) = \tan\theta - \cot\theta - \theta, \quad (0, \pi/2)$

Finding Functions from Derivatives

23. Suppose that $f(-1) = 3$ and that $f'(x) = 0$ for all x. Must $f(x) = 3$ for all x? Give reasons for your answer.

24. Suppose that $f(0) = 5$ and that $f'(x) = 2$ for all x. Must $f(x) = 2x + 5$ for all x. Give reasons for your answer.

25. Suppose that $f'(x) = 2x$ for all x. Find $f(2)$ if
    a. $f(0) = 0$ **b.** $f(1) = 0$ **c.** $f(-2) = 3$.

26. What can be said about functions whose derivatives are constant? Give reasons for your answer.

In Exercises 27–32, find all possible functions with the given derivative.

27. **a.** $y' = x$ **b.** $y' = x^2$ **c.** $y' = x^3$

28. **a.** $y' = 2x$ **b.** $y' = 2x - 1$ **c.** $y' = 3x^2 + 2x - 1$

29. **a.** $y' = -\dfrac{1}{x^2}$ **b.** $y' = 1 - \dfrac{1}{x^2}$ **c.** $y' = 5 + \dfrac{1}{x^2}$

30. **a.** $y' = \dfrac{1}{2\sqrt{x}}$ **b.** $y' = \dfrac{1}{\sqrt{x}}$ **c.** $y' = 4x - \dfrac{1}{\sqrt{x}}$

31. **a.** $y' = \sin 2t$ **b.** $y' = \cos\dfrac{t}{2}$ **c.** $y' = \sin 2t + \cos\dfrac{t}{2}$

32. **a.** $y' = \sec^2\theta$ **b.** $y' = \sqrt{\theta}$ **c.** $y' = \sqrt{\theta} - \sec^2\theta$

In Exercises 33–36, find the function with the given derivative whose graph passes through the point P.

33. $f'(x) = 2x - 1, \quad P(0, 0)$

34. $g'(x) = \dfrac{1}{x^2} + 2x, \quad P(-1, 1)$

35. $r'(\theta) = 8 - \csc^2\theta, \quad P\left(\dfrac{\pi}{4}, 0\right)$

36. $r'(t) = \sec t \tan t - 1, \quad P(0, 0)$

Finding Position from Velocity

Exercises 37–40 give the velocity $v = ds/dt$ and initial position of a body moving along a coordinate line. Find the body's position at time t.

37. $v = 9.8t + 5, \quad s(0) = 10$ 38. $v = 32t - 2, \quad s(0.5) = 4$

39. $v = \sin \pi t, \quad s(0) = 0$ 40. $v = \dfrac{2}{\pi}\cos\dfrac{2t}{\pi}, \quad s(\pi^2) = 1$

Finding Position from Acceleration

Exercises 41–44 give the acceleration $a = d^2s/dt^2$, initial velocity, and initial position of a body moving on a coordinate line. Find the body's position at time t.

41. $a = 32, \quad v(0) = 20, \quad s(0) = 5$

42. $a = 9.8, \quad v(0) = -3, \quad s(0) = 0$

43. $a = -4\sin 2t, \quad v(0) = 2, \quad s(0) = -3$

44. $a = \dfrac{9}{\pi^2}\cos\dfrac{3t}{\pi}, \quad v(0) = 0, \quad s(0) = -1$

Applications

45. **Temperature change** It took 14 sec for a mercury thermometer to rise from $-19°C$ to $100°C$ when it was taken from a freezer and placed in boiling water. Show that somewhere along the way the mercury was rising at the rate of $8.5°C/sec$.

46. A trucker handed in a ticket at a toll booth showing that in 2 hours she had covered 159 mi on a toll road with speed limit 65 mph. The trucker was cited for speeding. Why?

47. Classical accounts tell us that a 170-oar trireme (ancient Greek or Roman warship) once covered 184 sea miles in 24 hours. Explain why at some point during this feat the trireme's speed exceeded 7.5 knots (sea miles per hour).

48. A marathoner ran the 26.2-mi New York City Marathon in 2.2 hours. Show that at least twice the marathoner was running at exactly 11 mph.

49. Show that at some instant during a 2-hour automobile trip the car's speedometer reading will equal the average speed for the trip.

50. **Free fall on the moon** On our moon, the acceleration of gravity is 1.6 m/sec^2. If a rock is dropped into a crevasse, how fast will it be going just before it hits bottom 30 sec later?

Theory and Examples

51. The geometric mean of *a* and *b* The *geometric mean* of two positive numbers *a* and *b* is the number $\sqrt{ab}$. Show that the value of *c* in the conclusion of the Mean Value Theorem for $f(x) = 1/x$ on an interval of positive numbers $[a, b]$ is $c = \sqrt{ab}$.

52. The arithmetic mean of *a* and *b* The *arithmetic mean* of two numbers *a* and *b* is the number $(a + b)/2$. Show that the value of *c* in the conclusion of the Mean Value Theorem for $f(x) = x^2$ on any interval $[a, b]$ is $c = (a + b)/2$.

T 53. Graph the function

$$f(x) = \sin x \sin (x + 2) - \sin^2 (x + 1).$$

What does the graph do? Why does the function behave this way? Give reasons for your answers.

54. Rolle's Theorem

a. Construct a polynomial $f(x)$ that has zeros at $x = -2, -1, 0, 1,$ and 2.

b. Graph *f* and its derivative *f'* together. How is what you see related to Rolle's Theorem?

c. Do $g(x) = \sin x$ and its derivative *g'* illustrate the same phenomenon?

55. Unique solution Assume that *f* is continuous on $[a, b]$ and differentiable on (a, b). Also assume that $f(a)$ and $f(b)$ have opposite signs and that $f' \neq 0$ between *a* and *b*. Show that $f(x) = 0$ exactly once between *a* and *b*.

56. Parallel tangents Assume that *f* and *g* are differentiable on $[a, b]$ and that $f(a) = g(a)$ and $f(b) = g(b)$. Show that there is at least one point between *a* and *b* where the tangents to the graphs of *f* and *g* are parallel or the same line. Illustrate with a sketch.

57. If the graphs of two differentiable functions $f(x)$ and $g(x)$ start at the same point in the plane and the functions have the same rate of change at every point, do the graphs have to be identical? Give reasons for your answer.

58. Show that for any numbers *a* and *b*, the inequality $|\sin b - \sin a| \leq |b - a|$ is true.

59. Assume that *f* is differentiable on $a \leq x \leq b$ and that $f(b) < f(a)$. Show that *f'* is negative at some point between *a* and *b*.

60. Let *f* be a function defined on an interval $[a, b]$. What conditions could you place on *f* to guarantee that

$$\min f' \leq \frac{f(b) - f(a)}{b - a} \leq \max f',$$

where $\min f'$ and $\max f'$ refer to the minimum and maximum values of *f'* on $[a, b]$? Give reasons for your answers.

T 61. Use the inequalities in Exercise 60 to estimate $f(0.1)$ if $f'(x) = 1/(1 + x^4 \cos x)$ for $0 \leq x \leq 0.1$ and $f(0) = 1$.

T 62. Use the inequalities in Exercise 60 to estimate $f(0.1)$ if $f'(x) = 1/(1 - x^4)$ for $0 \leq x \leq 0.1$ and $f(0) = 2$.

63. Let *f* be differentiable at every value of *x* and suppose that $f(1) = 1$, that $f' < 0$ on $(-\infty, 1)$, and that $f' > 0$ on $(1, \infty)$.

a. Show that $f(x) \geq 1$ for all *x*.

b. Must $f'(1) = 0$? Explain.

64. Let $f(x) = px^2 + qx + r$ be a quadratic function defined on a closed interval $[a, b]$. Show that there is exactly one point *c* in (a, b) at which *f* satisfies the conclusion of the Mean Value Theorem.

4.3 Monotonic Functions and The First Derivative Test

In sketching the graph of a differentiable function it is useful to know where it increases (rises from left to right) and where it decreases (falls from left to right) over an interval. This section defines precisely what it means for a function to be increasing or decreasing over an interval, and gives a test to determine where it increases and where it decreases. We also show how to test the critical points of a function for the presence of local extreme values.

Increasing Functions and Decreasing Functions

What kinds of functions have positive derivatives or negative derivatives? The answer, provided by the Mean Value Theorem's third corollary, is this: The only functions with positive derivatives are increasing functions; the only functions with negative derivatives are decreasing functions.

> **DEFINITIONS**   Increasing, Decreasing Function
>
> Let f be a function defined on an interval I and let x_1 and x_2 be any two points in I.
>
> **1.**   If $f(x_1) < f(x_2)$ whenever $x_1 < x_2$, then f is said to be **increasing** on I.
>
> **2.**   If $f(x_2) < f(x_1)$ whenever $x_1 < x_2$, then f is said to be **decreasing** on I.
>
> A function that is increasing or decreasing on I is called **monotonic** on I.

It is important to realize that the definitions of increasing and decreasing functions must be satisfied for *every* pair of points x_1 and x_2 in I with $x_1 < x_2$. Because of the inequality $<$ comparing the function values, and not $\leq$, some books say that f is *strictly* increasing or decreasing on I. The interval I may be finite or infinite.

The function $f(x) = x^2$ decreases on $(-\infty, 0]$ and increases on $[0, \infty)$ as can be seen from its graph (Figure 4.21). The function f is monotonic on $(-\infty, 0]$ and $[0, \infty)$, but it is not monotonic on $(-\infty, \infty)$. Notice that on the interval $(-\infty, 0)$ the tangents have negative slopes, so the first derivative is always negative there; for $(0, \infty)$ the tangents have positive slopes and the first derivative is positive. The following result confirms these observations.

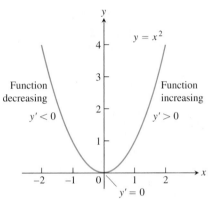

FIGURE 4.21   The function $f(x) = x^2$ is monotonic on the intervals $(-\infty, 0]$ and $[0, \infty)$, but it is not monotonic on $(-\infty, \infty)$.

> **COROLLARY 3**   First Derivative Test for Monotonic Functions
>
> Suppose that f is continuous on $[a, b]$ and differentiable on (a, b).
>
>> If $f'(x) > 0$ at each point $x \in (a, b)$, then f is increasing on $[a, b]$.
>>
>> If $f'(x) < 0$ at each point $x \in (a, b)$, then f is decreasing on $[a, b]$.

Proof   Let x_1 and x_2 be any two points in $[a, b]$ with $x_1 < x_2$. The Mean Value Theorem applied to f on $[x_1, x_2]$ says that

$$f(x_2) - f(x_1) = f'(c)(x_2 - x_1)$$

for some c between x_1 and x_2. The sign of the right-hand side of this equation is the same as the sign of $f'(c)$ because $x_2 - x_1$ is positive. Therefore, $f(x_2) > f(x_1)$ if f' is positive on (a, b) and $f(x_2) < f(x_1)$ if f' is negative on (a, b).   ∎

Here is how to apply the First Derivative Test to find where a function is increasing and decreasing. If $a < b$ are two critical points for a function f, and if f' exists but is not zero on the interval (a, b), then f' must be positive on (a, b) or negative there (Theorem 2, Section 3.1). One way we can determine the sign of f' on the interval is simply by evaluating f' for some point x in (a, b). Then we apply Corollary 3.

EXAMPLE 1   Using the First Derivative Test for Monotonic Functions

Find the critical points of $f(x) = x^3 - 12x - 5$ and identify the intervals on which f is increasing and decreasing.

Solution   The function f is everywhere continuous and differentiable. The first derivative

$$f'(x) = 3x^2 - 12 = 3(x^2 - 4)$$
$$= 3(x + 2)(x - 2)$$

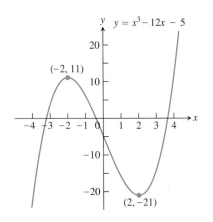

FIGURE 4.22 The function $f(x) = x^3 - 12x - 5$ is monotonic on three separate intervals (Example 1).

is zero at $x = -2$ and $x = 2$. These critical points subdivide the domain of f into intervals $(-\infty, -2)$, $(-2, 2)$, and $(2, \infty)$ on which f' is either positive or negative. We determine the sign of f' by evaluating f at a convenient point in each subinterval. The behavior of f is determined by then applying Corollary 3 to each subinterval. The results are summarized in the following table, and the graph of f is given in Figure 4.22.

Intervals	$-\infty < x < -2$	$-2 < x < 2$	$2 < x < \infty$
f' Evaluated	$f'(-3) = 15$	$f'(0) = -12$	$f'(3) = 15$
Sign of f'	$+$	$-$	$+$
Behavior of f	increasing	decreasing	increasing

■

Corollary 3 is valid for infinite as well as finite intervals, and we used that fact in our analysis in Example 1.

Knowing where a function increases and decreases also tells us how to test for the nature of local extreme values.

HISTORICAL BIOGRAPHY

Edmund Halley
(1656–1742)

First Derivative Test for Local Extrema

In Figure 4.23, at the points where f has a minimum value, $f' < 0$ immediately to the left and $f' > 0$ immediately to the right. (If the point is an endpoint, there is only one side to consider.) Thus, the function is decreasing on the left of the minimum value and it is increasing on its right. Similarly, at the points where f has a maximum value, $f' > 0$ immediately to the left and $f' < 0$ immediately to the right. Thus, the function is increasing on the left of the maximum value and decreasing on its right. In summary, at a local extreme point, the sign of $f'(x)$ changes.

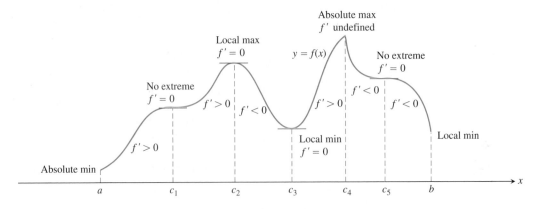

FIGURE 4.23 A function's first derivative tells how the graph rises and falls.

These observations lead to a test for the presence and nature of local extreme values of differentiable functions.

First Derivative Test for Local Extrema

Suppose that c is a critical point of a continuous function f, and that f is differentiable at every point in some interval containing c except possibly at c itself. Moving across c from left to right,

1. if f' changes from negative to positive at c, then f has a local minimum at c;

2. if f' changes from positive to negative at c, then f has a local maximum at c;

3. if f' does not change sign at c (that is, f' is positive on both sides of c or negative on both sides), then f has no local extremum at c.

The test for local extrema at endpoints is similar, but there is only one side to consider.

Proof Part (1). Since the sign of f' changes from negative to positive at c, these are numbers a and b such that $f' < 0$ on (a, c) and $f' > 0$ on (c, b). If $x \in (a, c)$, then $f(c) < f(x)$ because $f' < 0$ implies that f is decreasing on $[a, c]$. If $x \in (c, b)$, then $f(c) < f(x)$ because $f' > 0$ implies that f is increasing on $[c, b]$. Therefore, $f(x) \geq f(c)$ for every $x \in (a, b)$. By definition, f has a local minimum at c.

Parts (2) and (3) are proved similarly. ∎

EXAMPLE 2   Using the First Derivative Test for Local Extrema

Find the critical points of

$$f(x) = x^{1/3}(x - 4) = x^{4/3} - 4x^{1/3}.$$

Identify the intervals on which f is increasing and decreasing. Find the function's local and absolute extreme values.

Solution   The function f is continuous at all x since it is the product of two continuous functions, $x^{1/3}$ and $(x - 4)$. The first derivative

$$f'(x) = \frac{d}{dx}\left(x^{4/3} - 4x^{1/3}\right) = \frac{4}{3}x^{1/3} - \frac{4}{3}x^{-2/3}$$

$$= \frac{4}{3}x^{-2/3}\left(x - 1\right) = \frac{4(x - 1)}{3x^{2/3}}$$

is zero at $x = 1$ and undefined at $x = 0$. There are no endpoints in the domain, so the critical points $x = 0$ and $x = 1$ are the only places where f might have an extreme value.

The critical points partition the x-axis into intervals on which f' is either positive or negative. The sign pattern of f' reveals the behavior of f between and at the critical points. We can display the information in a table like the following:

Intervals	$x < 0$	$0 < x < 1$	$x > 1$
Sign of f'	−	−	+
Behavior of f	decreasing	decreasing	increasing

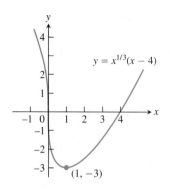

$y = x^{1/3}(x - 4)$

$(1, -3)$

FIGURE 4.24 The function $f(x) = x^{1/3}(x - 4)$ decreases when $x < 1$ and increases when $x > 1$ (Example 2).

Corollary 3 to the Mean Value Theorem tells us that f decreases on $(-\infty, 0)$, decreases on $(0, 1)$, and increases on $(1, \infty)$. The First Derivative Test for Local Extrema tells us that f does not have an extreme value at $x = 0$ (f' does not change sign) and that f has a local minimum at $x = 1$ (f' changes from negative to positive).

The value of the local minimum is $f(1) = 1^{1/3}(1 - 4) = -3$. This is also an absolute minimum because the function's values fall toward it from the left and rise away from it on the right. Figure 4.24 shows this value in relation to the function's graph. Note that $\lim_{x \to 0} f'(x) = -\infty$, so the graph of f has a vertical tangent at the origin.

■

EXERCISES 4.3

Analyzing f Given f'

Answer the following questions about the functions whose derivatives are given in Exercises 1–8:

a. What are the critical points of f?

b. On what intervals is f increasing or decreasing?

c. At what points, if any, does f assume local maximum and minimum values?

1. $f'(x) = x(x - 1)$

2. $f'(x) = (x - 1)(x + 2)$

3. $f'(x) = (x - 1)^2(x + 2)$

4. $f'(x) = (x - 1)^2(x + 2)^2$

5. $f'(x) = (x - 1)(x + 2)(x - 3)$

6. $f'(x) = (x - 7)(x + 1)(x + 5)$

7. $f'(x) = x^{-1/3}(x + 2)$

8. $f'(x) = x^{-1/2}(x - 3)$

Extremes of Given Functions

In Exercises 9–28:

a. Find the intervals on which the function is increasing and decreasing.

b. Then identify the function's local extreme values, if any, saying where they are taken on.

c. Which, if any, of the extreme values are absolute?

T d. Support your findings with a graphing calculator or computer grapher.

9. $g(t) = -t^2 - 3t + 3$

10. $g(t) = -3t^2 + 9t + 5$

11. $h(x) = -x^3 + 2x^2$

12. $h(x) = 2x^3 - 18x$

13. $f(\theta) = 3\theta^2 - 4\theta^3$

14. $f(\theta) = 6\theta - \theta^3$

15. $f(r) = 3r^3 + 16r$

16. $h(r) = (r + 7)^3$

17. $f(x) = x^4 - 8x^2 + 16$

18. $g(x) = x^4 - 4x^3 + 4x^2$

19. $H(t) = \dfrac{3}{2}t^4 - t^6$

20. $K(t) = 15t^3 - t^5$

21. $g(x) = x\sqrt{8 - x^2}$

22. $g(x) = x^2\sqrt{5 - x}$

23. $f(x) = \dfrac{x^2 - 3}{x - 2}, \quad x \neq 2$

24. $f(x) = \dfrac{x^3}{3x^2 + 1}$

25. $f(x) = x^{1/3}(x + 8)$

26. $g(x) = x^{2/3}(x + 5)$

27. $h(x) = x^{1/3}(x^2 - 4)$

28. $k(x) = x^{2/3}(x^2 - 4)$

Extreme Values on Half-Open Intervals

In Exercises 29–36:

a. Identify the function's local extreme values in the given domain, and say where they are assumed.

b. Which of the extreme values, if any, are absolute?

T c. Support your findings with a graphing calculator or computer grapher.

29. $f(x) = 2x - x^2, \quad -\infty < x \leq 2$

30. $f(x) = (x + 1)^2, \quad -\infty < x \leq 0$

31. $g(x) = x^2 - 4x + 4, \quad 1 \leq x < \infty$

32. $g(x) = -x^2 - 6x - 9, \quad -4 \leq x < \infty$

33. $f(t) = 12t - t^3, \quad -3 \leq t < \infty$

34. $f(t) = t^3 - 3t^2, \quad -\infty < t \leq 3$

35. $h(x) = \dfrac{x^3}{3} - 2x^2 + 4x, \quad 0 \leq x < \infty$

36. $k(x) = x^3 + 3x^2 + 3x + 1, \quad -\infty < x \leq 0$

Graphing Calculator or Computer Grapher

In Exercises 37–40:

a. Find the local extrema of each function on the given interval, and say where they are assumed.

T b. Graph the function and its derivative together. Comment on the behavior of f in relation to the signs and values of f'.

37. $f(x) = \dfrac{x}{2} - 2 \sin \dfrac{x}{2}, \quad 0 \le x \le 2\pi$

38. $f(x) = -2 \cos x - \cos^2 x, \quad -\pi \le x \le \pi$

39. $f(x) = \csc^2 x - 2 \cot x, \quad 0 < x < \pi$

40. $f(x) = \sec^2 x - 2 \tan x, \quad \dfrac{-\pi}{2} < x < \dfrac{\pi}{2}$

Theory and Examples

Show that the functions in Exercises 41 and 42 have local extreme values at the given values of θ, and say which kind of local extreme the function has.

41. $h(\theta) = 3 \cos \dfrac{\theta}{2}, \quad 0 \le \theta \le 2\pi, \quad \text{at } \theta = 0 \text{ and } \theta = 2\pi$

42. $h(\theta) = 5 \sin \dfrac{\theta}{2}, \quad 0 \le \theta \le \pi, \quad \text{at } \theta = 0 \text{ and } \theta = \pi$

43. Sketch the graph of a differentiable function $y = f(x)$ through the point $(1, 1)$ if $f'(1) = 0$ and
a. $f'(x) > 0$ for $x < 1$ and $f'(x) < 0$ for $x > 1$;
b. $f'(x) < 0$ for $x < 1$ and $f'(x) > 0$ for $x > 1$;
c. $f'(x) > 0$ for $x \ne 1$;
d. $f'(x) < 0$ for $x \ne 1$.

44. Sketch the graph of a differentiable function $y = f(x)$ that has
a. a local minimum at $(1, 1)$ and a local maximum at $(3, 3)$;
b. a local maximum at $(1, 1)$ and a local minimum at $(3, 3)$;
c. local maxima at $(1, 1)$ and $(3, 3)$;
d. local minima at $(1, 1)$ and $(3, 3)$.

45. Sketch the graph of a continuous function $y = g(x)$ such that
a. $g(2) = 2, \quad 0 < g' < 1$ for $x < 2, \quad g'(x) \to 1^-$ as $x \to 2^-, \quad -1 < g' < 0$ for $x > 2$, and $g'(x) \to -1^+$ as $x \to 2^+$;
b. $g(2) = 2, \quad g' < 0$ for $x < 2, \quad g'(x) \to -\infty$ as $x \to 2^-, \quad g' > 0$ for $x > 2$, and $g'(x) \to \infty$ as $x \to 2^+$.

46. Sketch the graph of a continuous function $y = h(x)$ such that
a. $h(0) = 0, -2 \le h(x) \le 2$ for all $x, h'(x) \to \infty$ as $x \to 0^-$, and $h'(x) \to \infty$ as $x \to 0^+$;
b. $h(0) = 0, -2 \le h(x) \le 0$ for all $x, h'(x) \to \infty$ as $x \to 0^-$, and $h'(x) \to -\infty$ as $x \to 0^+$.

47. As x moves from left to right through the point $c = 2$, is the graph of $f(x) = x^3 - 3x + 2$ rising, or is it falling? Give reasons for your answer.

48. Find the intervals on which the function $f(x) = ax^2 + bx + c$, $a \ne 0$, is increasing and decreasing. Describe the reasoning behind your answer.

Concavity and Curve Sketching

In Section 4.3 we saw how the first derivative tells us where a function is increasing and where it is decreasing. At a critical point of a differentiable function, the First Derivative Test tells us whether there is a local maximum or a local minimum, or whether the graph just continues to rise or fall there.

In this section we see how the second derivative gives information about the way the graph of a differentiable function bends or turns. This additional information enables us to capture key aspects of the behavior of a function and its graph, and then present these features in a sketch of the graph.

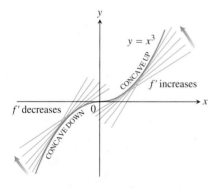

FIGURE 4.25 The graph of $f(x) = x^3$ is concave down on $(-\infty, 0)$ and concave up on $(0, \infty)$ (Example 1a).

Concavity

As you can see in Figure 4.25, the curve $y = x^3$ rises as x increases, but the portions defined on the intervals $(-\infty, 0)$ and $(0, \infty)$ turn in different ways. As we approach the origin from the left along the curve, the curve turns to our right and falls below its tangents. The slopes of the tangents are decreasing on the interval $(-\infty, 0)$. As we move away from the origin along the curve to the right, the curve turns to our left and rises above its tangents. The slopes of the tangents are increasing on the interval $(0, \infty)$. This turning or bending behavior defines the *concavity* of the curve.

> **DEFINITION** Concave Up, Concave Down
> The graph of a differentiable function $y = f(x)$ is
>
> **(a) concave up** on an open interval I if f' is increasing on I
>
> **(b) concave down** on an open interval I if f' is decreasing on I.

If $y = f(x)$ has a second derivative, we can apply Corollary 3 of the Mean Value Theorem to conclude that f' increases if $f'' > 0$ on I, and decreases if $f'' < 0$.

> **The Second Derivative Test for Concavity**
> Let $y = f(x)$ be twice-differentiable on an interval I.
>
> 1. If $f'' > 0$ on I, the graph of f over I is concave up.
> 2. If $f'' < 0$ on I, the graph of f over I is concave down.

If $y = f(x)$ is twice-differentiable, we will use the notations f'' and y'' interchangeably when denoting the second derivative.

EXAMPLE 1 Applying the Concavity Test

(a) The curve $y = x^3$ (Figure 4.25) is concave down on $(-\infty, 0)$ where $y'' = 6x < 0$ and concave up on $(0, \infty)$ where $y'' = 6x > 0$.

(b) The curve $y = x^2$ (Figure 4.26) is concave up on $(-\infty, \infty)$ because its second derivative $y'' = 2$ is always positive. ∎

EXAMPLE 2 Determining Concavity

Determine the concavity of $y = 3 + \sin x$ on $[0, 2\pi]$.

Solution The graph of $y = 3 + \sin x$ is concave down on $(0, \pi)$, where $y'' = -\sin x$ is negative. It is concave up on $(\pi, 2\pi)$, where $y'' = -\sin x$ is positive (Figure 4.27). ∎

Points of Inflection

The curve $y = 3 + \sin x$ in Example 2 changes concavity at the point $(\pi, 3)$. We call $(\pi, 3)$ a *point of inflection* of the curve.

> **DEFINITION** Point of Inflection
> A point where the graph of a function has a tangent line and where the concavity changes is a **point of inflection**.

A point on a curve where y'' is positive on one side and negative on the other is a point of inflection. At such a point, y'' is either zero (because derivatives have the Intermediate Value Property) or undefined. If y is a twice-differentiable function, $y'' = 0$ at a point of inflection and y' has a local maximum or minimum.

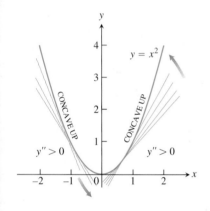

FIGURE 4.26 The graph of $f(x) = x^2$ is concave up on every interval (Example 1b).

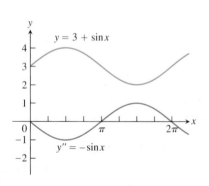

FIGURE 4.27 Using the graph of y'' to determine the concavity of y (Example 2).

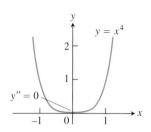

FIGURE 4.28 The graph of $y = x^4$ has no inflection point at the origin, even though $y'' = 0$ there (Example 3).

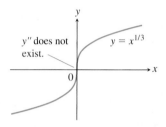

FIGURE 4.29 A point where y'' fails to exist can be a point of inflection (Example 4).

EXAMPLE 3   An Inflection Point May Not Exist Where $y'' = 0$

The curve $y = x^4$ has no inflection point at $x = 0$ (Figure 4.28). Even though $y'' = 12x^2$ is zero there, it does not change sign.   ■

EXAMPLE 4   An Inflection Point May Occur Where y'' Does Not Exist

The curve $y = x^{1/3}$ has a point of inflection at $x = 0$ (Figure 4.29), but y'' does not exist there.

$$y'' = \frac{d^2}{dx^2}\left(x^{1/3}\right) = \frac{d}{dx}\left(\frac{1}{3}x^{-2/3}\right) = -\frac{2}{9}x^{-5/3}.$$ ■

We see from Example 3 that a zero second derivative does not always produce a point of inflection. From Example 4, we see that inflection points can also occur where there *is* no second derivative.

To study the motion of a body moving along a line as a function of time, we often are interested in knowing when the body's acceleration, given by the second derivative, is positive or negative. The points of inflection on the graph of the body's position function reveal where the acceleration changes sign.

EXAMPLE 5   Studying Motion Along a Line

A particle is moving along a horizontal line with position function

$$s(t) = 2t^3 - 14t^2 + 22t - 5, \qquad t \geq 0.$$

Find the velocity and acceleration, and describe the motion of the particle.

Solution   The velocity is

$$v(t) = s'(t) = 6t^2 - 28t + 22 = 2(t - 1)(3t - 11),$$

and the acceleration is

$$a(t) = v'(t) = s''(t) = 12t - 28 = 4(3t - 7).$$

When the function $s(t)$ is increasing, the particle is moving to the right; when $s(t)$ is decreasing, the particle is moving to the left.

Notice that the first derivative ($v = s'$) is zero when $t = 1$ and $t = 11/3$.

Intervals	$0 < t < 1$	$1 < t < 11/3$	$11/3 < t$
Sign of $v = s'$	+	−	+
Behavior of s	increasing	decreasing	increasing
Particle motion	right	left	right

The particle is moving to the right in the time intervals $[0, 1)$ and $(11/3, \infty)$, and moving to the left in $(1, 11/3)$. It is momentarily stationary (at rest), at $t = 1$ and $t = 11/3$.

The acceleration $a(t) = s''(t) = 4(3t - 7)$ is zero when $t = 7/3$.

Intervals	$0 < t < 7/3$	$7/3 < t$
Sign of $a = s''$	−	+
Graph of s	concave down	concave up

The accelerating force is directed toward the left during the time interval [0, 7/3], is momentarily zero at $t = 7/3$, and is directed toward the right thereafter. ∎

Second Derivative Test for Local Extrema

Instead of looking for sign changes in f' at critical points, we can sometimes use the following test to determine the presence and character of local extrema.

THEOREM 5   Second Derivative Test for Local Extrema

Suppose f'' is continuous on an open interval that contains $x = c$.

1. If $f'(c) = 0$ and $f''(c) < 0$, then f has a local maximum at $x = c$.
2. If $f'(c) = 0$ and $f''(c) > 0$, then f has a local minimum at $x = c$.
3. If $f'(c) = 0$ and $f''(c) = 0$, then the test fails. The function f may have a local maximum, a local minimum, or neither.

$f' = 0, f'' < 0$
⇒ local max

$f' = 0, f'' > 0$
⇒ local min

Proof   Part (1). If $f''(c) < 0$, then $f''(x) < 0$ on some open interval I containing the point c, since f'' is continuous. Therefore, f' is decreasing on I. Since $f'(c) = 0$, the sign of f' changes from positive to negative at c so f has a local maximum at c by the First Derivative Test.

The proof of Part (2) is similar.

For Part (3), consider the three functions $y = x^4$, $y = -x^4$, and $y = x^3$. For each function, the first and second derivatives are zero at $x = 0$. Yet the function $y = x^4$ has a local minimum there, $y = -x^4$ has a local maximum, and $y = x^3$ is increasing in any open interval containing $x = 0$ (having neither a maximum nor a minimum there). Thus the test fails. ∎

This test requires us to know f'' *only at c itself* and not in an interval about c. This makes the test easy to apply. That's the good news. The bad news is that the test is inconclusive if $f'' = 0$ or if f'' does not exist at $x = c$. When this happens, use the First Derivative Test for local extreme values.

Together f' and f'' tell us the shape of the function's graph, that is, where the critical points are located and what happens at a critical point, where the function is increasing and where it is decreasing, and how the curve is turning or bending as defined by its concavity. We use this information to sketch a graph of the function that captures its key features.

EXAMPLE 6   Using f' and f'' to Graph f

Sketch a graph of the function

$$f(x) = x^4 - 4x^3 + 10$$

using the following steps.

(a) Identify where the extrema of f occur.
(b) Find the intervals on which f is increasing and the intervals on which f is decreasing.
(c) Find where the graph of f is concave up and where it is concave down.
(d) Sketch the general shape of the graph for f.

(e) Plot some specific points, such as local maximum and minimum points, points of inflection, and intercepts. Then sketch the curve.

Solution f is continuous since $f'(x) = 4x^3 - 12x^2$ exists. The domain of f is $(-\infty, \infty)$, and the domain of f' is also $(-\infty, \infty)$. Thus, the critical points of f occur only at the zeros of f'. Since

$$f'(x) = 4x^3 - 12x^2 = 4x^2(x - 3)$$

the first derivative is zero at $x = 0$ and $x = 3$.

Intervals	$x < 0$	$0 < x < 3$	$3 < x$
Sign of f'	$-$	$-$	$+$
Behavior of f	decreasing	decreasing	increasing

(a) Using the First Derivative Test for local extrema and the table above, we see that there is no extremum at $x = 0$ and a local minimum at $x = 3$.

(b) Using the table above, we see that f is decreasing on $(-\infty, 0]$ and $[0, 3]$, and increasing on $[3, \infty)$.

(c) $f''(x) = 12x^2 - 24x = 12x(x - 2)$ is zero at $x = 0$ and $x = 2$.

Intervals	$x < 0$	$0 < x < 2$	$2 < x$
Sign of f''	$+$	$-$	$+$
Behavior of f	concave up	concave down	concave up

We see that f is concave up on the intervals $(-\infty, 0)$ and $(2, \infty)$, and concave down on $(0, 2)$.

(d) Summarizing the information in the two tables above, we obtain

$x < 0$	$0 < x < 2$	$2 < x < 3$	$3 < x$
decreasing	decreasing	decreasing	increasing
concave up	concave down	concave up	concave up

The general shape of the curve is

General shape.

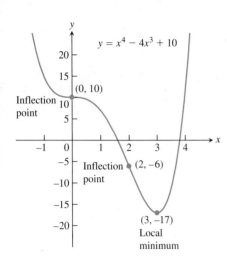

FIGURE 4.30 The graph of $f(x) = x^4 - 4x^3 + 10$ (Example 6).

(e) Plot the curve's intercepts (if possible) and the points where y' and y'' are zero. Indicate any local extreme values and inflection points. Use the general shape as a guide to sketch the curve. (Plot additional points as needed.) Figure 4.30 shows the graph of f. ∎

The steps in Example 6 help in giving a procedure for graphing to capture the key features of a function and its graph.

Strategy for Graphing $y = f(x)$

1. Identify the domain of f and any symmetries the curve may have.
2. Find y' and y''.
3. Find the critical points of f, and identify the function's behavior at each one.
4. Find where the curve is increasing and where it is decreasing.
5. Find the points of inflection, if any occur, and determine the concavity of the curve.
6. Identify any asymptotes.
7. Plot key points, such as the intercepts and the points found in Steps 3–5, and sketch the curve.

EXAMPLE 7 Using the Graphing Strategy

Sketch the graph of $f(x) = \dfrac{(x + 1)^2}{1 + x^2}$.

Solution

1. The domain of f is $(-\infty, \infty)$ and there are no symmetries about either axis or the origin (Section 1.4).

2. *Find f' and f''.*

$$f(x) = \frac{(x + 1)^2}{1 + x^2}$$ *x-intercept at $x = -1$, y-intercept ($y = 1$) at $x = 0$*

$$f'(x) = \frac{(1 + x^2) \cdot 2(x + 1) - (x + 1)^2 \cdot 2x}{(1 + x^2)^2}$$

$$= \frac{2(1 - x^2)}{(1 + x^2)^2}$$ *Critical points: $x = -1, x = 1$*

$$f''(x) = \frac{(1 + x^2)^2 \cdot 2(-2x) - 2(1 - x^2)[2(1 + x^2) \cdot 2x]}{(1 + x^2)^4}$$

$$= \frac{4x(x^2 - 3)}{(1 + x^2)^3}$$ *After some algebra*

3. *Behavior at critical points.* The critical points occur only at $x = \pm 1$ where $f'(x) = 0$ (Step 2) since f' exists everywhere over the domain of f. At $x = -1$, $f''(-1) = 1 > 0$ yielding a relative minimum by the Second Derivative Test. At $x = 1$, $f''(1) = -1 < 0$ yielding a relative maximum by the Second Derivative Test. We will see in Step 6 that both are absolute extrema as well.

4. *Increasing and decreasing.* We see that on the interval $(-\infty, -1)$ the derivative $f'(x) < 0$, and the curve is decreasing. On the interval $(-1, 1)$, $f'(x) > 0$ and the curve is increasing; it is decreasing on $(1, \infty)$ where $f'(x) < 0$ again.

5. *Inflection points.* Notice that the denominator of the second derivative (Step 2) is always positive. The second derivative f'' is zero when $x = -\sqrt{3}, 0$, and $\sqrt{3}$. The second derivative changes sign at each of these points: negative on $\left(-\infty, -\sqrt{3}\right)$, positive on $\left(-\sqrt{3}, 0\right)$, negative on $\left(0, \sqrt{3}\right)$, and positive again on $\left(\sqrt{3}, \infty\right)$. Thus each point is a point of inflection. The curve is concave down on the interval $\left(-\infty, -\sqrt{3}\right)$, concave up on $\left(-\sqrt{3}, 0\right)$, concave down on $\left(0, \sqrt{3}\right)$, and concave up again on $\left(\sqrt{3}, \infty\right)$.

6. *Asymptotes.* Expanding the numerator of $f(x)$ and then dividing both numerator and denominator by x^2 gives

$$f(x) = \frac{(x + 1)^2}{1 + x^2} = \frac{x^2 + 2x + 1}{1 + x^2} \qquad \text{Expanding numerator}$$

$$= \frac{1 + (2/x) + (1/x^2)}{(1/x^2) + 1}. \qquad \text{Dividing by } x^2$$

We see that $f(x) \rightarrow 1^+$ as $x \rightarrow \infty$ and that $f(x) \rightarrow 1^-$ as $x \rightarrow -\infty$. Thus, the line $y = 1$ is a horizontal asymptote.

Since f decreases on $(-\infty, -1)$ and then increases on $(-1, 1)$, we know that $f(-1) = 0$ is a local minimum. Although f decreases on $(1, \infty)$, it never crosses the horizontal asymptote $y = 1$ on that interval (it approaches the asymptote from above). So the graph never becomes negative, and $f(-1) = 0$ is an absolute minimum as well. Likewise, $f(1) = 2$ is an absolute maximum because the graph never crosses the asymptote $y = 1$ on the interval $(-\infty, -1)$, approaching it from below. Therefore, there are no vertical asymptotes (the range of f is $0 \leq y \leq 2$).

7. The graph of f is sketched in Figure 4.31. Notice how the graph is concave down as it approaches the horizontal asymptote $y = 1$ as $x \rightarrow -\infty$, and concave up in its approach to $y = 1$ as $x \rightarrow \infty$. ∎

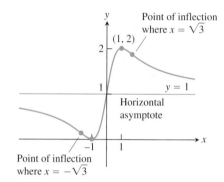

FIGURE 4.31 The graph of $y = \dfrac{(x + 1)^2}{1 + x^2}$ (Example 7).

Learning About Functions from Derivatives

As we saw in Examples 6 and 7, we can learn almost everything we need to know about a twice-differentiable function $y = f(x)$ by examining its first derivative. We can find where the function's graph rises and falls and where any local extrema are assumed. We can differentiate y' to learn how the graph bends as it passes over the intervals of rise and fall. We can determine the shape of the function's graph. Information we cannot get from the derivative is how to place the graph in the xy-plane. But, as we discovered in Section 4.2, the only additional information we need to position the graph is the value of f at one point. The derivative does not give us information about the asymptotes, which are found using limits (Sections 2.4 and 2.5).

$y = f(x)$ Differentiable $\Rightarrow$ smooth, connected; graph may rise and fall	$y = f(x)$ $y' > 0 \Rightarrow$ rises from left to right; may be wavy	$y = f(x)$ $y' < 0 \Rightarrow$ falls from left to right; may be wavy
or $y'' > 0 \Rightarrow$ concave up throughout; no waves; graph may rise or fall	or $y'' < 0 \Rightarrow$ concave down throughout; no waves; graph may rise or fall	y'' changes sign Inflection point
$-$ $+$ or $+$ $-$ y' changes sign $\Rightarrow$ graph has local maximum or local minimum	$y' = 0$ and $y'' < 0$ at a point; graph has local maximum	$y' = 0$ and $y'' > 0$ at a point; graph has local minimum

EXERCISES 4.4

Analyzing Graphed Functions

Identify the inflection points and local maxima and minima of the functions graphed in Exercises 1–8. Identify the intervals on which the functions are concave up and concave down.

1.
$$y = \frac{x^3}{3} - \frac{x^2}{2} - 2x + \frac{1}{3}$$

2.
$$y = \frac{x^4}{4} - 2x^2 + 4$$

3.
$$y = \frac{3}{4}(x^2 - 1)^{2/3}$$

4.
$$y = \frac{9}{14}x^{1/3}(x^2 - 7)$$

5.
$$y = x + \sin 2x, \quad -\frac{2\pi}{3} \le x \le \frac{2\pi}{3}$$

6.
$$y = \tan x - 4x, \quad -\frac{\pi}{2} < x < \frac{\pi}{2}$$

7. $y = \sin |x|, \quad -2\pi \le x \le 2\pi$

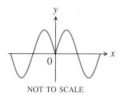

NOT TO SCALE

8.
$$y = 2 \cos x - \sqrt{2}x, \quad -\pi \le x \le \frac{3\pi}{2}$$

Graphing Equations

Use the steps of the graphing procedure on page 272 to graph the equations in Exercises 9–40. Include the coordinates of any local extreme points and inflection points.

9. $y = x^2 - 4x + 3$

10. $y = 6 - 2x - x^2$

11. $y = x^3 - 3x + 3$

12. $y = x(6 - 2x)^2$

13. $y = -2x^3 + 6x^2 - 3$

14. $y = 1 - 9x - 6x^2 - x^3$

15. $y = (x - 2)^3 + 1$

16. $y = 1 - (x + 1)^3$

17. $y = x^4 - 2x^2 = x^2(x^2 - 2)$

18. $y = -x^4 + 6x^2 - 4 = x^2(6 - x^2) - 4$

19. $y = 4x^3 - x^4 = x^3(4 - x)$

20. $y = x^4 + 2x^3 = x^3(x + 2)$

21. $y = x^5 - 5x^4 = x^4(x - 5)$

22. $y = x\left(\frac{x}{2} - 5\right)^4$

23. $y = x + \sin x, \quad 0 \le x \le 2\pi$

24. $y = x - \sin x, \quad 0 \le x \le 2\pi$

25. $y = x^{1/5}$

26. $y = x^{3/5}$

27. $y = x^{2/5}$

28. $y = x^{4/5}$

29. $y = 2x - 3x^{2/3}$

30. $y = 5x^{2/5} - 2x$

31. $y = x^{2/3}\left(\frac{5}{2} - x\right)$

32. $y = x^{2/3}(x - 5)$

33. $y = x\sqrt{8 - x^2}$

34. $y = (2 - x^2)^{3/2}$

35. $y = \frac{x^2 - 3}{x - 2}, \quad x \ne 2$

36. $y = \frac{x^3}{3x^2 + 1}$

37. $y = |x^2 - 1|$

38. $y = |x^2 - 2x|$

39. $y = \sqrt{|x|} = \begin{cases} \sqrt{-x}, & x \le 0 \\ \sqrt{x}, & x > 0 \end{cases}$

40. $y = \sqrt{|x - 4|}$

Sketching the General Shape Knowing y'

Each of Exercises 41–62 gives the first derivative of a continuous function $y = f(x)$. Find y'' and then use steps 2–4 of the graphing procedure on page 272 to sketch the general shape of the graph of f.

41. $y' = 2 + x - x^2$

42. $y' = x^2 - x - 6$

43. $y' = x(x - 3)^2$

44. $y' = x^2(2 - x)$

45. $y' = x(x^2 - 12)$

46. $y' = (x - 1)^2(2x + 3)$

47. $y' = (8x - 5x^2)(4 - x)^2$

48. $y' = (x^2 - 2x)(x - 5)^2$

49. $y' = \sec^2 x, \quad -\frac{\pi}{2} < x < \frac{\pi}{2}$

50. $y' = \tan x, \quad -\frac{\pi}{2} < x < \frac{\pi}{2}$

51. $y' = \cot\frac{\theta}{2}, \quad 0 < \theta < 2\pi$

52. $y' = \csc^2\frac{\theta}{2}, \quad 0 < \theta < 2\pi$

53. $y' = \tan^2 \theta - 1, \quad -\frac{\pi}{2} < \theta < \frac{\pi}{2}$

54. $y' = 1 - \cot^2 \theta, \quad 0 < \theta < \pi$

55. $y' = \cos t, \quad 0 \le t \le 2\pi$

56. $y' = \sin t, \quad 0 \le t \le 2\pi$

57. $y' = (x + 1)^{-2/3}$

58. $y' = (x - 2)^{-1/3}$

59. $y' = x^{-2/3}(x - 1)$

60. $y' = x^{-4/5}(x + 1)$

61. $y' = 2|x| = \begin{cases} -2x, & x \le 0 \\ 2x, & x > 0 \end{cases}$

62. $y' = \begin{cases} -x^2, & x \le 0 \\ x^2, & x > 0 \end{cases}$

Sketching y from Graphs of y' and y''

Each of Exercises 63–66 shows the graphs of the first and second derivatives of a function $y = f(x)$. Copy the picture and add to it a sketch of the approximate graph of f, given that the graph passes through the point P.

63.

64.

65.

66.

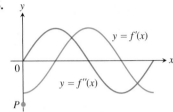

Theory and Examples

67. The accompanying figure shows a portion of the graph of a twice-differentiable function $y = f(x)$. At each of the five labeled points, classify y' and y'' as positive, negative, or zero.

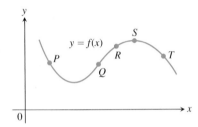

68. Sketch a smooth connected curve $y = f(x)$ with

$$f(-2) = 8, \qquad\qquad f'(2) = f'(-2) = 0,$$
$$f(0) = 4, \qquad\qquad f'(x) < 0 \quad \text{for} \quad |x| < 2,$$
$$f(2) = 0, \qquad\qquad f''(x) < 0 \quad \text{for} \quad x < 0,$$
$$f'(x) > 0 \quad \text{for} \quad |x| > 2, \qquad f''(x) > 0 \quad \text{for} \quad x > 0.$$

69. Sketch the graph of a twice-differentiable function $y = f(x)$ with the following properties. Label coordinates where possible.

x	y	Derivatives
$x < 2$		$y' < 0, \quad y'' > 0$
2	1	$y' = 0, \quad y'' > 0$
$2 < x < 4$		$y' > 0, \quad y'' > 0$
4	4	$y' > 0, \quad y'' = 0$
$4 < x < 6$		$y' > 0, \quad y'' < 0$
6	7	$y' = 0, \quad y'' < 0$
$x > 6$		$y' < 0, \quad y'' < 0$

70. Sketch the graph of a twice-differentiable function $y = f(x)$ that passes through the points $(-2, 2), (-1, 1), (0, 0), (1, 1)$ and $(2, 2)$ and whose first two derivatives have the following sign patterns:

$$y': \quad \frac{\quad + \quad - \quad + \quad -}{-2 \quad 0 \quad 2}$$

$$y'': \quad \frac{\quad - \quad + \quad -}{-1 \quad 1}$$

Motion Along a Line The graphs in Exercises 71 and 72 show the position $s = f(t)$ of a body moving back and forth on a coordinate line. (a) When is the body moving away from the origin? Toward the origin? At approximately what times is the (b) velocity equal to zero? (c) Acceleration equal to zero? (d) When is the acceleration positive? Negative?

71.

72.

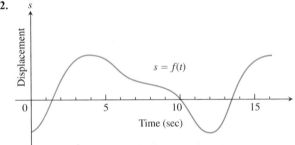

73. Marginal cost The accompanying graph shows the hypothetical cost $c = f(x)$ of manufacturing x items. At approximately what production level does the marginal cost change from decreasing to increasing?

74. The accompanying graph shows the monthly revenue of the Widget Corporation for the last 12 years. During approximately what time intervals was the marginal revenue increasing? decreasing?

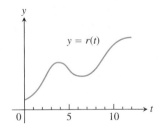

75. Suppose the derivative of the function $y = f(x)$ is

$$y' = (x - 1)^2(x - 2).$$

At what points, if any, does the graph of f have a local minimum, local maximum, or point of inflection? (*Hint:* Draw the sign pattern for y'.)

76. Suppose the derivative of the function $y = f(x)$ is

$$y' = (x - 1)^2(x - 2)(x - 4).$$

At what points, if any, does the graph of f have a local minimum, local maximum, or point of inflection?

77. For $x > 0$, sketch a curve $y = f(x)$ that has $f(1) = 0$ and $f'(x) = 1/x$. Can anything be said about the concavity of such a curve? Give reasons for your answer.

78. Can anything be said about the graph of a function $y = f(x)$ that has a continuous second derivative that is never zero? Give reasons for your answer.

79. If b, c, and d are constants, for what value of b will the curve $y = x^3 + bx^2 + cx + d$ have a point of inflection at $x = 1$? Give reasons for your answer.

80. Horizontal tangents   True, or false? Explain.

a. The graph of every polynomial of even degree (largest exponent even) has at least one horizontal tangent.

b. The graph of every polynomial of odd degree (largest exponent odd) has at least one horizontal tangent.

81. Parabolas

a. Find the coordinates of the vertex of the parabola $y = ax^2 + bx + c, a \neq 0$.

b. When is the parabola concave up? Concave down? Give reasons for your answers.

82. Is it true that the concavity of the graph of a twice-differentiable function $y = f(x)$ changes every time $f''(x) = 0$? Give reasons for your answer.

83. Quadratic curves   What can you say about the inflection points of a quadratic curve $y = ax^2 + bx + c, a \neq 0$? Give reasons for your answer.

84. Cubic curves   What can you say about the inflection points of a cubic curve $y = ax^3 + bx^2 + cx + d, a \neq 0$? Give reasons for your answer.

COMPUTER EXPLORATIONS

In Exercises 85–88, find the inflection points (if any) on the graph of the function and the coordinates of the points on the graph where the function has a local maximum or local minimum value. Then graph the function in a region large enough to show all these points simultaneously. Add to your picture the graphs of the function's first and second derivatives. How are the values at which these graphs intersect the

x-axis related to the graph of the function? In what other ways are the graphs of the derivatives related to the graph of the function?

85. $y = x^5 - 5x^4 - 240$ **86.** $y = x^3 - 12x^2$

87. $y = \dfrac{4}{5}x^5 + 16x^2 - 25$

88. $y = \dfrac{x^4}{4} - \dfrac{x^3}{3} - 4x^2 + 12x + 20$

89. Graph $f(x) = 2x^4 - 4x^2 + 1$ and its first two derivatives together. Comment on the behavior of f in relation to the signs and values of f' and f''.

90. Graph $f(x) = x \cos x$ and its second derivative together for $0 \leq x \leq 2\pi$. Comment on the behavior of the graph of f in relation to the signs and values of f''.

91. a. On a common screen, graph $f(x) = x^3 + kx$ for $k = 0$ and nearby positive and negative values of k. How does the value of k seem to affect the shape of the graph?

b. Find $f'(x)$. As you will see, $f'(x)$ is a quadratic function of x. Find the discriminant of the quadratic (the discriminant of $ax^2 + bx + c$ is $b^2 - 4ac$). For what values of k is the discriminant positive? Zero? Negative? For what values of k does f' have two zeros? One or no zeros? Now explain what the value of k has to do with the shape of the graph of f.

c. Experiment with other values of k. What appears to happen as $k \to -\infty$? as $k \to \infty$?

92. a. On a common screen, graph $f(x) = x^4 + kx^3 + 6x^2$, $-2 \leq x \leq 2$ for $k = -4$, and some nearby integer values of k. How does the value of k seem to affect the shape of the graph?

b. Find $f''(x)$. As you will see, $f''(x)$ is a quadratic function of x. What is the discriminant of this quadratic (see Exercise 91(b))? For what values of k is the discriminant positive? Zero? Negative? For what values of k does $f''(x)$ have two zeros? One or no zeros? Now explain what the value of k has to do with the shape of the graph of f.

93. a. Graph $y = x^{2/3}(x^2 - 2)$ for $-3 \leq x \leq 3$. Then use calculus to confirm what the screen shows about concavity, rise, and fall. (Depending on your grapher, you may have to enter $x^{2/3}$ as $(x^2)^{1/3}$ to obtain a plot for negative values of x.)

b. Does the curve have a cusp at $x = 0$, or does it just have a corner with different right-hand and left-hand derivatives?

94. a. Graph $y = 9x^{2/3}(x - 1)$ for $-0.5 \leq x \leq 1.5$. Then use calculus to confirm what the screen shows about concavity, rise, and fall. What concavity does the curve have to the left of the origin? (Depending on your grapher, you may have to enter $x^{2/3}$ as $(x^2)^{1/3}$ to obtain a plot for negative values of x.)

b. Does the curve have a cusp at $x = 0$, or does it just have a corner with different right-hand and left-hand derivatives?

95. Does the curve $y = x^2 + 3 \sin 2x$ have a horizontal tangent near $x = -3$? Give reasons for your answer.

4.5	Applied Optimization Problems

(a)

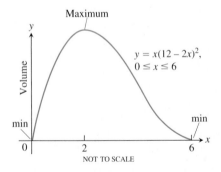

(b)

FIGURE 4.32 An open box made by cutting the corners from a square sheet of tin. What size corners maximize the box's volume (Example 1)?

To optimize something means to maximize or minimize some aspect of it. What are the dimensions of a rectangle with fixed perimeter having maximum area? What is the least expensive shape for a cylindrical can? What is the size of the most profitable production run? The differential calculus is a powerful tool for solving problems that call for maximizing or minimizing a function. In this section we solve a variety of optimization problems from business, mathematics, physics, and economics.

Examples from Business and Industry

EXAMPLE 1   Fabricating a Box

An open-top box is to be made by cutting small congruent squares from the corners of a 12-in.-by-12-in. sheet of tin and bending up the sides. How large should the squares cut from the corners be to make the box hold as much as possible?

Solution   We start with a picture (Figure 4.32). In the figure, the corner squares are x in. on a side. The volume of the box is a function of this variable:

$$V(x) = x(12 - 2x)^2 = 144x - 48x^2 + 4x^3. \qquad V = hlw$$

Since the sides of the sheet of tin are only 12 in. long, $x \le 6$ and the domain of V is the interval $0 \le x \le 6$.

A graph of V (Figure 4.33) suggests a minimum value of 0 at $x = 0$ and $x = 6$ and a maximum near $x = 2$. To learn more, we examine the first derivative of V with respect to x:

$$\frac{dV}{dx} = 144 - 96x + 12x^2 = 12(12 - 8x + x^2) = 12(2 - x)(6 - x).$$

Of the two zeros, $x = 2$ and $x = 6$, only $x = 2$ lies in the interior of the function's domain and makes the critical-point list. The values of V at this one critical point and two endpoints are

Critical-point value: $V(2) = 128$

Endpoint values: $V(0) = 0, \qquad V(6) = 0.$

The maximum volume is 128 in.^3. The cutout squares should be 2 in. on a side. ∎

EXAMPLE 2   Designing an Efficient Cylindrical Can

You have been asked to design a 1-liter can shaped like a right circular cylinder (Figure 4.34). What dimensions will use the least material?

Solution   *Volume of can:*   If r and h are measured in centimeters, then the volume of the can in cubic centimeters is

$$\pi r^2 h = 1000. \qquad \text{1 liter} = 1000 \text{ cm}^3$$

Surface area of can: $A = \underbrace{2\pi r^2}_{\substack{\text{circular} \\ \text{ends}}} + \underbrace{2\pi rh}_{\substack{\text{circular} \\ \text{wall}}}$

FIGURE 4.33 The volume of the box in Figure 4.32 graphed as a function of x.

FIGURE 4.34 This 1-L can uses the least material when $h = 2r$ (Example 2).

How can we interpret the phrase "least material"? First, it is customary to ignore the thickness of the material and the waste in manufacturing. Then we ask for dimensions r and h that make the total surface area as small as possible while satisfying the constraint $\pi r^2 h = 1000$.

To express the surface area as a function of one variable, we solve for one of the variables in $\pi r^2 h = 1000$ and substitute that expression into the surface area formula. Solving for h is easier:

$$h = \frac{1000}{\pi r^2}.$$

Thus,

$$\begin{aligned} A &= 2\pi r^2 + 2\pi rh \\ &= 2\pi r^2 + 2\pi r\left(\frac{1000}{\pi r^2}\right) \\ &= 2\pi r^2 + \frac{2000}{r}. \end{aligned}$$

Our goal is to find a value of $r > 0$ that minimizes the value of A. Figure 4.35 suggests that such a value exists.

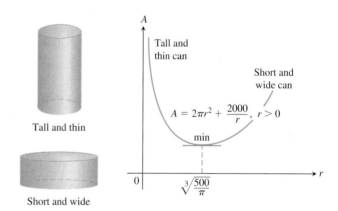

FIGURE 4.35 The graph of $A = 2\pi r^2 + 2000/r$ is concave up.

Notice from the graph that for small r (a tall thin container, like a piece of pipe), the term $2000/r$ dominates and A is large. For large r (a short wide container, like a pizza pan), the term $2\pi r^2$ dominates and A again is large.

Since A is differentiable on $r > 0$, an interval with no endpoints, it can have a minimum value only where its first derivative is zero.

$$\frac{dA}{dr} = 4\pi r - \frac{2000}{r^2}$$

$$0 = 4\pi r - \frac{2000}{r^2} \qquad \text{Set } dA/dr = 0.$$

$$4\pi r^3 = 2000 \qquad \text{Multiply by } r^2.$$

$$r = \sqrt[3]{\frac{500}{\pi}} \approx 5.42 \qquad \text{Solve for } r.$$

What happens at $r = \sqrt[3]{500/\pi}$?

The second derivative

$$\frac{d^2A}{dr^2} = 4\pi + \frac{4000}{r^3}$$

is positive throughout the domain of A. The graph is therefore everywhere concave up and the value of A at $r = \sqrt[3]{500/\pi}$ an absolute minimum.

The corresponding value of h (after a little algebra) is

$$h = \frac{1000}{\pi r^2} = 2\sqrt[3]{\frac{500}{\pi}} = 2r.$$

The 1-L can that uses the least material has height equal to the diameter, here with $r \approx 5.42$ cm and $h \approx 10.84$ cm. ∎

Solving Applied Optimization Problems

1. *Read the problem.* Read the problem until you understand it. What is given? What is the unknown quantity to be optimized?

2. *Draw a picture.* Label any part that may be important to the problem.

3. *Introduce variables.* List every relation in the picture and in the problem as an equation or algebraic expression, and identify the unknown variable.

4. *Write an equation for the unknown quantity.* If you can, express the unknown as a function of a single variable or in two equations in two unknowns. This may require considerable manipulation.

5. *Test the critical points and endpoints in the domain of the unknown.* Use what you know about the shape of the function's graph. Use the first and second derivatives to identify and classify the function's critical points.

Examples from Mathematics and Physics

EXAMPLE 3   Inscribing Rectangles

A rectangle is to be inscribed in a semicircle of radius 2. What is the largest area the rectangle can have, and what are its dimensions?

Solution   Let $(x, \sqrt{4 - x^2})$ be the coordinates of the corner of the rectangle obtained by placing the circle and rectangle in the coordinate plane (Figure 4.36). The length, height, and area of the rectangle can then be expressed in terms of the position x of the lower right-hand corner:

Length: $2x$,   Height: $\sqrt{4 - x^2}$,   Area: $2x \cdot \sqrt{4 - x^2}$.

Notice that the values of x are to be found in the interval $0 \le x \le 2$, where the selected corner of the rectangle lies.

Our goal is to find the absolute maximum value of the function

$$A(x) = 2x\sqrt{4 - x^2}$$

on the domain $[0, 2]$.

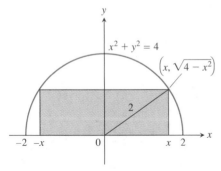

FIGURE 4.36 The rectangle inscribed in the semicircle in Example 3.

The derivative

$$\frac{dA}{dx} = \frac{-2x^2}{\sqrt{4 - x^2}} + 2\sqrt{4 - x^2}$$

is not defined when $x = 2$ and is equal to zero when

$$\frac{-2x^2}{\sqrt{4 - x^2}} + 2\sqrt{4 - x^2} = 0$$
$$-2x^2 + 2(4 - x^2) = 0$$
$$8 - 4x^2 = 0$$
$$x^2 = 2 \text{ or } x = \pm\sqrt{2}.$$

Of the two zeros, $x = \sqrt{2}$ and $x = -\sqrt{2}$, only $x = \sqrt{2}$ lies in the interior of A's domain and makes the critical-point list. The values of A at the endpoints and at this one critical point are

$$\text{Critical-point value:} \quad A(\sqrt{2}) = 2\sqrt{2}\sqrt{4 - 2} = 4$$
$$\text{Endpoint values:} \quad A(0) = 0, \quad A(2) = 0.$$

The area has a maximum value of 4 when the rectangle is $\sqrt{4 - x^2} = \sqrt{2}$ units high and $2x = 2\sqrt{2}$ unit long. ∎

EXAMPLE 4 Fermat's Principle and Snell's Law

The speed of light depends on the medium through which it travels, and is generally slower in denser media.

Fermat's principle in optics states that light travels from one point to another along a path for which the time of travel is a minimum. Find the path that a ray of light will follow in going from a point A in a medium where the speed of light is c_1 to a point B in a second medium where its speed is c_2.

Solution Since light traveling from A to B follows the quickest route, we look for a path that will minimize the travel time. We assume that A and B lie in the xy-plane and that the line separating the two media is the x-axis (Figure 4.37).

In a uniform medium, where the speed of light remains constant, "shortest time" means "shortest path," and the ray of light will follow a straight line. Thus the path from A to B will consist of a line segment from A to a boundary point P, followed by another line segment from P to B. Distance equals rate times time, so

$$\text{Time} = \frac{\text{distance}}{\text{rate}}.$$

The time required for light to travel from A to P is

$$t_1 = \frac{AP}{c_1} = \frac{\sqrt{a^2 + x^2}}{c_1}.$$

From P to B, the time is

$$t_2 = \frac{PB}{c_2} = \frac{\sqrt{b^2 + (d - x)^2}}{c_2}.$$

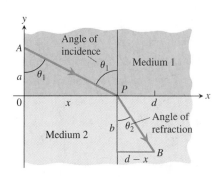

FIGURE 4.37 A light ray refracted (deflected from its path) as it passes from one medium to a denser medium (Example 4).

The time from A to B is the sum of these:

$$t = t_1 + t_2 = \frac{\sqrt{a^2 + x^2}}{c_1} + \frac{\sqrt{b^2 + (d - x)^2}}{c_2}.$$

This equation expresses t as a differentiable function of x whose domain is $[0, d]$. We want to find the absolute minimum value of t on this closed interval. We find the derivative

$$\frac{dt}{dx} = \frac{x}{c_1 \sqrt{a^2 + x^2}} - \frac{d - x}{c_2 \sqrt{b^2 + (d - x)^2}}.$$

In terms of the angles θ_1 and θ_2 in Figure 4.37,

$$\frac{dt}{dx} = \frac{\sin \theta_1}{c_1} - \frac{\sin \theta_2}{c_2}.$$

If we restrict x to the interval $0 \le x \le d$, then t has a negative derivative at $x = 0$ and a positive derivative at $x = d$. By the Intermediate Value Theorem for Derivatives (Section 3.1), there is a point $x_0 \in [0, d]$ where $dt/dx = 0$ (Figure 4.38). There is only one such point because dt/dx is an increasing function of x (Exercise 54). At this point

$$\frac{\sin \theta_1}{c_1} = \frac{\sin \theta_2}{c_2}.$$

This equation is **Snell's Law** or the **Law of Refraction**, and is an important principle in the theory of optics. It describes the path the ray of light follows. ∎

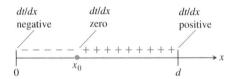

FIGURE 4.38 The sign pattern of dt/dx in Example 4.

Examples from Economics

In these examples we point out two ways that calculus makes a contribution to economics. The first has to do with maximizing profit. The second has to do with minimizing average cost.

Suppose that

$$r(x) = \text{the revenue from selling } x \text{ items}$$
$$c(x) = \text{the cost of producing the } x \text{ items}$$
$$p(x) = r(x) - c(x) = \text{the profit from producing and selling } x \text{ items}.$$

The **marginal revenue, marginal cost,** and **marginal profit** when producing and selling x items are

$$\frac{dr}{dx} = \text{marginal revenue},$$

$$\frac{dc}{dx} = \text{marginal cost},$$

$$\frac{dp}{dx} = \text{marginal profit}.$$

The first observation is about the relationship of p to these derivatives.

If $r(x)$ and $c(x)$ are differentiable for all $x > 0$, and if $p(x) = r(x) - c(x)$ has a maximum value, it occurs at a production level at which $p'(x) = 0$. Since $p'(x) = r'(x) - c'(x)$, $p'(x) = 0$ implies that

$$r'(x) - c'(x) = 0 \qquad \text{or} \qquad r'(x) = c'(x).$$

Therefore

> At a production level yielding maximum profit, marginal revenue equals marginal cost (Figure 4.39).

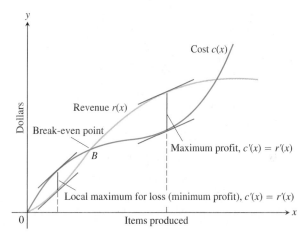

FIGURE 4.39 The graph of a typical cost function starts concave down and later turns concave up. It crosses the revenue curve at the break-even point B. To the left of B, the company operates at a loss. To the right, the company operates at a profit, with the maximum profit occurring where $c'(x) = r'(x)$. Farther to the right, cost exceeds revenue (perhaps because of a combination of rising labor and material costs and market saturation) and production levels become unprofitable again.

EXAMPLE 5 Maximizing Profit

Suppose that $r(x) = 9x$ and $c(x) = x^3 - 6x^2 + 15x$, where x represents thousands of units. Is there a production level that maximizes profit? If so, what is it?

Solution   Notice that $r'(x) = 9$ and $c'(x) = 3x^2 - 12x + 15$.

$$3x^2 - 12x + 15 = 9 \qquad \text{Set } c'(x) = r'(x).$$
$$3x^2 - 12x + 6 = 0$$

The two solutions of the quadratic equation are

$$x_1 = \frac{12 - \sqrt{72}}{6} = 2 - \sqrt{2} \approx 0.586 \qquad \text{and}$$

$$x_2 = \frac{12 + \sqrt{72}}{6} = 2 + \sqrt{2} \approx 3.414.$$

The possible production levels for maximum profit are $x \approx 0.586$ thousand units or $x \approx 3.414$ thousand units. The second derivative of $p(x) = r(x) - c(x)$ is $p''(x) = -c''(x)$ since $r''(x)$ is everywhere zero. Thus, $p''(x) = 6(2 - x)$ which is negative at $x = 2 + \sqrt{2}$ and positive at $x = 2 - \sqrt{2}$. By the Second Derivative Test, a maximum profit occurs at about $x = 3.414$ (where revenue exceeds costs) and maximum loss occurs at about $x = 0.586$. The graph of $r(x)$ is shown in Figure 4.40.

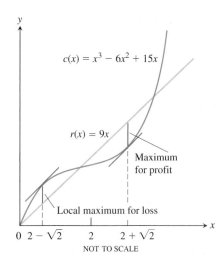

FIGURE 4.40 The cost and revenue curves for Example 5.

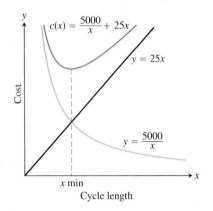

FIGURE 4.41 The average daily cost $c(x)$ is the sum of a hyperbola and a linear function (Example 6).

EXAMPLE 6   Minimizing Costs

A cabinetmaker uses plantation-farmed mahogany to produce 5 furnishings each day. Each delivery of one container of wood is $5000, whereas the storage of that material is $10 per day per unit stored, where a unit is the amount of material needed by her to produce 1 furnishing. How much material should be ordered each time and how often should the material be delivered to minimize her average daily cost in the production cycle between deliveries?

Solution   If she asks for a delivery every x days, then she must order $5x$ units to have enough material for that delivery cycle. The *average* amount in storage is approximately one-half of the delivery amount, or $5x/2$. Thus, the cost of delivery and storage for each cycle is approximately

$$\text{Cost per cycle} = \text{delivery costs} + \text{storage costs}$$

$$\text{Cost per cycle} = \underbrace{5000}_{\substack{\text{delivery} \\ \text{cost}}} + \underbrace{\left(\frac{5x}{2}\right)}_{\substack{\text{average} \\ \text{amount stored}}} \cdot \underbrace{x}_{\substack{\text{number of} \\ \text{days stored}}} \cdot \underbrace{10}_{\substack{\text{storage cost} \\ \text{per day}}}$$

We compute the *average daily cost* $c(x)$ by dividing the cost per cycle by the number of days x in the cycle (see Figure 4.41).

$$c(x) = \frac{5000}{x} + 25x, \qquad x > 0.$$

As $x \to 0$ and as $x \to \infty$, the average daily cost becomes large. So we expect a minimum to exist, but where? Our goal is to determine the number of days x between deliveries that provides the absolute minimum cost.

We find the critical points by determining where the derivative is equal to zero:

$$c'(x) = -\frac{5000}{x^2} + 25 = 0$$

$$x = \pm\sqrt{200} \approx \pm 14.14.$$

Of the two critical points, only $\sqrt{200}$ lies in the domain of $c(x)$. The critical-point value of the average daily cost is

$$c\left(\sqrt{200}\right) = \frac{5000}{\sqrt{200}} + 25\sqrt{200} = 500\sqrt{2} \approx \$707.11.$$

We note that $c(x)$ is defined over the open interval $(0, \infty)$ with $c''(x) = 10000/x^3 > 0$. Thus, an absolute minimum exists at $x = \sqrt{200} \approx 14.14$ days.

The cabinetmaker should schedule a delivery of $5(14) = 70$ units of the exotic wood every 14 days. ∎

In Examples 5 and 6 we allowed the number of items x to be any positive real number. In reality it usually only makes sense for x to be a positive integer (or zero). If we must round our answers, should we round up or down?

EXAMPLE 7   Sensitivity of the Minimum Cost

Should we round the number of days between deliveries up or down for the best solution in Example 6?

Solution   The average daily cost will increase by about \$0.03 if we round down from 14.14 to 14 days:

$$c(14) = \frac{5000}{14} + 25(14) = \$707.14$$

and

$$c(14) - c(14.14) = \$707.14 - \$707.11 = \$0.03.$$

On the other hand, $c(15) = \$708.33$, and our cost would increase by $\$708.33 - \$707.11 = \$1.22$ if we round up. Thus, it is better that we round x down to 14 days.   ∎

EXERCISES 4.5

Whenever you are maximizing or minimizing a function of a single variable, we urge you to graph it over the domain that is appropriate to the problem you are solving. The graph will provide insight before you calculate and will furnish a visual context for understanding your answer.

Applications in Geometry

1. **Minimizing perimeter**   What is the smallest perimeter possible for a rectangle whose area is 16 in.^{2}, and what are its dimensions?

2. Show that among all rectangles with an 8-m perimeter, the one with largest area is a square.

3. The figure shows a rectangle inscribed in an isosceles right triangle whose hypotenuse is 2 units long.

   a. Express the y-coordinate of P in terms of x. (*Hint*: Write an equation for the line AB.)

   b. Express the area of the rectangle in terms of x.

   c. What is the largest area the rectangle can have, and what are its dimensions?

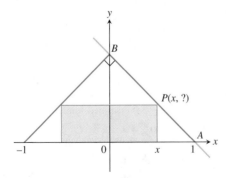

4. A rectangle has its base on the x-axis and its upper two vertices on the parabola $y = 12 - x^2$. What is the largest area the rectangle can have, and what are its dimensions?

5. You are planning to make an open rectangular box from an 8-in.-by-15-in. piece of cardboard by cutting congruent squares from the corners and folding up the sides. What are the dimensions of the box of largest volume you can make this way, and what is its volume?

6. You are planning to close off a corner of the first quadrant with a line segment 20 units long running from $(a, 0)$ to $(0, b)$. Show that the area of the triangle enclosed by the segment is largest when $a = b$.

7. **The best fencing plan**   A rectangular plot of farmland will be bounded on one side by a river and on the other three sides by a single-strand electric fence. With 800m of wire at your disposal, what is the largest area you can enclose, and what are its dimensions?

8. **The shortest fence**   A 216 m^2 rectangular pea patch is to be enclosed by a fence and divided into two equal parts by another fence parallel to one of the sides. What dimensions for the outer rectangle will require the smallest total length of fence? How much fence will be needed?

9. **Designing a tank**   Your iron works has contracted to design and build a 500 ft^3, square-based, open-top, rectangular steel holding tank for a paper company. The tank is to be made by welding thin stainless steel plates together along their edges. As the production engineer, your job is to find dimensions for the base and height that will make the tank weigh as little as possible.

   a. What dimensions do you tell the shop to use?

   b. Briefly describe how you took weight into account.

10. **Catching rainwater**   A 1125 ft^3 open-top rectangular tank with a square base x ft on a side and y ft deep is to be built with its top flush with the ground to catch runoff water. The costs associated with the tank involve not only the material from which the tank is made but also an excavation charge proportional to the product xy.

   a. If the total cost is

   $$c = 5(x^2 + 4xy) + 10xy,$$

   what values of x and y will minimize it?

   b. Give a possible scenario for the cost function in part (a).

11. **Designing a poster** You are designing a rectangular poster to contain 50 in.² of printing with a 4-in. margin at the top and bottom and a 2-in. margin at each side. What overall dimensions will minimize the amount of paper used?

12. Find the volume of the largest right circular cone that can be inscribed in a sphere of radius 3.

13. Two sides of a triangle have lengths a and b, and the angle between them is θ. What value of θ will maximize the triangle's area? (*Hint:* $A = (1/2)ab \sin \theta$.)

14. **Designing a can** What are the dimensions of the lightest open-top right circular cylindrical can that will hold a volume of 1000 cm³? Compare the result here with the result in Example 2.

15. **Designing a can** You are designing a 1000 cm³ right circular cylindrical can whose manufacture will take waste into account. There is no waste in cutting the aluminum for the side, but the top and bottom of radius r will be cut from squares that measure $2r$ units on a side. The total amount of aluminum used up by the can will therefore be

$$A = 8r^2 + 2\pi rh$$

rather than the $A = 2\pi r^2 + 2\pi rh$ in Example 2. In Example 2, the ratio of h to r for the most economical can was 2 to 1. What is the ratio now?

16. **Designing a box with a lid** A piece of cardboard measures 10 in. by 15 in. Two equal squares are removed from the corners of a 10-in. side as shown in the figure. Two equal rectangles are removed from the other corners so that the tabs can be folded to form a rectangular box with lid.

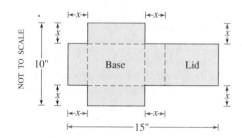

a. Write a formula $V(x)$ for the volume of the box.

b. Find the domain of V for the problem situation and graph V over this domain.

c. Use a graphical method to find the maximum volume and the value of x that gives it.

d. Confirm your result in part (c) analytically.

17. **Designing a suitcase** A 24-in.-by-36-in. sheet of cardboard is folded in half to form a 24-in.-by-18-in. rectangle as shown in the accompanying figure. Then four congruent squares of side length x are cut from the corners of the folded rectangle. The sheet is unfolded, and the six tabs are folded up to form a box with sides and a lid.

a. Write a formula $V(x)$ for the volume of the box.

b. Find the domain of V for the problem situation and graph V over this domain.

c. Use a graphical method to find the maximum volume and the value of x that gives it.

d. Confirm your result in part (c) analytically.

e. Find a value of x that yields a volume of 1120 in.³.

f. Write a paragraph describing the issues that arise in part (b).

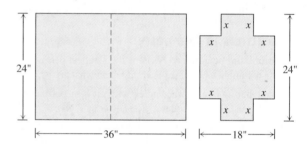

The sheet is then unfolded.

18. A rectangle is to be inscribed under the arch of the curve $y = 4 \cos (0.5x)$ from $x = -\pi$ to $x = \pi$. What are the dimensions of the rectangle with largest area, and what is the largest area?

19. Find the dimensions of a right circular cylinder of maximum volume that can be inscribed in a sphere of radius 10 cm. What is the maximum volume?

20. a. The U.S. Postal Service will accept a box for domestic shipment only if the sum of its length and girth (distance around) does not exceed 108 in. What dimensions will give a box with a square end the largest possible volume?

Girth = distance
around here

Length

Square end

T **b.** Graph the volume of a 108-in. box (length plus girth equals 108 in.) as a function of its length and compare what you see with your answer in part (a).

21. (*Continuation of Exercise 20.*)

a. Suppose that instead of having a box with square ends you have a box with square sides so that its dimensions are h by h by w and the girth is $2h + 2w$. What dimensions will give the box its largest volume now?

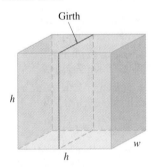

Girth

h

h

w

T **b.** Graph the volume as a function of h and compare what you see with your answer in part (a).

22. A window is in the form of a rectangle surmounted by a semicircle. The rectangle is of clear glass, whereas the semicircle is of tinted glass that transmits only half as much light per unit area as clear glass does. The total perimeter is fixed. Find the proportions of the window that will admit the most light. Neglect the thickness of the frame.

23. A silo (base not included) is to be constructed in the form of a cylinder surmounted by a hemisphere. The cost of construction per square unit of surface area is twice as great for the hemisphere as it is for the cylindrical sidewall. Determine the dimensions to be used if the volume is fixed and the cost of construction is to be kept to a minimum. Neglect the thickness of the silo and waste in construction.

24. The trough in the figure is to be made to the dimensions shown. Only the angle θ can be varied. What value of θ will maximize the trough's volume?

25. **Paper folding** A rectangular sheet of 8.5-in.-by-11-in. paper is placed on a flat surface. One of the corners is placed on the opposite longer edge, as shown in the figure, and held there as the paper is smoothed flat. The problem is to make the length of the crease as small as possible. Call the length L. Try it with paper.

a. Show that $L^2 = 2x^3/(2x - 8.5)$.

b. What value of x minimizes L^2?

c. What is the minimum value of L?

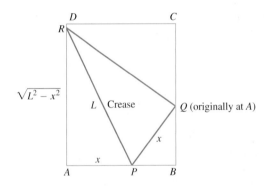

26. **Constructing cylinders** Compare the answers to the following two construction problems.

a. A rectangular sheet of perimeter 36 cm and dimensions x cm by y cm to be rolled into a cylinder as shown in part (a) of the figure. What values of x and y give the largest volume?

b. The same sheet is to be revolved about one of the sides of length y to sweep out the cylinder as shown in part (b) of the figure. What values of x and y give the largest volume?

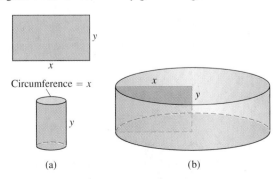

(a)

(b)

27. Constructing cones A right triangle whose hypotenuse is $\sqrt{3}$ m long is revolved about one of its legs to generate a right circular cone. Find the radius, height, and volume of the cone of greatest volume that can be made this way.

28. What value of a makes $f(x) = x^2 + (a/x)$ have

a. a local minimum at $x = 2$?

b. a point of inflection at $x = 1$?

29. Show that $f(x) = x^2 + (a/x)$ cannot have a local maximum for any value of a.

30. What values of a and b make $f(x) = x^3 + ax^2 + bx$ have

a. a local maximum at $x = -1$ and a local minimum at $x = 3$?

b. a local minimum at $x = 4$ and a point of inflection at $x = 1$?

Physical Applications

31. Vertical motion The height of an object moving vertically is given by

$$s = -16t^2 + 96t + 112,$$

with s in feet and t in seconds. Find

a. the object's velocity when $t = 0$

b. its maximum height and when it occurs

c. its velocity when $s = 0$.

32. Quickest route Jane is 2 mi offshore in a boat and wishes to reach a coastal village 6 mi down a straight shoreline from the point nearest the boat. She can row 2 mph and can walk 5 mph. Where should she land her boat to reach the village in the least amount of time?

33. Shortest beam The 8-ft wall shown here stands 27 ft from the building. Find the length of the shortest straight beam that will reach to the side of the building from the ground outside the wall.

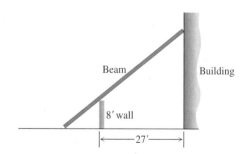

T 34. Strength of a beam The strength S of a rectangular wooden beam is proportional to its width times the square of its depth. (See accompanying figure.)

a. Find the dimensions of the strongest beam that can be cut from a 12-in.-diameter cylindrical log.

b. Graph S as a function of the beam's width w, assuming the proportionality constant to be $k = 1$. Reconcile what you see with your answer in part (a).

c. On the same screen, graph S as a function of the beam's depth d, again taking $k = 1$. Compare the graphs with one another and with your answer in part (a). What would be the effect of changing to some other value of k? Try it.

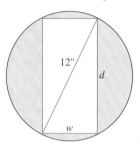

T 35. Stiffness of a beam The stiffness S of a rectangular beam is proportional to its width times the cube of its depth.

a. Find the dimensions of the stiffest beam that can be cut from a 12-in.-diameter cylindrical log.

b. Graph S as a function of the beam's width w, assuming the proportionality constant to be $k = 1$. Reconcile what you see with your answer in part (a).

c. On the same screen, graph S as a function of the beam's depth d, again taking $k = 1$. Compare the graphs with one another and with your answer in part (a). What would be the effect of changing to some other value of k? Try it.

36. Motion on a line The positions of two particles on the s-axis are $s_1 = \sin t$ and $s_2 = \sin (t + \pi/3)$, with s_1 and s_2 in meters and t in seconds.

a. At what time(s) in the interval $0 \le t \le 2\pi$ do the particles meet?

b. What is the farthest apart that the particles ever get?

c. When in the interval $0 \le t \le 2\pi$ is the distance between the particles changing the fastest?

37. Frictionless cart A small frictionless cart, attached to the wall by a spring, is pulled 10 cm from its rest position and released at time $t = 0$ to roll back and forth for 4 sec. Its position at time t is $s = 10 \cos \pi t$.

a. What is the cart's maximum speed? When is the cart moving that fast? Where is it then? What is the magnitude of the acceleration then?

b. Where is the cart when the magnitude of the acceleration is greatest? What is the cart's speed then?

38. Two masses hanging side by side from springs have positions $s_1 = 2 \sin t$ and $s_2 = \sin 2t$, respectively.

a. At what times in the interval $0 < t$ do the masses pass each other? (*Hint:* $\sin 2t = 2 \sin t \cos t$.)

b. When in the interval $0 \le t \le 2\pi$ is the vertical distance between the masses the greatest? What is this distance? (*Hint:* $\cos 2t = 2 \cos^2 t - 1$.)

39. Distance between two ships At noon, ship A was 12 nautical miles due north of ship B. Ship A was sailing south at 12 knots (nautical miles per hour; a nautical mile is 2000 yd) and continued to do so all day. Ship B was sailing east at 8 knots and continued to do so all day.

a. Start counting time with $t = 0$ at noon and express the distance s between the ships as a function of t.

b. How rapidly was the distance between the ships changing at noon? One hour later?

c. The visibility that day was 5 nautical miles. Did the ships ever sight each other?

T d. Graph s and ds/dt together as functions of t for $-1 \le t \le 3$, using different colors if possible. Compare the graphs and reconcile what you see with your answers in parts (b) and (c).

e. The graph of ds/dt looks as if it might have a horizontal asymptote in the first quadrant. This in turn suggests that ds/dt approaches a limiting value as $t \to \infty$. What is this value? What is its relation to the ships' individual speeds?

40. Fermat's principle in optics Fermat's principle in optics states that light always travels from one point to another along a path that minimizes the travel time. Light from a source A is reflected by a plane mirror to a receiver at point B, as shown in the figure. Show that for the light to obey Fermat's principle, the angle of incidence must equal the angle of reflection, both measured from the line normal to the reflecting surface. (This result can also be derived without calculus. There is a purely geometric argument, which you may prefer.)

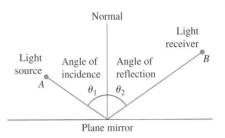

41. Tin pest When metallic tin is kept below 13.2°C, it slowly becomes brittle and crumbles to a gray powder. Tin objects eventually crumble to this gray powder spontaneously if kept in a cold climate for years. The Europeans who saw tin organ pipes in their churches crumble away years ago called the change *tin pest* because it seemed to be contagious, and indeed it was, for the gray powder is a catalyst for its own formation.

A *catalyst* for a chemical reaction is a substance that controls the rate of reaction without undergoing any permanent change in itself. An *autocatalytic reaction* is one whose product is a catalyst for its own formation. Such a reaction may proceed slowly at first if the amount of catalyst present is small and slowly again at the end, when most of the original substance is used up. But in between, when both the substance and its catalyst product are abundant, the reaction proceeds at a faster pace.

In some cases, it is reasonable to assume that the rate $v = dx/dt$ of the reaction is proportional both to the amount of the original substance present and to the amount of product. That is, v may be considered to be a function of x alone, and

$$v = kx(a - x) = kax - kx^2,$$

where

$x = $ the amount of product

$a = $ the amount of substance at the beginning

$k = $ a positive constant.

At what value of x does the rate v have a maximum? What is the maximum value of v?

42. Airplane landing path An airplane is flying at altitude H when it begins its descent to an airport runway that is at horizontal ground distance L from the airplane, as shown in the figure. Assume that the landing path of the airplane is the graph of a cubic polynomial function $y = ax^3 + bx^2 + cx + d$, where $y(-L) = H$ and $y(0) = 0$.

a. What is dy/dx at $x = 0$?

b. What is dy/dx at $x = -L$?

c. Use the values for dy/dx at $x = 0$ and $x = -L$ together with $y(0) = 0$ and $y(-L) = H$ to show that

$$y(x) = H\left[2\left(\frac{x}{L}\right)^3 + 3\left(\frac{x}{L}\right)^2\right].$$

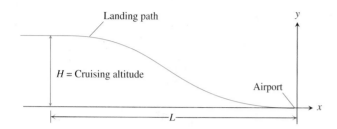

Landing path

H = Cruising altitude

Airport

L

Business and Economics

43. It costs you c dollars each to manufacture and distribute backpacks. If the backpacks sell at x dollars each, the number sold is given by

$$n = \frac{a}{x - c} + b(100 - x),$$

where a and b are positive constants. What selling price will bring a maximum profit?

44. You operate a tour service that offers the following rates:

$200 per person if 50 people (the minimum number to book the tour) go on the tour.

For each additional person, up to a maximum of 80 people total, the rate per person is reduced by $2.

It costs $6000 (a fixed cost) plus $32 per person to conduct the tour. How many people does it take to maximize your profit?

45. Wilson lot size formula One of the formulas for inventory management says that the average weekly cost of ordering, paying for, and holding merchandise is

$$A(q) = \frac{km}{q} + cm + \frac{hq}{2},$$

where q is the quantity you order when things run low (shoes, radios, brooms, or whatever the item might be), k is the cost of placing an order (the same, no matter how often you order), c is the cost of one item (a constant), m is the number of items sold each week (a constant), and h is the weekly holding cost per item (a constant that takes into account things such as space, utilities, insurance, and security).

a. Your job, as the inventory manager for your store, is to find the quantity that will minimize $A(q)$. What is it? (The formula you get for the answer is called the *Wilson lot size formula*.)

b. Shipping costs sometimes depend on order size. When they do, it is more realistic to replace k by $k + bq$, the sum of k and a constant multiple of q. What is the most economical quantity to order now?

46. Production level Prove that the production level (if any) at which average cost is smallest is a level at which average cost equals marginal cost.

47. Show that if $r(x) = 6x$ and $c(x) = x^3 - 6x^2 + 15x$ are your revenue and cost functions, then the best you can do is break even (have revenue equal cost).

48. Production level Suppose that $c(x) = x^3 - 20x^2 + 20{,}000x$ is the cost of manufacturing x items. Find a production level that will minimize the average cost of making x items.

49. Average daily cost In Example 6, assume for any material that a cost of d is incurred per delivery, the storage cost is s dollars per unit stored per day, and the production rate is p units per day.

a. How much should be delivered every x days?

b. Show that

$$\text{cost per cycle} = d + \frac{px}{2}\, sx.$$

c. Find the time between deliveries x^* and the amount to deliver that minimizes the *average daily cost* of delivery and storage.

d. Show that x^* occurs at the intersection of the hyperbola $y = d/x$ and the line $y = psx/2$.

50. Minimizing average cost Suppose that $c(x) = 2000 + 96x + 4x^{3/2}$, where x represents thousands of units. Is there a production level that minimizes average cost? If so, what is it?

Medicine

51. Sensitivity to medicine (*Continuation of Exercise 50, Section 3.2.*) Find the amount of medicine to which the body is most sensitive by finding the value of M that maximizes the derivative dR/dM, where

$$R = M^2\left(\frac{C}{2} - \frac{M}{3}\right)$$

and C is a constant.

52. How we cough

a. When we cough, the trachea (windpipe) contracts to increase the velocity of the air going out. This raises the questions of how much it should contract to maximize the velocity and whether it really contracts that much when we cough.

Under reasonable assumptions about the elasticity of the tracheal wall and about how the air near the wall is slowed by friction, the average flow velocity v can be modeled by the equation

$$v = c(r_0 - r)r^2 \text{ cm/sec}, \qquad \frac{r_0}{2} \le r \le r_0,$$

where r_0 is the rest radius of the trachea in centimeters and c is a positive constant whose value depends in part on the length of the trachea.

Show that v is greatest when $r = (2/3)r_0$, that is, when the trachea is about 33% contracted. The remarkable fact is that X-ray photographs confirm that the trachea contracts about this much during a cough.

T b. Take r_0 to be 0.5 and c to be 1 and graph v over the interval $0 \le r \le 0.5$. Compare what you see with the claim that v is at a maximum when $r = (2/3)r_0$.

Theory and Examples

53. An inequality for positive integers   Show that if a, b, c, and d are positive integers, then

$$\frac{(a^2 + 1)(b^2 + 1)(c^2 + 1)(d^2 + 1)}{abcd} \geq 16.$$

54. The derivative dt/dx in Example 4

   a. Show that

$$f(x) = \frac{x}{\sqrt{a^2 + x^2}}$$

   is an increasing function of x.

   b. Show that

$$g(x) = \frac{d - x}{\sqrt{b^2 + (d - x)^2}}$$

   is a decreasing function of x.

   c. Show that

$$\frac{dt}{dx} = \frac{x}{c_1 \sqrt{a^2 + x^2}} - \frac{d - x}{c_2 \sqrt{b^2 + (d - x)^2}}$$

   is an increasing function of x.

55. Let $f(x)$ and $g(x)$ be the differentiable functions graphed here. Point c is the point where the vertical distance between the curves is the greatest. Is there anything special about the tangents to the two curves at c? Give reasons for your answer.

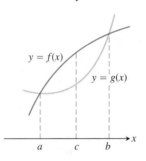

56. You have been asked to determine whether the function $f(x) = 3 + 4 \cos x + \cos 2x$ is ever negative.

   a. Explain why you need to consider values of x only in the interval $[0, 2\pi]$.

   b. Is f ever negative? Explain.

57. a. The function $y = \cot x - \sqrt{2} \csc x$ has an absolute maximum value on the interval $0 < x < \pi$. Find it.

   T b. Graph the function and compare what you see with your answer in part (a).

58. a. The function $y = \tan x + 3 \cot x$ has an absolute minimum value on the interval $0 < x < \pi/2$. Find it.

   T b. Graph the function and compare what you see with your answer in part (a).

59. a. How close does the curve $y = \sqrt{x}$ come to the point $(3/2, 0)$? (*Hint*: If you minimize the *square* of the distance, you can avoid square roots.)

   T b. Graph the distance function and $y = \sqrt{x}$ together and reconcile what you see with your answer in part (a).

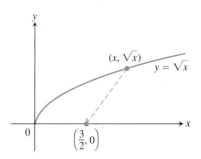

60. a. How close does the semicircle $y = \sqrt{16 - x^2}$ come to the point $\left(1, \sqrt{3}\right)$?

   T b. Graph the distance function and $y = \sqrt{16 - x^2}$ together and reconcile what you see with your answer in part (a).

COMPUTER EXPLORATIONS

In Exercises 61 and 62, you may find it helpful to use a CAS.

61. Generalized cone problem   A cone of height h and radius r is constructed from a flat, circular disk of radius a in. by removing a sector AOC of arc length x in. and then connecting the edges OA and OC.

   a. Find a formula for the volume V of the cone in terms of x and a.

   b. Find r and h in the cone of maximum volume for $a = 4, 5, 6, 8$.

   c. Find a simple relationship between r and h that is independent of a for the cone of maximum volume. Explain how you arrived at your relationship.

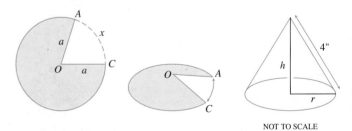

NOT TO SCALE

62. Circumscribing an ellipse   Let $P(x, a)$ and $Q(-x, a)$ be two points on the upper half of the ellipse

$$\frac{x^2}{100} + \frac{(y - 5)^2}{25} = 1$$

centered at $(0, 5)$. A triangle RST is formed by using the tangent lines to the ellipse at Q and P as shown in the figure.

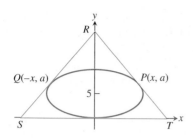

a. Show that the area of the triangle is

$$A(x) = -f'(x)\left[x - \frac{f(x)}{f'(x)}\right]^2,$$

where $y = f(x)$ is the function representing the upper half of the ellipse.

b. What is the domain of A? Draw the graph of A. How are the asymptotes of the graph related to the problem situation?

c. Determine the height of the triangle with minimum area. How is it related to the y coordinate of the center of the ellipse?

d. Repeat parts (a) through (c) for the ellipse

$$\frac{x^2}{C^2} + \frac{(y - B)^2}{B^2} = 1$$

centered at $(0, B)$. Show that the triangle has minimum area when its height is $3B$.

4.6 Indeterminate Forms and L'Hôpital's Rule

HISTORICAL BIOGRAPHY

Guillaume François
Antoine de l'Hôpital
(1661–1704)

John Bernoulli discovered a rule for calculating limits of fractions whose numerators and denominators both approach zero or $+\infty$. The rule is known today as **l'Hôpital's Rule**, after Guillaume de l'Hôpital. He was a French nobleman who wrote the first introductory differential calculus text, where the rule first appeared in print.

Indeterminate Form 0/0

If the continuous functions $f(x)$ and $g(x)$ are both zero at $x = a$, then

$$\lim_{x \to a} \frac{f(x)}{g(x)}$$

cannot be found by substituting $x = a$. The substitution produces $0/0$, a meaningless expression, which we cannot evaluate. We use $0/0$ as a notation for an expression known as an **indeterminate form**. Sometimes, but not always, limits that lead to indeterminate forms may be found by cancellation, rearrangement of terms, or other algebraic manipulations. This was our experience in Chapter 2. It took considerable analysis in Section 2.4 to find $\lim_{x \to 0} (\sin x)/x$. But we have had success with the limit

$$f'(a) = \lim_{x \to a} \frac{f(x) - f(a)}{x - a},$$

from which we calculate derivatives and which always produces the equivalent of $0/0$ when we substitute $x = a$. L'Hôpital's Rule enables us to draw on our success with derivatives to evaluate limits that otherwise lead to indeterminate forms.

THEOREM 6   **L'Hôpital's Rule (First Form)**

Suppose that $f(a) = g(a) = 0$, that $f'(a)$ and $g'(a)$ exist, and that $g'(a) \neq 0$. Then

$$\lim_{x \to a} \frac{f(x)}{g(x)} = \frac{f'(a)}{g'(a)}.$$

Caution

To apply l'Hôpital's Rule to f/g, divide the derivative of f by the derivative of g. Do not fall into the trap of taking the derivative of f/g. The quotient to use is f'/g', not $(f/g)'$.

Proof Working backward from $f'(a)$ and $g'(a)$, which are themselves limits, we have

$$\frac{f'(a)}{g'(a)} = \frac{\displaystyle\lim_{x \to a} \frac{f(x) - f(a)}{x - a}}{\displaystyle\lim_{x \to a} \frac{g(x) - g(a)}{x - a}} = \lim_{x \to a} \frac{\dfrac{f(x) - f(a)}{x - a}}{\dfrac{g(x) - g(a)}{x - a}}$$

$$= \lim_{x \to a} \frac{f(x) - f(a)}{g(x) - g(a)} = \lim_{x \to a} \frac{f(x) - 0}{g(x) - 0} = \lim_{x \to a} \frac{f(x)}{g(x)}. \qquad \blacksquare$$

EXAMPLE 1 Using L'Hôpital's Rule

(a) $\displaystyle\lim_{x \to 0} \frac{3x - \sin x}{x} = \left. \frac{3 - \cos x}{1} \right|_{x=0} = 2$

(b) $\displaystyle\lim_{x \to 0} \frac{\sqrt{1 + x} - 1}{x} = \left. \frac{\dfrac{1}{2\sqrt{1 + x}}}{1} \right|_{x=0} = \frac{1}{2}$ ∎

Sometimes after differentiation, the new numerator and denominator both equal zero at $x = a$, as we see in Example 2. In these cases, we apply a stronger form of l'Hôpital's Rule.

THEOREM 7 L'Hôpital's Rule (Stronger Form)

Suppose that $f(a) = g(a) = 0$, that f and g are differentiable on an open interval I containing a, and that $g'(x) \neq 0$ on I if $x \neq a$. Then

$$\lim_{x \to a} \frac{f(x)}{g(x)} = \lim_{x \to a} \frac{f'(x)}{g'(x)},$$

assuming that the limit on the right side exists.

Before we give a proof of Theorem 7, let's consider an example.

EXAMPLE 2 Applying the Stronger Form of L'Hôpital's Rule

(a) $\displaystyle\lim_{x \to 0} \frac{\sqrt{1 + x} - 1 - x/2}{x^2}$ $\quad \frac{0}{0}$

$$= \lim_{x \to 0} \frac{(1/2)(1 + x)^{-1/2} - 1/2}{2x} \qquad \text{Still } \tfrac{0}{0}; \text{ differentiate again.}$$

$$= \lim_{x \to 0} \frac{-(1/4)(1 + x)^{-3/2}}{2} = -\frac{1}{8} \qquad \text{Not } \tfrac{0}{0}; \text{ limit is found.}$$

(b) $\displaystyle\lim_{x \to 0} \frac{x - \sin x}{x^3}$ $\quad \frac{0}{0}$

$$= \lim_{x \to 0} \frac{1 - \cos x}{3x^2} \qquad \text{Still } \tfrac{0}{0}$$

$$= \lim_{x \to 0} \frac{\sin x}{6x} \qquad \text{Still } \tfrac{0}{0}$$

$$= \lim_{x \to 0} \frac{\cos x}{6} = \frac{1}{6} \qquad \text{Not } \tfrac{0}{0}; \text{ limit is found.} \quad \blacksquare$$

The proof of the stronger form of l'Hôpital's Rule is based on Cauchy's Mean Value Theorem, a Mean Value Theorem that involves two functions instead of one. We prove Cauchy's Theorem first and then show how it leads to l'Hôpital's Rule.

THEOREM 8   Cauchy's Mean Value Theorem

Suppose functions f and g are continuous on $[a, b]$ and differentiable throughout (a, b) and also suppose $g'(x) \neq 0$ throughout (a, b). Then there exists a number c in (a, b) at which

$$\frac{f'(c)}{g'(c)} = \frac{f(b) - f(a)}{g(b) - g(a)}.$$

Proof   We apply the Mean Value Theorem of Section 4.2 twice. First we use it to show that $g(a) \neq g(b)$. For if $g(b)$ did equal $g(a)$, then the Mean Value Theorem would give

$$g'(c) = \frac{g(b) - g(a)}{b - a} = 0$$

for some c between a and b, which cannot happen because $g'(x) \neq 0$ in (a, b).

We next apply the Mean Value Theorem to the function

$$F(x) = f(x) - f(a) - \frac{f(b) - f(a)}{g(b) - g(a)} [g(x) - g(a)].$$

This function is continuous and differentiable where f and g are, and $F(b) = F(a) = 0$. Therefore, there is a number c between a and b for which $F'(c) = 0$. When expressed in terms of f and g, this equation becomes

$$F'(c) = f'(c) - \frac{f(b) - f(a)}{g(b) - g(a)} [g'(c)] = 0$$

or

$$\frac{f'(c)}{g'(c)} = \frac{f(b) - f(a)}{g(b) - g(a)}.$$ ∎

Notice that the Mean Value Theorem in Section 4.2 is Theorem 8 with $g(x) = x$.

Cauchy's Mean Value Theorem has a geometric interpretation for a curve C defined by the parametric equations $x = g(t)$ and $y = f(t)$. From Equation (2) in Section 3.5, the slope of the parametric curve at t is given by

$$\frac{dy/dt}{dx/dt} = \frac{f'(t)}{g'(t)},$$

so $f'(c)/g'(c)$ is the slope of the tangent to the curve when $t = c$. The secant line joining the two points $(g(a), f(a))$ and $(g(b), f(b))$ on C has slope

$$\frac{f(b) - f(a)}{g(b) - g(a)}.$$

Theorem 8 says that there is a parameter value c in the interval (a, b) for which the slope of the tangent to the curve at the point $(g(c), f(c))$ is the same as the slope of the secant line joining the points $(g(a), f(a))$ and $(g(b), f(b))$. This geometric result is shown in Figure 4.42. Note that more than one such value c of the parameter may exist.

We now prove Theorem 7.

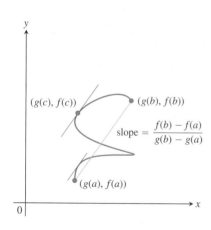

FIGURE 4.42   There is at least one value of the parameter $t = c, a < c < b$, for which the slope of the tangent to the curve at $(g(c), f(c))$ is the same as the slope of the secant line joining the points $(g(a), f(a))$ and $(g(b), f(b))$.

Proof of the Stronger Form of l'Hôpital's Rule   We first establish the limit equation for the case $x \rightarrow a^+$. The method needs almost no change to apply to $x \rightarrow a^-$, and the combination of these two cases establishes the result.

Suppose that x lies to the right of a. Then $g'(x) \neq 0$, and we can apply Cauchy's Mean Value Theorem to the closed interval from a to x. This step produces a number c between a and x such that

$$\frac{f'(c)}{g'(c)} = \frac{f(x) - f(a)}{g(x) - g(a)}.$$

But $f(a) = g(a) = 0$, so

$$\frac{f'(c)}{g'(c)} = \frac{f(x)}{g(x)}.$$

As x approaches a, c approaches a because it always lies between a and x. Therefore,

$$\lim_{x \rightarrow a^+} \frac{f(x)}{g(x)} = \lim_{c \rightarrow a^+} \frac{f'(c)}{g'(c)} = \lim_{x \rightarrow a^+} \frac{f'(x)}{g'(x)},$$

which establishes l'Hôpital's Rule for the case where x approaches a from above. The case where x approaches a from below is proved by applying Cauchy's Mean Value Theorem to the closed interval $[x, a]$, $x < a$.   ∎

Most functions encountered in the real world and most functions in this book satisfy the conditions of l'Hôpital's Rule.

Using L'Hôpital's Rule

To find

$$\lim_{x \rightarrow a} \frac{f(x)}{g(x)}$$

by l'Hôpital's Rule, continue to differentiate f and g, so long as we still get the form $0/0$ at $x = a$. But as soon as one or the other of these derivatives is different from zero at $x = a$ we stop differentiating. L'Hôpital's Rule does not apply when either the numerator or denominator has a finite nonzero limit.

EXAMPLE 3   Incorrectly Applying the Stronger Form of L'Hôpital's Rule

$$\lim_{x \rightarrow 0} \frac{1 - \cos x}{x + x^2} \qquad \frac{0}{0}$$

$$= \lim_{x \rightarrow 0} \frac{\sin x}{1 + 2x} = \frac{0}{1} = 0 \qquad \text{Not } \tfrac{0}{0}; \text{ limit is found.}$$

Up to now the calculation is correct, but if we continue to differentiate in an attempt to apply l'Hôpital's Rule once more, we get

$$\lim_{x \rightarrow 0} \frac{1 - \cos x}{x + x^2} = \lim_{x \rightarrow 0} \frac{\sin x}{1 + 2x} = \lim_{x \rightarrow 0} \frac{\cos x}{2} = \frac{1}{2},$$

which is wrong. L'Hôpital's Rule can only be applied to limits which give indeterminate forms, and $0/1$ is not an indeterminate form.   ∎

L'Hôpital's Rule applies to one-sided limits as well, which is apparent from the proof of Theorem 7.

EXAMPLE 4   Using L'Hôpital's Rule with One-Sided Limits

> Recall that ∞ and $+\infty$ mean the same thing.

(a) $\displaystyle \lim_{x \to 0^+} \frac{\sin x}{x^2}$ $\qquad \frac{0}{0}$

$\displaystyle = \lim_{x \to 0^+} \frac{\cos x}{2x} = \infty$ $\qquad$ Positive for $x > 0$.

(b) $\displaystyle \lim_{x \to 0^-} \frac{\sin x}{x^2}$ $\qquad \frac{0}{0}$

$\displaystyle = \lim_{x \to 0^-} \frac{\cos x}{2x} = -\infty$ $\qquad$ Negative for $x < 0$. ∎

Indeterminate Forms ∞/∞, $\infty \cdot 0$, $\infty - \infty$

Sometimes when we try to evaluate a limit as $x \to a$ by substituting $x = a$ we get an ambiguous expression like ∞/∞, $\infty \cdot 0$, or $\infty - \infty$, instead of $0/0$. We first consider the form ∞/∞.

In more advanced books it is proved that l'Hôpital's Rule applies to the indeterminate form ∞/∞ as well as to $0/0$. If $f(x) \to \pm\infty$ and $g(x) \to \pm\infty$ as $x \to a$, then

$$\lim_{x \to a} \frac{f(x)}{g(x)} = \lim_{x \to a} \frac{f'(x)}{g'(x)}$$

provided the limit on the right exists. In the notation $x \to a$, a may be either finite or infinite. Moreover $x \to a$ may be replaced by the one-sided limits $x \to a^+$ or $x \to a^-$.

EXAMPLE 5   Working with the Indeterminate Form ∞/∞

Find

(a) $\displaystyle \lim_{x \to \pi/2} \frac{\sec x}{1 + \tan x}$

(b) $\displaystyle \lim_{x \to \infty} \frac{x - 2x^2}{3x^2 + 5x}$

Solution

(a) The numerator and denominator are discontinuous at $x = \pi/2$, so we investigate the one-sided limits there. To apply l'Hôpital's Rule, we can choose I to be any open interval with $x = \pi/2$ as an endpoint.

$$\lim_{x \to (\pi/2)^-} \frac{\sec x}{1 + \tan x} \qquad \frac{\infty}{\infty} \text{ from the left}$$

$$= \lim_{x \to (\pi/2)^-} \frac{\sec x \tan x}{\sec^2 x} = \lim_{x \to (\pi/2)^-} \sin x = 1$$

The right-hand limit is 1 also, with $(-\infty)/(-\infty)$ as the indeterminate form. Therefore, the two-sided limit is equal to 1.

(b) $\displaystyle \lim_{x \to \infty} \frac{x - 2x^2}{3x^2 + 5x} = \lim_{x \to \infty} \frac{1 - 4x}{6x + 5} = \lim_{x \to \infty} \frac{-4}{6} = -\frac{2}{3}.$ ∎

Next we turn our attention to the indeterminate forms $\infty \cdot 0$ and $\infty - \infty$. Sometimes these forms can be handled by using algebra to convert them to a $0/0$ or ∞/∞ form. Here again we do not mean to suggest that $\infty \cdot 0$ or $\infty - \infty$ is a number. They are only notations for functional behaviors when considering limits. Here are examples of how we might work with these indeterminate forms.

EXAMPLE 6   Working with the Indeterminate Form $\infty \cdot 0$

Find

$$\lim_{x \to \infty} \left(x \sin \frac{1}{x} \right)$$

Solution

$$\lim_{x \to \infty} \left(x \sin \frac{1}{x} \right) \qquad \infty \cdot 0$$

$$= \lim_{h \to 0^+} \left(\frac{1}{h} \sin h \right) \qquad \text{Let } h = 1/x.$$

$$= 1$$ ∎

EXAMPLE 7   Working with the Indeterminate Form $\infty - \infty$

Find

$$\lim_{x \to 0} \left(\frac{1}{\sin x} - \frac{1}{x} \right).$$

Solution   If $x \to 0^+$, then $\sin x \to 0^+$ and

$$\frac{1}{\sin x} - \frac{1}{x} \to \infty - \infty.$$

Similarly, if $x \to 0^-$, then $\sin x \to 0^-$ and

$$\frac{1}{\sin x} - \frac{1}{x} \to -\infty - (-\infty) = -\infty + \infty.$$

Neither form reveals what happens in the limit. To find out, we first combine the fractions:

$$\frac{1}{\sin x} - \frac{1}{x} = \frac{x - \sin x}{x \sin x} \qquad \text{Common denominator is } x \sin x$$

Then apply l'Hôpital's Rule to the result:

$$\lim_{x \to 0} \left(\frac{1}{\sin x} - \frac{1}{x} \right) = \lim_{x \to 0} \frac{x - \sin x}{x \sin x} \qquad \frac{0}{0}$$

$$= \lim_{x \to 0} \frac{1 - \cos x}{\sin x + x \cos x} \qquad \text{Still } \frac{0}{0}$$

$$= \lim_{x \to 0} \frac{\sin x}{2 \cos x - x \sin x} = \frac{0}{2} = 0.$$ ∎

EXERCISES 4.6

Finding Limits

In Exercises 1–6, use l'Hôpital's Rule to evaluate the limit. Then evaluate the limit using a method studied in Chapter 2.

1. $\lim\limits_{x\to 2} \dfrac{x-2}{x^2-4}$

2. $\lim\limits_{x\to 0} \dfrac{\sin 5x}{x}$

3. $\lim\limits_{x\to\infty} \dfrac{5x^2-3x}{7x^2+1}$

4. $\lim\limits_{x\to 1} \dfrac{x^3-1}{4x^3-x-3}$

5. $\lim\limits_{x\to 0} \dfrac{1-\cos x}{x^2}$

6. $\lim\limits_{x\to\infty} \dfrac{2x^2+3x}{x^3+x+1}$

Applying l'Hôpital's Rule

Use l'Hôpital's Rule to find the limits in Exercises 7–26.

7. $\lim\limits_{t\to 0} \dfrac{\sin t^2}{t}$

8. $\lim\limits_{x\to\pi/2} \dfrac{2x-\pi}{\cos x}$

9. $\lim\limits_{\theta\to\pi} \dfrac{\sin\theta}{\pi-\theta}$

10. $\lim\limits_{x\to\pi/2} \dfrac{1-\sin x}{1+\cos 2x}$

11. $\lim\limits_{x\to\pi/4} \dfrac{\sin x-\cos x}{x-\pi/4}$

12. $\lim\limits_{x\to\pi/3} \dfrac{\cos x-0.5}{x-\pi/3}$

13. $\lim\limits_{x\to(\pi/2)} -\left(x-\dfrac{\pi}{2}\right)\tan x$

14. $\lim\limits_{x\to 0} \dfrac{2x}{x+7\sqrt{x}}$

15. $\lim\limits_{x\to 1} \dfrac{2x^2-(3x+1)\sqrt{x}+2}{x-1}$

16. $\lim\limits_{x\to 2} \dfrac{\sqrt{x^2+5}-3}{x^2-4}$

17. $\lim\limits_{x\to 0} \dfrac{\sqrt{a(a+x)}-a}{x}, \quad a>0$

18. $\lim\limits_{t\to 0} \dfrac{10(\sin t-t)}{t^3}$

19. $\lim\limits_{x\to 0} \dfrac{x(\cos x-1)}{\sin x-x}$

20. $\lim\limits_{h\to 0} \dfrac{\sin(a+h)-\sin a}{h}$

21. $\lim\limits_{r\to 1} \dfrac{a(r^n-1)}{r-1}, \quad n$ a positive integer

22. $\lim\limits_{x\to 0^+}\left(\dfrac{1}{x}-\dfrac{1}{\sqrt{x}}\right)$

23. $\lim\limits_{x\to\infty} (x-\sqrt{x^2+x})$

24. $\lim\limits_{x\to\infty} x\tan\dfrac{1}{x}$

25. $\lim\limits_{x\to\pm\infty} \dfrac{3x-5}{2x^2-x+2}$

26. $\lim\limits_{x\to 0} \dfrac{\sin 7x}{\tan 11x}$

Theory and Applications

L'Hôpital's Rule does not help with the limits in Exercises 27–30. Try it; you just keep on cycling. Find the limits some other way.

27. $\lim\limits_{x\to\infty} \dfrac{\sqrt{9x+1}}{\sqrt{x+1}}$

28. $\lim\limits_{x\to 0^+} \dfrac{\sqrt{x}}{\sqrt{\sin x}}$

29. $\lim\limits_{x\to(\pi/2)^-} \dfrac{\sec x}{\tan x}$

30. $\lim\limits_{x\to 0^+} \dfrac{\cot x}{\csc x}$

31. Which one is correct, and which one is wrong? Give reasons for your answers.

   a. $\lim\limits_{x\to 3} \dfrac{x-3}{x^2-3} = \lim\limits_{x\to 3} \dfrac{1}{2x} = \dfrac{1}{6}$

   b. $\lim\limits_{x\to 3} \dfrac{x-3}{x^2-3} = \dfrac{0}{6} = 0$

32. **∞/∞ Form** Give an example of two differentiable functions f and g with $\lim_{x\to\infty} f(x) = \lim_{x\to\infty} g(x) = \infty$ that satisfy the following.

   a. $\lim\limits_{x\to\infty} \dfrac{f(x)}{g(x)} = 3$

   b. $\lim\limits_{x\to\infty} \dfrac{f(x)}{g(x)} = 0$

   c. $\lim\limits_{x\to\infty} \dfrac{f(x)}{g(x)} = \infty$

33. **Continuous extension** Find a value of c that makes the function

$$f(x) = \begin{cases} \dfrac{9x-3\sin 3x}{5x^3}, & x\neq 0 \\ c, & x=0 \end{cases}$$

continuous at $x=0$. Explain why your value of c works.

34. Let

$$f(x) = \begin{cases} x+2, & x\neq 0 \\ 0, & x=0 \end{cases} \quad\text{and}\quad g(x) = \begin{cases} x+1, & x\neq 0 \\ 0, & x=0. \end{cases}$$

   a. Show that

$$\lim\limits_{x\to 0} \dfrac{f'(x)}{g'(x)} = 1 \quad\text{but}\quad \lim\limits_{x\to 0} \dfrac{f(x)}{g(x)} = 2.$$

   b. Explain why this does not contradict l'Hôpital's Rule.

T 35. **0/0 Form** Estimate the value of

$$\lim\limits_{x\to 1} \dfrac{2x^2-(3x+1)\sqrt{x}+2}{x-1}$$

by graphing. Then confirm your estimate with l'Hôpital's Rule.

T 36. **$\infty-\infty$ Form**

   a. Estimate the value of

$$\lim\limits_{x\to\infty} (x-\sqrt{x^2+x})$$

by graphing $f(x) = x-\sqrt{x^2+x}$ over a suitably large interval of x-values.

   b. Now confirm your estimate by finding the limit with l'Hôpital's Rule. As the first step, multiply $f(x)$ by the fraction $(x+\sqrt{x^2+x})/(x+\sqrt{x^2+x})$ and simplify the new numerator.

T **37.** Let

$$f(x) = \frac{1 - \cos x^6}{x^{12}}.$$

Explain why some graphs of f may give false information about $\lim_{x \to 0} f(x)$. (*Hint:* Try the window $[-1, 1]$ by $[-0.5, 1]$.)

38. Find all values of c, that satisfy the conclusion of Cauchy's Mean Value Theorem for the given functions and interval.

a. $f(x) = x, \quad g(x) = x^2, \quad (a, b) = (-2, 0)$

b. $f(x) = x, \quad g(x) = x^2, \quad (a, b)$ arbitrary

c. $f(x) = x^3/3 - 4x, \quad g(x) = x^2, \quad (a, b) = (0, 3)$

39. In the accompanying figure, the circle has radius OA equal to 1, and AB is tangent to the circle at A. The arc AC has radian measure θ and the segment AB also has length θ. The line through B and C crosses the x-axis at $P(x, 0)$.

a. Show that the length of PA is

$$1 - x = \frac{\theta(1 - \cos\theta)}{\theta - \sin\theta}.$$

b. Find $\lim_{\theta \to 0} (1 - x)$.

c. Show that $\lim_{\theta \to \infty} [(1 - x) - (1 - \cos\theta)] = 0$.

Interpret this geometrically.

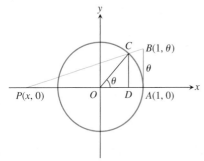

40. A right triangle has one leg of length 1, another of length y, and a hypotenuse of length r. The angle opposite y has radian measure θ. Find the limits as $\theta \to \pi/2$ of

a. $r - y$.

b. $r^2 - y^2$.

c. $r^3 - y^3$.

4.7 Newton's Method

HISTORICAL BIOGRAPHY

Niels Henrik Abel
(1802–1829)

One of the basic problems of mathematics is solving equations. Using the quadratic root formula, we know how to find a point (solution) where $x^2 - 3x + 2 = 0$. There are more complicated formulas to solve cubic or quartic equations (polynomials of degree 3 or 4), but the Norwegian mathematician Niels Abel showed that no simple formulas exist to solve polynomials of degree equal to five. There is also no simple formula for solving equations like $\sin x = x^2$, which involve transcendental functions as well as polynomials or other algebraic functions.

In this section we study a numerical method, called *Newton's method* or the *Newton–Raphson method*, which is a technique to approximate the solution to an equation $f(x) = 0$. Essentially it uses tangent lines in place of the graph of $y = f(x)$ near the points where f is zero. (A value of x where f is zero is a *root* of the function f and a *solution* of the equation $f(x) = 0$.)

Procedure for Newton's Method

The goal of Newton's method for estimating a solution of an equation $f(x) = 0$ is to produce a sequence of approximations that approach the solution. We pick the first number x_0 of the sequence. Then, under favorable circumstances, the method does the rest by moving step by step toward a point where the graph of f crosses the x-axis (Figure 4.43). At each

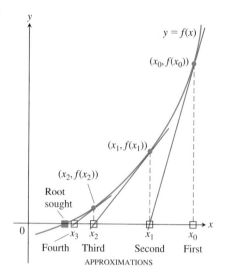

FIGURE 4.43 Newton's method starts with an initial guess x_0 and (under favorable circumstances) improves the guess one step at a time.

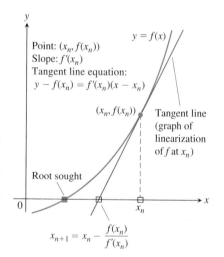

FIGURE 4.44 The geometry of the successive steps of Newton's method. From x_n we go up to the curve and follow the tangent line down to find x_{n+1}.

step the method approximates a zero of f with a zero of one of its linearizations. Here is how it works.

The initial estimate, x_0, may be found by graphing or just plain guessing. The method then uses the tangent to the curve $y = f(x)$ at $(x_0, f(x_0))$ to approximate the curve, calling the point x_1 where the tangent meets the x-axis (Figure 4.43). The number x_1 is usually a better approximation to the solution than is x_0. The point x_2 where the tangent to the curve at $(x_1, f(x_1))$ crosses the x-axis is the next approximation in the sequence. We continue on, using each approximation to generate the next, until we are close enough to the root to stop.

We can derive a formula for generating the successive approximations in the following way. Given the approximation x_n, the point-slope equation for the tangent to the curve at $(x_n, f(x_n))$ is

$$y = f(x_n) + f'(x_n)(x - x_n).$$

We can find where it crosses the x-axis by setting $y = 0$ (Figure 4.44).

$$0 = f(x_n) + f'(x_n)(x - x_n)$$

$$-\frac{f(x_n)}{f'(x_n)} = x - x_n$$

$$x = x_n - \frac{f(x_n)}{f'(x_n)} \qquad \text{If } f'(x_n) \neq 0$$

This value of x is the next approximation x_{n+1}. Here is a summary of Newton's method.

Procedure for Newton's Method

1. Guess a first approximation to a solution of the equation $f(x) = 0$. A graph of $y = f(x)$ may help.

2. Use the first approximation to get a second, the second to get a third, and so on, using the formula

$$x_{n+1} = x_n - \frac{f(x_n)}{f'(x_n)}, \qquad \text{if } f'(x_n) \neq 0 \tag{1}$$

Applying Newton's Method

Applications of Newton's method generally involve many numerical computations, making them well suited for computers or calculators. Nevertheless, even when the calculations are done by hand (which may be very tedious), they give a powerful way to find solutions of equations.

In our first example, we find decimal approximations to $\sqrt{2}$ by estimating the positive root of the equation $f(x) = x^2 - 2 = 0$.

EXAMPLE 1   Finding the Square Root of 2

Find the positive root of the equation

$$f(x) = x^2 - 2 = 0.$$

Solution   With $f(x) = x^2 - 2$ and $f'(x) = 2x$, Equation (1) becomes

$$x_{n+1} = x_n - \frac{x_n^2 - 2}{2x_n}$$

$$= x_n - \frac{x_n}{2} + \frac{1}{x_n}$$

$$= \frac{x_n}{2} + \frac{1}{x_n}.$$

The equation

$$x_{n+1} = \frac{x_n}{2} + \frac{1}{x_n}$$

enables us to go from each approximation to the next with just a few keystrokes. With the starting value $x_0 = 1$, we get the results in the first column of the following table. (To five decimal places, $\sqrt{2} = 1.41421$.)

	Error	Number of correct digits
$x_0 = 1$	-0.41421	1
$x_1 = 1.5$	0.08579	1
$x_2 = 1.41667$	0.00246	3
$x_3 = 1.41422$	0.00001	5

■

Newton's method is the method used by most calculators to calculate roots because it converges so fast (more about this later). If the arithmetic in the table in Example 1 had been carried to 13 decimal places instead of 5, then going one step further would have given $\sqrt{2}$ correctly to more than 10 decimal places.

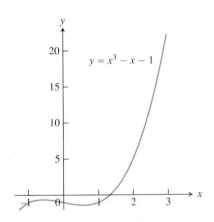

FIGURE 4.45   The graph of $f(x) = x^3 - x - 1$ crosses the x-axis once; this is the root we want to find (Example 2).

EXAMPLE 2   Using Newton's Method

Find the x-coordinate of the point where the curve $y = x^3 - x$ crosses the horizontal line $y = 1$.

Solution   The curve crosses the line when $x^3 - x = 1$ or $x^3 - x - 1 = 0$. When does $f(x) = x^3 - x - 1$ equal zero? Since $f(1) = -1$ and $f(2) = 5$, we know by the Intermediate Value Theorem there is a root in the interval $(1, 2)$ (Figure 4.45).

We apply Newton's method to f with the starting value $x_0 = 1$. The results are displayed in Table 4.1 and Figure 4.46.

At $n = 5$, we come to the result $x_6 = x_5 = 1.3247\,17957$. When $x_{n+1} = x_n$, Equation (1) shows that $f(x_n) = 0$. We have found a solution of $f(x) = 0$ to nine decimals.   ■

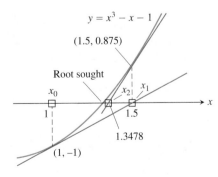

FIGURE 4.46   The first three x-values in Table 4.1 (four decimal places).

In Figure 4.47 we have indicated that the process in Example 2 might have started at the point $B_0(3, 23)$ on the curve, with $x_0 = 3$. Point B_0 is quite far from the x-axis, but the tangent at B_0 crosses the x-axis at about $(2.12, 0)$, so x_1 is still an improvement over x_0. If we use Equation (1) repeatedly as before, with $f(x) = x^3 - x - 1$ and $f'(x) = 3x^2 - 1$, we confirm the nine-place solution $x_7 = x_6 = 1.3247\,17957$ in seven steps.

TABLE 4.1 The result of applying Newton's method to $f(x) = x^3 - x - 1$ with $x_0 = 1$

n	x_n	$f(x_n)$	$f'(x_n)$	$x_{n+1} = x_n - \dfrac{f(x_n)}{f'(x_n)}$
0	1	-1	2	1.5
1	1.5	0.875	5.75	1.3478 26087
2	1.3478 26087	0.1006 82173	4.4499 05482	1.3252 00399
3	1.3252 00399	0.0020 58362	4.2684 68292	1.3247 18174
4	1.3247 18174	0.0000 00924	4.2646 34722	1.3247 17957
5	1.3247 17957	$-1.8672\text{E-}13$	4.2646 32999	1.3247 17957

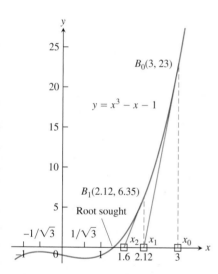

FIGURE 4.47 Any starting value x_0 to the right of $x = 1/\sqrt{3}$ will lead to the root.

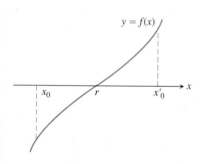

FIGURE 4.48 Newton's method will converge to r from either starting point.

The curve in Figure 4.47 has a local maximum at $x = -1/\sqrt{3}$ and a local minimum at $x = 1/\sqrt{3}$. We would not expect good results from Newton's method if we were to start with x_0 between these points, but we can start any place to the right of $x = 1/\sqrt{3}$ and get the answer. It would not be very clever to do so, but we could even begin far to the right of B_0, for example with $x_0 = 10$. It takes a bit longer, but the process still converges to the same answer as before.

Convergence of Newton's Method

In practice, Newton's method usually converges with impressive speed, but this is not guaranteed. One way to test convergence is to begin by graphing the function to estimate a good starting value for x_0. You can test that you are getting closer to a zero of the function by evaluating $|f(x_n)|$ and check that the method is converging by evaluating $|x_n - x_{n+1}|$.

Theory does provide some help. A theorem from advanced calculus says that if

$$\left| \frac{f(x)f''(x)}{(f'(x))^2} \right| < 1 \tag{2}$$

for all x in an interval about a root r, then the method will converge to r for any starting value x_0 in that interval. Note that this condition is satisfied if the graph of f is not too horizontal near where it crosses the x-axis.

Newton's method always converges if, between r and x_0, the graph of f is concave up when $f(x_0) > 0$ and concave down when $f(x_0) < 0$. (See Figure 4.48.) In most cases, the speed of the convergence to the root r is expressed by the advanced calculus formula

$$\underbrace{|x_{n+1} - r|}_{\text{error } e_{n+1}} \le \frac{\max|f''|}{2\min|f'|} |x_n - r|^2 = \text{constant} \cdot \underbrace{|x_n - r|^2}_{\text{error } e_n}, \tag{3}$$

where max and min refer to the maximum and minimum values in an interval surrounding r. The formula says that the error in step $n + 1$ is no greater than a constant times the square of the error in step n. This may not seem like much, but think of what it says. If the constant is less than or equal to 1 and $|x_n - r| < 10^{-3}$, then $|x_{n+1} - r| < 10^{-6}$. *In a single step*, the method moves from three decimal places of accuracy to six, and the number of decimals of accuracy continues to double with each successive step.

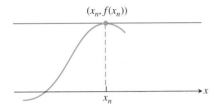

FIGURE 4.49 If $f'(x_n) = 0$, there is no intersection point to define x_{n+1}.

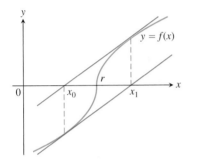

FIGURE 4.50 Newton's method fails to converge. You go from x_0 to x_1 and back to x_0, never getting any closer to r.

But Things Can Go Wrong

Newton's method stops if $f'(x_n) = 0$ (Figure 4.49). In that case, try a new starting point. Of course, f and f' may have the same root. To detect whether this is so, you could first find the solutions of $f'(x) = 0$ and check f at those values, or you could graph f and f' together.

Newton's method does not always converge. For instance, if

$$f(x) = \begin{cases} -\sqrt{r - x}, & x < r \\ \sqrt{x - r}, & x \ge r, \end{cases}$$

the graph will be like the one in Figure 4.50. If we begin with $x_0 = r - h$, we get $x_1 = r + h$, and successive approximations go back and forth between these two values. No amount of iteration brings us closer to the root than our first guess.

If Newton's method does converge, it converges to a root. Be careful, however. There are situations in which the method appears to converge but there is no root there. Fortunately, such situations are rare.

When Newton's method converges to a root, it may not be the root you have in mind. Figure 4.51 shows two ways this can happen.

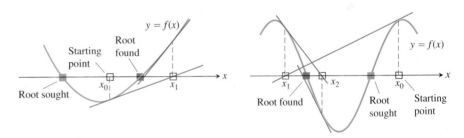

FIGURE 4.51 If you start too far away, Newton's method may miss the root you want.

Fractal Basins and Newton's Method

The process of finding roots by Newton's method can be uncertain in the sense that for some equations, the final outcome can be extremely sensitive to the starting value's location.

The equation $4x^4 - 4x^2 = 0$ is a case in point (Figure 4.52a). Starting values in the blue zone on the x-axis lead to root A. Starting values in the black lead to root B, and starting values in the red zone lead to root C. The points $\pm \sqrt{2}/2$ give horizontal tangents. The points $\pm \sqrt{21}/7$ "cycle," each leading to the other, and back (Figure 4.52b).

The interval between $\sqrt{21}/7$ and $\sqrt{2}/2$ contains infinitely many open intervals of points leading to root A, alternating with intervals of points leading to root C (Figure 4.52c). The boundary points separating consecutive intervals (there are infinitely many) do not lead to roots, but cycle back and forth from one to another. Moreover, as we select points that approach $\sqrt{21}/7$ from the right, it becomes increasingly difficult to distinguish which lead to root A and which to root C. On the same side of $\sqrt{21}/7$, we find arbitrarily close together points whose ultimate destinations are far apart.

If we think of the roots as "attractors" of other points, the coloring in Figure 4.52 shows the intervals of the points they attract (the "intervals of attraction"). You might think that points between roots A and B would be attracted to either A or B, but, as we see, that is not the case. Between A and B there are infinitely many intervals of points attracted to C. Similarly between B and C lie infinitely many intervals of points attracted to A.

We encounter an even more dramatic example of such behavior when we apply Newton's method to solve the complex-number equation $z^6 - 1 = 0$. It has six solutions: $1, -1$, and the four numbers $\pm(1/2) \pm \left(\sqrt{3}/2\right)i$. As Figure 4.53 suggests, each of the

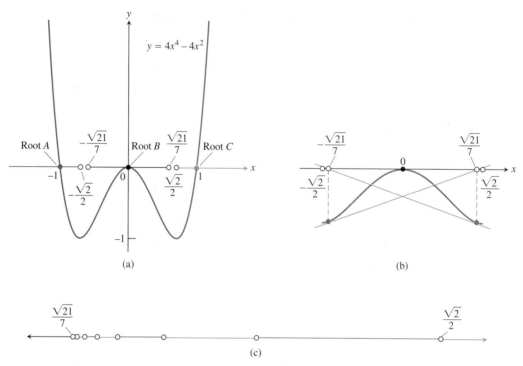

FIGURE 4.52 (a) Starting values in $\left(-\infty, -\sqrt{2}/2\right)$, $\left(-\sqrt{21}/7, \sqrt{21}/7\right)$, and $\left(\sqrt{2}/2, \infty\right)$ lead respectively to roots A, B, and C. (b) The values $x = \pm\sqrt{21}/7$ lead only to each other. (c) Between $\sqrt{21}/7$ and $\sqrt{2}/2$, there are infinitely many open intervals of points attracted to A alternating with open intervals of points attracted to C. This behavior is mirrored in the interval $\left(-\sqrt{2}/2, -\sqrt{21}/7\right)$.

FIGURE 4.53 This computer-generated initial value portrait uses color to show where different points in the complex plane end up when they are used as starting values in applying Newton's method to solve the equation $z^6 - 1 = 0$. Red points go to 1, green points to $(1/2) + \left(\sqrt{3}/2\right)i$, dark blue points to $(-1/2) + \left(\sqrt{3}/2\right)i$, and so on. Starting values that generate sequences that do not arrive within 0.1 unit of a root after 32 steps are colored black.

six roots has infinitely many "basins" of attraction in the complex plane (Appendix 5). Starting points in red basins are attracted to the root 1, those in the green basin to the root $(1/2) + \left(\sqrt{3}/2\right)i$, and so on. Each basin has a boundary whose complicated pattern repeats without end under successive magnifications. These basins are called **fractal basins**.

EXERCISES 4.7

Root-Finding

1. Use Newton's method to estimate the solutions of the equation $x^2 + x - 1 = 0$. Start with $x_0 = -1$ for the left-hand solution and with $x_0 = 1$ for the solution on the right. Then, in each case, find x_2.

2. Use Newton's method to estimate the one real solution of $x^3 + 3x + 1 = 0$. Start with $x_0 = 0$ and then find x_2.

3. Use Newton's method to estimate the two zeros of the function $f(x) = x^4 + x - 3$. Start with $x_0 = -1$ for the left-hand zero and with $x_0 = 1$ for the zero on the right. Then, in each case, find x_2.

4. Use Newton's method to estimate the two zeros of the function $f(x) = 2x - x^2 + 1$. Start with $x_0 = 0$ for the left-hand zero and with $x_0 = 2$ for the zero on the right. Then, in each case, find x_2.

5. Use Newton's method to find the positive fourth root of 2 by solving the equation $x^4 - 2 = 0$. Start with $x_0 = 1$ and find x_2.

6. Use Newton's method to find the negative fourth root of 2 by solving the equation $x^4 - 2 = 0$. Start with $x_0 = -1$ and find x_2.

Theory, Examples, and Applications

7. **Guessing a root** Suppose that your first guess is lucky, in the sense that x_0 is a root of $f(x) = 0$. Assuming that $f'(x_0)$ is defined and not 0, what happens to x_1 and later approximations?

8. **Estimating pi** You plan to estimate $\pi/2$ to five decimal places by using Newton's method to solve the equation $\cos x = 0$. Does it matter what your starting value is? Give reasons for your answer.

9. **Oscillation** Show that if $h > 0$, applying Newton's method to

$$f(x) = \begin{cases} \sqrt{x}, & x \geq 0 \\ \sqrt{-x}, & x < 0 \end{cases}$$

leads to $x_1 = -h$ if $x_0 = h$ and to $x_1 = h$ if $x_0 = -h$. Draw a picture that shows what is going on.

10. **Approximations that get worse and worse** Apply Newton's method to $f(x) = x^{1/3}$ with $x_0 = 1$ and calculate x_1, x_2, x_3, and x_4. Find a formula for $|x_n|$. What happens to $|x_n|$ as $n \to \infty$? Draw a picture that shows what is going on.

11. Explain why the following four statements ask for the same information:

    i) Find the roots of $f(x) = x^3 - 3x - 1$.

    ii) Find the x-coordinates of the intersections of the curve $y = x^3$ with the line $y = 3x + 1$.

    iii) Find the x-coordinates of the points where the curve $y = x^3 - 3x$ crosses the horizontal line $y = 1$.

    iv) Find the values of x where the derivative of $g(x) = (1/4)x^4 - (3/2)x^2 - x + 5$ equals zero.

12. **Locating a planet** To calculate a planet's space coordinates, we have to solve equations like $x = 1 + 0.5 \sin x$. Graphing the function $f(x) = x - 1 - 0.5 \sin x$ suggests that the function has a root near $x = 1.5$. Use one application of Newton's method to improve this estimate. That is, start with $x_0 = 1.5$ and find x_1. (The value of the root is 1.49870 to five decimal places.) Remember to use radians.

T 13. **A program for using Newton's method on a grapher** Let $f(x) = x^3 + 3x + 1$. Here is a home screen program to perform the computations in Newton's method.

   a. Let $y_0 = f(x)$ and $y_1 = $ NDER $f(x)$.

   b. Store $x_0 = -0.3$ into x.

   c. Then store $x - (y_0/y_1)$ into x and press the Enter key over and over. Watch as the numbers converge to the zero of f.

   d. Use different values for x_0 and repeat steps (b) and (c).

   e. Write your own equation and use this approach to solve it using Newton's method. Compare your answer with the answer given by the built-in feature of your calculator that gives zeros of functions.

T 14. (*Continuation of Exercise 11.*)

   a. Use Newton's method to find the two negative zeros of $f(x) = x^3 - 3x - 1$ to five decimal places.

   b. Graph $f(x) = x^3 - 3x - 1$ for $-2 \leq x \leq 2.5$. Use the Zoom and Trace features to estimate the zeros of f to five decimal places.

   c. Graph $g(x) = 0.25x^4 - 1.5x^2 - x + 5$. Use the Zoom and Trace features with appropriate rescaling to find, to five decimal places, the values of x where the graph has horizontal tangents.

T 15. **Intersecting curves** The curve $y = \tan x$ crosses the line $y = 2x$ between $x = 0$ and $x = \pi/2$. Use Newton's method to find where.

T 16. **Real solutions of a quartic** Use Newton's method to find the two real solutions of the equation $x^4 - 2x^3 - x^2 - 2x + 2 = 0$.

T 17. a. How many solutions does the equation $\sin 3x = 0.99 - x^2$ have?

   b. Use Newton's method to find them.

T **18. Intersection of curves**

    a. Does $\cos 3x$ ever equal x? Give reasons for your answer.

    b. Use Newton's method to find where.

T **19.** Find the four real zeros of the function $f(x) = 2x^4 - 4x^2 + 1$.

T **20. Estimating pi**   Estimate π to as many decimal places as your calculator will display by using Newton's method to solve the equation $\tan x = 0$ with $x_0 = 3$.

21. At what values(s) of x does $\cos x = 2x$?

22. At what value(s) of x does $\cos x = -x$?

23. Use the Intermediate Value Theorem from Section 2.6 to show that $f(x) = x^3 + 2x - 4$ has a root between $x = 1$ and $x = 2$. Then find the root to five decimal places.

24. Factoring a quartic   Find the approximate values of r_1 through r_4 in the factorization

$$8x^4 - 14x^3 - 9x^2 + 11x - 1 = 8(x - r_1)(x - r_2)(x - r_3)(x - r_4).$$

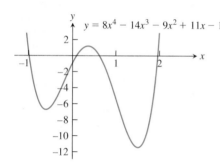

$y = 8x^4 - 14x^3 - 9x^2 + 11x - 1$

T **25. Converging to different zeros**   Use Newton's method to find the zeros of $f(x) = 4x^4 - 4x^2$ using the given starting values (Figure 4.52).

    a. $x_0 = -2$ and $x_0 = -0.8$, lying in $\left(-\infty, -\sqrt{2}/2\right)$

    b. $x_0 = -0.5$ and $x_0 = 0.25$, lying in $\left(-\sqrt{21}/7, \sqrt{21}/7\right)$

    c. $x_0 = 0.8$ and $x_0 = 2$, lying in $\left(\sqrt{2}/2, \infty\right)$

    d. $x_0 = -\sqrt{21}/7$ and $x_0 = \sqrt{21}/7$

26. The sonobuoy problem   In submarine location problems, it is often necessary to find a submarine's closest point of approach (CPA) to a sonobuoy (sound detector) in the water. Suppose that the submarine travels on the parabolic path $y = x^2$ and that the buoy is located at the point $(2, -1/2)$.

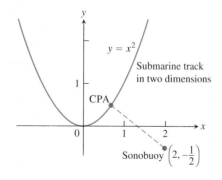

$y = x^2$

Submarine track in two dimensions

CPA

Sonobuoy $\left(2, -\frac{1}{2}\right)$

    a. Show that the value of x that minimizes the distance between the submarine and the buoy is a solution of the equation $x = 1/(x^2 + 1)$.

    b. Solve the equation $x = 1/(x^2 + 1)$ with Newton's method.

27. Curves that are nearly flat at the root   Some curves are so flat that, in practice, Newton's method stops too far from the root to give a useful estimate. Try Newton's method on $f(x) = (x - 1)^{40}$ with a starting value of $x_0 = 2$ to see how close your machine comes to the root $x = 1$.

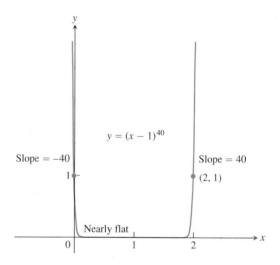

$y = (x - 1)^{40}$

Slope = −40

Slope = 40

(2, 1)

Nearly flat

28. Finding a root different from the one sought   All three roots of $f(x) = 4x^4 - 4x^2$ can be found by starting Newton's method near $x = \sqrt{21}/7$. Try it. (See Figure 4.52.)

29. Finding an ion concentration   While trying to find the acidity of a saturated solution of magnesium hydroxide in hydrochloric acid, you derive the equation

$$\frac{3.64 \times 10^{-11}}{[H_3O^+]^2} = [H_3O^+] + 3.6 \times 10^{-4}$$

for the hydronium ion concentration $[H_3O^+]$. To find the value of $[H_3O^+]$, you set $x = 10^4[H_3O^+]$ and convert the equation to

$$x^3 + 3.6x^2 - 36.4 = 0.$$

You then solve this by Newton's method. What do you get for x? (Make it good to two decimal places.) For $[H_3O^+]$?

T **30. Complex roots**   If you have a computer or a calculator that can be programmed to do complex-number arithmetic, experiment with Newton's method to solve the equation $z^6 - 1 = 0$. The recursion relation to use is

$$z_{n+1} = z_n - \frac{z_n^6 - 1}{6z_n^5} \quad \text{or} \quad z_{n+1} = \frac{5}{6}z_n + \frac{1}{6z_n^5}.$$

Try these starting values (among others): $2, i, \sqrt{3} + i$.

4.8 Antiderivatives

We have studied how to find the derivative of a function. However, many problems require that we recover a function from its known derivative (from its known rate of change). For instance, we may know the velocity function of an object falling from an initial height and need to know its height at any time over some period. More generally, we want to find a function F from its derivative f. If such a function F exists, it is called an *antiderivative* of f.

Finding Antiderivatives

> **DEFINITION** **Antiderivative**
> A function F is an **antiderivative** of f on an interval I if $F'(x) = f(x)$ for all x in I.

The process of recovering a function $F(x)$ from its derivative $f(x)$ is called *antidifferentiation*. We use capital letters such as F to represent an antiderivative of a function f, G to represent an antiderivative of g, and so forth.

EXAMPLE 1 Finding Antiderivatives

Find an antiderivative for each of the following functions.

(a) $f(x) = 2x$

(b) $g(x) = \cos x$

(c) $h(x) = 2x + \cos x$

Solution

(a) $F(x) = x^2$

(b) $G(x) = \sin x$

(c) $H(x) = x^2 + \sin x$

Each answer can be checked by differentiating. The derivative of $F(x) = x^2$ is $2x$. The derivative of $G(x) = \sin x$ is $\cos x$ and the derivative of $H(x) = x^2 + \sin x$ is $2x + \cos x$. ∎

The function $F(x) = x^2$ is not the only function whose derivative is $2x$. The function $x^2 + 1$ has the same derivative. So does $x^2 + C$ for any constant C. Are there others?

Corollary 2 of the Mean Value Theorem in Section 4.2 gives the answer: Any two antiderivatives of a function differ by a constant. So the functions $x^2 + C$, where C is an **arbitrary constant**, form *all* the antiderivatives of $f(x) = 2x$. More generally, we have the following result.

If F is an antiderivative of f on an interval I, then the most general antiderivative of f on I is

$$F(x) + C$$

where C is an arbitrary constant.

Thus the most general antiderivative of f on I is a *family* of functions $F(x) + C$ whose graphs are vertical translates of one another. We can select a particular antiderivative from this family by assigning a specific value to C. Here is an example showing how such an assignment might be made.

EXAMPLE 2   Finding a Particular Antiderivative

Find an antiderivative of $f(x) = \sin x$ that satisfies $F(0) = 3$.

Solution   Since the derivative of $-\cos x$ is $\sin x$, the general antiderivative

$$F(x) = -\cos x + C$$

gives all the antiderivatives of $f(x)$. The condition $F(0) = 3$ determines a specific value for C. Substituting $x = 0$ into $F(x) = -\cos x + C$ gives

$$F(0) = -\cos 0 + C = -1 + C.$$

Since $F(0) = 3$, solving for C gives $C = 4$. So

$$F(x) = -\cos x + 4$$

is the antiderivative satisfying $F(0) = 3$.   ∎

By working backward from assorted differentiation rules, we can derive formulas and rules for antiderivatives. In each case there is an arbitrary constant C in the general expression representing all antiderivatives of a given function. Table 4.2 gives antiderivative formulas for a number of important functions.

TABLE 4.2 Antiderivative formulas

	Function	**General antiderivative**
1.	x^n	$\dfrac{x^{n+1}}{n+1} + C, \quad n \neq -1, n$ rational
2.	$\sin kx$	$-\dfrac{\cos kx}{k} + C, \quad k$ a constant, $k \neq 0$
3.	$\cos kx$	$\dfrac{\sin kx}{k} + C, \quad k$ a constant, $k \neq 0$
4.	$\sec^2 x$	$\tan x + C$
5.	$\csc^2 x$	$-\cot x + C$
6.	$\sec x \tan x$	$\sec x + C$
7.	$\csc x \cot x$	$-\csc x + C$

The rules in Table 4.2 are easily verified by differentiating the general antiderivative formula to obtain the function to its left. For example, the derivative of $\tan x + C$ is $\sec^2 x$, whatever the value of the constant C, and this establishes the formula for the most general antiderivative of $\sec^2 x$.

EXAMPLE 3   Finding Antiderivatives Using Table 4.2

Find the general antiderivative of each of the following functions.

(a) $f(x) = x^5$

(b) $g(x) = \dfrac{1}{\sqrt{x}}$

(c) $h(x) = \sin 2x$

(d) $i(x) = \cos \dfrac{x}{2}$

Solution

(a) $F(x) = \dfrac{x^6}{6} + C$ ⟶ Formula 1 with $n = 5$

(b) $g(x) = x^{-1/2}$, so

$$G(x) = \frac{x^{1/2}}{1/2} + C = 2\sqrt{x} + C$$ ⟶ Formula 1 with $n = -1/2$

(c) $H(x) = \dfrac{-\cos 2x}{2} + C$ ⟶ Formula 2 with $k = 2$

(d) $I(x) = \dfrac{\sin(x/2)}{1/2} + C = 2\sin \dfrac{x}{2} + C$ ⟶ Formula 3 with $k = 1/2$ ∎

Other derivative rules also lead to corresponding antiderivative rules. We can add and subtract antiderivatives, and multiply them by constants.

The formulas in Table 4.3 are easily proved by differentiating the antiderivatives and verifying that the result agrees with the original function. Formula 2 is the special case $k = -1$ in Formula 1.

TABLE 4.3 Antiderivative linearity rules

		Function	General antiderivative
1.	Constant Multiple Rule:	$kf(x)$	$kF(x) + C$, k a constant
2.	Negative Rule:	$-f(x)$	$-F(x) + C$,
3.	Sum or Difference Rule:	$f(x) \pm g(x)$	$F(x) \pm G(x) + C$

EXAMPLE 4   Using the Linearity Rules for Antiderivatives

Find the general antiderivative of

$$f(x) = \frac{3}{\sqrt{x}} + \sin 2x.$$

Solution   We have that $f(x) = 3g(x) + h(x)$ for the functions g and h in Example 3. Since $G(x) = 2\sqrt{x}$ is an antiderivative of $g(x)$ from Example 3b, it follows from the Constant Multiple Rule for antiderivatives that $3G(x) = 3 \cdot 2\sqrt{x} = 6\sqrt{x}$ is an antiderivative of $3g(x) = 3/\sqrt{x}$. Likewise, from Example 3c we know that $H(x) = (-1/2)\cos 2x$ is an antiderivative of $h(x) = \sin 2x$. From the Sum Rule for antiderivatives, we then get that

$$F(x) = 3G(x) + H(x) + C$$

$$= 6\sqrt{x} - \frac{1}{2}\cos 2x + C$$

is the general antiderivative formula for $f(x)$, where C is an arbitrary constant.   ∎

Antiderivatives play several important roles, and methods and techniques for finding them are a major part of calculus. (This is the subject of Chapter 8.)

Initial Value Problems and Differential Equations

Finding an antiderivative for a function $f(x)$ is the same problem as finding a function $y(x)$ that satisfies the equation

$$\frac{dy}{dx} = f(x).$$

This is called a **differential equation**, since it is an equation involving an unknown function y that is being differentiated. To solve it, we need a function $y(x)$ that satisfies the equation. This function is found by taking the antiderivative of $f(x)$. We fix the arbitrary constant arising in the antidifferentiation process by specifying an initial condition

$$y(x_0) = y_0.$$

This condition means the function $y(x)$ has the value y_0 when $x = x_0$. The combination of a differential equation and an initial condition is called an **initial value problem**. Such problems play important roles in all branches of science. Here's an example of solving an initial value problem.

EXAMPLE 5   Finding a Curve from Its Slope Function and a Point

Find the curve whose slope at the point (x, y) is $3x^2$ if the curve is required to pass through the point $(1, -1)$.

Solution   In mathematical language, we are asked to solve the initial value problem that consists of the following.

The differential equation: $\dfrac{dy}{dx} = 3x^2$ The curve's slope is $3x^2$.

The initial condition: $y(1) = -1$

1. *Solve the differential equation:* The function y is an antiderivative of $f(x) = 3x^2$, so

$$y = x^3 + C.$$

This result tells us that y equals $x^3 + C$ for some value of C. We find that value from the initial condition $y(1) = -1$.

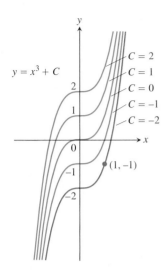

FIGURE 4.54 The curves $y = x^3 + C$ fill the coordinate plane without overlapping. In Example 5, we identify the curve $y = x^3 - 2$ as the one that passes through the given point $(1, -1)$.

2. *Evaluate C*:

$$y = x^3 + C$$
$$-1 = (1)^3 + C \qquad \text{Initial condition } y(1) = -1$$
$$C = -2.$$

The curve we want is $y = x^3 - 2$ (Figure 4.54). ∎

The most general antiderivative $F(x) + C$ (which is $x^3 + C$ in Example 5) of the function $f(x)$ gives the **general solution** $y = F(x) + C$ of the differential equation $dy/dx = f(x)$. The general solution gives *all* the solutions of the equation (there are infinitely many, one for each value of C). We **solve** the differential equation by finding its general solution. We then solve the initial value problem by finding the **particular solution** that satisfies the initial condition $y(x_0) = y_0$.

Antiderivatives and Motion

We have seen that the derivative of the position of an object gives its velocity, and the derivative of its velocity gives its acceleration. If we know an object's acceleration, then by finding an antiderivative we can recover the velocity, and from an antiderivative of the velocity we can recover its position function. This procedure was used as an application of Corollary 2 in Section 4.2. Now that we have a terminology and conceptual framework in terms of antiderivatives, we revisit the problem from the point of view of differential equations.

EXAMPLE 6 Dropping a Package from an Ascending Balloon

A balloon ascending at the rate of 12 ft/sec is at a height 80 ft above the ground when a package is dropped. How long does it take the package to reach the ground?

Solution Let $v(t)$ denote the velocity of the package at time t, and let $s(t)$ denote its height above the ground. The acceleration of gravity near the surface of the earth is 32 ft/sec². Assuming no other forces act on the dropped package, we have

$$\frac{dv}{dt} = -32. \qquad \text{Negative because gravity acts in the direction of decreasing } s.$$

This leads to the initial value problem.

Differential equation: $\quad \dfrac{dv}{dt} = -32$

Initial condition: $\qquad v(0) = 12,$

which is our mathematical model for the package's motion. We solve the initial value problem to obtain the velocity of the package.

1. *Solve the differential equation*: The general formula for an antiderivative of -32 is

$$v = -32t + C.$$

Having found the general solution of the differential equation, we use the initial condition to find the particular solution that solves our problem.

2. *Evaluate C*:

$$12 = -32(0) + C \qquad \text{Initial condition } v(0) = 12$$
$$C = 12.$$

The solution of the initial value problem is

$$v = -32t + 12.$$

Since velocity is the derivative of height and the height of the package is 80 ft at the time $t = 0$ when it is dropped, we now have a second initial value problem.

Differential equation: $\dfrac{ds}{dt} = -32t + 12$ Set $v = ds/dt$ in the last equation.

Initial condition: $s(0) = 80$

We solve this initial value problem to find the height as a function of t.

1. *Solve the differential equation*: Finding the general antiderivative of $-32t + 12$ gives

$$s = -16t^2 + 12t + C.$$

2. *Evaluate C*:

$$80 = -16(0)^2 + 12(0) + C \qquad \text{Initial condition } s(0) = 80$$
$$C = 80.$$

The package's height above ground at time t is

$$s = -16t^2 + 12t + 80.$$

Use the solution: To find how long it takes the package to reach the ground, we set s equal to 0 and solve for t:

$$-16t^2 + 12t + 80 = 0$$
$$-4t^2 + 3t + 20 = 0$$
$$t = \frac{-3 \pm \sqrt{329}}{-8} \qquad \text{Quadratic formula}$$
$$t \approx -1.89, \qquad t \approx 2.64.$$

The package hits the ground about 2.64 sec after it is dropped from the balloon. (The negative root has no physical meaning.) ∎

Indefinite Integrals

A special symbol is used to denote the collection of all antiderivatives of a function f.

DEFINITION   Indefinite Integral, Integrand

The set of all antiderivatives of f is the **indefinite integral** of f with respect to x, denoted by

$$\int f(x)\, dx.$$

The symbol $\int$ is an **integral sign**. The function f is the **integrand** of the integral, and x is the **variable of integration**.

Using this notation, we restate the solutions of Example 1, as follows:

$$\int 2x \, dx = x^2 + C,$$

$$\int \cos x \, dx = \sin x + C,$$

$$\int (2x + \cos x) \, dx = x^2 + \sin x + C.$$

This notation is related to the main application of antiderivatives, which will be explored in Chapter 5. Antiderivatives play a key role in computing limits of infinite sums, an unexpected and wonderfully useful role that is described in a central result of Chapter 5, called the Fundamental Theorem of Calculus.

EXAMPLE 7 Indefinite Integration Done Term-by-Term and Rewriting the Constant of Integration

Evaluate

$$\int (x^2 - 2x + 5) \, dx.$$

Solution If we recognize that $(x^3/3) - x^2 + 5x$ is an antiderivative of $x^2 - 2x + 5$, we can evaluate the integral as

$$\int (x^2 - 2x + 5) \, dx = \overbrace{\frac{x^3}{3} - x^2 + 5x}^{\text{antiderivative}} + \underbrace{C}_{\text{arbitrary constant}}.$$

If we do not recognize the antiderivative right away, we can generate it term-by-term with the Sum, Difference, and Constant Multiple Rules:

$$\int (x^2 - 2x + 5) \, dx = \int x^2 \, dx - \int 2x \, dx + \int 5 \, dx$$

$$= \int x^2 \, dx - 2 \int x \, dx + 5 \int 1 \, dx$$

$$= \left(\frac{x^3}{3} + C_1\right) - 2\left(\frac{x^2}{2} + C_2\right) + 5(x + C_3)$$

$$= \frac{x^3}{3} + C_1 - x^2 - 2C_2 + 5x + 5C_3.$$

This formula is more complicated than it needs to be. If we combine C_1, $-2C_2$, and $5C_3$ into a single arbitrary constant $C = C_1 - 2C_2 + 5C_3$, the formula simplifies to

$$\frac{x^3}{3} - x^2 + 5x + C$$

and *still* gives all the antiderivatives there are. For this reason, we recommend that you go right to the final form even if you elect to integrate term-by-term. Write

$$\int (x^2 - 2x + 5)\, dx = \int x^2\, dx - \int 2x\, dx + \int 5\, dx$$

$$= \frac{x^3}{3} - x^2 + 5x + C.$$

Find the simplest antiderivative you can for each part and add the arbitrary constant of integration at the end. ∎

EXERCISES 4.8

Finding Antiderivatives

In Exercises 1–16, find an antiderivative for each function. Do as many as you can mentally. Check your answers by differentiation.

1. **a.** $2x$ **b.** x^2 **c.** $x^2 - 2x + 1$

2. **a.** $6x$ **b.** x^7 **c.** $x^7 - 6x + 8$

3. **a.** $-3x^{-4}$ **b.** x^{-4} **c.** $x^{-4} + 2x + 3$

4. **a.** $2x^{-3}$ **b.** $\dfrac{x^{-3}}{2} + x^2$ **c.** $-x^{-3} + x - 1$

5. **a.** $\dfrac{1}{x^2}$ **b.** $\dfrac{5}{x^2}$ **c.** $2 - \dfrac{5}{x^2}$

6. **a.** $-\dfrac{2}{x^3}$ **b.** $\dfrac{1}{2x^3}$ **c.** $x^3 - \dfrac{1}{x^3}$

7. **a.** $\dfrac{3}{2}\sqrt{x}$ **b.** $\dfrac{1}{2\sqrt{x}}$ **c.** $\sqrt{x} + \dfrac{1}{\sqrt{x}}$

8. **a.** $\dfrac{4}{3}\sqrt[3]{x}$ **b.** $\dfrac{1}{3\sqrt[3]{x}}$ **c.** $\sqrt[3]{x} + \dfrac{1}{\sqrt[3]{x}}$

9. **a.** $\dfrac{2}{3}x^{-1/3}$ **b.** $\dfrac{1}{3}x^{-2/3}$ **c.** $-\dfrac{1}{3}x^{-4/3}$

10. **a.** $\dfrac{1}{2}x^{-1/2}$ **b.** $-\dfrac{1}{2}x^{-3/2}$ **c.** $-\dfrac{3}{2}x^{-5/2}$

11. **a.** $-\pi \sin \pi x$ **b.** $3 \sin x$ **c.** $\sin \pi x - 3 \sin 3x$

12. **a.** $\pi \cos \pi x$ **b.** $\dfrac{\pi}{2} \cos \dfrac{\pi x}{2}$ **c.** $\cos \dfrac{\pi x}{2} + \pi \cos x$

13. **a.** $\sec^2 x$ **b.** $\dfrac{2}{3} \sec^2 \dfrac{x}{3}$ **c.** $-\sec^2 \dfrac{3x}{2}$

14. **a.** $\csc^2 x$ **b.** $-\dfrac{3}{2} \csc^2 \dfrac{3x}{2}$ **c.** $1 - 8 \csc^2 2x$

15. **a.** $\csc x \cot x$ **b.** $-\csc 5x \cot 5x$ **c.** $-\pi \csc \dfrac{\pi x}{2} \cot \dfrac{\pi x}{2}$

16. **a.** $\sec x \tan x$ **b.** $4 \sec 3x \tan 3x$ **c.** $\sec \dfrac{\pi x}{2} \tan \dfrac{\pi x}{2}$

Finding Indefinite Integrals

In Exercises 17–54, find the most general antiderivative or indefinite integral. Check your answers by differentiation.

17. $\displaystyle\int (x + 1)\, dx$

18. $\displaystyle\int (5 - 6x)\, dx$

19. $\displaystyle\int \left(3t^2 + \dfrac{t}{2}\right) dt$

20. $\displaystyle\int \left(\dfrac{t^2}{2} + 4t^3\right) dt$

21. $\displaystyle\int (2x^3 - 5x + 7)\, dx$

22. $\displaystyle\int (1 - x^2 - 3x^5)\, dx$

23. $\displaystyle\int \left(\dfrac{1}{x^2} - x^2 - \dfrac{1}{3}\right) dx$

24. $\displaystyle\int \left(\dfrac{1}{5} - \dfrac{2}{x^3} + 2x\right) dx$

25. $\displaystyle\int x^{-1/3}\, dx$

26. $\displaystyle\int x^{-5/4}\, dx$

27. $\displaystyle\int \left(\sqrt{x} + \sqrt[3]{x}\right) dx$

28. $\displaystyle\int \left(\dfrac{\sqrt{x}}{2} + \dfrac{2}{\sqrt{x}}\right) dx$

29. $\displaystyle\int \left(8y - \dfrac{2}{y^{1/4}}\right) dy$

30. $\displaystyle\int \left(\dfrac{1}{7} - \dfrac{1}{y^{5/4}}\right) dy$

31. $\displaystyle\int 2x(1 - x^{-3})\, dx$

32. $\displaystyle\int x^{-3}(x + 1)\, dx$

33. $\displaystyle\int \dfrac{t\sqrt{t} + \sqrt{t}}{t^2}\, dt$

34. $\displaystyle\int \dfrac{4 + \sqrt{t}}{t^3}\, dt$

35. $\displaystyle\int (-2 \cos t)\, dt$

36. $\displaystyle\int (-5 \sin t)\, dt$

37. $\displaystyle\int 7 \sin \dfrac{\theta}{3}\, d\theta$

38. $\displaystyle\int 3 \cos 5\theta\, d\theta$

39. $\displaystyle\int (-3 \csc^2 x)\, dx$

40. $\displaystyle\int \left(-\dfrac{\sec^2 x}{3}\right) dx$

41. $\displaystyle\int \dfrac{\csc \theta \cot \theta}{2}\, d\theta$

42. $\displaystyle\int \dfrac{2}{5} \sec \theta \tan \theta\, d\theta$

43. $\int (4 \sec x \tan x - 2 \sec^2 x)\, dx$ **44.** $\int \frac{1}{2} (\csc^2 x - \csc x \cot x)\, dx$

45. $\int (\sin 2x - \csc^2 x)\, dx$ **46.** $\int (2 \cos 2x - 3 \sin 3x)\, dx$

47. $\int \frac{1 + \cos 4t}{2}\, dt$ **48.** $\int \frac{1 - \cos 6t}{2}\, dt$

49. $\int (1 + \tan^2 \theta)\, d\theta$ **50.** $\int (2 + \tan^2 \theta)\, d\theta$

(*Hint:* $1 + \tan^2 \theta = \sec^2 \theta$)

51. $\int \cot^2 x\, dx$ **52.** $\int (1 - \cot^2 x)\, dx$

(*Hint:* $1 + \cot^2 x = \csc^2 x$)

53. $\int \cos \theta (\tan \theta + \sec \theta)\, d\theta$ **54.** $\int \frac{\csc \theta}{\csc \theta - \sin \theta}\, d\theta$

Checking Antiderivative Formulas

Verify the formulas in Exercises 55–60 by differentiation.

55. $\int (7x - 2)^3\, dx = \frac{(7x - 2)^4}{28} + C$

56. $\int (3x + 5)^{-2}\, dx = -\frac{(3x + 5)^{-1}}{3} + C$

57. $\int \sec^2 (5x - 1)\, dx = \frac{1}{5} \tan (5x - 1) + C$

58. $\int \csc^2 \left(\frac{x - 1}{3} \right) dx = -3 \cot \left(\frac{x - 1}{3} \right) + C$

59. $\int \frac{1}{(x + 1)^2}\, dx = -\frac{1}{x + 1} + C$

60. $\int \frac{1}{(x + 1)^2}\, dx = \frac{x}{x + 1} + C$

61. Right, or wrong? Say which for each formula and give a brief reason for each answer.

a. $\int x \sin x\, dx = \frac{x^2}{2} \sin x + C$

b. $\int x \sin x\, dx = -x \cos x + C$

c. $\int x \sin x\, dx = -x \cos x + \sin x + C$

62. Right, or wrong? Say which for each formula and give a brief reason for each answer.

a. $\int \tan \theta \sec^2 \theta\, d\theta = \frac{\sec^3 \theta}{3} + C$

b. $\int \tan \theta \sec^2 \theta\, d\theta = \frac{1}{2} \tan^2 \theta + C$

c. $\int \tan \theta \sec^2 \theta\, d\theta = \frac{1}{2} \sec^2 \theta + C$

63. Right, or wrong? Say which for each formula and give a brief reason for each answer.

a. $\int (2x + 1)^2\, dx = \frac{(2x + 1)^3}{3} + C$

b. $\int 3(2x + 1)^2\, dx = (2x + 1)^3 + C$

c. $\int 6(2x + 1)^2\, dx = (2x + 1)^3 + C$

64. Right, or wrong? Say which for each formula and give a brief reason for each answer.

a. $\int \sqrt{2x + 1}\, dx = \sqrt{x^2 + x} + C$

b. $\int \sqrt{2x + 1}\, dx = \sqrt{x^2 + x} + C$

c. $\int \sqrt{2x + 1}\, dx = \frac{1}{3} \left(\sqrt{2x + 1} \right)^3 + C$

Initial Value Problems

65. Which of the following graphs shows the solution of the initial value problem

$$\frac{dy}{dx} = 2x, \quad y = 4 \text{ when } x = 1?$$

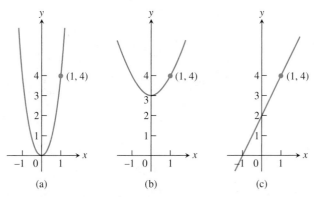

(a)   (b)   (c)

Give reasons for your answer.

66. Which of the following graphs shows the solution of the initial value problem

$$\frac{dy}{dx} = -x, \quad y = 1 \text{ when } x = -1?$$

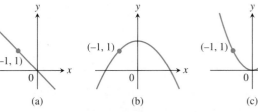

(a)   (b)   (c)

Give reasons for your answer.

Solve the initial value problems in Exercises 67–86.

67. $\dfrac{dy}{dx} = 2x - 7, \quad y(2) = 0$

68. $\dfrac{dy}{dx} = 10 - x, \quad y(0) = -1$

69. $\dfrac{dy}{dx} = \dfrac{1}{x^2} + x, \quad x > 0; \quad y(2) = 1$

70. $\dfrac{dy}{dx} = 9x^2 - 4x + 5, \quad y(-1) = 0$

71. $\dfrac{dy}{dx} = 3x^{-2/3}, \quad y(-1) = -5$

72. $\dfrac{dy}{dx} = \dfrac{1}{2\sqrt{x}}, \quad y(4) = 0$

73. $\dfrac{ds}{dt} = 1 + \cos t, \quad s(0) = 4$

74. $\dfrac{ds}{dt} = \cos t + \sin t, \quad s(\pi) = 1$

75. $\dfrac{dr}{d\theta} = -\pi \sin \pi\theta, \quad r(0) = 0$

76. $\dfrac{dr}{d\theta} = \cos \pi\theta, \quad r(0) = 1$

77. $\dfrac{dv}{dt} = \dfrac{1}{2} \sec t \tan t, \quad v(0) = 1$

78. $\dfrac{dv}{dt} = 8t + \csc^2 t, \quad v\left(\dfrac{\pi}{2}\right) = -7$

79. $\dfrac{d^2y}{dx^2} = 2 - 6x; \quad y'(0) = 4, \quad y(0) = 1$

80. $\dfrac{d^2y}{dx^2} = 0; \quad y'(0) = 2, \quad y(0) = 0$

81. $\dfrac{d^2r}{dt^2} = \dfrac{2}{t^3}; \quad \left.\dfrac{dr}{dt}\right|_{t=1} = 1, \quad r(1) = 1$

82. $\dfrac{d^2s}{dt^2} = \dfrac{3t}{8}; \quad \left.\dfrac{ds}{dt}\right|_{t=4} = 3, \quad s(4) = 4$

83. $\dfrac{d^3y}{dx^3} = 6; \quad y''(0) = -8, \quad y'(0) = 0, \quad y(0) = 5$

84. $\dfrac{d^3\theta}{dt^3} = 0; \quad \theta''(0) = -2, \quad \theta'(0) = -\dfrac{1}{2}, \quad \theta(0) = \sqrt{2}$

85. $y^{(4)} = -\sin t + \cos t;$
$y'''(0) = 7, \quad y''(0) = y'(0) = -1, \quad y(0) = 0$

86. $y^{(4)} = -\cos x + 8 \sin 2x;$
$y'''(0) = 0, \quad y''(0) = y'(0) = 1, \quad y(0) = 3$

Finding Curves

87. Find the curve $y = f(x)$ in the xy-plane that passes through the point $(9, 4)$ and whose slope at each point is $3\sqrt{x}$.

88. a. Find a curve $y = f(x)$ with the following properties:

    i) $\dfrac{d^2y}{dx^2} = 6x$

    ii) Its graph passes through the point $(0, 1)$, and has a horizontal tangent there.

  b. How many curves like this are there? How do you know?

Solution (Integral) Curves

Exercises 89–92 show solution curves of differential equations. In each exercise, find an equation for the curve through the labeled point.

89. $\dfrac{dy}{dx} = 1 - \dfrac{4}{3} x^{1/3}$

90. $\dfrac{dy}{dx} = x - 1$

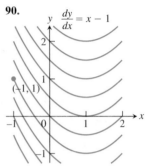

91. $\dfrac{dy}{dx} = \sin x - \cos x$

92. $\dfrac{dy}{dx} = \dfrac{1}{2\sqrt{x}} + \pi \sin \pi x$

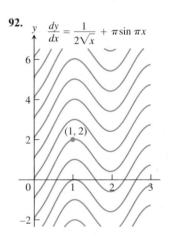

Applications

93. Finding displacement from an antiderivative of velocity

  a. Suppose that the velocity of a body moving along the s-axis is

$$\dfrac{ds}{dt} = v = 9.8t - 3.$$

    i) Find the body's displacement over the time interval from $t = 1$ to $t = 3$ given that $s = 5$ when $t = 0$.

    ii) Find the body's displacement from $t = 1$ to $t = 3$ given that $s = -2$ when $t = 0$.

    iii) Now find the body's displacement from $t = 1$ to $t = 3$ given that $s = s_0$ when $t = 0$.

b. Suppose that the position s of a body moving along a coordinate line is a differentiable function of time t. Is it true that once you know an antiderivative of the velocity function ds/dt you can find the body's displacement from $t = a$ to $t = b$ even if you do not know the body's exact position at either of those times? Give reasons for your answer.

94. Liftoff from Earth A rocket lifts off the surface of Earth with a constant acceleration of 20 m/sec². How fast will the rocket be going 1 min later?

95. Stopping a car in time You are driving along a highway at a steady 60 mph (88 ft/sec) when you see an accident ahead and slam on the brakes. What constant deceleration is required to stop your car in 242 ft? To find out, carry out the following steps.

1. Solve the initial value problem

   Differential equation: $\dfrac{d^2s}{dt^2} = -k$ (k constant)

   Initial conditions: $\dfrac{ds}{dt} = 88$ and $s = 0$ when $t = 0$.

   > Measuring time and distance from when the brakes are applied.

2. Find the value of t that makes $ds/dt = 0$. (The answer will involve k.)

3. Find the value of k that makes $s = 242$ for the value of t you found in Step 2.

96. Stopping a motorcycle The State of Illinois Cycle Rider Safety Program requires riders to be able to brake from 30 mph (44 ft/sec) to 0 in 45 ft. What constant deceleration does it take to do that?

97. Motion along a coordinate line A particle moves on a coordinate line with acceleration $a = d^2s/dt^2 = 15\sqrt{t} - \left(3/\sqrt{t}\right)$, subject to the conditions that $ds/dt = 4$ and $s = 0$ when $t = 1$. Find

a. the velocity $v = ds/dt$ in terms of t

b. the position s in terms of t.

T **98. The hammer and the feather** When *Apollo 15* astronaut David Scott dropped a hammer and a feather on the moon to demonstrate that in a vacuum all bodies fall with the same (constant) acceleration, he dropped them from about 4 ft above the ground. The television footage of the event shows the hammer and the feather falling more slowly than on Earth, where, in a vacuum, they would have taken only half a second to fall the 4 ft. How long did it take the hammer and feather to fall 4 ft on the moon? To find out, solve the following initial value problem for s as a function of t. Then find the value of t that makes s equal to 0.

Differential equation: $\dfrac{d^2s}{dt^2} = -5.2$ ft/sec²

Initial conditions: $\dfrac{ds}{dt} = 0$ and $s = 4$ when $t = 0$

99. Motion with constant acceleration The standard equation for the position s of a body moving with a constant acceleration a along a coordinate line is

$$s = \frac{a}{2}t^2 + v_0 t + s_0, \tag{1}$$

where v_0 and s_0 are the body's velocity and position at time $t = 0$. Derive this equation by solving the initial value problem

Differential equation: $\dfrac{d^2s}{dt^2} = a$

Initial conditions: $\dfrac{ds}{dt} = v_0$ and $s = s_0$ when $t = 0$.

100. Free fall near the surface of a planet For free fall near the surface of a planet where the acceleration due to gravity has a constant magnitude of g length-units/sec², Equation (1) in Exercise 99 takes the form

$$s = -\frac{1}{2}gt^2 + v_0 t + s_0, \tag{2}$$

where s is the body's height above the surface. The equation has a minus sign because the acceleration acts downward, in the direction of decreasing s. The velocity v_0 is positive if the object is rising at time $t = 0$ and negative if the object is falling.

Instead of using the result of Exercise 99, you can derive Equation (2) directly by solving an appropriate initial value problem. What initial value problem? Solve it to be sure you have the right one, explaining the solution steps as you go along.

Theory and Examples

101. Suppose that

$$f(x) = \frac{d}{dx}\left(1 - \sqrt{x}\right) \quad \text{and} \quad g(x) = \frac{d}{dx}(x + 2).$$

Find:

a. $\displaystyle\int f(x)\,dx$

b. $\displaystyle\int g(x)\,dx$

c. $\displaystyle\int [-f(x)]\,dx$

d. $\displaystyle\int [-g(x)]\,dx$

e. $\displaystyle\int [f(x) + g(x)]\,dx$

f. $\displaystyle\int [f(x) - g(x)]\,dx$

102. Uniqueness of solutions If differentiable functions $y = F(x)$ and $y = G(x)$ both solve the initial value problem

$$\frac{dy}{dx} = f(x), \qquad y(x_0) = y_0,$$

on an interval I, must $F(x) = G(x)$ for every x in I? Give reasons for your answer.

COMPUTER EXPLORATIONS

Use a CAS to solve the initial problems in Exercises 103–106. Plot the solution curves.

103. $y' = \cos^2 x + \sin x, \quad y(\pi) = 1$

104. $y' = \dfrac{1}{x} + x, \quad y(1) = -1$

105. $y' = \dfrac{1}{\sqrt{4 - x^2}}, \quad y(0) = 2$

106. $y'' = \dfrac{2}{x} + \sqrt{x}, \quad y(1) = 0, \quad y'(1) = 0$

Chapter 4   Questions to Guide Your Review

1. What can be said about the extreme values of a function that is continuous on a closed interval?

2. What does it mean for a function to have a local extreme value on its domain? An absolute extreme value? How are local and absolute extreme values related, if at all? Give examples.

3. How do you find the absolute extrema of a continuous function on a closed interval? Give examples.

4. What are the hypotheses and conclusion of Rolle's Theorem? Are the hypotheses really necessary? Explain.

5. What are the hypotheses and conclusion of the Mean Value Theorem? What physical interpretations might the theorem have?

6. State the Mean Value Theorem's three corollaries.

7. How can you sometimes identify a function $f(x)$ by knowing f' and knowing the value of f at a point $x = x_0$? Give an example.

8. What is the First Derivative Test for Local Extreme Values? Give examples of how it is applied.

9. How do you test a twice-differentiable function to determine where its graph is concave up or concave down? Give examples.

10. What is an inflection point? Give an example. What physical significance do inflection points sometimes have?

11. What is the Second Derivative Test for Local Extreme Values? Give examples of how it is applied.

12. What do the derivatives of a function tell you about the shape of its graph?

13. List the steps you would take to graph a polynomial function. Illustrate with an example.

14. What is a cusp? Give examples.

15. List the steps you would take to graph a rational function. Illustrate with an example.

16. Outline a general strategy for solving max-min problems. Give examples.

17. Describe l'Hôpital's Rule. How do you know when to use the rule and when to stop? Give an example.

18. How can you sometimes handle limits that lead to indeterminate forms ∞/∞, $\infty \cdot 0$, and $\infty - \infty$. Give examples.

19. Describe Newton's method for solving equations. Give an example. What is the theory behind the method? What are some of the things to watch out for when you use the method?

20. Can a function have more than one antiderivative? If so, how are the antiderivatives related? Explain.

21. What is an indefinite integral? How do you evaluate one? What general formulas do you know for finding indefinite integrals?

22. How can you sometimes solve a differential equation of the form $dy/dx = f(x)$?

23. What is an initial value problem? How do you solve one? Give an example.

24. If you know the acceleration of a body moving along a coordinate line as a function of time, what more do you need to know to find the body's position function? Give an example.

Chapter 4   Practice Exercises

Existence of Extreme Values

1. Does $f(x) = x^3 + 2x + \tan x$ have any local maximum or minimum values? Give reasons for your answer.

2. Does $g(x) = \csc x + 2 \cot x$ have any local maximum values? Give reasons for your answer.

3. Does $f(x) = (7 + x)(11 - 3x)^{1/3}$ have an absolute minimum value? An absolute maximum? If so, find them or give reasons why they fail to exist. List all critical points of f.

4. Find values of a and b such that the function

$$f(x) = \frac{ax + b}{x^2 - 1}$$

has a local extreme value of 1 at $\bar{x} = 3$. Is this extreme value a local maximum, or a local minimum? Give reasons for your answer.

5. The greatest integer function $f(x) = \lfloor x \rfloor$, defined for all values of x, assumes a local maximum value of 0 at each point of $[0, 1)$. Could any of these local maximum values also be local minimum values of f? Give reasons for your answer.

6. a. Give an example of a differentiable function f whose first derivative is zero at some point c even though f has neither a local maximum nor a local minimum at c.

   b. How is this consistent with Theorem 2 in Section 4.1? Give reasons for your answer.

7. The function $y = 1/x$ does not take on either a maximum or a minimum on the interval $0 < x < 1$ even though the function is continuous on this interval. Does this contradict the Extreme Value Theorem for continuous functions? Why?

8. What are the maximum and minimum values of the function $y = |x|$ on the interval $-1 \le x < 1$? Notice that the interval is not closed. Is this consistent with the Extreme Value Theorem for continuous functions? Why?

T 9. A graph that is large enough to show a function's global behavior may fail to reveal important local features. The graph of $f(x) = (x^8/8) - (x^6/2) - x^5 + 5x^3$ is a case in point.

   a. Graph f over the interval $-2.5 \le x \le 2.5$. Where does the graph appear to have local extreme values or points of inflection?

   b. Now factor $f'(x)$ and show that f has a local maximum at $x = \sqrt[5]{5} \approx 1.70998$ and local minima at $x = \pm\sqrt{3} \approx \pm1.73205$.

   c. Zoom in on the graph to find a viewing window that shows the presence of the extreme values at $x = \sqrt[5]{5}$ and $x = \sqrt{3}$.

      The moral here is that without calculus the existence of two of the three extreme values would probably have gone unnoticed. On any normal graph of the function, the values would lie close enough together to fall within the dimensions of a single pixel on the screen.

      (*Source*: *Uses of Technology in the Mathematics Curriculum*, by Benny Evans and Jerry Johnson, Oklahoma State University, published in 1990 under National Science Foundation Grant USE-8950044.)

T 10. (*Continuation of Exercise 9.*)

   a. Graph $f(x) = (x^8/8) - (2/5)x^5 - 5x - (5/x^2) + 11$ over the interval $-2 \le x \le 2$. Where does the graph appear to have local extreme values or points of inflection?

   b. Show that f has a local maximum value at $x = \sqrt[7]{5} \approx 1.2585$ and a local minimum value at $x = \sqrt[3]{2} \approx 1.2599$.

   c. Zoom in to find a viewing window that shows the presence of the extreme values at $x = \sqrt[7]{5}$ and $x = \sqrt[3]{2}$.

The Mean Value Theorem

11. a. Show that $g(t) = \sin^2 t - 3t$ decreases on every interval in its domain.

    b. How many solutions does the equation $\sin^2 t - 3t = 5$ have? Give reasons for your answer.

12. a. Show that $y = \tan \theta$ increases on every interval in its domain.

    b. If the conclusion in part (a) is really correct, how do you explain the fact that $\tan \pi = 0$ is less than $\tan (\pi/4) = 1$?

13. a. Show that the equation $x^4 + 2x^2 - 2 = 0$ has exactly one solution on $[0, 1]$.

   T b. Find the solution to as many decimal places as you can.

14. a. Show that $f(x) = x/(x + 1)$ increases on every interval in its domain.

    b. Show that $f(x) = x^3 + 2x$ has no local maximum or minimum values.

15. **Water in a reservoir** As a result of a heavy rain, the volume of water in a reservoir increased by 1400 acre-ft in 24 hours. Show that at some instant during that period the reservoir's volume was increasing at a rate in excess of 225,000 gal/min. (An acre-foot is 43,560 ft^3, the volume that would cover 1 acre to the depth of 1 ft. A cubic foot holds 7.48 gal.)

16. The formula $F(x) = 3x + C$ gives a different function for each value of C. All of these functions, however, have the same derivative with respect to x, namely $F'(x) = 3$. Are these the only differentiable functions whose derivative is 3? Could there be any others? Give reasons for your answers.

17. Show that

$$\frac{d}{dx}\left(\frac{x}{x + 1}\right) = \frac{d}{dx}\left(-\frac{1}{x + 1}\right)$$

even though

$$\frac{x}{x + 1} \ne -\frac{1}{x + 1}.$$

Doesn't this contradict Corollary 2 of the Mean Value Theorem? Give reasons for your answer.

18. Calculate the first derivatives of $f(x) = x^2/(x^2 + 1)$ and $g(x) = -1/(x^2 + 1)$. What can you conclude about the graphs of these functions?

Conclusions from Graphs

In Exercises 19 and 20, use the graph to answer the questions.

19. Identify any global extreme values of f and the values of x at which they occur.

20. Estimate the intervals on which the function $y = f(x)$ is

    a. increasing.

    b. decreasing.

    c. Use the given graph of f' to indicate where any local extreme
    values of the function occur, and whether each extreme is a
    relative maximum or minimum.

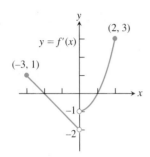

Each of the graphs in Exercises 21 and 22 is the graph of the position
function $s = f(t)$ of a body moving on a coordinate line
(t represents time). At approximately what times (if any) is each
body's **(a)** velocity equal to zero? **(b)** Acceleration equal to zero? During approximately what time intervals does the body move **(c)** forward? **(d)** Backward?

21.

22.

Graphs and Graphing

Graph the curves in Exercises 23–32.

23. $y = x^2 - (x^3/6)$ **24.** $y = x^3 - 3x^2 + 3$

25. $y = -x^3 + 6x^2 - 9x + 3$

26. $y = (1/8)(x^3 + 3x^2 - 9x - 27)$

27. $y = x^3(8 - x)$ **28.** $y = x^2(2x^2 - 9)$

29. $y = x - 3x^{2/3}$ **30.** $y = x^{1/3}(x - 4)$

31. $y = x\sqrt{3 - x}$ **32.** $y = x\sqrt{4 - x^2}$

Each of Exercises 33–38 gives the first derivative of a function
$y = f(x)$. **(a)** At what points, if any, does the graph of f have a local
maximum, local minimum, or inflection point? **(b)** Sketch the general
shape of the graph.

33. $y' = 16 - x^2$ **34.** $y' = x^2 - x - 6$

35. $y' = 6x(x + 1)(x - 2)$ **36.** $y' = x^2(6 - 4x)$

37. $y' = x^4 - 2x^2$ **38.** $y' = 4x^2 - x^4$

In Exercises 39–42, graph each function. Then use the function's first
derivative to explain what you see.

39. $y = x^{2/3} + (x - 1)^{1/3}$ **40.** $y = x^{2/3} + (x - 1)^{2/3}$

41. $y = x^{1/3} + (x - 1)^{1/3}$ **42.** $y = x^{2/3} - (x - 1)^{1/3}$

Sketch the graphs of the functions in Exercises 43–50.

43. $y = \dfrac{x + 1}{x - 3}$ **44.** $y = \dfrac{2x}{x + 5}$

45. $y = \dfrac{x^2 + 1}{x}$ **46.** $y = \dfrac{x^2 - x + 1}{x}$

47. $y = \dfrac{x^3 + 2}{2x}$ **48.** $y = \dfrac{x^4 - 1}{x^2}$

49. $y = \dfrac{x^2 - 4}{x^2 - 3}$ **50.** $y = \dfrac{x^2}{x^2 - 4}$

Applying l'Hôpital's Rule

Use l'Hôpital's Rule to find the limits in Exercises 51–62.

51. $\lim\limits_{x \to 1} \dfrac{x^2 + 3x - 4}{x - 1}$ **52.** $\lim\limits_{x \to 1} \dfrac{x^a - 1}{x^b - 1}$

53. $\lim\limits_{x \to \pi} \dfrac{\tan x}{x}$ **54.** $\lim\limits_{x \to 0} \dfrac{\tan x}{x + \sin x}$

55. $\lim\limits_{x \to 0} \dfrac{\sin^2 x}{\tan (x^2)}$ **56.** $\lim\limits_{x \to 0} \dfrac{\sin mx}{\sin nx}$

57. $\lim\limits_{x \to \pi/2^-} \sec 7x \cos 3x$ **58.** $\lim\limits_{x \to 0^+} \sqrt{x} \sec x$

59. $\lim\limits_{x \to 0} (\csc x - \cot x)$ **60.** $\lim\limits_{x \to 0} \left(\dfrac{1}{x^4} - \dfrac{1}{x^2} \right)$

61. $\lim\limits_{x \to \infty} \left(\sqrt{x^2 + x + 1} - \sqrt{x^2 - x} \right)$

62. $\lim\limits_{x \to \infty} \left(\dfrac{x^3}{x^2 - 1} - \dfrac{x^3}{x^2 + 1} \right)$

Optimization

63. The sum of two nonnegative numbers is 36. Find the numbers if

    a. the difference of their square roots is to be as large as
    possible.

    b. the sum of their square roots is to be as large as possible.

64. The sum of two nonnegative numbers is 20. Find the numbers

    a. if the product of one number and the square root of the other
    is to be as large as possible.

    b. if one number plus the square root of the other is to be as
    large as possible.

65. An isosceles triangle has its vertex at the origin and its base parallel to the x-axis with the vertices above the axis on the curve
$y = 27 - x^2$. Find the largest area the triangle can have.

66. A customer has asked you to design an open-top rectangular stainless steel vat. It is to have a square base and a volume of 32 ft³, to be welded from quarter-inch plate, and to weigh no more than necessary. What dimensions do you recommend?

67. Find the height and radius of the largest right circular cylinder that can be put in a sphere of radius $\sqrt{3}$.

68. The figure here shows two right circular cones, one upside down inside the other. The two bases are parallel, and the vertex of the smaller cone lies at the center of the larger cone's base. What values of r and h will give the smaller cone the largest possible volume?

69. Manufacturing tires Your company can manufacture x hundred grade A tires and y hundred grade B tires a day, where $0 \le x \le 4$ and

$$y = \frac{40 - 10x}{5 - x}.$$

Your profit on a grade A tire is twice your profit on a grade B tire. What is the most profitable number of each kind to make?

70. Particle motion The positions of two particles on the s-axis are $s_1 = \cos t$ and $s_2 = \cos(t + \pi/4)$.

a. What is the farthest apart the particles ever get?

b. When do the particles collide?

T 71. Open-top box An open-top rectangular box is constructed from a 10-in.-by-16-in. piece of cardboard by cutting squares of equal side length from the corners and folding up the sides. Find analytically the dimensions of the box of largest volume and the maximum volume. Support your answers graphically.

72. The ladder problem What is the approximate length (in feet) of the longest ladder you can carry horizontally around the corner of the corridor shown here? Round your answer down to the nearest foot.

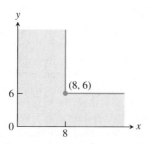

Newton's Method

73. Let $f(x) = 3x - x^3$. Show that the equation $f(x) = -4$ has a solution in the interval [2, 3] and use Newton's method to find it.

74. Let $f(x) = x^4 - x^3$. Show that the equation $f(x) = 75$ has a solution in the interval [3, 4] and use Newton's method to find it.

Finding Indefinite Integrals

Find the indefinite integrals (most general antiderivatives) in Exercises 75–90. Check your answers by differentiation.

75. $\int (x^3 + 5x - 7)\, dx$

76. $\int \left(8t^3 - \frac{t^2}{2} + t\right) dt$

77. $\int \left(3\sqrt{t} + \frac{4}{t^2}\right) dt$

78. $\int \left(\frac{1}{2\sqrt{t}} - \frac{3}{t^4}\right) dt$

79. $\int \frac{dr}{(r + 5)^2}$

80. $\int \frac{6\, dr}{(r - \sqrt{2})^3}$

81. $\int 3\theta\sqrt{\theta^2 + 1}\, d\theta$

82. $\int \frac{\theta}{\sqrt{7 + \theta^2}}\, d\theta$

83. $\int x^3(1 + x^4)^{-1/4}\, dx$ **84.** $\int (2 - x)^{3/5}\, dx$

85. $\int \sec^2 \frac{s}{10}\, ds$ **86.** $\int \csc^2 \pi s\, ds$

87. $\int \csc\sqrt{2}\theta \cot\sqrt{2}\theta\, d\theta$ **88.** $\int \sec\frac{\theta}{3}\tan\frac{\theta}{3}\, d\theta$

89. $\int \sin^2 \frac{x}{4}\, dx$

90. $\int \cos^2 \frac{x}{2}\, dx \left(Hint: \cos^2\theta = \frac{1 + \cos 2\theta}{2}\right)$

Initial Value Problems

Solve the initial value problems in Exercises 91–94.

91. $\frac{dy}{dx} = \frac{x^2 + 1}{x^2}, \quad y(1) = -1$

92. $\frac{dy}{dx} = \left(x + \frac{1}{x}\right)^2, \quad y(1) = 1$

93. $\frac{d^2r}{dt^2} = 15\sqrt{t} + \frac{3}{\sqrt{t}}; \quad r'(1) = 8, \quad r(1) = 0$

94. $\frac{d^3r}{dt^3} = -\cos t; \quad r''(0) = r'(0) = 0, \quad r(0) = -1$

1. What can you say about a function whose maximum and minimum values on an interval are equal? Give reasons for your answer.

2. Is it true that a discontinuous function cannot have both an absolute maximum and an absolute minimum value on a closed interval? Give reasons for your answer.

3. Can you conclude anything about the extreme values of a continuous function on an open interval? On a half-open interval? Give reasons for your answer.

4. **Local extrema** Use the sign pattern for the derivative

$$\frac{df}{dx} = 6(x - 1)(x - 2)^2(x - 3)^3(x - 4)^4$$

to identify the points where f has local maximum and minimum values.

5. **Local extrema**

   a. Suppose that the first derivative of $y = f(x)$ is

   $$y' = 6(x + 1)(x - 2)^2.$$

   At what points, if any, does the graph of f have a local maximum, local minimum, or point of inflection?

   b. Suppose that the first derivative of $y = f(x)$ is

   $$y' = 6x(x + 1)(x - 2).$$

   At what points, if any, does the graph of f have a local maximum, local minimum, or point of inflection?

6. If $f'(x) \le 2$ for all x, what is the most the values of f can increase on $[0, 6]$? Give reasons for your answer.

7. **Bounding a function** Suppose that f is continuous on $[a, b]$ and that c is an interior point of the interval. Show that if $f'(x) \le 0$ on $[a, c)$ and $f'(x) \ge 0$ on $(c, b]$, then $f(x)$ is never less than $f(c)$ on $[a, b]$.

8. **An inequality**

   a. Show that $-1/2 \le x/(1 + x^2) \le 1/2$ for every value of x.

   b. Suppose that f is a function whose derivative is $f'(x) = x/(1 + x^2)$. Use the result in part (a) to show that

   $$|f(b) - f(a)| \le \frac{1}{2}|b - a|$$

   for any a and b.

9. The derivative of $f(x) = x^2$ is zero at $x = 0$, but f is not a constant function. Doesn't this contradict the corollary of the Mean Value Theorem that says that functions with zero derivatives are constant? Give reasons for your answer.

10. **Extrema and inflection points** Let $h = fg$ be the product of two differentiable functions of x.

   a. If f and g are positive, with local maxima at $x = a$, and if f' and g' change sign at a, does h have a local maximum at a?

   b. If the graphs of f and g have inflection points at $x = a$, does the graph of h have an inflection point at a?

   In either case, if the answer is yes, give a proof. If the answer is no, give a counterexample.

11. **Finding a function** Use the following information to find the values of a, b, and c in the formula $f(x) = (x + a)/(bx^2 + cx + 2)$.

   i) The values of a, b, and c are either 0 or 1.

   ii) The graph of f passes through the point $(-1, 0)$.

   iii) The line $y = 1$ is an asymptote of the graph of f.

12. **Horizontal tangent** For what value or values of the constant k will the curve $y = x^3 + kx^2 + 3x - 4$ have exactly one horizontal tangent?

13. **Largest inscribed triangle** Points A and B lie at the ends of a diameter of a unit circle and point C lies on the circumference. Is it true that the area of triangle ABC is largest when the triangle is isosceles? How do you know?

14. **Proving the second derivative test** The Second Derivative Test for Local Maxima and Minima (Section 4.4) says:

   a. f has a local maximum value at $x = c$ if $f'(c) = 0$ and $f''(c) < 0$

   b. f has a local minimum value at $x = c$ if $f'(c) = 0$ and $f''(c) > 0$.

   To prove statement (a), let $\epsilon = (1/2)|f''(c)|$. Then use the fact that

   $$f''(c) = \lim_{h \to 0} \frac{f'(c + h) - f'(c)}{h} = \lim_{h \to 0} \frac{f'(c + h)}{h}$$

   to conclude that for some $\delta > 0$,

   $$0 < |h| < \delta \quad \Rightarrow \quad \frac{f'(c + h)}{h} < f''(c) + \epsilon < 0.$$

   Thus, $f'(c + h)$ is positive for $-\delta < h < 0$ and negative for $0 < h < \delta$. Prove statement (b) in a similar way.

15. **Hole in a water tank** You want to bore a hole in the side of the tank shown here at a height that will make the stream of water coming out hit the ground as far from the tank as possible. If you drill the hole near the top, where the pressure is low, the water will exit slowly but spend a relatively long time in the air. If you drill the hole near the bottom, the water will exit at a higher velocity but have only a short time to fall. Where is the best place, if any, for the hole? (*Hint:* How long will it take an exiting particle of water to fall from height y to the ground?)

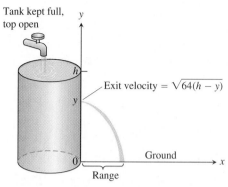

Tank kept full, top open

Exit velocity $= \sqrt{64(h - y)}$

Ground

Range

16. Kicking a field goal An American football player wants to kick a field goal with the ball being on a right hash mark. Assume that the goal posts are b feet apart and that the hash mark line is a distance $a > 0$ feet from the right goal post. (See the accompanying figure.) Find the distance h from the goal post line that gives the kicker his largest angle β. Assume that the football field is flat.

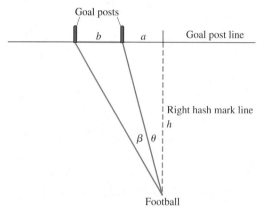

Goal posts

b a Goal post line

Right hash mark line

h

β θ

Football

17. A max-min problem with a variable answer Sometimes the solution of a max-min problem depends on the proportions of the shapes involved. As a case in point, suppose that a right circular cylinder of radius r and height h is inscribed in a right circular cone of radius R and height H, as shown here. Find the value of r (in terms of R and H) that maximizes the total surface area of the cylinder (including top and bottom). As you will see, the solution depends on whether $H \le 2R$ or $H > 2R$.

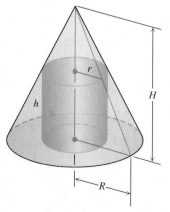

r

H

h

R

18. Minimizing a parameter Find the smallest value of the positive constant m that will make $mx - 1 + (1/x)$ greater than or equal to zero for all positive values of x.

19. Evaluate the following limits.

a. $\lim\limits_{x \to 0} \dfrac{2 \sin 5x}{3x}$ b. $\lim\limits_{x \to 0} \sin 5x \cot 3x$

c. $\lim\limits_{x \to 0} x \csc^2 \sqrt{2x}$ d. $\lim\limits_{x \to \pi/2} (\sec x - \tan x)$

e. $\lim\limits_{x \to 0} \dfrac{x - \sin x}{x - \tan x}$ f. $\lim\limits_{x \to 0} \dfrac{\sin x^2}{x \sin x}$

g. $\lim\limits_{x \to 0} \dfrac{\sec x - 1}{x^2}$ h. $\lim\limits_{x \to 2} \dfrac{x^3 - 8}{x^2 - 4}$

20. L'Hôpital's Rule does not help with the following limits. Find them some other way.

a. $\lim\limits_{x \to \infty} \dfrac{\sqrt{x + 5}}{\sqrt{x + 5}}$ b. $\lim\limits_{x \to \infty} \dfrac{2x}{x + 7\sqrt{x}}$

21. Suppose that it costs a company $y = a + bx$ dollars to produce x units per week. It can sell x units per week at a price of $P = c - ex$ dollars per unit. Each of a, b, c, and e represents a positive constant. **(a)** What production level maximizes the profit? **(b)** What is the corresponding price? **(c)** What is the weekly profit at this level of production? **(d)** At what price should each item be sold to maximize profits if the government imposes a tax of t dollars per item sold? Comment on the difference between this price and the price before the tax.

22. Estimating reciprocals without division You can estimate the value of the reciprocal of a number a without ever dividing by a if you apply Newton's method to the function $f(x) = (1/x) - a$. For example, if $a = 3$, the function involved is $f(x) = (1/x) - 3$.

a. Graph $y = (1/x) - 3$. Where does the graph cross the x-axis?

b. Show that the recursion formula in this case is

$$x_{n+1} = x_n(2 - 3x_n),$$

so there is no need for division.

23. To find $x = \sqrt[q]{a}$, we apply Newton's method to $f(x) = x^q - a$. Here we assume that a is a positive real number and q is a positive integer. Show that x_1 is a "weighted average" of x_0 and a/x_0^{q-1}, and find the coefficients m_0, m_1 such that

$$x_1 = m_0 x_0 + m_1\left(\frac{a}{x_0^{q-1}}\right), \qquad \begin{aligned} &m_0 > 0, m_1 > 0, \\ &m_0 + m_1 = 1. \end{aligned}$$

What conclusion would you reach if x_0 and a/x_0^{q-1} were equal? What would be the value of x_1 in that case?

24. The family of straight lines $y = ax + b$ (a, b arbitrary constants) can be characterized by the relation $y'' = 0$. Find a similar relation satisfied by the family of all circles

$$(x - h)^2 + (y - h)^2 = r^2,$$

where h and r are arbitrary constants. (*Hint:* Eliminate h and r from the set of three equations including the given one and two obtained by successive differentiation.)

25. Assume that the brakes of an automobile produce a constant deceleration of k ft/sec^2. **(a)** Determine what k must be to bring an automobile traveling 60 mi/hr (88 ft/sec) to rest in a distance of 100 ft from the point where the brakes are applied. **(b)** With the same k, how far would a car traveling 30 mi/hr travel before being brought to a stop?

26. Let $f(x)$, $g(x)$ be two continuously differentiable functions satisfying the relationships $f'(x) = g(x)$ and $f''(x) = -f(x)$. Let $h(x) = f^2(x) + g^2(x)$. If $h(0) = 5$, find $h(10)$.

27. Can there be a curve satisfying the following conditions? d^2y/dx^2 is everywhere equal to zero and, when $x = 0$, $y = 0$ and $dy/dx = 1$. Give a reason for your answer.

28. Find the equation for the curve in the xy-plane that passes through the point $(1, -1)$ if its slope at x is always $3x^2 + 2$.

29. A particle moves along the x-axis. Its acceleration is $a = -t^2$. At $t = 0$, the particle is at the origin. In the course of its motion, it reaches the point $x = b$, where $b > 0$, but no point beyond b. Determine its velocity at $t = 0$.

30. A particle moves with acceleration $a = \sqrt{t} - \left(1/\sqrt{t}\right)$. Assuming that the velocity $v = 4/3$ and the position $s = -4/15$ when $t = 0$, find

    a. the velocity v in terms of t.

    b. the position s in terms of t.

31. Given $f(x) = ax^2 + 2bx + c$ with $a > 0$. By considering the minimum, prove that $f(x) \geq 0$ for all real x if, and only if, $b^2 - ac \leq 0$.

32. Schwarz's inequality

    a. In Exercise 31, let

$$f(x) = (a_1x + b_1)^2 + (a_2x + b_2)^2 + \cdots + (a_nx + b_n)^2,$$

and deduce Schwarz's inequality:

$$(a_1b_1 + a_2b_2 + \cdots + a_nb_n)^2$$
$$\leq (a_1^2 + a_2^2 + \cdots + a_n^2)(b_1^2 + b_2^2 + \cdots + b_n^2).$$

    b. Show that equality holds in Schwarz's inequality only if there exists a real number x that makes a_ix equal $-b_i$ for every value of i from 1 to n.

| Chapter 4 | **Technology Application Projects** |

Mathematica/Maple Module
Motion Along a Straight Line: Position → Velocity → Acceleration
You will observe the shape of a graph through dramatic animated visualizations of the derivative relations among the position, velocity, and acceleration. Figures in the text can be animated.

Mathematica/Maple Module
Newton's Method: Estimate π to How Many Places?
Plot a function, observe a root, pick a starting point near the root, and use Newton's Iteration Procedure to approximate the root to a desired accuracy. The numbers π, e, and $\sqrt{2}$ are approximated.

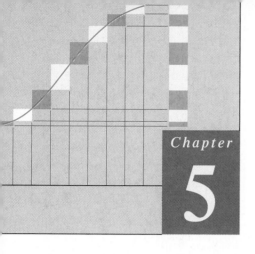

5

INTEGRATION

OVERVIEW One of the great achievements of classical geometry was to obtain formulas for the areas and volumes of triangles, spheres, and cones. In this chapter we study a method to calculate the areas and volumes of these and other more general shapes. The method we develop, called *integration*, is a tool for calculating much more than areas and volumes. The *integral* has many applications in statistics, economics, the sciences, and engineering. It allows us to calculate quantities ranging from probabilities and averages to energy consumption and the forces against a dam's floodgates.

The idea behind integration is that we can effectively compute many quantities by breaking them into small pieces, and then summing the contributions from each small part. We develop the theory of the integral in the setting of area, where it most clearly reveals its nature. We begin with examples involving finite sums. These lead naturally to the question of what happens when more and more terms are summed. Passing to the limit, as the number of terms goes to infinity, then gives an integral. While integration and differentiation are closely connected, we will not see the roles of the derivative and antiderivative emerge until Section 5.4. The nature of their connection, contained in the Fundamental Theorem of Calculus, is one of the most important ideas in calculus.

5.1 Estimating with Finite Sums

This section shows how area, average values, and the distance traveled by an object over time can all be approximated by finite sums. Finite sums are the basis for defining the integral in Section 5.3.

Area

The area of a region with a curved boundary can be approximated by summing the areas of a collection of rectangles. Using more rectangles can increase the accuracy of the approximation.

EXAMPLE 1   Approximating Area

What is the area of the shaded region R that lies above the x-axis, below the graph of $y = 1 - x^2$, and between the vertical lines $x = 0$ and $x = 1$? (See Figure 5.1.) An architect might want to know this area to calculate the weight of a custom window with a shape described by R. Unfortunately, there is no simple geometric formula for calculating the areas of shapes having curved boundaries like the region R.

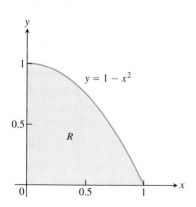

FIGURE 5.1 The area of the region R cannot be found by a simple geometry formula (Example 1).

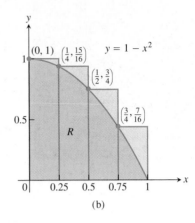

FIGURE 5.2 (a) We get an upper estimate of the area of R by using two rectangles containing R. (b) Four rectangles give a better upper estimate. Both estimates overshoot the true value for the area.

While we do not yet have a method for determining the exact area of R, we can approximate it in a simple way. Figure 5.2a shows two rectangles that together contain the region R. Each rectangle has width $1/2$ and they have heights 1 and $3/4$, moving from left to right. The height of each rectangle is the maximum value of the function f, obtained by evaluating f at the left endpoint of the subinterval of $[0, 1]$ forming the base of the rectangle. The total area of the two rectangles approximates the area A of the region R,

$$A \approx 1 \cdot \frac{1}{2} + \frac{3}{4} \cdot \frac{1}{2} = \frac{7}{8} = 0.875.$$

This estimate is larger than the true area A, since the two rectangles contain R. We say that 0.875 is an **upper sum** because it is obtained by taking the height of each rectangle as the maximum (uppermost) value of $f(x)$ for x a point in the base interval of the rectangle. In Figure 5.2b, we improve our estimate by using four thinner rectangles, each of width $1/4$, which taken together contain the region R. These four rectangles give the approximation

$$A \approx 1 \cdot \frac{1}{4} + \frac{15}{16} \cdot \frac{1}{4} + \frac{3}{4} \cdot \frac{1}{4} + \frac{7}{16} \cdot \frac{1}{4} = \frac{25}{32} = 0.78125,$$

which is still greater than A since the four rectangles contain R.

Suppose instead we use four rectangles contained *inside* the region R to estimate the area, as in Figure 5.3a. Each rectangle has width $1/4$ as before, but the rectangles are shorter and lie entirely beneath the graph of f. The function $f(x) = 1 - x^2$ is decreasing on $[0, 1]$, so the height of each of these rectangles is given by the value of f at the right endpoint of the subinterval forming its base. The fourth rectangle has zero height and therefore contributes no area. Summing these rectangles with heights equal to the minimum value of $f(x)$ for x a point in each base subinterval, gives a **lower sum** approximation to the area,

$$A \approx \frac{15}{16} \cdot \frac{1}{4} + \frac{3}{4} \cdot \frac{1}{4} + \frac{7}{16} \cdot \frac{1}{4} + 0 \cdot \frac{1}{4} = \frac{17}{32} = 0.53125.$$

This estimate is smaller than the area A since the rectangles all lie inside of the region R. The true value of A lies somewhere between these lower and upper sums:

$$0.53125 < A < 0.78125.$$

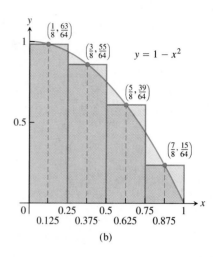

FIGURE 5.3   (a) Rectangles contained in R give an estimate for the area that undershoots the true value. (b) The midpoint rule uses rectangles whose height is the value of $y = f(x)$ at the midpoints of their bases.

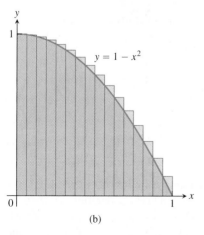

FIGURE 5.4   (a) A lower sum using 16 rectangles of equal width $\Delta x = 1/16$. (b) An upper sum using 16 rectangles.

By considering both lower and upper sum approximations we get not only estimates for the area, but also a bound on the size of the possible error in these estimates since the true value of the area lies somewhere between them. Here the error cannot be greater than the difference $0.78125 - 0.53125 = 0.25$.

Yet another estimate can be obtained by using rectangles whose heights are the values of f at the midpoints of their bases (Figure 5.3b). This method of estimation is called the **midpoint rule** for approximating the area. The midpoint rule gives an estimate that is between a lower sum and an upper sum, but it is not clear whether it overestimates or underestimates the true area. With four rectangles of width $1/4$ as before, the midpoint rule estimates the area of R to be

$$A \approx \frac{63}{64} \cdot \frac{1}{4} + \frac{55}{64} \cdot \frac{1}{4} + \frac{39}{64} \cdot \frac{1}{4} + \frac{15}{64} \cdot \frac{1}{4} = \frac{172}{64} \cdot \frac{1}{4} = 0.671875.$$

In each of our computed sums, the interval $[a, b]$ over which the function f is defined was subdivided into n subintervals of equal width (also called length) $\Delta x = (b - a)/n$, and f was evaluated at a point in each subinterval: c_1 in the first subinterval, c_2 in the second subinterval, and so on. The finite sums then all take the form

$$f(c_1)\,\Delta x + f(c_2)\,\Delta x + f(c_3)\,\Delta x + \cdots + f(c_n)\,\Delta x.$$

By taking more and more rectangles, with each rectangle thinner than before, it appears that these finite sums give better and better approximations to the true area of the region R.

Figure 5.4a shows a lower sum approximation for the area of R using 16 rectangles of equal width. The sum of their areas is 0.634765625, which appears close to the true area, but is still smaller since the rectangles lie inside R.

Figure 5.4b shows an upper sum approximation using 16 rectangles of equal width. The sum of their areas is 0.697265625, which is somewhat larger than the true area because the rectangles taken together contain R. The midpoint rule for 16 rectangles gives a total area approximation of 0.6669921875, but it is not immediately clear whether this estimate is larger or smaller than the true area.

TABLE 5.1 Finite approximations for the area of R

Number of subintervals	Lower sum	Midpoint rule	Upper sum
2	.375	.6875	.875
4	.53125	.671875	.78125
16	.634765625	.6669921875	.697265625
50	.6566	.6667	.6766
100	.66165	.666675	.67165
1000	.6661665	.66666675	.6671665

Table 5.1 shows the values of upper and lower sum approximations to the area of R using up to 1000 rectangles. In Section 5.2 we will see how to get an exact value of the areas of regions such as R by taking a limit as the base width of each rectangle goes to zero and the number of rectangles goes to infinity. With the techniques developed there, we will be able to show that the area of R is exactly $2/3$. ∎

Distance Traveled

Suppose we know the velocity function $v(t)$ of a car moving down a highway, without changing direction, and want to know how far it traveled between times $t = a$ and $t = b$. If we already know an antiderivative $F(t)$ of $v(t)$ we can find the car's position function $s(t)$ by setting $s(t) = F(t) + C$. The distance traveled can then be found by calculating the change in position, $s(b) - s(a)$ (see Exercise 93, Section 4.8). If the velocity function is determined by recording a speedometer reading at various times on the car, then we have no formula from which to obtain an antiderivative function for velocity. So what do we do in this situation?

When we don't know an antiderivative for the velocity function $v(t)$, we can approximate the distance traveled in the following way. Subdivide the interval $[a, b]$ into short time intervals on each of which the velocity is considered to be fairly constant. Then approximate the distance traveled on each time subinterval with the usual distance formula

$$\text{distance} = \text{velocity} \times \text{time}$$

and add the results across $[a, b]$.

Suppose the subdivided interval looks like

with the subintervals all of equal length Δt. Pick a number t_1 in the first interval. If Δt is so small that the velocity barely changes over a short time interval of duration Δt, then the distance traveled in the first time interval is about $v(t_1) \Delta t$. If t_2 is a number in the second interval, the distance traveled in the second time interval is about $v(t_2) \Delta t$. The sum of the distances traveled over all the time intervals is

$$D \approx v(t_1) \Delta t + v(t_2) \Delta t + \cdots + v(t_n) \Delta t,$$

where n is the total number of subintervals.

EXAMPLE 2   Estimating the Height of a Projectile

The velocity function of a projectile fired straight into the air is $f(t) = 160 - 9.8t$ m/sec. Use the summation technique just described to estimate how far the projectile rises during the first 3 sec. How close do the sums come to the exact figure of 435.9 m?

Solution   We explore the results for different numbers of intervals and different choices of evaluation points. Notice that $f(t)$ is decreasing, so choosing left endpoints gives an upper sum estimate; choosing right endpoints gives a lower sum estimate.

(a) *Three subintervals of length 1, with f evaluated at left endpoints giving an upper sum:*

With f evaluated at $t = 0, 1$, and 2, we have

$$D \approx f(t_1)\,\Delta t + f(t_2)\,\Delta t + f(t_3)\,\Delta t$$
$$= [160 - 9.8(0)](1) + [160 - 9.8(1)](1) + [160 - 9.8(2)](1)$$
$$= 450.6.$$

(b) *Three subintervals of length 1, with f evaluated at right endpoints giving a lower sum:*

With f evaluated at $t = 1, 2$, and 3, we have

$$D \approx f(t_1)\,\Delta t + f(t_2)\,\Delta t + f(t_3)\,\Delta t$$
$$= [160 - 9.8(1)](1) + [160 - 9.8(2)](1) + [160 - 9.8(3)](1)$$
$$= 421.2.$$

(c) *With six subintervals of length 1/2, we get*

An upper sum using left endpoints: $D \approx 443.25$; a lower sum using right endpoints: $D \approx 428.55$.

These six-interval estimates are somewhat closer than the three-interval estimates. The results improve as the subintervals get shorter.

As we can see in Table 5.2, the left-endpoint upper sums approach the true value 435.9 from above, whereas the right-endpoint lower sums approach it from below. The true

TABLE 5.2 Travel-distance estimates			
Number of subintervals	**Length of each subinterval**	**Upper sum**	**Lower sum**
3	1	450.6	421.2
6	1/2	443.25	428.55
12	1/4	439.57	432.22
24	1/8	437.74	434.06
48	1/16	436.82	434.98
96	1/32	436.36	435.44
192	1/64	436.13	435.67

value lies between these upper and lower sums. The magnitude of the error in the closest entries is 0.23, a small percentage of the true value.

$$\text{Error magnitude} = |\text{true value} - \text{calculated value}|$$
$$= |435.9 - 435.67| = 0.23.$$
$$\text{Error percentage} = \frac{0.23}{435.9} \approx 0.05\%.$$

It would be reasonable to conclude from the table's last entries that the projectile rose about 436 m during its first 3 sec of flight. ∎

Displacement Versus Distance Traveled

If a body with position function $s(t)$ moves along a coordinate line without changing direction, we can calculate the total distance it travels from $t = a$ to $t = b$ by summing the distance traveled over small intervals, as in Example 2. If the body changes direction one or more times during the trip, then we need to use the body's *speed* $|v(t)|$, which is the absolute value of its velocity function, $v(t)$, to find the total distance traveled. Using the velocity itself, as in Example 2, only gives an estimate to the body's **displacement**, $s(b) - s(a)$, the difference between its initial and final positions.

To see why, partition the time interval $[a, b]$ into small enough equal subintervals Δt so that the body's velocity does not change very much from time t_{k-1} to t_k. Then $v(t_k)$ gives a good approximation of the velocity throughout the interval. Accordingly, the change in the body's position coordinate during the time interval is about

$$v(t_k) \, \Delta t.$$

The change is positive if $v(t_k)$ is positive and negative if $v(t_k)$ is negative.

In either case, the distance traveled during the subinterval is about

$$|v(t_k)| \, \Delta t.$$

The **total distance traveled** is approximately the sum

$$|v(t_1)| \, \Delta t + |v(t_2)| \Delta t + \cdots + |v(t_n)| \, \Delta t.$$

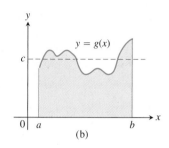

FIGURE 5.5 (a) The average value of $f(x) = c$ on $[a, b]$ is the area of the rectangle divided by $b - a$. (b) The average value of $g(x)$ on $[a, b]$ is the area beneath its graph divided by $b - a$.

Average Value of a Nonnegative Function

The average value of a collection of n numbers $x_1, x_2, \ldots, x_n$ is obtained by adding them together and dividing by n. But what is the average value of a continuous function f on an interval $[a, b]$? Such a function can assume infinitely many values. For example, the temperature at a certain location in a town is a continuous function that goes up and down each day. What does it mean to say that the average temperature in the town over the course of a day is 73 degrees?

When a function is constant, this question is easy to answer. A function with constant value c on an interval $[a, b]$ has average value c. When c is positive, its graph over $[a, b]$ gives a rectangle of height c. The average value of the function can then be interpreted geometrically as the area of this rectangle divided by its width $b - a$ (Figure 5.5a).

What if we want to find the average value of a nonconstant function, such as the function g in Figure 5.5b? We can think of this graph as a snapshot of the height of some water that is sloshing around in a tank, between enclosing walls at $x = a$ and $x = b$. As the water moves, its height over each point changes, but its average height remains the same. To get the average height of the water, we let it settle down until it is level and its height is constant. The resulting height c equals the area under the graph of g divided by $b - a$. We are led to *define* the average value of a nonnegative function on an interval $[a, b]$ to be the area under its graph divided by $b - a$. For this definition to be valid, we need a precise understanding of what is meant by the area under a graph. This will be obtained in Section 5.3, but for now we look at two simple examples.

EXAMPLE 3   The Average Value of a Linear Function

What is the average value of the function $f(x) = 3x$ on the interval $[0, 2]$?

Solution   The average equals the area under the graph divided by the width of the interval. In this case we do not need finite approximation to estimate the area of the region under the graph: a triangle of height 6 and base 2 has area 6 (Figure 5.6). The width of the interval is $b - a = 2 - 0 = 2$. The average value of the function is $6/2 = 3$. ∎

EXAMPLE 4   The Average Value of sin x

Estimate the average value of the function $f(x) = \sin x$ on the interval $[0, \pi]$.

Solution   Looking at the graph of $\sin x$ between 0 and π in Figure 5.7, we can see that its average height is somewhere between 0 and 1. To find the average we need to

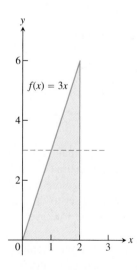

FIGURE 5.6 The average value of $f(x) = 3x$ over $[0, 2]$ is 3 (Example 3).

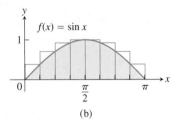

(a) (b)

FIGURE 5.7 Approximating the area under $f(x) = \sin x$ between 0 and π to compute the average value of $\sin x$ over $[0, \pi]$, using (a) four rectangles; (b) eight rectangles (Example 4).

calculate the area A under the graph and then divide this area by the length of the interval, $\pi - 0 = \pi$.

We do not have a simple way to determine the area, so we approximate it with finite sums. To get an upper sum estimate, we add the areas of four rectangles of equal width $\pi/4$ that together contain the region beneath the graph of $y = \sin x$ and above the x-axis on $[0, \pi]$. We choose the heights of the rectangles to be the largest value of $\sin x$ on each subinterval. Over a particular subinterval, this largest value may occur at the left endpoint, the right endpoint, or somewhere between them. We evaluate $\sin x$ at this point to get the height of the rectangle for an upper sum. The sum of the rectangle areas then estimates the total area (Figure 5.7a):

$$A \approx \left(\sin \frac{\pi}{4} \right) \cdot \frac{\pi}{4} + \left(\sin \frac{\pi}{2} \right) \cdot \frac{\pi}{4} + \left(\sin \frac{\pi}{2} \right) \cdot \frac{\pi}{4} + \left(\sin \frac{3\pi}{4} \right) \cdot \frac{\pi}{4}$$

$$= \left(\frac{1}{\sqrt{2}} + 1 + 1 + \frac{1}{\sqrt{2}} \right) \cdot \frac{\pi}{4} \approx (3.42) \cdot \frac{\pi}{4} \approx 2.69.$$

To estimate the average value of $\sin x$ we divide the estimated area by π and obtain the approximation $2.69/\pi \approx 0.86$.

If we use eight rectangles of equal width $\pi/8$ all lying above the graph of $y = \sin x$ (Figure 5.7b), we get the area estimate

$$A \approx \left(\sin \frac{\pi}{8} + \sin \frac{\pi}{4} + \sin \frac{3\pi}{8} + \sin \frac{\pi}{2} + \sin \frac{\pi}{2} + \sin \frac{5\pi}{8} + \sin \frac{3\pi}{4} + \sin \frac{7\pi}{8} \right) \cdot \frac{\pi}{8}$$

$$\approx (.38 + .71 + .92 + 1 + 1 + .92 + .71 + .38) \cdot \frac{\pi}{8} = (6.02) \cdot \frac{\pi}{8} \approx 2.365.$$

Dividing this result by the length π of the interval gives a more accurate estimate of 0.753 for the average. Since we used an upper sum to approximate the area, this estimate is still greater than the actual average value of $\sin x$ over $[0, \pi]$. If we use more and more rectangles, with each rectangle getting thinner and thinner, we get closer and closer to the true average value. Using the techniques of Section 5.3, we will show that the true average value is $2/\pi \approx 0.64$.

As before, we could just as well have used rectangles lying under the graph of $y = \sin x$ and calculated a lower sum approximation, or we could have used the midpoint rule. In Section 5.3, we will see that it doesn't matter whether our approximating rectangles are chosen to give upper sums, lower sums, or a sum in between. In each case, the approximations are close to the true area if all the rectangles are sufficiently thin. ∎

Summary

The area under the graph of a positive function, the distance traveled by a moving object that doesn't change direction, and the average value of a nonnegative function over an interval can all be approximated by finite sums. First we subdivide the interval into subintervals, treating the appropriate function f as if it were constant over each particular subinterval. Then we multiply the width of each subinterval by the value of f at some point within it, and add these products together. If the interval $[a, b]$ is subdivided into n subintervals of equal widths $\Delta x = (b - a)/n$, and if $f(c_k)$ is the value of f at the chosen point c_k in the kth subinterval, this process gives a finite sum of the form

$$f(c_1)\,\Delta x + f(c_2)\,\Delta x + f(c_3)\,\Delta x + \cdots + f(c_n)\,\Delta x.$$

The choices for the c_k could maximize or minimize the value of f in the kth subinterval, or give some value in between. The true value lies somewhere between the approximations given by upper sums and lower sums. The finite sum approximations we looked at improved as we took more subintervals of thinner width.

EXERCISES 5.1

Area

In Exercises 1–4 use finite approximations to estimate the area under the graph of the function using

  a. a lower sum with two rectangles of equal width.

  b. a lower sum with four rectangles of equal width.

  c. an upper sum with two rectangles of equal width.

  d. an upper sum with four rectangles of equal width.

  1. $f(x) = x^2$ between $x = 0$ and $x = 1$.

  2. $f(x) = x^3$ between $x = 0$ and $x = 1$.

  3. $f(x) = 1/x$ between $x = 1$ and $x = 5$.

  4. $f(x) = 4 - x^2$ between $x = -2$ and $x = 2$.

  Using rectangles whose height is given by the value of the function at the midpoint of the rectangle's base (*the midpoint rule*) estimate the area under the graphs of the following functions, using first two and then four rectangles.

  5. $f(x) = x^2$ between $x = 0$ and $x = 1$.

  6. $f(x) = x^3$ between $x = 0$ and $x = 1$.

  7. $f(x) = 1/x$ between $x = 1$ and $x = 5$.

  8. $f(x) = 4 - x^2$ between $x = -2$ and $x = 2$.

Distance

  9. Distance traveled The accompanying table shows the velocity of a model train engine moving along a track for 10 sec. Estimate the distance traveled by the engine using 10 subintervals of length 1 with

  a. left-endpoint values.

  b. right-endpoint values.

Time (sec)	Velocity (in./sec)	Time (sec)	Velocity (in./sec)
0	0	6	11
1	12	7	6
2	22	8	2
3	10	9	6
4	5	10	0
5	13		

10. Distance traveled upstream You are sitting on the bank of a tidal river watching the incoming tide carry a bottle upstream. You record the velocity of the flow every 5 minutes for an hour, with the results shown in the accompanying table. About how far upstream did the bottle travel during that hour? Find an estimate using 12 subintervals of length 5 with

  a. left-endpoint values.

  b. right-endpoint values.

Time (min)	Velocity (m/sec)	Time (min)	Velocity (m/sec)
0	1	35	1.2
5	1.2	40	1.0
10	1.7	45	1.8
15	2.0	50	1.5
20	1.8	55	1.2
25	1.6	60	0
30	1.4		

11. Length of a road   You and a companion are about to drive a twisty stretch of dirt road in a car whose speedometer works but whose odometer (mileage counter) is broken. To find out how long this particular stretch of road is, you record the car's velocity at 10-sec intervals, with the results shown in the accompanying table. Estimate the length of the road using

   a. left-endpoint values.

   b. right-endpoint values.

Time (sec)	Velocity (converted to ft/sec) (30 mi/h = 44 ft/sec)	Time (sec)	Velocity (converted to ft/sec) (30 mi/h = 44 ft/sec)
0	0	70	15
10	44	80	22
20	15	90	35
30	35	100	44
40	30	110	30
50	44	120	35
60	35		

12. Distance from velocity data   The accompanying table gives data for the velocity of a vintage sports car accelerating from 0 to 142 mi/h in 36 sec (10 thousandths of an hour).

Time (h)	Velocity (mi/h)	Time (h)	Velocity (mi/h)
0.0	0	0.006	116
0.001	40	0.007	125
0.002	62	0.008	132
0.003	82	0.009	137
0.004	96	0.010	142
0.005	108		

a. Use rectangles to estimate how far the car traveled during the 36 sec it took to reach 142 mi/h.

b. Roughly how many seconds did it take the car to reach the halfway point? About how fast was the car going then?

Velocity and Distance

13. Free fall with air resistance   An object is dropped straight down from a helicopter. The object falls faster and faster but its acceleration (rate of change of its velocity) decreases over time because of air resistance. The acceleration is measured in ft/sec^2 and recorded every second after the drop for 5 sec, as shown:

t	0	1	2	3	4	5
a	32.00	19.41	11.77	7.14	4.33	2.63

   a. Find an upper estimate for the speed when $t = 5$.

   b. Find a lower estimate for the speed when $t = 5$.

   c. Find an upper estimate for the distance fallen when $t = 3$.

14. Distance traveled by a projectile   An object is shot straight upward from sea level with an initial velocity of 400 ft/sec.

   a. Assuming that gravity is the only force acting on the object, give an upper estimate for its velocity after 5 sec have elapsed. Use $g = 32$ ft/sec^2 for the gravitational acceleration.

   b. Find a lower estimate for the height attained after 5 sec.

Average Value of a Function

In Exercises 15–18, use a finite sum to estimate the average value of f on the given interval by partitioning the interval into four subintervals of equal length and evaluating f at the subinterval midpoints.

15. $f(x) = x^3$ on $[0, 2]$ **16.** $f(x) = 1/x$ on $[1, 9]$

17. $f(t) = (1/2) + \sin^2 \pi t$ on $[0, 2]$

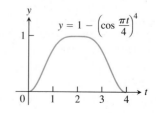

18. $f(t) = 1 - \left(\cos \dfrac{\pi t}{4}\right)^4$ on $[0, 4]$

Pollution Control

19. Water pollution Oil is leaking out of a tanker damaged at sea. The damage to the tanker is worsening as evidenced by the increased leakage each hour, recorded in the following table.

Time (h)	0	1	2	3	4
Leakage (gal/h)	50	70	97	136	190

Time (h)	5	6	7	8
Leakage (gal/h)	265	369	516	720

a. Give an upper and a lower estimate of the total quantity of oil that has escaped after 5 hours.

b. Repeat part (a) for the quantity of oil that has escaped after 8 hours.

c. The tanker continues to leak 720 gal/h after the first 8 hours. If the tanker originally contained 25,000 gal of oil, approximately how many more hours will elapse in the worst case before all the oil has spilled? In the best case?

20. Air pollution A power plant generates electricity by burning oil. Pollutants produced as a result of the burning process are removed by scrubbers in the smokestacks. Over time, the scrubbers become less efficient and eventually they must be replaced when the amount of pollution released exceeds government standards. Measurements are taken at the end of each month determining the rate at which pollutants are released into the atmosphere, recorded as follows.

Month	Jan	Feb	Mar	Apr	May	Jun
Pollutant Release rate (tons/day)	0.20	0.25	0.27	0.34	0.45	0.52

Month	Jul	Aug	Sep	Oct	Nov	Dec
Pollutant Release rate (tons/day)	0.63	0.70	0.81	0.85	0.89	0.95

a. Assuming a 30-day month and that new scrubbers allow only 0.05 ton/day released, give an upper estimate of the total tonnage of pollutants released by the end of June. What is a lower estimate?

b. In the best case, approximately when will a total of 125 tons of pollutants have been released into the atmosphere?

Area of a Circle

21. Inscribe a regular n-sided polygon inside a circle of radius 1 and compute the area of the polygon for the following values of n:

a. 4 (square)   b. 8 (octagon)   c. 16

d. Compare the areas in parts (a), (b), and (c) with the area of the circle.

22. (*Continuation of Exercise 21*)

a. Inscribe a regular n-sided polygon inside a circle of radius 1 and compute the area of one of the n congruent triangles formed by drawing radii to the vertices of the polygon.

b. Compute the limit of the area of the inscribed polygon as $n \to \infty$.

c. Repeat the computations in parts (a) and (b) for a circle of radius r.

COMPUTER EXPLORATIONS

In Exercises 23–26, use a CAS to perform the following steps.

a. Plot the functions over the given interval.

b. Subdivide the interval into $n = 100, 200$, and 1000 subintervals of equal length and evaluate the function at the midpoint of each subinterval.

c. Compute the average value of the function values generated in part (b).

d. Solve the equation $f(x) = $ (average value) for x using the average value calculated in part (c) for the $n = 1000$ partitioning.

23. $f(x) = \sin x$ on $[0, \pi]$ **24.** $f(x) = \sin^2 x$ on $[0, \pi]$

25. $f(x) = x \sin \dfrac{1}{x}$ on $\left[\dfrac{\pi}{4}, \pi \right]$

26. $f(x) = x \sin^2 \dfrac{1}{x}$ on $\left[\dfrac{\pi}{4}, \pi \right]$

5.2 Sigma Notation and Limits of Finite Sums

In estimating with finite sums in Section 5.1, we often encountered sums with many terms (up to 1000 in Table 5.1, for instance). In this section we introduce a notation to write sums with a large number of terms. After describing the notation and stating several of its properties, we look at what happens to a finite sum approximation as the number of terms approaches infinity.

Finite Sums and Sigma Notation

Sigma notation enables us to write a sum with many terms in the compact form

$$\sum_{k=1}^{n} a_k = a_1 + a_2 + a_3 + \cdots + a_{n-1} + a_n.$$

The Greek letter Σ (capital sigma, corresponding to our letter S), stands for "sum." The **index of summation** k tells us where the sum begins (at the number below the Σ symbol) and where it ends (at the number above Σ). Any letter can be used to denote the index, but the letters $i, j,$ and k are customary.

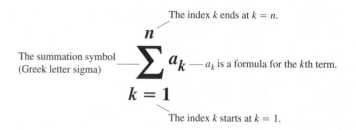

The index k ends at $k = n$.

The summation symbol (Greek letter sigma) — a_k is a formula for the kth term.

The index k starts at $k = 1$.

Thus we can write

$$1^2 + 2^2 + 3^2 + 4^2 + 5^2 + 6^2 + 7^2 + 8^2 + 9^2 + 10^2 + 11^2 = \sum_{k=1}^{11} k^2,$$

and

$$f(1) + f(2) + f(3) + \cdots + f(100) = \sum_{i=1}^{100} f(i).$$

The sigma notation used on the right side of these equations is much more compact than the summation expressions on the left side.

EXAMPLE 1 Using Sigma Notation

The sum in sigma notation	The sum written out, one term for each value of k	The value of the sum
$\displaystyle\sum_{k=1}^{5} k$	$1 + 2 + 3 + 4 + 5$	15
$\displaystyle\sum_{k=1}^{3} (-1)^k k$	$(-1)^1(1) + (-1)^2(2) + (-1)^3(3)$	$-1 + 2 - 3 = -2$
$\displaystyle\sum_{k=1}^{2} \dfrac{k}{k+1}$	$\dfrac{1}{1+1} + \dfrac{2}{2+1}$	$\dfrac{1}{2} + \dfrac{2}{3} = \dfrac{7}{6}$
$\displaystyle\sum_{k=4}^{5} \dfrac{k^2}{k-1}$	$\dfrac{4^2}{4-1} + \dfrac{5^2}{5-1}$	$\dfrac{16}{3} + \dfrac{25}{4} = \dfrac{139}{12}$

The lower limit of summation does not have to be 1; it can be any integer.

EXAMPLE 2   Using Different Index Starting Values

Express the sum $1 + 3 + 5 + 7 + 9$ in sigma notation.

Solution   The formula generating the terms changes with the lower limit of summation, but the terms generated remain the same. It is often simplest to start with $k = 0$ or $k = 1$.

$$\textit{Starting with } k = 0: \qquad 1 + 3 + 5 + 7 + 9 = \sum_{k=0}^{4}(2k + 1)$$

$$\textit{Starting with } k = 1: \qquad 1 + 3 + 5 + 7 + 9 = \sum_{k=1}^{5}(2k - 1)$$

$$\textit{Starting with } k = 2: \qquad 1 + 3 + 5 + 7 + 9 = \sum_{k=2}^{6}(2k - 3)$$

$$\textit{Starting with } k = -3: \qquad 1 + 3 + 5 + 7 + 9 = \sum_{k=-3}^{1}(2k + 7)$$ ∎

When we have a sum such as

$$\sum_{k=1}^{3}(k + k^2)$$

we can rearrange its terms,

$$\sum_{k=1}^{3}(k + k^2) = (1 + 1^2) + (2 + 2^2) + (3 + 3^2)$$

$$= (1 + 2 + 3) + (1^2 + 2^2 + 3^2) \qquad \text{Regroup terms.}$$

$$= \sum_{k=1}^{3} k + \sum_{k=1}^{3} k^2$$

This illustrates a general rule for finite sums:

$$\sum_{k=1}^{n}(a_k + b_k) = \sum_{k=1}^{n} a_k + \sum_{k=1}^{n} b_k$$

Four such rules are given below. A proof that they are valid can be obtained using mathematical induction (see Appendix 1).

Algebra Rules for Finite Sums

1.   *Sum Rule:* $\displaystyle\sum_{k=1}^{n}(a_k + b_k) = \sum_{k=1}^{n} a_k + \sum_{k=1}^{n} b_k$

2.   *Difference Rule:* $\displaystyle\sum_{k=1}^{n}(a_k - b_k) = \sum_{k=1}^{n} a_k - \sum_{k=1}^{n} b_k$

3.   *Constant Multiple Rule:* $\displaystyle\sum_{k=1}^{n} c a_k = c \cdot \sum_{k=1}^{n} a_k$ (Any number c)

4.   *Constant Value Rule:* $\displaystyle\sum_{k=1}^{n} c = n \cdot c$ (c is any constant value.)

EXAMPLE 3 Using the Finite Sum Algebra Rules

(a) $\sum_{k=1}^{n}(3k - k^2) = 3\sum_{k=1}^{n}k - \sum_{k=1}^{n}k^2$ Difference Rule and Constant Multiple Rule

(b) $\sum_{k=1}^{n}(-a_k) = \sum_{k=1}^{n}(-1)\cdot a_k = -1\cdot\sum_{k=1}^{n}a_k = -\sum_{k=1}^{n}a_k$ Constant Multiple Rule

(c) $\sum_{k=1}^{3}(k + 4) = \sum_{k=1}^{3}k + \sum_{k=1}^{3}4$ Sum Rule

$= (1 + 2 + 3) + (3 \cdot 4)$ Constant Value Rule

$= 6 + 12 = 18$

(d) $\sum_{k=1}^{n}\dfrac{1}{n} = n\cdot\dfrac{1}{n} = 1$ Constant Value Rule ($1/n$ is constant) ∎

Over the years people have discovered a variety of formulas for the values of finite sums. The most famous of these are the formula for the sum of the first n integers (Gauss may have discovered it at age 8) and the formulas for the sums of the squares and cubes of the first n integers.

EXAMPLE 4 The Sum of the First n Integers

Show that the sum of the first n integers is

$$\sum_{k=1}^{n}k = \frac{n(n + 1)}{2}.$$

Solution: The formula tells us that the sum of the first 4 integers is

$$\frac{(4)(5)}{2} = 10.$$

Addition verifies this prediction:

$$1 + 2 + 3 + 4 = 10.$$

To prove the formula in general, we write out the terms in the sum twice, once forward and once backward.

$$
\begin{array}{ccccccccc}
1 & + & 2 & + & 3 & + & \cdots & + & n \\
n & + & (n - 1) & + & (n - 2) & + & \cdots & + & 1
\end{array}
$$

If we add the two terms in the first column we get $1 + n = n + 1$. Similarly, if we add the two terms in the second column we get $2 + (n - 1) = n + 1$. The two terms in any column sum to $n + 1$. When we add the n columns together we get n terms, each equal to $n + 1$, for a total of $n(n + 1)$. Since this is twice the desired quantity, the sum of the first n integers is $(n)(n + 1)/2$. ∎

Formulas for the sums of the squares and cubes of the first n integers are proved using mathematical induction (see Appendix 1). We state them here.

The first n squares: $\sum_{k=1}^{n}k^2 = \dfrac{n(n + 1)(2n + 1)}{6}$

The first n cubes: $\sum_{k=1}^{n}k^3 = \left(\dfrac{n(n + 1)}{2}\right)^2$

Limits of Finite Sums

The finite sum approximations we considered in Section 5.1 got more accurate as the number of terms increased and the subinterval widths (lengths) became thinner. The next example shows how to calculate a limiting value as the widths of the subintervals go to zero and their number grows to infinity.

EXAMPLE 5   The Limit of Finite Approximations to an Area

Find the limiting value of lower sum approximations to the area of the region R below the graph of $y = 1 - x^2$ and above the interval $[0, 1]$ on the x-axis using equal width rectangles whose widths approach zero and whose number approaches infinity. (See Figure 5.4a.)

Solution   We compute a lower sum approximation using n rectangles of equal width $\Delta x = (1 - 0)/n$, and then we see what happens as $n \to \infty$. We start by subdividing $[0, 1]$ into n equal width subintervals

$$\left[0, \frac{1}{n}\right], \left[\frac{1}{n}, \frac{2}{n}\right], \cdots, \left[\frac{n-1}{n}, \frac{n}{n}\right].$$

Each subinterval has width $1/n$. The function $1 - x^2$ is decreasing on $[0, 1]$, and its smallest value in a subinterval occurs at the subinterval's right endpoint. So a lower sum is constructed with rectangles whose height over the subinterval $[(k-1)/n, k/n]$ is $f(k/n) = 1 - (k/n)^2$, giving the sum

$$f\left(\frac{1}{n}\right)\left(\frac{1}{n}\right) + f\left(\frac{2}{n}\right)\left(\frac{1}{n}\right) + \cdots + f\left(\frac{k}{n}\right)\left(\frac{1}{n}\right) + \cdots + f\left(\frac{n}{n}\right)\left(\frac{1}{n}\right).$$

We write this in sigma notation and simplify,

$$\sum_{k=1}^{n} f\left(\frac{k}{n}\right)\left(\frac{1}{n}\right) = \sum_{k=1}^{n}\left(1 - \left(\frac{k}{n}\right)^2\right)\left(\frac{1}{n}\right)$$

$$= \sum_{k=1}^{n}\left(\frac{1}{n} - \frac{k^2}{n^3}\right)$$

$$= \sum_{k=1}^{n}\frac{1}{n} - \sum_{k=1}^{n}\frac{k^2}{n^3} \qquad \text{Difference Rule}$$

$$= n \cdot \frac{1}{n} - \frac{1}{n^3}\sum_{k=1}^{n}k^2 \qquad \begin{array}{l}\text{Constant Value and}\\ \text{Constant Multiple Rules}\end{array}$$

$$= 1 - \left(\frac{1}{n^3}\right)\frac{(n)(n+1)(2n+1)}{6} \qquad \text{Sum of the First } n \text{ Squares}$$

$$= 1 - \frac{2n^3 + 3n^2 + n}{6n^3}. \qquad \text{Numerator expanded}$$

We have obtained an expression for the lower sum that holds for any n. Taking the limit of this expression as $n \to \infty$, we see that the lower sums converge as the number of subintervals increases and the subinterval widths approach zero:

$$\lim_{n \to \infty}\left(1 - \frac{2n^3 + 3n^2 + n}{6n^3}\right) = 1 - \frac{2}{6} = \frac{2}{3}.$$

The lower sum approximations converge to $2/3$. A similar calculation shows that the upper sum approximations also converge to $2/3$ (Exercise 35). Any finite sum approximation, in the sense of our summary at the end of Section 5.1, also converges to the same value

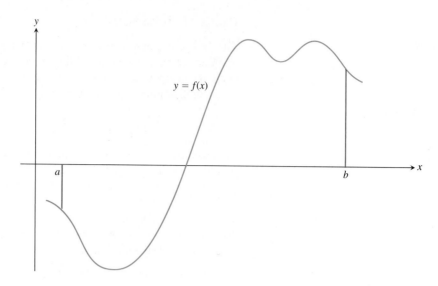

FIGURE 5.8 A typical continuous function $y = f(x)$ over a closed interval $[a, b]$.

2/3. This is because it is possible to show that any finite sum approximation is trapped between the lower and upper sum approximations. For this reason we are led to *define* the area of the region R as this limiting value. In Section 5.3 we study the limits of such finite approximations in their more general setting. ∎

Riemann Sums

The theory of limits of finite approximations was made precise by the German mathematician Bernhard Riemann. We now introduce the notion of a *Riemann sum*, which underlies the theory of the definite integral studied in the next section.

We begin with an arbitrary function f defined on a closed interval $[a, b]$. Like the function pictured in Figure 5.8, f may have negative as well as positive values. We subdivide the interval $[a, b]$ into subintervals, not necessarily of equal widths (or lengths), and form sums in the same way as for the finite approximations in Section 5.1. To do so, we choose $n - 1$ points $\{x_1, x_2, x_3, \ldots, x_{n-1}\}$ between a and b and satisfying

$$a < x_1 < x_2 < \cdots < x_{n-1} < b.$$

To make the notation consistent, we denote a by x_0 and b by x_n, so that

$$a = x_0 < x_1 < x_2 < \cdots < x_{n-1} < x_n = b.$$

The set

$$P = \{x_0, x_1, x_2, \ldots, x_{n-1}, x_n\}$$

is called a **partition** of $[a, b]$.

The partition P divides $[a, b]$ into n closed subintervals

$$[x_0, x_1], [x_1, x_2], \ldots, [x_{n-1}, x_n].$$

The first of these subintervals is $[x_0, x_1]$, the second is $[x_1, x_2]$, and the **kth subinterval of** P is $[x_{k-1}, x_k]$, for k an integer between 1 and n.

The width of the first subinterval $[x_0, x_1]$ is denoted Δx_1, the width of the second $[x_1, x_2]$ is denoted Δx_2, and the width of the kth subinterval is $\Delta x_k = x_k - x_{k-1}$. If all n subintervals have equal width, then the common width Δx is equal to $(b - a)/n$.

In each subinterval we select some point. The point chosen in the kth subinterval $[x_{k-1}, x_k]$ is called c_k. Then on each subinterval we stand a vertical rectangle that stretches from the x-axis to touch the curve at $(c_k, f(c_k))$. These rectangles can be above or below the x-axis, depending on whether $f(c_k)$ is positive or negative, or on it if $f(c_k) = 0$ (Figure 5.9).

On each subinterval we form the product $f(c_k) \cdot \Delta x_k$. This product is positive, negative or zero, depending on the sign of $f(c_k)$. When $f(c_k) > 0$, the product $f(c_k) \cdot \Delta x_k$ is the area of a rectangle with height $f(c_k)$ and width Δx_k. When $f(c_k) < 0$, the product $f(c_k) \cdot \Delta x_k$ is a negative number, the negative of the area of a rectangle of width Δx_k that drops from the x-axis to the negative number $f(c_k)$.

Finally we sum all these products to get

$$S_P = \sum_{k=1}^{n} f(c_k) \, \Delta x_k.$$

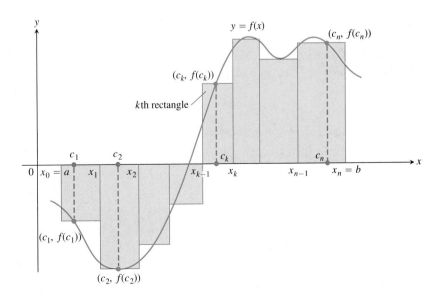

FIGURE 5.9 The rectangles approximate the region between the graph of the function $y = f(x)$ and the x-axis.

(a)

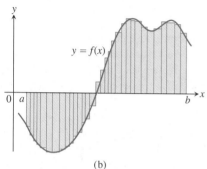

(b)

FIGURE 5.10 The curve of Figure 5.9 with rectangles from finer partitions of $[a, b]$. Finer partitions create collections of rectangles with thinner bases that approximate the region between the graph of f and the x-axis with increasing accuracy.

The sum S_P is called a **Riemann sum for f on the interval $[a, b]$.** There are many such sums, depending on the partition P we choose, and the choices of the points c_k in the subintervals.

In Example 5, where the subintervals all had equal widths $\Delta x = 1/n$, we could make them thinner by simply increasing their number n. When a partition has subintervals of varying widths, we can ensure they are all thin by controlling the width of a widest (longest) subinterval. We define the **norm** of a partition P, written $\|P\|$, to be the largest of all the subinterval widths. If $\|P\|$ is a small number, then all of the subintervals in the partition P have a small width. Let's look at an example of these ideas.

EXAMPLE 6   Partitioning a Closed Interval

The set $P = \{0, 0.2, 0.6, 1, 1.5, 2\}$ is a partition of $[0, 2]$. There are five subintervals of P: $[0, 0.2], [0.2, 0.6], [0.6, 1], [1, 1.5],$ and $[1.5, 2]$:

The lengths of the subintervals are $\Delta x_1 = 0.2$, $\Delta x_2 = 0.4$, $\Delta x_3 = 0.4$, $\Delta x_4 = 0.5$, and $\Delta x_5 = 0.5$. The longest subinterval length is 0.5, so the norm of the partition is $\|P\| = 0.5$. In this example, there are two subintervals of this length. ∎

Any Riemann sum associated with a partition of a closed interval $[a, b]$ defines rectangles that approximate the region between the graph of a continuous function f and the x-axis. Partitions with norm approaching zero lead to collections of rectangles that approximate this region with increasing accuracy, as suggested by Figure 5.10. We will see in the next section that if the function f is continuous over the closed interval $[a, b]$, then no matter how we choose the partition P and the points c_k in its subintervals to construct a Riemann sum, a single limiting value is approached as the subinterval widths, controlled by the norm of the partition, approach zero.

EXERCISES 5.2

Sigma Notation

Write the sums in Exercises 1–6 without sigma notation. Then evaluate them.

1. $\displaystyle\sum_{k=1}^{2} \frac{6k}{k+1}$

2. $\displaystyle\sum_{k=1}^{3} \frac{k-1}{k}$

3. $\displaystyle\sum_{k=1}^{4} \cos k\pi$

4. $\displaystyle\sum_{k=1}^{5} \sin k\pi$

5. $\displaystyle\sum_{k=1}^{3} (-1)^{k+1} \sin \frac{\pi}{k}$

6. $\displaystyle\sum_{k=1}^{4} (-1)^k \cos k\pi$

7. Which of the following express $1 + 2 + 4 + 8 + 16 + 32$ in sigma notation?

a. $\displaystyle\sum_{k=1}^{6} 2^{k-1}$

b. $\displaystyle\sum_{k=0}^{5} 2^k$

c. $\displaystyle\sum_{k=-1}^{4} 2^{k+1}$

8. Which of the following express $1 - 2 + 4 - 8 + 16 - 32$ in sigma notation?

a. $\displaystyle\sum_{k=1}^{6} (-2)^{k-1}$

b. $\displaystyle\sum_{k=0}^{5} (-1)^k 2^k$

c. $\displaystyle\sum_{k=-2}^{3} (-1)^{k+1} 2^{k+2}$

9. Which formula is not equivalent to the other two?

a. $\displaystyle\sum_{k=2}^{4} \frac{(-1)^{k-1}}{k-1}$

b. $\displaystyle\sum_{k=0}^{2} \frac{(-1)^k}{k+1}$

c. $\displaystyle\sum_{k=-1}^{1} \frac{(-1)^k}{k+2}$

10. Which formula is not equivalent to the other two?

a. $\displaystyle\sum_{k=1}^{4} (k-1)^2$

b. $\displaystyle\sum_{k=-1}^{3} (k+1)^2$

c. $\displaystyle\sum_{k=-3}^{-1} k^2$

Express the sums in Exercises 11–16 in sigma notation. The form of your answer will depend on your choice of the lower limit of summation.

11. $1 + 2 + 3 + 4 + 5 + 6$ **12.** $1 + 4 + 9 + 16$

13. $\dfrac{1}{2} + \dfrac{1}{4} + \dfrac{1}{8} + \dfrac{1}{16}$ **14.** $2 + 4 + 6 + 8 + 10$

15. $1 - \dfrac{1}{2} + \dfrac{1}{3} - \dfrac{1}{4} + \dfrac{1}{5}$ **16.** $-\dfrac{1}{5} + \dfrac{2}{5} - \dfrac{3}{5} + \dfrac{4}{5} - \dfrac{5}{5}$

Values of Finite Sums

17. Suppose that $\displaystyle\sum_{k=1}^{n} a_k = -5$ and $\displaystyle\sum_{k=1}^{n} b_k = 6$. Find the values of

   a. $\displaystyle\sum_{k=1}^{n} 3a_k$ **b.** $\displaystyle\sum_{k=1}^{n} \dfrac{b_k}{6}$ **c.** $\displaystyle\sum_{k=1}^{n} (a_k + b_k)$

   d. $\displaystyle\sum_{k=1}^{n} (a_k - b_k)$ **e.** $\displaystyle\sum_{k=1}^{n} (b_k - 2a_k)$

18. Suppose that $\displaystyle\sum_{k=1}^{n} a_k = 0$ and $\displaystyle\sum_{k=1}^{n} b_k = 1$. Find the values of

   a. $\displaystyle\sum_{k=1}^{n} 8a_k$ **b.** $\displaystyle\sum_{k=1}^{n} 250b_k$

   c. $\displaystyle\sum_{k=1}^{n} (a_k + 1)$ **d.** $\displaystyle\sum_{k=1}^{n} (b_k - 1)$

Evaluate the sums in Exercises 19–28.

19. a. $\displaystyle\sum_{k=1}^{10} k$ **b.** $\displaystyle\sum_{k=1}^{10} k^2$ **c.** $\displaystyle\sum_{k=1}^{10} k^3$

20. a. $\displaystyle\sum_{k=1}^{13} k$ **b.** $\displaystyle\sum_{k=1}^{13} k^2$ **c.** $\displaystyle\sum_{k=1}^{13} k^3$

21. $\displaystyle\sum_{k=1}^{7} (-2k)$ **22.** $\displaystyle\sum_{k=1}^{5} \dfrac{\pi k}{15}$

23. $\displaystyle\sum_{k=1}^{6} (3 - k^2)$ **24.** $\displaystyle\sum_{k=1}^{6} (k^2 - 5)$

25. $\displaystyle\sum_{k=1}^{5} k(3k + 5)$ **26.** $\displaystyle\sum_{k=1}^{7} k(2k + 1)$

27. $\displaystyle\sum_{k=1}^{5} \dfrac{k^3}{225} + \left(\sum_{k=1}^{5} k\right)^3$ **28.** $\left(\displaystyle\sum_{k=1}^{7} k\right)^2 - \displaystyle\sum_{k=1}^{7} \dfrac{k^3}{4}$

Rectangles for Riemann Sums

In Exercises 29–32, graph each function $f(x)$ over the given interval. Partition the interval into four subintervals of equal length. Then add to your sketch the rectangles associated with the Riemann sum $\sum_{k=1}^{4} f(c_k)\, \Delta x_k$, given that c_k is the (a) left-hand endpoint, (b) right-hand endpoint, (c) midpoint of the kth subinterval. (Make a separate sketch for each set of rectangles.)

29. $f(x) = x^2 - 1$, $[0, 2]$

30. $f(x) = -x^2$, $[0, 1]$

31. $f(x) = \sin x$, $[-\pi, \pi]$

32. $f(x) = \sin x + 1$, $[-\pi, \pi]$

33. Find the norm of the partition $P = \{0, 1.2, 1.5, 2.3, 2.6, 3\}$.

34. Find the norm of the partition $P = \{-2, -1.6, -0.5, 0, 0.8, 1\}$.

Limits of Upper Sums

For the functions in Exercises 35–40 find a formula for the upper sum obtained by dividing the interval $[a, b]$ into n equal subintervals. Then take a limit of these sums as $n \to \infty$ to calculate the area under the curve over $[a, b]$.

35. $f(x) = 1 - x^2$ over the interval $[0, 1]$.

36. $f(x) = 2x$ over the interval $[0, 3]$.

37. $f(x) = x^2 + 1$ over the interval $[0, 3]$.

38. $f(x) = 3x^2$ over the interval $[0, 1]$.

39. $f(x) = x + x^2$ over the interval $[0, 1]$.

40. $f(x) = 3x + 2x^2$ over the interval $[0, 1]$.

5.3   The Definite Integral

In Section 5.2 we investigated the limit of a finite sum for a function defined over a closed interval $[a, b]$ using n subintervals of equal width (or length), $(b - a)/n$. In this section we consider the limit of more general Riemann sums as the norm of the partitions of $[a, b]$ approaches zero. For general Riemann sums the subintervals of the partitions need not have equal widths. The limiting process then leads to the definition of the *definite integral* of a function over a closed interval $[a, b]$.

Limits of Riemann Sums

The definition of the definite integral is based on the idea that for certain functions, as the norm of the partitions of $[a, b]$ approaches zero, the values of the corresponding Riemann sums approach a limiting value I. What we mean by this converging idea is that a Riemann sum will be close to the number I provided that the norm of its partition is sufficiently small (so that all of its subintervals have thin enough widths). We introduce the symbol ϵ as a small positive number that specifies how close to I the Riemann sum must be, and the symbol δ as a second small positive number that specifies how small the norm of a partition must be in order for that to happen. Here is a precise formulation.

DEFINITION   The Definite Integral as a Limit of Riemann Sums

Let $f(x)$ be a function defined on a closed interval $[a, b]$. We say that a number I is the **definite integral of f over $[a, b]$** and that I is the limit of the Riemann sums $\sum_{k=1}^{n} f(c_k)\,\Delta x_k$ if the following condition is satisfied:

Given any number $\epsilon > 0$ there is a corresponding number $\delta > 0$ such that for every partition $P = \{x_0, x_1, \ldots, x_n\}$ of $[a, b]$ with $\|P\| < \delta$ and any choice of c_k in $[x_{k-1}, x_k]$, we have

$$\left| \sum_{k=1}^{n} f(c_k)\,\Delta x_k - I \right| < \epsilon.$$

Leibniz introduced a notation for the definite integral that captures its construction as a limit of Riemann sums. He envisioned the finite sums $\sum_{k=1}^{n} f(c_k)\,\Delta x_k$ becoming an infinite sum of function values $f(x)$ multiplied by "infinitesimal" subinterval widths dx. The sum symbol $\sum$ is replaced in the limit by the integral symbol $\int$, whose origin is in the letter "S." The function values $f(c_k)$ are replaced by a continuous selection of function values $f(x)$. The subinterval widths Δx_k become the differential dx. It is as if we are summing all products of the form $f(x) \cdot dx$ as x goes from a to b. While this notation captures the process of constructing an integral, it is Riemann's definition that gives a precise meaning to the definite integral.

Notation and Existence of the Definite Integral

The symbol for the number I in the definition of the definite integral is

$$\int_{a}^{b} f(x)\,dx$$

which is read as "the integral from a to b of f of x dee x" or sometimes as "the integral from a to b of f of x with respect to x." The component parts in the integral symbol also have names:

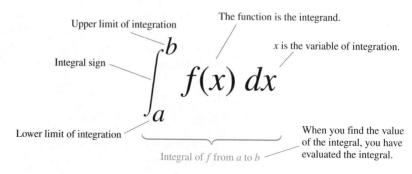

When the definition is satisfied, we say the Riemann sums of f on $[a, b]$ **converge** to the definite integral $I = \int_a^b f(x)\, dx$ and that f is **integrable** over $[a, b]$. We have many choices for a partition P with norm going to zero, and many choices of points c_k for each partition. The definite integral exists when we always get the same limit I, no matter what choices are made. When the limit exists we write it as the definite integral

$$\lim_{\|P\| \to 0} \sum_{k=1}^{n} f(c_k)\, \Delta x_k = I = \int_a^b f(x)\, dx.$$

When each partition has n equal subintervals, each of width $\Delta x = (b - a)/n$, we will also write

$$\lim_{n \to \infty} \sum_{k=1}^{n} f(c_k)\, \Delta x = I = \int_a^b f(x)\, dx.$$

The limit is always taken as the norm of the partitions approaches zero and the number of subintervals goes to infinity.

The value of the definite integral of a function over any particular interval depends on the function, not on the letter we choose to represent its independent variable. If we decide to use t or u instead of x, we simply write the integral as

$$\int_a^b f(t)\, dt \qquad \text{or} \qquad \int_a^b f(u)\, du \qquad \text{instead of} \qquad \int_a^b f(x)\, dx.$$

No matter how we write the integral, it is still the same number, defined as a limit of Riemann sums. Since it does not matter what letter we use, the variable of integration is called a **dummy variable**.

Since there are so many choices to be made in taking a limit of Riemann sums, it might seem difficult to show that such a limit exists. It turns out, however, that no matter what choices are made, the Riemann sums associated with a *continuous* function converge to the same limit.

THEOREM 1   **The Existence of Definite Integrals**

A continuous function is integrable. That is, if a function f is continuous on an interval $[a, b]$, then its definite integral over $[a, b]$ exists.

By the Extreme Value Theorem (Theorem 1, Section 4.1), when f is continuous we can choose c_k so that $f(c_k)$ gives the maximum value of f on $[x_{k-1}, x_k]$, giving an **upper sum**. We can choose c_k to give the minimum value of f on $[x_{k-1}, x_k]$, giving a **lower sum**. We can pick c_k to be the midpoint of $[x_{k-1}, x_k]$, the rightmost point x_k, or a random point. We can take the partitions of equal or varying widths. In each case we get the same limit for $\sum_{k=1}^n f(c_k)\, \Delta x_k$ as $\|P\| \to 0$. The idea behind Theorem 1 is that a Riemann sum associated with a partition is no more than the upper sum of that partition and no less than the lower sum. The upper and lower sums converge to the same value when $\|P\| \to 0$. All other Riemann sums lie between the upper and lower sums and have the same limit. A proof of Theorem 1 involves a careful analysis of functions, partitions, and limits along this line of thinking and is left to a more advanced text. An indication of this proof is given in Exercises 80 and 81.

Theorem 1 says nothing about how to *calculate* definite integrals. A method of calculation will be developed in Section 5.4, through a connection to the process of taking antiderivatives.

Integrable and Nonintegrable Functions

Theorem 1 tells us that functions continuous over the interval $[a, b]$ are integrable there. Functions that are not continuous may or may not be integrable. Discontinuous functions that are integrable include those that are increasing on $[a, b]$ (Exercise 77), and the *piecewise-continuous functions* defined in the Additional Exercises at the end of this chapter. (The latter are continuous except at a finite number of points in $[a, b]$.) For integrability to fail, a function needs to be sufficiently discontinuous so that the region between its graph and the x-axis cannot be approximated well by increasingly thin rectangles. Here is an example of a function that is not integrable.

EXAMPLE 1   A Nonintegrable Function on $[0, 1]$

The function

$$f(x) = \begin{cases} 1, & \text{if } x \text{ is rational} \\ 0, & \text{if } x \text{ is irrational} \end{cases}$$

has no Riemann integral over $[0, 1]$. Underlying this is the fact that between any two numbers there is both a rational number and an irrational number. Thus the function jumps up and down too erratically over $[0, 1]$ to allow the region beneath its graph and above the x-axis to be approximated by rectangles, no matter how thin they are. We show, in fact, that upper sum approximations and lower sum approximations converge to different limiting values.

If we pick a partition P of $[0, 1]$ and choose c_k to be the maximum value for f on $[x_{k-1}, x_k]$ then the corresponding Riemann sum is

$$U = \sum_{k=1}^{n} f(c_k)\,\Delta x_k = \sum_{k=1}^{n} (1)\,\Delta x_k = 1,$$

since each subinterval $[x_{k-1}, x_k]$ contains a rational number where $f(c_k) = 1$. Note that the lengths of the intervals in the partition sum to 1, $\sum_{k=1}^{n} \Delta x_k = 1$. So each such Riemann sum equals 1, and a limit of Riemann sums using these choices equals 1.

On the other hand, if we pick c_k to be the minimum value for f on $[x_{k-1}, x_k]$, then the Riemann sum is

$$L = \sum_{k=1}^{n} f(c_k)\,\Delta x_k = \sum_{k=1}^{n} (0)\,\Delta x_k = 0,$$

since each subinterval $[x_{k-1}, x_k]$ contains an irrational number c_k where $f(c_k) = 0$. The limit of Riemann sums using these choices equals zero. Since the limit depends on the choices of c_k, the function f is not integrable. ∎

Properties of Definite Integrals

In defining $\int_a^b f(x)\,dx$ as a limit of sums $\sum_{k=1}^{n} f(c_k)\,\Delta x_k$, we moved from left to right across the interval $[a, b]$. What would happen if we instead move right to left, starting with $x_0 = b$ and ending at $x_n = a$. Each Δx_k in the Riemann sum would change its sign, with $x_k - x_{k-1}$ now negative instead of positive. With the same choices of c_k in each subinterval, the sign of any Riemann sum would change, as would the sign of the limit, the integral

$\int_b^a f(x)\, dx$. Since we have not previously given a meaning to integrating backward, we are led to define

$$\int_b^a f(x)\, dx = -\int_a^b f(x)\, dx.$$

Another extension of the integral is to an interval of zero width, when $a = b$. Since $f(c_k)\, \Delta x_k$ is zero when the interval width $\Delta x_k = 0$, we define

$$\int_a^a f(x)\, dx = 0.$$

Theorem 2 states seven properties of integrals, given as rules that they satisfy, including the two above. These rules become very useful in the process of computing integrals. We will refer to them repeatedly to simplify our calculations.

Rules 2 through 7 have geometric interpretations, shown in Figure 5.11. The graphs in these figures are of positive functions, but the rules apply to general integrable functions.

THEOREM 2

When f and g are integrable, the definite integral satisfies Rules 1 to 7 in Table 5.3.

TABLE 5.3 Rules satisfied by definite integrals

1.	*Order of Integration:*	$\displaystyle\int_b^a f(x)\, dx = -\int_a^b f(x)\, dx$	A Definition
2.	*Zero Width Interval:*	$\displaystyle\int_a^a f(x)\, dx = 0$	Also a Definition
3.	*Constant Multiple:*	$\displaystyle\int_a^b kf(x)\, dx = k\int_a^b f(x)\, dx$	Any Number k
		$\displaystyle\int_a^b -f(x)\, dx = -\int_a^b f(x)\, dx$	$k = -1$
4.	*Sum and Difference:*	$\displaystyle\int_a^b (f(x) \pm g(x))\, dx = \int_a^b f(x)\, dx \pm \int_a^b g(x)\, dx$	
5.	*Additivity:*	$\displaystyle\int_a^b f(x)\, dx + \int_b^c f(x)\, dx = \int_a^c f(x)\, dx$	
6.	*Max-Min Inequality:*	If f has maximum value max f and minimum value min f on $[a, b]$, then	

$$\min f \cdot (b - a) \le \int_a^b f(x)\, dx \le \max f \cdot (b - a).$$

7.	*Domination:*	$f(x) \ge g(x)$ on $[a, b] \Rightarrow \displaystyle\int_a^b f(x)\, dx \ge \int_a^b g(x)\, dx$	

$$f(x) \ge 0 \text{ on } [a, b] \Rightarrow \int_a^b f(x)\, dx \ge 0 \quad \text{(Special Case)}$$

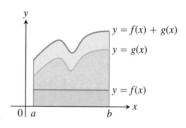

(a) *Zero Width Interval*:

$$\int_a^a f(x)\,dx = 0.$$

(The area over a point is 0.)

(b) *Constant Multiple*:

$$\int_a^b kf(x)\,dx = k\int_a^b f(x)\,dx.$$

(Shown for $k = 2$.)

(c) *Sum*:

$$\int_a^b (f(x) + g(x))\,dx = \int_a^b f(x)\,dx + \int_a^b g(x)\,dx$$

(Areas add)

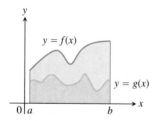

(d) *Additivity for definite integrals*:

$$\int_a^b f(x)\,dx + \int_b^c f(x)\,dx = \int_a^c f(x)\,dx$$

(e) *Max-Min Inequality*:

$$\min f \cdot (b - a) \le \int_a^b f(x)\,dx$$
$$\le \max f \cdot (b - a)$$

(f) *Domination*:

$$f(x) \ge g(x) \text{ on } [a, b]$$
$$\Rightarrow \int_a^b f(x)\,dx \ge \int_a^b g(x)\,dx$$

FIGURE 5.11

While Rules 1 and 2 are definitions, Rules 3 to 7 of Table 5.3 must be proved. The proofs are based on the definition of the definite integral as a limit of Riemann sums. The following is a proof of one of these rules. Similar proofs can be given to verify the other properties in Table 5.3.

Proof of Rule 6   Rule 6 says that the integral of f over $[a, b]$ is never smaller than the minimum value of f times the length of the interval and never larger than the maximum value of f times the length of the interval. The reason is that for every partition of $[a, b]$ and for every choice of the points c_k,

$$\min f \cdot (b - a) = \min f \cdot \sum_{k=1}^{n} \Delta x_k \qquad \sum_{k=1}^{n} \Delta x_k = b - a$$

$$= \sum_{k=1}^{n} \min f \cdot \Delta x_k \qquad \text{Constant Multiple Rule}$$

$$\le \sum_{k=1}^{n} f(c_k)\, \Delta x_k \qquad \min f \le f(c_k)$$

$$\le \sum_{k=1}^{n} \max f \cdot \Delta x_k \qquad f(c_k) \le \max f$$

$$= \max f \cdot \sum_{k=1}^{n} \Delta x_k \qquad \text{Constant Multiple Rule}$$

$$= \max f \cdot (b - a).$$

In short, all Riemann sums for f on $[a, b]$ satisfy the inequality

$$\min f \cdot (b - a) \le \sum_{k=1}^{n} f(c_k) \, \Delta x_k \le \max f \cdot (b - a).$$

Hence their limit, the integral, does too. ∎

EXAMPLE 2   Using the Rules for Definite Integrals

Suppose that

$$\int_{-1}^{1} f(x) \, dx = 5, \qquad \int_{1}^{4} f(x) \, dx = -2, \qquad \int_{-1}^{1} h(x) \, dx = 7.$$

Then

1. $\displaystyle\int_{4}^{1} f(x) \, dx = -\int_{1}^{4} f(x) \, dx = -(-2) = 2$ Rule 1

2. $\displaystyle\int_{-1}^{1} [2f(x) + 3h(x)] \, dx = 2\int_{-1}^{1} f(x) \, dx + 3\int_{-1}^{1} h(x) \, dx$ Rules 3 and 4

$$= 2(5) + 3(7) = 31$$

3. $\displaystyle\int_{-1}^{4} f(x) \, dx = \int_{-1}^{1} f(x) \, dx + \int_{1}^{4} f(x) \, dx = 5 + (-2) = 3$ Rule 5   ∎

EXAMPLE 3   Finding Bounds for an Integral

Show that the value of $\int_{0}^{1} \sqrt{1 + \cos x} \, dx$ is less than $3/2$.

Solution   The Max-Min Inequality for definite integrals (Rule 6) says that $\min f \cdot (b - a)$ is a *lower bound* for the value of $\int_{a}^{b} f(x) \, dx$ and that $\max f \cdot (b - a)$ is an *upper bound*. The maximum value of $\sqrt{1 + \cos x}$ on $[0, 1]$ is $\sqrt{1 + 1} = \sqrt{2}$, so

$$\int_{0}^{1} \sqrt{1 + \cos x} \, dx \le \sqrt{2} \cdot (1 - 0) = \sqrt{2}.$$

Since $\int_{0}^{1} \sqrt{1 + \cos x} \, dx$ is bounded from above by $\sqrt{2}$ (which is $1.414 \ldots$), the integral is less than $3/2$. ∎

Area Under the Graph of a Nonnegative Function

We now make precise the notion of the area of a region with curved boundary, capturing the idea of approximating a region by increasingly many rectangles. The area under the graph of a nonnegative continuous function is defined to be a definite integral.

DEFINITION   Area Under a Curve as a Definite Integral

If $y = f(x)$ is nonnegative and integrable over a closed interval $[a, b]$, then the **area under the curve $y = f(x)$ over $[a, b]$** is the integral of f from a to b,

$$A = \int_{a}^{b} f(x) \, dx.$$

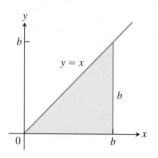

FIGURE 5.12 The region in Example 4 is a triangle.

For the first time we have a rigorous definition for the area of a region whose boundary is the graph of any continuous function. We now apply this to a simple example, the area under a straight line, where we can verify that our new definition agrees with our previous notion of area.

EXAMPLE 4   Area Under the Line $y = x$

Compute $\int_0^b x \, dx$ and find the area A under $y = x$ over the interval $[0, b]$, $b > 0$.

Solution   The region of interest is a triangle (Figure 5.12). We compute the area in two ways.

(a) To compute the definite integral as the limit of Riemann sums, we calculate $\lim_{\|P\|\to 0} \sum_{k=1}^{n} f(c_k) \, \Delta x_k$ for partitions whose norms go to zero. Theorem 1 tells us that it does not matter how we choose the partitions or the points c_k as long as the norms approach zero. All choices give the exact same limit. So we consider the partition P that subdivides the interval $[0, b]$ into n subintervals of equal width $\Delta x = (b - 0)/n = b/n$, and we choose c_k to be the right endpoint in each subinterval. The partition is

$$P = \left\{ 0, \frac{b}{n}, \frac{2b}{n}, \frac{3b}{n}, \cdots, \frac{nb}{n} \right\} \text{ and } c_k = \frac{kb}{n}. \text{ So}$$

$$\sum_{k=1}^{n} f(c_k) \, \Delta x = \sum_{k=1}^{n} \frac{kb}{n} \cdot \frac{b}{n} \qquad f(c_k) = c_k$$

$$= \sum_{k=1}^{n} \frac{kb^2}{n^2}$$

$$= \frac{b^2}{n^2} \sum_{k=1}^{n} k \qquad \text{Constant Multiple Rule}$$

$$= \frac{b^2}{n^2} \cdot \frac{n(n + 1)}{2} \qquad \text{Sum of First } n \text{ Integers}$$

$$= \frac{b^2}{2} \left(1 + \frac{1}{n}\right)$$

As $n \to \infty$ and $\|P\| \to 0$, this last expression on the right has the limit $b^2/2$. Therefore,

$$\int_0^b x \, dx = \frac{b^2}{2}.$$

(b) Since the area equals the definite integral for a nonnegative function, we can quickly derive the definite integral by using the formula for the area of a triangle having base length b and height $y = b$. The area is $A = (1/2) \, b \cdot b = b^2/2$. Again we have that $\int_0^b x \, dx = b^2/2$. ∎

Example 4 can be generalized to integrate $f(x) = x$ over any closed interval $[a, b]$, $0 < a < b$.

$$\int_a^b x \, dx = \int_a^0 x \, dx + \int_0^b x \, dx \qquad \text{Rule 5}$$

$$= -\int_0^a x \, dx + \int_0^b x \, dx \qquad \text{Rule 1}$$

$$= -\frac{a^2}{2} + \frac{b^2}{2}. \qquad \text{Example 4}$$

In conclusion, we have the following rule for integrating $f(x) = x$:

$$\int_a^b x\, dx = \frac{b^2}{2} - \frac{a^2}{2}, \qquad a < b \tag{1}$$

This computation gives the area of a trapezoid (Figure 5.13). Equation (1) remains valid when a and b are negative. When $a < b < 0$, the definite integral value $(b^2 - a^2)/2$ is a negative number, the negative of the area of a trapezoid dropping down to the line $y = x$ below the x-axis. When $a < 0$ and $b > 0$, Equation (1) is still valid and the definite integral gives the difference between two areas, the area under the graph and above $[0, b]$ minus the area below $[a, 0]$ and over the graph.

The following results can also be established using a Riemann sum calculation similar to that in Example 4 (Exercises 75 and 76).

$$\int_a^b c\, dx = c(b - a), \qquad c \text{ any constant} \tag{2}$$

$$\int_a^b x^2\, dx = \frac{b^3}{3} - \frac{a^3}{3}, \qquad a < b \tag{3}$$

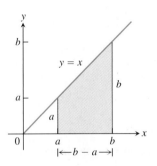

FIGURE 5.13 The area of this trapezoidal region is $A = (b^2 - a^2)/2$.

Average Value of a Continuous Function Revisited

In Section 5.1 we introduced informally the average value of a nonnegative continuous function f over an interval $[a, b]$, leading us to define this average as the area under the graph of $y = f(x)$ divided by $b - a$. In integral notation we write this as

$$\text{Average} = \frac{1}{b - a} \int_a^b f(x)\, dx.$$

We can use this formula to give a precise definition of the average value of any continuous (or integrable) function, whether positive, negative or both.

Alternately, we can use the following reasoning. We start with the idea from arithmetic that the average of n numbers is their sum divided by n. A continuous function f on $[a, b]$ may have infinitely many values, but we can still sample them in an orderly way. We divide $[a, b]$ into n subintervals of equal width $\Delta x = (b - a)/n$ and evaluate f at a point c_k in each (Figure 5.14). The average of the n sampled values is

$$\frac{f(c_1) + f(c_2) + \cdots + f(c_n)}{n} = \frac{1}{n} \sum_{k=1}^n f(c_k)$$

$$= \frac{\Delta x}{b - a} \sum_{k=1}^n f(c_k) \qquad \Delta x = \frac{b - a}{n}, \text{ so } \frac{1}{n} = \frac{\Delta x}{b - a}$$

$$= \frac{1}{b - a} \sum_{k=1}^n f(c_k)\, \Delta x$$

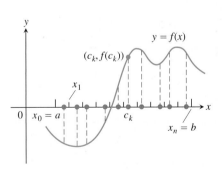

FIGURE 5.14 A sample of values of a function on an interval $[a, b]$.

The average is obtained by dividing a Riemann sum for f on $[a, b]$ by $(b - a)$. As we increase the size of the sample and let the norm of the partition approach zero, the average approaches $(1/(b - a)) \int_a^b f(x) \, dx$. Both points of view lead us to the following definition.

DEFINITION   The Average or Mean Value of a Function

If f is integrable on $[a, b]$, then its **average value on** $[a, b]$, also called its **mean value**, is

$$\text{av}(f) = \frac{1}{b - a} \int_a^b f(x) \, dx.$$

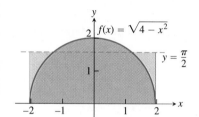

FIGURE 5.15   The average value of $f(x) = \sqrt{4 - x^2}$ on $[-2, 2]$ is $\pi/2$ (Example 5).

EXAMPLE 5   Finding an Average Value

Find the average value of $f(x) = \sqrt{4 - x^2}$ on $[-2, 2]$.

Solution   We recognize $f(x) = \sqrt{4 - x^2}$ as a function whose graph is the upper semicircle of radius 2 centered at the origin (Figure 5.15).

The area between the semicircle and the x-axis from -2 to 2 can be computed using the geometry formula

$$\text{Area} = \frac{1}{2} \cdot \pi r^2 = \frac{1}{2} \cdot \pi (2)^2 = 2\pi.$$

Because f is nonnegative, the area is also the value of the integral of f from -2 to 2,

$$\int_{-2}^2 \sqrt{4 - x^2} \, dx = 2\pi.$$

Therefore, the average value of f is

$$\text{av}(f) = \frac{1}{2 - (-2)} \int_{-2}^2 \sqrt{4 - x^2} \, dx = \frac{1}{4} (2\pi) = \frac{\pi}{2}. \qquad \blacksquare$$

EXERCISES 5.3

Expressing Limits as Integrals

Express the limits in Exercises 1–8 as definite integrals.

1. $\displaystyle \lim_{\|P\| \to 0} \sum_{k=1}^n c_k^2 \, \Delta x_k$, where P is a partition of $[0, 2]$

2. $\displaystyle \lim_{\|P\| \to 0} \sum_{k=1}^n 2c_k^3 \, \Delta x_k$, where P is a partition of $[-1, 0]$

3. $\displaystyle \lim_{\|P\| \to 0} \sum_{k=1}^n (c_k^2 - 3c_k) \, \Delta x_k$, where P is a partition of $[-7, 5]$

4. $\displaystyle \lim_{\|P\| \to 0} \sum_{k=1}^n \left(\frac{1}{c_k} \right) \Delta x_k$, where P is a partition of $[1, 4]$

5. $\displaystyle \lim_{\|P\| \to 0} \sum_{k=1}^n \frac{1}{1 - c_k} \Delta x_k$, where P is a partition of $[2, 3]$

6. $\displaystyle \lim_{\|P\| \to 0} \sum_{k=1}^n \sqrt{4 - c_k^2} \, \Delta x_k$, where P is a partition of $[0, 1]$

7. $\displaystyle \lim_{\|P\| \to 0} \sum_{k=1}^n (\sec c_k) \, \Delta x_k$, where P is a partition of $[-\pi/4, 0]$

8. $\displaystyle \lim_{\|P\| \to 0} \sum_{k=1}^n (\tan c_k) \, \Delta x_k$, where P is a partition of $[0, \pi/4]$

Using Properties and Known Values to Find Other Integrals

9. Suppose that f and g are integrable and that

$$\int_1^2 f(x)\,dx = -4, \quad \int_1^5 f(x)\,dx = 6, \quad \int_1^5 g(x)\,dx = 8.$$

Use the rules in Table 5.3 to find

a. $\displaystyle\int_2^2 g(x)\,dx$

b. $\displaystyle\int_5^1 g(x)\,dx$

c. $\displaystyle\int_1^2 3f(x)\,dx$

d. $\displaystyle\int_2^5 f(x)\,dx$

e. $\displaystyle\int_1^5 [f(x) - g(x)]\,dx$

f. $\displaystyle\int_1^5 [4f(x) - g(x)]\,dx$

10. Suppose that f and h are integrable and that

$$\int_1^9 f(x)\,dx = -1, \quad \int_7^9 f(x)\,dx = 5, \quad \int_7^9 h(x)\,dx = 4.$$

Use the rules in Table 5.3 to find

a. $\displaystyle\int_1^9 -2f(x)\,dx$

b. $\displaystyle\int_7^9 [f(x) + h(x)]\,dx$

c. $\displaystyle\int_7^9 [2f(x) - 3h(x)]\,dx$

d. $\displaystyle\int_9^1 f(x)\,dx$

e. $\displaystyle\int_1^7 f(x)\,dx$

f. $\displaystyle\int_9^7 [h(x) - f(x)]\,dx$

11. Suppose that $\int_1^2 f(x)\,dx = 5$. Find

a. $\displaystyle\int_1^2 f(u)\,du$

b. $\displaystyle\int_1^2 \sqrt{3}f(z)\,dz$

c. $\displaystyle\int_2^1 f(t)\,dt$

d. $\displaystyle\int_1^2 [-f(x)]\,dx$

12. Suppose that $\int_{-3}^0 g(t)\,dt = \sqrt{2}$. Find

a. $\displaystyle\int_0^{-3} g(t)\,dt$

b. $\displaystyle\int_{-3}^0 g(u)\,du$

c. $\displaystyle\int_{-3}^0 [-g(x)]\,dx$

d. $\displaystyle\int_{-3}^0 \frac{g(r)}{\sqrt{2}}\,dr$

13. Suppose that f is integrable and that $\int_0^3 f(z)\,dz = 3$ and $\int_0^4 f(z)\,dz = 7$. Find

a. $\displaystyle\int_3^4 f(z)\,dz$

b. $\displaystyle\int_4^3 f(t)\,dt$

14. Suppose that h is integrable and that $\int_{-1}^1 h(r)\,dr = 0$ and $\int_{-1}^3 h(r)\,dr = 6$. Find

a. $\displaystyle\int_1^3 h(r)\,dr$

b. $-\displaystyle\int_3^1 h(u)\,du$

Using Area to Evaluate Definite Integrals

In Exercises 15–22, graph the integrands and use areas to evaluate the integrals.

15. $\displaystyle\int_{-2}^4 \left(\frac{x}{2} + 3\right) dx$

16. $\displaystyle\int_{1/2}^{3/2} (-2x + 4)\,dx$

17. $\displaystyle\int_{-3}^3 \sqrt{9 - x^2}\,dx$

18. $\displaystyle\int_{-4}^0 \sqrt{16 - x^2}\,dx$

19. $\displaystyle\int_{-2}^1 |x|\,dx$

20. $\displaystyle\int_{-1}^1 (1 - |x|)\,dx$

21. $\displaystyle\int_{-1}^1 (2 - |x|)\,dx$

22. $\displaystyle\int_{-1}^1 \left(1 + \sqrt{1 - x^2}\right) dx$

Use areas to evaluate the integrals in Exercises 23–26.

23. $\displaystyle\int_0^b \frac{x}{2}\,dx, \quad b > 0$

24. $\displaystyle\int_0^b 4x\,dx, \quad b > 0$

25. $\displaystyle\int_a^b 2s\,ds, \quad 0 < a < b$

26. $\displaystyle\int_a^b 3t\,dt, \quad 0 < a < b$

Evaluations

Use the results of Equations (1) and (3) to evaluate the integrals in Exercises 27–38.

27. $\displaystyle\int_1^{\sqrt{2}} x\,dx$

28. $\displaystyle\int_{0.5}^{2.5} x\,dx$

29. $\displaystyle\int_\pi^{2\pi} \theta\,d\theta$

30. $\displaystyle\int_{\sqrt{2}}^{5\sqrt{2}} r\,dr$

31. $\displaystyle\int_0^{\sqrt[3]{7}} x^2\,dx$

32. $\displaystyle\int_0^{0.3} s^2\,ds$

33. $\displaystyle\int_0^{1/2} t^2\,dt$

34. $\displaystyle\int_0^{\pi/2} \theta^2\,d\theta$

35. $\displaystyle\int_a^{2a} x\,dx$

36. $\displaystyle\int_a^{\sqrt{3}a} x\,dx$

37. $\displaystyle\int_0^{\sqrt[3]{b}} x^2\,dx$

38. $\displaystyle\int_0^{3b} x^2\,dx$

Use the rules in Table 5.3 and Equations (1)–(3) to evaluate the integrals in Exercises 39–50.

39. $\displaystyle\int_3^1 7\,dx$

40. $\displaystyle\int_0^{-2} \sqrt{2}\,dx$

41. $\displaystyle\int_0^2 5x\,dx$

42. $\displaystyle\int_3^5 \frac{x}{8}\,dx$

43. $\displaystyle\int_0^2 (2t - 3)\,dt$

44. $\displaystyle\int_0^{\sqrt{2}} \left(t - \sqrt{2}\right) dt$

45. $\displaystyle\int_2^1 \left(1 + \frac{z}{2}\right) dz$

46. $\displaystyle\int_3^0 (2z - 3)\,dz$

47. $\displaystyle\int_1^2 3u^2\,du$

48. $\displaystyle\int_{1/2}^1 24u^2\,du$

49. $\displaystyle\int_0^2 (3x^2 + x - 5)\,dx$

50. $\displaystyle\int_1^0 (3x^2 + x - 5)\,dx$

Finding Area

In Exercises 51–54 use a definite integral to find the area of the region between the given curve and the x-axis on the interval $[0, b]$.

51. $y = 3x^2$

52. $y = \pi x^2$

53. $y = 2x$

54. $y = \frac{x}{2} + 1$

Average Value

In Exercises 55–62, graph the function and find its average value over the given interval.

55. $f(x) = x^2 - 1$ on $[0, \sqrt{3}]$

56. $f(x) = -\dfrac{x^2}{2}$ on $[0, 3]$ **57.** $f(x) = -3x^2 - 1$ on $[0, 1]$

58. $f(x) = 3x^2 - 3$ on $[0, 1]$

59. $f(t) = (t - 1)^2$ on $[0, 3]$

60. $f(t) = t^2 - t$ on $[-2, 1]$

61. $g(x) = |x| - 1$ on   **a.** $[-1, 1]$, **b.** $[1, 3]$, and **c.** $[-1, 3]$

62. $h(x) = -|x|$ on   **a.** $[-1, 0]$, **b.** $[0, 1]$, and **c.** $[-1, 1]$

Theory and Examples

63. What values of a and b maximize the value of

$$\int_a^b (x - x^2)\, dx?$$

(*Hint:* Where is the integrand positive?)

64. What values of a and b minimize the value of

$$\int_a^b (x^4 - 2x^2)\, dx?$$

65. Use the Max-Min Inequality to find upper and lower bounds for the value of

$$\int_0^1 \frac{1}{1 + x^2}\, dx.$$

66. (*Continuation of Exercise 65*) Use the Max-Min Inequality to find upper and lower bounds for

$$\int_0^{0.5} \frac{1}{1 + x^2}\, dx \quad \text{and} \quad \int_{0.5}^1 \frac{1}{1 + x^2}\, dx.$$

Add these to arrive at an improved estimate of

$$\int_0^1 \frac{1}{1 + x^2}\, dx.$$

67. Show that the value of $\int_0^1 \sin(x^2)\, dx$ cannot possibly be 2.

68. Show that the value of $\int_1^0 \sqrt{x + 8}\, dx$ lies between $2\sqrt{2} \approx 2.8$ and 3.

69. Integrals of nonnegative functions   Use the Max-Min Inequality to show that if f is integrable then

$$f(x) \geq 0 \quad \text{on} \quad [a, b] \quad \Rightarrow \quad \int_a^b f(x)\, dx \geq 0.$$

70. Integrals of nonpositive functions   Show that if f is integrable then

$$f(x) \leq 0 \quad \text{on} \quad [a, b] \quad \Rightarrow \quad \int_a^b f(x)\, dx \leq 0.$$

71. Use the inequality $\sin x \leq x$, which holds for $x \geq 0$, to find an upper bound for the value of $\int_0^1 \sin x\, dx$.

72. The inequality $\sec x \geq 1 + (x^2/2)$ holds on $(-\pi/2, \pi/2)$. Use it to find a lower bound for the value of $\int_0^1 \sec x\, dx$.

73. If av(f) really is a typical value of the integrable function $f(x)$ on $[a, b]$, then the number av(f) should have the same integral over $[a, b]$ that f does. Does it? That is, does

$$\int_a^b av(f)\, dx = \int_a^b f(x)\, dx?$$

Give reasons for your answer.

74. It would be nice if average values of integrable functions obeyed the following rules on an interval $[a, b]$.

a. $av(f + g) = av(f) + av(g)$

b. $av(kf) = k\, av(f)$ (any number k)

c. $av(f) \leq av(g)$ if $f(x) \leq g(x)$ on $[a, b]$.

Do these rules ever hold? Give reasons for your answers.

75. Use limits of Riemann sums as in Example 4a to establish Equation (2).

76. Use limits of Riemann sums as in Example 4a to establish Equation (3).

77. Upper and lower sums for increasing functions

a. Suppose the graph of a continuous function $f(x)$ rises steadily as x moves from left to right across an interval $[a, b]$. Let P be a partition of $[a, b]$ into n subintervals of length $\Delta x = (b - a)/n$. Show by referring to the accompanying figure that the difference between the upper and lower sums for f on this partition can be represented graphically as the area of a rectangle R whose dimensions are $[f(b) - f(a)]$ by Δx. (*Hint:* The difference $U - L$ is the sum of areas of rectangles whose diagonals $Q_0Q_1, Q_1Q_2, \ldots, Q_{n-1}Q_n$ lie along the curve. There is no overlapping when these rectangles are shifted horizontally onto R.)

b. Suppose that instead of being equal, the lengths Δx_k of the subintervals of the partition of $[a, b]$ vary in size. Show that

$$U - L \leq |f(b) - f(a)|\, \Delta x_{max},$$

where Δx_{max} is the norm of P, and hence that $\lim_{\|P\| \to 0} (U - L) = 0$.

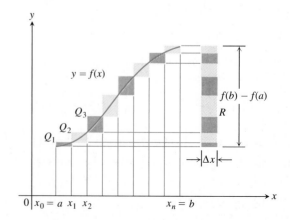

78. Upper and lower sums for decreasing functions (*Continuation of Exercise 77*)

a. Draw a figure like the one in Exercise 77 for a continuous function $f(x)$ whose values decrease steadily as x moves from left to right across the interval $[a, b]$. Let P be a partition of $[a, b]$ into subintervals of equal length. Find an expression for $U - L$ that is analogous to the one you found for $U - L$ in Exercise 77a.

b. Suppose that instead of being equal, the lengths Δx_k of the subintervals of P vary in size. Show that the inequality

$$U - L \le |f(b) - f(a)| \, \Delta x_{max}$$

of Exercise 77b still holds and hence that $\lim_{\|P\| \to 0} (U - L) = 0$.

79. Use the formula

$$\sin h + \sin 2h + \sin 3h + \cdots + \sin mh$$
$$= \frac{\cos (h/2) - \cos ((m + (1/2))h)}{2 \sin (h/2)}$$

to find the area under the curve $y = \sin x$ from $x = 0$ to $x = \pi/2$ in two steps:

a. Partition the interval $[0, \pi/2]$ into n subintervals of equal length and calculate the corresponding upper sum U; then

b. Find the limit of U as $n \to \infty$ and $\Delta x = (b - a)/n \to 0$.

80. Suppose that f is continuous and nonnegative over $[a, b]$, as in the figure at the right. By inserting points

$$x_1, x_2, \ldots, x_{k-1}, x_k, \ldots, x_{n-1}$$

as shown, divide $[a, b]$ into n subintervals of lengths $\Delta x_1 = x_1 - a$, $\Delta x_2 = x_2 - x_1, \ldots, \Delta x_n = b - x_{n-1}$, which need not be equal.

a. If $m_k = \min \{f(x)$ for x in the kth subinterval$\}$, explain the connection between the *lower sum*

$$L = m_1 \Delta x_1 + m_2 \Delta x_2 + \cdots + m_n \Delta x_n$$

and the shaded region in the first part of the figure.

b. If $M_k = \max \{f(x)$ for x in the kth subinterval$\}$, explain the connection between the *upper sum*
$$U = M_1 \Delta x_1 + M_2 \Delta x_2 + \cdots + M_n \Delta x_n$$

and the shaded region in the second part of the figure.

c. Explain the connection between $U - L$ and the shaded regions along the curve in the third part of the figure.

81. We say f is **uniformly continuous** on $[a, b]$ if given any $\epsilon > 0$ there is a $\delta > 0$ such that if x_1, x_2 are in $[a, b]$ and $|x_1 - x_2| < \delta$ then $|f(x_1) - f(x_2)| < \epsilon$. It can be shown that a continuous function on $[a, b]$ is uniformly continuous. Use this and the figure at the right to show that if f is continuous and $\epsilon > 0$ is given, it is possible to make $U - L \le \epsilon \cdot (b - a)$ by making the largest of the Δx_k's sufficiently small.

82. If you average 30 mi/h on a 150-mi trip and then return over the same 150 mi at the rate of 50 mi/h, what is your average speed for the trip? Give reasons for your answer. (Source: David H.

Pleacher, *The Mathematics Teacher*, Vol. 85, No. 6, pp. 445–446, September 1992.)

COMPUTER EXPLORATIONS

Finding Riemann Sums

If your CAS can draw rectangles associated with Riemann sums, use it to draw rectangles associated with Riemann sums that converge to the integrals in Exercises 83–88. Use $n = 4, 10, 20$, and 50 subintervals of equal length in each case.

83. $\int_0^1 (1 - x) \, dx = \frac{1}{2}$ **84.** $\int_0^1 (x^2 + 1) \, dx = \frac{4}{3}$

85. $\int_{-\pi}^{\pi} \cos x \, dx = 0$ **86.** $\int_{0}^{\pi/4} \sec^2 x \, dx = 1$

87. $\int_{-1}^{1} |x| \, dx = 1$

88. $\int_{1}^{2} \frac{1}{x} \, dx$ (The integral's value is about 0.693.)

Average Value

In Exercises 89–92, use a CAS to perform the following steps:

a. Plot the functions over the given interval.

b. Partition the interval into $n = 100, 200$, and 1000 subintervals of equal length, and evaluate the function at the midpoint of each subinterval.

c. Compute the average value of the function values generated in part (b).

d. Solve the equation $f(x) = $ (average value) for x using the average value calculated in part (c) for the $n = 1000$ partitioning.

89. $f(x) = \sin x$ on $[0, \pi]$

90. $f(x) = \sin^2 x$ on $[0, \pi]$

91. $f(x) = x \sin \frac{1}{x}$ on $\left[\frac{\pi}{4}, \pi\right]$

92. $f(x) = x \sin^2 \frac{1}{x}$ on $\left[\frac{\pi}{4}, \pi\right]$

5.4   The Fundamental Theorem of Calculus

HISTORICAL BIOGRAPHY

Sir Isaac Newton
(1642–1727)

In this section we present the Fundamental Theorem of Calculus, which is the central theorem of integral calculus. It connects integration and differentiation, enabling us to compute integrals using an antiderivative of the integrand function rather than by taking limits of Riemann sums as we did in Section 5.3. Leibniz and Newton exploited this relationship and started mathematical developments that fueled the scientific revolution for the next 200 years.

Along the way, we present the integral version of the Mean Value Theorem, which is another important theorem of integral calculus and used to prove the Fundamental Theorem.

Mean Value Theorem for Definite Integrals

In the previous section, we defined the average value of a continuous function over a closed interval $[a, b]$ as the definite integral $\int_a^b f(x) \, dx$ divided by the length or width $b - a$ of the interval. The Mean Value Theorem for Definite Integrals asserts that this average value is *always* taken on at least once by the function f in the interval.

The graph in Figure 5.16 shows a *positive* continuous function $y = f(x)$ defined over the interval $[a, b]$. Geometrically, the Mean Value Theorem says that there is a number c in $[a, b]$ such that the rectangle with height equal to the average value $f(c)$ of the function and base width $b - a$ has exactly the same area as the region beneath the graph of f from a to b.

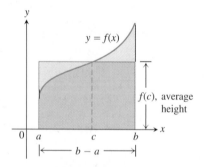

FIGURE 5.16   The value $f(c)$ in the Mean Value Theorem is, in a sense, the average (or *mean*) height of f on $[a, b]$. When $f \geq 0$, the area of the rectangle is the area under the graph of f from a to b,

$$f(c)(b - a) = \int_a^b f(x) \, dx.$$

THEOREM 3   **The Mean Value Theorem for Definite Integrals**

If f is continuous on $[a, b]$, then at some point c in $[a, b]$,

$$f(c) = \frac{1}{b - a} \int_a^b f(x) \, dx.$$

Proof If we divide both sides of the Max-Min Inequality (Table 5.3, Rule 6) by $(b - a)$, we obtain

$$\min f \le \frac{1}{b - a} \int_a^b f(x)\,dx \le \max f.$$

Since f is continuous, the Intermediate Value Theorem for Continuous Functions (Section 2.6) says that f must assume every value between $\min f$ and $\max f$. It must therefore assume the value $(1/(b - a)) \int_a^b f(x)\,dx$ at some point c in $[a, b]$. ∎

The continuity of f is important here. It is possible that a discontinuous function never equals its average value (Figure 5.17).

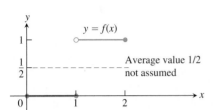

FIGURE 5.17 A discontinuous function need not assume its average value.

EXAMPLE 1 Applying the Mean Value Theorem for Integrals

Find the average value of $f(x) = 4 - x$ on $[0, 3]$ and where f actually takes on this value at some point in the given domain.

Solution

$$\begin{aligned}
\operatorname{av}(f) &= \frac{1}{b - a} \int_a^b f(x)\,dx \\
&= \frac{1}{3 - 0} \int_0^3 (4 - x)\,dx = \frac{1}{3}\left(\int_0^3 4\,dx - \int_0^3 x\,dx \right) \\
&= \frac{1}{3}\left(4(3 - 0) - \left(\frac{3^2}{2} - \frac{0^2}{2} \right) \right) \qquad \text{Section 5.3, Eqs. (1) and (2)} \\
&= 4 - \frac{3}{2} = \frac{5}{2}.
\end{aligned}$$

The average value of $f(x) = 4 - x$ over $[0, 3]$ is $5/2$. The function assumes this value when $4 - x = 5/2$ or $x = 3/2$, which is the point c in Theorem 3. (Figure 5.18) ∎

FIGURE 5.18 The area of the rectangle with base $[0, 3]$ and height $5/2$ (the average value of the function $f(x) = 4 - x$) is equal to the area between the graph of f and the x-axis from 0 to 3 (Example 1).

In Example 1, we actually found a point c where f assumed its average value by setting $f(x)$ equal to the calculated average value and solving for x. It's not always possible to solve easily for the value c. What else can we learn from the Mean Value Theorem for integrals? Here's an example.

EXAMPLE 2 Show that if f is continuous on $[a, b]$, $a \ne b$, and if

$$\int_a^b f(x)\,dx = 0,$$

then $f(x) = 0$ at least once in $[a, b]$.

Solution The average value of f on $[a, b]$ is

$$\operatorname{av}(f) = \frac{1}{b - a} \int_a^b f(x)\,dx = \frac{1}{b - a} \cdot 0 = 0.$$

By the Mean Value Theorem, f assumes this value at some point $c \in [a, b]$. ∎

Fundamental Theorem, Part 1

If $f(t)$ is an integrable function over a finite interval I, then the integral from any fixed number $a \in I$ to another number $x \in I$ defines a new function F whose value at x is

$$F(x) = \int_a^x f(t)\, dt. \tag{1}$$

For example, if f is nonnegative and x lies to the right of a, then $F(x)$ is the area under the graph from a to x (Figure 5.19). The variable x is the upper limit of integration of an integral, but F is just like any other real-valued function of a real variable. For each value of the input x, there is a well-defined numerical output, in this case the definite integral of f from a to x.

Equation (1) gives a way to define new functions, but its importance now is the connection it makes between integrals and derivatives. If f is any continuous function, then the Fundamental Theorem asserts that F is a differentiable function of x whose derivative is f itself. At every value of x,

$$\frac{d}{dx} F(x) = \frac{d}{dx} \int_a^x f(t)\, dt = f(x).$$

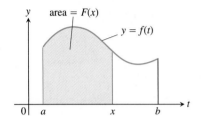

FIGURE 5.19 The function $F(x)$ defined by Equation (1) gives the area under the graph of f from a to x when f is nonnegative and $x > a$.

To gain some insight into why this result holds, we look at the geometry behind it.

If $f \geq 0$ on $[a, b]$, then the computation of $F'(x)$ from the definition of the derivative means taking the limit as $h \to 0$ of the difference quotient

$$\frac{F(x + h) - F(x)}{h}.$$

For $h > 0$, the numerator is obtained by subtracting two areas, so it is the area under the graph of f from x to $x + h$ (Figure 5.20). If h is small, this area is approximately equal to the area of the rectangle of height $f(x)$ and width h, which can be seen from Figure 5.20. That is,

$$F(x + h) - F(x) \approx hf(x).$$

Dividing both sides of this approximation by h and letting $h \to 0$, it is reasonable to expect that

$$F'(x) = \lim_{h \to 0} \frac{F(x + h) - F(x)}{h} = f(x).$$

This result is true even if the function f is not positive, and it forms the first part of the Fundamental Theorem of Calculus.

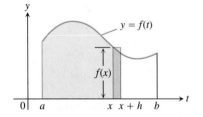

FIGURE 5.20 In Equation (1), $F(x)$ is the area to the left of x. Also, $F(x + h)$ is the area to the left of $x + h$. The difference quotient $[F(x + h) - F(x)]/h$ is then approximately equal to $f(x)$, the height of the rectangle shown here.

THEOREM 4   The Fundamental Theorem of Calculus, Part 1

If f is continuous on $[a, b]$ then $F(x) = \int_a^x f(t)\, dt$ is continuous on $[a, b]$ and differentiable on (a, b) and its derivative is $f(x)$;

$$F'(x) = \frac{d}{dx} \int_a^x f(t)\, dt = f(x). \tag{2}$$

Before proving Theorem 4, we look at several examples to gain a better understanding of what it says.

EXAMPLE 3   Applying the Fundamental Theorem

Use the Fundamental Theorem to find

(a) $\dfrac{d}{dx}\displaystyle\int_a^x \cos t\, dt$

(b) $\dfrac{d}{dx}\displaystyle\int_0^x \dfrac{1}{1+t^2}\, dt$

(c) $\dfrac{dy}{dx}$ if $y = \displaystyle\int_x^5 3t \sin t\, dt$

(d) $\dfrac{dy}{dx}$ if $y = \displaystyle\int_1^{x^2} \cos t\, dt$

Solution

(a) $\dfrac{d}{dx}\displaystyle\int_a^x \cos t\, dt = \cos x$ Eq. 2 with $f(t) = \cos t$

(b) $\dfrac{d}{dx}\displaystyle\int_0^x \dfrac{1}{1+t^2}\, dt = \dfrac{1}{1+x^2}$ Eq. 2 with $f(t) = \dfrac{1}{1+t^2}$

(c) Rule 1 for integrals in Table 5.3 of Section 5.3 sets this up for the Fundamental Theorem.

$$\dfrac{dy}{dx} = \dfrac{d}{dx}\int_x^5 3t \sin t\, dt = \dfrac{d}{dx}\left(-\int_5^x 3t \sin t\, dt\right) \quad \text{Rule 1}$$

$$= -\dfrac{d}{dx}\int_5^x 3t \sin t\, dt$$

$$= -3x \sin x$$

(d) The upper limit of integration is not x but x^2. This makes y a composite of the two functions,

$$y = \int_1^u \cos t\, dt \qquad \text{and} \qquad u = x^2.$$

We must therefore apply the Chain Rule when finding dy/dx.

$$\dfrac{dy}{dx} = \dfrac{dy}{du} \cdot \dfrac{du}{dx}$$

$$= \left(\dfrac{d}{du}\int_1^u \cos t\, dt\right) \cdot \dfrac{du}{dx}$$

$$= \cos u \cdot \dfrac{du}{dx}$$

$$= \cos(x^2) \cdot 2x$$

$$= 2x \cos x^2$$

∎

EXAMPLE 4   Constructing a Function with a Given Derivative and Value

Find a function $y = f(x)$ on the domain $(-\pi/2, \pi/2)$ with derivative

$$\frac{dy}{dx} = \tan x$$

that satisfies the condition $f(3) = 5$.

Solution   The Fundamental Theorem makes it easy to construct a function with derivative $\tan x$ that equals 0 at $x = 3$:

$$y = \int_3^x \tan t \, dt.$$

Since $y(3) = \int_3^3 \tan t \, dt = 0$, we have only to add 5 to this function to construct one with derivative $\tan x$ whose value at $x = 3$ is 5:

$$f(x) = \int_3^x \tan t \, dt + 5. \qquad \blacksquare$$

Although the solution to the problem in Example 4 satisfies the two required conditions, you might ask whether it is in a useful form. The answer is yes, since today we have computers and calculators that are capable of approximating integrals. In Chapter 7 we will learn to write the solution in Example 4 exactly as

$$y = \ln\left|\frac{\cos 3}{\cos x}\right| + 5.$$

We now give a proof of the Fundamental Theorem for an arbitrary continuous function.

Proof of Theorem 4   We prove the Fundamental Theorem by applying the definition of the derivative directly to the function $F(x)$, when x and $x + h$ are in (a, b). This means writing out the difference quotient

$$\frac{F(x + h) - F(x)}{h} \qquad (3)$$

and showing that its limit as $h \to 0$ is the number $f(x)$ for each x in (a, b). Thus,

$$F'(x) = \lim_{h \to 0} \frac{F(x + h) - F(x)}{h}$$

$$= \lim_{h \to 0} \frac{1}{h}\left[\int_a^{x+h} f(t) \, dt - \int_a^x f(t) \, dt\right]$$

$$= \lim_{h \to 0} \frac{1}{h}\int_x^{x+h} f(t) \, dt \qquad \text{Table 5.3, Rule 5}$$

According to the Mean Value Theorem for Definite Integrals, the value before taking the limit in the last expression is one of the values taken on by f in the interval between x and $x + h$. That is, for some number c in this interval,

$$\frac{1}{h} \int_x^{x+h} f(t)\, dt = f(c). \tag{4}$$

As $h \to 0$, $x + h$ approaches x, forcing c to approach x also (because c is trapped between x and $x + h$). Since f is continuous at x, $f(c)$ approaches $f(x)$:

$$\lim_{h \to 0} f(c) = f(x). \tag{5}$$

In conclusion, we have

$$F'(x) = \lim_{h \to 0} \frac{1}{h} \int_x^{x+h} f(t)\, dt$$

$$= \lim_{h \to 0} f(c) \qquad\qquad \text{Eq. (4)}$$

$$= f(x). \qquad\qquad\qquad \text{Eq. (5)}$$

If $x = a$ or b, then the limit of Equation (3) is interpreted as a one-sided limit with $h \to 0^+$ or $h \to 0^-$, respectively. Then Theorem 1 in Section 3.1 shows that F is continuous for every point of $[a, b]$. This concludes the proof. ∎

Fundamental Theorem, Part 2 (The Evaluation Theorem)

We now come to the second part of the Fundamental Theorem of Calculus. This part describes how to evaluate definite integrals without having to calculate limits of Riemann sums. Instead we find and evaluate an antiderivative at the upper and lower limits of integration.

THEOREM 4 (Continued)   **The Fundamental Theorem of Calculus, Part 2**

If f is continuous at every point of $[a, b]$ and F is any antiderivative of f on $[a, b]$, then

$$\int_a^b f(x)\, dx = F(b) - F(a).$$

Proof Part 1 of the Fundamental Theorem tells us that an antiderivative of f exists, namely

$$G(x) = \int_a^x f(t)\, dt.$$

Thus, if F is *any* antiderivative of f, then $F(x) = G(x) + C$ for some constant C for $a < x < b$ (by Corollary 2 of the Mean Value Theorem for Derivatives, Section 4.2). Since both F and G are continuous on $[a, b]$, we see that $F(x) = G(x) + C$ also holds when $x = a$ and $x = b$ by taking one-sided limits (as $x \to a^+$ and $x \to b^-$).

Evaluating $F(b) - F(a)$, we have

$$
\begin{aligned}
F(b) - F(a) &= [G(b) + C] - [G(a) + C] \\
&= G(b) - G(a) \\
&= \int_a^b f(t)\, dt - \int_a^a f(t)\, dt \\
&= \int_a^b f(t)\, dt - 0 \\
&= \int_a^b f(t)\, dt.
\end{aligned}
$$
$\blacksquare$

The theorem says that to calculate the definite integral of f over $[a, b]$ all we need to do is:

1. Find an antiderivative F of f, and
2. Calculate the number $\int_a^b f(x)\, dx = F(b) - F(a)$.

The usual notation for $F(b) - F(a)$ is

$$
F(x) \Big]_a^b \quad \text{or} \quad \left[F(x) \right]_a^b,
$$

depending on whether F has one or more terms.

EXAMPLE 5   Evaluating Integrals

(a) $\displaystyle \int_0^\pi \cos x\, dx = \sin x \Big]_0^\pi = \sin \pi - \sin 0 = 0 - 0 = 0$

(b) $\displaystyle \int_{-\pi/4}^0 \sec x \tan x\, dx = \sec x \Big]_{-\pi/4}^0 = \sec 0 - \sec\left(-\frac{\pi}{4}\right) = 1 - \sqrt{2}$

(c) $\displaystyle \int_1^4 \left(\frac{3}{2}\sqrt{x} - \frac{4}{x^2} \right) dx = \left[x^{3/2} + \frac{4}{x} \right]_1^4$

$$
\begin{aligned}
&= \left[(4)^{3/2} + \frac{4}{4} \right] - \left[(1)^{3/2} + \frac{4}{1} \right] \\
&= [8 + 1] - [5] = 4.
\end{aligned}
$$
$\blacksquare$

The process used in Example 5 was much easier than a Riemann sum computation.

The conclusions of the Fundamental Theorem tell us several things. Equation (2) can be rewritten as

$$
\frac{d}{dx} \int_a^x f(t)\, dt = \frac{dF}{dx} = f(x),
$$

which says that if you first integrate the function f and then differentiate the result, you get the function f back again. Likewise, the equation

$$
\int_a^x \frac{dF}{dt}\, dt = \int_a^x f(t)\, dt = F(x) - F(a)
$$

says that if you first differentiate the function F and then integrate the result, you get the function F back (adjusted by an integration constant). In a sense, the processes of integration and differentiation are "inverses" of each other. The Fundamental Theorem also says that every continuous function f has an antiderivative F. And it says that the differential equation $dy/dx = f(x)$ has a solution (namely, the function $y = F(x)$) for every continuous function f.

Total Area

The Riemann sum contains terms such as $f(c_k)\,\Delta_k$ which give the area of a rectangle when $f(c_k)$ is positive. When $f(c_k)$ is negative, then the product $f(c_k)\,\Delta_k$ is the negative of the rectangle's area. When we add up such terms for a negative function we get the negative of the area between the curve and the x-axis. If we then take the absolute value, we obtain the correct positive area.

EXAMPLE 6   Finding Area Using Antiderivatives

Calculate the area bounded by the x-axis and the parabola $y = 6 - x - x^2$.

Solution   We find where the curve crosses the x-axis by setting

$$y = 0 = 6 - x - x^2 = (3 + x)(2 - x),$$

which gives

$$x = -3 \quad \text{or} \quad x = 2.$$

The curve is sketched in Figure 5.21, and is nonnegative on $[-3, 2]$.
The area is

$$\int_{-3}^{2} (6 - x - x^2)\,dx = \left[6x - \frac{x^2}{2} - \frac{x^3}{3} \right]_{-3}^{2}$$

$$= \left(12 - 2 - \frac{8}{3} \right) - \left(-18 - \frac{9}{2} + \frac{27}{3} \right) = 20\tfrac{5}{6}.$$

The curve in Figure 5.21 is an arch of a parabola, and it is interesting to note that the area under such an arch is exactly equal to two-thirds the base times the altitude:

$$\frac{2}{3}(5)\left(\frac{25}{4} \right) = \frac{125}{6} = 20\tfrac{5}{6}. \qquad \blacksquare$$

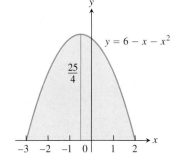

FIGURE 5.21   The area of this parabolic arch is calculated with a definite integral (Example 6).

To compute the area of the region bounded by the graph of a function $y = f(x)$ and the x-axis requires more care when the function takes on both positive and negative values. We must be careful to break up the interval $[a, b]$ into subintervals on which the function doesn't change sign. Otherwise we might get cancellation between positive and negative signed areas, leading to an incorrect total. The correct total area is obtained by adding the absolute value of the definite integral over each subinterval where $f(x)$ does not change sign. The term "area" will be taken to mean *total area*.

EXAMPLE 7   Canceling Areas

Figure 5.22 shows the graph of the function $f(x) = \sin x$ between $x = 0$ and $x = 2\pi$. Compute

(a) the definite integral of $f(x)$ over $[0, 2\pi]$.

(b) the area between the graph of $f(x)$ and the x-axis over $[0, 2\pi]$.

FIGURE 5.22   The total area between $y = \sin x$ and the x-axis for $0 \le x \le 2\pi$ is the sum of the absolute values of two integrals (Example 7).

Solution   The definite integral for $f(x) = \sin x$ is given by

$$\int_0^{2\pi} \sin x \, dx = -\cos x \Big]_0^{2\pi} = -[\cos 2\pi - \cos 0] = -[1 - 1] = 0.$$

The definite integral is zero because the portions of the graph above and below the x-axis make canceling contributions.

The area between the graph of $f(x)$ and the x-axis over $[0, 2\pi]$ is calculated by breaking up the domain of $\sin x$ into two pieces: the interval $[0, \pi]$ over which it is nonnegative and the interval $[\pi, 2\pi]$ over which it is nonpositive.

$$\int_0^{\pi} \sin x \, dx = -\cos x \Big]_0^{\pi} = -[\cos \pi - \cos 0] = -[-1 - 1] = 2.$$

$$\int_{\pi}^{2\pi} \sin x \, dx = -\cos x \Big]_{\pi}^{2\pi} = -[\cos 2\pi - \cos \pi] = -[1 - (-1)] = -2.$$

The second integral gives a negative value. The area between the graph and the axis is obtained by adding the absolute values

$$\text{Area} = |2| + |-2| = 4.$$ ∎

Summary:

To find the area between the graph of $y = f(x)$ and the x-axis over the interval $[a, b]$, do the following:

1. Subdivide $[a, b]$ at the zeros of f.
2. Integrate f over each subinterval.
3. Add the absolute values of the integrals.

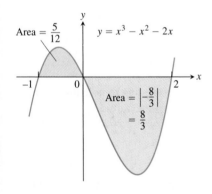

FIGURE 5.23   The region between the curve $y = x^3 - x^2 - 2x$ and the x-axis (Example 8).

EXAMPLE 8   Finding Area Using Antiderivatives

Find the area of the region between the x-axis and the graph of $f(x) = x^3 - x^2 - 2x$, $-1 \le x \le 2$.

Solution   First find the zeros of f. Since

$$f(x) = x^3 - x^2 - 2x = x(x^2 - x - 2) = x(x + 1)(x - 2),$$

the zeros are $x = 0, -1$, and 2 (Figure 5.23). The zeros subdivide $[-1, 2]$ into two subintervals: $[-1, 0]$, on which $f \ge 0$, and $[0, 2]$, on which $f \le 0$. We integrate f over each subinterval and add the absolute values of the calculated integrals.

$$\int_{-1}^0 (x^3 - x^2 - 2x) \, dx = \left[\frac{x^4}{4} - \frac{x^3}{3} - x^2\right]_{-1}^0 = 0 - \left[\frac{1}{4} + \frac{1}{3} - 1\right] = \frac{5}{12}$$

$$\int_0^2 (x^3 - x^2 - 2x) \, dx = \left[\frac{x^4}{4} - \frac{x^3}{3} - x^2\right]_0^2 = \left[4 - \frac{8}{3} - 4\right] - 0 = -\frac{8}{3}$$

The total enclosed area is obtained by adding the absolute values of the calculated integrals,

$$\text{Total enclosed area} = \frac{5}{12} + \left|-\frac{8}{3}\right| = \frac{37}{12}.$$ ∎

EXERCISES 5.4

Evaluating Integrals

Evaluate the integrals in Exercises 1–26.

1. $\displaystyle\int_{-2}^{0} (2x + 5)\, dx$

2. $\displaystyle\int_{-3}^{4} \left(5 - \frac{x}{2}\right) dx$

3. $\displaystyle\int_{0}^{4} \left(3x - \frac{x^3}{4}\right) dx$

4. $\displaystyle\int_{-2}^{2} (x^3 - 2x + 3)\, dx$

5. $\displaystyle\int_{0}^{1} \left(x^2 + \sqrt{x}\right) dx$

6. $\displaystyle\int_{0}^{5} x^{3/2}\, dx$

7. $\displaystyle\int_{1}^{32} x^{-6/5}\, dx$

8. $\displaystyle\int_{-2}^{-1} \frac{2}{x^2}\, dx$

9. $\displaystyle\int_{0}^{\pi} \sin x\, dx$

10. $\displaystyle\int_{0}^{\pi} (1 + \cos x)\, dx$

11. $\displaystyle\int_{0}^{\pi/3} 2 \sec^2 x\, dx$

12. $\displaystyle\int_{\pi/6}^{5\pi/6} \csc^2 x\, dx$

13. $\displaystyle\int_{\pi/4}^{3\pi/4} \csc\theta \cot\theta\, d\theta$

14. $\displaystyle\int_{0}^{\pi/3} 4 \sec u \tan u\, du$

15. $\displaystyle\int_{\pi/2}^{0} \frac{1 + \cos 2t}{2}\, dt$

16. $\displaystyle\int_{-\pi/3}^{\pi/3} \frac{1 - \cos 2t}{2}\, dt$

17. $\displaystyle\int_{-\pi/2}^{\pi/2} (8y^2 + \sin y)\, dy$

18. $\displaystyle\int_{-\pi/3}^{-\pi/4} \left(4 \sec^2 t + \frac{\pi}{t^2}\right) dt$

19. $\displaystyle\int_{1}^{-1} (r + 1)^2\, dr$

20. $\displaystyle\int_{-\sqrt{3}}^{\sqrt{3}} (t + 1)(t^2 + 4)\, dt$

21. $\displaystyle\int_{\sqrt{2}}^{1} \left(\frac{u^7}{2} - \frac{1}{u^5}\right) du$

22. $\displaystyle\int_{1/2}^{1} \left(\frac{1}{v^3} - \frac{1}{v^4}\right) dv$

23. $\displaystyle\int_{1}^{\sqrt{2}} \frac{s^2 + \sqrt{s}}{s^2}\, ds$

24. $\displaystyle\int_{9}^{4} \frac{1 - \sqrt{u}}{\sqrt{u}}\, du$

25. $\displaystyle\int_{-4}^{4} |x|\, dx$

26. $\displaystyle\int_{0}^{\pi} \frac{1}{2}(\cos x + |\cos x|)\, dx$

Derivatives of Integrals

Find the derivatives in Exercises 27–30

a. by evaluating the integral and differentiating the result.

b. by differentiating the integral directly.

27. $\displaystyle\frac{d}{dx}\int_{0}^{\sqrt{x}} \cos t\, dt$

28. $\displaystyle\frac{d}{dx}\int_{1}^{\sin x} 3t^2\, dt$

29. $\displaystyle\frac{d}{dt}\int_{0}^{t^4} \sqrt{u}\, du$

30. $\displaystyle\frac{d}{d\theta}\int_{0}^{\tan\theta} \sec^2 y\, dy$

Find dy/dx in Exercises 31–36.

31. $\displaystyle y = \int_{0}^{x} \sqrt{1 + t^2}\, dt$

32. $\displaystyle y = \int_{1}^{x} \frac{1}{t}\, dt, \quad x > 0$

33. $\displaystyle y = \int_{\sqrt{x}}^{0} \sin(t^2)\, dt$

34. $\displaystyle y = \int_{0}^{x^2} \cos \sqrt{t}\, dt$

35. $\displaystyle y = \int_{0}^{\sin x} \frac{dt}{\sqrt{1 - t^2}}, \quad |x| < \frac{\pi}{2}$

36. $\displaystyle y = \int_{\tan x}^{0} \frac{dt}{1 + t^2}$

Area

In Exercises 37–42, find the total area between the region and the x-axis.

37. $y = -x^2 - 2x, \quad -3 \le x \le 2$

38. $y = 3x^2 - 3, \quad -2 \le x \le 2$

39. $y = x^3 - 3x^2 + 2x, \quad 0 \le x \le 2$

40. $y = x^3 - 4x, \quad -2 \le x \le 2$

41. $y = x^{1/3}, \quad -1 \le x \le 8$

42. $y = x^{1/3} - x, \quad -1 \le x \le 8$

Find the areas of the shaded regions in Exercises 43–46.

43.

44.

45.   **46.**

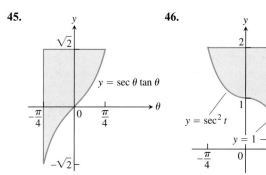

Initial Value Problems

Each of the following functions solves one of the initial value problems in Exercises 47–50. Which function solves which problem? Give brief reasons for your answers.

a. $y = \int_1^x \frac{1}{t}\, dt - 3$

b. $y = \int_0^x \sec t\, dt + 4$

c. $y = \int_{-1}^x \sec t\, dt + 4$

d. $y = \int_\pi^x \frac{1}{t}\, dt - 3$

47. $\dfrac{dy}{dx} = \dfrac{1}{x}, \quad y(\pi) = -3$

48. $y' = \sec x, \quad y(-1) = 4$

49. $y' = \sec x, \quad y(0) = 4$

50. $y' = \dfrac{1}{x}, \quad y(1) = -3$

Express the solutions of the initial value problems in Exercises 51–54 in terms of integrals.

51. $\dfrac{dy}{dx} = \sec x, \quad y(2) = 3$

52. $\dfrac{dy}{dx} = \sqrt{1 + x^2}, \quad y(1) = -2$

53. $\dfrac{ds}{dt} = f(t), \quad s(t_0) = s_0$

54. $\dfrac{dv}{dt} = g(t), \quad v(t_0) = v_0$

Applications

55. Archimedes' area formula for parabolas Archimedes (287–212 B.C.), inventor, military engineer, physicist, and the greatest mathematician of classical times in the Western world, discovered that the area under a parabolic arch is two-thirds the base times the height. Sketch the parabolic arch $y = h - (4h/b^2)x^2$, $-b/2 \le x \le b/2$, assuming that h and b are positive. Then use calculus to find the area of the region enclosed between the arch and the x-axis.

56. Revenue from marginal revenue Suppose that a company's marginal revenue from the manufacture and sale of egg beaters is

$$\frac{dr}{dx} = 2 - 2/(x + 1)^2,$$

where r is measured in thousands of dollars and x in thousands of units. How much money should the company expect from a production run of $x = 3$ thousand egg beaters? To find out, integrate the marginal revenue from $x = 0$ to $x = 3$.

57. Cost from marginal cost The marginal cost of printing a poster when x posters have been printed is

$$\frac{dc}{dx} = \frac{1}{2\sqrt{x}}$$

dollars. Find $c(100) - c(1)$, the cost of printing posters 2–100.

58. (*Continuation of Exercise 57.*) Find $c(400) - c(100)$, the cost of printing posters 101–400.

Drawing Conclusions About Motion from Graphs

59. Suppose that f is the differentiable function shown in the accompanying graph and that the position at time t (sec) of a particle moving along a coordinate axis is

$$s = \int_0^t f(x)\, dx$$

meters. Use the graph to answer the following questions. Give reasons for your answers.

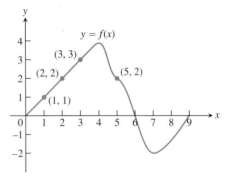

a. What is the particle's velocity at time $t = 5$?

b. Is the acceleration of the particle at time $t = 5$ positive, or negative?

c. What is the particle's position at time $t = 3$?

d. At what time during the first 9 sec does s have its largest value?

e. Approximately when is the acceleration zero?

f. When is the particle moving toward the origin? away from the origin?

g. On which side of the origin does the particle lie at time $t = 9$?

60. Suppose that g is the differentiable function graphed here and that the position at time t (sec) of a particle moving along a coordinate axis is

$$s = \int_0^t g(x)\, dx$$

meters. Use the graph to answer the following questions. Give reasons for your answers.

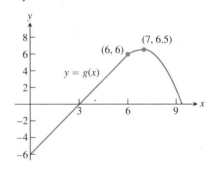

a. What is the particle's velocity at $t = 3$?

b. Is the acceleration at time $t = 3$ positive, or negative?

c. What is the particle's position at time $t = 3$?

d. When does the particle pass through the origin?

e. When is the acceleration zero?

f. When is the particle moving away from the origin? toward the origin?

g. On which side of the origin does the particle lie at $t = 9$?

Theory and Examples

61. Show that if k is a positive constant, then the area between the x-axis and one arch of the curve $y = \sin kx$ is $2/k$.

62. Find

$$\lim_{x \to 0} \frac{1}{x^3} \int_0^x \frac{t^2}{t^4 + 1} \, dt.$$

63. Suppose $\int_1^x f(t) \, dt = x^2 - 2x + 1$. Find $f(x)$.

64. Find $f(4)$ if $\int_0^x f(t) \, dt = x \cos \pi x$.

65. Find the linearization of

$$f(x) = 2 - \int_2^{x+1} \frac{9}{1 + t} \, dt$$

at $x = 1$.

66. Find the linearization of

$$g(x) = 3 + \int_1^{x^2} \sec(t - 1) \, dt$$

at $x = -1$.

67. Suppose that f has a positive derivative for all values of x and that $f(1) = 0$. Which of the following statements must be true of the function

$$g(x) = \int_0^x f(t) \, dt?$$

Give reasons for your answers.

a. g is a differentiable function of x.

b. g is a continuous function of x.

c. The graph of g has a horizontal tangent at $x = 1$.

d. g has a local maximum at $x = 1$.

e. g has a local minimum at $x = 1$.

f. The graph of g has an inflection point at $x = 1$.

g. The graph of dg/dx crosses the x-axis at $x = 1$.

68. Another proof of The Evaluation Theorem

a. Let $a = x_0 < x_1 < x_2 < \cdots < x_n = b$ be any partition of $[a, b]$, and let F be any antiderivative of f. Show that

$$F(b) - F(a) = \sum_{i=1}^{n} [F(x_i) - F(x_{i-1})]$$

b. Apply the Mean Value Theorem to each term to show $F(x_i) - F(x_{i-1}) = f(c_i)(x_i - x_{i-1})$ for some c_i in the interval (x_{i-1}, x_i). Then show that $F(b) - F(a)$ is a Riemann sum for f on $[a, b]$.

c. From part b and the definition of the definite integral, show that

$$F(b) - F(a) = \int_a^b f(x) \, dx.$$

T 69. The Fundamental Theorem If f is continuous, we expect

$$\lim_{h \to 0} \frac{1}{h} \int_x^{x+h} f(t) \, dt$$

to equal $f(x)$, as in the proof of Part 1 of the Fundamental Theorem. For instance, if $f(t) = \cos t$, then

$$\frac{1}{h} \int_x^{x+h} \cos t \, dt = \frac{\sin(x + h) - \sin x}{h}. \tag{6}$$

The right-hand side of Equation (6) is the difference quotient for the derivative of the sine, and we expect its limit as $h \to 0$ to be $\cos x$.

Graph $\cos x$ for $-\pi \le x \le 2\pi$. Then, in a different color if possible, graph the right-hand side of Equation (6) as a function of x for $h = 2, 1, 0.5$, and 0.1. Watch how the latter curves converge to the graph of the cosine as $h \to 0$.

T 70. Repeat Exercise 69 for $f(t) = 3t^2$. What is

$$\lim_{h \to 0} \frac{1}{h} \int_x^{x+h} 3t^2 \, dt = \lim_{h \to 0} \frac{(x + h)^3 - x^3}{h}?$$

Graph $f(x) = 3x^2$ for $-1 \le x \le 1$. Then graph the quotient $((x + h)^3 - x^3)/h$ as a function of x for $h = 1, 0.5, 0.2$, and 0.1. Watch how the latter curves converge to the graph of $3x^2$ as $h \to 0$.

COMPUTER EXPLORATIONS

In Exercises 71–74, let $F(x) = \int_a^x f(t) \, dt$ for the specified function f and interval $[a, b]$. Use a CAS to perform the following steps and answer the questions posed.

a. Plot the functions f and F together over $[a, b]$.

b. Solve the equation $F'(x) = 0$. What can you see to be true about the graphs of f and F at points where $F'(x) = 0$? Is your observation borne out by Part 1 of the Fundamental Theorem coupled with information provided by the first derivative? Explain your answer.

c. Over what intervals (approximately) is the function F increasing and decreasing? What is true about f over those intervals?

d. Calculate the derivative f' and plot it together with F. What can you see to be true about the graph of F at points where $f'(x) = 0$? Is your observation borne out by Part 1 of the Fundamental Theorem? Explain your answer.

71. $f(x) = x^3 - 4x^2 + 3x$, $[0, 4]$

72. $f(x) = 2x^4 - 17x^3 + 46x^2 - 43x + 12$, $\left[0, \dfrac{9}{2}\right]$

73. $f(x) = \sin 2x \cos \dfrac{x}{3}$, $[0, 2\pi]$

74. $f(x) = x \cos \pi x$, $[0, 2\pi]$

In Exercises 75–78, let $F(x) = \int_a^{u(x)} f(t)\, dt$ for the specified a, u, and f. Use a CAS to perform the following steps and answer the questions posed.

a. Find the domain of F.

b. Calculate $F'(x)$ and determine its zeros. For what points in its domain is F increasing? decreasing?

c. Calculate $F''(x)$ and determine its zero. Identify the local extrema and the points of inflection of F.

d. Using the information from parts (a)–(c), draw a rough hand-sketch of $y = F(x)$ over its domain. Then graph $F(x)$ on your CAS to support your sketch.

75. $a = 1$, $u(x) = x^2$, $f(x) = \sqrt{1 - x^2}$

76. $a = 0$, $u(x) = x^2$, $f(x) = \sqrt{1 - x^2}$

77. $a = 0$, $u(x) = 1 - x$, $f(x) = x^2 - 2x - 3$

78. $a = 0$, $u(x) = 1 - x^2$, $f(x) = x^2 - 2x - 3$

In Exercises 79 and 80, assume that f is continuous and $u(x)$ is twice-differentiable.

79. Calculate $\dfrac{d}{dx} \displaystyle\int_a^{u(x)} f(t)\, dt$ and check your answer using a CAS.

80. Calculate $\dfrac{d^2}{dx^2} \displaystyle\int_a^{u(x)} f(t)\, dt$ and check your answer using a CAS.

5.5   Indefinite Integrals and the Substitution Rule

A definite integral is a number defined by taking the limit of Riemann sums associated with partitions of a finite closed interval whose norms go to zero. The Fundamental Theorem of Calculus says that a definite integral of a continuous function can be computed easily if we can find an antiderivative of the function. Antiderivatives generally turn out to be more difficult to find than derivatives. However, it is well worth the effort to learn techniques for computing them.

Recall from Section 4.8 that the set of *all* antiderivatives of the function f is called the **indefinite integral** of f with respect to x, and is symbolized by

$$\int f(x)\, dx.$$

The connection between antiderivatives and the definite integral stated in the Fundamental Theorem now explains this notation. When finding the indefinite integral of a function f, remember that it always includes an arbitrary constant C.

We must distinguish carefully between definite and indefinite integrals. A definite integral $\int_a^b f(x)\, dx$ is a *number*. An indefinite integral $\int f(x)\, dx$ is a *function* plus an arbitrary constant C.

So far, we have only been able to find antiderivatives of functions that are clearly recognizable as derivatives. In this section we begin to develop more general techniques for finding antiderivatives. The first integration techniques we develop are obtained by inverting rules for finding derivatives, such as the Power Rule and the Chain Rule.

The Power Rule in Integral Form

If u is a differentiable function of x and n is a rational number different from -1, the Chain Rule tells us that

$$\frac{d}{dx}\left(\frac{u^{n+1}}{n+1} \right) = u^n \frac{du}{dx}.$$

From another point of view, this same equation says that $u^{n+1}/(n+1)$ is one of the anti-derivatives of the function $u^n(du/dx)$. Therefore,

$$\int \left(u^n \frac{du}{dx} \right) dx = \frac{u^{n+1}}{n+1} + C.$$

The integral on the left-hand side of this equation is usually written in the simpler "differential" form,

$$\int u^n \, du,$$

obtained by treating the dx's as differentials that cancel. We are thus led to the following rule.

If u is any differentiable function, then

$$\int u^n \, du = \frac{u^{n+1}}{n+1} + C \qquad (n \neq -1, n \text{ rational}). \qquad (1)$$

Equation (1) actually holds for any real exponent $n \neq -1$, as we see in Chapter 7.

In deriving Equation (1), we assumed u to be a differentiable function of the variable x, but the name of the variable does not matter and does not appear in the final formula. We could have represented the variable with θ, t, y, or any other letter. Equation (1) says that whenever we can cast an integral in the form

$$\int u^n \, du, \qquad (n \neq -1),$$

with u a differentiable function and du its differential, we can evaluate the integral as $[u^{n+1}/(n+1)] + C$.

EXAMPLE 1   Using the Power Rule

$$\int \sqrt{1+y^2} \cdot 2y \, dy = \int \sqrt{u} \cdot \left(\frac{du}{dy} \right) dy \qquad \text{Let } u = 1 + y^2,$$
$$\qquad\qquad\qquad du/dy = 2y$$

$$= \int u^{1/2} \, du$$

$$= \frac{u^{(1/2)+1}}{(1/2)+1} + C \qquad \text{Integrate, using Eq. (1)}$$
$$\text{with } n = 1/2.$$

$$= \frac{2}{3} u^{3/2} + C \qquad \text{Simpler form}$$

$$= \frac{2}{3}(1+y^2)^{3/2} + C \qquad \text{Replace } u \text{ by } 1+y^2. \qquad \blacksquare$$

EXAMPLE 2 Adjusting the Integrand by a Constant

$$\int \sqrt{4t-1}\; dt = \int \frac{1}{4} \cdot \sqrt{4t-1} \cdot 4\; dt$$

$$= \frac{1}{4}\int \sqrt{u} \cdot \left(\frac{du}{dt}\right) dt \qquad \text{Let } u = 4t-1,\; du/dt = 4.$$

$$= \frac{1}{4}\int u^{1/2}\; du \qquad \text{With the 1/4 out front, the integral is now in standard form.}$$

$$= \frac{1}{4} \cdot \frac{u^{3/2}}{3/2} + C \qquad \text{Integrate, using Eq. (1) with } n = 1/2.$$

$$= \frac{1}{6} u^{3/2} + C \qquad \text{Simpler form}$$

$$= \frac{1}{6}(4t-1)^{3/2} + C \qquad \text{Replace } u \text{ by } 4t-1. \qquad ■$$

Substitution: Running the Chain Rule Backwards

The substitutions in Examples 1 and 2 are instances of the following general rule.

THEOREM 5 The Substitution Rule

If $u = g(x)$ is a differentiable function whose range is an interval I and f is continuous on I, then

$$\int f(g(x))g'(x)\; dx = \int f(u)\; du.$$

Proof The rule is true because, by the Chain Rule, $F(g(x))$ is an antiderivative of $f(g(x)) \cdot g'(x)$ whenever F is an antiderivative of f:

$$\frac{d}{dx} F(g(x)) = F'(g(x)) \cdot g'(x) \qquad \text{Chain Rule}$$

$$= f(g(x)) \cdot g'(x). \qquad \text{Because } F' = f$$

If we make the substitution $u = g(x)$ then

$$\int f(g(x))g'(x)\; dx = \int \frac{d}{dx} F(g(x))\; dx$$

$$= F(g(x)) + C \qquad \text{Fundamental Theorem}$$

$$= F(u) + C \qquad u = g(x)$$

$$= \int F'(u)\; du \qquad \text{Fundamental Theorem}$$

$$= \int f(u)\; du \qquad F' = f \qquad ■$$

The Substitution Rule provides the following method to evaluate the integral

$$\int f(g(x))g'(x)\,dx,$$

when f and g' are continuous functions:

1. Substitute $u = g(x)$ and $du = g'(x)\,dx$ to obtain the integral

$$\int f(u)\,du.$$

2. Integrate with respect to u.

3. Replace u by $g(x)$ in the result.

EXAMPLE 3   Using Substitution

$$\int \cos(7\theta + 5)\,d\theta = \int \cos u \cdot \frac{1}{7}\,du \qquad \text{Let } u = 7\theta + 5, du = 7\,d\theta, \\ (1/7)\,du = d\theta.$$

$$= \frac{1}{7}\int \cos u\,du \qquad \text{With the (1/7) out front, the integral is now in standard form.}$$

$$= \frac{1}{7}\sin u + C \qquad \text{Integrate with respect to } u, \text{ Table 4.2.}$$

$$= \frac{1}{7}\sin(7\theta + 5) + C \qquad \text{Replace } u \text{ by } 7\theta + 5.$$

We can verify this solution by differentiating and checking that we obtain the original function $\cos(7\theta + 5)$. ∎

EXAMPLE 4   Using Substitution

$$\int x^2 \sin(x^3)\,dx = \int \sin(x^3) \cdot x^2\,dx$$

$$= \int \sin u \cdot \frac{1}{3}\,du \qquad \text{Let } u = x^3, \\ du = 3x^2\,dx, \\ (1/3)\,du = x^2\,dx.$$

$$= \frac{1}{3}\int \sin u\,du$$

$$= \frac{1}{3}(-\cos u) + C \qquad \text{Integrate with respect to } u.$$

$$= -\frac{1}{3}\cos(x^3) + C \qquad \text{Replace } u \text{ by } x^3. \qquad ∎$$

EXAMPLE 5 Using Identities and Substitution

$$\int \frac{1}{\cos^2 2x}\,dx = \int \sec^2 2x\,dx \qquad \frac{1}{\cos 2x} = \sec 2x$$

$$= \int \sec^2 u \cdot \frac{1}{2}\,du \qquad \begin{array}{l} u = 2x, \\ du = 2\,dx, \\ dx = (1/2)\,du \end{array}$$

$$= \frac{1}{2}\int \sec^2 u\,du$$

$$= \frac{1}{2}\tan u + C \qquad \frac{d}{du}\tan u = \sec^2 u$$

$$= \frac{1}{2}\tan 2x + C \qquad u = 2x \qquad ■$$

   The success of the substitution method depends on finding a substitution that changes an integral we cannot evaluate directly into one that we can. If the first substitution fails, try to simplify the integrand further with an additional substitution or two (see Exercises 49 and 50). Alternatively, we can start fresh. There can be more than one good way to start, as in the next example.

EXAMPLE 6 Using Different Substitutions

Evaluate

$$\int \frac{2z\,dz}{\sqrt[3]{z^2 + 1}}.$$

Solution   We can use the substitution method of integration as an exploratory tool: Substitute for the most troublesome part of the integrand and see how things work out. For the integral here, we might try $u = z^2 + 1$ or we might even press our luck and take u to be the entire cube root. Here is what happens in each case.

Solution 1: Substitute $u = z^2 + 1$.

$$\int \frac{2z\,dz}{\sqrt[3]{z^2 + 1}} = \int \frac{du}{u^{1/3}} \qquad \begin{array}{l} \text{Let } u = z^2 + 1, \\ du = 2z\,dz. \end{array}$$

$$= \int u^{-1/3}\,du \qquad \text{In the form } \int u^n\,du$$

$$= \frac{u^{2/3}}{2/3} + C \qquad \text{Integrate with respect to } u.$$

$$= \frac{3}{2}u^{2/3} + C$$

$$= \frac{3}{2}(z^2 + 1)^{2/3} + C \qquad \text{Replace } u \text{ by } z^2 + 1.$$

Solution 2: Substitute $u = \sqrt[3]{z^2 + 1}$ instead.

$$\int \frac{2z\,dz}{\sqrt[3]{z^2 + 1}} = \int \frac{3u^2\,du}{u} \qquad \begin{array}{l} \text{Let } u = \sqrt[3]{z^2 + 1}, \\ u^3 = z^2 + 1, \\ 3u^2\,du = 2z\,dz. \end{array}$$

$$= 3\int u\,du$$

$$= 3 \cdot \frac{u^2}{2} + C \qquad \text{Integrate with respect to } u.$$

$$= \frac{3}{2}(z^2 + 1)^{2/3} + C \qquad \text{Replace } u \text{ by } (z^2 + 1)^{1/3}. \qquad \blacksquare$$

The Integrals of $\sin^2 x$ and $\cos^2 x$

Sometimes we can use trigonometric identities to transform integrals we do not know how to evaluate into ones we can using the substitution rule. Here is an example giving the integral formulas for $\sin^2 x$ and $\cos^2 x$ which arise frequently in applications.

EXAMPLE 7

(a) $\displaystyle\int \sin^2 x\,dx = \int \frac{1 - \cos 2x}{2}\,dx \qquad \sin^2 x = \frac{1 - \cos 2x}{2}$

$$= \frac{1}{2}\int (1 - \cos 2x)\,dx = \frac{1}{2}\int dx - \frac{1}{2}\int \cos 2x\,dx$$

$$= \frac{1}{2}x - \frac{1}{2}\frac{\sin 2x}{2} + C = \frac{x}{2} - \frac{\sin 2x}{4} + C$$

(b) $\displaystyle\int \cos^2 x\,dx = \int \frac{1 + \cos 2x}{2}\,dx \qquad \cos^2 x = \frac{1 + \cos 2x}{2}$

$$= \frac{x}{2} + \frac{\sin 2x}{4} + C \qquad \begin{array}{l} \text{As in part (a), but} \\ \text{with a sign change} \end{array} \qquad \blacksquare$$

EXAMPLE 8   Area Beneath the Curve $y = \sin^2 x$

Figure 5.24 shows the graph of $g(x) = \sin^2 x$ over the interval $[0, 2\pi]$. Find

(a) the definite integral of $g(x)$ over $[0, 2\pi]$.

(b) the area between the graph of the function and the x-axis over $[0, 2\pi]$.

Solution

(a) From Example 7(a), the definite integral is

$$\int_0^{2\pi} \sin^2 x\,dx = \left[\frac{x}{2} - \frac{\sin 2x}{4}\right]_0^{2\pi} = \left[\frac{2\pi}{2} - \frac{\sin 4\pi}{4}\right] - \left[\frac{0}{2} - \frac{\sin 0}{4}\right]$$

$$= [\pi - 0] - [0 - 0] = \pi.$$

(b) The function $\sin^2 x$ is nonnegative, so the area is equal to the definite integral, or π. $\blacksquare$

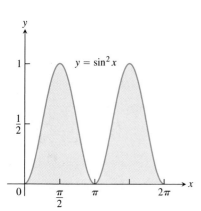

FIGURE 5.24 The area beneath the curve $y = \sin^2 x$ over $[0, 2\pi]$ equals π square units (Example 8).

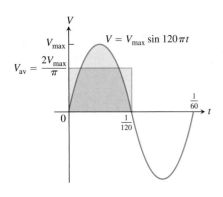

FIGURE 5.25 The graph of the voltage $V = V_{max} \sin 120\pi t$ over a full cycle. Its average value over a half-cycle is $2V_{max}/\pi$. Its average value over a full cycle is zero (Example 9).

EXAMPLE 9 Household Electricity

We can model the voltage in our home wiring with the sine function

$$V = V_{max} \sin 120\pi t,$$

which expresses the voltage V in volts as a function of time t in seconds. The function runs through 60 cycles each second (its frequency is 60 hertz, or 60 Hz). The positive constant V_{max} ("vee max") is the **peak voltage**.

The average value of V over the half-cycle from 0 to 1/120 sec (see Figure 5.25) is

$$\begin{aligned}
V_{av} &= \frac{1}{(1/120) - 0} \int_0^{1/120} V_{max} \sin 120\pi t \, dt \\
&= 120 V_{max} \left[-\frac{1}{120\pi} \cos 120\pi t \right]_0^{1/120} \\
&= \frac{V_{max}}{\pi} [-\cos \pi + \cos 0] \\
&= \frac{2V_{max}}{\pi}.
\end{aligned}$$

The average value of the voltage over a full cycle is zero, as we can see from Figure 5.25. (Also see Exercise 63.) If we measured the voltage with a standard moving-coil galvanometer, the meter would read zero.

To measure the voltage effectively, we use an instrument that measures the square root of the average value of the square of the voltage, namely

$$V_{rms} = \sqrt{(V^2)_{av}}.$$

The subscript "rms" (read the letters separately) stands for "root mean square." Since the average value of $V^2 = (V_{max})^2 \sin^2 120\pi t$ over a cycle is

$$(V^2)_{av} = \frac{1}{(1/60) - 0} \int_0^{1/60} (V_{max})^2 \sin^2 120\pi t \, dt = \frac{(V_{max})^2}{2},$$

(Exercise 63, part c), the rms voltage is

$$V_{rms} = \sqrt{\frac{(V_{max})^2}{2}} = \frac{V_{max}}{\sqrt{2}}.$$

The values given for household currents and voltages are always rms values. Thus, "115 volts ac" means that the rms voltage is 115. The peak voltage, obtained from the last equation, is

$$V_{max} = \sqrt{2} \, V_{rms} = \sqrt{2} \cdot 115 \approx 163 \text{ volts},$$

which is considerably higher. ∎

EXERCISES 5.5

Evaluating Integrals

Evaluate the indefinite integrals in Exercises 1–12 by using the given substitutions to reduce the integrals to standard form.

1. $\int \sin 3x \, dx, \quad u = 3x$

2. $\int x \sin (2x^2) \, dx, \quad u = 2x^2$

3. $\int \sec 2t \tan 2t \, dt, \quad u = 2t$

4. $\int \left(1 - \cos \frac{t}{2}\right)^2 \sin \frac{t}{2} \, dt, \quad u = 1 - \cos \frac{t}{2}$

5. $\int 28(7x - 2)^{-5} \, dx, \quad u = 7x - 2$

6. $\int x^3 (x^4 - 1)^2 \, dx, \quad u = x^4 - 1$

7. $\int \dfrac{9r^2 \, dr}{\sqrt{1 - r^3}}, \quad u = 1 - r^3$

8. $\int 12(y^4 + 4y^2 + 1)^2 (y^3 + 2y) \, dy, \quad u = y^4 + 4y^2 + 1$

9. $\int \sqrt{x} \sin^2 (x^{3/2} - 1) \, dx, \quad u = x^{3/2} - 1$

10. $\int \dfrac{1}{x^2} \cos^2 \left(\dfrac{1}{x} \right) dx, \quad u = -\dfrac{1}{x}$

11. $\int \csc^2 2\theta \cot 2\theta \, d\theta$

   a. Using $u = \cot 2\theta$ **b.** Using $u = \csc 2\theta$

12. $\int \dfrac{dx}{\sqrt{5x + 8}}$

   a. Using $u = 5x + 8$ **b.** Using $u = \sqrt{5x + 8}$

Evaluate the integrals in Exercises 13–48.

13. $\int \sqrt{3 - 2s} \, ds$

14. $\int (2x + 1)^3 \, dx$

15. $\int \dfrac{1}{\sqrt{5s + 4}} \, ds$

16. $\int \dfrac{3 \, dx}{(2 - x)^2}$

17. $\int \theta \sqrt[4]{1 - \theta^2} \, d\theta$

18. $\int 8\theta \sqrt[3]{\theta^2 - 1} \, d\theta$

19. $\int 3y \sqrt{7 - 3y^2} \, dy$

20. $\int \dfrac{4y \, dy}{\sqrt{2y^2 + 1}}$

21. $\int \dfrac{1}{\sqrt{x} (1 + \sqrt{x})^2} \, dx$

22. $\int \dfrac{(1 + \sqrt{x})^3}{\sqrt{x}} \, dx$

23. $\int \cos (3z + 4) \, dz$

24. $\int \sin (8z - 5) \, dz$

25. $\int \sec^2 (3x + 2) \, dx$

26. $\int \tan^2 x \sec^2 x \, dx$

27. $\int \sin^5 \dfrac{x}{3} \cos \dfrac{x}{3} \, dx$

28. $\int \tan^7 \dfrac{x}{2} \sec^2 \dfrac{x}{2} \, dx$

29. $\int r^2 \left(\dfrac{r^3}{18} - 1 \right)^5 dr$

30. $\int r^4 \left(7 - \dfrac{r^5}{10} \right)^3 dr$

31. $\int x^{1/2} \sin (x^{3/2} + 1) \, dx$

32. $\int x^{1/3} \sin (x^{4/3} - 8) \, dx$

33. $\int \sec \left(v + \dfrac{\pi}{2} \right) \tan \left(v + \dfrac{\pi}{2} \right) dv$

34. $\int \csc \left(\dfrac{v - \pi}{2} \right) \cot \left(\dfrac{v - \pi}{2} \right) dv$

35. $\int \dfrac{\sin (2t + 1)}{\cos^2 (2t + 1)} \, dt$

36. $\int \dfrac{6 \cos t}{(2 + \sin t)^3} \, dt$

37. $\int \sqrt{\cot y} \, \csc^2 y \, dy$

38. $\int \dfrac{\sec z \tan z}{\sqrt{\sec z}} \, dz$

39. $\int \dfrac{1}{t^2} \cos \left(\dfrac{1}{t} - 1 \right) dt$

40. $\int \dfrac{1}{\sqrt{t}} \cos (\sqrt{t} + 3) \, dt$

41. $\int \dfrac{1}{\theta^2} \sin \dfrac{1}{\theta} \cos \dfrac{1}{\theta} \, d\theta$

42. $\int \dfrac{\cos \sqrt{\theta}}{\sqrt{\theta} \sin^2 \sqrt{\theta}} \, d\theta$

43. $\int (s^3 + 2s^2 - 5s + 5)(3s^2 + 4s - 5) \, ds$

44. $\int (\theta^4 - 2\theta^2 + 8\theta - 2)(\theta^3 - \theta + 2) \, d\theta$

45. $\int t^3 (1 + t^4)^3 \, dt$

46. $\int \sqrt{\dfrac{x - 1}{x^5}} \, dx$

47. $\int x^3 \sqrt{x^2 + 1} \, dx$

48. $\int 3x^5 \sqrt{x^3 + 1} \, dx$

Simplifying Integrals Step by Step

If you do not know what substitution to make, try reducing the integral step by step, using a trial substitution to simplify the integral a bit and then another to simplify it some more. You will see what we mean if you try the sequences of substitutions in Exercises 49 and 50.

49. $\int \dfrac{18 \tan^2 x \sec^2 x}{(2 + \tan^3 x)^2} \, dx$

   a. $u = \tan x$, followed by $v = u^3$, then by $w = 2 + v$

   b. $u = \tan^3 x$, followed by $v = 2 + u$

   c. $u = 2 + \tan^3 x$

50. $\int \sqrt{1 + \sin^2 (x - 1)} \sin (x - 1) \cos (x - 1) \, dx$

   a. $u = x - 1$, followed by $v = \sin u$, then by $w = 1 + v^2$

   b. $u = \sin (x - 1)$, followed by $v = 1 + u^2$

   c. $u = 1 + \sin^2 (x - 1)$

Evaluate the integrals in Exercises 51 and 52.

51. $\int \dfrac{(2r - 1) \cos \sqrt{3(2r - 1)^2 + 6}}{\sqrt{3(2r - 1)^2 + 6}} \, dr$

52. $\int \dfrac{\sin \sqrt{\theta}}{\sqrt{\theta \cos^3 \sqrt{\theta}}} \, d\theta$

Initial Value Problems

Solve the initial value problems in Exercises 53–58.

53. $\dfrac{ds}{dt} = 12t (3t^2 - 1)^3, \quad s(1) = 3$

54. $\dfrac{dy}{dx} = 4x (x^2 + 8)^{-1/3}, \quad y(0) = 0$

55. $\dfrac{ds}{dt} = 8 \sin^2 \left(t + \dfrac{\pi}{12} \right), \quad s(0) = 8$

56. $\dfrac{dr}{d\theta} = 3 \cos^2 \left(\dfrac{\pi}{4} - \theta \right), \quad r(0) = \dfrac{\pi}{8}$

57. $\dfrac{d^2s}{dt^2} = -4\sin\left(2t - \dfrac{\pi}{2}\right), \quad s'(0) = 100, \quad s(0) = 0$

58. $\dfrac{d^2y}{dx^2} = 4\sec^2 2x \tan 2x, \quad y'(0) = 4, \quad y(0) = -1$

59. The velocity of a particle moving back and forth on a line is $v = ds/dt = 6\sin 2t$ m/sec for all t. If $s = 0$ when $t = 0$, find the value of s when $t = \pi/2$ sec.

60. The acceleration of a particle moving back and forth on a line is $a = d^2s/dt^2 = \pi^2 \cos \pi t$ m/sec^2 for all t. If $s = 0$ and $v = 8$ m/sec when $t = 0$, find s when $t = 1$ sec.

Theory and Examples

61. It looks as if we can integrate $2\sin x \cos x$ with respect to x in three different ways:

a. $\displaystyle\int 2\sin x \cos x \, dx = \int 2u \, du \qquad u = \sin x,$

$\qquad = u^2 + C_1 = \sin^2 x + C_1$

b. $\displaystyle\int 2\sin x \cos x \, dx = \int -2u \, du \qquad u = \cos x,$

$\qquad = -u^2 + C_2 = -\cos^2 x + C_2$

c. $\displaystyle\int 2\sin x \cos x \, dx = \int \sin 2x \, dx \quad 2\sin x \cos x = \sin 2x$

$\qquad = -\dfrac{\cos 2x}{2} + C_3.$

Can all three integrations be correct? Give reasons for your answer.

62. The substitution $u = \tan x$ gives

$$\int \sec^2 x \tan x \, dx = \int u \, du = \frac{u^2}{2} + C = \frac{\tan^2 x}{2} + C.$$

The substitution $u = \sec x$ gives

$$\int \sec^2 x \tan x \, dx = \int u \, du = \frac{u^2}{2} + C = \frac{\sec^2 x}{2} + C.$$

Can both integrations be correct? Give reasons for your answer.

63. (*Continuation of Example 9.*)

a. Show by evaluating the integral in the expression

$$\frac{1}{(1/60) - 0} \int_0^{1/60} V_{max} \sin 120\,\pi t \, dt$$

that the average value of $V = V_{max} \sin 120\,\pi t$ over a full cycle is zero.

b. The circuit that runs your electric stove is rated 240 volts rms. What is the peak value of the allowable voltage?

c. Show that

$$\int_0^{1/60} (V_{max})^2 \sin^2 120\,\pi t \, dt = \frac{(V_{max})^2}{120}.$$

5.6   Substitution and Area Between Curves

There are two methods for evaluating a definite integral by substitution. The first method is to find an antiderivative using substitution, and then to evaluate the definite integral by applying the Fundamental Theorem. We used this method in Examples 8 and 9 of the preceding section. The second method extends the process of substitution directly to *definite* integrals. We apply the new formula introduced here to the problem of computing the area between two curves.

Substitution Formula

In the following formula, the limits of integration change when the variable of integration is changed by substitution.

THEOREM 6   Substitution in Definite Integrals

If g' is continuous on the interval $[a, b]$ and f is continuous on the range of g, then

$$\int_a^b f(g(x)) \cdot g'(x) \, dx = \int_{g(a)}^{g(b)} f(u) \, du.$$

Proof   Let F denote any antiderivative of f. Then,

$$\int_a^b f(g(x)) \cdot g'(x)\, dx = F(g(x)) \Big]_{x=a}^{x=b}$$

$$= F(g(b)) - F(g(a))$$

$$= F(u) \Big]_{u=g(a)}^{u=g(b)}$$

$$= \int_{g(a)}^{g(b)} f(u)\, du. \qquad \text{Fundamental Theorem, Part 2} \qquad \blacksquare$$

$$\frac{d}{dx} F(g(x))$$
$$= F'(g(x))g'(x)$$
$$= f(g(x))g'(x)$$

To use the formula, make the same u-substitution $u = g(x)$ and $du = g'(x)\, dx$ you would use to evaluate the corresponding indefinite integral. Then integrate the transformed integral with respect to u from the value $g(a)$ (the value of u at $x = a$) to the value $g(b)$ (the value of u at $x = b$).

EXAMPLE 1   Substitution by Two Methods

Evaluate $\displaystyle\int_{-1}^{1} 3x^2 \sqrt{x^3 + 1}\, dx.$

Solution   We have two choices.

Method 1: Transform the integral and evaluate the transformed integral with the transformed limits given in Theorem 6.

$$\int_{-1}^{1} 3x^2 \sqrt{x^3 + 1}\, dx$$

$$= \int_{0}^{2} \sqrt{u}\, du \qquad \begin{array}{l}\text{Let } u = x^3 + 1,\, du = 3x^2\, dx.\\ \text{When } x = -1,\, u = (-1)^3 + 1 = 0.\\ \text{When } x = 1,\, u = (1)^3 + 1 = 2.\end{array}$$

$$= \frac{2}{3} u^{3/2} \Big]_0^2 \qquad \text{Evaluate the new definite integral.}$$

$$= \frac{2}{3}\left[2^{3/2} - 0^{3/2}\right] = \frac{2}{3}\left[2\sqrt{2}\right] = \frac{4\sqrt{2}}{3}$$

Method 2: Transform the integral as an indefinite integral, integrate, change back to x, and use the original x-limits.

$$\int 3x^2 \sqrt{x^3 + 1}\, dx = \int \sqrt{u}\, du \qquad \text{Let } u = x^3 + 1,\, du = 3x^2\, dx.$$

$$= \frac{2}{3} u^{3/2} + C \qquad \text{Integrate with respect to } u.$$

$$= \frac{2}{3}(x^3 + 1)^{3/2} + C \qquad \text{Replace } u \text{ by } x^3 + 1.$$

$$\int_{-1}^{1} 3x^2 \sqrt{x^3 + 1}\, dx = \frac{2}{3}(x^3 + 1)^{3/2} \Big]_{-1}^{1} \qquad \begin{array}{l}\text{Use the integral just found,}\\ \text{with limits of integration for } x.\end{array}$$

$$= \frac{2}{3}\left[((1)^3 + 1)^{3/2} - ((-1)^3 + 1)^{3/2}\right]$$

$$= \frac{2}{3}\left[2^{3/2} - 0^{3/2}\right] = \frac{2}{3}\left[2\sqrt{2}\right] = \frac{4\sqrt{2}}{3} \qquad \blacksquare$$

Which method is better—evaluating the transformed definite integral with transformed limits using Theorem 6, or transforming the integral, integrating, and transforming back to use the original limits of integration? In Example 1, the first method seems easier, but that is not always the case. Generally, it is best to know both methods and to use whichever one seems better at the time.

EXAMPLE 2 Using the Substitution Formula

$$\int_{\pi/4}^{\pi/2} \cot \theta \csc^2 \theta \, d\theta = \int_1^0 u \cdot (-du)$$

Let $u = \cot \theta$, $du = -\csc^2 \theta \, d\theta$,
$\quad -du = \csc^2 \theta \, d\theta$.
When $\theta = \pi/4$, $u = \cot(\pi/4) = 1$.
When $\theta = \pi/2$, $u = \cot(\pi/2) = 0$.

$$= -\int_1^0 u \, du$$

$$= -\left[\frac{u^2}{2}\right]_1^0$$

$$= -\left[\frac{(0)^2}{2} - \frac{(1)^2}{2}\right] = \frac{1}{2} \qquad \blacksquare$$

Definite Integrals of Symmetric Functions

The Substitution Formula in Theorem 6 simplifies the calculation of definite integrals of even and odd functions (Section 1.4) over a symmetric interval $[-a, a]$ (Figure 5.26).

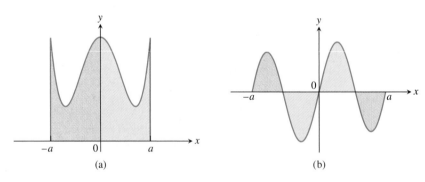

FIGURE 5.26 (a) f even, $\int_{-a}^a f(x)\,dx = 2\int_0^a f(x)\,dx$ (b) f odd, $\int_{-a}^a f(x)\,dx = 0$

Theorem 7

Let f be continuous on the symmetric interval $[-a, a]$.

(a) If f is even, then $\displaystyle\int_{-a}^a f(x)\,dx = 2\int_0^a f(x)\,dx$.

(b) If f is odd, then $\displaystyle\int_{-a}^a f(x)\,dx = 0$.

Proof of Part (a)

$$\int_{-a}^{a} f(x)\, dx = \int_{-a}^{0} f(x)\, dx + \int_{0}^{a} f(x)\, dx \qquad \text{Additivity Rule for Definite Integrals}$$

$$= -\int_{0}^{-a} f(x)\, dx + \int_{0}^{a} f(x)\, dx \qquad \text{Order of Integration Rule}$$

$$= -\int_{0}^{a} f(-u)(-du) + \int_{0}^{a} f(x)\, dx \qquad \begin{matrix}\text{Let } u = -x, du = -dx.\\ \text{When } x = 0, u = 0.\\ \text{When } x = -a, u = a.\end{matrix}$$

$$= \int_{0}^{a} f(-u)\, du + \int_{0}^{a} f(x)\, dx$$

$$= \int_{0}^{a} f(u)\, du + \int_{0}^{a} f(x)\, dx \qquad \begin{matrix}f \text{ is even, so}\\ f(-u) = f(u).\end{matrix}$$

$$= 2\int_{0}^{a} f(x)\, dx$$

The proof of part (b) is entirely similar and you are asked to give it in Exercise 86. ■

The assertions of Theorem 7 remain true when f is an integrable function (rather than having the stronger property of being continuous), but the proof is somewhat more difficult and best left to a more advanced course.

EXAMPLE 3   Integral of an Even Function

Evaluate $\int_{-2}^{2} (x^4 - 4x^2 + 6)\, dx$.

Solution   Since $f(x) = x^4 - 4x^2 + 6$ satisfies $f(-x) = f(x)$, it is even on the symmetric interval $[-2, 2]$, so

$$\int_{-2}^{2} (x^4 - 4x^2 + 6)\, dx = 2\int_{0}^{2} (x^4 - 4x^2 + 6)\, dx$$

$$= 2\left[\frac{x^5}{5} - \frac{4}{3}x^3 + 6x\right]_{0}^{2}$$

$$= 2\left(\frac{32}{5} - \frac{32}{3} + 12\right) = \frac{232}{15}. \qquad ■$$

Areas Between Curves

Suppose we want to find the area of a region that is bounded above by the curve $y = f(x)$, below by the curve $y = g(x)$, and on the left and right by the lines $x = a$ and $x = b$ (Figure 5.27). The region might accidentally have a shape whose area we could find with geometry, but if f and g are arbitrary continuous functions, we usually have to find the area with an integral.

To see what the integral should be, we first approximate the region with n vertical rectangles based on a partition $P = \{x_0, x_1, \ldots, x_n\}$ of $[a, b]$ (Figure 5.28). The area of the kth rectangle (Figure 5.29) is

$$\Delta A_k = \text{height} \times \text{width} = [f(c_k) - g(c_k)]\, \Delta x_k.$$

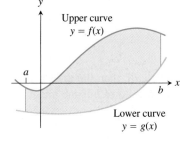
FIGURE 5.27 The region between the curves $y = f(x)$ and $y = g(x)$ and the lines $x = a$ and $x = b$.

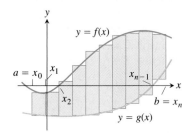
FIGURE 5.28 We approximate the region with rectangles perpendicular to the x-axis.

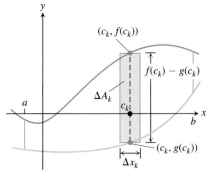
FIGURE 5.29 The area ΔA_k of the kth rectangle is the product of its height, $f(c_k) - g(c_k)$, and its width, Δx_k.

We then approximate the area of the region by adding the areas of the n rectangles:

$$A \approx \sum_{k=1}^{n} \Delta A_k = \sum_{k=1}^{n} [f(c_k) - g(c_k)] \, \Delta x_k. \qquad \text{Riemann Sum}$$

As $\|P\| \to 0$, the sums on the right approach the limit $\int_a^b [f(x) - g(x)] \, dx$ because f and g are continuous. We take the area of the region to be the value of this integral. That is,

$$A = \lim_{\|P\| \to 0} \sum_{k=1}^{n} [f(c_k) - g(c_k)] \, \Delta x_k = \int_a^b [f(x) - g(x)] \, dx.$$

DEFINITION   Area Between Curves

If f and g are continuous with $f(x) \geq g(x)$ throughout $[a, b]$, then the **area of the region between the curves $y = f(x)$ and $y = g(x)$ from a to b** is the integral of $(f - g)$ from a to b:

$$A = \int_a^b [f(x) - g(x)] \, dx.$$

When applying this definition it is helpful to graph the curves. The graph reveals which curve is the upper curve f and which is the lower curve g. It also helps you find the limits of integration if they are not already known. You may need to find where the curves intersect to determine the limits of integration, and this may involve solving the equation $f(x) = g(x)$ for values of x. Then you can integrate the function $f - g$ for the area between the intersections.

EXAMPLE 4   Area Between Intersecting Curves

Find the area of the region enclosed by the parabola $y = 2 - x^2$ and the line $y = -x$.

Solution   First we sketch the two curves (Figure 5.30). The limits of integration are found by solving $y = 2 - x^2$ and $y = -x$ simultaneously for x.

$$
\begin{aligned}
2 - x^2 &= -x & &\text{Equate } f(x) \text{ and } g(x). \\
x^2 - x - 2 &= 0 & &\text{Rewrite.} \\
(x + 1)(x - 2) &= 0 & &\text{Factor.} \\
x = -1, \quad x &= 2. & &\text{Solve.}
\end{aligned}
$$

The region runs from $x = -1$ to $x = 2$. The limits of integration are $a = -1, b = 2$. The area between the curves is

$$
\begin{aligned}
A &= \int_a^b [f(x) - g(x)] \, dx = \int_{-1}^{2} [(2 - x^2) - (-x)] \, dx \\
&= \int_{-1}^{2} (2 + x - x^2) \, dx = \left[2x + \frac{x^2}{2} - \frac{x^3}{3} \right]_{-1}^{2} \\
&= \left(4 + \frac{4}{2} - \frac{8}{3} \right) - \left(-2 + \frac{1}{2} + \frac{1}{3} \right) = \frac{9}{2}
\end{aligned}
$$

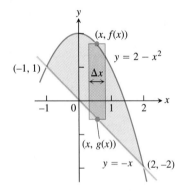

FIGURE 5.30 The region in Example 4 with a typical approximating rectangle.

HISTORICAL BIOGRAPHY

Richard Dedekind
(1831–1916)

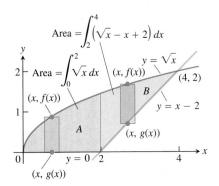

FIGURE 5.31 When the formula for a bounding curve changes, the area integral changes to become the sum of integrals to match, one integral for each of the shaded regions shown here for Example 5.

If the formula for a bounding curve changes at one or more points, we subdivide the region into subregions that correspond to the formula changes and apply the formula for the area between curves to each subregion.

EXAMPLE 5   Changing the Integral to Match a Boundary Change

Find the area of the region in the first quadrant that is bounded above by $y = \sqrt{x}$ and below by the x-axis and the line $y = x - 2$.

Solution   The sketch (Figure 5.31) shows that the region's upper boundary is the graph of $f(x) = \sqrt{x}$. The lower boundary changes from $g(x) = 0$ for $0 \le x \le 2$ to $g(x) = x - 2$ for $2 \le x \le 4$ (there is agreement at $x = 2$). We subdivide the region at $x = 2$ into subregions A and B, shown in Figure 5.31.

The limits of integration for region A are $a = 0$ and $b = 2$. The left-hand limit for region B is $a = 2$. To find the right-hand limit, we solve the equations $y = \sqrt{x}$ and $y = x - 2$ simultaneously for x:

$$\sqrt{x} = x - 2 \qquad \text{Equate } f(x) \text{ and } g(x).$$
$$x = (x - 2)^2 = x^2 - 4x + 4 \qquad \text{Square both sides.}$$
$$x^2 - 5x + 4 = 0 \qquad \text{Rewrite.}$$
$$(x - 1)(x - 4) = 0 \qquad \text{Factor.}$$
$$x = 1, \qquad x = 4. \qquad \text{Solve.}$$

Only the value $x = 4$ satisfies the equation $\sqrt{x} = x - 2$. The value $x = 1$ is an extraneous root introduced by squaring. The right-hand limit is $b = 4$.

$$\text{For } 0 \le x \le 2: \qquad f(x) - g(x) = \sqrt{x} - 0 = \sqrt{x}$$
$$\text{For } 2 \le x \le 4: \qquad f(x) - g(x) = \sqrt{x} - (x - 2) = \sqrt{x} - x + 2$$

We add the area of subregions A and B to find the total area:

$$\text{Total area} = \underbrace{\int_0^2 \sqrt{x}\, dx}_{\text{area of } A} + \underbrace{\int_2^4 (\sqrt{x} - x + 2)\, dx}_{\text{area of } B}$$

$$= \left[\frac{2}{3} x^{3/2} \right]_0^2 + \left[\frac{2}{3} x^{3/2} - \frac{x^2}{2} + 2x \right]_2^4$$

$$= \frac{2}{3}(2)^{3/2} - 0 + \left(\frac{2}{3}(4)^{3/2} - 8 + 8 \right) - \left(\frac{2}{3}(2)^{3/2} - 2 + 4 \right)$$

$$= \frac{2}{3}(8) - 2 = \frac{10}{3}. \qquad \blacksquare$$

Integration with Respect to y

If a region's bounding curves are described by functions of y, the approximating rectangles are horizontal instead of vertical and the basic formula has y in place of x.

For regions like these

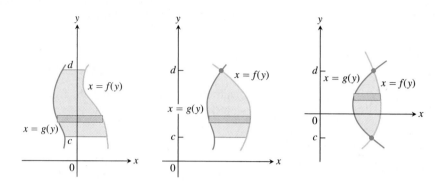

use the formula

$$A = \int_c^d [f(y) - g(y)]\, dy.$$

In this equation f always denotes the right-hand curve and g the left-hand curve, so $f(y) - g(y)$ is nonnegative.

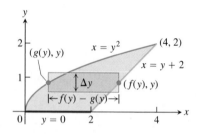

FIGURE 5.32 It takes two integrations to find the area of this region if we integrate with respect to x. It takes only one if we integrate with respect to y (Example 6).

EXAMPLE 6 Find the area of the region in Example 5 by integrating with respect to y.

Solution We first sketch the region and a typical *horizontal* rectangle based on a partition of an interval of y-values (Figure 5.32). The region's right-hand boundary is the line $x = y + 2$, so $f(y) = y + 2$. The left-hand boundary is the curve $x = y^2$, so $g(y) = y^2$. The lower limit of integration is $y = 0$. We find the upper limit by solving $x = y + 2$ and $x = y^2$ simultaneously for y:

$$y + 2 = y^2 \quad \text{Equate } f(y) = y + 2 \text{ and } g(y) = y^2.$$
$$y^2 - y - 2 = 0 \quad \text{Rewrite.}$$
$$(y + 1)(y - 2) = 0 \quad \text{Factor.}$$
$$y = -1, \quad y = 2 \quad \text{Solve.}$$

The upper limit of integration is $b = 2$. (The value $y = -1$ gives a point of intersection *below* the x-axis.)

The area of the region is

$$A = \int_a^b [f(y) - g(y)]\, dy = \int_0^2 [y + 2 - y^2]\, dy$$
$$= \int_0^2 [2 + y - y^2]\, dy$$
$$= \left[2y + \frac{y^2}{2} - \frac{y^3}{3} \right]_0^2$$
$$= 4 + \frac{4}{2} - \frac{8}{3} = \frac{10}{3}.$$

This is the result of Example 5, found with less work.

Combining Integrals with Formulas from Geometry

The fastest way to find an area may be to combine calculus and geometry.

EXAMPLE 7 The Area of the Region in Example 5 Found the Fastest Way

Find the area of the region in Example 5.

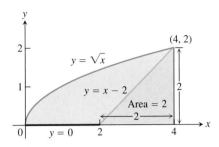

FIGURE 5.33 The area of the blue region is the area under the parabola $y = \sqrt{x}$ minus the area of the triangle (Example 7).

Solution The area we want is the area between the curve $y = \sqrt{x}, 0 \le x \le 4$, and the x-axis, *minus* the area of a triangle with base 2 and height 2 (Figure 5.33):

$$\text{Area} = \int_0^4 \sqrt{x}\, dx - \frac{1}{2}(2)(2)$$

$$= \frac{2}{3} x^{3/2} \Big]_0^4 - 2$$

$$= \frac{2}{3}(8) - 0 - 2 = \frac{10}{3}.$$

Conclusion from Examples 5–7 It is sometimes easier to find the area between two curves by integrating with respect to y instead of x. Also, it may help to combine geometry and calculus. After sketching the region, take a moment to think about the best way to proceed.

EXERCISES 5.6

Evaluating Definite Integrals

Use the Substitution Formula in Theorem 6 to evaluate the integrals in Exercises 1–24.

1. a. $\int_0^3 \sqrt{y+1}\, dy$ b. $\int_{-1}^0 \sqrt{y+1}\, dy$

2. a. $\int_0^1 r\sqrt{1-r^2}\, dr$ b. $\int_{-1}^1 r\sqrt{1-r^2}\, dr$

3. a. $\int_0^{\pi/4} \tan x \sec^2 x\, dx$ b. $\int_{-\pi/4}^0 \tan x \sec^2 x\, dx$

4. a. $\int_0^\pi 3\cos^2 x \sin x\, dx$ b. $\int_{2\pi}^{3\pi} 3\cos^2 x \sin x\, dx$

5. a. $\int_0^1 t^3(1+t^4)^3\, dt$ b. $\int_{-1}^1 t^3(1+t^4)^3\, dt$

6. a. $\int_0^{\sqrt{7}} t(t^2+1)^{1/3}\, dt$ b. $\int_{-\sqrt{7}}^0 t(t^2+1)^{1/3}\, dt$

7. a. $\int_{-1}^1 \frac{5r}{(4+r^2)^2}\, dr$ b. $\int_0^1 \frac{5r}{(4+r^2)^2}\, dr$

8. a. $\int_0^1 \frac{10\sqrt{v}}{(1+v^{3/2})^2}\, dv$ b. $\int_1^4 \frac{10\sqrt{v}}{(1+v^{3/2})^2}\, dv$

9. a. $\int_0^{\sqrt{3}} \frac{4x}{\sqrt{x^2+1}}\, dx$ b. $\int_{-\sqrt{3}}^{\sqrt{3}} \frac{4x}{\sqrt{x^2+1}}\, dx$

10. a. $\int_0^1 \frac{x^3}{\sqrt{x^4+9}}\, dx$ b. $\int_{-1}^0 \frac{x^3}{\sqrt{x^4+9}}\, dx$

11. a. $\int_0^{\pi/6} (1-\cos 3t)\sin 3t\, dt$ b. $\int_{\pi/6}^{\pi/3} (1-\cos 3t)\sin 3t\, dt$

12. a. $\int_{-\pi/2}^0 \left(2+\tan\frac{t}{2}\right)\sec^2\frac{t}{2}\, dt$ b. $\int_{-\pi/2}^{\pi/2} \left(2+\tan\frac{t}{2}\right)\sec^2\frac{t}{2}\, dt$

13. a. $\int_0^{2\pi} \frac{\cos z}{\sqrt{4+3\sin z}}\, dz$ b. $\int_{-\pi}^\pi \frac{\cos z}{\sqrt{4+3\sin z}}\, dz$

14. a. $\int_{-\pi/2}^0 \frac{\sin w}{(3+2\cos w)^2}\, dw$ b. $\int_0^{\pi/2} \frac{\sin w}{(3+2\cos w)^2}\, dw$

15. $\int_0^1 \sqrt{t^5+2t}\,(5t^4+2)\, dt$ 16. $\int_1^4 \frac{dy}{2\sqrt{y}(1+\sqrt{y})^2}$

17. $\int_0^{\pi/6} \cos^{-3} 2\theta \sin 2\theta\, d\theta$ 18. $\int_\pi^{3\pi/2} \cot^5\left(\frac{\theta}{6}\right)\sec^2\left(\frac{\theta}{6}\right)\, d\theta$

19. $\int_0^\pi 5(5-4\cos t)^{1/4}\sin t\, dt$ 20. $\int_0^{\pi/4} (1-\sin 2t)^{3/2}\cos 2t\, dt$

21. $\int_0^1 (4y-y^2+4y^3+1)^{-2/3}(12y^2-2y+4)\, dy$

22. $\int_0^1 (y^3+6y^2-12y+9)^{-1/2}(y^2+4y-4)\, dy$

23. $\displaystyle\int_0^{\sqrt[3]{\pi^2}} \sqrt{\theta}\,\cos^2\left(\theta^{3/2}\right) d\theta$ **24.** $\displaystyle\int_{-1}^{-1/2} t^{-2}\sin^2\left(1 + \frac{1}{t}\right) dt$

Area

Find the total areas of the shaded regions in Exercises 25–40.

25.

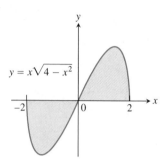

$y = x\sqrt{4 - x^2}$

26.

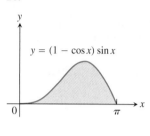

$y = (1 - \cos x)\sin x$

31.

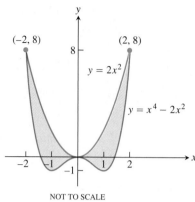

$(-2, 8)$ $(2, 8)$

$y = 2x^2$

$y = x^4 - 2x^2$

NOT TO SCALE

32.

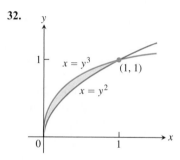

$x = y^3$

$(1, 1)$

$x = y^2$

27.

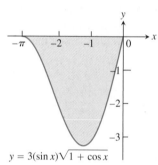

$y = 3(\sin x)\sqrt{1 + \cos x}$

28.

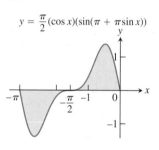

$y = \dfrac{\pi}{2}(\cos x)(\sin(\pi + \pi\sin x))$

33.

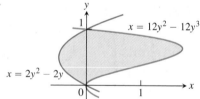

$x = 12y^2 - 12y^3$

$x = 2y^2 - 2y$

29.

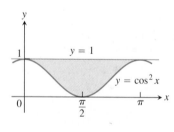

$y = 1$

$y = \cos^2 x$

30.

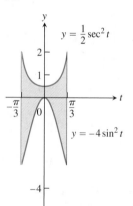

$y = \dfrac{1}{2}\sec^2 t$

$y = -4\sin^2 t$

34.

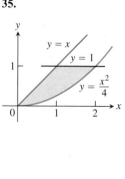

$y = x^2$

$y = -2x^4$

35.

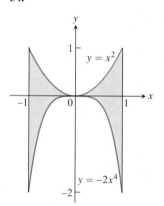

$y = x$

$y = 1$

$y = \dfrac{x^2}{4}$

36.

37.

38.

39.

40.

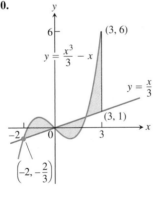

Find the areas of the regions enclosed by the lines and curves in Exercises 41–50.

41. $y = x^2 - 2$ and $y = 2$

42. $y = 2x - x^2$ and $y = -3$

43. $y = x^4$ and $y = 8x$

44. $y = x^2 - 2x$ and $y = x$

45. $y = x^2$ and $y = -x^2 + 4x$

46. $y = 7 - 2x^2$ and $y = x^2 + 4$

47. $y = x^4 - 4x^2 + 4$ and $y = x^2$

48. $y = x\sqrt{a^2 - x^2}$, $a > 0$, and $y = 0$

49. $y = \sqrt{|x|}$ and $5y = x + 6$ (How many intersection points are there?)

50. $y = |x^2 - 4|$ and $y = (x^2/2) + 4$

Find the areas of the regions enclosed by the lines and curves in Exercises 51–58.

51. $x = 2y^2$, $x = 0$, and $y = 3$

52. $x = y^2$ and $x = y + 2$

53. $y^2 - 4x = 4$ and $4x - y = 16$

54. $x - y^2 = 0$ and $x + 2y^2 = 3$

55. $x + y^2 = 0$ and $x + 3y^2 = 2$

56. $x - y^{2/3} = 0$ and $x + y^4 = 2$

57. $x = y^2 - 1$ and $x = |y|\sqrt{1 - y^2}$

58. $x = y^3 - y^2$ and $x = 2y$

Find the areas of the regions enclosed by the curves in Exercises 59–62.

59. $4x^2 + y = 4$ and $x^4 - y = 1$

60. $x^3 - y = 0$ and $3x^2 - y = 4$

61. $x + 4y^2 = 4$ and $x + y^4 = 1$, for $x \geq 0$

62. $x + y^2 = 3$ and $4x + y^2 = 0$

Find the areas of the regions enclosed by the lines and curves in Exercises 63–70.

63. $y = 2 \sin x$ and $y = \sin 2x$, $0 \leq x \leq \pi$

64. $y = 8 \cos x$ and $y = \sec^2 x$, $-\pi/3 \leq x \leq \pi/3$

65. $y = \cos(\pi x/2)$ and $y = 1 - x^2$

66. $y = \sin(\pi x/2)$ and $y = x$

67. $y = \sec^2 x$, $y = \tan^2 x$, $x = -\pi/4$, and $x = \pi/4$

68. $x = \tan^2 y$ and $x = -\tan^2 y$, $-\pi/4 \leq y \leq \pi/4$

69. $x = 3 \sin y \sqrt{\cos y}$ and $x = 0$, $0 \leq y \leq \pi/2$

70. $y = \sec^2(\pi x/3)$ and $y = x^{1/3}$, $-1 \leq x \leq 1$

71. Find the area of the propeller-shaped region enclosed by the curve $x - y^3 = 0$ and the line $x - y = 0$.

72. Find the area of the propeller-shaped region enclosed by the curves $x - y^{1/3} = 0$ and $x - y^{1/5} = 0$.

73. Find the area of the region in the first quadrant bounded by the line $y = x$, the line $x = 2$, the curve $y = 1/x^2$, and the x-axis.

74. Find the area of the "triangular" region in the first quadrant bounded on the left by the y-axis and on the right by the curves $y = \sin x$ and $y = \cos x$.

75. The region bounded below by the parabola $y = x^2$ and above by the line $y = 4$ is to be partitioned into two subsections of equal area by cutting across it with the horizontal line $y = c$.

  a. Sketch the region and draw a line $y = c$ across it that looks about right. In terms of c, what are the coordinates of the points where the line and parabola intersect? Add them to your figure.

b. Find c by integrating with respect to y. (This puts c in the limits of integration.)

c. Find c by integrating with respect to x. (This puts c into the integrand as well.)

76. Find the area of the region between the curve $y = 3 - x^2$ and the line $y = -1$ by integrating with respect to **a.** x,   **b.** y.

77. Find the area of the region in the first quadrant bounded on the left by the y-axis, below by the line $y = x/4$, above left by the curve $y = 1 + \sqrt{x}$, and above right by the curve $y = 2/\sqrt{x}$.

78. Find the area of the region in the first quadrant bounded on the left by the y-axis, below by the curve $x = 2\sqrt{y}$, above left by the curve $x = (y - 1)^2$, and above right by the line $x = 3 - y$.

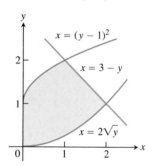

79. The figure here shows triangle AOC inscribed in the region cut from the parabola $y = x^2$ by the line $y = a^2$. Find the limit of the ratio of the area of the triangle to the area of the parabolic region as a approaches zero.

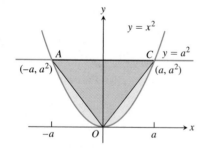

80. Suppose the area of the region between the graph of a positive continuous function f and the x-axis from $x = a$ to $x = b$ is 4 square units. Find the area between the curves $y = f(x)$ and $y = 2f(x)$ from $x = a$ to $x = b$.

81. Which of the following integrals, if either, calculates the area of the shaded region shown here? Give reasons for your answer.

a. $\displaystyle\int_{-1}^{1} (x - (-x)) \, dx = \int_{-1}^{1} 2x \, dx$

b. $\displaystyle\int_{-1}^{1} (-x - (x)) \, dx = \int_{-1}^{1} -2x \, dx$

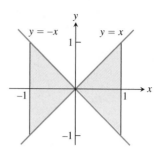

82. True, sometimes true, or never true? The area of the region between the graphs of the continuous functions $y = f(x)$ and $y = g(x)$ and the vertical lines $x = a$ and $x = b$ ($a < b$) is

$$\int_{a}^{b} [f(x) - g(x)] \, dx.$$

Give reasons for your answer.

Theory and Examples

83. Suppose that $F(x)$ is an antiderivative of $f(x) = (\sin x)/x$, $x > 0$. Express

$$\int_{1}^{3} \frac{\sin 2x}{x} \, dx$$

in terms of F.

84. Show that if f is continuous, then

$$\int_{0}^{1} f(x) \, dx = \int_{0}^{1} f(1 - x) \, dx.$$

85. Suppose that

$$\int_{0}^{1} f(x) \, dx = 3.$$

Find

$$\int_{-1}^{0} f(x) \, dx$$

if **a.** f is odd,   **b.** f is even.

86. a. Show that if f is odd on $[-a, a]$, then

$$\int_{-a}^{a} f(x) \, dx = 0.$$

b. Test the result in part (a) with $f(x) = \sin x$ and $a = \pi/2$.

87. If f is a continuous function, find the value of the integral

$$I = \int_{0}^{a} \frac{f(x) \, dx}{f(x) + f(a - x)}$$

by making the substitution $u = a - x$ and adding the resulting integral to I.

88. By using a substitution, prove that for all positive numbers x and y,

$$\int_x^{xy} \frac{1}{t}\, dt = \int_1^y \frac{1}{t}\, dt.$$

The Shift Property for Definite Integrals

A basic property of definite integrals is their invariance under translation, as expressed by the equation.

$$\int_a^b f(x)\, dx = \int_{a-c}^{b-c} f(x+c)\, dx. \tag{1}$$

The equation holds whenever f is integrable and defined for the necessary values of x. For example in the accompanying figure, show that

$$\int_{-2}^{-1} (x+2)^3\, dx = \int_0^1 x^3\, dx$$

because the areas of the shaded regions are congruent.

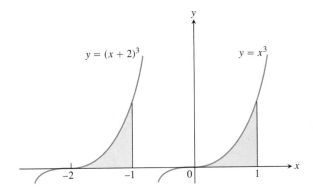

89. Use a substitution to verify Equation (1).

90. For each of the following functions, graph $f(x)$ over $[a, b]$ and $f(x + c)$ over $[a - c, b - c]$ to convince yourself that Equation (1) is reasonable.

   a. $f(x) = x^2$, $a = 0$, $b = 1$, $c = 1$

   b. $f(x) = \sin x$, $a = 0$, $b = \pi$, $c = \pi/2$

   c. $f(x) = \sqrt{x - 4}$, $a = 4$, $b = 8$, $c = 5$

COMPUTER EXPLORATIONS

In Exercises 91–94, you will find the area between curves in the plane when you cannot find their points of intersection using simple algebra. Use a CAS to perform the following steps:

   a. Plot the curves together to see what they look like and how many points of intersection they have.

   b. Use the numerical equation solver in your CAS to find all the points of intersection.

   c. Integrate $|f(x) - g(x)|$ over consecutive pairs of intersection values.

   d. Sum together the integrals found in part (c).

91. $f(x) = \dfrac{x^3}{3} - \dfrac{x^2}{2} - 2x + \dfrac{1}{3}$, $g(x) = x - 1$

92. $f(x) = \dfrac{x^4}{2} - 3x^3 + 10$, $g(x) = 8 - 12x$

93. $f(x) = x + \sin(2x)$, $g(x) = x^3$

94. $f(x) = x^2 \cos x$, $g(x) = x^3 - x$

<table>
<tr><td>Chapter 5</td><td></td></tr>
</table>

Questions to Guide Your Review

   1. How can you sometimes estimate quantities like distance traveled, area, and average value with finite sums? Why might you want to do so?

   2. What is sigma notation? What advantage does it offer? Give examples.

   3. What is a Riemann sum? Why might you want to consider such a sum?

   4. What is the norm of a partition of a closed interval?

   5. What is the definite integral of a function f over a closed interval $[a, b]$? When can you be sure it exists?

   6. What is the relation between definite integrals and area? Describe some other interpretations of definite integrals.

   7. What is the average value of an integrable function over a closed interval? Must the function assume its average value? Explain.

   8. Describe the rules for working with definite integrals (Table 5.3). Give examples.

   9. What is the Fundamental Theorem of Calculus? Why is it so important? Illustrate each part of the theorem with an example.

   10. How does the Fundamental Theorem provide a solution to the initial value problem $dy/dx = f(x), y(x_0) = y_0$, when f is continuous?

   11. How is integration by substitution related to the Chain Rule?

   12. How can you sometimes evaluate indefinite integrals by substitution? Give examples.

   13. How does the method of substitution work for definite integrals? Give examples.

   14. How do you define and calculate the area of the region between the graphs of two continuous functions? Give an example.

Chapter **5**   Practice Exercises

Finite Sums and Estimates

1. The accompanying figure shows the graph of the velocity (ft/sec) of a model rocket for the first 8 sec after launch. The rocket accelerated straight up for the first 2 sec and then coasted to reach its maximum height at $t = 8$ sec.

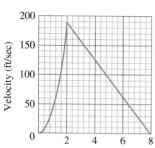

Time after launch (sec)

a. Assuming that the rocket was launched from ground level, about how high did it go? (This is the rocket in Section 3.3, Exercise 17, but you do not need to do Exercise 17 to do the exercise here.)

b. Sketch a graph of the rocket's height aboveground as a function of time for $0 \leq t \leq 8$.

2. a. The accompanying figure shows the velocity (m/sec) of a body moving along the s-axis during the time interval from $t = 0$ to $t = 10$ sec. About how far did the body travel during those 10 sec?

b. Sketch a graph of s as a function of t for $0 \leq t \leq 10$ assuming $s(0) = 0$.

Time (sec)

3. Suppose that $\sum_{k=1}^{10} a_k = -2$ and $\sum_{k=1}^{10} b_k = 25$. Find the value of

a. $\sum_{k=1}^{10} \dfrac{a_k}{4}$

b. $\sum_{k=1}^{10} (b_k - 3a_k)$

c. $\sum_{k=1}^{10} (a_k + b_k - 1)$

d. $\sum_{k=1}^{10} \left(\dfrac{5}{2} - b_k \right)$

4. Suppose that $\sum_{k=1}^{20} a_k = 0$ and $\sum_{k=1}^{20} b_k = 7$. Find the values of

a. $\sum_{k=1}^{20} 3a_k$

b. $\sum_{k=1}^{20} (a_k + b_k)$

c. $\sum_{k=1}^{20} \left(\dfrac{1}{2} - \dfrac{2b_k}{7} \right)$

d. $\sum_{k=1}^{20} (a_k - 2)$

Definite Integrals

In Exercises 5–8, express each limit as a definite integral. Then evaluate the integral to find the value of the limit. In each case, P is a partition of the given interval and the numbers c_k are chosen from the subintervals of P.

5. $\displaystyle \lim_{\|P\| \to 0} \sum_{k=1}^{n} (2c_k - 1)^{-1/2} \Delta x_k$, where P is a partition of $[1, 5]$

6. $\displaystyle \lim_{\|P\| \to 0} \sum_{k=1}^{n} c_k (c_k^2 - 1)^{1/3} \Delta x_k$, where P is a partition of $[1, 3]$

7. $\displaystyle \lim_{\|P\| \to 0} \sum_{k=1}^{n} \left(\cos \left(\dfrac{c_k}{2} \right) \right) \Delta x_k$, where P is a partition of $[-\pi, 0]$

8. $\displaystyle \lim_{\|P\| \to 0} \sum_{k=1}^{n} (\sin c_k)(\cos c_k) \Delta x_k$, where P is a partition of $[0, \pi/2]$

9. If $\int_{-2}^{2} 3f(x)\, dx = 12$, $\int_{-2}^{5} f(x)\, dx = 6$, and $\int_{-2}^{5} g(x)\, dx = 2$, find the values of the following.

a. $\displaystyle \int_{-2}^{2} f(x)\, dx$

b. $\displaystyle \int_{2}^{5} f(x)\, dx$

c. $\displaystyle \int_{5}^{-2} g(x)\, dx$

d. $\displaystyle \int_{-2}^{5} (-\pi g(x))\, dx$

e. $\displaystyle \int_{-2}^{5} \left(\dfrac{f(x) + g(x)}{5} \right) dx$

10. If $\int_{0}^{2} f(x)\, dx = \pi$, $\int_{0}^{2} 7g(x)\, dx = 7$, and $\int_{0}^{1} g(x)\, dx = 2$, find the values of the following.

a. $\displaystyle \int_{0}^{2} g(x)\, dx$

b. $\displaystyle \int_{1}^{2} g(x)\, dx$

c. $\displaystyle \int_{2}^{0} f(x)\, dx$

d. $\displaystyle \int_{0}^{2} \sqrt{2}\, f(x)\, dx$

e. $\displaystyle \int_{0}^{2} (g(x) - 3f(x))\, dx$

Area

In Exercise 11–14, find the total area of the region between the graph of f and the x-axis.

11. $f(x) = x^2 - 4x + 3$, $\quad 0 \leq x \leq 3$

12. $f(x) = 1 - (x^2/4)$, $\quad -2 \leq x \leq 3$

13. $f(x) = 5 - 5x^{2/3}, \quad -1 \le x \le 8$

14. $f(x) = 1 - \sqrt{x}, \quad 0 \le x \le 4$

Find the areas of the regions enclosed by the curves and lines in Exercises 15–26.

15. $y = x, \quad y = 1/x^2, \quad x = 2$

16. $y = x, \quad y = 1/\sqrt{x}, \quad x = 2$

17. $\sqrt{x} + \sqrt{y} = 1, \quad x = 0, \quad y = 0$

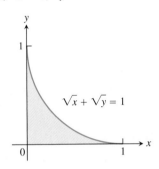

18. $x^3 + \sqrt{y} = 1, \quad x = 0, \quad y = 0, \quad \text{for} \quad 0 \le x \le 1$

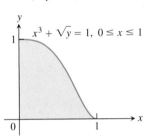

19. $x = 2y^2, \quad x = 0, \quad y = 3$ **20.** $x = 4 - y^2, \quad x = 0$

21. $y^2 = 4x, \quad y = 4x - 2$

22. $y^2 = 4x + 4, \quad y = 4x - 16$

23. $y = \sin x, \quad y = x, \quad 0 \le x \le \pi/4$

24. $y = |\sin x|, \quad y = 1, \quad -\pi/2 \le x \le \pi/2$

25. $y = 2 \sin x, \quad y = \sin 2x, \quad 0 \le x \le \pi$

26. $y = 8 \cos x, \quad y = \sec^2 x, \quad -\pi/3 \le x \le \pi/3$

27. Find the area of the "triangular" region bounded on the left by $x + y = 2$, on the right by $y = x^2$, and above by $y = 2$.

28. Find the area of the "triangular" region bounded on the left by $y = \sqrt{x}$, on the right by $y = 6 - x$, and below by $y = 1$.

29. Find the extreme values of $f(x) = x^3 - 3x^2$ and find the area of the region enclosed by the graph of f and the x-axis.

30. Find the area of the region cut from the first quadrant by the curve $x^{1/2} + y^{1/2} = a^{1/2}$.

31. Find the total area of the region enclosed by the curve $x = y^{2/3}$ and the lines $x = y$ and $y = -1$.

32. Find the total area of the region between the curves $y = \sin x$ and $y = \cos x$ for $0 \le x \le 3\pi/2$.

Initial Value Problems

33. Show that $y = x^2 + \int_1^x \dfrac{1}{t} \, dt$ solves the initial value problem

$$\frac{d^2 y}{dx^2} = 2 - \frac{1}{x^2}; \quad y'(1) = 3, \quad y(1) = 1.$$

34. Show that $y = \int_0^x \left(1 + 2\sqrt{\sec t}\right) dt$ solves the initial value problem

$$\frac{d^2 y}{dx^2} = \sqrt{\sec x} \tan x; \quad y'(0) = 3, \quad y(0) = 0.$$

Express the solutions of the initial value problems in Exercises 35 and 36 in terms of integrals.

35. $\dfrac{dy}{dx} = \dfrac{\sin x}{x}, \quad y(5) = -3$

36. $\dfrac{dy}{dx} = \sqrt{2 - \sin^2 x}, \quad y(-1) = 2$

Evaluating Indefinite Integrals

Evaluate the integrals in Exercises 37–44.

37. $\displaystyle\int 2(\cos x)^{-1/2} \sin x \, dx$ **38.** $\displaystyle\int (\tan x)^{-3/2} \sec^2 x \, dx$

39. $\displaystyle\int (2\theta + 1 + 2\cos(2\theta + 1)) \, d\theta$

40. $\displaystyle\int \left(\frac{1}{\sqrt{2\theta - \pi}} + 2\sec^2(2\theta - \pi) \right) d\theta$

41. $\displaystyle\int \left(t - \frac{2}{t} \right)\left(t + \frac{2}{t} \right) dt$ **42.** $\displaystyle\int \frac{(t+1)^2 - 1}{t^4} \, dt$

43. $\displaystyle\int \sqrt{t} \sin(2t^{3/2}) \, dt$ **44.** $\displaystyle\int \sec\theta \tan\theta \sqrt{1 + \sec\theta} \, d\theta$

Evaluating Definite Integrals

Evaluate the integrals in Exercises 45–70.

45. $\displaystyle\int_{-1}^{1} (3x^2 - 4x + 7) \, dx$ **46.** $\displaystyle\int_{0}^{1} (8s^3 - 12s^2 + 5) \, ds$

47. $\displaystyle\int_{1}^{2} \frac{4}{v^2} \, dv$ **48.** $\displaystyle\int_{1}^{27} x^{-4/3} \, dx$

49. $\displaystyle\int_{1}^{4} \frac{dt}{t\sqrt{t}}$ **50.** $\displaystyle\int_{1}^{4} \frac{\left(1 + \sqrt{u}\right)^{1/2}}{\sqrt{u}} \, du$

51. $\displaystyle\int_{0}^{1} \frac{36 \, dx}{(2x + 1)^3}$ **52.** $\displaystyle\int_{0}^{1} \frac{dr}{\sqrt[3]{(7 - 5r)^2}}$

53. $\displaystyle\int_{1/8}^{1} x^{-1/3}(1 - x^{2/3})^{3/2} \, dx$ **54.** $\displaystyle\int_{0}^{1/2} x^3(1 + 9x^4)^{-3/2} \, dx$

55. $\displaystyle\int_{0}^{\pi} \sin^2 5r \, dr$ **56.** $\displaystyle\int_{0}^{\pi/4} \cos^2\left(4t - \frac{\pi}{4}\right) dt$

57. $\displaystyle\int_0^{\pi/3} \sec^2 \theta \, d\theta$

58. $\displaystyle\int_{\pi/4}^{3\pi/4} \csc^2 x \, dx$

59. $\displaystyle\int_{\pi}^{3\pi} \cot^2 \frac{x}{6} \, dx$

60. $\displaystyle\int_0^{\pi} \tan^2 \frac{\theta}{3} \, d\theta$

61. $\displaystyle\int_{-\pi/3}^0 \sec x \tan x \, dx$

62. $\displaystyle\int_{\pi/4}^{3\pi/4} \csc z \cot z \, dz$

63. $\displaystyle\int_0^{\pi/2} 5(\sin x)^{3/2} \cos x \, dx$

64. $\displaystyle\int_{-1}^1 2x \sin(1 - x^2) \, dx$

65. $\displaystyle\int_{-\pi/2}^{\pi/2} 15 \sin^4 3x \cos 3x \, dx$

66. $\displaystyle\int_0^{2\pi/3} \cos^{-4}\left(\frac{x}{2}\right) \sin\left(\frac{x}{2}\right) dx$

67. $\displaystyle\int_0^{\pi/2} \frac{3 \sin x \cos x}{\sqrt{1 + 3 \sin^2 x}} \, dx$

68. $\displaystyle\int_0^{\pi/4} \frac{\sec^2 x}{(1 + 7 \tan x)^{2/3}} \, dx$

69. $\displaystyle\int_0^{\pi/3} \frac{\tan \theta}{\sqrt{2 \sec \theta}} \, d\theta$

70. $\displaystyle\int_{\pi^2/36}^{\pi^2/4} \frac{\cos \sqrt{t}}{\sqrt{t} \sin \sqrt{t}} \, dt$

Average Values

71. Find the average value of $f(x) = mx + b$

   a. over $[-1, 1]$

   b. over $[-k, k]$

72. Find the average value of

   a. $y = \sqrt{3x}$ over $[0, 3]$

   b. $y = \sqrt{ax}$ over $[0, a]$

73. Let f be a function that is differentiable on $[a, b]$. In Chapter 2 we defined the average rate of change of f over $[a, b]$ to be

$$\frac{f(b) - f(a)}{b - a}$$

and the instantaneous rate of change of f at x to be $f'(x)$. In this chapter we defined the average value of a function. For the new definition of average to be consistent with the old one, we should have

$$\frac{f(b) - f(a)}{b - a} = \text{average value of } f' \text{ on } [a, b].$$

Is this the case? Give reasons for your answer.

74. Is it true that the average value of an integrable function over an interval of length 2 is half the function's integral over the interval? Give reasons for your answer.

T 75. Compute the average value of the temperature function

$$f(x) = 37 \sin\left(\frac{2\pi}{365} (x - 101)\right) + 25$$

for a 365-day year. This is one way to estimate the annual mean air temperature in Fairbanks, Alaska. The National Weather Service's official figure, a numerical average of the daily normal mean air temperatures for the year, is 25.7°F, which is slightly higher than the average value of $f(x)$. Figure 3.33 shows why.

T 76. **Specific heat of a gas**   Specific heat C_v is the amount of heat required to raise the temperature of a given mass of gas with con-

stant volume by 1°C, measured in units of cal/deg-mole (calories per degree gram molecule). The specific heat of oxygen depends on its temperature T and satisfies the formula

$$C_v = 8.27 + 10^{-5}(26T - 1.87T^2).$$

Find the average value of C_v for $20° \leq T \leq 675°$C and the temperature at which it is attained.

Differentiating Integrals

In Exercises 77–80, find dy/dx.

77. $\displaystyle y = \int_2^x \sqrt{2 + \cos^3 t} \, dt$

78. $\displaystyle y = \int_2^{7x^2} \sqrt{2 + \cos^3 t} \, dt$

79. $\displaystyle y = \int_x^1 \frac{6}{3 + t^4} \, dt$

80. $\displaystyle y = \int_{\sec x}^2 \frac{1}{t^2 + 1} \, dt$

Theory and Examples

81. Is it true that every function $y = f(x)$ that is differentiable on $[a, b]$ is itself the derivative of some function on $[a, b]$? Give reasons for your answer.

82. Suppose that $F(x)$ is an antiderivative of $f(x) = \sqrt{1 + x^4}$. Express $\int_0^1 \sqrt{1 + x^4} \, dx$ in terms of F and give a reason for your answer.

83. Find dy/dx if $y = \int_x^1 \sqrt{1 + t^2} \, dt$. Explain the main steps in your calculation.

84. Find dy/dx if $y = \int_{\cos x}^0 (1/(1 - t^2)) \, dt$. Explain the main steps in your calculation.

85. **A new parking lot**   To meet the demand for parking, your town has allocated the area shown here. As the town engineer, you have been asked by the town council to find out if the lot can be built for $10,000. The cost to clear the land will be $0.10 a square foot, and the lot will cost $2.00 a square foot to pave. Can the job be done for $10,000? Use a lower sum estimate to see. (Answers may vary slightly, depending on the estimate used.)

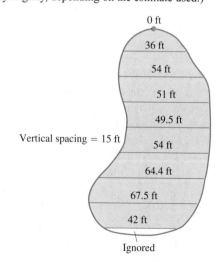

0 ft

36 ft

54 ft

51 ft

49.5 ft

Vertical spacing = 15 ft

54 ft

64.4 ft

67.5 ft

42 ft

Ignored

86. Skydivers A and B are in a helicopter hovering at 6400 ft. Skydiver A jumps and descends for 4 sec before opening her parachute. The helicopter then climbs to 7000 ft and hovers there. Forty-five seconds after A leaves the aircraft, B jumps and descends for 13 sec before opening his parachute. Both skydivers descend at 16 ft/sec with parachutes open. Assume that the skydivers fall freely (no effective air resistance) before their parachutes open.

   a. At what altitude does A's parachute open?

   b. At what altitude does B's parachute open?

   c. Which skydiver lands first?

Average Daily Inventory

Average value is used in economics to study such things as average daily inventory. If $I(t)$ is the number of radios, tires, shoes, or whatever product a firm has on hand on day t (we call I an **inventory function**), the average value of I over a time period $[0, T]$ is called the firm's average daily inventory for the period.

$$\textbf{Average daily inventory} = \text{av}(I) = \frac{1}{T}\int_0^T I(t)\,dt.$$

If h is the dollar cost of holding one item per day, the product $\text{av}(I) \cdot h$ is the **average daily holding cost** for the period.

87. As a wholesaler, Tracey Burr Distributors receives a shipment of 1200 cases of chocolate bars every 30 days. TBD sells the chocolate to retailers at a steady rate, and t days after a shipment arrives, its inventory of cases on hand is $I(t) = 1200 - 40t$, $0 \le t \le 30$. What is TBD's average daily inventory for the 30-day period? What is its average daily holding cost if the cost of holding one case is $3\textcent$ a day?

88. Rich Wholesale Foods, a manufacturer of cookies, stores its cases of cookies in an air-conditioned warehouse for shipment every 14 days. Rich tries to keep 600 cases on reserve to meet occasional peaks in demand, so a typical 14-day inventory function is $I(t) = 600 + 600t$, $0 \le t \le 14$. The daily holding cost for each case is $4\textcent$ per day. Find Rich's average daily inventory and average daily holding cost.

89. Solon Container receives 450 drums of plastic pellets every 30 days. The inventory function (drums on hand as a function of days) is $I(t) = 450 - t^2/2$. Find the average daily inventory. If the holding cost for one drum is $2\textcent$ per day, find the average daily holding cost.

90. Mitchell Mailorder receives a shipment of 600 cases of athletic socks every 60 days. The number of cases on hand t days after the shipment arrives is $I(t) = 600 - 20\sqrt{15t}$. Find the average daily inventory. If the holding cost for one case is $1/2\textcent$ per day, find the average daily holding cost.

Chapter 5   Additional and Advanced Exercises

Theory and Examples

1. a. If $\displaystyle\int_0^1 7f(x)\,dx = 7$, does $\displaystyle\int_0^1 f(x)\,dx = 1$?

   b. If $\displaystyle\int_0^1 f(x)\,dx = 4$ and $f(x) \ge 0$, does

   $$\int_0^1 \sqrt{f(x)}\,dx = \sqrt{4} = 2?$$

   Give reasons for your answers.

2. Suppose $\displaystyle\int_{-2}^2 f(x)\,dx = 4$, $\displaystyle\int_2^5 f(x)\,dx = 3$, $\displaystyle\int_{-2}^5 g(x)\,dx = 2$.

   Which, if any, of the following statements are true?

   a. $\displaystyle\int_5^2 f(x)\,dx = -3$ **b.** $\displaystyle\int_{-2}^5 (f(x) + g(x)) = 9$

   c. $f(x) \le g(x)$ on the interval $-2 \le x \le 5$

3. Initial value problem Show that

$$y = \frac{1}{a}\int_0^x f(t)\sin a(x - t)\,dt$$

solves the initial value problem

$$\frac{d^2y}{dx^2} + a^2y = f(x), \qquad \frac{dy}{dx} = 0 \quad \text{and} \quad y = 0 \text{ when } x = 0.$$

   (*Hint:* $\sin(ax - at) = \sin ax \cos at - \cos ax \sin at$.)

4. Proportionality Suppose that x and y are related by the equation

$$x = \int_0^y \frac{1}{\sqrt{1 + 4t^2}}\,dt.$$

   Show that d^2y/dx^2 is proportional to y and find the constant of proportionality.

5. Find $f(4)$ if

   a. $\displaystyle\int_0^{x^2} f(t)\,dt = x\cos \pi x$ **b.** $\displaystyle\int_0^{f(x)} t^2\,dt = x\cos \pi x$.

6. Find $f(\pi/2)$ from the following information.

   i. f is positive and continuous.

   ii. The area under the curve $y = f(x)$ from $x = 0$ to $x = a$ is

   $$\frac{a^2}{2} + \frac{a}{2}\sin a + \frac{\pi}{2}\cos a.$$

7. The area of the region in the xy-plane enclosed by the x-axis, the curve $y = f(x), f(x) \geq 0$, and the lines $x = 1$ and $x = b$ is equal to $\sqrt{b^2 + 1} - \sqrt{2}$ for all $b > 1$. Find $f(x)$.

8. Prove that

$$\int_0^x \left(\int_0^u f(t)\, dt \right) du = \int_0^x f(u)(x - u)\, du.$$

(*Hint:* Express the integral on the right-hand side as the difference of two integrals. Then show that both sides of the equation have the same derivative with respect to x.)

9. **Finding a curve** Find the equation for the curve in the xy-plane that passes through the point $(1, -1)$ if its slope at x is always $3x^2 + 2$.

10. **Shoveling dirt** You sling a shovelful of dirt up from the bottom of a hole with an initial velocity of 32 ft/sec. The dirt must rise 17 ft above the release point to clear the edge of the hole. Is that enough speed to get the dirt out, or had you better duck?

Piecewise Continuous Functions

Although we are mainly interested in continuous functions, many functions in applications are piecewise continuous. A function $f(x)$ is **piecewise continuous on a closed interval** I if f has only finitely many discontinuities in I, the limits

$$\lim_{x \to c^-} f(x) \quad \text{and} \quad \lim_{x \to c^+} f(x)$$

exist and are finite at every interior point of I, and the appropriate one-sided limits exist and are finite at the endpoints of I. All piecewise continuous functions are integrable. The points of discontinuity subdivide I into open and half-open subintervals on which f is continuous, and the limit criteria above guarantee that f has a continuous extension to the closure of each subinterval. To integrate a piecewise continuous function, we integrate the individual extensions and add the results. The integral of

$$f(x) = \begin{cases} 1 - x, & -1 \leq x < 0 \\ x^2, & 0 \leq x < 2 \\ -1, & 2 \leq x \leq 3 \end{cases}$$

(Figure 5.34) over $[-1, 3]$ is

$$\int_{-1}^3 f(x)\, dx = \int_{-1}^0 (1 - x)\, dx + \int_0^2 x^2\, dx + \int_2^3 (-1)\, dx$$

$$= \left[x - \frac{x^2}{2} \right]_{-1}^0 + \left[\frac{x^3}{3} \right]_0^2 + \left[-x \right]_2^3$$

$$= \frac{3}{2} + \frac{8}{3} - 1 = \frac{19}{6}.$$

The Fundamental Theorem applies to piecewise continuous functions with the restriction that $(d/dx) \int_a^x f(t)\, dt$ is expected to equal $f(x)$ only at values of x at which f is continuous. There is a similar restriction on Leibniz's Rule below.

Graph the functions in Exercises 11–16 and integrate them over their domains.

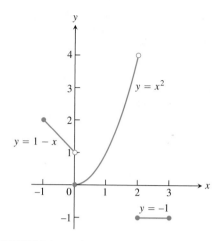

FIGURE 5.34 Piecewise continuous functions like this are integrated piece by piece.

11. $f(x) = \begin{cases} x^{2/3}, & -8 \leq x < 0 \\ -4, & 0 \leq x \leq 3 \end{cases}$

12. $f(x) = \begin{cases} \sqrt{-x}, & -4 \leq x < 0 \\ x^2 - 4, & 0 \leq x \leq 3 \end{cases}$

13. $g(t) = \begin{cases} t, & 0 \leq t < 1 \\ \sin \pi t, & 1 \leq t \leq 2 \end{cases}$

14. $h(z) = \begin{cases} \sqrt{1 - z}, & 0 \leq z < 1 \\ (7z - 6)^{-1/3}, & 1 \leq z \leq 2 \end{cases}$

15. $f(x) = \begin{cases} 1, & -2 \leq x < -1 \\ 1 - x^2, & -1 \leq x < 1 \\ 2, & 1 \leq x \leq 2 \end{cases}$

16. $h(r) = \begin{cases} r, & -1 \leq r < 0 \\ 1 - r^2, & 0 \leq r < 1 \\ 1, & 1 \leq r \leq 2 \end{cases}$

17. Find the average value of the function graphed in the accompanying figure.

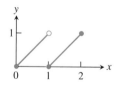

18. Find the average value of the function graphed in the accompanying figure.

Leibniz's Rule

In applications, we sometimes encounter functions like

$$f(x) = \int_{\sin x}^{x^2} (1 + t)\, dt \qquad \text{and} \qquad g(x) = \int_{\sqrt{x}}^{2\sqrt{x}} \sin t^2 \, dt,$$

defined by integrals that have variable upper limits of integration and variable lower limits of integration at the same time. The first integral can be evaluated directly, but the second cannot. We may find the derivative of either integral, however, by a formula called **Leibniz's Rule**.

Leibniz's Rule

If f is continuous on $[a, b]$ and if $u(x)$ and $v(x)$ are differentiable functions of x whose values lie in $[a, b]$, then

$$\frac{d}{dx} \int_{u(x)}^{v(x)} f(t)\, dt = f(v(x)) \frac{dv}{dx} - f(u(x)) \frac{du}{dx}.$$

Figure 5.35 gives a geometric interpretation of Leibniz's Rule. It shows a carpet of variable width $f(t)$ that is being rolled up at the left at the same time x as it is being unrolled at the right. (In this interpretation, time is x, not t.) At time x, the floor is covered from $u(x)$ to $v(x)$. The rate du/dx at which the carpet is being rolled up need not be the same as the rate dv/dx at which the carpet is being laid down. At any given time x, the area covered by carpet is

$$A(x) = \int_{u(x)}^{v(x)} f(t)\, dt.$$

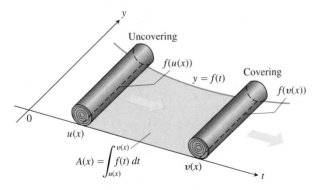

FIGURE 5.35 Rolling and unrolling a carpet: a geometric interpretation of Leibniz's Rule:

$$\frac{dA}{dx} = f(v(x)) \frac{dv}{dx} - f(u(x)) \frac{du}{dx}.$$

At what rate is the covered area changing? At the instant x, $A(x)$ is increasing by the width $f(v(x))$ of the unrolling carpet times the rate dv/dx at which the carpet is being unrolled. That is, $A(x)$ is being increased at the rate

$$f(v(x)) \frac{dv}{dx}.$$

At the same time, A is being decreased at the rate

$$f(u(x)) \frac{du}{dx},$$

the width at the end that is being rolled up times the rate du/dx. The net rate of change in A is

$$\frac{dA}{dx} = f(v(x)) \frac{dv}{dx} - f(u(x)) \frac{du}{dx},$$

which is precisely Leibniz's Rule.

To prove the rule, let F be an antiderivative of f on $[a, b]$. Then

$$\int_{u(x)}^{v(x)} f(t)\, dt = F(v(x)) - F(u(x)).$$

Differentiating both sides of this equation with respect to x gives the equation we want:

$$\frac{d}{dx} \int_{u(x)}^{v(x)} f(t)\, dt = \frac{d}{dx}\left[F(v(x)) - F(u(x)) \right]$$

$$= F'(v(x)) \frac{dv}{dx} - F'(u(x)) \frac{du}{dx} \qquad \text{Chain Rule}$$

$$= f(v(x)) \frac{dv}{dx} - f(u(x)) \frac{du}{dx}.$$

Use Leibniz's Rule to find the derivatives of the functions in Exercises 19–21.

19. $f(x) = \displaystyle\int_{1/x}^{x} \frac{1}{t}\, dt$ **20.** $f(x) = \displaystyle\int_{\cos x}^{\sin x} \frac{1}{1 - t^2}\, dt$

21. $g(y) = \displaystyle\int_{\sqrt{y}}^{2\sqrt{y}} \sin t^2 \, dt$

22. Use Leibniz's Rule to find the value of x that maximizes the value of the integral

$$\int_{x}^{x+3} t(5 - t)\, dt.$$

Problems like this arise in the mathematical theory of political elections. See "The Entry Problem in a Political Race," by Steven J. Brams and Philip D. Straffin, Jr., in *Political Equilibrium*, Peter Ordeshook and Kenneth Shepfle, Editors, Kluwer-Nijhoff, Boston, 1982, pp. 181–195.

Approximating Finite Sums with Integrals

In many applications of calculus, integrals are used to approximate finite sums—the reverse of the usual procedure of using finite sums to approximate integrals.

For example, let's estimate the sum of the square roots of the first n positive integers, $\sqrt{1} + \sqrt{2} + \cdots + \sqrt{n}$. The integral

$$\int_0^1 \sqrt{x}\, dx = \frac{2}{3}x^{3/2}\Big]_0^1 = \frac{2}{3}$$

is the limit of the upper sums

$$S_n = \sqrt{\frac{1}{n}} \cdot \frac{1}{n} + \sqrt{\frac{2}{n}} \cdot \frac{1}{n} + \cdots + \sqrt{\frac{n}{n}} \cdot \frac{1}{n}$$

$$= \frac{\sqrt{1} + \sqrt{2} + \cdots + \sqrt{n}}{n^{3/2}}.$$

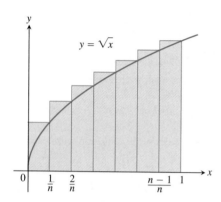

Therefore, when n is large, S_n will be close to $2/3$ and we will have

$$\text{Root sum} = \sqrt{1} + \sqrt{2} + \cdots + \sqrt{n} = S_n \cdot n^{3/2} \approx \frac{2}{3} n^{3/2}.$$

The following table shows how good the approximation can be.

n	Root sum	$(2/3)n^{3/2}$	Relative error
10	22.468	21.082	$1.386/22.468 \approx 6\%$
50	239.04	235.70	1.4%
100	671.46	666.67	0.7%
1000	21,097	21,082	0.07%

23. Evaluate

$$\lim_{n\to\infty} \frac{1^5 + 2^5 + 3^5 + \cdots + n^5}{n^6}$$

by showing that the limit is

$$\int_0^1 x^5\, dx$$

and evaluating the integral.

24. See Exercise 23. Evaluate

$$\lim_{n\to\infty} \frac{1}{n^4}(1^3 + 2^3 + 3^3 + \cdots + n^3).$$

25. Let $f(x)$ be a continuous function. Express

$$\lim_{n\to\infty} \frac{1}{n}\left[f\left(\frac{1}{n}\right) + f\left(\frac{2}{n}\right) + \cdots + f\left(\frac{n}{n}\right)\right]$$

as a definite integral.

26. Use the result of Exercise 25 to evaluate

a. $\displaystyle\lim_{n\to\infty} \frac{1}{n^2}(2 + 4 + 6 + \cdots + 2n)$,

b. $\displaystyle\lim_{n\to\infty} \frac{1}{n^{16}}(1^{15} + 2^{15} + 3^{15} + \cdots + n^{15})$,

c. $\displaystyle\lim_{n\to\infty} \frac{1}{n}\left(\sin\frac{\pi}{n} + \sin\frac{2\pi}{n} + \sin\frac{3\pi}{n} + \cdots + \sin\frac{n\pi}{n}\right)$.

What can be said about the following limits?

d. $\displaystyle\lim_{n\to\infty} \frac{1}{n^{17}}(1^{15} + 2^{15} + 3^{15} + \cdots + n^{15})$

e. $\displaystyle\lim_{n\to\infty} \frac{1}{n^{15}}(1^{15} + 2^{15} + 3^{15} + \cdots + n^{15})$

27. a. Show that the area A_n of an n-sided regular polygon in a circle of radius r is

$$A_n = \frac{nr^2}{2}\sin\frac{2\pi}{n}.$$

b. Find the limit of A_n as $n \to \infty$. Is this answer consistent with what you know about the area of a circle?

28. A differential equation Show that $y = \sin x + \int_x^\pi \cos 2t\, dt + 1$ satisfies both of the following conditions:

i. $y'' = -\sin x + 2\sin 2x$

ii. $y = 1$ and $y' = -2$ when $x = \pi$.

29. A function defined by an integral The graph of a function f consists of a semicircle and two line segments as shown. Let $g(x) = \int_1^x f(t)\, dt$.

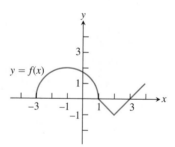

a. Find $g(1)$.   b. Find $g(3)$.   c. Find $g(-1)$.

d. Find all values of x on the open interval $(-3, 4)$ at which g has a relative maximum.

e. Write an equation for the line tangent to the graph of g at $x = -1$.

f. Find the x-coordinate of each point of inflection of the graph of g on the open interval $(-3, 4)$.

g. Find the range of g.

Chapter 5   Technology Application Projects

Mathematica/Maple Module
Using Riemann Sums to Estimate Areas, Volumes, and Lengths of Curves

Visualize and approximate areas and volumes in Part I.

Mathematica/Maple Module
Riemann Sums, Definite Integrals, and the Fundamental Theorem of Calculus

Parts I, II, and III develop Riemann sums and definite integrals. Part IV continues the development of the Riemann sum and definite integral using the Fundamental Theorem to solve problems previously investigated.

Mathematica/Maple Module
Rain Catchers, Elevators, and Rockets

Part I illustrates that the area under a curve is the same as the area of an appropriate rectangle for examples taken from the chapter. You will compute the amount of water accumulating in basins of different shapes as the basin is filled and drained.

Mathematica/Maple Module
Motion Along a Straight Line, Part II

You will observe the shape of a graph through dramatic animated visualizations of the derivative relations among the position, velocity, and acceleration. Figures in the text can be animated using this software.

Mathematica/Maple Module
Bending of Beams

Study bent shapes of beams, determine their maximum deflections, concavity and inflection points, and interpret the results in terms of a beam's compression and tension.

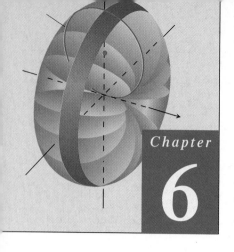

APPLICATIONS OF
DEFINITE INTEGRALS

OVERVIEW   In Chapter 5 we discovered the connection between Riemann sums

$$S_P = \sum_{k=1}^{n} f(c_k)\, \Delta x_k$$

associated with a partition P of the finite closed interval $[a, b]$ and the process of integration. We found that for a continuous function f on $[a, b]$, the limit of S_P as the norm of the partition $\|P\|$ approaches zero is the number

$$\int_a^b f(x)\, dx = F(b) - F(a)$$

where F is any antiderivative of f. We applied this to the problems of computing the area between the x-axis and the graph of $y = f(x)$ for $a \le x \le b$, and to finding the area between two curves.

In this chapter we extend the applications to finding volumes, lengths of plane curves, centers of mass, areas of surfaces of revolution, work, and fluid forces against planar walls. We define all these as limits of Riemann sums of continuous functions on closed intervals—that is, as definite integrals which can be evaluated using the Fundamental Theorem of Calculus.

6.1   Volumes by Slicing and Rotation About an Axis

In this section we define volumes of solids whose cross-sections are plane regions. A **cross-section** of a solid S is the plane region formed by intersecting S with a plane (Figure 6.1).

Suppose we want to find the volume of a solid S like the one in Figure 6.1. We begin by extending the definition of a cylinder from classical geometry to cylindrical solids with arbitrary bases (Figure 6.2). If the cylindrical solid has a known base area A and height h, then the volume of the cylindrical solid is

$$\text{Volume} = \text{area} \times \text{height} = A \cdot h.$$

This equation forms the basis for defining the volumes of many solids that are not cylindrical by the *method of slicing*.

If the cross-section of the solid S at each point x in the interval $[a, b]$ is a region $R(x)$ of area $A(x)$, and A is a continuous function of x, we can define and calculate the volume of the solid S as a definite integral in the following way.

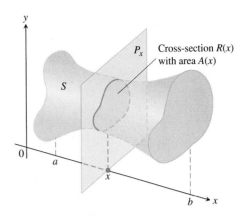

FIGURE 6.1 A cross-section of the solid S formed by intersecting S with a plane P_x perpendicular to the x-axis through the point x in the interval $[a, b]$.

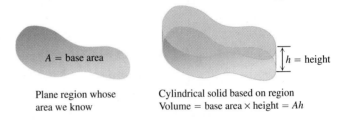

Plane region whose area we know

Cylindrical solid based on region Volume = base area × height = Ah

FIGURE 6.2 The volume of a cylindrical solid is always defined to be its base area times its height.

We partition $[a, b]$ into subintervals of width (length) Δx_k and slice the solid, as we would a loaf of bread, by planes perpendicular to the x-axis at the partition points $a = x_0 < x_1 < \cdots < x_n = b$. The planes P_{x_k}, perpendicular to the x-axis at the partition points, slice S into thin "slabs" (like thin slices of a loaf of bread). A typical slab is shown in Figure 6.3. We approximate the slab between the plane at x_{k-1} and the plane at x_k by a cylindrical solid with base area $A(x_k)$ and height $\Delta x_k = x_k - x_{k-1}$ (Figure 6.4). The volume V_k of this cylindrical solid is $A(x_k) \cdot \Delta x_k$, which is approximately the same volume as that of the slab:

Volume of the kth slab $\approx V_k = A(x_k)\, \Delta x_k$.

The volume V of the entire solid S is therefore approximated by the sum of these cylindrical volumes,

$$V \approx \sum_{k=1}^{n} V_k = \sum_{k=1}^{n} A(x_k)\, \Delta x_k.$$

This is a Riemann sum for the function $A(x)$ on $[a, b]$. We expect the approximations from these sums to improve as the norm of the partition of $[a, b]$ goes to zero. Taking a partition of $[a, b]$ into n subintervals with $\|P\| \to 0$ gives

$$V = \lim_{n \to \infty} \sum_{k=1}^{n} A(x_k)\, \Delta x_k = \int_a^b A(x)\, dx.$$

So we define their limiting definite integral to be the volume of the solid S.

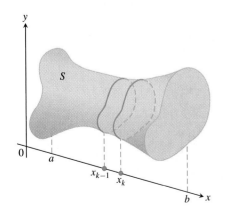

FIGURE 6.3 A typical thin slab in the solid S.

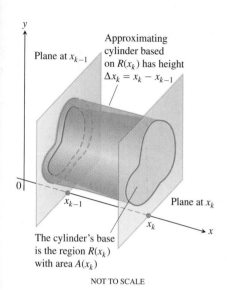

FIGURE 6.4 The solid thin slab in Figure 6.3 is approximated by the cylindrical solid with base $R(x_k)$ having area $A(x_k)$ and height $\Delta x_k = x_k - x_{k-1}$.

> **DEFINITION**   **Volume**
>
> The **volume** of a solid of known integrable cross-sectional area $A(x)$ from $x = a$ to $x = b$ is the integral of A from a to b,
>
> $$V = \int_a^b A(x)\,dx.$$

This definition applies whenever $A(x)$ is continuous, or more generally, when it is integrable. To apply the formula in the definition to calculate the volume of a solid, take the following steps:

> **Calculating the Volume of a Solid**
>
> 1. *Sketch the solid and a typical cross-section.*
> 2. *Find a formula for $A(x)$,* the area of a typical cross-section.
> 3. *Find the limits of integration.*
> 4. *Integrate $A(x)$* using the Fundamental Theorem.

EXAMPLE 1   Volume of a Pyramid

A pyramid 3 m high has a square base that is 3 m on a side. The cross-section of the pyramid perpendicular to the altitude x m down from the vertex is a square x m on a side. Find the volume of the pyramid.

Solution

1. *A sketch.* We draw the pyramid with its altitude along the x-axis and its vertex at the origin and include a typical cross-section (Figure 6.5).
2. *A formula for $A(x)$.* The cross-section at x is a square x meters on a side, so its area is

$$A(x) = x^2.$$

3. *The limits of integration.* The squares lie on the planes from $x = 0$ to $x = 3$.
4. *Integrate to find the volume.*

$$V = \int_0^3 A(x)\,dx = \int_0^3 x^2\,dx = \frac{x^3}{3}\Big]_0^3 = 9\ \text{m}^3 \qquad \blacksquare$$

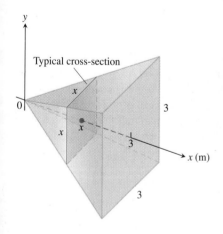

FIGURE 6.5 The cross-sections of the pyramid in Example 1 are squares.

EXAMPLE 2   Cavalieri's Principle

Cavalieri's principle says that solids with equal altitudes and identical cross-sectional areas at each height have the same volume (Figure 6.6). This follows immediately from the definition of volume, because the cross-sectional area function $A(x)$ and the interval $[a, b]$ are the same for both solids. $\qquad \blacksquare$

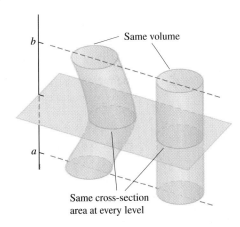

FIGURE 6.6 *Cavalieri's Principle:* These solids have the same volume, which can be illustrated with stacks of coins (Example 2).

EXAMPLE 3   Volume of a Wedge

A curved wedge is cut from a cylinder of radius 3 by two planes. One plane is perpendicular to the axis of the cylinder. The second plane crosses the first plane at a $45°$ angle at the center of the cylinder. Find the volume of the wedge.

Solution   We draw the wedge and sketch a typical cross-section perpendicular to the x-axis (Figure 6.7). The cross-section at x is a rectangle of area

$$A(x) = (\text{height})(\text{width}) = (x)\left(2\sqrt{9 - x^2}\right)$$

$$= 2x\sqrt{9 - x^2}.$$

The rectangles run from $x = 0$ to $x = 3$, so we have

$$V = \int_a^b A(x)\, dx = \int_0^3 2x\sqrt{9 - x^2}\, dx$$

$$= -\frac{2}{3}(9 - x^2)^{3/2}\Big]_0^3$$

Let $u = 9 - x^2$, $du = -2x\, dx$, integrate, and substitute back.

$$= 0 + \frac{2}{3}(9)^{3/2}$$

$$= 18. \qquad\blacksquare$$

The figure shows the wedge of Example 3 with labels $2\sqrt{9 - x^2}$, $45°$, 3, -3, and $\left(x, -\sqrt{9 - x^2}\right)$.

FIGURE 6.7 The wedge of Example 3, sliced perpendicular to the x-axis. The cross-sections are rectangles.

Solids of Revolution: The Disk Method

The solid generated by rotating a plane region about an axis in its plane is called a **solid of revolution**. To find the volume of a solid like the one shown in Figure 6.8, we need only observe that the cross-sectional area $A(x)$ is the area of a disk of radius $R(x)$, the distance of the planar region's boundary from the axis of revolution. The area is then

$$A(x) = \pi(\text{radius})^2 = \pi[R(x)]^2.$$

So the definition of volume gives

$$V = \int_a^b A(x)\, dx = \int_a^b \pi[R(x)]^2\, dx.$$

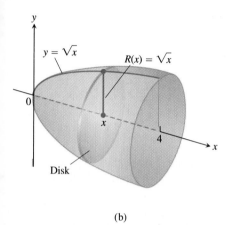

FIGURE 6.8 The region (a) and solid of revolution (b) in Example 4.

This method for calculating the volume of a solid of revolution is often called the **disk method** because a cross-section is a circular disk of radius $R(x)$.

EXAMPLE 4   A Solid of Revolution (Rotation About the x-Axis)

The region between the curve $y = \sqrt{x}$, $0 \le x \le 4$, and the x-axis is revolved about the x-axis to generate a solid. Find its volume.

Solution   We draw figures showing the region, a typical radius, and the generated solid (Figure 6.8). The volume is

$$V = \int_a^b \pi[R(x)]^2 \, dx$$

$$= \int_0^4 \pi\left[\sqrt{x}\right]^2 dx \qquad\qquad R(x) = \sqrt{x}$$

$$= \pi \int_0^4 x \, dx = \pi \left. \frac{x^2}{2} \right|_0^4 = \pi \frac{(4)^2}{2} = 8\pi. \qquad ■$$

EXAMPLE 5   Volume of a Sphere

The circle

$$x^2 + y^2 = a^2$$

is rotated about the x-axis to generate a sphere. Find its volume.

Solution   We imagine the sphere cut into thin slices by planes perpendicular to the x-axis (Figure 6.9). The cross-sectional area at a typical point x between $-a$ and a is

$$A(x) = \pi y^2 = \pi(a^2 - x^2).$$

Therefore, the volume is

$$V = \int_{-a}^{a} A(x) \, dx = \int_{-a}^{a} \pi(a^2 - x^2) \, dx = \pi \left[a^2 x - \frac{x^3}{3} \right]_{-a}^{a} = \frac{4}{3}\pi a^3.$$

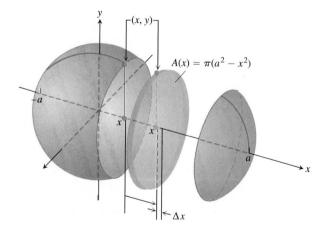

FIGURE 6.9 The sphere generated by rotating the circle $x^2 + y^2 = a^2$ about the x-axis. The radius is $R(x) = y = \sqrt{a^2 - x^2}$ (Example 5). ■

The axis of revolution in the next example is not the *x*-axis, but the rule for calculating the volume is the same: Integrate $\pi(\text{radius})^2$ between appropriate limits.

EXAMPLE 6   A Solid of Revolution (Rotation About the Line $y = 1$)

Find the volume of the solid generated by revolving the region bounded by $y = \sqrt{x}$ and the lines $y = 1, x = 4$ about the line $y = 1$.

Solution   We draw figures showing the region, a typical radius, and the generated solid (Figure 6.10). The volume is

$$V = \int_1^4 \pi[R(x)]^2 \, dx$$

$$= \int_1^4 \pi\left[\sqrt{x} - 1\right]^2 dx$$

$$= \pi \int_1^4 \left[x - 2\sqrt{x} + 1\right] dx$$

$$= \pi\left[\frac{x^2}{2} - 2 \cdot \frac{2}{3} x^{3/2} + x\right]_1^4 = \frac{7\pi}{6}.$$

(a)

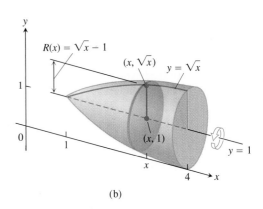

(b)

FIGURE 6.10   The region (a) and solid of revolution (b) in Example 6.

To find the volume of a solid generated by revolving a region between the *y*-axis and a curve $x = R(y), c \le y \le d$, about the *y*-axis, we use the same method with *x* replaced by *y*. In this case, the circular cross-section is

$$A(y) = \pi[\text{radius}]^2 = \pi[R(y)]^2.$$

EXAMPLE 7   Rotation About the y-Axis

Find the volume of the solid generated by revolving the region between the *y*-axis and the curve $x = 2/y, 1 \le y \le 4$, about the *y*-axis.

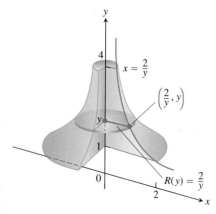

FIGURE 6.11 The region (a) and part of the solid of revolution (b) in Example 7.

Solution We draw figures showing the region, a typical radius, and the generated solid (Figure 6.11). The volume is

$$V = \int_1^4 \pi [R(y)]^2 \, dy$$

$$= \int_1^4 \pi \left(\frac{2}{y}\right)^2 dy$$

$$= \pi \int_1^4 \frac{4}{y^2} \, dy = 4\pi \left[-\frac{1}{y}\right]_1^4 = 4\pi \left[\frac{3}{4}\right]$$

$$= 3\pi.$$

EXAMPLE 8 Rotation About a Vertical Axis

Find the volume of the solid generated by revolving the region between the parabola $x = y^2 + 1$ and the line $x = 3$ about the line $x = 3$.

Solution We draw figures showing the region, a typical radius, and the generated solid (Figure 6.12). Note that the cross-sections are perpendicular to the line $x = 3$. The volume is

$$V = \int_{-\sqrt{2}}^{\sqrt{2}} \pi [R(y)]^2 \, dy$$

$$= \int_{-\sqrt{2}}^{\sqrt{2}} \pi [2 - y^2]^2 \, dy \qquad \begin{aligned} R(y) &= 3 - (y^2 + 1) \\ &= 2 - y^2 \end{aligned}$$

$$= \pi \int_{-\sqrt{2}}^{\sqrt{2}} [4 - 4y^2 + y^4] \, dy$$

$$= \pi \left[4y - \frac{4}{3}y^3 + \frac{y^5}{5}\right]_{-\sqrt{2}}^{\sqrt{2}}$$

$$= \frac{64\pi\sqrt{2}}{15}.$$

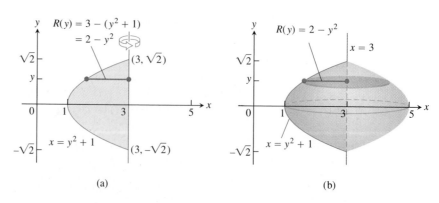

FIGURE 6.12 The region (a) and solid of revolution (b) in Example 8.

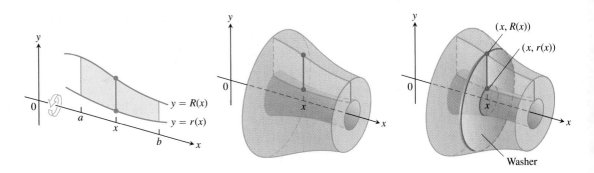

FIGURE 6.13 The cross-sections of the solid of revolution generated here are washers, not disks, so the integral $\int_a^b A(x)\,dx$ leads to a slightly different formula.

Solids of Revolution: The Washer Method

If the region we revolve to generate a solid does not border on or cross the axis of revolution, the solid has a hole in it (Figure 6.13). The cross-sections perpendicular to the axis of revolution are washers (the purplish circular surface in Figure 6.13) instead of disks. The dimensions of a typical washer are

Outer radius: $R(x)$

Inner radius: $r(x)$

The washer's area is

$$A(x) = \pi[R(x)]^2 - \pi[r(x)]^2 = \pi([R(x)]^2 - [r(x)]^2).$$

Consequently, the definition of volume gives

$$V = \int_a^b A(x)\,dx = \int_a^b \pi([R(x)]^2 - [r(x)]^2)\,dx.$$

This method for calculating the volume of a solid of revolution is called the **washer method** because a slab is a circular washer of outer radius $R(x)$ and inner radius $r(x)$.

EXAMPLE 9 A Washer Cross-Section (Rotation About the x-Axis)

The region bounded by the curve $y = x^2 + 1$ and the line $y = -x + 3$ is revolved about the x-axis to generate a solid. Find the volume of the solid.

Solution

1. Draw the region and sketch a line segment across it perpendicular to the axis of revolution (the red segment in Figure 6.14).

2. Find the outer and inner radii of the washer that would be swept out by the line segment if it were revolved about the x-axis along with the region.

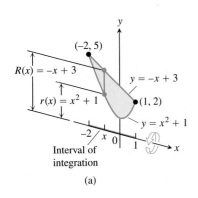

FIGURE 6.14 (a) The region in Example 9 spanned by a line segment perpendicular to the axis of revolution. (b) When the region is revolved about the x-axis, the line segment generates a washer.

These radii are the distances of the ends of the line segment from the axis of revolution (Figure 6.14).

$$\text{Outer radius:} \quad R(x) = -x + 3$$

$$\text{Inner radius:} \quad r(x) = x^2 + 1$$

3. Find the limits of integration by finding the x-coordinates of the intersection points of the curve and line in Figure 6.14a.

$$x^2 + 1 = -x + 3$$
$$x^2 + x - 2 = 0$$
$$(x + 2)(x - 1) = 0$$
$$x = -2, \quad x = 1$$

4. Evaluate the volume integral.

$$V = \int_a^b \pi([R(x)]^2 - [r(x)]^2)\, dx$$

$$= \int_{-2}^{1} \pi((-x + 3)^2 - (x^2 + 1)^2)\, dx \qquad \text{Values from Steps 2 and 3}$$

$$= \int_{-2}^{1} \pi(8 - 6x - x^2 - x^4)\, dx$$

$$= \pi\left[8x - 3x^2 - \frac{x^3}{3} - \frac{x^5}{5}\right]_{-2}^{1} = \frac{117\pi}{5} \qquad \blacksquare$$

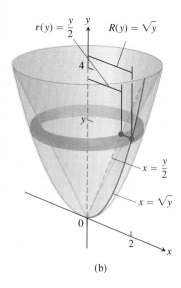

FIGURE 6.15 (a) The region being rotated about the y-axis, the washer radii, and limits of integration in Example 10. (b) The washer swept out by the line segment in part (a).

To find the volume of a solid formed by revolving a region about the y-axis, we use the same procedure as in Example 9, but integrate with respect to y instead of x. In this situation the line segment sweeping out a typical washer is perpendicular to the y-axis (the axis of revolution), and the outer and inner radii of the washer are functions of y.

EXAMPLE 10   A Washer Cross-Section (Rotation About the y-Axis)

The region bounded by the parabola $y = x^2$ and the line $y = 2x$ in the first quadrant is revolved about the y-axis to generate a solid. Find the volume of the solid.

Solution   First we sketch the region and draw a line segment across it perpendicular to the axis of revolution (the y-axis). See Figure 6.15a.

The radii of the washer swept out by the line segment are $R(y) = \sqrt{y}$, $r(y) = y/2$ (Figure 6.15).

The line and parabola intersect at $y = 0$ and $y = 4$, so the limits of integration are $c = 0$ and $d = 4$. We integrate to find the volume:

$$V = \int_c^d \pi([R(y)]^2 - [r(y)]^2)\, dy$$

$$= \int_0^4 \pi\left(\left[\sqrt{y}\right]^2 - \left[\frac{y}{2}\right]^2\right) dy$$

$$= \pi \int_0^4 \left(y - \frac{y^2}{4}\right) dy = \pi\left[\frac{y^2}{2} - \frac{y^3}{12}\right]_0^4 = \frac{8}{3}\pi. \qquad \blacksquare$$

Summary

In all of our volume examples, no matter how the cross-sectional area $A(x)$ of a typical slab is determined, the definition of volume as the definite integral $V = \int_a^b A(x)\,dx$ is the heart of the calculations we made.

EXERCISES 6.1

Cross-Sectional Areas

In Exercises 1 and 2, find a formula for the area $A(x)$ of the cross-sections of the solid perpendicular to the x-axis.

1. The solid lies between planes perpendicular to the x-axis at $x = -1$ and $x = 1$. In each case, the cross-sections perpendicular to the x-axis between these planes run from the semicircle $y = -\sqrt{1 - x^2}$ to the semicircle $y = \sqrt{1 - x^2}$.

a. The cross-sections are circular disks with diameters in the xy-plane.

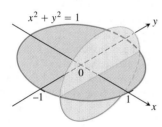

b. The cross-sections are squares with bases in the xy-plane.

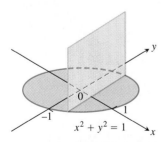

c. The cross-sections are squares with diagonals in the xy-plane. (The length of a square's diagonal is $\sqrt{2}$ times the length of its sides.)

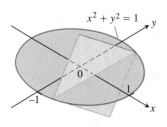

d. The cross-sections are equilateral triangles with bases in the xy-plane.

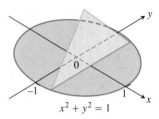

2. The solid lies between planes perpendicular to the x-axis at $x = 0$ and $x = 4$. The cross-sections perpendicular to the x-axis between these planes run from the parabola $y = -\sqrt{x}$ to the parabola $y = \sqrt{x}$.

a. The cross-sections are circular disks with diameters in the xy-plane.

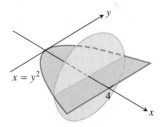

b. The cross-sections are squares with bases in the xy-plane.

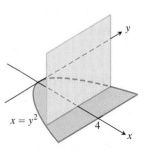

c. The cross-sections are squares with diagonals in the xy-plane.

d. The cross-sections are equilateral triangles with bases in the xy-plane.

Volumes by Slicing

Find the volumes of the solids in Exercises 3–10.

3. The solid lies between planes perpendicular to the x-axis at $x = 0$ and $x = 4$. The cross-sections perpendicular to the axis on the interval $0 \le x \le 4$ are squares whose diagonals run from the parabola $y = -\sqrt{x}$ to the parabola $y = \sqrt{x}$.

4. The solid lies between planes perpendicular to the x-axis at $x = -1$ and $x = 1$. The cross-sections perpendicular to the x-axis are circular disks whose diameters run from the parabola $y = x^2$ to the parabola $y = 2 - x^2$.

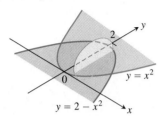

5. The solid lies between planes perpendicular to the x-axis at $x = -1$ and $x = 1$. The cross-sections perpendicular to the x-axis between these planes are squares whose bases run from the semicircle $y = -\sqrt{1 - x^2}$ to the semicircle $y = \sqrt{1 - x^2}$.

6. The solid lies between planes perpendicular to the x-axis at $x = -1$ and $x = 1$. The cross-sections perpendicular to the x-axis between these planes are squares whose diagonals run from the semicircle $y = -\sqrt{1 - x^2}$ to the semicircle $y = \sqrt{1 - x^2}$.

7. The base of a solid is the region between the curve $y = 2\sqrt{\sin x}$ and the interval $[0, \pi]$ on the x-axis. The cross-sections perpendicular to the x-axis are

a. equilateral triangles with bases running from the x-axis to the curve as shown in the figure.

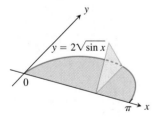

b. squares with bases running from the x-axis to the curve.

8. The solid lies between planes perpendicular to the x-axis at $x = -\pi/3$ and $x = \pi/3$. The cross-sections perpendicular to the x-axis are

a. circular disks with diameters running from the curve $y = \tan x$ to the curve $y = \sec x$.

b. squares whose bases run from the curve $y = \tan x$ to the curve $y = \sec x$.

9. The solid lies between planes perpendicular to the y-axis at $y = 0$ and $y = 2$. The cross-sections perpendicular to the y-axis are circular disks with diameters running from the y-axis to the parabola $x = \sqrt{5}y^2$.

10. The base of the solid is the disk $x^2 + y^2 \le 1$. The cross-sections by planes perpendicular to the y-axis between $y = -1$ and $y = 1$ are isosceles right triangles with one leg in the disk.

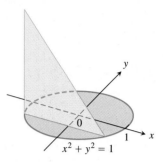

11. A twisted solid A square of side length s lies in a plane perpendicular to a line L. One vertex of the square lies on L. As this square moves a distance h along L, the square turns one revolution about L to generate a corkscrew-like column with square cross-sections.

a. Find the volume of the column.

b. What will the volume be if the square turns twice instead of once? Give reasons for your answer.

12. Cavalieri's Principle A solid lies between planes perpendicular to the x-axis at $x = 0$ and $x = 12$. The cross-sections by planes perpendicular to the x-axis are circular disks whose diameters run from the line $y = x/2$ to the line $y = x$ as shown in the accompanying figure. Explain why the solid has the same volume as a right circular cone with base radius 3 and height 12.

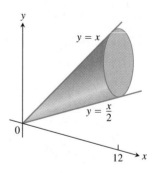

Volumes by the Disk Method

In Exercises 13–16, find the volume of the solid generated by revolving the shaded region about the given axis.

13. About the x-axis   **14.** About the y-axis

15. About the *y*-axis

16. About the *x*-axis

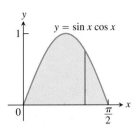

Find the volumes of the solids generated by revolving the regions bounded by the lines and curves in Exercises 17–22 about the *x*-axis.

17. $y = x^2$, $y = 0$, $x = 2$ **18.** $y = x^3$, $y = 0$, $x = 2$

19. $y = \sqrt{9 - x^2}$, $y = 0$ **20.** $y = x - x^2$, $y = 0$

21. $y = \sqrt{\cos x}$, $0 \le x \le \pi/2$, $y = 0$, $x = 0$

22. $y = \sec x$, $y = 0$, $x = -\pi/4$, $x = \pi/4$

In Exercises 23 and 24, find the volume of the solid generated by revolving the region about the given line.

23. The region in the first quadrant bounded above by the line $y = \sqrt{2}$, below by the curve $y = \sec x \tan x$, and on the left by the *y*-axis, about the line $y = \sqrt{2}$

24. The region in the first quadrant bounded above by the line $y = 2$, below by the curve $y = 2 \sin x$, $0 \le x \le \pi/2$, and on the left by the *y*-axis, about the line $y = 2$

Find the volumes of the solids generated by revolving the regions bounded by the lines and curves in Exercises 25–30 about the *y*-axis.

25. The region enclosed by $x = \sqrt{5}y^2$, $x = 0$, $y = -1$, $y = 1$

26. The region enclosed by $x = y^{3/2}$, $x = 0$, $y = 2$

27. The region enclosed by $x = \sqrt{2 \sin 2y}$, $0 \le y \le \pi/2$, $x = 0$

28. The region enclosed by $x = \sqrt{\cos (\pi y/4)}$, $-2 \le y \le 0$, $x = 0$

29. $x = 2/(y + 1)$, $x = 0$, $y = 0$, $y = 3$

30. $x = \sqrt{2y}/(y^2 + 1)$, $x = 0$, $y = 1$

Volumes by the Washer Method

Find the volumes of the solids generated by revolving the shaded regions in Exercises 31 and 32 about the indicated axes.

31. The *x*-axis

32. The *y*-axis

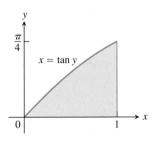

Find the volumes of the solids generated by revolving the regions bounded by the lines and curves in Exercises 33–38 about the *x*-axis.

33. $y = x$, $y = 1$, $x = 0$ **34.** $y = 2\sqrt{x}$, $y = 2$, $x = 0$

35. $y = x^2 + 1$, $y = x + 3$ **36.** $y = 4 - x^2$, $y = 2 - x$

37. $y = \sec x$, $y = \sqrt{2}$, $-\pi/4 \le x \le \pi/4$

38. $y = \sec x$, $y = \tan x$, $x = 0$, $x = 1$

In Exercises 39–42, find the volume of the solid generated by revolving each region about the *y*-axis.

39. The region enclosed by the triangle with vertices $(1, 0)$, $(2, 1)$, and $(1, 1)$

40. The region enclosed by the triangle with vertices $(0, 1)$, $(1, 0)$, and $(1, 1)$

41. The region in the first quadrant bounded above by the parabola $y = x^2$, below by the *x*-axis, and on the right by the line $x = 2$

42. The region in the first quadrant bounded on the left by the circle $x^2 + y^2 = 3$, on the right by the line $x = \sqrt{3}$, and above by the line $y = \sqrt{3}$

In Exercises 43 and 44, find the volume of the solid generated by revolving each region about the given axis.

43. The region in the first quadrant bounded above by the curve $y = x^2$, below by the *x*-axis, and on the right by the line $x = 1$, about the line $x = -1$

44. The region in the second quadrant bounded above by the curve $y = -x^3$, below by the *x*-axis, and on the left by the line $x = -1$, about the line $x = -2$

Volumes of Solids of Revolution

45. Find the volume of the solid generated by revolving the region bounded by $y = \sqrt{x}$ and the lines $y = 2$ and $x = 0$ about

    a. the *x*-axis.   **b.** the *y*-axis.

    c. the line $y = 2$.   **d.** the line $x = 4$.

46. Find the volume of the solid generated by revolving the triangular region bounded by the lines $y = 2x$, $y = 0$, and $x = 1$ about

    a. the line $x = 1$.   **b.** the line $x = 2$.

47. Find the volume of the solid generated by revolving the region bounded by the parabola $y = x^2$ and the line $y = 1$ about

    a. the line $y = 1$.   **b.** the line $y = 2$.

    c. the line $y = -1$.

48. By integration, find the volume of the solid generated by revolving the triangular region with vertices $(0, 0)$, $(b, 0)$, $(0, h)$ about

    a. the *x*-axis.   **b.** the *y*-axis.

Theory and Applications

49. The volume of a torus The disk $x^2 + y^2 \le a^2$ is revolved about the line $x = b$ ($b > a$) to generate a solid shaped like a doughnut and called a *torus*. Find its volume. (*Hint:* $\int_{-a}^{a} \sqrt{a^2 - y^2} \, dy = \pi a^2 / 2$, since it is the area of a semicircle of radius *a*.)

50. Volume of a bowl   A bowl has a shape that can be generated by revolving the graph of $y = x^2/2$ between $y = 0$ and $y = 5$ about the *y*-axis.

   a. Find the volume of the bowl.

   b. Related rates   If we fill the bowl with water at a constant rate of 3 cubic units per second, how fast will the water level in the bowl be rising when the water is 4 units deep?

51. Volume of a bowl

   a. A hemispherical bowl of radius *a* contains water to a depth *h*. Find the volume of water in the bowl.

   b. Related rates   Water runs into a sunken concrete hemispherical bowl of radius 5 m at the rate of 0.2 m³/sec. How fast is the water level in the bowl rising when the water is 4 m deep?

52. Explain how you could estimate the volume of a solid of revolution by measuring the shadow cast on a table parallel to its axis of revolution by a light shining directly above it.

53. Volume of a hemisphere   Derive the formula $V = (2/3)\pi R^3$ for the volume of a hemisphere of radius *R* by comparing its cross-sections with the cross-sections of a solid right circular cylinder of radius *R* and height *R* from which a solid right circular cone of base radius *R* and height *R* has been removed as suggested by the accompanying figure.

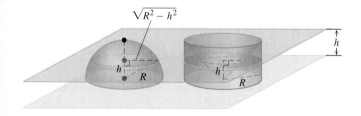

54. Volume of a cone   Use calculus to find the volume of a right circular cone of height *h* and base radius *r*.

55. Designing a wok   You are designing a wok frying pan that will be shaped like a spherical bowl with handles. A bit of experimentation at home persuades you that you can get one that holds about 3 L if you make it 9 cm deep and give the sphere a radius of 16 cm. To be sure, you picture the wok as a solid of revolution, as shown here, and calculate its volume with an integral. To the nearest cubic centimeter, what volume do you really get? (1 L = 1000 cm³.)

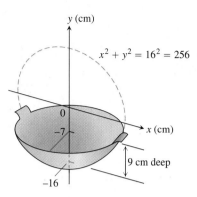

56. Designing a plumb bob   Having been asked to design a brass plumb bob that will weigh in the neighborhood of 190 g, you decide to shape it like the solid of revolution shown here. Find the plumb bob's volume. If you specify a brass that weighs 8.5 g/cm³, how much will the plumb bob weigh (to the nearest gram)?

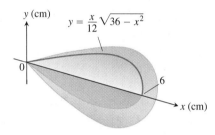

57. Max-min   The arch $y = \sin x$, $0 \le x \le \pi$, is revolved about the line $y = c$, $0 \le c \le 1$, to generate the solid in Figure 6.16.

   a. Find the value of *c* that minimizes the volume of the solid. What is the minimum volume?

   b. What value of *c* in [0, 1] maximizes the volume of the solid?

   T **c.** Graph the solid's volume as a function of *c*, first for $0 \le c \le 1$ and then on a larger domain. What happens to the volume of the solid as *c* moves away from [0, 1]? Does this make sense physically? Give reasons for your answers.

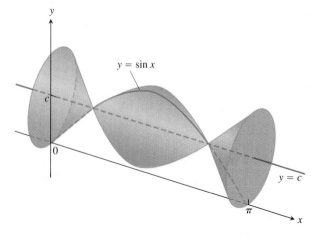

FIGURE 6.16

58. An auxiliary fuel tank You are designing an auxiliary fuel tank that will fit under a helicopter's fuselage to extend its range. After some experimentation at your drawing board, you decide to shape the tank like the surface generated by revolving the curve $y = 1 - (x^2/16)$, $-4 \leq x \leq 4$, about the x-axis (dimensions in feet).

a. How many cubic feet of fuel will the tank hold (to the nearest cubic foot)?

b. A cubic foot holds 7.481 gal. If the helicopter gets 2 mi to the gallon, how many additional miles will the helicopter be able to fly once the tank is installed (to the nearest mile)?

6.2 Volumes by Cylindrical Shells

In Section 6.1 we defined the volume of a solid S as the definite integral

$$V = \int_a^b A(x) \, dx,$$

where $A(x)$ is an integrable cross-sectional area of S from $x = a$ to $x = b$. The area $A(x)$ was obtained by slicing through the solid with a plane perpendicular to the x-axis. In this section we use the same integral definition for volume, but obtain the area by slicing through the solid in a different way. Now we slice through the solid using circular cylinders of increasing radii, like cookie cutters. We slice straight down through the solid perpendicular to the x-axis, with the axis of the cylinder parallel to the y-axis. The vertical axis of each cylinder is the same line, but the radii of the cylinders increase with each slice. In this way the solid S is sliced up into thin cylindrical shells of constant thickness that grow outward from their common axis, like circular tree rings. Unrolling a cylindrical shell shows that its volume is approximately that of a rectangular slab with area $A(x)$ and thickness Δx. This allows us to apply the same integral definition for volume as before. Before describing the method in general, let's look at an example to gain some insight.

EXAMPLE 1   Finding a Volume Using Shells

The region enclosed by the x-axis and the parabola $y = f(x) = 3x - x^2$ is revolved about the vertical line $x = -1$ to generate the shape of a solid (Figure 6.17). Find the volume of the solid.

Solution   Using the washer method from Section 6.1 would be awkward here because we would need to express the x-values of the left and right branches of the parabola in terms

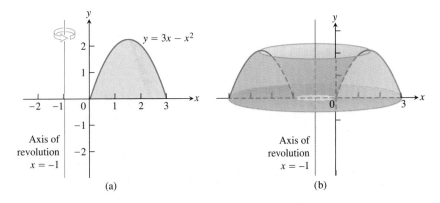

FIGURE 6.17   (a) The graph of the region in Example 1, before revolution. (b) The solid formed when the region in part (a) is revolved about the axis of revolution $x = -1$.

FIGURE 6.18 A cylindrical shell of height y_k obtained by rotating a vertical strip of thickness Δx about the line $x = -1$. The outer radius of the cylinder occurs at x_k, where the height of the parabola is $y_k = 3x_k - x_k^2$ (Example 1).

of y. (These x-values are the inner and outer radii for a typical washer, leading to complicated formulas.) Instead of rotating a horizontal strip of thickness Δy, we rotate a *vertical strip* of thickness Δx. This rotation produces a *cylindrical shell* of height y_k above a point x_k within the base of the vertical strip, and of thickness Δx. An example of a cylindrical shell is shown as the orange-shaded region in Figure 6.18. We can think of the cylindrical shell shown in the figure as approximating a slice of the solid obtained by cutting straight down through it, parallel to the axis of revolution, all the way around close to the inside hole. We then cut another cylindrical slice around the enlarged hole, then another, and so on, obtaining n cylinders. The radii of the cylinders gradually increase, and the heights of the cylinders follow the contour of the parabola: shorter to taller, then back to shorter (Figure 6.17a).

Each slice is sitting over a subinterval of the x-axis of length (width) Δx. Its radius is approximately $(1 + x_k)$, and its height is approximately $3x_k - x_k^2$. If we unroll the cylinder at x_k and flatten it out, it becomes (approximately) a rectangular slab with thickness Δx (Figure 6.19). The outer circumference of the kth cylinder is $2\pi \cdot \text{radius} = 2\pi(1 + x_k)$, and this is the length of the rolled-out rectangular slab. Its volume is approximated by that of a rectangular solid,

$$\Delta V_k = \text{circumference} \times \text{height} \times \text{thickness}$$
$$= 2\pi(1 + x_k) \cdot \left(3x_k - x_k^2\right) \cdot \Delta x.$$

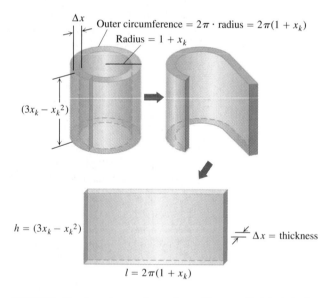

FIGURE 6.19 Imagine cutting and unrolling a cylindrical shell to get a flat (nearly) rectangular solid (Example 1).

Summing together the volumes ΔV_k of the individual cylindrical shells over the interval $[0, 3]$ gives the Riemann sum

$$\sum_{k=1}^{n} \Delta V_k = \sum_{k=1}^{n} 2\pi(x_k + 1)\left(3x_k - x_k^2\right) \Delta x.$$

Taking the limit as the thickness $\Delta x \to 0$ gives the volume integral

$$V = \lim_{n \to \infty} \sum_{k=1}^{n} 2\pi(x_k + 1)(3x_k - x_k^2)\,\Delta x$$

$$= \int_0^3 2\pi(x + 1)(3x - x^2)\,dx$$

$$= \int_0^3 2\pi(3x^2 + 3x - x^3 - x^2)\,dx$$

$$= 2\pi \int_0^3 (2x^2 + 3x - x^3)\,dx$$

$$= 2\pi \left[\frac{2}{3}x^3 + \frac{3}{2}x^2 - \frac{1}{4}x^4 \right]_0^3 = \frac{45\pi}{2}.$$

We now generalize the procedure used in Example 1.

The Shell Method

Suppose the region bounded by the graph of a nonnegative continuous function $y = f(x)$ and the x-axis over the finite closed interval $[a, b]$ lies to the right of the vertical line $x = L$ (Figure 6.20a). We assume $a \geq L$, so the vertical line may touch the region, but not pass through it. We generate a solid S by rotating this region about the vertical line L.

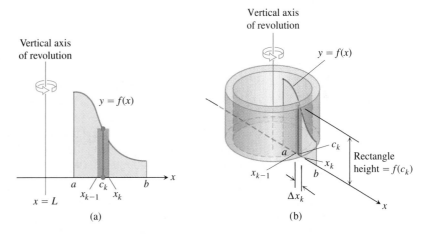

FIGURE 6.20 When the region shown in (a) is revolved about the vertical line $x = L$, a solid is produced which can be sliced into cylindrical shells. A typical shell is shown in (b).

Let P be a partition of the interval $[a, b]$ by the points $a = x_0 < x_1 < \cdots < x_n = b$, and let c_k be the midpoint of the kth subinterval $[x_{k-1}, x_k]$. We approximate the region in Figure 6.20a with rectangles based on this partition of $[a, b]$. A typical approximating rectangle has height $f(c_k)$ and width $\Delta x_k = x_k - x_{k-1}$. If this rectangle is rotated about the vertical line $x = L$, then a shell is swept out, as in Figure 6.20b. A formula from geometry tells us that the volume of the shell swept out by the rectangle is

$$\Delta V_k = 2\pi \times \text{average shell radius} \times \text{shell height} \times \text{thickness}$$
$$= 2\pi \cdot (c_k - L) \cdot f(c_k) \cdot \Delta x_k.$$

We approximate the volume of the solid S by summing the volumes of the shells swept out by the n rectangles based on P:

$$V \approx \sum_{k=1}^{n} \Delta V_k.$$

The limit of this Riemann sum as $\|P\| \rightarrow 0$ gives the volume of the solid as a definite integral:

$$V = \lim_{\|P\|\rightarrow 0} \sum_{k=1}^{n} \Delta V_k = \int_a^b 2\pi(\text{shell radius})(\text{shell height}) \, dx.$$

$$= \int_a^b 2\pi(x - L)f(x) \, dx.$$

We refer to the variable of integration, here x, as the **thickness variable**. We use the first integral, rather than the second containing a formula for the integrand, to emphasize the *process* of the shell method. This will allow for rotations about a horizontal line L as well.

Shell Formula for Revolution About a Vertical Line
The volume of the solid generated by revolving the region between the x-axis and the graph of a continuous function $y = f(x) \geq 0, L \leq a \leq x \leq b$, about a vertical line $x = L$ is

$$V = \int_a^b 2\pi \left(\begin{array}{c} \text{shell} \\ \text{radius} \end{array} \right) \left(\begin{array}{c} \text{shell} \\ \text{height} \end{array} \right) dx.$$

EXAMPLE 2   Cylindrical Shells Revolving About the y-Axis

The region bounded by the curve $y = \sqrt{x}$, the x-axis, and the line $x = 4$ is revolved about the y-axis to generate a solid. Find the volume of the solid.

Solution   Sketch the region and draw a line segment across it *parallel* to the axis of revolution (Figure 6.21a). Label the segment's height (shell height) and distance from the axis of revolution (shell radius). (We drew the shell in Figure 6.21b, but you need not do that.)

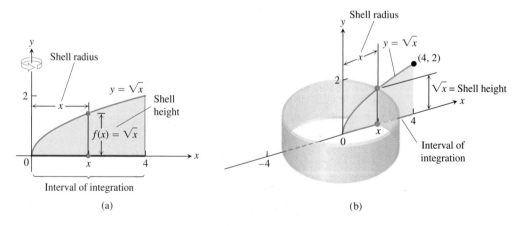

FIGURE 6.21   (a) The region, shell dimensions, and interval of integration in Example 2. (b) The shell swept out by the vertical segment in part (a) with a width Δx.

The shell thickness variable is x, so the limits of integration for the shell formula are $a = 0$ and $b = 4$ (Figure 6.21). The volume is then

$$V = \int_a^b 2\pi \left(\begin{array}{c}\text{shell}\\\text{radius}\end{array}\right)\left(\begin{array}{c}\text{shell}\\\text{height}\end{array}\right) dx$$

$$= \int_0^4 2\pi(x)\left(\sqrt{x}\right) dx$$

$$= 2\pi \int_0^4 x^{3/2} \, dx = 2\pi \left[\frac{2}{5} x^{5/2}\right]_0^4 = \frac{128\pi}{5}.$$ ∎

So far, we have used vertical axes of revolution. For horizontal axes, we replace the x's with y's.

EXAMPLE 3   Cylindrical Shells Revolving About the x-Axis

The region bounded by the curve $y = \sqrt{x}$, the x-axis, and the line $x = 4$ is revolved about the x-axis to generate a solid. Find the volume of the solid.

Solution   Sketch the region and draw a line segment across it *parallel* to the axis of revolution (Figure 6.22a). Label the segment's length (shell height) and distance from the axis of revolution (shell radius). (We drew the shell in Figure 6.22b, but you need not do that.)

In this case, the shell thickness variable is y, so the limits of integration for the shell formula method are $a = 0$ and $b = 2$ (along the y-axis in Figure 6.22). The volume of the solid is

$$V = \int_a^b 2\pi \left(\begin{array}{c}\text{shell}\\\text{radius}\end{array}\right)\left(\begin{array}{c}\text{shell}\\\text{height}\end{array}\right) dy$$

$$= \int_0^2 2\pi(y)(4 - y^2) \, dy$$

$$= \int_0^2 2\pi(4y - y^3) \, dy$$

$$= 2\pi \left[2y^2 - \frac{y^4}{4}\right]_0^2 = 8\pi.$$ ∎

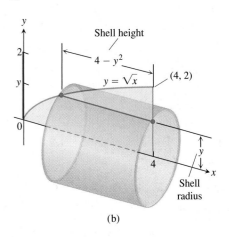

FIGURE 6.22   (a) The region, shell dimensions, and interval of integration in Example 3. (b) The shell swept out by the horizontal segment in part (a) with a width Δy.

> **Summary of the Shell Method**
>
> Regardless of the position of the axis of revolution (horizontal or vertical), the steps for implementing the shell method are these.
>
> 1. *Draw the region and sketch a line segment* across it *parallel* to the axis of revolution. *Label* the segment's height or length (shell height) and distance from the axis of revolution (shell radius).
> 2. *Find* the limits of integration for the thickness variable.
> 3. *Integrate* the product 2π (shell radius) (shell height) with respect to the thickness variable (x or y) to find the volume.

The shell method gives the same answer as the washer method when both are used to calculate the volume of a region. We do not prove that result here, but it is illustrated in Exercises 33 and 34. Both volume formulas are actually special cases of a general volume formula we look at in studying double and triple integrals in Chapter 15. That general formula also allows for computing volumes of solids other than those swept out by regions of revolution.

EXERCISES 6.2

In Exercises 1–6, use the shell method to find the volumes of the solids generated by revolving the shaded region about the indicated axis.

1.

2.

3.

4.

5. The y-axis

6. The y-axis

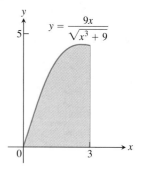

Revolution About the y-Axis

Use the shell method to find the volumes of the solids generated by revolving the regions bounded by the curves and lines in Exercises 7–14 about the y-axis.

7. $y = x$, $y = -x/2$, $x = 2$

8. $y = 2x$, $y = x/2$, $x = 1$

9. $y = x^2$, $y = 2 - x$, $x = 0$, for $x \geq 0$

10. $y = 2 - x^2$, $y = x^2$, $x = 0$

11. $y = 2x - 1$, $y = \sqrt{x}$, $x = 0$

12. $y = 3/(2\sqrt{x}), \quad y = 0, \quad x = 1, \quad x = 4$

13. Let $f(x) = \begin{cases} (\sin x)/x, & 0 < x \le \pi \\ 1, & x = 0 \end{cases}$

   a. Show that $x f(x) = \sin x, 0 \le x \le \pi$.

   b. Find the volume of the solid generated by revolving the shaded region about the y-axis.

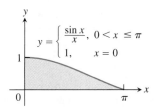

$$y = \begin{cases} \dfrac{\sin x}{x}, & 0 < x \le \pi \\ 1, & x = 0 \end{cases}$$

14. Let $g(x) = \begin{cases} (\tan x)^2/x, & 0 < x \le \pi/4 \\ 0, & x = 0 \end{cases}$

   a. Show that $x g(x) = (\tan x)^2, 0 \le x \le \pi/4$.

   b. Find the volume of the solid generated by revolving the shaded region about the y-axis.

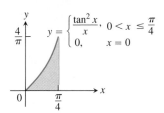

$$y = \begin{cases} \dfrac{\tan^2 x}{x}, & 0 < x \le \dfrac{\pi}{4} \\ 0, & x = 0 \end{cases}$$

Revolution About the x-Axis

Use the shell method to find the volumes of the solids generated by revolving the regions bounded by the curves and lines in Exercises 15–22 about the x-axis.

15. $x = \sqrt{y}, \quad x = -y, \quad y = 2$

16. $x = y^2, \quad x = -y, \quad y = 2, \quad y \ge 0$

17. $x = 2y - y^2, \quad x = 0$

18. $x = 2y - y^2, \quad x = y$

19. $y = |x|, \quad y = 1$

20. $y = x, \quad y = 2x, \quad y = 2$

21. $y = \sqrt{x}, \quad y = 0, \quad y = x - 2$

22. $y = \sqrt{x}, \quad y = 0, \quad y = 2 - x$

Revolution About Horizontal Lines

In Exercises 23 and 24, use the shell method to find the volumes of the solids generated by revolving the shaded regions about the indicated axes.

23. a. The x-axis   **b.** The line $y = 1$

    c. The line $y = 8/5$ **d.** The line $y = -2/5$

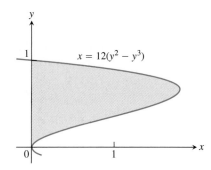

$x = 12(y^2 - y^3)$

24. a. The x-axis   **b.** The line $y = 2$

    c. The line $y = 5$ **d.** The line $y = -5/8$

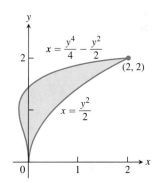

$x = \dfrac{y^4}{4} - \dfrac{y^2}{2}$

$(2, 2)$

$x = \dfrac{y^2}{2}$

Comparing the Washer and Shell Models

For some regions, both the washer and shell methods work well for the solid generated by revolving the region about the coordinate axes, but this is not always the case. When a region is revolved about the y-axis, for example, and washers are used, we must integrate with respect to y. It may not be possible, however, to express the integrand in terms of y. In such a case, the shell method allows us to integrate with respect to x instead. Exercises 25 and 26 provide some insight.

25. Compute the volume of the solid generated by revolving the region bounded by $y = x$ and $y = x^2$ about each coordinate axis using

   a. the shell method.   **b.** the washer method.

26. Compute the volume of the solid generated by revolving the triangular region bounded by the lines $2y = x + 4, y = x$, and $x = 0$ about

   a. the x-axis using the washer method.

   b. the y-axis using the shell method.

   c. the line $x = 4$ using the shell method.

   d. the line $y = 8$ using the washer method.

Choosing Shells or Washers

In Exercises 27–32, find the volumes of the solids generated by revolving the regions about the given axes. If you think it would be better to use washers in any given instance, feel free to do so.

27. The triangle with vertices $(1, 1)$, $(1, 2)$, and $(2, 2)$ about

    a. the x-axis   **b.** the y-axis

    c. the line $x = 10/3$ **d.** the line $y = 1$

28. The region bounded by $y = \sqrt{x}$, $y = 2$, $x = 0$ about

    a. the x-axis   **b.** the y-axis

    c. the line $x = 4$ **d.** the line $y = 2$

29. The region in the first quadrant bounded by the curve $x = y - y^3$ and the y-axis about

    a. the x-axis   **b.** the line $y = 1$

30. The region in the first quadrant bounded by $x = y - y^3$, $x = 1$, and $y = 1$ about

    a. the x-axis   **b.** the y-axis

    c. the line $x = 1$ **d.** the line $y = 1$

31. The region bounded by $y = \sqrt{x}$ and $y = x^2/8$ about

    a. the x-axis   **b.** the y-axis

32. The region bounded by $y = 2x - x^2$ and $y = x$ about

    a. the y-axis   **b.** the line $x = 1$

33. The region in the first quadrant that is bounded above by the curve $y = 1/x^{1/4}$, on the left by the line $x = 1/16$, and below by the line $y = 1$ is revolved about the x-axis to generate a solid. Find the volume of the solid by

    a. the washer method.   **b.** the shell method.

34. The region in the first quadrant that is bounded above by the curve $y = 1/\sqrt{x}$, on the left by the line $x = 1/4$, and below by the line $y = 1$ is revolved about the y-axis to generate a solid. Find the volume of the solid by

    a. the washer method.   **b.** the shell method.

Choosing Disks, Washers, or Shells

35. The region shown here is to be revolved about the x-axis to generate a solid. Which of the methods (disk, washer, shell) could you use to find the volume of the solid? How many integrals would be required in each case? Explain.

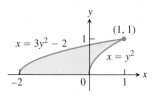

36. The region shown here is to be revolved about the y-axis to generate a solid. Which of the methods (disk, washer, shell) could you use to find the volume of the solid? How many integrals would be required in each case? Give reasons for your answers.

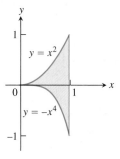

Lengths of Plane Curves

HISTORICAL BIOGRAPHY

Archimedes
(287–212 B.C.)

We know what is meant by the length of a straight line segment, but without calculus, we have no precise notion of the length of a general winding curve. The idea of approximating the length of a curve running from point A to point B by subdividing the curve into many pieces and joining successive points of division by straight line segments dates back to the ancient Greeks. Archimedes used this method to approximate the circumference of a circle by inscribing a polygon of n sides and then using geometry to compute its perimeter

FIGURE 6.23 Archimedes used the perimeters of inscribed polygons to approximate the circumference of a circle. For $n = 96$ the approximation method gives $\pi \approx 3.14103$ as the circumference of the unit circle.

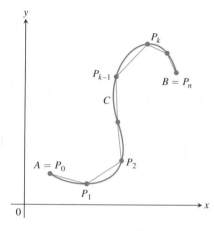

FIGURE 6.24 The curve C defined parametrically by the equations $x = f(t)$ and $y = g(t)$, $a \le t \le b$. The length of the curve from A to B is approximated by the sum of the lengths of the polygonal path (straight line segments) starting at $A = P_0$, then to P_1, and so on, ending at $B = P_n$.

(Figure 6.23). The extension of this idea to a more general curve is displayed in Figure 6.24, and we now describe how that method works.

Length of a Parametrically Defined Curve

Let C be a curve given parametrically by the equations

$$x = f(t) \quad \text{and} \quad y = g(t), \quad a \le t \le b.$$

We assume the functions f and g have continuous derivatives on the interval $[a, b]$ that are not simultaneously zero. Such functions are said to be **continuously differentiable**, and the curve C defined by them is called a **smooth curve**. It may be helpful to imagine the curve as the path of a particle moving from point $A = (f(a), g(a))$ at time $t = a$ to point $B = (f(b), g(b))$ in Figure 6.24. We subdivide the path (or arc) AB into n pieces at points $A = P_0, P_1, P_2, \ldots, P_n = B$. These points correspond to a partition of the interval $[a, b]$ by $a = t_0 < t_1 < t_2 < \cdots < t_n = b$, where $P_k = (f(t_k), g(t_k))$. Join successive points of this subdivision by straight line segments (Figure 6.24). A representative line segment has length

$$L_k = \sqrt{(\Delta x_k)^2 + (\Delta y_k)^2}$$
$$= \sqrt{[f(t_k) - f(t_{k-1})]^2 + [g(t_k) - g(t_{k-1})]^2}$$

(see Figure 6.25). If Δt_k is small, the length L_k is approximately the length of arc $P_{k-1}P_k$. By the Mean Value Theorem there are numbers t_k^* and t_k^{**} in $[t_{k-1}, t_k]$ such that

$$\Delta x_k = f(t_k) - f(t_{k-1}) = f'(t_k^*) \Delta t_k,$$
$$\Delta y_k = g(t_k) - g(t_{k-1}) = g'(t_k^{**}) \Delta t_k.$$

Assuming the path from A to B is traversed exactly once as t increases from $t = a$ to $t = b$, with no doubling back or retracing, an intuitive approximation to the "length" of the curve AB is the sum of all the lengths L_k:

$$\sum_{k=1}^{n} L_k = \sum_{k=1}^{n} \sqrt{(\Delta x_k)^2 + (\Delta y_k)^2}$$
$$= \sum_{k=1}^{n} \sqrt{[f'(t_k^*)]^2 + [g'(t_k^{**})]^2} \Delta t_k.$$

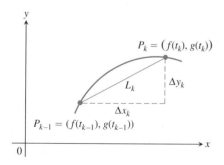

FIGURE 6.25 The arc $P_{k-1}P_k$ is approximated by the straight line segment shown here, which has length $L_k = \sqrt{(\Delta x_k)^2 + (\Delta y_k)^2}$.

Although this last sum on the right is not exactly a Riemann sum (because f' and g' are evaluated at different points), a theorem in advanced calculus guarantees its limit, as the norm of the partition tends to zero, to be the definite integral

$$\lim_{n \to \infty} \sum_{k=1}^{n} \sqrt{[f'(t_k^*)]^2 + [g'(t_k^{**})]^2} \, \Delta t_k = \int_a^b \sqrt{[f'(t)]^2 + [g'(t)]^2} \, dt.$$

Therefore, it is reasonable to define the length of the curve from A to B as this integral.

DEFINITION   Length of a Parametric Curve

If a curve C is defined parametrically by $x = f(t)$ and $y = g(t)$, $a \leq t \leq b$, where f' and g' are continuous and not simultaneously zero on $[a, b]$, and C is traversed exactly once as t increases from $t = a$ to $t = b$, then **the length of C** is the definite integral

$$L = \int_a^b \sqrt{[f'(t)]^2 + [g'(t)]^2} \, dt.$$

A smooth curve C does not double back or reverse the direction of motion over the time interval $[a, b]$ since $(f')^2 + (g')^2 > 0$ throughout the interval.

If $x = f(t)$ and $y = g(t)$, then using the Leibniz notation we have the following result for arc length:

$$L = \int_a^b \sqrt{\left(\frac{dx}{dt}\right)^2 + \left(\frac{dy}{dt}\right)^2} \, dt. \tag{1}$$

What if there are two different parametrizations for a curve C whose length we want to find; does it matter which one we use? The answer, from advanced calculus, is no, as long as the parametrization we choose meets the conditions stated in the definition of the length of C (see Exercise 29).

EXAMPLE 1   The Circumference of a Circle

Find the length of the circle of radius r defined parametrically by

$$x = r \cos t \quad \text{and} \quad y = r \sin t, \quad 0 \leq t \leq 2\pi.$$

Solution   As t varies from 0 to 2π, the circle is traversed exactly once, so the circumference is

$$L = \int_0^{2\pi} \sqrt{\left(\frac{dx}{dt}\right)^2 + \left(\frac{dy}{dt}\right)^2} \, dt.$$

We find

$$\frac{dx}{dt} = -r \sin t, \quad \frac{dy}{dt} = r \cos t$$

and

$$\left(\frac{dx}{dt}\right)^2 + \left(\frac{dy}{dt}\right)^2 = r^2(\sin^2 t + \cos^2 t) = r^2.$$

So

$$L = \int_0^{2\pi} \sqrt{r^2}\, dt = r\left[t\right]_0^{2\pi} = 2\pi r.$$

EXAMPLE 2 Applying the Parametric Formula for Length of a Curve

Find the length of the astroid (Figure 6.26)

$$x = \cos^3 t, \qquad y = \sin^3 t, \qquad 0 \le t \le 2\pi.$$

Solution Because of the curve's symmetry with respect to the coordinate axes, its length is four times the length of the first-quadrant portion. We have

$$x = \cos^3 t, \qquad y = \sin^3 t$$

$$\left(\frac{dx}{dt}\right)^2 = [3\cos^2 t(-\sin t)]^2 = 9\cos^4 t \sin^2 t$$

$$\left(\frac{dy}{dt}\right)^2 = [3\sin^2 t(\cos t)]^2 = 9\sin^4 t \cos^2 t$$

$$\sqrt{\left(\frac{dx}{dt}\right)^2 + \left(\frac{dy}{dt}\right)^2} = \sqrt{9\cos^2 t \sin^2 t \underbrace{(\cos^2 t + \sin^2 t)}_{1}}$$

$$= \sqrt{9\cos^2 t \sin^2 t}$$

$$= 3|\cos t \sin t|$$

$$= 3\cos t \sin t. \qquad \begin{array}{l}\cos t \sin t \ge 0 \text{ for} \\ 0 \le t \le \pi/2\end{array}$$

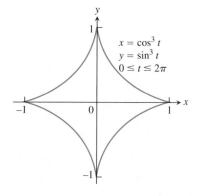

FIGURE 6.26 The astroid in Example 2.

Therefore,

$$\text{Length of first-quadrant portion} = \int_0^{\pi/2} 3\cos t \sin t \, dt$$

$$= \frac{3}{2}\int_0^{\pi/2} \sin 2t \, dt \qquad \begin{array}{l}\cos t \sin t = \\ (1/2)\sin 2t\end{array}$$

$$= -\frac{3}{4}\cos 2t \Big]_0^{\pi/2} = \frac{3}{2}.$$

The length of the astroid is four times this: $4(3/2) = 6$.

HISTORICAL BIOGRAPHY

Gregory St. Vincent
(1584–1667)

Length of a Curve $y = f(x)$

Given a continuously differentiable function $y = f(x)$, $a \le x \le b$, we can assign $x = t$ as a parameter. The graph of the function f is then the curve C defined parametrically by

$$x = t \qquad \text{and} \qquad y = f(t), \qquad a \le t \le b,$$

a special case of what we considered before. Then,

$$\frac{dx}{dt} = 1 \qquad \text{and} \qquad \frac{dy}{dt} = f'(t).$$

From our calculations in Section 3.5, we have

$$\frac{dy}{dx} = \frac{dy/dt}{dx/dt} = f'(t)$$

giving

$$\left(\frac{dx}{dt}\right)^2 + \left(\frac{dy}{dt}\right)^2 = 1 + [f'(t)]^2$$

$$= 1 + \left(\frac{dy}{dx}\right)^2$$

$$= 1 + [f'(x)]^2.$$

Substitution into Equation (1) gives the arc length formula for the graph of $y = f(x)$.

Formula for the Length of $y = f(x)$, $a \leq x \leq b$

If f is continuously differentiable on the closed interval $[a, b]$, the length of the curve (graph) $y = f(x)$ from $x = a$ to $x = b$ is

$$L = \int_a^b \sqrt{1 + \left(\frac{dy}{dx}\right)^2}\, dx = \int_a^b \sqrt{1 + [f'(x)]^2}\, dx. \qquad (2)$$

EXAMPLE 3   Applying the Arc Length Formula for a Graph

Find the length of the curve

$$y = \frac{4\sqrt{2}}{3} x^{3/2} - 1, \qquad 0 \leq x \leq 1.$$

Solution   We use Equation (2) with $a = 0, b = 1$, and

$$y = \frac{4\sqrt{2}}{3} x^{3/2} - 1$$

$$\frac{dy}{dx} = \frac{4\sqrt{2}}{3} \cdot \frac{3}{2} x^{1/2} = 2\sqrt{2} x^{1/2}$$

$$\left(\frac{dy}{dx}\right)^2 = \left(2\sqrt{2} x^{1/2}\right)^2 = 8x.$$

The length of the curve from $x = 0$ to $x = 1$ is

$$L = \int_0^1 \sqrt{1 + \left(\frac{dy}{dx}\right)^2}\, dx = \int_0^1 \sqrt{1 + 8x}\, dx \qquad \begin{array}{l} \text{Eq. (2) with} \\ a = 0, b = 1 \\ \text{Let } u = 1 + 8x, \\ \text{integrate, and} \\ \text{replace } u \text{ by} \\ 1 + 8x. \end{array}$$

$$= \frac{2}{3} \cdot \frac{1}{8} (1 + 8x)^{3/2} \Big]_0^1 = \frac{13}{6}. \qquad \blacksquare$$

Dealing with Discontinuities in dy/dx

At a point on a curve where dy/dx fails to exist, dx/dy may exist and we may be able to find the curve's length by expressing x as a function of y and applying the following analogue of Equation (2):

Formula for the Length of $x = g(y)$, $\quad c \leq y \leq d$

If g is continuously differentiable on $[c, d]$, the length of the curve $x = g(y)$ from $y = c$ to $y = d$ is

$$L = \int_c^d \sqrt{1 + \left(\frac{dx}{dy}\right)^2}\, dy = \int_c^d \sqrt{1 + [g'(y)]^2}\, dy. \qquad (3)$$

EXAMPLE 4 Length of a Graph Which Has a Discontinuity in dy/dx

Find the length of the curve $y = (x/2)^{2/3}$ from $x = 0$ to $x = 2$.

Solution The derivative

$$\frac{dy}{dx} = \frac{2}{3}\left(\frac{x}{2}\right)^{-1/3}\left(\frac{1}{2}\right) = \frac{1}{3}\left(\frac{2}{x}\right)^{1/3}$$

is not defined at $x = 0$, so we cannot find the curve's length with Equation (2).
We therefore rewrite the equation to express x in terms of y:

$$y = \left(\frac{x}{2}\right)^{2/3}$$

$$y^{3/2} = \frac{x}{2} \qquad \text{Raise both sides to the power 3/2.}$$

$$x = 2y^{3/2}. \qquad \text{Solve for } x.$$

From this we see that the curve whose length we want is also the graph of $x = 2y^{3/2}$ from $y = 0$ to $y = 1$ (Figure 6.27).
The derivative

$$\frac{dx}{dy} = 2\left(\frac{3}{2}\right)y^{1/2} = 3y^{1/2}$$

is continuous on $[0, 1]$. We may therefore use Equation (3) to find the curve's length:

$$L = \int_c^d \sqrt{1 + \left(\frac{dx}{dy}\right)^2}\, dy = \int_0^1 \sqrt{1 + 9y}\, dy \qquad \text{Eq. (3) with } c = 0, d = 1.$$

$$= \frac{1}{9} \cdot \frac{2}{3}(1 + 9y)^{3/2}\bigg]_0^1 \qquad \begin{array}{l}\text{Let } u = 1 + 9y,\\ du/9 = dy,\\ \text{integrate, and}\\ \text{substitute back.}\end{array}$$

$$= \frac{2}{27}\left(10\sqrt{10} - 1\right) \approx 2.27. \qquad \blacksquare$$

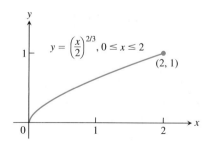

FIGURE 6.27 The graph of $y = (x/2)^{2/3}$ from $x = 0$ to $x = 2$ is also the graph of $x = 2y^{3/2}$ from $y = 0$ to $y = 1$ (Example 4).

The Short Differential Formula

Equation (1) is frequently written in terms of differentials in place of derivatives. This is done formally by writing $(dt)^2$ under the radical in place of the dt outside the radical, and then writing

$$\left(\frac{dx}{dt}\right)^2 (dt)^2 = \left(\frac{dx}{dt}\,dt\right)^2 = (dx)^2$$

and

$$\left(\frac{dy}{dt}\right)^2 (dt)^2 = \left(\frac{dy}{dt}\,dt\right)^2 = (dy)^2.$$

It is also customary to eliminate the parentheses in $(dx)^2$ and write dx^2 instead, so that Equation (1) is written

$$L = \int \sqrt{dx^2 + dy^2}. \tag{4}$$

We can think of these differentials as a way to summarize and simplify the properties of integrals. Differentials are given a precise mathematical definition in a more advanced text.

To do an integral computation, dx and dy must both be expressed in terms of one and the same variable, and appropriate limits must be supplied in Equation (4).

A useful way to remember Equation (4) is to write

$$ds = \sqrt{dx^2 + dy^2} \tag{5}$$

and treat ds as the differential of arc length, which can be integrated between appropriate limits to give the total length of a curve. Figure 6.28a gives the exact interpretation of ds corresponding to Equation (5). Figure 6.28b is not strictly accurate but is to be thought of as a simplified approximation of Figure 6.28a.

With Equation (5) in mind, the quickest way to recall the formulas for arc length is to remember the equation

$$\text{Arc length} = \int ds.$$

If we write $L = \int ds$ and have the graph of $y = f(x)$, we can rewrite Equation (5) to get

$$ds = \sqrt{dx^2 + dy^2} = \sqrt{dx^2 + \frac{dy^2}{dx^2}\,dx^2} = \sqrt{1 + \frac{dy^2}{dx^2}}\,dx = \sqrt{1 + \left(\frac{dy}{dx}\right)^2}\,dx,$$

resulting in Equation (2). If we have instead $x = g(y)$, we rewrite Equation (5)

$$ds = \sqrt{dx^2 + dy^2} = \sqrt{dy^2 + \frac{dx^2}{dy^2}\,dy^2} = \sqrt{1 + \frac{dx^2}{dy^2}}\,dy = \sqrt{1 + \left(\frac{dx}{dy}\right)^2}\,dy,$$

and obtain Equation (3).

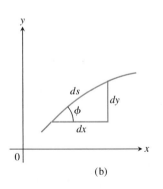

FIGURE 6.28 Diagrams for remembering the equation $ds = \sqrt{dx^2 + dy^2}$.

EXERCISES 6.3

Lengths of Parametrized Curves

Find the lengths of the curves in Exercises 1–6.

1. $x = 1 - t, \quad y = 2 + 3t, \quad -2/3 \le t \le 1$
2. $x = \cos t, \quad y = t + \sin t, \quad 0 \le t \le \pi$
3. $x = t^3, \quad y = 3t^2/2, \quad 0 \le t \le \sqrt{3}$
4. $x = t^2/2, \quad y = (2t + 1)^{3/2}/3, \quad 0 \le t \le 4$
5. $x = (2t + 3)^{3/2}/3, \quad y = t + t^2/2, \quad 0 \le t \le 3$
6. $x = 8 \cos t + 8t \sin t, \quad y = 8 \sin t - 8t \cos t, \quad 0 \le t \le \pi/2$

Finding Lengths of Curves

Find the lengths of the curves in Exercises 7–16. If you have a grapher, you may want to graph these curves to see what they look like.

7. $y = (1/3)(x^2 + 2)^{3/2} \quad$ from $\quad x = 0$ to $x = 3$
8. $y = x^{3/2} \quad$ from $\quad x = 0$ to $x = 4$
9. $x = (y^3/3) + 1/(4y) \quad$ from $\quad y = 1$ to $y = 3$
   (*Hint:* $1 + (dx/dy)^2$ is a perfect square.)
10. $x = (y^{3/2}/3) - y^{1/2} \quad$ from $\quad y = 1$ to $y = 9$
    (*Hint:* $1 + (dx/dy)^2$ is a perfect square.)
11. $x = (y^4/4) + 1/(8y^2) \quad$ from $\quad y = 1$ to $y = 2$
    (*Hint:* $1 + (dx/dy)^2$ is a perfect square.)
12. $x = (y^3/6) + 1/(2y) \quad$ from $\quad y = 2$ to $y = 3$
    (*Hint:* $1 + (dx/dy)^2$ is a perfect square.)
13. $y = (3/4)x^{4/3} - (3/8)x^{2/3} + 5, \quad 1 \le x \le 8$
14. $y = (x^3/3) + x^2 + x + 1/(4x + 4), \quad 0 \le x \le 2$
15. $x = \int_0^y \sqrt{\sec^4 t - 1} \, dt, \quad -\pi/4 \le y \le \pi/4$
16. $y = \int_{-2}^x \sqrt{3t^4 - 1} \, dt, \quad -2 \le x \le -1$

T Finding Integrals for Lengths of Curves

In Exercises 17–24, do the following.

a. Set up an integral for the length of the curve.

b. Graph the curve to see what it looks like.

c. Use your grapher's or computer's integral evaluator to find the curve's length numerically.

17. $y = x^2, \quad -1 \le x \le 2$
18. $y = \tan x, \quad -\pi/3 \le x \le 0$
19. $x = \sin y, \quad 0 \le y \le \pi$
20. $x = \sqrt{1 - y^2}, \quad -1/2 \le y \le 1/2$
21. $y^2 + 2y = 2x + 1 \quad$ from $\quad (-1, -1)$ to $(7, 3)$
22. $y = \sin x - x \cos x, \quad 0 \le x \le \pi$

23. $y = \int_0^x \tan t \, dt, \quad 0 \le x \le \pi/6$
24. $x = \int_0^y \sqrt{\sec^2 t - 1} \, dt, \quad -\pi/3 \le y \le \pi/4$

Theory and Applications

25. Is there a smooth (continuously differentiable) curve $y = f(x)$ whose length over the interval $0 \le x \le a$ is always $\sqrt{2a}$? Give reasons for your answer.

26. **Using tangent fins to derive the length formula for curves** Assume that f is smooth on $[a, b]$ and partition the interval $[a, b]$ in the usual way. In each subinterval $[x_{k-1}, x_k]$, construct the *tangent fin* at the point $(x_{k-1}, f(x_{k-1}))$, as shown in the accompanying figure.

    a. Show that the length of the kth tangent fin over the interval $[x_{k-1}, x_k]$ equals $\sqrt{(\Delta x_k)^2 + (f'(x_{k-1}) \, \Delta x_k)^2}$.

    b. Show that

    $$\lim_{n \to \infty} \sum_{k=1}^{n} (\text{length of } k\text{th tangent fin}) = \int_a^b \sqrt{1 + (f'(x))^2} \, dx,$$

    which is the length L of the curve $y = f(x)$ from a to b.

27. a. Find a curve through the point $(1, 1)$ whose length integral is

    $$L = \int_1^4 \sqrt{1 + \frac{1}{4x}} \, dx.$$

    b. How many such curves are there? Give reasons for your answer.

28. a. Find a curve through the point $(0, 1)$ whose length integral is

    $$L = \int_1^2 \sqrt{1 + \frac{1}{y^4}} \, dy.$$

    b. How many such curves are there? Give reasons for your answer.

29. **Length is independent of parametrization** To illustrate the fact that the numbers we get for length do not depend on the way

we parametrize our curves (except for the mild restrictions preventing doubling back mentioned earlier), calculate the length of the semicircle $y = \sqrt{1 - x^2}$ with these two different parametrizations:

a. $x = \cos 2t, \quad y = \sin 2t, \quad 0 \le t \le \pi/2$

b. $x = \sin \pi t, \quad y = \cos \pi t, \quad -1/2 \le t \le 1/2$

30. Find the length of one arch of the cycloid $x = a(\theta - \sin \theta)$, $y = a(1 - \cos \theta), 0 \le \theta \le 2\pi$, shown in the accompanying figure. A **cycloid** is the curve traced out by a point P on the circumference of a circle rolling along a straight line, such as the x-axis.

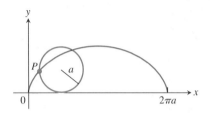

COMPUTER EXPLORATIONS

In Exercises 31–36, use a CAS to perform the following steps for the given curve over the closed interval.

a. Plot the curve together with the polygonal path approximations for $n = 2, 4, 8$ partition points over the interval. (See Figure 6.24.)

b. Find the corresponding approximation to the length of the curve by summing the lengths of the line segments.

c. Evaluate the length of the curve using an integral. Compare your approximations for $n = 2, 4, 8$ with the actual length given by the integral. How does the actual length compare with the approximations as n increases? Explain your answer.

31. $f(x) = \sqrt{1 - x^2}, \quad -1 \le x \le 1$

32. $f(x) = x^{1/3} + x^{2/3}, \quad 0 \le x \le 2$

33. $f(x) = \sin(\pi x^2), \quad 0 \le x \le \sqrt{2}$

34. $f(x) = x^2 \cos x, \quad 0 \le x \le \pi$

35. $f(x) = \dfrac{x - 1}{4x^2 + 1}, \quad -\dfrac{1}{2} \le x \le 1$

36. $f(x) = x^3 - x^2, \quad -1 \le x \le 1$

37. $x = \dfrac{1}{3}t^3, \quad y = \dfrac{1}{2}t^2, \quad 0 \le t \le 1$

38. $x = 2t^3 - 16t^2 + 25t + 5, \quad y = t^2 + t - 3,$
$0 \le t \le 6$

39. $x = t - \cos t, \quad y = 1 + \sin t, \quad -\pi \le t \le \pi$

40. $x = e^t \cos t, \quad y = e^t \sin t, \quad 0 \le t \le \pi$

6.4 Moments and Centers of Mass

Many structures and mechanical systems behave as if their masses were concentrated at a single point, called the *center of mass* (Figure 6.29). It is important to know how to locate this point, and doing so is basically a mathematical enterprise. For the moment, we deal with one- and two-dimensional objects. Three-dimensional objects are best done with the multiple integrals of Chapter 15.

Masses Along a Line

We develop our mathematical model in stages. The first stage is to imagine masses $m_1, m_2,$ and m_3 on a rigid x-axis supported by a fulcrum at the origin.

The resulting system might balance, or it might not. It depends on how large the masses are and how they are arranged.

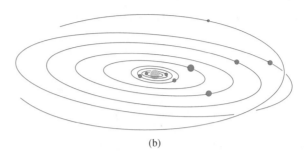

(b)

FIGURE 6.29 (a) The motion of this wrench gliding on ice seems haphazard until we notice that the wrench is simply turning about its center of mass as the center glides in a straight line. (b) The planets, asteroids, and comets of our solar system revolve about their collective center of mass. (It lies inside the sun.)

Each mass m_k exerts a downward force $m_k g$ (the weight of m_k) equal to the magnitude of the mass times the acceleration of gravity. Each of these forces has a tendency to turn the axis about the origin, the way you turn a seesaw. This turning effect, called a **torque**, is measured by multiplying the force $m_k g$ by the signed distance x_k from the point of application to the origin. Masses to the left of the origin exert negative (counterclockwise) torque. Masses to the right of the origin exert positive (clockwise) torque.

The sum of the torques measures the tendency of a system to rotate about the origin. This sum is called the **system torque**.

$$\text{System torque} = m_1 g x_1 + m_2 g x_2 + m_3 g x_3 \tag{1}$$

The system will balance if and only if its torque is zero.

If we factor out the g in Equation (1), we see that the system torque is

$$\underbrace{g}_{\substack{\text{a feature of the} \\ \text{environment}}} \cdot \underbrace{(m_1 x_1 + m_2 x_2 + m_3 x_3)}_{\substack{\text{a feature of} \\ \text{the system}}}$$

Thus, the torque is the product of the gravitational acceleration g, which is a feature of the environment in which the system happens to reside, and the number $(m_1 x_1 + m_2 x_2 + m_3 x_3)$, which is a feature of the system itself, a constant that stays the same no matter where the system is placed.

The number $(m_1 x_1 + m_2 x_2 + m_3 x_3)$ is called the **moment of the system about the origin**. It is the sum of the **moments** $m_1 x_1, m_2 x_2, m_3 x_3$ of the individual masses.

$$M_0 = \text{Moment of system about origin} = \sum m_k x_k.$$

(We shift to sigma notation here to allow for sums with more terms.)

We usually want to know where to place the fulcrum to make the system balance, that is, at what point $\bar{x}$ to place it to make the torques add to zero.

(a)

The torque of each mass about the fulcrum in this special location is

$$\text{Torque of } m_k \text{ about } \bar{x} = \begin{pmatrix} \text{signed distance} \\ \text{of } m_k \text{ from } \bar{x} \end{pmatrix} \begin{pmatrix} \text{downward} \\ \text{force} \end{pmatrix}$$

$$= (x_k - \bar{x}) m_k g.$$

When we write the equation that says that the sum of these torques is zero, we get an equation we can solve for $\bar{x}$:

$$\sum (x_k - \bar{x}) m_k g = 0 \qquad \text{Sum of the torques equals zero}$$

$$g \sum (x_k - \bar{x}) m_k = 0 \qquad \text{Constant Multiple Rule for Sums}$$

$$\sum (m_k x_k - \bar{x} m_k) = 0 \qquad g \text{ divided out, } m_k \text{ distributed}$$

$$\sum m_k x_k - \sum \bar{x} m_k = 0 \qquad \text{Difference Rule for Sums}$$

$$\sum m_k x_k = \bar{x} \sum m_k \qquad \text{Rearranged, Constant Multiple Rule again}$$

$$\bar{x} = \frac{\sum m_k x_k}{\sum m_k}. \qquad \text{Solved for } \bar{x}$$

This last equation tells us to find $\bar{x}$ by dividing the system's moment about the origin by the system's total mass:

$$\bar{x} = \frac{\sum m_k x_k}{\sum m_k} = \frac{\text{system moment about origin}}{\text{system mass}}.$$

The point $\bar{x}$ is called the system's **center of mass**.

Wires and Thin Rods

In many applications, we want to know the center of mass of a rod or a thin strip of metal. In cases like these where we can model the distribution of mass with a continuous function, the summation signs in our formulas become integrals in a manner we now describe.

Imagine a long, thin strip lying along the x-axis from $x = a$ to $x = b$ and cut into small pieces of mass Δm_k by a partition of the interval $[a, b]$. Choose x_k to be any point in the kth subinterval of the partition.

The kth piece is Δx_k units long and lies approximately x_k units from the origin. Now observe three things.

First, the strip's center of mass $\bar{x}$ is nearly the same as that of the system of point masses we would get by attaching each mass Δm_k to the point x_k:

$$\bar{x} \approx \frac{\text{system moment}}{\text{system mass}}.$$

Density

A material's density is its mass per unit volume. In practice, however, we tend to use units we can conveniently measure. For wires, rods, and narrow strips, we use mass per unit length. For flat sheets and plates, we use mass per unit area.

Second, the moment of each piece of the strip about the origin is approximately $x_k \, \Delta m_k$, so the system moment is approximately the sum of the $x_k \, \Delta m_k$:

$$\text{System moment} \approx \sum x_k \, \Delta m_k.$$

Third, if the density of the strip at x_k is $\delta(x_k)$, expressed in terms of mass per unit length and if δ is continuous, then Δm_k is approximately equal to $\delta(x_k) \, \Delta x_k$ (mass per unit length times length):

$$\Delta m_k \approx \delta(x_k) \, \Delta x_k.$$

Combining these three observations gives

$$\bar{x} \approx \frac{\text{system moment}}{\text{system mass}} \approx \frac{\sum x_k \, \Delta m_k}{\sum \Delta m_k} \approx \frac{\sum x_k \, \delta(x_k) \, \Delta x_k}{\sum \delta(x_k) \, \Delta x_k}. \qquad (2)$$

The sum in the last numerator in Equation (2) is a Riemann sum for the continuous function $x\delta(x)$ over the closed interval $[a, b]$. The sum in the denominator is a Riemann sum for the function $\delta(x)$ over this interval. We expect the approximations in Equation (2) to improve as the strip is partitioned more finely, and we are led to the equation

$$\bar{x} = \frac{\displaystyle\int_a^b x\delta(x) \, dx}{\displaystyle\int_a^b \delta(x) \, dx}.$$

This is the formula we use to find $\bar{x}$.

Moment, Mass, and Center of Mass of a Thin Rod or Strip Along the x-Axis with Density Function $\delta(x)$

$$\text{Moment about the origin:} \qquad M_0 = \int_a^b x\delta(x) \, dx \qquad (3a)$$

$$\text{Mass:} \qquad M = \int_a^b \delta(x) \, dx \qquad (3b)$$

$$\text{Center of mass:} \qquad \bar{x} = \frac{M_0}{M} \qquad (3c)$$

FIGURE 6.30 The center of mass of a straight, thin rod or strip of constant density lies halfway between its ends (Example 1).

EXAMPLE 1 Strips and Rods of Constant Density

Show that the center of mass of a straight, thin strip or rod of constant density lies halfway between its two ends.

Solution We model the strip as a portion of the x-axis from $x = a$ to $x = b$ (Figure 6.30). Our goal is to show that $\bar{x} = (a + b)/2$, the point halfway between a and b.

The key is the density's having a constant value. This enables us to regard the function $\delta(x)$ in the integrals in Equation (3) as a constant (call it δ), with the result that

$$M_0 = \int_a^b \delta x \, dx = \delta \int_a^b x \, dx = \delta \left[\frac{1}{2} x^2 \right]_a^b = \frac{\delta}{2} (b^2 - a^2)$$

$$M = \int_a^b \delta \, dx = \delta \int_a^b dx = \delta \left[x \right]_a^b = \delta(b - a)$$

$$\bar{x} = \frac{M_0}{M} = \frac{\frac{\delta}{2}(b^2 - a^2)}{\delta(b - a)}$$

$$= \frac{a + b}{2}.$$

The δ's cancel in the formula for $\bar{x}$.

∎

EXAMPLE 2   Variable-Density Rod

The 10-m-long rod in Figure 6.31 thickens from left to right so that its density, instead of being constant, is $\delta(x) = 1 + (x/10)$ kg/m. Find the rod's center of mass.

Solution   The rod's moment about the origin (Equation 3a) is

$$M_0 = \int_0^{10} x\delta(x) \, dx = \int_0^{10} x\left(1 + \frac{x}{10}\right) dx = \int_0^{10} \left(x + \frac{x^2}{10}\right) dx$$

$$= \left[\frac{x^2}{2} + \frac{x^3}{30} \right]_0^{10} = 50 + \frac{100}{3} = \frac{250}{3} \text{ kg} \cdot \text{m}.$$

The units of a moment are mass $\times$ length.

The rod's mass (Equation 3b) is

$$M = \int_0^{10} \delta(x) \, dx = \int_0^{10} \left(1 + \frac{x}{10}\right) dx = \left[x + \frac{x^2}{20} \right]_0^{10} = 10 + 5 = 15 \text{ kg}.$$

The center of mass (Equation 3c) is located at the point

$$\bar{x} = \frac{M_0}{M} = \frac{250}{3} \cdot \frac{1}{15} = \frac{50}{9} \approx 5.56 \text{ m}.$$

∎

Masses Distributed over a Plane Region

Suppose that we have a finite collection of masses located in the plane, with mass m_k at the point (x_k, y_k) (see Figure 6.32). The mass of the system is

$$\text{System mass:} \quad M = \sum m_k.$$

Each mass m_k has a moment about each axis. Its moment about the x-axis is $m_k y_k$, and its moment about the y-axis is $m_k x_k$. The moments of the entire system about the two axes are

$$\text{Moment about } x\text{-axis:} \quad M_x = \sum m_k y_k,$$

$$\text{Moment about } y\text{-axis:} \quad M_y = \sum m_k x_k.$$

The x-coordinate of the system's center of mass is defined to be

$$\bar{x} = \frac{M_y}{M} = \frac{\sum m_k x_k}{\sum m_k}. \tag{4}$$

FIGURE 6.31   We can treat a rod of variable thickness as a rod of variable density (Example 2).

FIGURE 6.32   Each mass m_k has a moment about each axis.

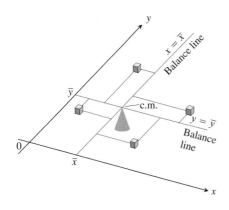

With this choice of $\bar{x}$, as in the one-dimensional case, the system balances about the line $x = \bar{x}$ (Figure 6.33).

The y-coordinate of the system's center of mass is defined to be

$$\bar{y} = \frac{M_x}{M} = \frac{\sum m_k y_k}{\sum m_k}. \tag{5}$$

With this choice of $\bar{y}$, the system balances about the line $y = \bar{y}$ as well. The torques exerted by the masses about the line $y = \bar{y}$ cancel out. Thus, as far as balance is concerned, the system behaves as if all its mass were at the single point $(\bar{x}, \bar{y})$. We call this point the system's **center of mass**.

FIGURE 6.33 A two-dimensional array of masses balances on its center of mass.

Thin, Flat Plates

In many applications, we need to find the center of mass of a thin, flat plate: a disk of aluminum, say, or a triangular sheet of steel. In such cases, we assume the distribution of mass to be continuous, and the formulas we use to calculate $\bar{x}$ and $\bar{y}$ contain integrals instead of finite sums. The integrals arise in the following way.

Imagine the plate occupying a region in the xy-plane, cut into thin strips parallel to one of the axes (in Figure 6.34, the y-axis). The center of mass of a typical strip is $(\tilde{x}, \tilde{y})$. We treat the strip's mass Δm as if it were concentrated at $(\tilde{x}, \tilde{y})$. The moment of the strip about the y-axis is then $\tilde{x}\, \Delta m$. The moment of the strip about the x-axis is $\tilde{y}\, \Delta m$. Equations (4) and (5) then become

$$\bar{x} = \frac{M_y}{M} = \frac{\sum \tilde{x}\, \Delta m}{\sum \Delta m}, \qquad \bar{y} = \frac{M_x}{M} = \frac{\sum \tilde{y}\, \Delta m}{\sum \Delta m}.$$

As in the one-dimensional case, the sums are Riemann sums for integrals and approach these integrals as limiting values as the strips into which the plate is cut become narrower and narrower. We write these integrals symbolically as

$$\bar{x} = \frac{\int \tilde{x}\, dm}{\int dm} \qquad \text{and} \qquad \bar{y} = \frac{\int \tilde{y}\, dm}{\int dm}.$$

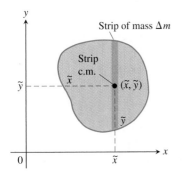

FIGURE 6.34 A plate cut into thin strips parallel to the y-axis. The moment exerted by a typical strip about each axis is the moment its mass Δm would exert if concentrated at the strip's center of mass $(\tilde{x}, \tilde{y})$.

Moments, Mass, and Center of Mass of a Thin Plate Covering a Region in the xy-Plane

Moment about the x-axis: $\quad M_x = \int \tilde{y}\, dm$

Moment about the y-axis: $\quad M_y = \int \tilde{x}\, dm \qquad (6)$

Mass: $\quad M = \int dm$

Center of mass: $\quad \bar{x} = \dfrac{M_y}{M}, \quad \bar{y} = \dfrac{M_x}{M}$

To evaluate these integrals, we picture the plate in the coordinate plane and sketch a strip of mass parallel to one of the coordinates axes. We then express the strip's mass dm and the coordinates $(\tilde{x}, \tilde{y})$ of the strip's center of mass in terms of x or y. Finally, we integrate $\tilde{y}\, dm$, $\tilde{x}\, dm$, and dm between limits of integration determined by the plate's location in the plane.

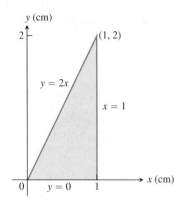

FIGURE 6.35   The plate in Example 3.

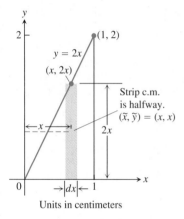

FIGURE 6.36   Modeling the plate in Example 3 with vertical strips.

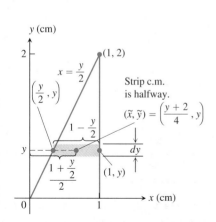

FIGURE 6.37   Modeling the plate in Example 3 with horizontal strips.

EXAMPLE 3   Constant-Density Plate

The triangular plate shown in Figure 6.35 has a constant density of $\delta = 3$ g/cm^2. Find

(a) the plate's moment M_y about the y-axis.

(b) the plate's mass M.

(c) the x-coordinate of the plate's center of mass (c.m.).

Solution
Method 1: Vertical Strips   (Figure 6.36)

(a) The moment M_y: The typical vertical strip has

center of mass (c.m.): $(\tilde{x}, \tilde{y}) = (x, x)$

length: $2x$

width: dx

area: $dA = 2x\,dx$

mass: $dm = \delta\,dA = 3 \cdot 2x\,dx = 6x\,dx$

distance of c.m. from y-axis: $\tilde{x} = x$.

The moment of the strip about the y-axis is

$$\tilde{x}\,dm = x \cdot 6x\,dx = 6x^2\,dx.$$

The moment of the plate about the y-axis is therefore

$$M_y = \int \tilde{x}\,dm = \int_0^1 6x^2\,dx = 2x^3 \Big]_0^1 = 2 \text{ g} \cdot \text{cm}.$$

(b) The plate's mass:

$$M = \int dm = \int_0^1 6x\,dx = 3x^2 \Big]_0^1 = 3 \text{ g}.$$

(c) The x-coordinate of the plate's center of mass:

$$\bar{x} = \frac{M_y}{M} = \frac{2 \text{ g} \cdot \text{cm}}{3 \text{ g}} = \frac{2}{3} \text{ cm}.$$

By a similar computation, we could find M_x and $\bar{y} = M_x/M$.

Method 2: Horizontal Strips   (Figure 6.37)

(a) The moment M_y: The y-coordinate of the center of mass of a typical horizontal strip is y (see the figure), so

$$\tilde{y} = y.$$

The x-coordinate is the x-coordinate of the point halfway across the triangle. This makes it the average of $y/2$ (the strip's left-hand x-value) and 1 (the strip's right-hand x-value):

$$\tilde{x} = \frac{(y/2) + 1}{2} = \frac{y}{4} + \frac{1}{2} = \frac{y + 2}{4}.$$

We also have

$$\text{length:} \quad 1 - \frac{y}{2} = \frac{2-y}{2}$$

$$\text{width:} \quad dy$$

$$\text{area:} \quad dA = \frac{2-y}{2}\,dy$$

$$\text{mass:} \quad dm = \delta\,dA = 3 \cdot \frac{2-y}{2}\,dy$$

$$\text{distance of c.m. to } y\text{-axis:} \quad \widetilde{x} = \frac{y+2}{4}.$$

The moment of the strip about the y-axis is

$$\widetilde{x}\,dm = \frac{y+2}{4} \cdot 3 \cdot \frac{2-y}{2}\,dy = \frac{3}{8}(4 - y^2)\,dy.$$

The moment of the plate about the y-axis is

$$M_y = \int \widetilde{x}\,dm = \int_0^2 \frac{3}{8}(4 - y^2)\,dy = \frac{3}{8}\left[4y - \frac{y^3}{3}\right]_0^2 = \frac{3}{8}\left(\frac{16}{3}\right) = 2\ \text{g}\cdot\text{cm}.$$

(b) The plate's mass:

$$M = \int dm = \int_0^2 \frac{3}{2}(2 - y)\,dy = \frac{3}{2}\left[2y - \frac{y^2}{2}\right]_0^2 = \frac{3}{2}(4 - 2) = 3\ \text{g}.$$

(c) The x-coordinate of the plate's center of mass:

$$\bar{x} = \frac{M_y}{M} = \frac{2\ \text{g}\cdot\text{cm}}{3\ \text{g}} = \frac{2}{3}\ \text{cm}.$$

By a similar computation, we could find M_x and $\bar{y}$.　■

If the distribution of mass in a thin, flat plate has an axis of symmetry, the center of mass will lie on this axis. If there are two axes of symmetry, the center of mass will lie at their intersection. These facts often help to simplify our work.

> **How to Find a Plate's Center of Mass**
>
> 1. Picture the plate in the xy-plane.
> 2. Sketch a strip of mass parallel to one of the coordinate axes and find its dimensions.
> 3. Find the strip's mass dm and center of mass $(\widetilde{x}, \widetilde{y})$.
> 4. Integrate $\widetilde{y}\,dm$, $\widetilde{x}\,dm$, and dm to find M_x, M_y, and M.
> 5. Divide the moments by the mass to calculate $\bar{x}$ and $\bar{y}$.

EXAMPLE 4　Constant-Density Plate

Find the center of mass of a thin plate of constant density δ covering the region bounded above by the parabola $y = 4 - x^2$ and below by the x-axis (Figure 6.38).

Solution　Since the plate is symmetric about the y-axis and its density is constant, the distribution of mass is symmetric about the y-axis and the center of mass lies on the y-axis. Thus, $\bar{x} = 0$. It remains to find $\bar{y} = M_x/M$.

A trial calculation with horizontal strips (Figure 6.38a) leads to an inconvenient integration

$$M_x = \int_0^4 2\delta y\sqrt{4 - y}\,dy.$$

We therefore model the distribution of mass with vertical strips instead (Figure 6.38b).

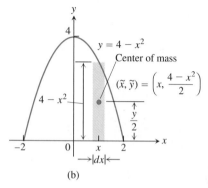

FIGURE 6.38 Modeling the plate in Example 4 with (a) horizontal strips leads to an inconvenient integration, so we model with (b) vertical strips instead.

The typical vertical strip has

$$\text{center of mass (c.m.):} \qquad (\tilde{x}, \tilde{y}) = \left(x, \frac{4 - x^2}{2}\right)$$

length: $\quad 4 - x^2$

width: $\quad dx$

area: $\quad dA = (4 - x^2)\,dx$

mass: $\quad dm = \delta\,dA = \delta(4 - x^2)\,dx$

distance from c.m. to x-axis: $\quad \tilde{y} = \dfrac{4 - x^2}{2}.$

The moment of the strip about the x-axis is

$$\tilde{y}\,dm = \frac{4 - x^2}{2} \cdot \delta(4 - x^2)\,dx = \frac{\delta}{2}(4 - x^2)^2\,dx.$$

The moment of the plate about the x-axis is

$$M_x = \int \tilde{y}\,dm = \int_{-2}^{2} \frac{\delta}{2}(4 - x^2)^2\,dx$$

$$= \frac{\delta}{2}\int_{-2}^{2}(16 - 8x^2 + x^4)\,dx = \frac{256}{15}\delta. \qquad (7)$$

The mass of the plate is

$$M = \int dm = \int_{-2}^{2} \delta(4 - x^2)\,dx = \frac{32}{3}\delta. \qquad (8)$$

Therefore,

$$\bar{y} = \frac{M_x}{M} = \frac{(256/15)\,\delta}{(32/3)\,\delta} = \frac{8}{5}.$$

The plate's center of mass is the point

$$(\bar{x}, \bar{y}) = \left(0, \frac{8}{5}\right). \qquad \blacksquare$$

EXAMPLE 5 Variable-Density Plate

Find the center of mass of the plate in Example 4 if the density at the point (x, y) is $\delta = 2x^2$, twice the square of the distance from the point to the y-axis.

Solution The mass distribution is still symmetric about the y-axis, so $\bar{x} = 0$. With $\delta = 2x^2$, Equations (7) and (8) become

$$M_x = \int \widetilde{y} \, dm = \int_{-2}^{2} \frac{\delta}{2} (4 - x^2)^2 \, dx = \int_{-2}^{2} x^2 (4 - x^2)^2 \, dx$$

$$= \int_{-2}^{2} (16x^2 - 8x^4 + x^6) \, dx = \frac{2048}{105} \qquad (7')$$

$$M = \int dm = \int_{-2}^{2} \delta(4 - x^2) \, dx = \int_{-2}^{2} 2x^2 (4 - x^2) \, dx$$

$$= \int_{-2}^{2} (8x^2 - 2x^4) \, dx = \frac{256}{15}. \qquad (8')$$

Therefore,

$$\bar{y} = \frac{M_x}{M} = \frac{2048}{105} \cdot \frac{15}{256} = \frac{8}{7}.$$

The plate's new center of mass is

$$(\bar{x}, \bar{y}) = \left(0, \frac{8}{7}\right). \qquad \blacksquare$$

EXAMPLE 6 Constant-Density Wire

Find the center of mass of a wire of constant density δ shaped like a semicircle of radius a.

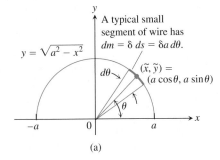

Solution We model the wire with the semicircle $y = \sqrt{a^2 - x^2}$ (Figure 6.39). The distribution of mass is symmetric about the y-axis, so $\bar{x} = 0$. To find $\bar{y}$, we imagine the wire divided into short segments. The typical segment (Figure 6.39a) has

length: $ds = a \, d\theta$

mass: $dm = \delta \, ds = \delta a \, d\theta$ Mass per unit length times length

distance of c.m. to x-axis: $\widetilde{y} = a \sin \theta$.

Hence,

$$\bar{y} = \frac{\int \widetilde{y} \, dm}{\int dm} = \frac{\int_0^\pi a \sin \theta \cdot \delta a \, d\theta}{\int_0^\pi \delta a \, d\theta} = \frac{\delta a^2 \left[-\cos \theta\right]_0^\pi}{\delta a \pi} = \frac{2}{\pi} a.$$

The center of mass lies on the axis of symmetry at the point $(0, 2a/\pi)$, about two-thirds of the way up from the origin (Figure 6.39b).

Centroids

When the density function is constant, it cancels out of the numerator and denominator of the formulas for $\bar{x}$ and $\bar{y}$. This happened in nearly every example in this section. As far as $\bar{x}$ and $\bar{y}$ were concerned, δ might as well have been 1. Thus, when the density is constant, the location of the center of mass is a feature of the geometry of the object and not of the material from which it is made. In such cases, engineers may call the center of mass the **centroid** of the shape, as in "Find the centroid of a triangle or a solid cone." To do so, just set δ equal to 1 and proceed to find $\bar{x}$ and $\bar{y}$ as before, by dividing moments by masses.

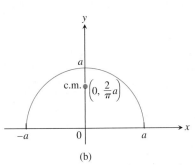

FIGURE 6.39 The semicircular wire in Example 6. (a) The dimensions and variables used in finding the center of mass. (b) The center of mass does not lie on the wire.

EXERCISES 6.4

Thin Rods

1. An 80-lb child and a 100-lb child are balancing on a seesaw. The 80-lb child is 5 ft from the fulcrum. How far from the fulcrum is the 100-lb child?

2. The ends of a log are placed on two scales. One scale reads 100 kg and the other 200 kg. Where is the log's center of mass?

3. The ends of two thin steel rods of equal length are welded together to make a right-angled frame. Locate the frame's center of mass. (*Hint:* Where is the center of mass of each rod?)

4. You weld the ends of two steel rods into a right-angled frame. One rod is twice the length of the other. Where is the frame's center of mass? (*Hint:* Where is the center of mass of each rod?)

Exercises 5–12 give density functions of thin rods lying along various intervals of the x-axis. Use Equations (3a) through (3c) to find each rod's moment about the origin, mass, and center of mass.

5. $\delta(x) = 4, \quad 0 \le x \le 2$

6. $\delta(x) = 4, \quad 1 \le x \le 3$

7. $\delta(x) = 1 + (x/3), \quad 0 \le x \le 3$

8. $\delta(x) = 2 - (x/4), \quad 0 \le x \le 4$

9. $\delta(x) = 1 + (1/\sqrt{x}), \quad 1 \le x \le 4$

10. $\delta(x) = 3(x^{-3/2} + x^{-5/2}), \quad 0.25 \le x \le 1$

11. $\delta(x) = \begin{cases} 2 - x, & 0 \le x < 1 \\ x, & 1 \le x \le 2 \end{cases}$

12. $\delta(x) = \begin{cases} x + 1, & 0 \le x < 1 \\ 2, & 1 \le x \le 2 \end{cases}$

Thin Plates with Constant Density

In Exercises 13–24, find the center of mass of a thin plate of constant density δ covering the given region.

13. The region bounded by the parabola $y = x^2$ and the line $y = 4$

14. The region bounded by the parabola $y = 25 - x^2$ and the x-axis

15. The region bounded by the parabola $y = x - x^2$ and the line $y = -x$

16. The region enclosed by the parabolas $y = x^2 - 3$ and $y = -2x^2$

17. The region bounded by the y-axis and the curve $x = y - y^3$, $0 \le y \le 1$

18. The region bounded by the parabola $x = y^2 - y$ and the line $y = x$

19. The region bounded by the x-axis and the curve $y = \cos x$, $-\pi/2 \le x \le \pi/2$

20. The region between the x-axis and the curve $y = \sec^2 x$, $-\pi/4 \le x \le \pi/4$

21. The region bounded by the parabolas $y = 2x^2 - 4x$ and $y = 2x - x^2$

22. **a.** The region cut from the first quadrant by the circle $x^2 + y^2 = 9$

    b. The region bounded by the x-axis and the semicircle $y = \sqrt{9 - x^2}$

    Compare your answer in part (b) with the answer in part (a).

23. The "triangular" region in the first quadrant between the circle $x^2 + y^2 = 9$ and the lines $x = 3$ and $y = 3$. (*Hint:* Use geometry to find the area.)

24. The region bounded above by the curve $y = 1/x^3$, below by the curve $y = -1/x^3$, and on the left and right by the lines $x = 1$ and $x = a > 1$. Also, find $\lim_{a \to \infty} \bar{x}$.

Thin Plates with Varying Density

25. Find the center of mass of a thin plate covering the region between the x-axis and the curve $y = 2/x^2$, $1 \le x \le 2$, if the plate's density at the point (x, y) is $\delta(x) = x^2$.

26. Find the center of mass of a thin plate covering the region bounded below by the parabola $y = x^2$ and above by the line $y = x$ if the plate's density at the point (x, y) is $\delta(x) = 12x$.

27. The region bounded by the curves $y = \pm 4/\sqrt{x}$ and the lines $x = 1$ and $x = 4$ is revolved about the y-axis to generate a solid.

    a. Find the volume of the solid.

    b. Find the center of mass of a thin plate covering the region if the plate's density at the point (x, y) is $\delta(x) = 1/x$.

    c. Sketch the plate and show the center of mass in your sketch.

28. The region between the curve $y = 2/x$ and the x-axis from $x = 1$ to $x = 4$ is revolved about the x-axis to generate a solid.

    a. Find the volume of the solid.

    b. Find the center of mass of a thin plate covering the region if the plate's density at the point (x, y) is $\delta(x) = \sqrt{x}$.

    c. Sketch the plate and show the center of mass in your sketch.

Centroids of Triangles

29. **The centroid of a triangle lies at the intersection of the triangle's medians** (*Figure 6.40a*) You may recall that the point

inside a triangle that lies one-third of the way from each side toward the opposite vertex is the point where the triangle's three medians intersect. Show that the centroid lies at the intersection of the medians by showing that it too lies one-third of the way from each side toward the opposite vertex. To do so, take the following steps.

i. Stand one side of the triangle on the x-axis as in Figure 6.40b. Express dm in terms of L and dy.

ii. Use similar triangles to show that $L = (b/h)(h - y)$. Substitute this expression for L in your formula for dm.

iii. Show that $\bar{y} = h/3$.

iv. Extend the argument to the other sides.

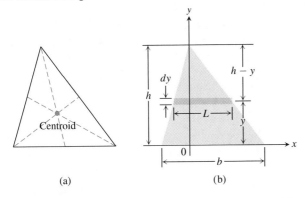

(a)   (b)

FIGURE 6.40 The triangle in Exercise 29. (a) The centroid. (b) The dimensions and variables to use in locating the center of mass.

Use the result in Exercise 29 to find the centroids of the triangles whose vertices appear in Exercises 30–34. Assume $a, b > 0$.

30. $(-1, 0), (1, 0), (0, 3)$ **31.** $(0, 0), (1, 0), (0, 1)$

32. $(0, 0), (a, 0), (0, a)$ **33.** $(0, 0), (a, 0), (0, b)$

34. $(0, 0), (a, 0), (a/2, b)$

Thin Wires

35. Constant density Find the moment about the x-axis of a wire of constant density that lies along the curve $y = \sqrt{x}$ from $x = 0$ to $x = 2$.

36. Constant density Find the moment about the x-axis of a wire of constant density that lies along the curve $y = x^3$ from $x = 0$ to $x = 1$.

37. Variable density Suppose that the density of the wire in Example 6 is $\delta = k \sin \theta$ (k constant). Find the center of mass.

38. Variable density Suppose that the density of the wire in Example 6 is $\delta = 1 + k|\cos \theta|$ (k constant). Find the center of mass.

Engineering Formulas

Verify the statements and formulas in Exercises 39–42.

39. The coordinates of the centroid of a differentiable plane curve are

$$\bar{x} = \frac{\int x\, ds}{\text{length}}, \qquad \bar{y} = \frac{\int y\, ds}{\text{length}}.$$

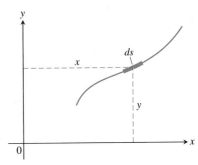

40. Whatever the value of $p > 0$ in the equation $y = x^2/(4p)$, the y-coordinate of the centroid of the parabolic segment shown here is $\bar{y} = (3/5)a$.

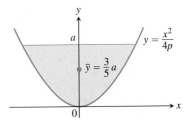

41. For wires and thin rods of constant density shaped like circular arcs centered at the origin and symmetric about the y-axis, the y-coordinate of the center of mass is

$$\bar{y} = \frac{a \sin \alpha}{\alpha} = \frac{ac}{s}.$$

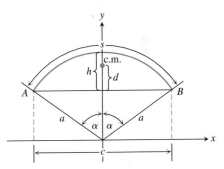

42. (*Continuation of Exercise 41.*)

a. Show that when α is small, the distance d from the centroid to chord AB is about $2h/3$ (in the notation of the figure here) by taking the following steps.

i. Show that

$$\frac{d}{h} = \frac{\sin \alpha - \alpha \cos \alpha}{\alpha - \alpha \cos \alpha}. \tag{9}$$

T **ii.** Graph

$$f(\alpha) = \frac{\sin \alpha - \alpha \cos \alpha}{\alpha - \alpha \cos \alpha}$$

and use the trace feature to show that $\lim_{\alpha \to 0^+} f(\alpha) \approx 2/3$.

b. The error (difference between d and $2h/3$) is small even for angles greater that $45°$. See for yourself by evaluating the right-hand side of Equation (9) for $\alpha = 0.2, 0.4, 0.6, 0.8,$ and 1.0 rad.

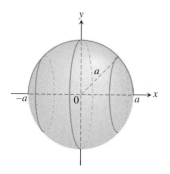

FIGURE 6.41 Rotating the semicircle $y = \sqrt{a^2 - x^2}$ of radius a with center at the origin generates a spherical surface with area $4\pi a^2$.

When you jump rope, the rope sweeps out a surface in the space around you called a *surface of revolution*. The "area" of this surface depends on the length of the rope and the distance of each of its segments from the axis of revolution. In this section we define areas of surfaces of revolution. More complicated surfaces are treated in Chapter 16.

Defining Surface Area

We want our definition of the area of a surface of revolution to be consistent with known results from classical geometry for the surface areas of spheres, circular cylinders, and cones. So if the jump rope discussed in the introduction takes the shape of a semicircle with radius a rotated about the x-axis (Figure 6.41), it generates a sphere with surface area $4\pi a^2$.

Before considering general curves, we begin by rotating horizontal and slanted line segments about the x-axis. If we rotate the horizontal line segment AB having length Δx about the x-axis (Figure 6.42a), we generate a cylinder with surface area $2\pi y\Delta x$. This area is the same as that of a rectangle with side lengths Δx and $2\pi y$ (Figure 6.42b). The length $2\pi y$ is the circumference of the circle of radius y generated by rotating the point (x, y) on the line AB about the x-axis.

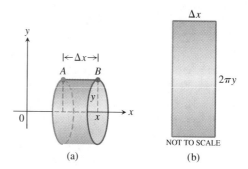

FIGURE 6.42 (a) A cylindrical surface generated by rotating the horizontal line segment AB of length Δx about the x-axis has area $2\pi y\Delta x$. (b) The cut and rolled out cylindrical surface as a rectangle.

Suppose the line segment AB has length Δs and is slanted rather than horizontal. Now when AB is rotated about the x-axis, it generates a frustum of a cone (Figure 6.43a). From classical geometry, the surface area of this frustum is $2\pi y^* \Delta s$, where $y^* = (y_1 + y_2)/2$ is the average height of the slanted segment AB above the x-axis. This surface area is the same as that of a rectangle with side lengths Δs and $2\pi y^*$ (Figure 6.43b).

Let's build on these geometric principles to define the area of a surface swept out by revolving more general curves about the x-axis. Suppose we want to find the area of the surface swept out by revolving the graph of a nonnegative continuous function $y = f(x), a \leq x \leq b$, about the x-axis. We partition the closed interval $[a, b]$ in the usual way and use the points in the partition to subdivide the graph into short arcs. Figure 6.44 shows a typical arc PQ and the band it sweeps out as part of the graph of f.

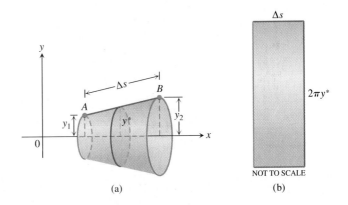

FIGURE 6.43   (a) The frustum of a cone generated by rotating the slanted line segment AB of length Δs about the x-axis has area $2\pi y^* \Delta s$. (b) The area of the rectangle for $y^* = \dfrac{y_1 + y_2}{2}$, the average height of AB above the x-axis.

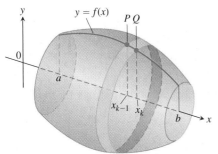

FIGURE 6.44   The surface generated by revolving the graph of a nonnegative function $y = f(x)$, $a \le x \le b$, about the x-axis. The surface is a union of bands like the one swept out by the arc PQ.

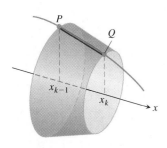

FIGURE 6.45   The line segment joining P and Q sweeps out a frustum of a cone.

As the arc PQ revolves about the x-axis, the line segment joining P and Q sweeps out a frustum of a cone whose axis lies along the x-axis (Figure 6.45). The surface area of this frustum approximates the surface area of the band swept out by the arc PQ. The surface area of the frustum of the cone shown in Figure 6.45 is $2\pi y^* L$, where y^* is the average height of the line segment joining P and Q, and L is its length (just as before). Since $f \ge 0$, from Figure 6.46 we see that the average height of the line segment is $y^* = (f(x_{k-1}) + f(x_k))/2$, and the slant length is $L = \sqrt{(\Delta x_k)^2 + (\Delta y_k)^2}$. Therefore,

$$\text{Frustum surface area} = 2\pi \cdot \frac{f(x_{k-1}) + f(x_k)}{2} \cdot \sqrt{(\Delta x_k)^2 + (\Delta y_k)^2}$$

$$= \pi(f(x_{k-1}) + f(x_k))\sqrt{(\Delta x_k)^2 + (\Delta y_k)^2}.$$

The area of the original surface, being the sum of the areas of the bands swept out by arcs like arc PQ, is approximated by the frustum area sum

$$\sum_{k=1}^{n} \pi(f(x_{k-1}) + f(x_k))\sqrt{(\Delta x_k)^2 + (\Delta y_k)^2}. \tag{1}$$

We expect the approximation to improve as the partition of $[a, b]$ becomes finer. Moreover, if the function f is differentiable, then by the Mean Value Theorem, there is a point $(c_k, f(c_k))$ on the curve between P and Q where the tangent is parallel to the segment PQ (Figure 6.47). At this point,

$$f'(c_k) = \frac{\Delta y_k}{\Delta x_k},$$

$$\Delta y_k = f'(c_k)\,\Delta x_k.$$

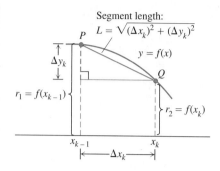

FIGURE 6.46 Dimensions associated with the arc and line segment PQ.

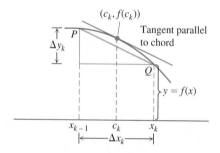

FIGURE 6.47 If f is smooth, the Mean Value Theorem guarantees the existence of a point c_k where the tangent is parallel to segment PQ.

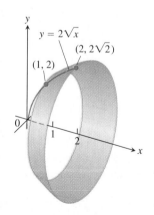

FIGURE 6.48 In Example 1 we calculate the area of this surface.

With this substitution for Δy_k, the sums in Equation (1) take the form

$$\sum_{k=1}^{n} \pi(f(x_{k-1}) + f(x_k))\sqrt{(\Delta x_k)^2 + (f'(c_k)\,\Delta x_k)^2}$$

$$= \sum_{k=1}^{n} \pi(f(x_{k-1}) + f(x_k))\sqrt{1 + (f'(c_k))^2}\,\Delta x_k. \tag{2}$$

These sums are not the Riemann sums of any function because the points x_{k-1}, x_k, and c_k are not the same. However, a theorem from advanced calculus assures us that as the norm of the partition of $[a, b]$ goes to zero, the sums in Equation (2) converge to the integral

$$\int_a^b 2\pi f(x)\sqrt{1 + (f'(x))^2}\,dx.$$

We therefore define this integral to be the area of the surface swept out by the graph of f from a to b.

DEFINITION   Surface Area for Revolution About the x-Axis
If the function $f(x) \geq 0$ is continuously differentiable on $[a, b]$, the **area** of the surface generated by revolving the curve $y = f(x)$ about the x-axis is

$$S = \int_a^b 2\pi y \sqrt{1 + \left(\frac{dy}{dx}\right)^2}\,dx = \int_a^b 2\pi f(x)\sqrt{1 + (f'(x))^2}\,dx. \tag{3}$$

The square root in Equation (3) is the same one that appears in the formula for the length of the generating curve in Equation (2) of Section 6.3.

EXAMPLE 1   Applying the Surface Area Formula

Find the area of the surface generated by revolving the curve $y = 2\sqrt{x}$, $1 \leq x \leq 2$, about the x-axis (Figure 6.48).

Solution   We evaluate the formula

$$S = \int_a^b 2\pi y \sqrt{1 + \left(\frac{dy}{dx}\right)^2}\,dx \qquad \text{Eq. (3)}$$

with

$$a = 1, \qquad b = 2, \qquad y = 2\sqrt{x}, \qquad \frac{dy}{dx} = \frac{1}{\sqrt{x}},$$

$$\sqrt{1 + \left(\frac{dy}{dx}\right)^2} = \sqrt{1 + \left(\frac{1}{\sqrt{x}}\right)^2}$$

$$= \sqrt{1 + \frac{1}{x}} = \sqrt{\frac{x + 1}{x}} = \frac{\sqrt{x + 1}}{\sqrt{x}}.$$

With these substitutions,

$$S = \int_1^2 2\pi \cdot 2\sqrt{x} \frac{\sqrt{x+1}}{\sqrt{x}} \, dx = 4\pi \int_1^2 \sqrt{x+1} \, dx$$

$$= 4\pi \cdot \frac{2}{3}(x+1)^{3/2} \Big|_1^2 = \frac{8\pi}{3}\left(3\sqrt{3} - 2\sqrt{2}\right). \qquad \blacksquare$$

Revolution About the y-Axis

For revolution about the y-axis, we interchange x and y in Equation (3).

Surface Area for Revolution About the y-Axis
If $x = g(y) \geq 0$ is continuously differentiable on $[c, d]$, the area of the surface generated by revolving the curve $x = g(y)$ about the y-axis is

$$S = \int_c^d 2\pi x \sqrt{1 + \left(\frac{dx}{dy}\right)^2} \, dy = \int_c^d 2\pi g(y)\sqrt{1 + (g'(y))^2} \, dy. \qquad (4)$$

EXAMPLE 2 Finding Area for Revolution about the y-Axis

The line segment $x = 1 - y, 0 \leq y \leq 1$, is revolved about the y-axis to generate the cone in Figure 6.49. Find its lateral surface area (which excludes the base area).

Solution Here we have a calculation we can check with a formula from geometry:

$$\text{Lateral surface area} = \frac{\text{base circumference}}{2} \times \text{slant height} = \pi\sqrt{2}.$$

To see how Equation (4) gives the same result, we take

$$c = 0, \qquad d = 1, \qquad x = 1 - y, \qquad \frac{dx}{dy} = -1,$$

$$\sqrt{1 + \left(\frac{dx}{dy}\right)^2} = \sqrt{1 + (-1)^2} = \sqrt{2}$$

and calculate

$$S = \int_c^d 2\pi x \sqrt{1 + \left(\frac{dx}{dy}\right)^2} \, dy = \int_0^1 2\pi(1-y)\sqrt{2} \, dy$$

$$= 2\pi\sqrt{2}\left[y - \frac{y^2}{2}\right]_0^1 = 2\pi\sqrt{2}\left(1 - \frac{1}{2}\right)$$

$$= \pi\sqrt{2}.$$

The results agree, as they should. $\qquad \blacksquare$

FIGURE 6.49 Revolving line segment AB about the y-axis generates a cone whose lateral surface area we can now calculate in two different ways (Example 2).

Parametrized Curves

Regardless of the coordinate axis of revolution, the square roots appearing in Equations (3) and (4) are the same ones that appear in the formulas for arc length in Section 6.3. If the curve is parametrized by the equations $x = f(t)$ and $y = g(t)$, $a \le t \le b$, where f and g are continuously differentiable on $[a, b]$, then the corresponding square root appearing in the arc length formula is

$$\sqrt{[f'(t)]^2 + [g'(t)]^2} = \sqrt{\left(\frac{dx}{dt}\right)^2 + \left(\frac{dy}{dt}\right)^2}.$$

This observation leads to the following formulas for area of surfaces of revolution for smooth parametrized curves.

Surface Area of Revolution for Parametrized Curves

If a smooth curve $x = f(t)$, $y = g(t)$, $a \le t \le b$, is traversed exactly once as t increases from a to b, then the areas of the surfaces generated by revolving the curve about the coordinate axes are as follows.

1. Revolution about the x-axis ($y \ge 0$):

$$S = \int_a^b 2\pi y \sqrt{\left(\frac{dx}{dt}\right)^2 + \left(\frac{dy}{dt}\right)^2} \, dt \tag{5}$$

2. Revolution about the y-axis ($x \ge 0$):

$$S = \int_a^b 2\pi x \sqrt{\left(\frac{dx}{dt}\right)^2 + \left(\frac{dy}{dt}\right)^2} \, dt \tag{6}$$

As with length, we can calculate surface area from any convenient parametrization that meets the stated criteria.

EXAMPLE 3 Applying Surface Area Formula

The standard parametrization of the circle of radius 1 centered at the point $(0, 1)$ in the xy-plane is

$$x = \cos t, \qquad y = 1 + \sin t, \qquad 0 \le t \le 2\pi.$$

Use this parametrization to find the area of the surface swept out by revolving the circle about the x-axis (Figure 6.50).

Solution We evaluate the formula

$$S = \int_a^b 2\pi y \sqrt{\left(\frac{dx}{dt}\right)^2 + \left(\frac{dy}{dt}\right)^2} \, dt \qquad \begin{array}{l}\text{Eq. (5) for revolution}\\ \text{about the } x\text{-axis;}\\ y = 1 + \sin t > 0\end{array}$$

$$= \int_0^{2\pi} 2\pi(1 + \sin t) \underbrace{\sqrt{(-\sin t)^2 + (\cos t)^2}}_{1} \, dt$$

$$= 2\pi \int_0^{2\pi} (1 + \sin t) \, dt$$

$$= 2\pi \Big[t - \cos t \Big]_0^{2\pi} = 4\pi^2. \qquad \blacksquare$$

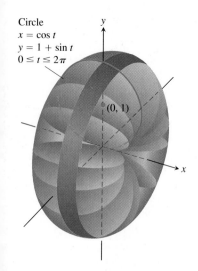

Circle
$x = \cos t$
$y = 1 + \sin t$
$0 \le t \le 2\pi$

$(0, 1)$

FIGURE 6.50 In Example 3 we calculate the area of the surface of revolution swept out by this parametrized curve.

The Differential Form

The equations

$$S = \int_a^b 2\pi y \sqrt{1 + \left(\frac{dy}{dx}\right)^2}\, dx \qquad \text{and} \qquad S = \int_c^d 2\pi x \sqrt{\left(\frac{dx}{dy}\right)^2}\, dy$$

are often written in terms of the arc length differential $ds = \sqrt{dx^2 + dy^2}$ as

$$S = \int_a^b 2\pi y\, ds \qquad \text{and} \qquad S = \int_c^d 2\pi x\, ds.$$

In the first of these, y is the distance from the x-axis to an element of arc length ds. In the second, x is the distance from the y-axis to an element of arc length ds. Both integrals have the form

$$S = \int 2\pi(\text{radius})(\text{band width}) = \int 2\pi\rho\, ds \qquad (7)$$

where ρ is the radius from the axis of revolution to an element of arc length ds (Figure 6.51).

In any particular problem, you would then express the radius function ρ and the arc length differential ds in terms of a common variable and supply limits of integration for that variable.

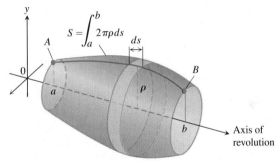

FIGURE 6.51 The area of the surface swept out by revolving arc AB about the axis shown here is $\int_a^b 2\pi\rho\, ds$. The exact expression depends on the formulas for ρ and ds.

EXAMPLE 4 Using the Differential Form for Surface Areas

Find the area of the surface generated by revolving the curve $y = x^3, 0 \le x \le 1/2$, about the x-axis (Figure 6.52).

Solution   We start with the short differential form:

$$S = \int 2\pi\rho\, ds$$

$$= \int 2\pi y\, ds$$

For revolution about the x-axis, the radius function is $\rho = y > 0$ on $0 \le x \le 1/2$.

$$= \int 2\pi y \sqrt{dx^2 + dy^2}.$$

$ds = \sqrt{dx^2 + dy^2}$

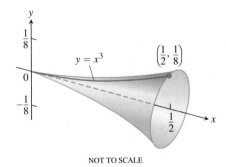

NOT TO SCALE

FIGURE 6.52 The surface generated by revolving the curve $y = x^3, 0 \le x \le 1/2$, about the x-axis could be the design for a champagne glass (Example 4).

We then decide whether to express dy in terms of dx or dx in terms of dy. The original form of the equation, $y = x^3$, makes it easier to express dy in terms of dx, so we continue the calculation with

$$y = x^3, \qquad dy = 3x^2 \, dx, \qquad \text{and} \qquad \sqrt{dx^2 + dy^2} = \sqrt{dx^2 + (3x^2 \, dx)^2}$$

$$= \sqrt{1 + 9x^4} \, dx.$$

With these substitutions, x becomes the variable of integration and

$$S = \int_{x=0}^{x=1/2} 2\pi y \sqrt{dx^2 + dy^2}$$

$$= \int_0^{1/2} 2\pi x^3 \sqrt{1 + 9x^4} \, dx$$

$$= 2\pi \left(\frac{1}{36}\right)\left(\frac{2}{3}\right)(1 + 9x^4)^{3/2} \Big]_0^{1/2}$$

$$= \frac{\pi}{27}\left[\left(1 + \frac{9}{16}\right)^{3/2} - 1\right]$$

$$= \frac{\pi}{27}\left[\left(\frac{25}{16}\right)^{3/2} - 1\right] = \frac{\pi}{27}\left(\frac{125}{64} - 1\right)$$

$$= \frac{61\pi}{1728}.$$

Substitute $u = 1 + 9x^4$, $du/36 = x^3 \, dx$; integrate, and substitute back.

Cylindrical Versus Conical Bands

Why not find the surface area by approximating with cylindrical bands instead of conical bands, as suggested in Figure 6.53? The Riemann sums we get this way converge just as nicely as the ones based on conical bands, and the resulting integral is simpler. For revolution about the x-axis in this case, the radius in Equation (7) is $\rho = y$ and the band width is $ds = dx$. This leads to the integral formula

$$S = \int_a^b 2\pi f(x) \, dx \tag{8}$$

rather than the defining Equation (3). The problem with this new formula is that it fails to give results consistent with the surface area formulas from classical geometry, and that was one of our stated goals at the outset. Just because we end up with a nice-looking integral from a Riemann sum derivation does not mean it will calculate what we intend. (See Exercise 40.)

CAUTION   Do not use Equation (8) to calculate surface area. It does *not* give the correct result.

The Theorems of Pappus

In the third century, an Alexandrian Greek named Pappus discovered two formulas that relate centroids to surfaces and solids of revolution. The formulas provide shortcuts to a number of otherwise lengthy calculations.

(a)

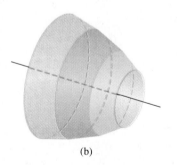

(b)

FIGURE 6.53   Why not use (a) cylindrical bands instead of (b) conical bands to approximate surface area?

> **THEOREM 1** **Pappus's Theorem for Volumes**
> If a plane region is revolved once about a line in the plane that does not cut through the region's interior, then the volume of the solid it generates is equal to the region's area times the distance traveled by the region's centroid during the revolution. If ρ is the distance from the axis of revolution to the centroid, then
> $$V = 2\pi\rho A. \qquad (9)$$

Proof We draw the axis of revolution as the x-axis with the region R in the first quadrant (Figure 6.54). We let $L(y)$ denote the length of the cross-section of R perpendicular to the y-axis at y. We assume $L(y)$ to be continuous.

By the method of cylindrical shells, the volume of the solid generated by revolving the region about the x-axis is

$$V = \int_c^d 2\pi(\text{shell radius})(\text{shell height})\, dy = 2\pi \int_c^d y\, L(y)\, dy. \qquad (10)$$

The y-coordinate of R's centroid is

$$\bar{y} = \frac{\int_c^d \tilde{y}\, dA}{A} = \frac{\int_c^d y\, L(y)\, dy}{A}, \qquad \tilde{y} = y,\, dA = L(y)dy$$

so that

$$\int_c^d y\, L(y)\, dy = A\bar{y}.$$

Substituting $A\bar{y}$ for the last integral in Equation (10) gives $V = 2\pi\bar{y}A$. With ρ equal to $\bar{y}$, we have $V = 2\pi\rho A$. ∎

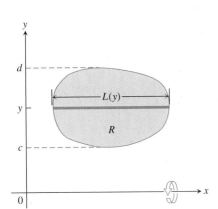

FIGURE 6.54 The region R is to be revolved (once) about the x-axis to generate a solid. A 1700-year-old theorem says that the solid's volume can be calculated by multiplying the region's area by the distance traveled by its centroid during the revolution.

EXAMPLE 5 Volume of a Torus

The volume of the torus (doughnut) generated by revolving a circular disk of radius a about an axis in its plane at a distance $b \geq a$ from its center (Figure 6.55) is

$$V = 2\pi(b)(\pi a^2) = 2\pi^2 b a^2. \qquad ∎$$

EXAMPLE 6 Locate the Centroid of a Semicircular Region

Solution We model the region as the region between the semicircle $y = \sqrt{a^2 - x^2}$ (Figure 6.56) and the x-axis and imagine revolving the region about the x-axis to generate a solid sphere. By symmetry, the x-coordinate of the centroid is $\bar{x} = 0$. With $\bar{y} = \rho$ in Equation (9), we have

$$\bar{y} = \frac{V}{2\pi A} = \frac{(4/3)\pi a^3}{2\pi(1/2)\pi a^2} = \frac{4}{3\pi}a. \qquad ∎$$

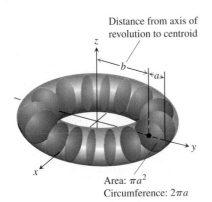

FIGURE 6.55 With Pappus's first theorem, we can find the volume of a torus without having to integrate (Example 5).

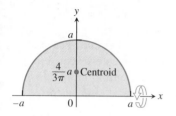

FIGURE 6.56 With Pappus's first theorem, we can locate the centroid of a semicircular region without having to integrate (Example 6).

> **THEOREM 2   Pappus's Theorem for Surface Areas**
> If an arc of a smooth plane curve is revolved once about a line in the plane that does not cut through the arc's interior, then the area of the surface generated by the arc equals the length of the arc times the distance traveled by the arc's centroid during the revolution. If ρ is the distance from the axis of revolution to the centroid, then
>
> $$S = 2\pi\rho L. \tag{11}$$

The proof we give assumes that we can model the axis of revolution as the x-axis and the arc as the graph of a continuously differentiable function of x.

Proof   We draw the axis of revolution as the x-axis with the arc extending from $x = a$ to $x = b$ in the first quadrant (Figure 6.57). The area of the surface generated by the arc is

$$S = \int_{x=a}^{x=b} 2\pi y \, ds = 2\pi \int_{x=a}^{x=b} y \, ds. \tag{12}$$

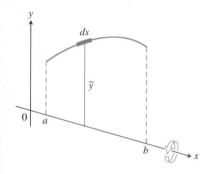

FIGURE 6.57 Figure for proving Pappus's area theorem.

The y-coordinate of the arc's centroid is

$$\bar{y} = \frac{\displaystyle\int_{x=a}^{x=b} \widetilde{y} \, ds}{\displaystyle\int_{x=a}^{x=b} ds} = \frac{\displaystyle\int_{x=a}^{x=b} y \, ds}{L}. \qquad \begin{array}{l} L = \int ds \text{ is the arc's} \\ \text{length and } \widetilde{y} = y. \end{array}$$

Hence

$$\int_{x=a}^{x=b} y \, ds = \bar{y}L.$$

Substituting $\bar{y}L$ for the last integral in Equation (12) gives $S = 2\pi\bar{y}L$. With ρ equal to $\bar{y}$, we have $S = 2\pi\rho L$.   ∎

EXAMPLE 7   Surface Area of a Torus

The surface area of the torus in Example 5 is

$$S = 2\pi(b)(2\pi a) = 4\pi^2 ba.$$ ∎

EXERCISES 6.5

Finding Integrals for Surface Area

In Exercises 1–8:

   a. Set up an integral for the area of the surface generated by revolving the given curve about the indicated axis.

T **b.** Graph the curve to see what it looks like. If you can, graph the surface, too.

T **c.** Use your grapher's or computer's integral evaluator to find the surface's area numerically.

1. $y = \tan x, \quad 0 \le x \le \pi/4; \quad x$-axis

2. $y = x^2, \quad 0 \le x \le 2; \quad x$-axis

3. $xy = 1, \quad 1 \le y \le 2; \quad y$-axis

4. $x = \sin y, \quad 0 \le y \le \pi; \quad y$-axis

5. $x^{1/2} + y^{1/2} = 3$ from $(4, 1)$ to $(1, 4); \quad x$-axis

6. $y + 2\sqrt{y} = x, \quad 1 \le y \le 2; \quad y$-axis

7. $x = \displaystyle\int_0^y \tan t \, dt, \quad 0 \le y \le \pi/3; \quad y$-axis

8. $y = \displaystyle\int_1^x \sqrt{t^2 - 1} \, dt, \quad 1 \le x \le \sqrt{5}; \quad x$-axis

Finding Surface Areas

9. Find the lateral (side) surface area of the cone generated by revolving the line segment $y = x/2, 0 \le x \le 4$, about the x-axis. Check your answer with the geometry formula

$$\text{Lateral surface area} = \frac{1}{2} \times \text{base circumference} \times \text{slant height}.$$

10. Find the lateral surface area of the cone generated by revolving the line segment $y = x/2, 0 \le x \le 4$ about the y-axis. Check your answer with the geometry formula

$$\text{Lateral surface area} = \frac{1}{2} \times \text{base circumference} \times \text{slant height}.$$

11. Find the surface area of the cone frustum generated by revolving the line segment $y = (x/2) + (1/2), 1 \le x \le 3$, about the x-axis. Check your result with the geometry formula

$$\text{Frustum surface area} = \pi(r_1 + r_2) \times \text{slant height}.$$

12. Find the surface area of the cone frustum generated by revolving the line segment $y = (x/2) + (1/2), 1 \le x \le 3$, about the y-axis. Check your result with the geometry formula

$$\text{Frustum surface area} = \pi(r_1 + r_2) \times \text{slant height}.$$

Find the areas of the surfaces generated by revolving the curves in Exercises 13–22 about the indicated axes. If you have a grapher, you may want to graph these curves to see what they look like.

13. $y = x^3/9, \quad 0 \le x \le 2; \quad x$-axis

14. $y = \sqrt{x}, \quad 3/4 \le x \le 15/4; \quad x$-axis

15. $y = \sqrt{2x - x^2}, \quad 0.5 \le x \le 1.5; \quad x$-axis

16. $y = \sqrt{x + 1}, \quad 1 \le x \le 5; \quad x$-axis

17. $x = y^3/3, \quad 0 \le y \le 1; \quad y$-axis

18. $x = (1/3)y^{3/2} - y^{1/2}, \quad 1 \le y \le 3; \quad y$-axis

19. $x = 2\sqrt{4 - y}, \quad 0 \le y \le 15/4; \quad y$-axis

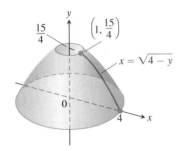

20. $x = \sqrt{2y - 1}, \quad 5/8 \le y \le 1; \quad y$-axis

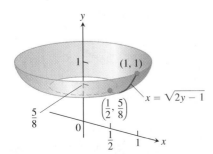

21. $x = (y^4/4) + 1/(8y^2), \quad 1 \le y \le 2; \quad x$-axis (*Hint:* Express $ds = \sqrt{dx^2 + dy^2}$ in terms of dy, and evaluate the integral $S = \int 2\pi y \, ds$ with appropriate limits.)

22. $y = (1/3)(x^2 + 2)^{3/2}, \quad 0 \le x \le \sqrt{2}; \quad y$-axis (*Hint:* Express $ds = \sqrt{dx^2 + dy^2}$ in terms of dx, and evaluate the integral $S = \int 2\pi x \, ds$ with appropriate limits.)

23. **Testing the new definition** Show that the surface area of a sphere of radius a is still $4\pi a^2$ by using Equation (3) to find the area of the surface generated by revolving the curve $y = \sqrt{a^2 - x^2}, -a \le x \le a$, about the x-axis.

24. **Testing the new definition** The lateral (side) surface area of a cone of height h and base radius r should be $\pi r \sqrt{r^2 + h^2}$, the semiperimeter of the base times the slant height. Show that this is still the case by finding the area of the surface generated by revolving the line segment $y = (r/h)x, 0 \le x \le h$, about the x-axis.

25. Write an integral for the area of the surface generated by revolving the curve $y = \cos x, -\pi/2 \le x \le \pi/2$, about the x-axis. In Section 8.5 we will see how to evaluate such integrals.

26. **The surface of an astroid** Find the area of the surface generated by revolving about the x-axis the portion of the astroid $x^{2/3} + y^{2/3} = 1$ shown here. (*Hint:* Revolve the first-quadrant portion $y = (1 - x^{2/3})^{3/2}, 0 \le x \le 1$, about the x-axis and double your result.)

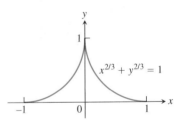

27. **Enameling woks** Your company decided to put out a deluxe version of the successful wok you designed in Section 6.1, Exercise 55. The plan is to coat it inside with white enamel and outside with blue enamel. Each enamel will be sprayed on 0.5 mm thick before baking. (See diagram here.) Your manufacturing department wants to know how much enamel to have on hand for a production run of 5000 woks. What do you tell them? (Neglect waste and unused material and give your answer in liters. Remember that $1 \text{ cm}^3 = 1 \text{ mL}$, so $1 \text{ L} = 1000 \text{ cm}^3$.)

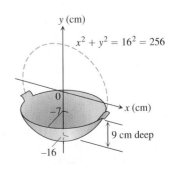

28. Slicing bread Did you know that if you cut a spherical loaf of bread into slices of equal width, each slice will have the same amount of crust? To see why, suppose the semicircle $y = \sqrt{r^2 - x^2}$ shown here is revolved about the x-axis to generate a sphere. Let AB be an arc of the semicircle that lies above an interval of length h on the x-axis. Show that the area swept out by AB does not depend on the location of the interval. (It does depend on the length of the interval.)

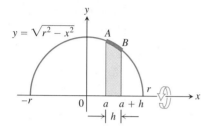

29. The shaded band shown here is cut from a sphere of radius R by parallel planes h units apart. Show that the surface area of the band is $2\pi Rh$.

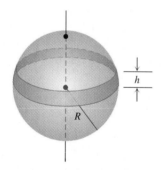

30. Here is a schematic drawing of the 90-ft dome used by the U.S. National Weather Service to house radar in Bozeman, Montana.

   a. How much outside surface is there to paint (not counting the bottom)?

   T **b.** Express the answer to the nearest square foot.

31. Surfaces generated by curves that cross the axis of revolution The surface area formula in Equation (3) was developed under the assumption that the function f whose graph generated the surface was nonnegative over the interval $[a, b]$. For curves that cross the axis of

revolution, we replace Equation (3) with the absolute value formula

$$S = \int 2\pi\rho \, ds = \int 2\pi |f(x)| \, ds. \qquad (13)$$

Use Equation (13) to find the surface area of the double cone generated by revolving the line segment $y = x$, $-1 \le x \le 2$, about the x-axis.

32. (*Continuation of Exercise 31.*) Find the area of the surface generated by revolving the curve $y = x^3/9$, $-\sqrt{3} \le x \le \sqrt{3}$, about the x-axis. What do you think will happen if you drop the absolute value bars from Equation (13) and attempt to find the surface area with the formula $S = \int 2\pi f(x) \, ds$ instead? Try it.

Parametrizations

Find the areas of the surfaces generated by revolving the curves in Exercises 33–35 about the indicated axes.

33. $x = \cos t$, $y = 2 + \sin t$, $0 \le t \le 2\pi$; x-axis

34. $x = (2/3)t^{3/2}$, $y = 2\sqrt{t}$, $0 \le t \le \sqrt{3}$; y-axis

35. $x = t + \sqrt{2}$, $y = (t^2/2) + \sqrt{2}t$, $-\sqrt{2} \le t \le \sqrt{2}$; y-axis

36. Set up, but do not evaluate, an integral that represents the area of the surface obtained by rotating the curve $x = a(t - \sin t)$, $y = a(1 - \cos t)$, $0 \le t \le 2\pi$, about the x-axis.

37. A cone frustum The line segment joining the points $(0, 1)$ and $(2, 2)$ is revolved about the x-axis to generate a frustum of a cone. Find the surface area of the frustum using the parametrization $x = 2t$, $y = t + 1$, $0 \le t \le 1$. Check your result with the geometry formula: Area $= \pi(r_1 + r_2)$(slant height).

38. A cone The line segment joining the origin to the point (h, r) is revolved about the x-axis to generate a cone of height h and base radius r. Find the cone's surface area with the parametric equations $x = ht$, $y = rt$, $0 \le t \le 1$. Check your result with the geometry formula: Area $= \pi r$(slant height).

39. An alternative derivation of the surface area formula Assume f is smooth on $[a, b]$ and partition $[a, b]$ in the usual way. In the kth subinterval $[x_{k-1}, x_k]$ construct the tangent line to the curve at the midpoint $m_k = (x_{k-1} + x_k)/2$, as in the figure here.

   a. Show that $r_1 = f(m_k) - f'(m_k)\dfrac{\Delta x_k}{2}$ and $r_2 = f(m_k) + f'(m_k)\dfrac{\Delta x_k}{2}$.

   b. Show that the length L_k of the tangent line segment in the kth subinterval is $L_k = \sqrt{(\Delta x_k)^2 + (f'(m_k)\,\Delta x_k)^2}$.

c. Show that the lateral surface area of the frustum of the cone swept out by the tangent line segment as it revolves about the x-axis is $2\pi f(m_k)\sqrt{1 + (f'(m_k))^2}\,\Delta x_k$.

d. Show that the area of the surface generated by revolving $y = f(x)$ about the x-axis over $[a, b]$ is

$$\lim_{n\to\infty}\sum_{k=1}^{n}\binom{\text{lateral surface area}}{\text{of } k\text{th frustum}} = \int_{a}^{b} 2\pi f(x)\sqrt{1 + (f'(x))^2}\,dx.$$

40. Modeling surface area The lateral surface area of the cone swept out by revolving the line segment $y = x/\sqrt{3}$, $0 \le x \le \sqrt{3}$, about the x-axis should be $(1/2)(\text{base circumference})(\text{slant height}) = (1/2)(2\pi)(2) = 2\pi$. What do you get if you use Equation (8) with $f(x) = x/\sqrt{3}$?

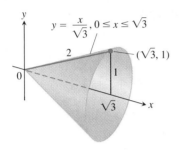

The Theorems of Pappus

41. The square region with vertices $(0, 2)$, $(2, 0)$, $(4, 2)$, and $(2, 4)$ is revolved about the x-axis to generate a solid. Find the volume and surface area of the solid.

42. Use a theorem of Pappus to find the volume generated by revolving about the line $x = 5$ the triangular region bounded by the coordinate axes and the line $2x + y = 6$. (As you saw in Exercise 29 of Section 6.4, the centroid of a triangle lies at the intersection of the medians, one-third of the way from the midpoint of each side toward the opposite vertex.)

43. Find the volume of the torus generated by revolving the circle $(x - 2)^2 + y^2 = 1$ about the y-axis.

44. Use the theorems of Pappus to find the lateral surface area and the volume of a right circular cone.

45. Use the Second Theorem of Pappus and the fact that the surface area of a sphere of radius a is $4\pi a^2$ to find the centroid of the semicircle $y = \sqrt{a^2 - x^2}$.

46. As found in Exercise 45, the centroid of the semicircle $y = \sqrt{a^2 - x^2}$ lies at the point $(0, 2a/\pi)$. Find the area of the surface swept out by revolving the semicircle about the line $y = a$.

47. The area of the region R enclosed by the semiellipse $y = (b/a)\sqrt{a^2 - x^2}$ and the x-axis is $(1/2)\pi ab$ and the volume of the ellipsoid generated by revolving R about the x-axis is $(4/3)\pi ab^2$. Find the centroid of R. Notice that the location is independent of a.

48. As found in Example 6, the centroid of the region enclosed by the x-axis and the semicircle $y = \sqrt{a^2 - x^2}$ lies at the point $(0, 4a/3\pi)$. Find the volume of the solid generated by revolving this region about the line $y = -a$.

49. The region of Exercise 48 is revolved about the line $y = x - a$ to generate a solid. Find the volume of the solid.

50. As found in Exercise 45, the centroid of the semicircle $y = \sqrt{a^2 - x^2}$ lies at the point $(0, 2a/\pi)$. Find the area of the surface generated by revolving the semicircle about the line $y = x - a$.

51. Find the moment about the x-axis of the semicircular region in Example 6. If you use results already known, you will not need to integrate.

6.6 Work

In everyday life, *work* means an activity that requires muscular or mental effort. In science, the term refers specifically to a force acting on a body and the body's subsequent displacement. This section shows how to calculate work. The applications run from compressing railroad car springs and emptying subterranean tanks to forcing electrons together and lifting satellites into orbit.

Work Done by a Constant Force

When a body moves a distance d along a straight line as a result of being acted on by a force of constant magnitude F in the direction of motion, we define the **work** W done by the force on the body with the formula

$$W = Fd \qquad \text{(Constant-force formula for work).} \qquad (1)$$

From Equation (1) we see that the unit of work in any system is the unit of force multiplied by the unit of distance. In SI units (SI stands for *Système International*, or International System), the unit of force is a newton, the unit of distance is a meter, and the unit of work is a newton-meter ($\text{N} \cdot \text{m}$). This combination appears so often it has a special name, the **joule**. In the British system, the unit of work is the foot-pound, a unit frequently used by engineers.

EXAMPLE 1   Jacking Up a Car

If you jack up the side of a 2000-lb car 1.25 ft to change a tire (you have to apply a constant vertical force of about 1000 lb) you will perform $1000 \times 1.25 = 1250$ ft-lb of work on the car. In SI units, you have applied a force of 4448 N through a distance of 0.381 m to do $4448 \times 0.381 \approx 1695$ J of work.   ∎

Work Done by a Variable Force Along a Line

If the force you apply varies along the way, as it will if you are compressing a spring, the formula $W = Fd$ has to be replaced by an integral formula that takes the variation in F into account.

Suppose that the force performing the work acts along a line that we take to be the x-axis and that its magnitude F is a continuous function of the position. We want to find the work done over the interval from $x = a$ to $x = b$. We partition $[a, b]$ in the usual way and choose an arbitrary point c_k in each subinterval $[x_{k-1}, x_k]$. If the subinterval is short enough, F, being continuous, will not vary much from x_{k-1} to x_k. The amount of work done across the interval will be about $F(c_k)$ times the distance Δx_k, the same as it would be if F were constant and we could apply Equation (1). The total work done from a to b is therefore approximated by the Riemann sum

$$\text{Work} \approx \sum_{k=1}^{n} F(c_k) \, \Delta x_k.$$

We expect the approximation to improve as the norm of the partition goes to zero, so we define the work done by the force from a to b to be the integral of F from a to b:

$$\lim_{n \to \infty} \sum_{k=1}^{n} F(c_k) \, \Delta x_k = \int_{a}^{b} F(x) \, dx.$$

DEFINITION   Work

The **work** done by a variable force $F(x)$ directed along the x-axis from $x = a$ to $x = b$ is

$$W = \int_{a}^{b} F(x) \, dx. \tag{2}$$

The units of the integral are joules if F is in newtons and x is in meters, and foot-pounds if F is in pounds and x in feet. So, the work done by a force of $F(x) = 1/x^2$ newtons along the x-axis from $x = 1$ m to $x = 10$ m is

$$W = \int_{1}^{10} \frac{1}{x^2} \, dx = -\frac{1}{x} \Big]_{1}^{10} = -\frac{1}{10} + 1 = 0.9 \text{ J}.$$

Hooke's Law for Springs: $F = kx$

Hooke's Law says that the force it takes to stretch or compress a spring x length units from its natural (unstressed) length is proportional to x. In symbols,

$$F = kx. \tag{3}$$

The constant k, measured in force units per unit length, is a characteristic of the spring, called the **force constant** (or **spring constant**) of the spring. Hooke's Law, Equation (3), gives good results as long as the force doesn't distort the metal in the spring. We assume that the forces in this section are too small to do that.

EXAMPLE 2   Compressing a Spring

Find the work required to compress a spring from its natural length of 1 ft to a length of 0.75 ft if the force constant is $k = 16\ \text{lb/ft}$.

Solution   We picture the uncompressed spring laid out along the x-axis with its movable end at the origin and its fixed end at $x = 1$ ft (Figure 6.58). This enables us to describe the force required to compress the spring from 0 to x with the formula $F = 16x$. To compress the spring from 0 to 0.25 ft, the force must increase from

$$F(0) = 16 \cdot 0 = 0\ \text{lb} \qquad \text{to} \qquad F(0.25) = 16 \cdot 0.25 = 4\ \text{lb}.$$

The work done by F over this interval is

$$W = \int_0^{0.25} 16x\,dx = 8x^2 \Big]_0^{0.25} = 0.5\ \text{ft-lb}. \qquad \begin{array}{l}\text{Eq. (2) with}\\ a = 0, b = 0.25,\\ F(x) = 16x\end{array}$$

■

EXAMPLE 3   Stretching a Spring

A spring has a natural length of 1 m. A force of 24 N stretches the spring to a length of 1.8 m.

(a) Find the force constant k.

(b) How much work will it take to stretch the spring 2 m beyond its natural length?

(c) How far will a 45-N force stretch the spring?

Solution

(a) *The force constant.* We find the force constant from Equation (3). A force of 24 N stretches the spring 0.8 m, so

$$24 = k(0.8) \qquad \begin{array}{l}\text{Eq. (3) with}\\ F = 24, x = 0.8\end{array}$$

$$k = 24/0.8 = 30\ \text{N/m}.$$

(b) *The work to stretch the spring* 2 m. We imagine the unstressed spring hanging along the x-axis with its free end at $x = 0$ (Figure 6.59). The force required to stretch the spring x m beyond its natural length is the force required to pull the free end of the spring x units from the origin. Hooke's Law with $k = 30$ says that this force is

$$F(x) = 30x.$$

Compressed

Uncompressed

(a)

$F = 16x$

Force (lb)

Work done by F
from $x = 0$ to $x = 0.25$

Amount compressed

(b)

FIGURE 6.58   The force F needed to hold a spring under compression increases linearly as the spring is compressed (Example 2).

$x = 0$

0.8

1

24 N

x (m)

FIGURE 6.59   A 24-N weight stretches this spring 0.8 m beyond its unstressed length (Example 3).

The work done by F on the spring from $x = 0$ m to $x = 2$ m is

$$W = \int_0^2 30x \, dx = 15x^2 \Big]_0^2 = 60 \text{ J}.$$

(c) *How far will a 45-N force stretch the spring?* We substitute $F = 45$ in the equation $F = 30x$ to find

$$45 = 30x, \quad \text{or} \quad x = 1.5 \text{ m}.$$

A 45-N force will stretch the spring 1.5 m. No calculus is required to find this. ∎

The work integral is useful to calculate the work done in lifting objects whose weights vary with their elevation.

EXAMPLE 4 Lifting a Rope and Bucket

A 5-lb bucket is lifted from the ground into the air by pulling in 20 ft of rope at a constant speed (Figure 6.60). The rope weighs 0.08 lb/ft. How much work was spent lifting the bucket and rope?

FIGURE 6.60 Lifting the bucket in Example 4.

Solution The bucket has constant weight so the work done lifting it alone is weight $\times$ distance $= 5 \cdot 20 = 100$ ft-lb.

The weight of the rope varies with the bucket's elevation, because less of it is freely hanging. When the bucket is x ft off the ground, the remaining proportion of the rope still being lifted weighs $(0.08) \cdot (20 - x)$ lb. So the work in lifting the rope is

$$\text{Work on rope} = \int_0^{20} (0.08)(20 - x) \, dx = \int_0^{20} (1.6 - 0.08x) \, dx$$

$$= \Big[1.6x - 0.04x^2 \Big]_0^{20} = 32 - 16 = 16 \text{ ft-lb}.$$

The total work for the bucket and rope combined is

$$100 + 16 = 116 \text{ ft-lb}. \qquad ∎$$

Pumping Liquids from Containers

How much work does it take to pump all or part of the liquid from a container? To find out, we imagine lifting the liquid out one thin horizontal slab at a time and applying the equation $W = Fd$ to each slab. We then evaluate the integral this leads to as the slabs become thinner and more numerous. The integral we get each time depends on the weight of the liquid and the dimensions of the container, but the way we find the integral is always the same. The next examples show what to do.

EXAMPLE 5 Pumping Oil from a Conical Tank

The conical tank in Figure 6.61 is filled to within 2 ft of the top with olive oil weighing 57 lb/ft^3. How much work does it take to pump the oil to the rim of the tank?

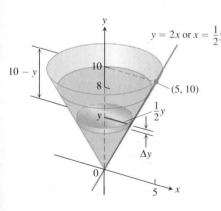

FIGURE 6.61 The olive oil and tank in Example 5.

Solution We imagine the oil divided into thin slabs by planes perpendicular to the y-axis at the points of a partition of the interval $[0, 8]$.

The typical slab between the planes at y and $y + \Delta y$ has a volume of about

$$\Delta V = \pi (\text{radius})^2 (\text{thickness}) = \pi \left(\frac{1}{2} y \right)^2 \Delta y = \frac{\pi}{4} y^2 \, \Delta y \text{ ft}^3.$$

The force $F(y)$ required to lift this slab is equal to its weight,

$$F(y) = 57 \, \Delta V = \frac{57\pi}{4} y^2 \, \Delta y \text{ lb}.$$

Weight = weight per unit volume × volume

The distance through which $F(y)$ must act to lift this slab to the level of the rim of the cone is about $(10 - y)$ ft, so the work done lifting the slab is about

$$\Delta W = \frac{57\pi}{4}(10 - y)y^2 \, \Delta y \text{ ft-lb}.$$

Assuming there are n slabs associated with the partition of $[0, 8]$, and that $y = y_k$ denotes the plane associated with the kth slab of thickness Δy_k, we can approximate the work done lifting all of the slabs with the Riemann sum

$$W \approx \sum_{k=1}^{n} \frac{57\pi}{4}(10 - y_k)y_k^2 \, \Delta y_k \text{ ft-lb}.$$

The work of pumping the oil to the rim is the limit of these sums as the norm of the partition goes to zero.

$$W = \lim_{n \to \infty} \sum_{k=1}^{n} \frac{57\pi}{4}(10 - y_k)y_k^2 \, \Delta y_k = \int_0^8 \frac{57\pi}{4}(10 - y)y^2 \, dy$$

$$= \frac{57\pi}{4} \int_0^8 (10y^2 - y^3) \, dy$$

$$= \frac{57\pi}{4}\left[\frac{10y^3}{3} - \frac{y^4}{4}\right]_0^8 \approx 30{,}561 \text{ ft-lb}. \quad \blacksquare$$

EXAMPLE 6   Pumping Water from a Glory Hole

A glory hole is a vertical drain pipe that keeps the water behind a dam from getting too high. The top of the glory hole for a dam is 14 ft below the top of the dam and 375 ft above the bottom (Figure 6.62). The hole needs to be pumped out from time to time to permit the removal of seasonal debris.

From the cross-section in Figure 6.62a, we see that the glory hole is a funnel-shaped drain. The throat of the funnel is 20 ft wide and the head is 120 ft across. The outside boundary of the head cross-section are quarter circles formed with 50-ft radii, shown in Figure 6.62b. The glory hole is formed by rotating a cross-section around its center. Consequently, all horizontal cross-sections are circular disks throughout the entire glory hole. We calculate the work required to pump water from

(a) the throat of the hole.

(b) the funnel portion.

Solution

(a) *Pumping from the throat.* A typical slab in the throat between the planes at y and $y + \Delta y$ has a volume of about

$$\Delta V = \pi(\text{radius})^2(\text{thickness}) = \pi(10)^2 \Delta y \text{ ft}^3.$$

The force $F(y)$ required to lift this slab is equal to its weight (about 62.4 lb/ft^3 for water),

$$F(y) = 62.4 \, \Delta V = 6240\pi \, \Delta y \text{ lb}.$$

389 ft — |← 120 ft →| 375 ft above bottom of dam

325 ft above bottom of dam

← Throat 20 ft wide

(a)

Quarter circle of radius 50 ft

r

(b)

FIGURE 6.62 (a) Cross-section of the glory hole for a dam and (b) the top of the glory hole (Example 6).

The distance through which $F(y)$ must act to lift this slab to the top of the hole is $(375 - y)$ ft, so the work done lifting the slab is

$$\Delta W = 6240\pi(375 - y)\,\Delta y \text{ ft-lb}.$$

We can approximate the work done in pumping the water from the throat by summing the work done lifting all the slabs individually, and then taking the limit of this Riemann sum as the norm of the partition goes to zero. This gives the integral

$$W = \int_{0}^{325} 6240\pi(375 - y)\,dy$$

$$= 6240\pi\left[375y - \frac{y^2}{2}\right]_{0}^{325}$$

$$\approx 1{,}353{,}869{,}354 \text{ ft-lb}.$$

(b) *Pumping from the funnel.* To compute the work necessary to pump water from the funnel portion of the glory hole, from $y = 325$ to $y = 375$, we need to compute ΔV for approximating elements in the funnel as shown in Figure 6.63. As can be seen from the figure, the radii of the slabs vary with height y.

In Exercises 33 and 34, you are asked to complete the analysis to determine the total work required to pump the water and to find the power of the pumps necessary to pump out the glory hole. ∎

FIGURE 6.63 The glory hole funnel portion.

EXERCISES 6.6

Springs

1. **Spring constant** It took 1800 J of work to stretch a spring from its natural length of 2 m to a length of 5 m. Find the spring's force constant.

2. **Stretching a spring** A spring has a natural length of 10 in. An 800-lb force stretches the spring to 14 in.

   a. Find the force constant.

   b. How much work is done in stretching the spring from 10 in. to 12 in.?

   c. How far beyond its natural length will a 1600-lb force stretch the spring?

3. **Stretching a rubber band** A force of 2 N will stretch a rubber band 2 cm (0.02 m). Assuming that Hooke's Law applies, how far will a 4-N force stretch the rubber band? How much work does it take to stretch the rubber band this far?

4. **Stretching a spring** If a force of 90 N stretches a spring 1 m beyond its natural length, how much work does it take to stretch the spring 5 m beyond its natural length?

5. **Subway car springs** It takes a force of 21,714 lb to compress a coil spring assembly on a New York City Transit Authority subway car from its free height of 8 in. to its fully compressed height of 5 in.

   a. What is the assembly's force constant?

   b. How much work does it take to compress the assembly the first half inch? the second half inch? Answer to the nearest in.-lb.

   (Data courtesy of Bombardier, Inc., Mass Transit Division, for spring assemblies in subway cars delivered to the New York City Transit Authority from 1985 to 1987.)

6. **Bathroom scale** A bathroom scale is compressed 1/16 in. when a 150-lb person stands on it. Assuming that the scale behaves like a spring that obeys Hooke's Law, how much does someone who compresses the scale 1/8 in. weigh? How much work is done compressing the scale 1/8 in.?

Work Done By a Variable Force

7. **Lifting a rope** A mountain climber is about to haul up a 50 m length of hanging rope. How much work will it take if the rope weighs 0.624 N/m?

8. **Leaky sandbag** A bag of sand originally weighing 144 lb was lifted at a constant rate. As it rose, sand also leaked out at a constant rate. The sand was half gone by the time the bag had been

lifted to 18 ft. How much work was done lifting the sand this far? (Neglect the weight of the bag and lifting equipment.)

9. **Lifting an elevator cable** An electric elevator with a motor at the top has a multistrand cable weighing 4.5 lb/ft. When the car is at the first floor, 180 ft of cable are paid out, and effectively 0 ft are out when the car is at the top floor. How much work does the motor do just lifting the cable when it takes the car from the first floor to the top?

10. **Force of attraction** When a particle of mass m is at $(x, 0)$, it is attracted toward the origin with a force whose magnitude is k/x^2. If the particle starts from rest at $x = b$ and is acted on by no other forces, find the work done on it by the time it reaches $x = a$, $0 < a < b$.

11. **Compressing gas** Suppose that the gas in a circular cylinder of cross-sectional area A is being compressed by a piston. If p is the pressure of the gas in pounds per square inch and V is the volume in cubic inches, show that the work done in compressing the gas from state (p_1, V_1) to state (p_2, V_2) is given by the equation

$$\text{Work} = \int_{(p_1, V_1)}^{(p_2, V_2)} p \, dV.$$

(*Hint:* In the coordinates suggested in the figure here, $dV = A \, dx$. The force against the piston is pA.)

12. (*Continuation of Exercise 11.*) Use the integral in Exercise 11 to find the work done in compressing the gas from $V_1 = 243$ in.^{3} to $V_2 = 32$ in.^{3} if $p_1 = 50$ lb/in.^{3} and p and V obey the gas law $pV^{1.4} = $ constant (for adiabatic processes).

13. **Leaky bucket** Assume the bucket in Example 4 is leaking. It starts with 2 gal of water (16 lb) and leaks at a constant rate. It finishes draining just as it reaches the top. How much work was spent lifting the water alone? (*Hint:* Do not include the rope and bucket, and find the proportion of water left at elevation x ft.)

14. (*Continuation of Exercise 13.*) The workers in Example 4 and Exercise 13 changed to a larger bucket that held 5 gal (40 lb) of water, but the new bucket had an even larger leak so that it, too, was empty by the time it reached the top. Assuming that the water leaked out at a steady rate, how much work was done lifting the water alone? (Do not include the rope and bucket.)

Pumping Liquids from Containers

The Weight of Water

Because of Earth's rotation and variations in its gravitational field, the weight of a cubic foot of water at sea level can vary from about 62.26 lb at the equator to as much as 62.59 lb near the poles, a variation of about 0.5%. A cubic foot that weighs about 62.4 lb in Melbourne and New York City will weigh 62.5 lb in Juneau and Stockholm. Although 62.4 is a typical figure and common textbook value, there is considerable variation.

15. **Pumping water** The rectangular tank shown here, with its top at ground level, is used to catch runoff water. Assume that the water weighs 62.4 lb/ft^3.

    a. How much work does it take to empty the tank by pumping the water back to ground level once the tank is full?

    b. If the water is pumped to ground level with a (5/11)-horsepower (hp) motor (work output 250 ft-lb/sec), how long will it take to empty the full tank (to the nearest minute)?

    c. Show that the pump in part (b) will lower the water level 10 ft (halfway) during the first 25 min of pumping.

    d. **The weight of water** What are the answers to parts (a) and (b) in a location where water weighs 62.26 lb/ft^3? 62.59 lb/ft^3?

16. **Emptying a cistern** The rectangular cistern (storage tank for rainwater) shown below has its top 10 ft below ground level. The cistern, currently full, is to be emptied for inspection by pumping its contents to ground level.

    a. How much work will it take to empty the cistern?

    b. How long will it take a 1/2 hp pump, rated at 275 ft-lb/sec, to pump the tank dry?

    c. How long will it take the pump in part (b) to empty the tank halfway? (It will be less than half the time required to empty the tank completely.)

    d. **The weight of water** What are the answers to parts (a) through (c) in a location where water weighs 62.26 lb/ft^3? 62.59 lb/ft^3?

Ground level

17. **Pumping oil**   How much work would it take to pump oil from the tank in Example 5 to the level of the top of the tank if the tank were completely full?

18. **Pumping a half-full tank**   Suppose that, instead of being full, the tank in Example 5 is only half full. How much work does it take to pump the remaining oil to a level 4 ft above the top of the tank?

19. **Emptying a tank**   A vertical right circular cylindrical tank measures 30 ft high and 20 ft in diameter. It is full of kerosene weighing 51.2 lb/ft³. How much work does it take to pump the kerosene to the level of the top of the tank?

20. The cylindrical tank shown here can be filled by pumping water from a lake 15 ft below the bottom of the tank. There are two ways to go about it. One is to pump the water through a hose attached to a valve in the bottom of the tank. The other is to attach the hose to the rim of the tank and let the water pour in. Which way will be faster? Give reasons for your answer.

Open top

2 ft

6 ft

Valve at base

21. a. **Pumping milk**   Suppose that the conical container in Example 5 contains milk (weighing 64.5 lb/ft³) instead of olive oil. How much work will it take to pump the contents to the rim?

   b. **Pumping oil**   How much work will it take to pump the oil in Example 5 to a level 3 ft above the cone's rim?

22. **Pumping seawater**   To design the interior surface of a huge stainless-steel tank, you revolve the curve $y = x^2, 0 \le x \le 4$, about the y-axis. The container, with dimensions in meters, is to be filled with seawater, which weighs 10,000 N/m³. How much work will it take to empty the tank by pumping the water to the tank's top?

23. **Emptying a water reservoir**   We model pumping from spherical containers the way we do from other containers, with the axis of integration along the vertical axis of the sphere. Use the figure here to find how much work it takes to empty a full hemispherical water reservoir of radius 5 m by pumping the water to a height of 4 m above the top of the reservoir. Water weighs 9800 N/m³.

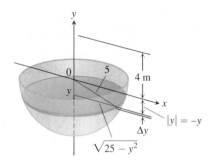

24. You are in charge of the evacuation and repair of the storage tank shown here. The tank is a hemisphere of radius 10 ft and is full of benzene weighing 56 lb/ft³. A firm you contacted says it can empty the tank for $1/2$¢ per foot-pound of work. Find the work required to empty the tank by pumping the benzene to an outlet 2 ft above the top of the tank. If you have $5000 budgeted for the job, can you afford to hire the firm?

Work and Kinetic Energy

25. **Kinetic energy**   If a variable force of magnitude $F(x)$ moves a body of mass m along the x-axis from x_1 to x_2, the body's velocity v can be written as dx/dt (where t represents time). Use Newton's second law of motion $F = m(dv/dt)$ and the Chain Rule

$$\frac{dv}{dt} = \frac{dv}{dx}\frac{dx}{dt} = v\frac{dv}{dx}$$

to show that the net work done by the force in moving the body from x_1 to x_2 is

$$W = \int_{x_1}^{x_2} F(x)\, dx = \frac{1}{2}mv_2{}^2 - \frac{1}{2}mv_1{}^2,$$

where v_1 and v_2 are the body's velocities at x_1 and x_2. In physics, the expression $(1/2)mv^2$ is called the *kinetic energy* of a body of mass m moving with velocity v. Therefore, *the work done by the force equals the change in the body's kinetic energy*, and we can find the work by calculating this change.

In Exercises 26–32, use the result of Exercise 25.

26. **Tennis**   A 2-oz tennis ball was served at 160 ft/sec (about 109 mph). How much work was done on the ball to make it go this fast? (To find the ball's mass from its weight, express the weight in pounds and divide by 32 ft/sec², the acceleration of gravity.)

27. **Baseball**   How many foot-pounds of work does it take to throw a baseball 90 mph? A baseball weighs 5 oz, or 0.3125 lb.

28. **Golf** A 1.6-oz golf ball is driven off the tee at a speed of 280 ft/sec (about 191 mph). How many foot-pounds of work are done on the ball getting it into the air?

29. **Tennis** During the match in which Pete Sampras won the 1990 U.S. Open men's tennis championship, Sampras hit a serve that was clocked at a phenomenal 124 mph. How much work did Sampras have to do on the 2-oz ball to get it to that speed?

30. **Football** A quarterback threw a 14.5-oz football 88 ft/sec (60 mph). How many foot-pounds of work were done on the ball to get it to this speed?

31. **Softball** How much work has to be performed on a 6.5-oz softball to pitch it 132 ft/sec (90 mph)?

32. **A ball bearing** A 2-oz steel ball bearing is placed on a vertical spring whose force constant is $k = 18$ lb/ft. The spring is compressed 2 in. and released. About how high does the ball bearing go?

33. **Pumping the funnel of the glory hole** (*Continuation of Example 6.*)
   a. Find the radius of the cross-section (funnel portion) of the glory hole in Example 6 as a function of the height y above the floor of the dam (from $y = 325$ to $y = 375$).
   b. Find ΔV for the funnel section of the glory hole (from $y = 325$ to $y = 375$).
   c. Find the work necessary to pump out the funnel section by formulating and evaluating the appropriate definite integral.

34. **Pumping water from a glory hole** (*Continuation of Exercise 33.*)
   a. Find the total work necessary to pump out the glory hole, by adding the work necessary to pump both the throat and funnel sections.
   b. Your answer to part (a) is in foot-pounds. A more useful form is horsepower-hours, since motors are rated in horsepower. To convert from foot-pounds to horsepower-hours, divide by 1.98×10^6. How many hours would it take a 1000-horsepower motor to pump out the glory hole, assuming that the motor was fully efficient?

35. **Drinking a milkshake** The truncated conical container shown here is full of strawberry milkshake that weighs $4/9$ oz/in.^{3} As you can see, the container is 7 in. deep, 2.5 in. across at the base, and 3.5 in. across at the top (a standard size at Brigham's in Boston). The straw sticks up an inch above the top. About how much work does it take to suck up the milkshake through the straw (neglecting friction)? Answer in inch-ounces.

Dimensions in inches

36. **Water tower** Your town has decided to drill a well to increase its water supply. As the town engineer, you have determined that a water tower will be necessary to provide the pressure needed for distribution, and you have designed the system shown here. The water is to be pumped from a 300 ft well through a vertical 4 in. pipe into the base of a cylindrical tank 20 ft in diameter and 25 ft high. The base of the tank will be 60 ft aboveground. The pump is a 3 hp pump, rated at 1650 ft·lb/sec. To the nearest hour, how long will it take to fill the tank the first time? (Include the time it takes to fill the pipe.) Assume that water weighs 62.4 lb/ft^3.

NOT TO SCALE

37. **Putting a satellite in orbit** The strength of Earth's gravitational field varies with the distance r from Earth's center, and the magnitude of the gravitational force experienced by a satellite of mass m during and after launch is

$$F(r) = \frac{mMG}{r^2}.$$

Here, $M = 5.975 \times 10^{24}$ kg is Earth's mass, $G = 6.6720 \times 10^{-11}$ N·m^2 kg^{-2} is the universal gravitational constant, and r is measured in meters. The work it takes to lift a 1000-kg satellite from Earth's surface to a circular orbit 35,780 km above Earth's center is therefore given by the integral

$$\text{Work} = \int_{6,370,000}^{35,780,000} \frac{1000MG}{r^2} \, dr \text{ joules}.$$

Evaluate the integral. The lower limit of integration is Earth's radius in meters at the launch site. (This calculation does not take into account energy spent lifting the launch vehicle or energy spent bringing the satellite to orbit velocity.)

38. **Forcing electrons together** Two electrons r meters apart repel each other with a force of

$$F = \frac{23 \times 10^{-29}}{r^2} \text{ newtons}.$$

   a. Suppose one electron is held fixed at the point $(1, 0)$ on the x-axis (units in meters). How much work does it take to move a second electron along the x-axis from the point $(-1, 0)$ to the origin?
   b. Suppose an electron is held fixed at each of the points $(-1, 0)$ and $(1, 0)$. How much work does it take to move a third electron along the x-axis from $(5, 0)$ to $(3, 0)$?

6.7   Fluid Pressures and Forces

FIGURE 6.64 To withstand the increasing pressure, dams are built thicker as they go down.

We make dams thicker at the bottom than at the top (Figure 6.64) because the pressure against them increases with depth. The pressure at any point on a dam depends only on how far below the surface the point is and not on how much the surface of the dam happens to be tilted at that point. The pressure, in pounds per square foot at a point h feet below the surface, is always $62.4h$. The number 62.4 is the weight-density of water in pounds per cubic foot. The pressure h feet below the surface of any fluid is the fluid's *weight-density* times h.

The Pressure-Depth Equation

In a fluid that is standing still, the pressure p at depth h is the fluid's weight-density w times h:

$$p = wh. \tag{1}$$

In this section we use the equation $p = wh$ to derive a formula for the total force exerted by a fluid against all or part of a vertical or horizontal containing wall.

The Constant-Depth Formula for Fluid Force

In a container of fluid with a flat horizontal base, the total force exerted by the fluid against the base can be calculated by multiplying the area of the base by the pressure at the base. We can do this because total force equals force per unit area (pressure) times area. (See Figure 6.65.) If F, p, and A are the total force, pressure, and area, then

$$F = \text{total force} = \text{force per unit area} \times \text{area}$$
$$= \text{pressure} \times \text{area} = pA$$
$$= whA. \qquad\qquad {\scriptstyle p = wh \text{ from Eq. (1)}}$$

Weight-density

A fluid's weight-density is its weight per unit volume. Typical values (lb/ft³) are

Gasoline	42
Mercury	849
Milk	64.5
Molasses	100
Olive oil	57
Seawater	64
Water	62.4

Fluid Force on a Constant-Depth Surface

$$F = pA = whA \tag{2}$$

For example, the weight-density of water is 62.4 lb/ft³, so the fluid force at the bottom of a 10 ft × 20 ft rectangular swimming pool 3 ft deep is

$$F = whA = (62.4 \text{ lb/ft}^3)(3 \text{ ft})(10 \cdot 20 \text{ ft}^2)$$
$$= 37{,}440 \text{ lb}.$$

For a flat plate submerged *horizontally*, like the bottom of the swimming pool just discussed, the downward force acting on its upper face due to liquid pressure is given by Equation (2). If the plate is submerged *vertically*, however, then the pressure against it will be different at different depths and Equation (2) no longer is usable in that form (because h varies). By dividing the plate into many narrow horizontal bands or strips, we can create a Riemann sum whose limit is the fluid force against the side of the submerged vertical plate. Here is the procedure.

FIGURE 6.65 These containers are filled with water to the same depth and have the same base area. The total force is therefore the same on the bottom of each container. The containers' shapes do not matter here.

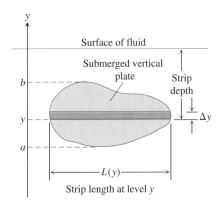

FIGURE 6.66 The force exerted by a fluid against one side of a thin, flat horizontal strip is about ΔF = pressure $\times$ area = $w \times$ (strip depth) $\times L(y)\Delta y$.

The Variable-Depth Formula

Suppose we want to know the force exerted by a fluid against one side of a vertical plate submerged in a fluid of weight-density w. To find it, we model the plate as a region extending from $y = a$ to $y = b$ in the xy-plane (Figure 6.66). We partition $[a, b]$ in the usual way and imagine the region to be cut into thin horizontal strips by planes perpendicular to the y-axis at the partition points. The typical strip from y to $y + \Delta y$ is Δy units wide by $L(y)$ units long. We assume $L(y)$ to be a continuous function of y.

The pressure varies across the strip from top to bottom. If the strip is narrow enough, however, the pressure will remain close to its bottom-edge value of $w \times$ (strip depth). The force exerted by the fluid against one side of the strip will be about

$$\Delta F = (\text{pressure along bottom edge}) \times (\text{area})$$

$$= w \cdot (\text{strip depth}) \cdot L(y)\,\Delta y.$$

Assume there are n strips associated with the partition of $a \le y \le b$ and that y_k is the bottom edge of the kth strip having length $L(y_k)$ and width Δy_k. The force against the entire plate is approximated by summing the forces against each strip, giving the Riemann sum

$$F \approx \sum_{k=1}^{n} (w \cdot (\text{strip depth})_k \cdot L(y_k))\,\Delta y_k. \tag{3}$$

The sum in Equation (3) is a Riemann sum for a continuous function on $[a, b]$, and we expect the approximations to improve as the norm of the partition goes to zero. The force against the plate is the limit of these sums:

$$\lim_{n\to\infty} \sum_{k=1}^{n} (w \cdot (\text{strip depth})_k \cdot L(y_k))\,\Delta y_k = \int_a^b w \cdot (\text{strip depth}) \cdot L(y)\,dy.$$

> **The Integral for Fluid Force Against a Vertical Flat Plate**
> Suppose that a plate submerged vertically in fluid of weight-density w runs from $y = a$ to $y = b$ on the y-axis. Let $L(y)$ be the length of the horizontal strip measured from left to right along the surface of the plate at level y. Then the force exerted by the fluid against one side of the plate is
> $$F = \int_a^b w \cdot (\text{strip depth}) \cdot L(y)\,dy. \tag{4}$$

EXAMPLE 1   Applying the Integral for Fluid Force

A flat isosceles right triangular plate with base 6 ft and height 3 ft is submerged vertically, base up, 2 ft below the surface of a swimming pool. Find the force exerted by the water against one side of the plate.

Solution   We establish a coordinate system to work in by placing the origin at the plate's bottom vertex and running the y-axis upward along the plate's axis of symmetry (Figure 6.67). The surface of the pool lies along the line $y = 5$ and the plate's top edge along the line $y = 3$. The plate's right-hand edge lies along the line $y = x$, with the upper right vertex at $(3, 3)$. The length of a thin strip at level y is

$$L(y) = 2x = 2y.$$

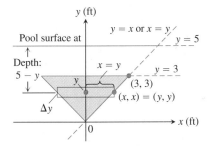

FIGURE 6.67 To find the force on one side of the submerged plate in Example 1, we can use a coordinate system like the one here.

The depth of the strip beneath the surface is $(5 - y)$. The force exerted by the water against one side of the plate is therefore

$$
F = \int_a^b w \cdot \left(\begin{array}{c}\text{strip}\\\text{depth}\end{array}\right) \cdot L(y) \, dy \qquad \text{Eq. (4)}
$$

$$
= \int_0^3 62.4(5 - y)2y \, dy
$$

$$
= 124.8 \int_0^3 (5y - y^2) \, dy
$$

$$
= 124.8 \left[\frac{5}{2} y^2 - \frac{y^3}{3} \right]_0^3 = 1684.8 \text{ lb.} \qquad \blacksquare
$$

Fluid Forces and Centroids

If we know the location of the centroid of a submerged flat vertical plate (Figure 6.68), we can take a shortcut to find the force against one side of the plate. From Equation (4),

$$
F = \int_a^b w \times (\text{strip depth}) \times L(y) \, dy
$$

$$
= w \int_a^b (\text{strip depth}) \times L(y) \, dy
$$

$$
= w \times (\text{moment about surface level line of region occupied by plate})
$$

$$
= w \times (\text{depth of plate's centroid}) \times (\text{area of plate}).
$$

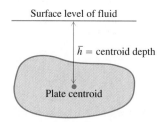

Surface level of fluid

$\bar{h}$ = centroid depth

Plate centroid

FIGURE 6.68 The force against one side of the plate is $w \cdot \bar{h} \cdot$ plate area.

Fluid Forces and Centroids
The force of a fluid of weight-density w against one side of a submerged flat vertical plate is the product of w, the distance $\bar{h}$ from the plate's centroid to the fluid surface, and the plate's area:

$$
F = w\bar{h}A. \tag{5}
$$

EXAMPLE 2   Finding Fluid Force Using Equation (5)

Use Equation (5) to find the force in Example 1.

Solution   The centroid of the triangle (Figure 6.67) lies on the y-axis, one-third of the way from the base to the vertex, so $\bar{h} = 3$. The triangle's area is

$$
A = \frac{1}{2}(\text{base})(\text{height})
$$

$$
= \frac{1}{2}(6)(3) = 9.
$$

Hence,

$$
F = w\bar{h}A = (62.4)(3)(9)
$$

$$
= 1684.8 \text{ lb.} \qquad \blacksquare
$$

EXERCISES 6.7

The weight-densities of the fluids in the following exercises can be found in the table on page 456.

1. Triangular plate Calculate the fluid force on one side of the plate in Example 1 using the coordinate system shown here.

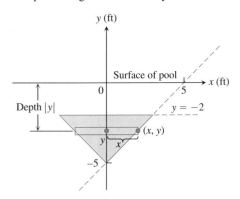

2. Triangular plate Calculate the fluid force on one side of the plate in Example 1 using the coordinate system shown here.

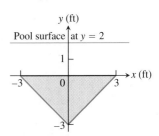

3. Lowered triangular plate The plate in Example 1 is lowered another 2 ft into the water. What is the fluid force on one side of the plate now?

4. Raised triangular plate The plate in Example 1 is raised to put its top edge at the surface of the pool. What is the fluid force on one side of the plate now?

5. Triangular plate The isosceles triangular plate shown here is submerged vertically 1 ft below the surface of a freshwater lake.

   a. Find the fluid force against one face of the plate.

   b. What would be the fluid force on one side of the plate if the water were seawater instead of freshwater?

6. Rotated triangular plate The plate in Exercise 5 is revolved 180° about line *AB* so that part of the plate sticks out of the lake, as shown here. What force does the water exert on one face of the plate now?

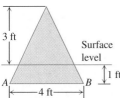

7. New England Aquarium The viewing portion of the rectangular glass window in a typical fish tank at the New England Aquarium in Boston is 63 in. wide and runs from 0.5 in. below the water's surface to 33.5 in. below the surface. Find the fluid force against this portion of the window. The weight-density of seawater is 64 lb/ft^3. (In case you were wondering, the glass is $3/4$ in. thick and the tank walls extend 4 in. above the water to keep the fish from jumping out.)

8. Fish tank A horizontal rectangular freshwater fish tank with base 2 ft × 4 ft and height 2 ft (interior dimensions) is filled to within 2 in. of the top.

   a. Find the fluid force against each side and end of the tank.

   b. If the tank is sealed and stood on end (without spilling), so that one of the square ends is the base, what does that do to the fluid forces on the rectangular sides?

9. Semicircular plate A semicircular plate 2 ft in diameter sticks straight down into freshwater with the diameter along the surface. Find the force exerted by the water on one side of the plate.

10. Milk truck A tank truck hauls milk in a 6-ft-diameter horizontal right circular cylindrical tank. How much force does the milk exert on each end of the tank when the tank is half full?

11. The cubical metal tank shown here has a parabolic gate, held in place by bolts and designed to withstand a fluid force of 160 lb without rupturing. The liquid you plan to store has a weight-density of 50 lb/ft^3.

   a. What is the fluid force on the gate when the liquid is 2 ft deep?

   b. What is the maximum height to which the container can be filled without exceeding its design limitation?

Parabolic gate

Enlarged view of
parabolic gate

12. The rectangular tank shown here has a 1 ft × 1 ft square window 1 ft above the base. The window is designed to withstand a fluid force of 312 lb without cracking.

    a. What fluid force will the window have to withstand if the tank is filled with water to a depth of 3 ft?

    b. To what level can the tank be filled with water without exceeding the window's design limitation?

13. The end plates of the trough shown here were designed to withstand a fluid force of 6667 lb. How many cubic feet of water can the tank hold without exceeding this limitation? Round down to the nearest cubic foot.

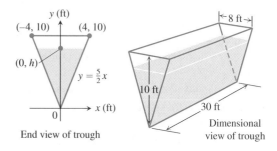

End view of trough   Dimensional view of trough

14. Water is running into the rectangular swimming pool shown here at the rate of 1000 ft³/h.

    a. Find the fluid force against the triangular drain plate after 9 h of filling.

    b. The drain plate is designed to withstand a fluid force of 520 lb. How high can you fill the pool without exceeding this limitation?

Triangular drain plate

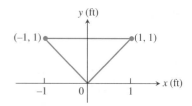

Enlarged view of drain plate

15. A vertical rectangular plate a units long by b units wide is submerged in a fluid of weight-density w with its long edges parallel to the fluid's surface. Find the average value of the pressure along the vertical dimension of the plate. Explain your answer.

16. (*Continuation of Exercise 15.*) Show that the force exerted by the fluid on one side of the plate is the average value of the pressure (found in Exercise 15) times the area of the plate.

17. Water pours into the tank here at the rate of 4 ft³/min. The tank's cross-sections are 4-ft-diameter semicircles. One end of the tank is movable, but moving it to increase the volume compresses a spring. The spring constant is $k = 100$ lb/ft. If the end of the tank moves 5 ft against the spring, the water will drain out of a safety hole in the bottom at the rate of 5 ft³/min. Will the movable end reach the hole before the tank overflows?

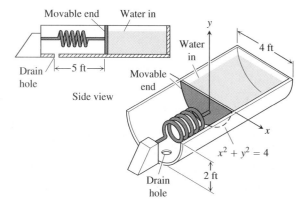

18. **Watering trough** The vertical ends of a watering trough are squares 3 ft on a side.

    a. Find the fluid force against the ends when the trough is full.

    b. How many inches do you have to lower the water level in the trough to reduce the fluid force by 25%?

19. **Milk carton** A rectangular milk carton measures 3.75 in. × 3.75 in. at the base and is 7.75 in. tall. Find the force of the milk on one side when the carton is full.

20. **Olive oil can** A standard olive oil can measures 5.75 in. × 3.5 in. at the base and is 10 in. tall. Find the fluid force against the base and each side when the can is full.

21. **Watering trough** The vertical ends of a watering trough are isosceles triangles like the one shown here (dimensions in feet).

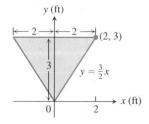

    a. Find the fluid force against the ends when the trough is full.

b. How many inches do you have to lower the water level in the trough to cut the fluid force on the ends in half? (Answer to the nearest half-inch.)

c. Does it matter how long the trough is? Give reasons for your answer.

22. The face of a dam is a rectangle, *ABCD*, of dimensions $AB = CD = 100$ ft, $AD = BC = 26$ ft. Instead of being vertical, the plane *ABCD* is inclined as indicated in the accompanying figure, so that the top of the dam is 24 ft higher than the bottom.

Find the force due to water pressure on the dam when the surface of the water is level with the top of the dam.

Chapter 6 Questions to Guide Your Review

1. How do you define and calculate the volumes of solids by the method of slicing? Give an example.

2. How are the disk and washer methods for calculating volumes derived from the method of slicing? Give examples of volume calculations by these methods.

3. Describe the method of cylindrical shells. Give an example.

4. How do you define the length of a smooth parametrized curve $x = f(t), y = g(t), a \le t \le b$? What does smoothness have to do with length? What else do you need to know about the parametrization to find the curve's length? Give examples.

5. How do you find the length of the graph of a smooth function over a closed interval? Give an example. What about functions that do not have continuous first derivatives?

6. What is a center of mass?

7. How do you locate the center of mass of a straight, narrow rod or strip of material? Give an example. If the density of the material is constant, you can tell right away where the center of mass is. Where is it?

8. How do you locate the center of mass of a thin flat plate of material? Give an example.

9. How do you define and calculate the area of the surface swept out by revolving the graph of a smooth function $y = f(x)$, $a \le x \le b$, about the *x*-axis? Give an example.

10. Under what conditions can you find the area of the surface generated by revolving a curve $x = f(t), y = g(t), a \le t \le b$, about the *x*-axis? The *y*-axis? Give examples.

11. What do Pappus's two theorems say? Give examples of how they are used to calculate surface areas and volumes and to locate centroids.

12. How do you define and calculate the work done by a variable force directed along a portion of the *x*-axis? How do you calculate the work it takes to pump a liquid from a tank? Give examples.

13. How do you calculate the force exerted by a liquid against a portion of a vertical wall? Give an example.

Chapter 6 Practice Exercises

Volumes

Find the volumes of the solids in Exercises 1–16.

1. The solid lies between planes perpendicular to the *x*-axis at $x = 0$ and $x = 1$. The cross-sections perpendicular to the *x*-axis

between these planes are circular disks whose diameters run from the parabola $y = x^2$ to the parabola $y = \sqrt{x}$.

2. The base of the solid is the region in the first quadrant between the line $y = x$ and the parabola $y = 2\sqrt{x}$. The cross-sections of the solid perpendicular to the x-axis are equilateral triangles whose bases stretch from the line to the curve.

3. The solid lies between planes perpendicular to the x-axis at $x = \pi/4$ and $x = 5\pi/4$. The cross-sections between these planes are circular disks whose diameters run from the curve $y = 2 \cos x$ to the curve $y = 2 \sin x$.

4. The solid lies between planes perpendicular to the x-axis at $x = 0$ and $x = 6$. The cross-sections between these planes are squares whose bases run from the x-axis up to the curve $x^{1/2} + y^{1/2} = \sqrt{6}$.

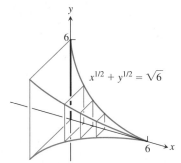

5. The solid lies between planes perpendicular to the x-axis at $x = 0$ and $x = 4$. The cross-sections of the solid perpendicular to the x-axis between these planes are circular disks whose diameters run from the curve $x^2 = 4y$ to the curve $y^2 = 4x$.

6. The base of the solid is the region bounded by the parabola $y^2 = 4x$ and the line $x = 1$ in the xy-plane. Each cross-section perpendicular to the x-axis is an equilateral triangle with one edge in the plane. (The triangles all lie on the same side of the plane.)

7. Find the volume of the solid generated by revolving the region bounded by the x-axis, the curve $y = 3x^4$, and the lines $x = 1$ and $x = -1$ about (a) the x-axis; (b) the y-axis; (c) the line $x = 1$; (d) the line $y = 3$.

8. Find the volume of the solid generated by revolving the "triangular" region bounded by the curve $y = 4/x^3$ and the lines $x = 1$ and $y = 1/2$ about (a) the x-axis; (b) the y-axis; (c) the line $x = 2$; (d) the line $y = 4$.

9. Find the volume of the solid generated by revolving the region bounded on the left by the parabola $x = y^2 + 1$ and on the right by the line $x = 5$ about (a) the x-axis; (b) the y-axis; (c) the line $x = 5$.

10. Find the volume of the solid generated by revolving the region bounded by the parabola $y^2 = 4x$ and the line $y = x$ about (a) the x-axis; (b) the y-axis; (c) the line $x = 4$; (d) the line $y = 4$.

11. Find the volume of the solid generated by revolving the "triangular" region bounded by the x-axis, the line $x = \pi/3$, and the curve $y = \tan x$ in the first quadrant about the x-axis.

12. Find the volume of the solid generated by revolving the region bounded by the curve $y = \sin x$ and the lines $x = 0$, $x = \pi$, and $y = 2$ about the line $y = 2$.

13. Find the volume of the solid generated by revolving the region between the x-axis and the curve $y = x^2 - 2x$ about (a) the x-axis; (b) the line $y = -1$; (c) the line $x = 2$; (d) the line $y = 2$.

14. Find the volume of the solid generated by revolving about the x-axis the region bounded by $y = 2 \tan x$, $y = 0$, $x = -\pi/4$, and $x = \pi/4$. (The region lies in the first and third quadrants and resembles a skewed bowtie.)

15. **Volume of a solid sphere hole** A round hole of radius $\sqrt{3}$ ft is bored through the center of a solid sphere of a radius 2 ft. Find the volume of material removed from the sphere.

16. **Volume of a football** The profile of a football resembles the ellipse shown here. Find the football's volume to the nearest cubic inch.

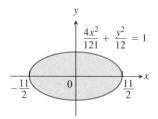

Lengths of Curves

Find the lengths of the curves in Exercises 17–23.

17. $y = x^{1/2} - (1/3)x^{3/2}$, $\quad 1 \leq x \leq 4$

18. $x = y^{2/3}$, $\quad 1 \leq y \leq 8$

19. $y = (5/12)x^{6/5} - (5/8)x^{4/5}$, $\quad 1 \leq x \leq 32$

20. $x = (y^3/12) + (1/y)$, $\quad 1 \leq y \leq 2$

21. $x = 5 \cos t - \cos 5t$, $\quad y = 5 \sin t - \sin 5t$, $\quad 0 \leq t \leq \pi/2$

22. $x = t^3 - 6t^2$, $\quad y = t^3 + 6t^2$, $\quad 0 \leq t \leq 1$

23. $x = 3 \cos \theta$, $\quad y = 3 \sin \theta$, $\quad 0 \leq \theta \leq \dfrac{3\pi}{2}$

24. Find the length of the enclosed loop $x = t^2$, $y = (t^3/3) - t$ shown here. The loop starts at $t = -\sqrt{3}$ and ends at $t = \sqrt{3}$.

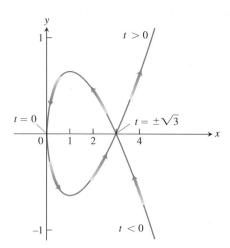

Centroids and Centers of Mass

25. Find the centroid of a thin, flat plate covering the region enclosed by the parabolas $y = 2x^2$ and $y = 3 - x^2$.

26. Find the centroid of a thin, flat plate covering the region enclosed by the x-axis, the lines $x = 2$ and $x = -2$, and the parabola $y = x^2$.

27. Find the centroid of a thin, flat plate covering the "triangular" region in the first quadrant bounded by the y-axis, the parabola $y = x^2/4$, and the line $y = 4$.

28. Find the centroid of a thin, flat plate covering the region enclosed by the parabola $y^2 = x$ and the line $x = 2y$.

29. Find the center of mass of a thin, flat plate covering the region enclosed by the parabola $y^2 = x$ and the line $x = 2y$ if the density function is $\delta(y) = 1 + y$. (Use horizontal strips.)

30. a. Find the center of mass of a thin plate of constant density covering the region between the curve $y = 3/x^{3/2}$ and the x-axis from $x = 1$ to $x = 9$.

   b. Find the plate's center of mass if, instead of being constant, the density is $\delta(x) = x$. (Use vertical strips.)

Areas of Surfaces of Revolution

In Exercises 31–36, find the areas of the surfaces generated by revolving the curves about the given axes.

31. $y = \sqrt{2x + 1}, \quad 0 \le x \le 3; \quad x\text{-axis}$

32. $y = x^3/3, \quad 0 \le x \le 1; \quad x\text{-axis}$

33. $x = \sqrt{4y - y^2}, \quad 1 \le y \le 2; \quad y\text{-axis}$

34. $x = \sqrt{y}, \quad 2 \le y \le 6; \quad y\text{-axis}$

35. $x = t^2/2, \quad y = 2t, \quad 0 \le t \le \sqrt{5}; \quad x\text{-axis}$

36. $x = t^2 + 1/(2t), \quad y = 4\sqrt{t}, \quad 1/\sqrt{2} \le t \le 1; \quad y\text{-axis}$

Work

37. Lifting equipment   A rock climber is about to haul up 100 N (about 22.5 lb) of equipment that has been hanging beneath her on 40 m of rope that weighs 0.8 newton per meter. How much work will it take? (*Hint:* Solve for the rope and equipment separately, then add.)

38. Leaky tank truck   You drove an 800-gal tank truck of water from the base of Mt. Washington to the summit and discovered on arrival that the tank was only half full. You started with a full tank, climbed at a steady rate, and accomplished the 4750-ft elevation change in 50 min. Assuming that the water leaked out at a steady rate, how much work was spent in carrying water to the top? Do not count the work done in getting yourself and the truck there. Water weighs 8 lb/U.S. gal.

39. Stretching a spring   If a force of 20 lb is required to hold a spring 1 ft beyond its unstressed length, how much work does it take to stretch the spring this far? An additional foot?

40. Garage door spring   A force of 200 N will stretch a garage door spring 0.8 m beyond its unstressed length. How far will a 300-N force stretch the spring? How much work does it take to stretch the spring this far from its unstressed length?

41. Pumping a reservoir   A reservoir shaped like a right circular cone, point down, 20 ft across the top and 8 ft deep, is full of water. How much work does it take to pump the water to a level 6 ft above the top?

42. Pumping a reservoir (*Continuation of Exercise 41.*) The reservoir is filled to a depth of 5 ft, and the water is to be pumped to the same level as the top. How much work does it take?

43. Pumping a conical tank   A right circular conical tank, point down, with top radius 5 ft and height 10 ft is filled with a liquid whose weight-density is 60 lb/ft³. How much work does it take to pump the liquid to a point 2 ft above the tank? If the pump is driven by a motor rated at 275 ft-lb/sec (1/2 hp), how long will it take to empty the tank?

44. Pumping a cylindrical tank   A storage tank is a right circular cylinder 20 ft long and 8 ft in diameter with its axis horizontal. If the tank is half full of olive oil weighing 57 lb/ft³, find the work done in emptying it through a pipe that runs from the bottom of the tank to an outlet that is 6 ft above the top of the tank.

Fluid Force

45. Trough of water   The vertical triangular plate shown here is the end plate of a trough full of water ($w = 62.4$). What is the fluid force against the plate?

UNITS IN FEET

46. Trough of maple syrup   The vertical trapezoid plate shown here is the end plate of a trough full of maple syrup weighing 75 lb/ft³. What is the force exerted by the syrup against the end plate of the trough when the syrup is 10 in. deep?

UNITS IN FEET

47. Force on a parabolic gate   A flat vertical gate in the face of a dam is shaped like the parabolic region between the curve $y = 4x^2$ and the line $y = 4$, with measurements in feet. The top of the gate lies 5 ft below the surface of the water. Find the force exerted by the water against the gate ($w = 62.4$).

T 48. You plan to store mercury ($w = 849$ lb/ft³) in a vertical rectangular tank with a 1 ft square base side whose interior side wall can withstand a total fluid force of 40,000 lb. About how many cubic feet of mercury can you store in the tank at any one time?

49. The container profiled in the accompanying figure is filled with two nonmixing liquids of weight-density w_1 and w_2. Find the fluid force on one side of the vertical square plate $ABCD$. The points B and D lie in the boundary layer and the square is $6\sqrt{2}$ ft on a side.

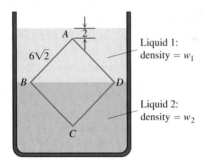

50. The isosceles trapezoidal plate shown here is submerged vertically in water ($w = 62.4$) with its upper edge 4 ft below the surface. Find the fluid force on one side of the plate in two different ways:

a. By evaluating an integral.

b. By dividing the plate into a parallelogram and an isosceles triangle, locating their centroids, and using the equation $F = w\bar{h}A$ from Section 6.7.

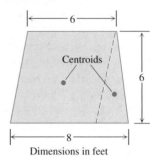

Dimensions in feet

Chapter **6** ## Additional and Advanced Exercises

Volume and Length

1. A solid is generated by revolving about the x-axis the region bounded by the graph of the positive continuous function $y = f(x)$, the x-axis, and the fixed line $x = a$ and the variable line $x = b$, $b > a$. Its volume, for all b, is $b^2 - ab$. Find $f(x)$.

2. A solid is generated by revolving about the x-axis the region bounded by the graph of the positive continuous function $y = f(x)$, the x-axis, and the lines $x = 0$ and $x = a$. Its volume, for all $a > 0$, is $a^2 + a$. Find $f(x)$.

3. Suppose that the increasing function $f(x)$ is smooth for $x \geq 0$ and that $f(0) = a$. Let $s(x)$ denote the length of the graph of f from $(0, a)$ to $(x, f(x))$, $x > 0$. Find $f(x)$ if $s(x) = Cx$ for some constant C. What are the allowable values for C?

4. a. Show that for $0 < \alpha \leq \pi/2$,

$$\int_0^\alpha \sqrt{1 + \cos^2\theta}\, d\theta > \sqrt{\alpha^2 + \sin^2\alpha}.$$

b. Generalize the result in part (a).

Moments and Centers of Mass

5. Find the centroid of the region bounded below by the x-axis and above by the curve $y = 1 - x^n$, n an even positive integer. What is the limiting position of the centroid as $n \to \infty$?

6. If you haul a telephone pole on a two-wheeled carriage behind a truck, you want the wheels to be 3 ft or so behind the pole's center of mass to provide an adequate "tongue" weight. NYNEX's class 1.40-ft wooden poles have a 27-in. circumference at the top and a 43.5-in. circumference at the base. About how far from the top is the center of mass?

7. Suppose that a thin metal plate of area A and constant density δ occupies a region R in the xy-plane, and let M_y be the plate's moment about the y-axis. Show that the plate's moment about the line $x = b$ is

a. $M_y - b\delta A$ if the plate lies to the right of the line, and

b. $b\delta A - M_y$ if the plate lies to the left of the line.

8. Find the center of mass of a thin plate covering the region bounded by the curve $y^2 = 4ax$ and the line $x = a$, $a =$ positive constant, if the density at (x, y) is directly proportional to (a) x, (b) $|y|$.

9. a. Find the centroid of the region in the first quadrant bounded by two concentric circles and the coordinate axes, if the circles have radii a and b, $0 < a < b$, and their centers are at the origin.

b. Find the limits of the coordinates of the centroid as a approaches b and discuss the meaning of the result.

10. A triangular corner is cut from a square 1 ft on a side. The area of the triangle removed is 36 in.^{2}. If the centroid of the remaining region is 7 in. from one side of the original square, how far is it from the remaining sides?

Surface Area

11. At points on the curve $y = 2\sqrt{x}$, line segments of length $h = y$ are drawn perpendicular to the xy-plane. (See accompanying figure.) Find the area of the surface formed by these perpendiculars from $(0, 0)$ to $(3, 2\sqrt{3})$.

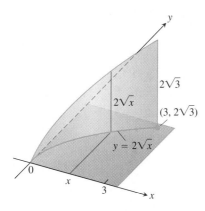

12. At points on a circle of radius a, line segments are drawn perpendicular to the plane of the circle, the perpendicular at each point P being of length ks, where s is the length of the arc of the circle measured counterclockwise from $(a, 0)$ to P and k is a positive constant, as shown here. Find the area of the surface formed by the perpendiculars along the arc beginning at $(a, 0)$ and extending once around the circle.

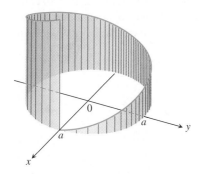

Work

13. A particle of mass m starts from rest at time $t = 0$ and is moved along the x-axis with constant acceleration a from $x = 0$ to $x = h$ against a variable force of magnitude $F(t) = t^2$. Find the work done.

14. Work and kinetic energy   Suppose a 1.6-oz golf ball is placed on a vertical spring with force constant $k = 2$ lb/in. The spring is compressed 6 in. and released. About how high does the ball go (measured from the spring's rest position)?

Fluid Force

15. A triangular plate ABC is submerged in water with its plane vertical. The side AB, 4 ft long, is 6 ft below the surface of the water, while the vertex C is 2 ft below the surface. Find the force exerted by the water on one side of the plate.

16. A vertical rectangular plate is submerged in a fluid with its top edge parallel to the fluid's surface. Show that the force exerted by the fluid on one side of the plate equals the average value of the pressure up and down the plate times the area of the plate.

17. The *center of pressure* on one side of a plane region submerged in a fluid is defined to be the point at which the total force exerted by the fluid can be applied without changing its total moment about any axis in the plane. Find the depth to the center of pressure **(a)** on a vertical rectangle of height h and width b if its upper edge is in the surface of the fluid; **(b)** on a vertical triangle of height h and base b if the vertex opposite b is a ft and the base b is $(a + h)$ ft below the surface of the fluid.

Chapter 6   Technology Application Projects

Mathematica/Maple Module
Using Riemann Sums to Estimate Areas, Volumes, and Lengths of Curves
Visualize and approximate areas and volumes in **Part I** and **Part II**: Volumes of Revolution; and **Part III**: Lengths of Curves.

Mathematica/Maple Module
Modeling a Bungee Cord Jump
Collect data (or use data previously collected) to build and refine a model for the force exerted by a jumper's bungee cord. Use the work-energy theorem to compute the distance fallen for a given jumper and a given length of bungee cord.

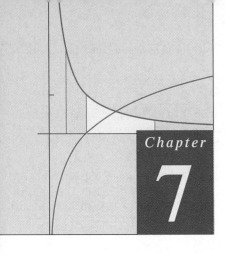

Chapter 7

TRANSCENDENTAL FUNCTIONS

OVERVIEW Functions can be classified into two broad groups (see Section 1.4). Polynomial functions are called *algebraic*, as are functions obtained from them by addition, multiplication, division, or taking powers and roots. Functions that are not algebraic are called *transcendental*. The trigonometric, exponential, logarithmic, and hyperbolic functions are transcendental, as are their inverses.

Transcendental functions occur frequently in many calculus settings and applications, including growths of populations, vibrations and waves, efficiencies of computer algorithms, and the stability of engineered structures. In this chapter we introduce several important transcendental functions and investigate their graphs, properties, derivatives, and integrals.

7.1 Inverse Functions and Their Derivatives

A function that undoes, or inverts, the effect of a function f is called the *inverse* of f. Many common functions, though not all, are paired with an inverse. Important inverse functions often show up in formulas for antiderivatives and solutions of differential equations. Inverse functions also play a key role in the development and properties of the logarithmic and exponential functions, as we will see in Section 7.3.

One-to-One Functions

A function is a rule that assigns a value from its range to each element in its domain. Some functions assign the same range value to more than one element in the domain. The function $f(x) = x^2$ assigns the same value, 1, to both of the numbers -1 and $+1$; the sines of $\pi/3$ and $2\pi/3$ are both $\sqrt{3}/2$. Other functions assume each value in their range no more than once. The square roots and cubes of different numbers are always different. A function that has distinct values at distinct elements in its domain is called one-to-one. These functions take on any one value in their range exactly once.

DEFINITION One-to-One Function

A function $f(x)$ is **one-to-one** on a domain D if $f(x_1) \neq f(x_2)$ whenever $x_1 \neq x_2$ in D.

EXAMPLE 1   Domains of One-to-One Functions

(a) $f(x) = \sqrt{x}$ is one-to-one on any domain of nonnegative numbers because $\sqrt{x_1} \neq \sqrt{x_2}$ whenever $x_1 \neq x_2$.

(b) $g(x) = \sin x$ is *not* one-to-one on the interval $[0, \pi]$ because $\sin(\pi/6) = \sin(5\pi/6)$. The sine *is* one-to-one on $[0, \pi/2]$, however, because it is a strictly increasing function on $[0, \pi/2]$.   ∎

The graph of a one-to-one function $y = f(x)$ can intersect a given horizontal line at most once. If it intersects the line more than once, it assumes the same y-value more than once, and is therefore not one-to-one (Figure 7.1).

The Horizontal Line Test for One-to-One Functions
A function $y = f(x)$ is one-to-one if and only if its graph intersects each horizontal line at most once.

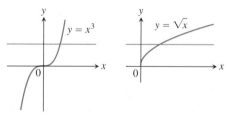

One-to-one: Graph meets each
horizontal line at most once.

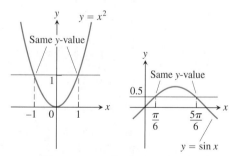

Not one-to-one: Graph meets one or
more horizontal lines more than once.

FIGURE 7.1   Using the horizontal line test, we see that $y = x^3$ and $y = \sqrt{x}$ are one-to-one on their domains $(-\infty, \infty)$ and $[0, \infty)$, but $y = x^2$ and $y = \sin x$ are not one-to-one on their domains $(-\infty, \infty)$.

Inverse Functions

Since each output of a one-to-one function comes from just one input, the effect of the function can be inverted to send an output back to the input from which it came.

DEFINITION   Inverse Function

Suppose that f is a one-to-one function on a domain D with range R. The **inverse function** f^{-1} is defined by

$$f^{-1}(a) = b \text{ if } f(b) = a.$$

The domain of f^{-1} is R and the range of f^{-1} is D.

The domains and ranges of f and f^{-1} are interchanged. The symbol f^{-1} for the inverse of f is read "f inverse." The "-1" in f^{-1} is *not* an exponent: $f^{-1}(x)$ does not mean $1/f(x)$.

If we apply f to send an input x to the output $f(x)$ and follow by applying f^{-1} to $f(x)$ we get right back to x, just where we started. Similarly, if we take some number y in the range of f, apply f^{-1} to it, and then apply f to the resulting value $f^{-1}(y)$, we get back the value y with which we began. Composing a function and its inverse has the same effect as doing nothing.

$$(f^{-1} \circ f)(x) = x, \qquad \text{for all } x \text{ in the domain of } f$$

$$(f \circ f^{-1})(y) = y, \qquad \text{for all } y \text{ in the domain of } f^{-1} \text{ (or range of } f)$$

Only a one-to-one function can have an inverse. The reason is that if $f(x_1) = y$ and $f(x_2) = y$ for two distinct inputs x_1 and x_2, then there is no way to assign a value to $f^{-1}(y)$ that satisfies both $f^{-1}(f(x_1)) = x_1$ and $f^{-1}(f(x_2)) = x_2$.

A function that is increasing on an interval, satisfying $f(x_2) > f(x_1)$ when $x_2 > x_1$, is one-to-one and has an inverse. Decreasing functions also have an inverse (Exercise 39). Functions that have positive derivatives at all x are increasing (Corollary 3 of the Mean Value Theorem, Section 4.2), and so they have inverses. Similarly, functions with negative derivatives at all x are decreasing and have inverses. Functions that are neither increasing nor decreasing may still be one-to-one and have an inverse, as with the function $\sec^{-1} x$ in Section 7.7.

Finding Inverses

The graphs of a function and its inverse are closely related. To read the value of a function from its graph, we start at a point x on the x-axis, go vertically to the graph, and then move horizontally to the y-axis to read the value of y. The inverse function can be read from the graph by reversing this process. Start with a point y on the y-axis, go horizontally to the graph, and then move vertically to the x-axis to read the value of $x = f^{-1}(y)$ (Figure 7.2).

We want to set up the graph of f^{-1} so that its input values lie along the x-axis, as is usually done for functions, rather then on the y-axis. To achieve this we interchange the x and y axes by reflecting across the 45° line $y = x$. After this reflection we have a new graph that represents f^{-1}. The value of $f^{-1}(x)$ can now be read from the graph in the usual way, by starting with a point x on the x-axis, going vertically to the graph and then horizontally to the y-axis to get the value of $f^{-1}(x)$. Figure 7.2 indicates the relation between the graphs of f and f^{-1}. The graphs are interchanged by reflection through the line $y = x$.

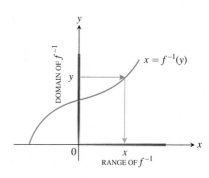

(a) To find the value of f at x, we start at x, go up to the curve, and then over to the y-axis.

(b) The graph of f is already the graph of f^{-1}, but with x and y interchanged. To find the x that gave y, we start at y and go over to the curve and down to the x-axis. The domain of f^{-1} is the range of f. The range of f^{-1} is the domain of f.

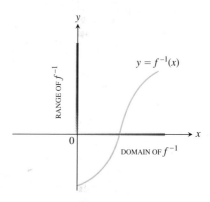

(c) To draw the graph of f^{-1} in the more usual way, we reflect the system in the line $y = x$.

(d) Then we interchange the letters x and y. We now have a normal-looking graph of f^{-1} as a function of x.

FIGURE 7.2 Determining the graph of $y = f^{-1}(x)$ from the graph of $y = f(x)$.

The process of passing from f to f^{-1} can be summarized as a two-step process.

1. Solve the equation $y = f(x)$ for x. This gives a formula $x = f^{-1}(y)$ where x is expressed as a function of y.

2. Interchange x and y, obtaining a formula $y = f^{-1}(x)$ where f^{-1} is expressed in the conventional format with x as the independent variable and y as the dependent variable.

EXAMPLE 2   Finding an Inverse Function

Find the inverse of $y = \dfrac{1}{2}x + 1$, expressed as a function of x.

Solution

1. *Solve for x in terms of y:*
$$y = \frac{1}{2}x + 1$$
$$2y = x + 2$$
$$x = 2y - 2.$$

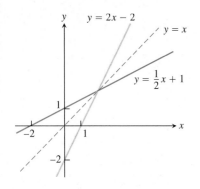

FIGURE 7.3 Graphing $f(x) = (1/2)x + 1$ and $f^{-1}(x) = 2x - 2$ together shows the graphs' symmetry with respect to the line $y = x$. The slopes are reciprocals of each other (Example 2).

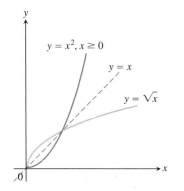

FIGURE 7.4 The functions $y = \sqrt{x}$ and $y = x^2, x \geq 0$, are inverses of one another (Example 3).

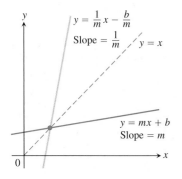

FIGURE 7.5 The slopes of nonvertical lines reflected through the line $y = x$ are reciprocals of each other.

2. *Interchange x and y:* $y = 2x - 2$.

The inverse of the function $f(x) = (1/2)x + 1$ is the function $f^{-1}(x) = 2x - 2$. To check, we verify that both composites give the identity function:

$$f^{-1}(f(x)) = 2\left(\frac{1}{2}x + 1\right) - 2 = x + 2 - 2 = x$$

$$f(f^{-1}(x)) = \frac{1}{2}(2x - 2) + 1 = x - 1 + 1 = x.$$

See Figure 7.3. ∎

EXAMPLE 3 Finding an Inverse Function

Find the inverse of the function $y = x^2, x \geq 0$, expressed as a function of x.

Solution We first solve for x in terms of y:

$$y = x^2$$
$$\sqrt{y} = \sqrt{x^2} = |x| = x \qquad |x| = x \text{ because } x \geq 0$$

We then interchange x and y, obtaining

$$y = \sqrt{x}.$$

The inverse of the function $y = x^2, x \geq 0$, is the function $y = \sqrt{x}$ (Figure 7.4).

Notice that, unlike the restricted function $y = x^2, x \geq 0$, the unrestricted function $y = x^2$ is not one-to-one and therefore has no inverse. ∎

Derivatives of Inverses of Differentiable Functions

If we calculate the derivatives of $f(x) = (1/2)x + 1$ and its inverse $f^{-1}(x) = 2x - 2$ from Example 2, we see that

$$\frac{d}{dx}f(x) = \frac{d}{dx}\left(\frac{1}{2}x + 1\right) = \frac{1}{2}$$

$$\frac{d}{dx}f^{-1}(x) = \frac{d}{dx}(2x - 2) = 2.$$

The derivatives are reciprocals of one another. The graph of f is the line $y = (1/2)x + 1$, and the graph of f^{-1} is the line $y = 2x - 2$ (Figure 7.3). Their slopes are reciprocals of one another.

This is not a special case. Reflecting any nonhorizontal or nonvertical line across the line $y = x$ always inverts the line's slope. If the original line has slope $m \neq 0$ (Figure 7.5), the reflected line has slope $1/m$ (Exercise 36).

The reciprocal relationship between the slopes of f and f^{-1} holds for other functions as well, but we must be careful to compare slopes at corresponding points. If the slope of $y = f(x)$ at the point $(a, f(a))$ is $f'(a)$ and $f'(a) \neq 0$, then the slope of $y = f^{-1}(x)$ at the point $(f(a), a)$ is the reciprocal $1/f'(a)$ (Figure 7.6). If we set $b = f(a)$, then

$$(f^{-1})'(b) = \frac{1}{f'(a)} = \frac{1}{f'(f^{-1}(b))}.$$

If $y = f(x)$ has a horizontal tangent line at $(a, f(a))$ then the inverse function f^{-1} has a vertical tangent line at $(f(a), a)$, and this infinite slope implies that f^{-1} is not differentiable

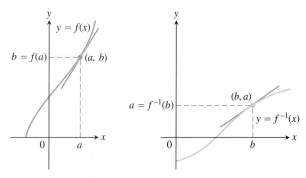

The slopes are reciprocal: $(f^{-1})'(b) = \dfrac{1}{f'(a)}$ or $(f^{-1})'(b) = \dfrac{1}{f'(f^{-1}(b))}$

FIGURE 7.6 The graphs of inverse functions have reciprocal slopes at corresponding points.

at $f(a)$. Theorem 1 gives the conditions under which f^{-1} is differentiable in its domain, which is the same as the range of f.

THEOREM 1   The Derivative Rule for Inverses

If f has an interval I as domain and $f'(x)$ exists and is never zero on I, then f^{-1} is differentiable at every point in its domain. The value of $(f^{-1})'$ at a point b in the domain of f^{-1} is the reciprocal of the value of f' at the point $a = f^{-1}(b)$:

$$(f^{-1})'(b) = \frac{1}{f'(f^{-1}(b))}$$

or

$$\left. \frac{df^{-1}}{dx} \right|_{x=b} = \frac{1}{\left. \dfrac{df}{dx} \right|_{x=f^{-1}(b)}} \tag{1}$$

The proof of Theorem 1 is omitted, but here is another way to view it. When $y = f(x)$ is differentiable at $x = a$ and we change x by a small amount dx, the corresponding change in y is approximately

$$dy = f'(a)\, dx.$$

This means that y changes about $f'(a)$ times as fast as x when $x = a$ and that x changes about $1/f'(a)$ times as fast as y when $y = b$. It is reasonable that the derivative of f^{-1} at b is the reciprocal of the derivative of f at a.

EXAMPLE 4   Applying Theorem 1

The function $f(x) = x^2, x \geq 0$ and its inverse $f^{-1}(x) = \sqrt{x}$ have derivatives $f'(x) = 2x$ and $(f^{-1})'(x) = 1/(2\sqrt{x})$.

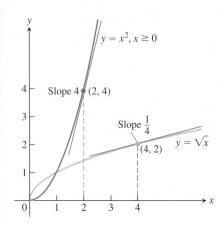

FIGURE 7.7 The derivative of $f^{-1}(x) = \sqrt{x}$ at the point $(4, 2)$ is the reciprocal of the derivative of $f(x) = x^2$ at $(2, 4)$ (Example 4).

Theorem 1 predicts that the derivative of $f^{-1}(x)$ is

$$(f^{-1})'(x) = \frac{1}{f'(f^{-1}(x))}$$

$$= \frac{1}{2(f^{-1}(x))}$$

$$= \frac{1}{2(\sqrt{x})}.$$

Theorem 1 gives a derivative that agrees with our calculation using the Power Rule for the derivative of the square root function.

Let's examine Theorem 1 at a specific point. We pick $x = 2$ (the number a) and $f(2) = 4$ (the value b). Theorem 1 says that the derivative of f at 2, $f'(2) = 4$, and the derivative of f^{-1} at $f(2)$, $(f^{-1})'(4)$, are reciprocals. It states that

$$(f^{-1})'(4) = \frac{1}{f'(f^{-1}(4))} = \frac{1}{f'(2)} = \frac{1}{2x}\bigg|_{x=2} = \frac{1}{4}.$$

See Figure 7.7. ∎

Equation (1) sometimes enables us to find specific values of df^{-1}/dx without knowing a formula for f^{-1}.

EXAMPLE 5 Finding a Value of the Inverse Derivative

Let $f(x) = x^3 - 2$. Find the value of df^{-1}/dx at $x = 6 = f(2)$ without finding a formula for $f^{-1}(x)$.

Solution

$$\frac{df}{dx}\bigg|_{x=2} = 3x^2\bigg|_{x=2} = 12$$

$$\frac{df^{-1}}{dx}\bigg|_{x=f(2)} = \frac{1}{\dfrac{df}{dx}\bigg|_{x=2}} = \frac{1}{12} \qquad \text{Eq. (1)}$$

See Figure 7.8. ∎

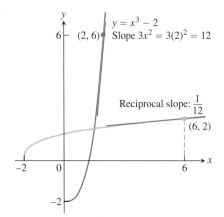

FIGURE 7.8 The derivative of $f(x) = x^3 - 2$ at $x = 2$ tells us the derivative of f^{-1} at $x = 6$ (Example 5).

Parametrizing Inverse Functions

We can graph or represent any function $y = f(x)$ parametrically as

$$x = t \qquad \text{and} \qquad y = f(t).$$

Interchanging t and $f(t)$ produces parametric equations for the inverse:

$$x = f(t) \qquad \text{and} \qquad y = t$$

(see Section 3.5).

For example, to graph the one-to-one function $f(x) = x^2, x \geq 0$, on a grapher together with its inverse and the line $y = x, x \geq 0$, use the parametric graphing option with

$$\text{Graph of } f: \quad x_1 = t, \qquad y_1 = t^2, \qquad t \geq 0$$
$$\text{Graph of } f^{-1}: \quad x_2 = t^2, \qquad y_2 = t$$
$$\text{Graph of } y = x: \quad x_3 = t, \qquad y_3 = t$$

EXERCISES 7.1

Identifying One-to-One Functions Graphically

Which of the functions graphed in Exercises 1–6 are one-to-one, and which are not?

1.

$y = -3x^3$

2.

$y = x^4 - x^2$

3.

$y = 2|x|$

4.
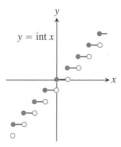
$y = \text{int } x$

5.

$y = \dfrac{1}{x}$

6.

$y = x^{1/3}$

Graphing Inverse Functions

Each of Exercises 7–10 shows the graph of a function $y = f(x)$. Copy the graph and draw in the line $y = x$. Then use symmetry with respect to the line $y = x$ to add the graph of f^{-1} to your sketch. (It is not necessary to find a formula for f^{-1}.) Identify the domain and range of f^{-1}.

7.
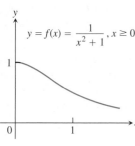
$y = f(x) = \dfrac{1}{x^2 + 1}, x \geq 0$

8.
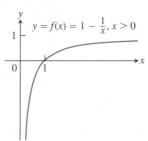
$y = f(x) = 1 - \dfrac{1}{x}, x > 0$

9.
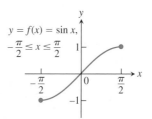
$y = f(x) = \sin x,$
$-\dfrac{\pi}{2} \leq x \leq \dfrac{\pi}{2}$

10.
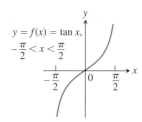
$y = f(x) = \tan x,$
$-\dfrac{\pi}{2} < x < \dfrac{\pi}{2}$

11. a. Graph the function $f(x) = \sqrt{1 - x^2}, 0 \leq x \leq 1$. What symmetry does the graph have?

 b. Show that f is its own inverse. (Remember that $\sqrt{x^2} = x$ if $x \geq 0$.)

12. a. Graph the function $f(x) = 1/x$. What symmetry does the graph have?

 b. Show that f is its own inverse.

Formulas for Inverse Functions

Each of Exercises 13–18 gives a formula for a function $y = f(x)$ and shows the graphs of f and f^{-1}. Find a formula for f^{-1} in each case.

13. $f(x) = x^2 + 1, \quad x \geq 0$
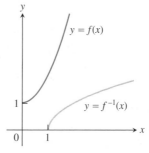

14. $f(x) = x^2, \quad x \leq 0$
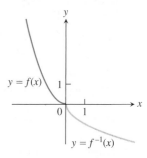

15. $f(x) = x^3 - 1$
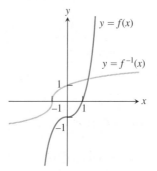

16. $f(x) = x^2 - 2x + 1, \quad x \geq 1$

17. $f(x) = (x + 1)^2$, $x \geq -1$ **18.** $f(x) = x^{2/3}$, $x \geq 0$

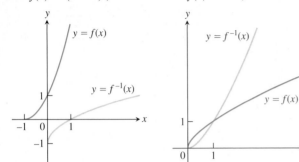

Each of Exercises 19–24 gives a formula for a function $y = f(x)$. In each case, find $f^{-1}(x)$ and identify the domain and range of f^{-1}. As a check, show that $f(f^{-1}(x)) = f^{-1}(f(x)) = x$.

19. $f(x) = x^5$ **20.** $f(x) = x^4$, $x \geq 0$

21. $f(x) = x^3 + 1$ **22.** $f(x) = (1/2)x - 7/2$

23. $f(x) = 1/x^2$, $x > 0$ **24.** $f(x) = 1/x^3$, $x \neq 0$

Derivatives of Inverse Functions

In Exercises 25–28:

a. Find $f^{-1}(x)$.

b. Graph f and f^{-1} together.

c. Evaluate df/dx at $x = a$ and df^{-1}/dx at $x = f(a)$ to show that at these points $df^{-1}/dx = 1/(df/dx)$.

25. $f(x) = 2x + 3$, $a = -1$ **26.** $f(x) = (1/5)x + 7$, $a = -1$

27. $f(x) = 5 - 4x$, $a = 1/2$ **28.** $f(x) = 2x^2$, $x \geq 0$, $a = 5$

29. a. Show that $f(x) = x^3$ and $g(x) = \sqrt[3]{x}$ are inverses of one another.

b. Graph f and g over an x-interval large enough to show the graphs intersecting at $(1, 1)$ and $(-1, -1)$. Be sure the picture shows the required symmetry about the line $y = x$.

c. Find the slopes of the tangents to the graphs of f and g at $(1, 1)$ and $(-1, -1)$ (four tangents in all).

d. What lines are tangent to the curves at the origin?

30. a. Show that $h(x) = x^3/4$ and $k(x) = (4x)^{1/3}$ are inverses of one another.

b. Graph h and k over an x-interval large enough to show the graphs intersecting at $(2, 2)$ and $(-2, -2)$. Be sure the picture shows the required symmetry about the line $y = x$.

c. Find the slopes of the tangents to the graphs at h and k at $(2, 2)$ and $(-2, -2)$.

d. What lines are tangent to the curves at the origin?

31. Let $f(x) = x^3 - 3x^2 - 1$, $x \geq 2$. Find the value of df^{-1}/dx at the point $x = -1 = f(3)$.

32. Let $f(x) = x^2 - 4x - 5$, $x > 2$. Find the value of df^{-1}/dx at the point $x = 0 = f(5)$.

33. Suppose that the differentiable function $y = f(x)$ has an inverse and that the graph of f passes through the point $(2, 4)$ and has a slope of $1/3$ there. Find the value of df^{-1}/dx at $x = 4$.

34. Suppose that the differentiable function $y = g(x)$ has an inverse and that the graph of g passes through the origin with slope 2. Find the slope of the graph of g^{-1} at the origin.

Inverses of Lines

35. a. Find the inverse of the function $f(x) = mx$, where m is a constant different from zero.

b. What can you conclude about the inverse of a function $y = f(x)$ whose graph is a line through the origin with a nonzero slope m?

36. Show that the graph of the inverse of $f(x) = mx + b$, where m and b are constants and $m \neq 0$, is a line with slope $1/m$ and y-intercept $-b/m$.

37. a. Find the inverse of $f(x) = x + 1$. Graph f and its inverse together. Add the line $y = x$ to your sketch, drawing it with dashes or dots for contrast.

b. Find the inverse of $f(x) = x + b$ (b constant). How is the graph of f^{-1} related to the graph of f?

c. What can you conclude about the inverses of functions whose graphs are lines parallel to the line $y = x$?

38. a. Find the inverse of $f(x) = -x + 1$. Graph the line $y = -x + 1$ together with the line $y = x$. At what angle do the lines intersect?

b. Find the inverse of $f(x) = -x + b$ (b constant). What angle does the line $y = -x + b$ make with the line $y = x$?

c. What can you conclude about the inverses of functions whose graphs are lines perpendicular to the line $y = x$?

Increasing and Decreasing Functions

39. As in Section 4.3, a function $f(x)$ increases on an interval I if for any two points x_1 and x_2 in I,

$$x_2 > x_1 \quad \Rightarrow \quad f(x_2) > f(x_1).$$

Similarly, a function decreases on I if for any two points x_1 and x_2 in I,

$$x_2 > x_1 \quad \Rightarrow \quad f(x_2) < f(x_1).$$

Show that increasing functions and decreasing functions are one-to-one. That is, show that for any x_1 and x_2 in I, $x_2 \neq x_1$ implies $f(x_2) \neq f(x_1)$.

Use the results of Exercise 39 to show that the functions in Exercises 40–44 have inverses over their domains. Find a formula for df^{-1}/dx using Theorem 1.

40. $f(x) = (1/3)x + (5/6)$ **41.** $f(x) = 27x^3$

42. $f(x) = 1 - 8x^3$ **43.** $f(x) = (1 - x)^3$

44. $f(x) = x^{5/3}$

Theory and Applications

45. If $f(x)$ is one-to-one, can anything be said about $g(x) = -f(x)$? Is it also one-to-one? Give reasons for your answer.

46. If $f(x)$ is one-to-one and $f(x)$ is never zero, can anything be said about $h(x) = 1/f(x)$? Is it also one-to-one? Give reasons for your answer.

47. Suppose that the range of g lies in the domain of f so that the composite $f \circ g$ is defined. If f and g are one-to-one, can anything be said about $f \circ g$? Give reasons for your answer.

48. If a composite $f \circ g$ is one-to-one, must g be one-to-one? Give reasons for your answer.

49. Suppose $f(x)$ is positive, continuous, and increasing over the interval $[a, b]$. By interpreting the graph of f show that

$$\int_a^b f(x)\,dx + \int_{f(a)}^{f(b)} f^{-1}(y)\,dy = bf(b) - af(a).$$

50. Determine conditions on the constants a, b, c, and d so that the rational function

$$f(x) = \frac{ax + b}{cx + d}$$

has an inverse.

51. If we write $g(x)$ for $f^{-1}(x)$, Equation (1) can be written as

$$g'(f(a)) = \frac{1}{f'(a)}, \quad \text{or} \quad g'(f(a)) \cdot f'(a) = 1.$$

If we then write x for a, we get

$$g'(f(x)) \cdot f'(x) = 1.$$

The latter equation may remind you of the Chain Rule, and indeed there is a connection.

Assume that f and g are differentiable functions that are inverses of one another, so that $(g \circ f)(x) = x$. Differentiate both sides of this equation with respect to x, using the Chain Rule to express $(g \circ f)'(x)$ as a product of derivatives of g and f. What do you find? (This is not a proof of Theorem 1 because we assume here the theorem's conclusion that $g = f^{-1}$ is differentiable.)

52. Equivalence of the washer and shell methods for finding volume Let f be differentiable and increasing on the interval $a \le x \le b$, with $a > 0$, and suppose that f has a differentiable inverse, f^{-1}. Revolve about the y-axis the region bounded by the graph of f and the lines $x = a$ and $y = f(b)$ to generate a solid. Then the values of the integrals given by the washer and shell methods for the volume have identical values:

$$\int_{f(a)}^{f(b)} \pi((f^{-1}(y))^2 - a^2)\,dy = \int_a^b 2\pi x(f(b) - f(x))\,dx.$$

To prove this equality, define

$$W(t) = \int_{f(a)}^{f(t)} \pi((f^{-1}(y))^2 - a^2)\,dy$$

$$S(t) = \int_a^t 2\pi x(f(t) - f(x))\,dx.$$

Then show that the functions W and S agree at a point of $[a, b]$ and have identical derivatives on $[a, b]$. As you saw in Section 4.8, Exercise 102, this will guarantee $W(t) = S(t)$ for all t in $[a, b]$. In particular, $W(b) = S(b)$. (*Source:* "Disks and Shells Revisited," by Walter Carlip, *American Mathematical Monthly*, Vol. 98, No. 2, Feb. 1991, pp. 154–156.)

COMPUTER EXPLORATIONS

In Exercises 53–60, you will explore some functions and their inverses together with their derivatives and linear approximating functions at specified points. Perform the following steps using your CAS:

a. Plot the function $y = f(x)$ together with its derivative over the given interval. Explain why you know that f is one-to-one over the interval.

b. Solve the equation $y = f(x)$ for x as a function of y, and name the resulting inverse function g.

c. Find the equation for the tangent line to f at the specified point $(x_0, f(x_0))$.

d. Find the equation for the tangent line to g at the point $(f(x_0), x_0)$ located symmetrically across the 45° line $y = x$ (which is the graph of the identity function). Use Theorem 1 to find the slope of this tangent line.

e. Plot the functions f and g, the identity, the two tangent lines, and the line segment joining the points $(x_0, f(x_0))$ and $(f(x_0), x_0)$. Discuss the symmetries you see across the main diagonal.

53. $y = \sqrt{3x - 2}, \quad \frac{2}{3} \le x \le 4, \quad x_0 = 3$

54. $y = \frac{3x + 2}{2x - 11}, \quad -2 \le x \le 2, \quad x_0 = 1/2$

55. $y = \frac{4x}{x^2 + 1}, \quad -1 \le x \le 1, \quad x_0 = 1/2$

56. $y = \frac{x^3}{x^2 + 1}, \quad -1 \le x \le 1, \quad x_0 = 1/2$

57. $y = x^3 - 3x^2 - 1, \quad 2 \le x \le 5, \quad x_0 = \frac{27}{10}$

58. $y = 2 - x - x^3, \quad -2 \le x \le 2, \quad x_0 = \frac{3}{2}$

59. $y = e^x, \quad -3 \le x \le 5, \quad x_0 = 1$

60. $y = \sin x, \quad -\frac{\pi}{2} \le x \le \frac{\pi}{2}, \quad x_0 = 1$

In Exercises 61 and 62, repeat the steps above to solve for the functions $y = f(x)$ and $x = f^{-1}(y)$ defined implicitly by the given equations over the interval.

61. $y^{1/3} - 1 = (x + 2)^3, \quad -5 \le x \le 5, \quad x_0 = -3/2$

62. $\cos y = x^{1/5}, \quad 0 \le x \le 1, \quad x_0 = 1/2$

7.2 Natural Logarithms

For any positive number a, the function value $f(x) = a^x$ is easy to define when x is an integer or rational number. When x is irrational, the meaning of a^x is not so clear. Similarly, the definition of the logarithm $\log_a x$, the inverse function of $f(x) = a^x$, is not completely obvious. In this section we use integral calculus to define the *natural logarithm* function, for which the number a is a particularly important value. This function allows us to define and analyze general exponential and logarithmic functions, $y = a^x$ and $y = \log_a x$.

Logarithms originally played important roles in arithmetic computations. Historically, considerable labor went into producing long tables of logarithms, correct to five, eight, or even more, decimal places of accuracy. Prior to the modern age of electronic calculators and computers, every engineer owned slide rules marked with logarithmic scales. Calculations with logarithms made possible the great seventeenth-century advances in offshore navigation and celestial mechanics. Today we know such calculations are done using calculators or computers, but the properties and numerous applications of logarithms are as important as ever.

Definition of the Natural Logarithm Function

One solid approach to defining and understanding logarithms begins with a study of the natural logarithm function defined as an integral through the Fundamental Theorem of Calculus. While this approach may seem indirect, it enables us to derive quickly the familiar properties of logarithmic and exponential functions. The functions we have studied so far were analyzed using the techniques of calculus, but here we do something more fundamental. We use calculus for the very definition of the logarithmic and exponential functions.

The natural logarithm of a positive number x, written as $\ln x$, is the value of an integral.

DEFINITION The Natural Logarithm Function

$$\ln x = \int_1^x \frac{1}{t}\, dt, \qquad x > 0$$

If $x > 1$, then $\ln x$ is the area under the curve $y = 1/t$ from $t = 1$ to $t = x$ (Figure 7.9). For $0 < x < 1$, $\ln x$ gives the negative of the area under the curve from x to 1. The function is not defined for $x \leq 0$. From the Zero Width Interval Rule for definite integrals, we also have

$$\ln 1 = \int_1^1 \frac{1}{t}\, dt = 0.$$

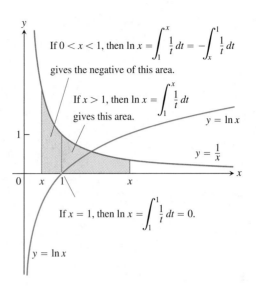

FIGURE 7.9 The graph of $y = \ln x$ and its relation to the function $y = 1/x, x > 0$. The graph of the logarithm rises above the x-axis as x moves from 1 to the right, and it falls below the axis as x moves from 1 to the left.

TABLE 7.1 Typical 2-place values of ln x

x	$\ln x$
0	undefined
0.05	-3.00
0.5	-0.69
1	0
2	0.69
3	1.10
4	1.39
10	2.30

Notice that we show the graph of $y = 1/x$ in Figure 7.9 but use $y = 1/t$ in the integral. Using x for everything would have us writing

$$\ln x = \int_1^x \frac{1}{x} \, dx,$$

with x meaning two different things. So we change the variable of integration to t.

By using rectangles to obtain finite approximations of the area under the graph of $y = 1/t$ and over the interval between $t = 1$ and $t = x$, as in Section 5.1, we can approximate the values of the function $\ln x$. Several values are given in Table 7.1. There is an important number whose natural logarithm equals 1.

DEFINITION   **The Number e**

The number e is that number in the domain of the natural logarithm satisfying

$$\ln (e) = 1$$

Geometrically, the number e corresponds to the point on the x-axis for which the area under the graph of $y = 1/t$ and above the interval $[1, e]$ is the exact area of the unit square. The area of the region shaded blue in Figure 7.9 is 1 sq unit when $x = e$.

The Derivative of $y = \ln x$

By the first part of the Fundamental Theorem of Calculus (Section 5.4),

$$\frac{d}{dx}\ln x = \frac{d}{dx}\int_1^x \frac{1}{t}\,dt = \frac{1}{x}.$$

For every positive value of x, we have

$$\frac{d}{dx}\ln x = \frac{1}{x}.$$

Therefore, the function $y = \ln x$ is a solution to the initial value problem $dy/dx = 1/x$, $x > 0$, with $y(1) = 0$. Notice that the derivative is always positive so the natural logarithm is an increasing function, hence it is one-to-one and invertible. Its inverse is studied in Section 7.3.

If u is a differentiable function of x whose values are positive, so that $\ln u$ is defined, then applying the Chain Rule

$$\frac{dy}{dx} = \frac{dy}{du}\frac{du}{dx}$$

to the function $y = \ln u$ gives

$$\frac{d}{dx}\ln u = \frac{d}{du}\ln u \cdot \frac{du}{dx} = \frac{1}{u}\frac{du}{dx}.$$

$$\frac{d}{dx}\ln u = \frac{1}{u}\frac{du}{dx}, \qquad u > 0 \tag{1}$$

EXAMPLE 1 Derivatives of Natural Logarithms

(a) $\dfrac{d}{dx}\ln 2x = \dfrac{1}{2x}\dfrac{d}{dx}(2x) = \dfrac{1}{2x}(2) = \dfrac{1}{x}$

(b) Equation (1) with $u = x^2 + 3$ gives

$$\frac{d}{dx}\ln(x^2 + 3) = \frac{1}{x^2 + 3}\cdot\frac{d}{dx}(x^2 + 3) = \frac{1}{x^2 + 3}\cdot 2x = \frac{2x}{x^2 + 3}. \qquad \blacksquare$$

Notice the remarkable occurrence in Example 1a. The function $y = \ln 2x$ has the same derivative as the function $y = \ln x$. This is true of $y = \ln ax$ for any positive number a:

$$\frac{d}{dx} \ln ax = \frac{1}{ax} \cdot \frac{d}{dx}(ax) = \frac{1}{ax}(a) = \frac{1}{x}. \tag{2}$$

Since they have the same derivative, the functions $y = \ln ax$ and $y = \ln x$ differ by a constant.

Properties of Logarithms

Logarithms were invented by John Napier and were the single most important improvement in arithmetic calculation before the modern electronic computer. What made them so useful is that the properties of logarithms enable multiplication of positive numbers by addition of their logarithms, division of positive numbers by subtraction of their logarithms, and exponentiation of a number by multiplying its logarithm by the exponent. We summarize these properties as a series of rules in Theorem 2. For the moment, we restrict the exponent r in Rule 4 to be a rational number; you will see why when we prove the rule.

THEOREM 2   Properties of Logarithms

For any numbers $a > 0$ and $x > 0$, the natural logarithm satisfies the following rules:

1. *Product Rule*: $\ln ax = \ln a + \ln x$

2. *Quotient Rule*: $\ln \dfrac{a}{x} = \ln a - \ln x$

3. *Reciprocal Rule*: $\ln \dfrac{1}{x} = -\ln x$ Rule 2 with $a = 1$

4. *Power Rule*: $\ln x^r = r \ln x$ r rational

We illustrate how these rules apply.

EXAMPLE 2   Interpreting the Properties of Logarithms

(a) $\ln 6 = \ln (2 \cdot 3) = \ln 2 + \ln 3$ Product

(b) $\ln 4 - \ln 5 = \ln \dfrac{4}{5} = \ln 0.8$ Quotient

(c) $\ln \dfrac{1}{8} = -\ln 8$ Reciprocal

$\qquad = -\ln 2^3 = -3 \ln 2$ Power   ∎

EXAMPLE 3   Applying the Properties to Function Formulas

(a) $\ln 4 + \ln \sin x = \ln (4 \sin x)$ Product

(b) $\ln \dfrac{x + 1}{2x - 3} = \ln (x + 1) - \ln (2x - 3)$ Quotient

(c) $\ln \sec x = \ln \dfrac{1}{\cos x} = -\ln \cos x$ Reciprocal

(d) $\ln \sqrt[3]{x + 1} = \ln (x + 1)^{1/3} = \dfrac{1}{3} \ln (x + 1)$ Power   ■

We now give the proof of Theorem 2. The steps in the proof are similar to those used in solving problems involving logarithms.

Proof that $\ln ax = \ln a + \ln x$ The argument is unusual—and elegant. It starts by observing that $\ln ax$ and $\ln x$ have the same derivative (Equation 2). According to Corollary 2 of the Mean Value Theorem, then, the functions must differ by a constant, which means that

$$\ln ax = \ln x + C$$

for some C.

Since this last equation holds for all positive values of x, it must hold for $x = 1$. Hence,

$$\ln (a \cdot 1) = \ln 1 + C$$

$$\ln a = 0 + C \qquad \ln 1 = 0$$

$$C = \ln a.$$

By substituting we conclude,

$$\ln ax = \ln a + \ln x.$$

Proof that $\ln x^r = r \ln x$ (assuming r rational)   We use the same-derivative argument again. For all positive values of x,

$$\frac{d}{dx} \ln x^r = \frac{1}{x^r} \frac{d}{dx} (x^r) \qquad\qquad \text{Eq. (1) with } u = x^r$$

$$= \frac{1}{x^r} r x^{r-1} \qquad\qquad \begin{array}{l} \text{Here is where we need } r \text{ to be rational,} \\ \text{at least for now. We have proved the} \\ \text{Power Rule only for rational} \\ \text{exponents.} \end{array}$$

$$= r \cdot \frac{1}{x} = \frac{d}{dx} (r \ln x).$$

Since $\ln x^r$ and $r \ln x$ have the same derivative,

$$\ln x^r = r \ln x + C$$

for some constant C. Taking x to be 1 identifies C as zero, and we're done.

You are asked to prove Rule 2 in Exercise 84. Rule 3 is a special case of Rule 2, obtained by setting $a = 1$ and noting that $\ln 1 = 0$. So we have established all cases of Theorem 2. ■

We have not yet proved Rule 4 for r irrational; we will return to this case in Section 7.3. The rule does hold for all r, rational or irrational.

The Graph and Range of ln x

The derivative $d(\ln x)/dx = 1/x$ is positive for $x > 0$, so $\ln x$ is an increasing function of x. The second derivative, $-1/x^2$, is negative, so the graph of $\ln x$ is concave down.

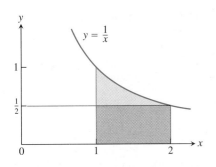

FIGURE 7.10 The rectangle of height $y = 1/2$ fits beneath the graph of $y = 1/x$ for the interval $1 \leq x \leq 2$.

We can estimate the value of ln 2 by considering the area under the graph of $y = 1/x$ and above the interval $[1, 2]$. In Figure 7.10 a rectangle of height $1/2$ over the interval $[1, 2]$ fits under the graph. Therefore the area under the graph, which is ln 2, is greater than the area, $1/2$, of the rectangle. So $\ln 2 > 1/2$. Knowing this we have,

$$\ln 2^n = n \ln 2 > n\left(\frac{1}{2}\right) = \frac{n}{2}$$

and

$$\ln 2^{-n} = -n \ln 2 < -n\left(\frac{1}{2}\right) = -\frac{n}{2}.$$

It follows that

$$\lim_{x \to \infty} \ln x = \infty \qquad \text{and} \qquad \lim_{x \to 0^+} \ln x = -\infty.$$

We defined ln x for $x > 0$, so the domain of ln x is the set of positive real numbers. The above discussion and the Intermediate Value Theorem show that its range is the entire real line giving the graph of $y = \ln x$ shown in Figure 7.9.

The Integral $\int (1/u)\, du$

Equation (1) leads to the integral formula

$$\int \frac{1}{u}\, du = \ln u + C \tag{3}$$

when u is a positive differentiable function, but what if u is negative? If u is negative, then $-u$ is positive and

$$\int \frac{1}{u}\, du = \int \frac{1}{(-u)}\, d(-u) \qquad \text{Eq. (3) with } u \text{ replaced by } -u$$

$$= \ln(-u) + C. \tag{4}$$

We can combine Equations (3) and (4) into a single formula by noticing that in each case the expression on the right is $\ln |u| + C$. In Equation (3), $\ln u = \ln |u|$ because $u > 0$; in Equation (4), $\ln(-u) = \ln |u|$ because $u < 0$. Whether u is positive or negative, the integral of $(1/u)\, du$ is $\ln |u| + C$.

If u is a differentiable function that is never zero,

$$\int \frac{1}{u}\, du = \ln |u| + C. \tag{5}$$

Equation (5) applies anywhere on the domain of $1/u$, the points where $u \neq 0$.

We know that

$$\int u^n\, du = \frac{u^{n+1}}{n+1} + C, \qquad n \neq -1 \text{ and rational}$$

Equation (5) explains what to do when n equals -1. Equation (5) says integrals of a certain *form* lead to logarithms. If $u = f(x)$, then $du = f'(x)\, dx$ and

$$\int \frac{1}{u}\, du = \int \frac{f'(x)}{f(x)}\, dx.$$

So Equation (5) gives

$$\int \frac{f'(x)}{f(x)}\, dx = \ln |f(x)| + C$$

whenever $f(x)$ is a differentiable function that maintains a constant sign on the domain given for it.

EXAMPLE 4   Applying Equation (5)

(a) $\displaystyle \int_0^2 \frac{2x}{x^2 - 5}\, dx = \int_{-5}^{-1} \frac{du}{u} = \ln |u| \,\Big]_{-5}^{-1}$ $\qquad$ $u = x^2 - 5, \quad du = 2x\, dx,$ $u(0) = -5, \quad u(2) = -1$

$$= \ln |-1| - \ln |-5| = \ln 1 - \ln 5 = -\ln 5$$

(b) $\displaystyle \int_{-\pi/2}^{\pi/2} \frac{4 \cos \theta}{3 + 2 \sin \theta}\, d\theta = \int_1^5 \frac{2}{u}\, du$ $\qquad$ $u = 3 + 2 \sin \theta, \quad du = 2 \cos \theta\, d\theta,$ $u(-\pi/2) = 1, \quad u(\pi/2) = 5$

$$= 2 \ln |u| \,\Big]_1^5$$

$$= 2 \ln |5| - 2 \ln |1| = 2 \ln 5$$

Note that $u = 3 + 2 \sin \theta$ is always positive on $[-\pi/2, \pi/2]$, so Equation (5) applies. ∎

The Integrals of tan x and cot x

Equation (5) tells us at last how to integrate the tangent and cotangent functions. For the tangent function,

$$\int \tan x\, dx = \int \frac{\sin x}{\cos x}\, dx = \int \frac{-du}{u}$$ $\qquad$ $u = \cos x > 0$ on $(-\pi/2, \pi/2),$ $du = -\sin x\, dx$

$$= -\int \frac{du}{u} = -\ln |u| + C$$

$$= -\ln |\cos x| + C = \ln \frac{1}{|\cos x|} + C \qquad \text{Reciprocal Rule}$$

$$= \ln |\sec x| + C.$$

For the cotangent,

$$\int \cot x\, dx = \int \frac{\cos x\, dx}{\sin x} = \int \frac{du}{u}$$ $\qquad$ $u = \sin x,$ $du = \cos x\, dx$

$$= \ln |u| + C = \ln |\sin x| + C = -\ln |\csc x| + C.$$

$$\int \tan u \, du = -\ln |\cos u| + C = \ln |\sec u| + C$$

$$\int \cot u \, du = \ln |\sin u| + C = -\ln |\csc x| + C$$

EXAMPLE 5

$$\int_0^{\pi/6} \tan 2x \, dx = \int_0^{\pi/3} \tan u \cdot \frac{du}{2} = \frac{1}{2}\int_0^{\pi/3} \tan u \, du$$

Substitute $u = 2x$,
$dx = du/2$,
$u(0) = 0$,
$u(\pi/6) = \pi/3$

$$= \frac{1}{2} \ln |\sec u| \Big]_0^{\pi/3} = \frac{1}{2}(\ln 2 - \ln 1) = \frac{1}{2} \ln 2 \qquad \blacksquare$$

Logarithmic Differentiation

The derivatives of positive functions given by formulas that involve products, quotients, and powers can often be found more quickly if we take the natural logarithm of both sides before differentiating. This enables us to use the laws of logarithms to simplify the formulas before differentiating. The process, called **logarithmic differentiation**, is illustrated in the next example.

EXAMPLE 6   Using Logarithmic Differentiation

Find dy/dx if

$$y = \frac{(x^2 + 1)(x + 3)^{1/2}}{x - 1}, \qquad x > 1.$$

Solution   We take the natural logarithm of both sides and simplify the result with the properties of logarithms:

$$\ln y = \ln \frac{(x^2 + 1)(x + 3)^{1/2}}{x - 1}$$

$$= \ln \left((x^2 + 1)(x + 3)^{1/2} \right) - \ln (x - 1) \qquad \text{Rule 2}$$

$$= \ln (x^2 + 1) + \ln (x + 3)^{1/2} - \ln (x - 1) \qquad \text{Rule 1}$$

$$= \ln (x^2 + 1) + \frac{1}{2} \ln (x + 3) - \ln (x - 1). \qquad \text{Rule 3}$$

We then take derivatives of both sides with respect to x, using Equation (1) on the left:

$$\frac{1}{y}\frac{dy}{dx} = \frac{1}{x^2 + 1} \cdot 2x + \frac{1}{2} \cdot \frac{1}{x + 3} - \frac{1}{x - 1}.$$

Next we solve for dy/dx:

$$\frac{dy}{dx} = y \left(\frac{2x}{x^2 + 1} + \frac{1}{2x + 6} - \frac{1}{x - 1} \right).$$

Finally, we substitute for y:

$$\frac{dy}{dx} = \frac{(x^2 + 1)(x + 3)^{1/2}}{x - 1}\left(\frac{2x}{x^2 + 1} + \frac{1}{2x + 6} - \frac{1}{x - 1}\right).$$

A direct computation in Example 6, using the Quotient and Product Rules, would be much longer. ∎

EXERCISES 7.2

Using the Properties of Logarithms

1. Express the following logarithms in terms of ln 2 and ln 3.

  a. ln 0.75   **b.** $\ln(4/9)$ **c.** $\ln(1/2)$

  d. $\ln\sqrt[3]{9}$ **e.** $\ln 3\sqrt{2}$ **f.** $\ln\sqrt{13.5}$

2. Express the following logarithms in terms of ln 5 and ln 7.

  a. $\ln(1/125)$ **b.** ln 9.8   **c.** $\ln 7\sqrt{7}$

  d. ln 1225   **e.** ln 0.056

  f. $(\ln 35 + \ln(1/7))/(\ln 25)$

Use the properties of logarithms to simplify the expressions in Exercises 3 and 4.

3. a. $\ln\sin\theta - \ln\left(\dfrac{\sin\theta}{5}\right)$ **b.** $\ln(3x^2 - 9x) + \ln\left(\dfrac{1}{3x}\right)$

  c. $\dfrac{1}{2}\ln(4t^4) - \ln 2$

4. a. $\ln\sec\theta + \ln\cos\theta$ **b.** $\ln(8x + 4) - 2\ln 2$

  c. $3\ln\sqrt[3]{t^2 - 1} - \ln(t + 1)$

Derivatives of Logarithms

In Exercises 5–36, find the derivative of y with respect to x, t, or θ, as appropriate.

5. $y = \ln 3x$ **6.** $y = \ln kx$, k constant

7. $y = \ln(t^2)$ **8.** $y = \ln(t^{3/2})$

9. $y = \ln\dfrac{3}{x}$ **10.** $y = \ln\dfrac{10}{x}$

11. $y = \ln(\theta + 1)$ **12.** $y = \ln(2\theta + 2)$

13. $y = \ln x^3$ **14.** $y = (\ln x)^3$

15. $y = t(\ln t)^2$ **16.** $y = t\sqrt{\ln t}$

17. $y = \dfrac{x^4}{4}\ln x - \dfrac{x^4}{16}$ **18.** $y = \dfrac{x^3}{3}\ln x - \dfrac{x^3}{9}$

19. $y = \dfrac{\ln t}{t}$ **20.** $y = \dfrac{1 + \ln t}{t}$

21. $y = \dfrac{\ln x}{1 + \ln x}$ **22.** $y = \dfrac{x\ln x}{1 + \ln x}$

23. $y = \ln(\ln x)$ **24.** $y = \ln(\ln(\ln x))$

25. $y = \theta(\sin(\ln\theta) + \cos(\ln\theta))$

26. $y = \ln(\sec\theta + \tan\theta)$

27. $y = \ln\dfrac{1}{x\sqrt{x + 1}}$ **28.** $y = \dfrac{1}{2}\ln\dfrac{1 + x}{1 - x}$

29. $y = \dfrac{1 + \ln t}{1 - \ln t}$ **30.** $y = \sqrt{\ln\sqrt{t}}$

31. $y = \ln(\sec(\ln\theta))$ **32.** $y = \ln\left(\dfrac{\sqrt{\sin\theta\cos\theta}}{1 + 2\ln\theta}\right)$

33. $y = \ln\left(\dfrac{(x^2 + 1)^5}{\sqrt{1 - x}}\right)$ **34.** $y = \ln\sqrt{\dfrac{(x + 1)^5}{(x + 2)^{20}}}$

35. $y = \displaystyle\int_{x^2/2}^{x^2} \ln\sqrt{t}\, dt$ **36.** $y = \displaystyle\int_{\sqrt{x}}^{\sqrt[3]{x}} \ln t\, dt$

Integration

Evaluate the integrals in Exercises 37–54.

37. $\displaystyle\int_{-3}^{-2} \dfrac{dx}{x}$ **38.** $\displaystyle\int_{-1}^{0} \dfrac{3\, dx}{3x - 2}$

39. $\displaystyle\int \dfrac{2y\, dy}{y^2 - 25}$ **40.** $\displaystyle\int \dfrac{8r\, dr}{4r^2 - 5}$

41. $\displaystyle\int_0^\pi \dfrac{\sin t}{2 - \cos t}\, dt$ **42.** $\displaystyle\int_0^{\pi/3} \dfrac{4\sin\theta}{1 - 4\cos\theta}\, d\theta$

43. $\displaystyle\int_1^2 \dfrac{2\ln x}{x}\, dx$ **44.** $\displaystyle\int_2^4 \dfrac{dx}{x\ln x}$

45. $\displaystyle\int_2^4 \dfrac{dx}{x(\ln x)^2}$ **46.** $\displaystyle\int_2^{16} \dfrac{dx}{2x\sqrt{\ln x}}$

47. $\displaystyle\int \dfrac{3\sec^2 t}{6 + 3\tan t}\, dt$ **48.** $\displaystyle\int \dfrac{\sec y\tan y}{2 + \sec y}\, dy$

49. $\displaystyle\int_0^{\pi/2} \tan\dfrac{x}{2}\, dx$ **50.** $\displaystyle\int_{\pi/4}^{\pi/2} \cot t\, dt$

51. $\displaystyle\int_{\pi/2}^{\pi} 2\cot\dfrac{\theta}{3}\, d\theta$ **52.** $\displaystyle\int_0^{\pi/12} 6\tan 3x\, dx$

53. $\displaystyle\int \dfrac{dx}{2\sqrt{x} + 2x}$ **54.** $\displaystyle\int \dfrac{\sec x\, dx}{\sqrt{\ln(\sec x + \tan x)}}$

Logarithmic Differentiation

In Exercises 55–68, use logarithmic differentiation to find the derivative of y with respect to the given independent variable.

55. $y = \sqrt{x(x + 1)}$

56. $y = \sqrt{(x^2 + 1)(x - 1)^2}$

57. $y = \sqrt{\dfrac{t}{t + 1}}$

58. $y = \sqrt{\dfrac{1}{t(t + 1)}}$

59. $y = \sqrt{\theta + 3} \sin \theta$

60. $y = (\tan \theta)\sqrt{2\theta + 1}$

61. $y = t(t + 1)(t + 2)$

62. $y = \dfrac{1}{t(t + 1)(t + 2)}$

63. $y = \dfrac{\theta + 5}{\theta \cos \theta}$

64. $y = \dfrac{\theta \sin \theta}{\sqrt{\sec \theta}}$

65. $y = \dfrac{x\sqrt{x^2 + 1}}{(x + 1)^{2/3}}$

66. $y = \sqrt{\dfrac{(x + 1)^{10}}{(2x + 1)^5}}$

67. $y = \sqrt[3]{\dfrac{x(x - 2)}{x^2 + 1}}$

68. $y = \sqrt[3]{\dfrac{x(x + 1)(x - 2)}{(x^2 + 1)(2x + 3)}}$

Theory and Applications

69. Locate and identify the absolute extreme values of

   a. $\ln (\cos x)$ on $[-\pi/4, \pi/3]$,

   b. $\cos (\ln x)$ on $[1/2, 2]$.

70. a. Prove that $f(x) = x - \ln x$ is increasing for $x > 1$.

   b. Using part (a), show that $\ln x < x$ if $x > 1$.

71. Find the area between the curves $y = \ln x$ and $y = \ln 2x$ from $x = 1$ to $x = 5$.

72. Find the area between the curve $y = \tan x$ and the x-axis from $x = -\pi/4$ to $x = \pi/3$.

73. The region in the first quadrant bounded by the coordinate axes, the line $y = 3$, and the curve $x = 2/\sqrt{y + 1}$ is revolved about the y-axis to generate a solid. Find the volume of the solid.

74. The region between the curve $y = \sqrt{\cot x}$ and the x-axis from $x = \pi/6$ to $x = \pi/2$ is revolved about the x-axis to generate a solid. Find the volume of the solid.

75. The region between the curve $y = 1/x^2$ and the x-axis from $x = 1/2$ to $x = 2$ is revolved about the y-axis to generate a solid. Find the volume of the solid.

76. In Section 6.2, Exercise 6, we revolved about the y-axis the region between the curve $y = 9x/\sqrt{x^3 + 9}$ and the x-axis from $x = 0$ to $x = 3$ to generate a solid of volume 36π. What volume do you get if you revolve the region about the x-axis instead? (See Section 6.2, Exercise 6, for a graph.)

77. Find the lengths of the following curves.

   a. $y = (x^2/8) - \ln x$, $\quad 4 \le x \le 8$

   b. $x = (y/4)^2 - 2 \ln (y/4)$, $\quad 4 \le y \le 12$

78. Find a curve through the point $(1, 0)$ whose length from $x = 1$ to $x = 2$ is

$$L = \int_1^2 \sqrt{1 + \dfrac{1}{x^2}}\, dx.$$

T 79. a. Find the centroid of the region between the curve $y = 1/x$ and the x-axis from $x = 1$ to $x = 2$. Give the coordinates to two decimal places.

   b. Sketch the region and show the centroid in your sketch.

80. a. Find the center of mass of a thin plate of constant density covering the region between the curve $y = 1/\sqrt{x}$ and the x-axis from $x = 1$ to $x = 16$.

   b. Find the center of mass if, instead of being constant, the density function is $\delta(x) = 4/\sqrt{x}$.

Solve the initial value problems in Exercises 81 and 82.

81. $\dfrac{dy}{dx} = 1 + \dfrac{1}{x}, \quad y(1) = 3$

82. $\dfrac{d^2y}{dx^2} = \sec^2 x, \quad y(0) = 0 \quad \text{and} \quad y'(0) = 1$

T 83. The linearization of $\ln (1 + x)$ at $x = 0$ Instead of approximating $\ln x$ near $x = 1$, we approximate $\ln (1 + x)$ near $x = 0$. We get a simpler formula this way.

   a. Derive the linearization $\ln (1 + x) \approx x$ at $x = 0$.

   b. Estimate to five decimal places the error involved in replacing $\ln (1 + x)$ by x on the interval $[0, 0.1]$.

   c. Graph $\ln (1 + x)$ and x together for $0 \le x \le 0.5$. Use different colors, if available. At what points does the approximation of $\ln (1 + x)$ seem best? Least good? By reading coordinates from the graphs, find as good an upper bound for the error as your grapher will allow.

84. Use the same-derivative argument, as was done to prove Rules 1 and 4 of Theorem 2, to prove the Quotient Rule property of logarithms.

Grapher Explorations

85. Graph $\ln x$, $\ln 2x$, $\ln 4x$, $\ln 8x$, and $\ln 16x$ (as many as you can) together for $0 < x \le 10$. What is going on? Explain.

86. Graph $y = \ln |\sin x|$ in the window $0 \le x \le 22$, $-2 \le y \le 0$. Explain what you see. How could you change the formula to turn the arches upside down?

87. a. Graph $y = \sin x$ and the curves $y = \ln (a + \sin x)$ for $a = 2$, 4, 8, 20, and 50 together for $0 \le x \le 23$.

   b. Why do the curves flatten as a increases? (*Hint:* Find an a-dependent upper bound for $|y'|$.)

88. Does the graph of $y = \sqrt{x} - \ln x$, $x > 0$, have an inflection point? Try to answer the question **(a)** by graphing, **(b)** by using calculus.

7.3   The Exponential Function

Having developed the theory of the function $\ln x$, we introduce the exponential function $\exp x = e^x$ as the inverse of $\ln x$. We study its properties and compute its derivative and integral. Knowing its derivative, we prove the power rule to differentiate x^n when n is *any* real number, rational or irrational.

The Inverse of ln *x* and the Number *e*

The function $\ln x$, being an increasing function of x with domain $(0, \infty)$ and range $(-\infty, \infty)$, has an inverse $\ln^{-1} x$ with domain $(-\infty, \infty)$ and range $(0, \infty)$. The graph of $\ln^{-1} x$ is the graph of $\ln x$ reflected across the line $y = x$. As you can see in Figure 7.11,

$$\lim_{x \to \infty} \ln^{-1} x = \infty \qquad \text{and} \qquad \lim_{x \to -\infty} \ln^{-1} x = 0.$$

The function $\ln^{-1} x$ is also denoted by $\exp x$.

In Section 7.2 we defined the number e by the equation $\ln (e) = 1$, so $e = \ln^{-1}(1) = \exp (1)$. Although e is not a rational number, later in this section we see one way to express it as a limit. In Chapter 11, we will calculate its value with a computer to as many places of accuracy as we want with a different formula (Section 11.9, Example 6). To 15 places,

$$e = 2.718281828459045.$$

The Function *y* = *e*^x

We can raise the number e to a rational power r in the usual way:

$$e^2 = e \cdot e, \qquad e^{-2} = \frac{1}{e^2}, \qquad e^{1/2} = \sqrt{e},$$

and so on. Since e is positive, e^r is positive too. Thus, e^r has a logarithm. When we take the logarithm, we find that

$$\ln e^r = r \ln e = r \cdot 1 = r.$$

Since $\ln x$ is one-to-one and $\ln (\ln^{-1} r) = r$, this equation tells us that

$$e^r = \ln^{-1} r = \exp r \qquad \text{for } r \text{ rational.} \tag{1}$$

We have not yet found a way to give an obvious meaning to e^x for x irrational. But $\ln^{-1} x$ has meaning for any x, rational or irrational. So Equation (1) provides a way to extend the definition of e^x to irrational values of x. The function $\ln^{-1} x$ is defined for all x, so we use it to assign a value to e^x at every point where e^x had no previous definition.

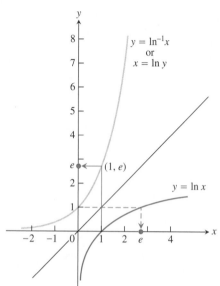

FIGURE 7.11   The graphs of $y = \ln x$ and $y = \ln^{-1} x = \exp x$. The number e is $\ln^{-1} 1 = \exp (1)$.

Typical values of e^x

x	e^x (rounded)
-1	0.37
0	1
1	2.72
2	7.39
10	22026
100	2.6881×10^{43}

> **DEFINITION**   **The Natural Exponential Function**
> For every real number x, $e^x = \ln^{-1} x = \exp x$.

For the first time we have a precise meaning for an irrational exponent. Usually the exponential function is denoted by e^x rather than $\exp x$. Since $\ln x$ and e^x are inverses of one another, we have

---

Inverse Equations for e^x and $\ln x$

$$e^{\ln x} = x \qquad (\text{all } x > 0) \tag{2}$$

$$\ln(e^x) = x \qquad (\text{all } x) \tag{3}$$

Transcendental Numbers and Transcendental Functions

Numbers that are solutions of polynomial equations with rational coefficients are called **algebraic**: -2 is algebraic because it satisfies the equation $x + 2 = 0$, and $\sqrt{3}$ is algebraic because it satisfies the equation $x^2 - 3 = 0$. Numbers that are not algebraic are called **transcendental**, like e and π. In 1873, Charles Hermite proved the transcendence of e in the sense that we describe. In 1882, C.L.F. Lindemann proved the transcendence of π.

Today, we call a function $y = f(x)$ algebraic if it satisfies an equation of the form

$$P_n y^n + \cdots + P_1 y + P_0 = 0$$

in which the P's are polynomials in x with rational coefficients. The function $y = 1/\sqrt{x + 1}$ is algebraic because it satisfies the equation $(x + 1)y^2 - 1 = 0$. Here the polynomials are $P_2 = x + 1, P_1 = 0$, and $P_0 = -1$. Functions that are not algebraic are called transcendental.

The domain of $\ln x$ is $(0, \infty)$ and its range is $(-\infty, \infty)$. So the domain of e^x is $(-\infty, \infty)$ and its range is $(0, \infty)$.

EXAMPLE 1 Using the Inverse Equations

(a) $\ln e^2 = 2$

(b) $\ln e^{-1} = -1$

(c) $\ln \sqrt{e} = \dfrac{1}{2}$

(d) $\ln e^{\sin x} = \sin x$

(e) $e^{\ln 2} = 2$

(f) $e^{\ln(x^2 + 1)} = x^2 + 1$

(g) $e^{3\ln 2} = e^{\ln 2^3} = e^{\ln 8} = 8$ One way

(h) $e^{3\ln 2} = (e^{\ln 2})^3 = 2^3 = 8$ Another way ∎

EXAMPLE 2 Solving for an Exponent

Find k if $e^{2k} = 10$.

Solution Take the natural logarithm of both sides:

$$e^{2k} = 10$$

$$\ln e^{2k} = \ln 10$$

$$2k = \ln 10 \qquad \text{Eq. (3)}$$

$$k = \frac{1}{2} \ln 10.$$

∎

The General Exponential Function a^x

Since $a = e^{\ln a}$ for any positive number a, we can think of a^x as $(e^{\ln a})^x = e^{x \ln a}$. We therefore make the following definition.

DEFINITION **General Exponential Functions**

For any numbers $a > 0$ and x, the exponential function with base a is

$$a^x = e^{x \ln a}.$$

When $a = e$, the definition gives $a^x = e^{x \ln a} = e^{x \ln e} = e^{x \cdot 1} = e^x$.

EXAMPLE 3 Evaluating Exponential Functions

(a) $2^{\sqrt{3}} = e^{\sqrt{3}\ln 2} \approx e^{1.20} \approx 3.32$

(b) $2^{\pi} = e^{\pi \ln 2} \approx e^{2.18} \approx 8.8$ ∎

We study the calculus of general exponential functions and their inverses in the next section. Here we need the definition in order to discuss the laws of exponents for e^x.

Laws of Exponents

Even though e^x is defined in a seemingly roundabout way as $\ln^{-1} x$, it obeys the familiar laws of exponents from algebra. Theorem 3 shows us that these laws are consequences of the definitions of $\ln x$ and e^x.

THEOREM 3 Laws of Exponents for e^x

For all numbers x, x_1, and x_2, the natural exponential e^x obeys the following laws:

1. $e^{x_1} \cdot e^{x_2} = e^{x_1 + x_2}$

2. $e^{-x} = \dfrac{1}{e^x}$

3. $\dfrac{e^{x_1}}{e^{x_2}} = e^{x_1 - x_2}$

4. $(e^{x_1})^{x_2} = e^{x_1 x_2} = (e^{x_2})^{x_1}$

Proof of Law 1 Let

$$y_1 = e^{x_1} \qquad \text{and} \qquad y_2 = e^{x_2}. \tag{4}$$

Then

$$x_1 = \ln y_1 \quad \text{and} \quad x_2 = \ln y_2 \qquad \text{Take logs of both sides of Eqs. (4).}$$

$$x_1 + x_2 = \ln y_1 + \ln y_2$$

$$= \ln y_1 y_2 \qquad \text{Product Rule for logarithms}$$

$$e^{x_1 + x_2} = e^{\ln y_1 y_2} \qquad \text{Exponentiate.}$$

$$= y_1 y_2 \qquad e^{\ln u} = u$$

$$= e^{x_1} e^{x_2}. \qquad \qquad ∎$$

The proof of Law 4 is similar. Laws 2 and 3 follow from Law 1 (Exercise 78).

EXAMPLE 4 Applying the Exponent Laws

(a) $e^{x + \ln 2} = e^x \cdot e^{\ln 2} = 2e^x$ Law 1

(b) $e^{-\ln x} = \dfrac{1}{e^{\ln x}} = \dfrac{1}{x}$ Law 2

(c) $\dfrac{e^{2x}}{e} = e^{2x - 1}$ Law 3

(d) $(e^3)^x = e^{3x} = (e^x)^3$ Law 4 ∎

Theorem 3 is also valid for a^x, the exponential function with base a. For example,

$$a^{x_1} \cdot a^{x_2} = e^{x_1 \ln a} \cdot e^{x_2 \ln a} \qquad \text{Definition of } a^x$$

$$= e^{x_1 \ln a + x_2 \ln a} \qquad \text{Law 1}$$

$$= e^{(x_1 + x_2)\ln a} \qquad \text{Factor } \ln a$$

$$= a^{x_1 + x_2}. \qquad \text{Definition of } a^x$$

The Derivative and Integral of e^x

The exponential function is differentiable because it is the inverse of a differentiable function whose derivative is never zero (Theorem 1). We calculate its derivative using Theorem 1 and our knowledge of the derivative of $\ln x$. Let

$$f(x) = \ln x \quad \text{and} \quad y = e^x = \ln^{-1} x = f^{-1}(x).$$

Then,

$$\frac{dy}{dx} = \frac{d}{dx}(e^x) = \frac{d}{dx}\ln^{-1} x$$

$$= \frac{d}{dx}f^{-1}(x)$$

$$= \frac{1}{f'(f^{-1}(x))} \qquad \text{Theorem 1}$$

$$= \frac{1}{f'(e^x)} \qquad f^{-1}(x) = e^x$$

$$= \frac{1}{\left(\dfrac{1}{e^x}\right)} \qquad f'(z) = \frac{1}{z} \text{ with } z = e^x$$

$$= e^x.$$

That is, for $y = e^x$, we find that $dy/dx = e^x$ so the natural exponential function e^x is its own derivative. We will see in Section 7.5 that the only functions that behave this way are constant multiples of e^x. In summary,

$$\frac{d}{dx}e^x = e^x \tag{5}$$

EXAMPLE 5 Differentiating an Exponential

$$\frac{d}{dx}(5e^x) = 5\frac{d}{dx}e^x$$

$$= 5e^x$$

The Chain Rule extends Equation (5) in the usual way to a more general form.

If u is any differentiable function of x, then

$$\frac{d}{dx} e^u = e^u \frac{du}{dx}.$$ (6)

EXAMPLE 6 Applying the Chain Rule with Exponentials

(a) $\dfrac{d}{dx} e^{-x} = e^{-x} \dfrac{d}{dx}(-x) = e^{-x}(-1) = -e^{-x}$ Eq. (6) with $u = -x$

(b) $\dfrac{d}{dx} e^{\sin x} = e^{\sin x} \dfrac{d}{dx}(\sin x) = e^{\sin x} \cdot \cos x$ Eq. (6) with $u = \sin x$ ∎

The integral equivalent of Equation (6) is

$$\int e^u \, du = e^u + C.$$

EXAMPLE 7 Integrating Exponentials

(a) $\displaystyle \int_0^{\ln 2} e^{3x} \, dx = \int_0^{\ln 8} e^u \cdot \frac{1}{3} \, du$ $u = 3x, \quad \frac{1}{3} du = dx, \quad u(0) = 0,$
$u(\ln 2) = 3 \ln 2 = \ln 2^3 = \ln 8$

$\qquad\qquad\qquad = \dfrac{1}{3} \displaystyle\int_0^{\ln 8} e^u \, du$

$\qquad\qquad\qquad = \dfrac{1}{3} e^u \Big]_0^{\ln 8}$

$\qquad\qquad\qquad = \dfrac{1}{3}(8 - 1) = \dfrac{7}{3}$

(b) $\displaystyle \int_0^{\pi/2} e^{\sin x} \cos x \, dx = e^{\sin x} \Big]_0^{\pi/2}$ Antiderivative from Example 6

$\qquad\qquad\qquad\qquad = e^1 - e^0 = e - 1$ ∎

EXAMPLE 8 Solving an Initial Value Problem

Solve the initial value problem

$$e^y \frac{dy}{dx} = 2x, \qquad x > \sqrt{3}; \qquad y(2) = 0.$$

Solution   We integrate both sides of the differential equation with respect to x to obtain

$$e^y = x^2 + C.$$

We use the initial condition $y(2) = 0$ to determine C:

$$C = e^0 - (2)^2$$
$$= 1 - 4 = -3.$$

This completes the formula for e^y:

$$e^y = x^2 - 3.$$

To find y, we take logarithms of both sides:

$$\ln e^y = \ln (x^2 - 3)$$
$$y = \ln (x^2 - 3).$$

Notice that the solution is valid for $x > \sqrt{3}$.

Let's check the solution in the original equation.

$$e^y \frac{dy}{dx} = e^y \frac{d}{dx} \ln (x^2 - 3)$$

$$= e^y \frac{2x}{x^2 - 3} \qquad \text{Derivative of } \ln (x^2 - 3)$$

$$= e^{\ln (x^2 - 3)} \frac{2x}{x^2 - 3} \qquad y = \ln (x^2 - 3)$$

$$= (x^2 - 3) \frac{2x}{x^2 - 3} \qquad e^{\ln y} = y$$

$$= 2x.$$

The solution checks. ∎

The Number e Expressed as a Limit

We have defined the number e as the number for which $\ln e = 1$, or the value $\exp(1)$. We see that e is an important constant for the logarithmic and exponential functions, but what is its numerical value? The next theorem shows one way to calculate e as a limit.

THEOREM 4 **The Number e as a Limit**

The number e can be calculated as the limit

$$e = \lim_{x \to 0} (1 + x)^{1/x}.$$

Proof If $f(x) = \ln x$, then $f'(x) = 1/x$, so $f'(1) = 1$. But, by the definition of derivative,

$$f'(1) = \lim_{h \to 0} \frac{f(1 + h) - f(1)}{h} = \lim_{x \to 0} \frac{f(1 + x) - f(1)}{x}$$

$$= \lim_{x \to 0} \frac{\ln (1 + x) - \ln 1}{x} = \lim_{x \to 0} \frac{1}{x} \ln (1 + x) \qquad \ln 1 = 0$$

$$= \lim_{x \to 0} \ln (1 + x)^{1/x} = \ln \left[\lim_{x \to 0} (1 + x)^{1/x} \right] \qquad \ln \text{ is continuous.}$$

Because $f'(1) = 1$, we have

$$\ln \left[\lim_{x \to 0} (1 + x)^{1/x} \right] = 1$$

Therefore,

$$\lim_{x \to 0} (1 + x)^{1/x} = e \qquad \text{ln } e = 1 \text{ and ln is one-to-one} \qquad \blacksquare$$

By substituting $y = 1/x$, we can also express the limit in Theorem 4 as

$$e = \lim_{y \to \infty} \left(1 + \frac{1}{y} \right)^y. \tag{7}$$

At the beginning of the section we noted that $e = 2.718281828459045$ to 15 decimal places.

The Power Rule (General Form)

We can now define x^n for any $x > 0$ and any real number n as $x^n = e^{n \ln x}$. Therefore, the n in the equation $\ln x^n = n \ln x$ no longer needs to be rational—it can be any number as long as $x > 0$:

$$\ln x^n = \ln (e^{n \ln x}) = n \ln x \qquad \text{ln } e^u = u, \text{ any } u$$

Together, the law $a^x/a^y = a^{x-y}$ and the definition $x^n = e^{n \ln x}$ enable us to establish the Power Rule for differentiation in its final form. Differentiating x^n with respect to x gives

$$\frac{d}{dx} x^n = \frac{d}{dx} e^{n \ln x} \qquad \text{Definition of } x^n, \ x > 0$$

$$= e^{n \ln x} \cdot \frac{d}{dx} (n \ln x) \qquad \text{Chain Rule for } e^u$$

$$= x^n \cdot \frac{n}{x} \qquad \text{The definition again}$$

$$= nx^{n-1}.$$

In short, as long as $x > 0$,

$$\frac{d}{dx} x^n = nx^{n-1}.$$

The Chain Rule extends this equation to the Power Rule's general form.

Power Rule (General Form)

If u is a positive differentiable function of x and n is any real number, then u^n is a differentiable function of x and

$$\frac{d}{dx} u^n = nu^{n-1} \frac{du}{dx}.$$

EXAMPLE 9 Using the Power Rule with Irrational Powers

(a) $\dfrac{d}{dx}x^{\sqrt{2}} = \sqrt{2}x^{\sqrt{2}-1}$ $(x > 0)$

(b) $\dfrac{d}{dx}(2 + \sin 3x)^{\pi} = \pi(2 + \sin 3x)^{\pi-1}(\cos 3x) \cdot 3$

$$= 3\pi(2 + \sin 3x)^{\pi-1}(\cos 3x).$$ ∎

EXERCISES 7.3

Algebraic Calculations with the Exponential and Logarithm

Find simpler expressions for the quantities in Exercises 1–4.

1. a. $e^{\ln 7.2}$ **b.** $e^{-\ln x^2}$ **c.** $e^{\ln x - \ln y}$

2. a. $e^{\ln(x^2+y^2)}$ **b.** $e^{-\ln 0.3}$ **c.** $e^{\ln \pi x - \ln 2}$

3. a. $2\ln\sqrt{e}$ **b.** $\ln(\ln e^e)$ **c.** $\ln(e^{-x^2-y^2})$

4. a. $\ln(e^{\sec\theta})$ **b.** $\ln(e^{(e^x)})$ **c.** $\ln(e^{2\ln x})$

Solving Equations with Logarithmic or Exponential Terms

In Exercises 5–10, solve for y in terms of t or x, as appropriate.

5. $\ln y = 2t + 4$ **6.** $\ln y = -t + 5$

7. $\ln(y - 40) = 5t$ **8.** $\ln(1 - 2y) = t$

9. $\ln(y - 1) - \ln 2 = x + \ln x$

10. $\ln(y^2 - 1) - \ln(y + 1) = \ln(\sin x)$

In Exercises 11 and 12, solve for k.

11. a. $e^{2k} = 4$ **b.** $100e^{10k} = 200$ **c.** $e^{k/1000} = a$

12. a. $e^{5k} = \dfrac{1}{4}$ **b.** $80e^k = 1$ **c.** $e^{(\ln 0.8)k} = 0.8$

In Exercises 13–16, solve for t.

13. a. $e^{-0.3t} = 27$ **b.** $e^{kt} = \dfrac{1}{2}$ **c.** $e^{(\ln 0.2)t} = 0.4$

14. a. $e^{-0.01t} = 1000$ **b.** $e^{kt} = \dfrac{1}{10}$ **c.** $e^{(\ln 2)t} = \dfrac{1}{2}$

15. $e^{\sqrt{t}} = x^2$ **16.** $e^{(x^2)}e^{(2x+1)} = e^t$

Derivatives

In Exercises 17–36, find the derivative of y with respect to x, t, or θ, as appropriate.

17. $y = e^{-5x}$ **18.** $y = e^{2x/3}$

19. $y = e^{5-7x}$ **20.** $y = e^{(4\sqrt{x}+x^2)}$

21. $y = xe^x - e^x$ **22.** $y = (1 + 2x)e^{-2x}$

23. $y = (x^2 - 2x + 2)e^x$ **24.** $y = (9x^2 - 6x + 2)e^{3x}$

25. $y = e^{\theta}(\sin\theta + \cos\theta)$ **26.** $y = \ln(3\theta e^{-\theta})$

27. $y = \cos(e^{-\theta^2})$ **28.** $y = \theta^3 e^{-2\theta}\cos 5\theta$

29. $y = \ln(3te^{-t})$ **30.** $y = \ln(2e^{-t}\sin t)$

31. $y = \ln\left(\dfrac{e^{\theta}}{1 + e^{\theta}}\right)$ **32.** $y = \ln\left(\dfrac{\sqrt{\theta}}{1 + \sqrt{\theta}}\right)$

33. $y = e^{(\cos t + \ln t)}$ **34.** $y = e^{\sin t}(\ln t^2 + 1)$

35. $y = \displaystyle\int_0^{\ln x} \sin e^t\, dt$ **36.** $y = \displaystyle\int_{e^{4\sqrt{x}}}^{e^{2x}} \ln t\, dt$

In Exercises 37–40, find dy/dx.

37. $\ln y = e^y \sin x$ **38.** $\ln xy = e^{x+y}$

39. $e^{2x} = \sin(x + 3y)$ **40.** $\tan y = e^x + \ln x$

Integrals

Evaluate the integrals in Exercises 41–62.

41. $\displaystyle\int (e^{3x} + 5e^{-x})\, dx$ **42.** $\displaystyle\int (2e^x - 3e^{-2x})\, dx$

43. $\displaystyle\int_{\ln 2}^{\ln 3} e^x\, dx$ **44.** $\displaystyle\int_{-\ln 2}^{0} e^{-x}\, dx$

45. $\displaystyle\int 8e^{(x+1)}\, dx$ **46.** $\displaystyle\int 2e^{(2x-1)}\, dx$

47. $\displaystyle\int_{\ln 4}^{\ln 9} e^{x/2}\, dx$ **48.** $\displaystyle\int_0^{\ln 16} e^{x/4}\, dx$

49. $\displaystyle\int \dfrac{e^{\sqrt{r}}}{\sqrt{r}}\, dr$ **50.** $\displaystyle\int \dfrac{e^{-\sqrt{r}}}{\sqrt{r}}\, dr$

51. $\displaystyle\int 2t\, e^{-t^2}\, dt$ **52.** $\displaystyle\int t^3 e^{(t^4)}\, dt$

53. $\displaystyle\int \dfrac{e^{1/x}}{x^2}\, dx$ **54.** $\displaystyle\int \dfrac{e^{-1/x^2}}{x^3}\, dx$

55. $\displaystyle\int_0^{\pi/4} (1 + e^{\tan\theta})\sec^2\theta\, d\theta$ **56.** $\displaystyle\int_{\pi/4}^{\pi/2} (1 + e^{\cot\theta})\csc^2\theta\, d\theta$

57. $\displaystyle\int e^{\sec\pi t}\sec\pi t \tan\pi t\, dt$

58. $\displaystyle\int e^{\csc(\pi+t)}\csc(\pi + t)\cot(\pi + t)\, dt$

59. $\displaystyle\int_{\ln(\pi/6)}^{\ln(\pi/2)} 2e^v \cos e^v \, dv$ **60.** $\displaystyle\int_0^{\sqrt{\ln \pi}} 2x \, e^{x^2} \cos(e^{x^2}) \, dx$

61. $\displaystyle\int \frac{e^r}{1+e^r} \, dr$ **62.** $\displaystyle\int \frac{dx}{1+e^x}$

Initial Value Problems

Solve the initial value problems in Exercises 63–66.

63. $\dfrac{dy}{dt} = e^t \sin(e^t - 2), \quad y(\ln 2) = 0$

64. $\dfrac{dy}{dt} = e^{-t} \sec^2(\pi e^{-t}), \quad y(\ln 4) = 2/\pi$

65. $\dfrac{d^2y}{dx^2} = 2e^{-x}, \quad y(0) = 1 \quad \text{and} \quad y'(0) = 0$

66. $\dfrac{d^2y}{dt^2} = 1 - e^{2t}, \quad y(1) = -1 \quad \text{and} \quad y'(1) = 0$

Theory and Applications

67. Find the absolute maximum and minimum values of $f(x) = e^x - 2x$ on $[0, 1]$.

68. Where does the periodic function $f(x) = 2e^{\sin(x/2)}$ take on its extreme values and what are these values?

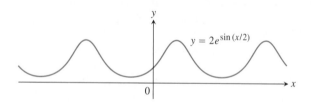

69. Find the absolute maximum value of $f(x) = x^2 \ln(1/x)$ and say where it is assumed.

T 70. Graph $f(x) = (x - 3)^2 e^x$ and its first derivative together. Comment on the behavior of f in relation to the signs and values of f'. Identify significant points on the graphs with calculus, as necessary.

71. Find the area of the "triangular" region in the first quadrant that is bounded above by the curve $y = e^{2x}$, below by the curve $y = e^x$, and on the right by the line $x = \ln 3$.

72. Find the area of the "triangular" region in the first quadrant that is bounded above by the curve $y = e^{x/2}$, below by the curve $y = e^{-x/2}$, and on the right by the line $x = 2 \ln 2$.

73. Find a curve through the origin in the xy-plane whose length from $x = 0$ to $x = 1$ is

$$L = \int_0^1 \sqrt{1 + \frac{1}{4}e^x} \, dx.$$

74. Find the area of the surface generated by revolving the curve $x = (e^y + e^{-y})/2, \, 0 \le y \le \ln 2$, about the y-axis.

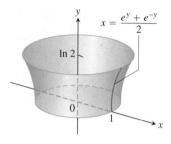

75. a. Show that $\int \ln x \, dx = x \ln x - x + C$.

   b. Find the average value of $\ln x$ over $[1, e]$.

76. Find the average value of $f(x) = 1/x$ on $[1, 2]$.

77. The linearization of e^x at $x = 0$

   a. Derive the linear approximation $e^x \approx 1 + x$ at $x = 0$.

   T b. Estimate to five decimal places the magnitude of the error involved in replacing e^x by $1 + x$ on the interval $[0, 0.2]$.

   T c. Graph e^x and $1 + x$ together for $-2 \le x \le 2$. Use different colors, if available. On what intervals does the approximation appear to overestimate e^x? Underestimate e^x?

78. Laws of Exponents

   a. Starting with the equation $e^{x_1}e^{x_2} = e^{x_1+x_2}$, derived in the text, show that $e^{-x} = 1/e^x$ for any real number x. Then show that $e^{x_1}/e^{x_2} = e^{x_1-x_2}$ for any numbers x_1 and x_2.

   b. Show that $(e^{x_1})^{x_2} = e^{x_1 x_2} = (e^{x_2})^{x_1}$ for any numbers x_1 and x_2.

T 79. **A decimal representation of e** Find e to as many decimal places as your calculator allows by solving the equation $\ln x = 1$.

T 80. **The inverse relation between e^x and $\ln x$** Find out how good your calculator is at evaluating the composites

$$e^{\ln x} \quad \text{and} \quad \ln(e^x).$$

81. Show that for any number $a > 1$

$$\int_1^a \ln x \, dx + \int_0^{\ln a} e^y \, dy = a \ln a.$$

(See accompanying figure.)

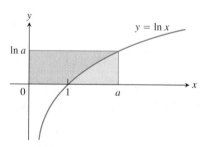

82. The geometric, logarithmic, and arithmetic mean inequality

   a. Show that the graph of e^x is concave up over every interval of x-values.

b. Show, by reference to the accompanying figure, that if $0 < a < b$ then

$$e^{(\ln a + \ln b)/2} \cdot (\ln b - \ln a) < \int_{\ln a}^{\ln b} e^x \, dx < \frac{e^{\ln a} + e^{\ln b}}{2} \cdot (\ln b - \ln a).$$

c. Use the inequality in part (b) to conclude that

$$\sqrt{ab} < \frac{b - a}{\ln b - \ln a} < \frac{a + b}{2}.$$

This inequality says that the geometric mean of two positive numbers is less than their logarithmic mean, which in turn is less than their arithmetic mean.

(For more about this inequality, see "The Geometric, Logarithmic, and Arithmetic Mean Inequality" by Frank Burk,

American Mathematical Monthly, Vol. 94, No. 6, June–July 1987, pp. 527–528.)

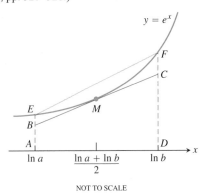

NOT TO SCALE

7.4 a^x and $\log_a x$

We have defined general exponential functions such as 2^x, 10^x, and π^x. In this section we compute their derivatives and integrals. We also define the general logarithmic functions such as $\log_2 x$, $\log_{10} x$, and $\log_\pi x$, and find their derivatives and integrals as well.

The Derivative of a^u

We start with the definition $a^x = e^{x \ln a}$:

$$\frac{d}{dx} a^x = \frac{d}{dx} e^{x \ln a} = e^{x \ln a} \cdot \frac{d}{dx} (x \ln a) \qquad \frac{d}{dx} e^u = e^u \frac{du}{dx}$$

$$= a^x \ln a.$$

If $a > 0$, then

$$\frac{d}{dx} a^x = a^x \ln a.$$

With the Chain Rule, we get a more general form.

If $a > 0$ and u is a differentiable function of x, then a^u is a differentiable function of x and

$$\frac{d}{dx} a^u = a^u \ln a \frac{du}{dx}. \tag{1}$$

These equations show why e^x is the exponential function preferred in calculus. If $a = e$, then $\ln a = 1$ and the derivative of a^x simplifies to

$$\frac{d}{dx} e^x = e^x \ln e = e^x.$$

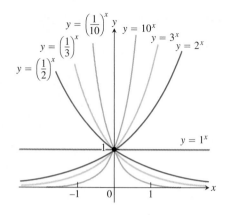

FIGURE 7.12 Exponential functions decrease if $0 < a < 1$ and increase if $a > 1$. As $x \to \infty$, we have $a^x \to 0$ if $0 < a < 1$ and $a^x \to \infty$ if $a > 1$. As $x \to -\infty$, we have $a^x \to \infty$ if $0 < a < 1$ and $a^x \to 0$ if $a > 1$.

EXAMPLE 1 Differentiating General Exponential Functions

(a) $\dfrac{d}{dx} 3^x = 3^x \ln 3$

(b) $\dfrac{d}{dx} 3^{-x} = 3^{-x}(\ln 3)\dfrac{d}{dx}(-x) = -3^{-x}\ln 3$

(c) $\dfrac{d}{dx} 3^{\sin x} = 3^{\sin x}(\ln 3)\dfrac{d}{dx}(\sin x) = 3^{\sin x}(\ln 3)\cos x$ ∎

From Equation (1), we see that the derivative of a^x is positive if $\ln a > 0$, or $a > 1$, and negative if $\ln a < 0$, or $0 < a < 1$. Thus, a^x is an increasing function of x if $a > 1$ and a decreasing function of x if $0 < a < 1$. In each case, a^x is one-to-one. The second derivative

$$\frac{d^2}{dx^2}(a^x) = \frac{d}{dx}(a^x \ln a) = (\ln a)^2\, a^x$$

is positive for all x, so the graph of a^x is concave up on every interval of the real line (Figure 7.12).

Other Power Functions

The ability to raise positive numbers to arbitrary real powers makes it possible to define functions like x^x and $x^{\ln x}$ for $x > 0$. We find the derivatives of such functions by rewriting the functions as powers of e.

EXAMPLE 2 Differentiating a General Power Function

Find dy/dx if $y = x^x$, $x > 0$.

Solution Write x^x as a power of e:

$$y = x^x = e^{x \ln x}. \qquad a^x \text{ with } a = x.$$

Then differentiate as usual:

$$\frac{dy}{dx} = \frac{d}{dx} e^{x \ln x}$$

$$= e^{x \ln x}\frac{d}{dx}(x \ln x)$$

$$= x^x \left(x \cdot \frac{1}{x} + \ln x \right)$$

$$= x^x(1 + \ln x). \qquad\blacksquare$$

The Integral of a^u

If $a \neq 1$, so that $\ln a \neq 0$, we can divide both sides of Equation (1) by $\ln a$ to obtain

$$a^u \frac{du}{dx} = \frac{1}{\ln a}\frac{d}{dx}(a^u).$$

Integrating with respect to x then gives

$$\int a^u \frac{du}{dx}\,dx = \int \frac{1}{\ln a}\frac{d}{dx}(a^u)\,dx = \frac{1}{\ln a}\int \frac{d}{dx}(a^u)\,dx = \frac{1}{\ln a}a^u + C.$$

Writing the first integral in differential form gives

$$\int a^u\,du = \frac{a^u}{\ln a} + C. \qquad\qquad (2)$$

EXAMPLE 3   Integrating General Exponential Functions

(a) $\displaystyle\int 2^x\,dx = \frac{2^x}{\ln 2} + C$ \qquad Eq. (2) with $a = 2$, $u = x$

(b) $\displaystyle\int 2^{\sin x}\cos x\,dx$

$$= \int 2^u\,du = \frac{2^u}{\ln 2} + C \qquad u = \sin x,\, du = \cos x\,dx,\text{ and Eq. (2)}$$

$$= \frac{2^{\sin x}}{\ln 2} + C \qquad\qquad u \text{ replaced by } \sin x \qquad\blacksquare$$

Logarithms with Base a

As we saw earlier, if a is any positive number other than 1, the function a^x is one-to-one and has a nonzero derivative at every point. It therefore has a differentiable inverse. We call the inverse the **logarithm of x with base a** and denote it by $\log_a x$.

DEFINITION $\log_a x$

For any positive number $a \ne 1$,

$$\log_a x \text{ is the inverse function of } a^x.$$

The graph of $y = \log_a x$ can be obtained by reflecting the graph of $y = a^x$ across the 45° line $y = x$ (Figure 7.13). When $a = e$, we have $\log_e x = $ inverse of $e^x = \ln x$. Since $\log_a x$ and a^x are inverses of one another, composing them in either order gives the identity function.

Inverse Equations for a^x and $\log_a x$

$$a^{\log_a x} = x \qquad (x > 0) \qquad\qquad (3)$$

$$\log_a (a^x) = x \qquad (\text{all } x) \qquad\qquad (4)$$

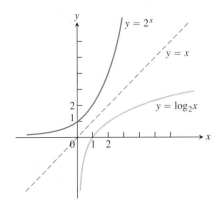

FIGURE 7.13   The graph of 2^x and its inverse, $\log_2 x$.

EXAMPLE 4 Applying the Inverse Equations

(a) $\log_2 (2^5) = 5$ **(b)** $\log_{10} (10^{-7}) = -7$

(c) $2^{\log_2 (3)} = 3$ **(d)** $10^{\log_{10} (4)} = 4$ ∎

Evaluation of $\log_a x$

The evaluation of $\log_a x$ is simplified by the observation that $\log_a x$ is a numerical multiple of $\ln x$.

$$\log_a x = \frac{1}{\ln a} \cdot \ln x = \frac{\ln x}{\ln a} \tag{5}$$

We can derive this equation from Equation (3):

$$a^{\log_a (x)} = x \qquad \text{Eq. (3)}$$
$$\ln a^{\log_a (x)} = \ln x \qquad \text{Take the natural logarithm of both sides.}$$
$$\log_a (x) \cdot \ln a = \ln x \qquad \text{The Power Rule in Theorem 2}$$
$$\log_a x = \frac{\ln x}{\ln a} \qquad \text{Solve for } \log_a x.$$

For example,

$$\log_{10} 2 = \frac{\ln 2}{\ln 10} \approx \frac{0.69315}{2.30259} \approx 0.30103$$

The arithmetic rules satisfied by $\log_a x$ are the same as the ones for $\ln x$ (Theorem 2). These rules, given in Table 7.2, can be proved by dividing the corresponding rules for the natural logarithm function by $\ln a$. For example,

$$\ln xy = \ln x + \ln y \qquad \text{Rule 1 for natural logarithms} \ldots$$
$$\frac{\ln xy}{\ln a} = \frac{\ln x}{\ln a} + \frac{\ln y}{\ln a} \qquad \ldots \text{divided by } \ln a \ldots$$
$$\log_a xy = \log_a x + \log_a y. \qquad \ldots \text{gives Rule 1 for base } a \text{ logarithms.}$$

Derivatives and Integrals Involving $\log_a x$

To find derivatives or integrals involving base a logarithms, we convert them to natural logarithms.

If u is a positive differentiable function of x, then

$$\frac{d}{dx} (\log_a u) = \frac{d}{dx} \left(\frac{\ln u}{\ln a} \right) = \frac{1}{\ln a} \frac{d}{dx} (\ln u) = \frac{1}{\ln a} \cdot \frac{1}{u} \frac{du}{dx}.$$

$$\frac{d}{dx} (\log_a u) = \frac{1}{\ln a} \cdot \frac{1}{u} \frac{du}{dx}$$

TABLE 7.2 Rules for base a logarithms

For any numbers $x > 0$ and $y > 0$,

1. *Product Rule:*
   $\log_a xy = \log_a x + \log_a y$

2. *Quotient Rule:*
   $\log_a \dfrac{x}{y} = \log_a x - \log_a y$

3. *Reciprocal Rule:*
   $\log_a \dfrac{1}{y} = -\log_a y$

4. *Power Rule:*
   $\log_a x^y = y \log_a x$

EXAMPLE 5

(a) $\dfrac{d}{dx} \log_{10}(3x + 1) = \dfrac{1}{\ln 10} \cdot \dfrac{1}{3x + 1} \dfrac{d}{dx}(3x + 1) = \dfrac{3}{(\ln 10)(3x + 1)}$

(b) $\displaystyle\int \dfrac{\log_2 x}{x}\, dx = \dfrac{1}{\ln 2}\int \dfrac{\ln x}{x}\, dx$ $\qquad \log_2 x = \dfrac{\ln x}{\ln 2}$

$\qquad\qquad = \dfrac{1}{\ln 2}\displaystyle\int u\, du$ $\qquad u = \ln x, \quad du = \dfrac{1}{x} dx$

$\qquad\qquad = \dfrac{1}{\ln 2}\dfrac{u^2}{2} + C = \dfrac{1}{\ln 2}\dfrac{(\ln x)^2}{2} + C = \dfrac{(\ln x)^2}{2 \ln 2} + C$ ∎

Indeterminate Powers

Limits that lead to the indeterminate forms 1^∞, 0^0, and ∞^0 can sometimes be handled by first taking the logarithm of the function. We use l'Hôpital's Rule to find the limit of the logarithm expression and then exponentiate the result to find the original function limit. This procedure is formulated as follows.

> If $\lim_{x \to a} \ln f(x) = L$, then
> $$\lim_{x \to a} f(x) = \lim_{x \to a} e^{\ln f(x)} = e^L.$$
> Here a may be either finite or infinite.

EXAMPLE 6 Working with the Indeterminate Form 1^∞

Apply l'Hôpital's Rule to show that $\lim_{x \to 0^+}(1 + x)^{1/x} = e$.

Solution The limit leads to the indeterminate form 1^∞. We let $f(x) = (1 + x)^{1/x}$ and find $\lim_{x \to 0^+} \ln f(x)$. Since

$$\ln f(x) = \ln(1 + x)^{1/x} = \dfrac{1}{x}\ln(1 + x),$$

l'Hôpital's Rule now applies to give

$$\lim_{x \to 0^+} \ln f(x) = \lim_{x \to 0^+} \dfrac{\ln(1 + x)}{x} \qquad \dfrac{0}{0}$$

$$= \lim_{x \to 0^+} \dfrac{\dfrac{1}{1 + x}}{1}$$

$$= \dfrac{1}{1} = 1.$$

Therefore,

$$\lim_{x \to 0^+}(1 + x)^{1/x} = \lim_{x \to 0^+} f(x) = \lim_{x \to 0^+} e^{\ln f(x)} = e^1 = e.$$ ∎

EXAMPLE 7 An Indeterminant Form ∞^0

Find $\lim_{x \to \infty} x^{1/x}$.

Solution   The limit leads to the indeterminate form ∞^0. We let $f(x) = x^{1/x}$ and find $\lim_{x \to \infty} \ln f(x)$. Since

$$\ln f(x) = \ln x^{1/x} = \frac{\ln x}{x},$$

l'Hôpital's Rule gives

$$\lim_{x \to \infty} \ln f(x) = \lim_{x \to \infty} \frac{\ln x}{x} \qquad \frac{\infty}{\infty}$$

$$= \lim_{x \to \infty} \frac{1/x}{1}$$

$$= \frac{0}{1} = 0.$$

Therefore,

$$\lim_{x \to \infty} x^{1/x} = \lim_{x \to \infty} f(x) = \lim_{x \to \infty} e^{\ln f(x)} = e^0 = 1. \qquad \blacksquare$$

EXERCISES 7.4

Algebraic Calculations With a^x and $\log_a x$

Simplify the expressions in Exercises 1–4.

1. a. $5^{\log_5 7}$ **b.** $8^{\log_8 \sqrt{2}}$ **c.** $1.3^{\log_{1.3} 75}$

d. $\log_4 16$ **e.** $\log_3 \sqrt{3}$ **f.** $\log_4 \left(\dfrac{1}{4}\right)$

2. a. $2^{\log_2 3}$ **b.** $10^{\log_{10}(1/2)}$ **c.** $\pi^{\log_\pi 7}$

d. $\log_{11} 121$ **e.** $\log_{121} 11$ **f.** $\log_3 \left(\dfrac{1}{9}\right)$

3. a. $2^{\log_4 x}$ **b.** $9^{\log_3 x}$ **c.** $\log_2 (e^{(\ln 2)(\sin x)})$

4. a. $25^{\log_5 (3x^2)}$ **b.** $\log_e (e^x)$ **c.** $\log_4 (2^{e^x \sin x})$

Express the ratios in Exercises 5 and 6 as ratios of natural logarithms and simplify.

5. a. $\dfrac{\log_2 x}{\log_3 x}$ **b.** $\dfrac{\log_2 x}{\log_8 x}$ **c.** $\dfrac{\log_x a}{\log_{x^2} a}$

6. a. $\dfrac{\log_9 x}{\log_3 x}$ **b.** $\dfrac{\log_{\sqrt{10}} x}{\log_{\sqrt{2}} x}$ **c.** $\dfrac{\log_a b}{\log_b a}$

Solve the equations in Exercises 7–10 for x.

7. $3^{\log_3 (7)} + 2^{\log_2 (5)} = 5^{\log_5 (x)}$

8. $8^{\log_8 (3)} - e^{\ln 5} = x^2 - 7^{\log_7 (3x)}$

9. $3^{\log_3 (x^2)} = 5e^{\ln x} - 3 \cdot 10^{\log_{10} (2)}$

10. $\ln e + 4^{-2 \log_4 (x)} = \dfrac{1}{x} \log_{10} (100)$

Derivatives

In Exercises 11–38, find the derivative of y with respect to the given independent variable.

11. $y = 2^x$ **12.** $y = 3^{-x}$

13. $y = 5^{\sqrt{s}}$ **14.** $y = 2^{(s^2)}$

15. $y = x^\pi$ **16.** $y = t^{1-e}$

17. $y = (\cos \theta)^{\sqrt{2}}$ **18.** $y = (\ln \theta)^\pi$

19. $y = 7^{\sec \theta} \ln 7$ **20.** $y = 3^{\tan \theta} \ln 3$

21. $y = 2^{\sin 3t}$ **22.** $y = 5^{-\cos 2t}$

23. $y = \log_2 5\theta$ **24.** $y = \log_3 (1 + \theta \ln 3)$

25. $y = \log_4 x + \log_4 x^2$ **26.** $y = \log_{25} e^x - \log_5 \sqrt{x}$

27. $y = \log_2 r \cdot \log_4 r$ **28.** $y = \log_3 r \cdot \log_9 r$

29. $y = \log_3 \left(\left(\dfrac{x+1}{x-1}\right)^{\ln 3}\right)$ **30.** $y = \log_5 \sqrt{\left(\dfrac{7x}{3x+2}\right)^{\ln 5}}$

31. $y = \theta \sin (\log_7 \theta)$ **32.** $y = \log_7 \left(\dfrac{\sin \theta \cos \theta}{e^\theta 2^\theta}\right)$

33. $y = \log_5 e^x$ **34.** $y = \log_2 \left(\dfrac{x^2 e^2}{2\sqrt{x+1}}\right)$

35. $y = 3^{\log_2 t}$ **36.** $y = 3 \log_8 (\log_2 t)$

37. $y = \log_2 (8t^{\ln 2})$ **38.** $y = t \log_3 \left(e^{(\sin t)(\ln 3)}\right)$

Logarithmic Differentiation

In Exercises 39–46, use logarithmic differentiation to find the derivative of y with respect to the given independent variable.

39. $y = (x + 1)^x$ **40.** $y = x^{(x+1)}$

41. $y = (\sqrt{t})^t$ **42.** $y = t^{\sqrt{t}}$

43. $y = (\sin x)^x$ **44.** $y = x^{\sin x}$

45. $y = x^{\ln x}$ **46.** $y = (\ln x)^{\ln x}$

Integration

Evaluate the integrals in Exercises 47–56.

47. $\displaystyle \int 5^x \, dx$ **48.** $\displaystyle \int (1.3)^x \, dx$

49. $\displaystyle\int_0^1 2^{-\theta} \, d\theta$

50. $\displaystyle\int_{-2}^0 5^{-\theta} \, d\theta$

51. $\displaystyle\int_1^{\sqrt{2}} x 2^{(x^2)} \, dx$

52. $\displaystyle\int_1^4 \frac{2^{\sqrt{x}}}{\sqrt{x}} \, dx$

53. $\displaystyle\int_0^{\pi/2} 7^{\cos t} \sin t \, dt$

54. $\displaystyle\int_0^{\pi/4} \left(\frac{1}{3}\right)^{\tan t} \sec^2 t \, dt$

55. $\displaystyle\int_2^4 x^{2x}(1 + \ln x) \, dx$

56. $\displaystyle\int_1^2 \frac{2^{\ln x}}{x} \, dx$

Evaluate the integrals in Exercises 57–60.

57. $\displaystyle\int 3x^{\sqrt{3}} \, dx$

58. $\displaystyle\int x^{\sqrt{2}-1} \, dx$

59. $\displaystyle\int_0^3 (\sqrt{2} + 1)x^{\sqrt{2}} \, dx$

60. $\displaystyle\int_1^e x^{(\ln 2)-1} \, dx$

Evaluate the integrals in Exercises 61–70.

61. $\displaystyle\int \frac{\log_{10} x}{x} \, dx$

62. $\displaystyle\int_1^4 \frac{\log_2 x}{x} \, dx$

63. $\displaystyle\int_1^4 \frac{\ln 2 \log_2 x}{x} \, dx$

64. $\displaystyle\int_1^e \frac{2 \ln 10 \log_{10} x}{x} \, dx$

65. $\displaystyle\int_0^2 \frac{\log_2 (x + 2)}{x + 2} \, dx$

66. $\displaystyle\int_{1/10}^{10} \frac{\log_{10} (10x)}{x} \, dx$

67. $\displaystyle\int_0^9 \frac{2 \log_{10} (x + 1)}{x + 1} \, dx$

68. $\displaystyle\int_2^3 \frac{2 \log_2 (x - 1)}{x - 1} \, dx$

69. $\displaystyle\int \frac{dx}{x \log_{10} x}$

70. $\displaystyle\int \frac{dx}{x(\log_8 x)^2}$

Evaluate the integrals in Exercises 71–74.

71. $\displaystyle\int_1^{\ln x} \frac{1}{t} \, dt, \quad x > 1$

72. $\displaystyle\int_1^{e^x} \frac{1}{t} \, dt$

73. $\displaystyle\int_1^{1/x} \frac{1}{t} \, dt, \quad x > 0$

74. $\displaystyle\frac{1}{\ln a}\int_1^x \frac{1}{t} \, dt, \quad x > 0$

Theory and Applications

75. Find the area of the region between the curve $y = 2x/(1 + x^2)$ and the interval $-2 \le x \le 2$ of the x-axis.

76. Find the area of the region between the curve $y = 2^{1-x}$ and the interval $-1 \le x \le 1$ of the x-axis.

77. Blood pH The pH of human blood normally falls between 7.37 and 7.44. Find the corresponding bounds for $[H_3O^+]$.

78. Brain fluid pH The cerebrospinal fluid in the brain has a hydronium ion concentration of about $[H_3O^+] = 4.8 \times 10^{-8}$ moles per liter. What is the pH?

79. Audio amplifiers By what factor k do you have to multiply the intensity of I of the sound from your audio amplifier to add 10 dB to the sound level?

80. Audio amplifiers You multiplied the intensity of the sound of your audio system by a factor of 10. By how many decibels did this increase the sound level?

81. In any solution, the product of the hydronium ion concentration $[H_3O^+]$ (moles/L) and the hydroxyl ion concentration $[OH^-]$ (moles/L) is about 10^{-14}.

   a. What value of $[H_3O^+]$ minimizes the sum of the concentrations, $S = [H_3O^+] + [OH^-]$? (*Hint:* Change notation. Let $x = [H_3O^+]$.)

   b. What is the pH of a solution in which S has this minimum value?

   c. What ratio of $[H_3O^+]$ to $[OH^-]$ minimizes S?

82. Could $\log_a b$ possibly equal $1/\log_b a$? Give reasons for your answer.

T **83.** The equation $x^2 = 2^x$ has three solutions: $x = 2, x = 4$, and one other. Estimate the third solution as accurately as you can by graphing.

T **84.** Could $x^{\ln 2}$ possibly be the same as $2^{\ln x}$ for $x > 0$? Graph the two functions and explain what you see.

85. The linearization of 2^x

   a. Find the linearization of $f(x) = 2^x$ at $x = 0$. Then round its coefficients to two decimal places.

   T **b.** Graph the linearization and function together for $-3 \le x \le 3$ and $-1 \le x \le 1$.

86. The linearization of $\log_3 x$

   a. Find the linearization of $f(x) = \log_3 x$ at $x = 3$. Then round its coefficients to two decimal places.

   T **b.** Graph the linearization and function together in the window $0 \le x \le 8$ and $2 \le x \le 4$.

Calculations with Other Bases

T **87.** Most scientific calculators have keys for $\log_{10} x$ and $\ln x$. To find logarithms to other bases, we use the Equation (5), $\log_a x = (\ln x)/(\ln a)$.

   Find the following logarithms to five decimal places.

   a. $\log_3 8$ **b.** $\log_7 0.5$

   c. $\log_{20} 17$ **d.** $\log_{0.5} 7$

   e. $\ln x$, given that $\log_{10} x = 2.3$

   f. $\ln x$, given that $\log_2 x = 1.4$

   g. $\ln x$, given that $\log_2 x = -1.5$

   h. $\ln x$, given that $\log_{10} x = -0.7$

88. Conversion factors

   a. Show that the equation for converting base 10 logarithms to base 2 logarithms is

   $$\log_2 x = \frac{\ln 10}{\ln 2} \log_{10} x.$$

   b. Show that the equation for converting base a logarithms to base b logarithms is

   $$\log_b x = \frac{\ln a}{\ln b} \log_a x.$$

89. Orthogonal families of curves   Prove that all curves in the family

$$y = -\frac{1}{2}x^2 + k$$

(k any constant) are perpendicular to all curves in the family $y = \ln x + c$ (c any constant) at their points of intersection. (See the accompanying figure.)

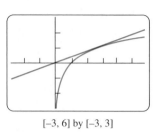

[-3, 6] by [-3, 3]

b. Give an argument based on the graphs of $y = \ln x$ and the tangent line to explain why $\ln x < x/e$ for all positive $x \neq e$.

c. Show that $\ln(x^e) < x$ for all positive $x \neq e$.

d. Conclude that $x^e < e^x$ for all positive $x \neq e$.

e. So which is bigger, π^e or e^π?

T 90. Which is bigger, π^e or e^π?   Calculators have taken some of the mystery out of this once-challenging question. (Go ahead and check; you will see that it is a surprisingly close call.) You can answer the question without a calculator, though.

a. Find an equation for the line through the origin tangent to the graph of $y = \ln x$.

Find the limits in Exercise 91–100.

91. $\displaystyle\lim_{x \to 1^+} x^{1/(1-x)}$

92. $\displaystyle\lim_{x \to 1^+} x^{1/(x-1)}$

93. $\displaystyle\lim_{x \to \infty} (\ln x)^{1/x}$

94. $\displaystyle\lim_{x \to e^+} (\ln x)^{1/(x-e)}$

95. $\displaystyle\lim_{x \to 0^+} x^{-1/\ln x}$

96. $\displaystyle\lim_{x \to \infty} x^{1/\ln x}$

97. $\displaystyle\lim_{x \to \infty} (1 + 2x)^{1/(2 \ln x)}$

98. $\displaystyle\lim_{x \to 0} (e^x + x)^{1/x}$

99. $\displaystyle\lim_{x \to 0^+} x^x$

100. $\displaystyle\lim_{x \to 0^+} \left(1 + \frac{1}{x}\right)^x$

7.5 Exponential Growth and Decay

Exponential functions increase or decrease very rapidly with changes in the independent variable. They describe growth or decay in a wide variety of natural and industrial situations. The variety of models based on these functions partly accounts for their importance.

The Law of Exponential Change

In modeling many real-world situations, a quantity y increases or decreases at a rate proportional to its size at a given time t. Examples of such quantities include the amount of a decaying radioactive material, funds earning interest in a bank account, the size of a population, and the temperature difference between a hot cup of coffee and the room in which it sits. Such quantities change according to the *law of exponential change*, which we derive in this section.

   If the amount present at time $t = 0$ is called y_0, then we can find y as a function of t by solving the following initial value problem:

Differential equation: $\dfrac{dy}{dt} = ky$

Initial condition: $y = y_0$ when $t = 0$.

(1)

If y is positive and increasing, then k is positive, and we use Equation (1) to say that the rate of growth is proportional to what has already been accumulated. If y is positive and decreasing, then k is negative, and we use Equation (1) to say that the rate of decay is proportional to the amount still left.

We see right away that the constant function $y = 0$ is a solution of Equation (1) if $y_0 = 0$. To find the nonzero solutions, we divide Equation (1) by y:

$$\frac{1}{y} \cdot \frac{dy}{dt} = k$$

$$\int \frac{1}{y}\frac{dy}{dt}\, dt = \int k\, dt \qquad \text{Integrate with respect to } t;$$

$$\ln |y| = kt + C \qquad \int (1/u)\, du = \ln |u| + C.$$

$$|y| = e^{kt+C} \qquad \text{Exponentiate.}$$

$$|y| = e^{C} \cdot e^{kt} \qquad e^{a+b} = e^{a} \cdot e^{b}$$

$$y = \pm e^{C} e^{kt} \qquad \text{If } |y| = r, \text{ then } y = \pm r.$$

$$y = Ae^{kt}. \qquad \begin{array}{l} A \text{ is a shorter name for} \\ \pm e^{C}. \end{array}$$

By allowing A to take on the value 0 in addition to all possible values $\pm e^{C}$, we can include the solution $y = 0$ in the formula.

We find the value of A for the initial value problem by solving for A when $y = y_0$ and $t = 0$:

$$y_0 = Ae^{k \cdot 0} = A.$$

The solution of the initial value problem is therefore $y = y_0 e^{kt}$.

Quantities changing in this way are said to undergo **exponential growth** if $k > 0$, and **exponential decay** if $k < 0$.

The Law of Exponential Change

$$y = y_0 e^{kt} \qquad\qquad (2)$$

Growth: $k > 0$ Decay: $k < 0$

The number k is the **rate constant** of the equation.

The derivation of Equation (2) shows that the only functions that are their own derivatives are constant multiples of the exponential function.

Unlimited Population Growth

Strictly speaking, the number of individuals in a population (of people, plants, foxes, or bacteria, for example) is a discontinuous function of time because it takes on discrete values. However, when the number of individuals becomes large enough, the population can be approximated by a continuous function. Differentiability of the approximating function is another reasonable hypothesis in many settings, allowing for the use of calculus to model and predict population sizes.

If we assume that the proportion of reproducing individuals remains constant and assume a constant fertility, then at any instant t the birth rate is proportional to the number $y(t)$ of individuals present. Let's assume, too, that the death rate of the population is stable and proportional to $y(t)$. If, further, we neglect departures and arrivals, the growth rate

dy/dt is the birth rate minus the death rate, which is the difference of the two proportionalities under our assumptions. In other words, $dy/dt = ky$, so that $y = y_0 e^{kt}$, where y_0 is the size of the population at time $t = 0$. As with all kinds of growth, there may be limitations imposed by the surrounding environment, but we will not go into these here. (This situation is analyzed in Section 9.5.)

In the following example we assume this population model to look at how the number of individuals infected by a disease within a given population decreases as the disease is appropriately treated.

EXAMPLE 1   Reducing the Cases of an Infectious Disease

One model for the way diseases die out when properly treated assumes that the rate dy/dt at which the number of infected people changes is proportional to the number y. The number of people cured is proportional to the number that have the disease. Suppose that in the course of any given year the number of cases of a disease is reduced by 20%. If there are 10,000 cases today, how many years will it take to reduce the number to 1000?

Solution   We use the equation $y = y_0 e^{kt}$. There are three things to find: the value of y_0, the value of k, and the time t when $y = 1000$.

The value of y_0. We are free to count time beginning anywhere we want. If we count from today, then $y = 10,000$ when $t = 0$, so $y_0 = 10,000$. Our equation is now

$$y = 10,000 e^{kt}. \tag{3}$$

The value of k. When $t = 1$ year, the number of cases will be 80% of its present value, or 8000. Hence,

$$8000 = 10,000 e^{k(1)} \qquad \text{Eq. (3) with } t = 1 \text{ and } y = 8000$$

$$e^k = 0.8$$

$$\ln(e^k) = \ln 0.8 \qquad \text{Logs of both sides}$$

$$k = \ln 0.8 < 0.$$

At any given time t,

$$y = 10,000 e^{(\ln 0.8)t}. \tag{4}$$

The value of t that makes $y = 1000$. We set y equal to 1000 in Equation (4) and solve for t:

$$1000 = 10,000 e^{(\ln 0.8)t}$$

$$e^{(\ln 0.8)t} = 0.1$$

$$(\ln 0.8)t = \ln 0.1 \qquad \text{Logs of both sides}$$

$$t = \frac{\ln 0.1}{\ln 0.8} \approx 10.32 \text{ years}.$$

It will take a little more than 10 years to reduce the number of cases to 1000.   ■

Continuously Compounded Interest

If you invest an amount A_0 of money at a fixed annual interest rate r (expressed as a decimal) and if interest is added to your account k times a year, the formula for the amount of money you will have at the end of t years is

$$A_t = A_0 \left(1 + \frac{r}{k}\right)^{kt}. \tag{5}$$

The interest might be added ("compounded," bankers say) monthly ($k = 12$), weekly ($k = 52$), daily ($k = 365$), or even more frequently, say by the hour or by the minute. By taking the limit as interest is compounded more and more often, we arrive at the following formula for the amount after t years,

$$\lim_{k \to \infty} A_t = \lim_{k \to \infty} A_0 \left(1 + \frac{r}{k} \right)^{kt}$$

$$= A_0 \lim_{k \to \infty} \left(1 + \frac{r}{k} \right)^{\frac{k}{r} \cdot rt}$$

$$= A_0 \left[\lim_{\frac{r}{k} \to 0} \left(1 + \frac{r}{k} \right)^{\frac{k}{r}} \right]^{rt} \qquad \text{As } k \to \infty, \frac{r}{k} \to 0$$

$$= A_0 \left[\lim_{x \to 0} (1 + x)^{1/x} \right]^{rt} \qquad \text{Substitute } x = \frac{r}{k}$$

$$= A_0 e^{rt} \qquad \text{Theorem 4}$$

The resulting formula for the amount of money in your account after t years is

$$A(t) = A_0 e^{rt}. \qquad (6)$$

Interest paid according to this formula is said to be **compounded continuously**. The number r is called the **continuous interest rate**. The amount of money after t years is calculated with the law of exponential change given in Equation (6).

EXAMPLE 2   A Savings Account

Suppose you deposit \$621 in a bank account that pays 6% compounded continuously. How much money will you have 8 years later?

Solution   We use Equation (6) with $A_0 = 621$, $r = 0.06$, and $t = 8$:

$$A(8) = 621e^{(0.06)(8)} = 621e^{0.48} = 1003.58 \qquad \text{Nearest cent}$$

Had the bank paid interest quarterly ($k = 4$ in Equation 5), the amount in your account would have been \$1000.01. Thus the effect of continuous compounding, as compared with quarterly compounding, has been an addition of \$3.57. A bank might decide it would be worth this additional amount to be able to advertise, "We compound interest every second, night and day—better yet, we compound the interest continuously." ■

Radioactivity

Some atoms are unstable and can spontaneously emit mass or radiation. This process is called **radioactive decay**, and an element whose atoms go spontaneously through this process is called **radioactive**. Sometimes when an atom emits some of its mass through this process of radioactivity, the remainder of the atom re-forms to make an atom of some new element. For example, radioactive carbon-14 decays into nitrogen; radium, through a number of intermediate radioactive steps, decays into lead.

Experiments have shown that at any given time the rate at which a radioactive element decays (as measured by the number of nuclei that change per unit time) is approximately proportional to the number of radioactive nuclei present. Thus, the decay of a radioactive element is described by the equation $dy/dt = -ky$, $k > 0$. It is conventional to use

For radon-222 gas, t is measured in days and $k = 0.18$. For radium-226, which used to be painted on watch dials to make them glow at night (a dangerous practice), t is measured in years and $k = 4.3 \times 10^{-4}$.

$-k(k > 0)$ here instead of $k(k < 0)$ to emphasize that y is decreasing. If y_0 is the number of radioactive nuclei present at time zero, the number still present at any later time t will be

$$y = y_0 e^{-kt}, \qquad k > 0.$$

EXAMPLE 3   Half-Life of a Radioactive Element

The **half-life** of a radioactive element is the time required for half of the radioactive nuclei present in a sample to decay. It is an interesting fact that the half-life is a constant that does not depend on the number of radioactive nuclei initially present in the sample, but only on the radioactive substance.

To see why, let y_0 be the number of radioactive nuclei initially present in the sample. Then the number y present at any later time t will be $y = y_0 e^{-kt}$. We seek the value of t at which the number of radioactive nuclei present equals half the original number:

$$y_0 e^{-kt} = \frac{1}{2} y_0$$

$$e^{-kt} = \frac{1}{2}$$

$$-kt = \ln \frac{1}{2} = -\ln 2 \qquad \text{Reciprocal Rule for logarithms}$$

$$t = \frac{\ln 2}{k}$$

This value of t is the half-life of the element. It depends only on the value of k; the number y_0 does not enter in.

$$\text{Half-life} = \frac{\ln 2}{k} \qquad\qquad (7)$$

■

EXAMPLE 4   Half-Life of Polonium-210

The effective radioactive lifetime of polonium-210 is so short we measure it in days rather than years. The number of radioactive atoms remaining after t days in a sample that starts with y_0 radioactive atoms is

$$y = y_0 e^{-5 \times 10^{-3} t}.$$

Find the element's half-life.

Solution

$$\text{Half-life} = \frac{\ln 2}{k} \qquad \text{Eq. (7)}$$

$$= \frac{\ln 2}{5 \times 10^{-3}} \qquad \text{The } k \text{ from polonium's decay equation}$$

$$\approx 139 \text{ days}$$

■

EXAMPLE 5   Carbon-14 Dating

The decay of radioactive elements can sometimes be used to date events from the Earth's past. In a living organism, the ratio of radioactive carbon, carbon-14, to ordinary carbon stays fairly constant during the lifetime of the organism, being approximately equal to the ratio in the organism's surroundings at the time. After the organism's death, however, no new carbon is ingested, and the proportion of carbon-14 in the organism's remains decreases as the carbon-14 decays.

Scientists who do carbon-14 dating use a figure of 5700 years for its half-life (more about carbon-14 dating in the exercises). Find the age of a sample in which 10% of the radioactive nuclei originally present have decayed.

Solution   We use the decay equation $y = y_0 e^{-kt}$. There are two things to find: the value of k and the value of t when y is $0.9y_0$ (90% of the radioactive nuclei are still present). That is, find t when $y_0 e^{-kt} = 0.9y_0$, or $e^{-kt} = 0.9$.

The value of k. We use the half-life Equation (7):

$$k = \frac{\ln 2}{\text{half-life}} = \frac{\ln 2}{5700} \qquad (\text{about } 1.2 \times 10^{-4})$$

The value of t that makes $e^{-kt} = 0.9$:

$$e^{-kt} = 0.9$$

$$e^{-(\ln 2/5700)t} = 0.9$$

$$-\frac{\ln 2}{5700} t = \ln 0.9 \qquad\qquad \text{Logs of both sides}$$

$$t = -\frac{5700 \ln 0.9}{\ln 2} \approx 866 \text{ years}.$$

The sample is about 866 years old. ∎

Heat Transfer: Newton's Law of Cooling

Hot soup left in a tin cup cools to the temperature of the surrounding air. A hot silver ingot immersed in a large tub of water cools to the temperature of the surrounding water. In situations like these, the rate at which an object's temperature is changing at any given time is roughly proportional to the difference between its temperature and the temperature of the surrounding medium. This observation is called *Newton's law of cooling*, although it applies to warming as well, and there is an equation for it.

If H is the temperature of the object at time t and H_S is the constant surrounding temperature, then the differential equation is

$$\frac{dH}{dt} = -k(H - H_S). \qquad (8)$$

If we substitute y for $(H - H_S)$, then

$$\frac{dy}{dt} = \frac{d}{dt}(H - H_S) = \frac{dH}{dt} - \frac{d}{dt}(H_S)$$

$$= \frac{dH}{dt} - 0 \qquad\qquad H_S \text{ is a constant.}$$

$$= \frac{dH}{dt}$$

$$= -k(H - H_S) \qquad\qquad \text{Eq. (8)}$$

$$= -ky. \qquad\qquad H - H_S = y.$$

Now we know that the solution of $dy/dt = -ky$ is $y = y_0 e^{-kt}$, where $y(0) = y_0$. Substituting $(H - H_S)$ for y, this says that

$$H - H_S = (H_0 - H_S)e^{-kt}, \tag{9}$$

where H_0 is the temperature at $t = 0$. This is the equation for Newton's Law of Cooling.

EXAMPLE 6   Cooling a Hard-Boiled Egg

A hard-boiled egg at 98°C is put in a sink of 18°C water. After 5 min, the egg's temperature is 38°C. Assuming that the water has not warmed appreciably, how much longer will it take the egg to reach 20°C?

Solution   We find how long it would take the egg to cool from 98°C to 20°C and subtract the 5 min that have already elapsed. Using Equation (9) with $H_S = 18$ and $H_0 = 98$, the egg's temperature t min after it is put in the sink is

$$H = 18 + (98 - 18)e^{-kt} = 18 + 80e^{-kt}.$$

To find k, we use the information that $H = 38$ when $t = 5$:

$$38 = 18 + 80e^{-5k}$$

$$e^{-5k} = \frac{1}{4}$$

$$-5k = \ln\frac{1}{4} = -\ln 4$$

$$k = \frac{1}{5}\ln 4 = 0.2\ln 4 \qquad \text{(about 0.28)}.$$

The egg's temperature at time t is $H = 18 + 80e^{-(0.2\ln 4)t}$. Now find the time t when $H = 20$:

$$20 = 18 + 80e^{-(0.2\ln 4)t}$$

$$80e^{-(0.2\ln 4)t} = 2$$

$$e^{-(0.2\ln 4)t} = \frac{1}{40}$$

$$-(0.2\ln 4)t = \ln\frac{1}{40} = -\ln 40$$

$$t = \frac{\ln 40}{0.2\ln 4} \approx 13 \text{ min}.$$

The egg's temperature will reach 20°C about 13 min after it is put in the water to cool. Since it took 5 min to reach 38°C, it will take about 8 min more to reach 20°C.   ∎

EXERCISES 7.5

The answers to most of the following exercises are in terms of logarithms and exponentials. A calculator can be helpful, enabling you to express the answers in decimal form.

1. **Human evolution continues**   The analysis of tooth shrinkage by C. Loring Brace and colleagues at the University of Michi-gan's Museum of Anthropology indicates that human tooth size is continuing to decrease and that the evolutionary process did not come to a halt some 30,000 years ago as many scientists contend. In northern Europeans, for example, tooth size reduction now has a rate of 1% per 1000 years.

a. If t represents time in years and y represents tooth size, use the condition that $y = 0.99y_0$ when $t = 1000$ to find the value of k in the equation $y = y_0e^{kt}$. Then use this value of k to answer the following questions.

b. In about how many years will human teeth be 90% of their present size?

c. What will be our descendants' tooth size 20,000 years from now (as a percentage of our present tooth size)?

(*Source: LSA Magazine*, Spring 1989, Vol. 12, No. 2, p. 19, Ann Arbor, MI.)

2. Atmospheric pressure The earth's atmospheric pressure p is often modeled by assuming that the rate dp/dh at which p changes with the altitude h above sea level is proportional to p. Suppose that the pressure at sea level is 1013 millibars (about 14.7 pounds per square inch) and that the pressure at an altitude of 20 km is 90 millibars.

a. Solve the initial value problem

Differential equation: $dp/dh = kp$ (k a constant)
Initial condition: $p = p_0$ when $h = 0$

to express p in terms of h. Determine the values of p_0 and k from the given altitude-pressure data.

b. What is the atmospheric pressure at $h = 50\ \text{km}$?

c. At what altitude does the pressure equal 900 millibars?

3. First-order chemical reactions In some chemical reactions, the rate at which the amount of a substance changes with time is proportional to the amount present. For the change of δ-glucono lactone into gluconic acid, for example,

$$\frac{dy}{dt} = -0.6y$$

when t is measured in hours. If there are 100 grams of δ-glucono lactone present when $t = 0$, how many grams will be left after the first hour?

4. The inversion of sugar The processing of raw sugar has a step called "inversion" that changes the sugar's molecular structure. Once the process has begun, the rate of change of the amount of raw sugar is proportional to the amount of raw sugar remaining. If 1000 kg of raw sugar reduces to 800 kg of raw sugar during the first 10 hours, how much raw sugar will remain after another 14 hours?

5. Working underwater The intensity $L(x)$ of light x feet beneath the surface of the ocean satisfies the differential equation

$$\frac{dL}{dx} = -kL.$$

As a diver, you know from experience that diving to 18 ft in the Caribbean Sea cuts the intensity in half. You cannot work without artificial light when the intensity falls below one-tenth of the surface value. About how deep can you expect to work without artificial light?

6. Voltage in a discharging capacitor Suppose that electricity is draining from a capacitor at a rate that is proportional to the voltage V across its terminals and that, if t is measured in seconds,

$$\frac{dV}{dt} = -\frac{1}{40}V.$$

Solve this equation for V, using V_0 to denote the value of V when $t = 0$. How long will it take the voltage to drop to 10% of its original value?

7. Cholera bacteria Suppose that the bacteria in a colony can grow unchecked, by the law of exponential change. The colony starts with 1 bacterium and doubles every half-hour. How many bacteria will the colony contain at the end of 24 hours? (Under favorable laboratory conditions, the number of cholera bacteria can double every 30 min. In an infected person, many bacteria are destroyed, but this example helps explain why a person who feels well in the morning may be dangerously ill by evening.)

8. Growth of bacteria A colony of bacteria is grown under ideal conditions in a laboratory so that the population increases exponentially with time. At the end of 3 hours there are 10,000 bacteria. At the end of 5 hours there are 40,000. How many bacteria were present initially?

9. The incidence of a disease (*Continuation of Example 1.*) Suppose that in any given year the number of cases can be reduced by 25% instead of 20%.

a. How long will it take to reduce the number of cases to 1000?

b. How long will it take to eradicate the disease, that is, reduce the number of cases to less than 1?

10. The U.S. population The Museum of Science in Boston displays a running total of the U.S. population. On May 11, 1993, the total was increasing at the rate of 1 person every 14 sec. The displayed population figure for 3:45 P.M. that day was 257,313,431.

a. Assuming exponential growth at a constant rate, find the rate constant for the population's growth (people per 365-day year).

b. At this rate, what will the U.S. population be at 3:45 P.M. Boston time on May 11, 2008?

11. Oil depletion Suppose the amount of oil pumped from one of the canyon wells in Whittier, California, decreases at the continuous rate of 10% per year. When will the well's output fall to one-fifth of its present value?

12. Continuous price discounting To encourage buyers to place 100-unit orders, your firm's sales department applies a continuous discount that makes the unit price a function $p(x)$ of the number of units x ordered. The discount decreases the price at the rate of $0.01 per unit ordered. The price per unit for a 100-unit order is $p(100) = \$20.09$.

a. Find $p(x)$ by solving the following initial value problem:

Differential equation: $\dfrac{dp}{dx} = -\dfrac{1}{100}p$
Initial condition: $p(100) = 20.09$.

b. Find the unit price $p(10)$ for a 10-unit order and the unit price $p(90)$ for a 90-unit order.

c. The sales department has asked you to find out if it is discounting so much that the firm's revenue, $r(x) = x \cdot p(x)$, will actually be less for a 100-unit order than, say, for a 90-unit order. Reassure them by showing that r has its maximum value at $x = 100$.

T **d.** Graph the revenue function $r(x) = xp(x)$ for $0 \le x \le 200$.

13. Continuously compounded interest   You have just placed A_0 dollars in a bank account that pays 4% interest, compounded continuously.

a. How much money will you have in the account in 5 years?

b. How long will it take your money to double? To triple?

14. John Napier's question   John Napier (1550–1617), the Scottish laird who invented logarithms, was the first person to answer the question, What happens if you invest an amount of money at 100% interest, compounded continuously?

a. What does happen?

b. How long does it take to triple your money?

c. How much can you earn in a year?

Give reasons for your answers.

15. Benjamin Franklin's will   The Franklin Technical Institute of Boston owes its existence to a provision in a codicil to Benjamin Franklin's will. In part the codicil reads:

> I wish to be useful even after my Death, if possible, in forming and advancing other young men that may be serviceable to their Country in both Boston and Philadelphia. To this end I devote Two thousand Pounds Sterling, which I give, one thousand thereof to the Inhabitants of the Town of Boston in Massachusetts, and the other thousand to the inhabitants of the City of Philadelphia, in Trust and for the Uses, Interests and Purposes hereinafter mentioned and declared.

Franklin's plan was to lend money to young apprentices at 5% interest with the provision that each borrower should pay each year along

> ... with the yearly Interest, one tenth part of the Principal, which sums of Principal and Interest shall be again let to fresh Borrowers.... If this plan is executed and succeeds as projected without interruption for one hundred Years, the Sum will then be one hundred and thirty-one thousand Pounds of which I would have the Managers of the Donation to the Inhabitants of the Town of Boston, then lay out at their discretion one hundred thousand Pounds in Public Works.... The remaining thirty-one thousand Pounds, I would have continued to be let out on Interest in the manner above directed for another hundred Years.... At the end of this second term if no unfortunate accident has prevented the operation the sum will be Four Millions and Sixty-one Thousand Pounds.

It was not always possible to find as many borrowers as Franklin had planned, but the managers of the trust did the best they could. At the end of 100 years from the reception of the Franklin gift, in January 1894, the fund had grown from 1000 pounds to almost exactly 90,000 pounds. In 100 years the original capital had multiplied about 90 times instead of the 131 times Franklin had imagined.

What rate of interest, compounded continuously for 100 years, would have multiplied Benjamin Franklin's original capital by 90?

16. (*Continuation of Exercise 15.*) In Benjamin Franklin's estimate that the original 1000 pounds would grow to 131,000 in 100 years, he was using an annual rate of 5% and compounding once each year. What rate of interest per year when compounded continuously for 100 years would multiply the original amount by 131?

17. Radon-222   The decay equation for radon-222 gas is known to be $y = y_0 e^{-0.18t}$, with t in days. About how long will it take the radon in a sealed sample of air to fall to 90% of its original value?

18. Polonium-210   The half-life of polonium is 139 days, but your sample will not be useful to you after 95% of the radioactive nuclei present on the day the sample arrives has disintegrated. For about how many days after the sample arrives will you be able to use the polonium?

19. The mean life of a radioactive nucleus   Physicists using the radioactivity equation $y = y_0 e^{-kt}$ call the number $1/k$ the *mean life* of a radioactive nucleus. The mean life of a radon nucleus is about $1/0.18 = 5.6$ days. The mean life of a carbon-14 nucleus is more than 8000 years. Show that 95% of the radioactive nuclei originally present in a sample will disintegrate within three mean lifetimes, i.e., by time $t = 3/k$. Thus, the mean life of a nucleus gives a quick way to estimate how long the radioactivity of a sample will last.

20. Californium-252   What costs $27 million per gram and can be used to treat brain cancer, analyze coal for its sulfur content, and detect explosives in luggage? The answer is californium-252, a radioactive isotope so rare that only 8 g of it have been made in the western world since its discovery by Glenn Seaborg in 1950. The half-life of the isotope is 2.645 years—long enough for a useful service life and short enough to have a high radioactivity per unit mass. One microgram of the isotope releases 170 million neutrons per second.

a. What is the value of k in the decay equation for this isotope?

b. What is the isotope's mean life? (See Exercise 19.)

c. How long will it take 95% of a sample's radioactive nuclei to disintegrate?

21. Cooling soup   Suppose that a cup of soup cooled from 90°C to 60°C after 10 min in a room whose temperature was 20°C. Use Newton's law of cooling to answer the following questions.

a. How much longer would it take the soup to cool to 35°C?

b. Instead of being left to stand in the room, the cup of 90°C soup is put in a freezer whose temperature is −15°C. How long will it take the soup to cool from 90°C to 35°C?

22. **A beam of unknown temperature** An aluminum beam was brought from the outside cold into a machine shop where the temperature was held at 65°F. After 10 min, the beam warmed to 35°F and after another 10 min it was 50°F. Use Newton's law of cooling to estimate the beam's initial temperature.

23. **Surrounding medium of unknown temperature** A pan of warm water (46°C) was put in a refrigerator. Ten minutes later, the water's temperature was 39°C; 10 min after that, it was 33°C. Use Newton's law of cooling to estimate how cold the refrigerator was.

24. **Silver cooling in air** The temperature of an ingot of silver is 60°C above room temperature right now. Twenty minutes ago, it was 70°C above room temperature. How far above room temperature will the silver be

   a. 15 min from now?

   b. 2 hours from now?

   c. When will the silver be 10°C above room temperature?

25. **The age of Crater Lake** The charcoal from a tree killed in the volcanic eruption that formed Crater Lake in Oregon contained 44.5% of the carbon-14 found in living matter. About how old is Crater Lake?

26. **The sensitivity of carbon-14 dating to measurement** To see the effect of a relatively small error in the estimate of the amount of carbon-14 in a sample being dated, consider this hypothetical situation:

   a. A fossilized bone found in central Illinois in the year A.D. 2000 contains 17% of its original carbon-14 content. Estimate the year the animal died.

   b. Repeat part (a) assuming 18% instead of 17%.

   c. Repeat part (a) assuming 16% instead of 17%.

27. **Art forgery** A painting attributed to Vermeer (1632–1675), which should contain no more than 96.2% of its original carbon-14, contains 99.5% instead. About how old is the forgery?

7.6 Relative Rates of Growth

It is often important in mathematics, computer science, and engineering to compare the rates at which functions of x grow as x becomes large. Exponential functions are important in these comparisons because of their very fast growth, and logarithmic functions because of their very slow growth. In this section we introduce the *little-oh* and *big-oh* notation used to describe the results of these comparisons. We restrict our attention to functions whose values eventually become and remain positive as $x \to \infty$.

Growth Rates of Functions

You may have noticed that exponential functions like 2^x and e^x seem to grow more rapidly as x gets large than do polynomials and rational functions. These exponentials certainly grow more rapidly than x itself, and you can see 2^x outgrowing x^2 as x increases in Figure 7.14. In fact, as $x \to \infty$, the functions 2^x and e^x grow faster than any power of x, even $x^{1,000,000}$ (Exercise 19).

To get a feeling for how rapidly the values of $y = e^x$ grow with increasing x, think of graphing the function on a large blackboard, with the axes scaled in centimeters. At $x = 1$ cm, the graph is $e^1 \approx 3$ cm above the x-axis. At $x = 6$ cm, the graph is $e^6 \approx 403$ cm ≈ 4 m high (it is about to go through the ceiling if it hasn't done so already). At $x = 10$ cm, the graph is $e^{10} \approx 22{,}026$ cm ≈ 220 m high, higher than most buildings. At $x = 24$ cm, the graph is more than halfway to the moon, and at $x = 43$ cm from the origin, the graph is high enough to reach past the sun's closest stellar neighbor, the red dwarf star Proxima Centauri:

$$e^{43} \approx 4.73 \times 10^{18} \text{ cm}$$

$$= 4.73 \times 10^{13} \text{ km}$$

$$\approx 1.58 \times 10^8 \text{ light-seconds}$$

$$\approx 5.0 \text{ light-years}$$

In a vacuum, light travels at 300,000 km/sec.

FIGURE 7.14 The graphs of e^x, 2^x, and x^2.

FIGURE 7.15 Scale drawings of the graphs of e^x and $\ln x$.

The distance to Proxima Centauri is about 4.22 light-years. Yet with $x = 43$ cm from the origin, the graph is still less than 2 feet to the right of the y-axis.

In contrast, logarithmic functions like $y = \log_2 x$ and $y = \ln x$ grow more slowly as $x \to \infty$ than any positive power of x (Exercise 21). With axes scaled in centimeters, you have to go nearly 5 light-years out on the x-axis to find a point where the graph of $y = \ln x$ is even $y = 43$ cm high. See Figure 7.15.

These important comparisons of exponential, polynomial, and logarithmic functions can be made precise by defining what it means for a function $f(x)$ to grow faster than another function $g(x)$ as $x \to \infty$.

DEFINITION Rates of Growth as $x \to \infty$

Let $f(x)$ and $g(x)$ be positive for x sufficiently large.

1. f **grows faster than** g as $x \to \infty$ if

$$\lim_{x \to \infty} \frac{f(x)}{g(x)} = \infty$$

or, equivalently, if

$$\lim_{x \to \infty} \frac{g(x)}{f(x)} = 0.$$

We also say that g **grows slower than** f as $x \to \infty$.

2. f and g **grow at the same rate** as $x \to \infty$ if

$$\lim_{x \to \infty} \frac{f(x)}{g(x)} = L$$

where L is finite and positive.

According to these definitions, $y = 2x$ does not grow faster than $y = x$. The two functions grow at the same rate because

$$\lim_{x \to \infty} \frac{2x}{x} = \lim_{x \to \infty} 2 = 2,$$

which is a finite, nonzero limit. The reason for this apparent disregard of common sense is that we want "f grows faster than g" to mean that for large x-values g is negligible when compared with f.

EXAMPLE 1 Several Useful Comparisons of Growth Rates

(a) e^x grows faster than x^2 as $x \to \infty$ because

$$\lim_{x \to \infty} \frac{e^x}{x^2} = \lim_{x \to \infty} \frac{e^x}{2x} = \lim_{x \to \infty} \frac{e^x}{2} = \infty. \qquad \text{Using l'Hôpital's Rule twice}$$

$$\underbrace{\quad\quad}_{\infty / \infty} \quad \underbrace{\quad\quad}_{\infty / \infty}$$

(b) 3^x grows faster than 2^x as $x \to \infty$ because

$$\lim_{x \to \infty} \frac{3^x}{2^x} = \lim_{x \to \infty} \left(\frac{3}{2}\right)^x = \infty.$$

(c) x^2 grows faster than $\ln x$ as $x \to \infty$, because

$$\lim_{x\to\infty} \frac{x^2}{\ln x} = \lim_{x\to\infty} \frac{2x}{1/x} = \lim_{x\to\infty} 2x^2 = \infty. \qquad \text{l'Hôpital's Rule}$$

(d) $\ln x$ grows slower than x as $x \to \infty$ because

$$\lim_{x\to\infty} \frac{\ln x}{x} = \lim_{x\to\infty} \frac{1/x}{1} \qquad \text{l'Hôpital's Rule}$$

$$= \lim_{x\to\infty} \frac{1}{x} = 0. \qquad\blacksquare$$

EXAMPLE 2   Exponential and Logarithmic Functions with Different Bases

(a) As Example 1b suggests, exponential functions with different bases never grow at the same rate as $x \to \infty$. If $a > b > 0$, then a^x grows faster than b^x. Since $(a/b) > 1$,

$$\lim_{x\to\infty} \frac{a^x}{b^x} = \lim_{x\to\infty} \left(\frac{a}{b}\right)^x = \infty.$$

(b) In contrast to exponential functions, logarithmic functions with different bases a and b always grow at the same rate as $x \to \infty$:

$$\lim_{x\to\infty} \frac{\log_a x}{\log_b x} = \lim_{x\to\infty} \frac{\ln x/\ln a}{\ln x/\ln b} = \frac{\ln b}{\ln a}.$$

The limiting ratio is always finite and never zero. $\qquad\blacksquare$

If f grows at the same rate as g as $x \to \infty$, and g grows at the same rate as h as $x \to \infty$, then f grows at the same rate as h as $x \to \infty$. The reason is that

$$\lim_{x\to\infty} \frac{f}{g} = L_1 \qquad \text{and} \qquad \lim_{x\to\infty} \frac{g}{h} = L_2$$

together imply

$$\lim_{x\to\infty} \frac{f}{h} = \lim_{x\to\infty} \frac{f}{g} \cdot \frac{g}{h} = L_1 L_2.$$

If L_1 and L_2 are finite and nonzero, then so is $L_1 L_2$.

EXAMPLE 3   Functions Growing at the Same Rate

Show that $\sqrt{x^2 + 5}$ and $(2\sqrt{x} - 1)^2$ grow at the same rate as $x \to \infty$.

Solution   We show that the functions grow at the same rate by showing that they both grow at the same rate as the function $g(x) = x$:

$$\lim_{x\to\infty} \frac{\sqrt{x^2 + 5}}{x} = \lim_{x\to\infty} \sqrt{1 + \frac{5}{x^2}} = 1,$$

$$\lim_{x\to\infty} \frac{(2\sqrt{x} - 1)^2}{x} = \lim_{x\to\infty} \left(\frac{2\sqrt{x} - 1}{\sqrt{x}}\right)^2 = \lim_{x\to\infty} \left(2 - \frac{1}{\sqrt{x}}\right)^2 = 4. \qquad\blacksquare$$

Order and Oh-Notation

Here we introduce the "little-oh" and "big-oh" notation invented by number theorists a hundred years ago and now commonplace in mathematical analysis and computer science.

DEFINITION   Little-oh

A function f is **of smaller order than** g as $x \to \infty$ if $\lim\limits_{x \to \infty} \dfrac{f(x)}{g(x)} = 0$. We indicate this by writing $\boldsymbol{f = o(g)}$ ("f is little-oh of g").

Notice that saying $f = o(g)$ as $x \to \infty$ is another way to say that f grows slower than g as $x \to \infty$.

EXAMPLE 4   Using Little-oh Notation

(a) $\ln x = o(x)$ as $x \to \infty$ because $\lim\limits_{x \to \infty} \dfrac{\ln x}{x} = 0$

(b) $x^2 = o(x^3 + 1)$ as $x \to \infty$ because $\lim\limits_{x \to \infty} \dfrac{x^2}{x^3 + 1} = 0$ ∎

DEFINITION   Big-oh

Let $f(x)$ and $g(x)$ be positive for x sufficiently large. Then f is **of at most the order of** g as $x \to \infty$ if there is a positive integer M for which

$$\frac{f(x)}{g(x)} \leq M,$$

for x sufficiently large. We indicate this by writing $\boldsymbol{f = O(g)}$ ("f is big-oh of g").

EXAMPLE 5   Using Big-oh Notation

(a) $x + \sin x = O(x)$ as $x \to \infty$ because $\dfrac{x + \sin x}{x} \leq 2$ for x sufficiently large.

(b) $e^x + x^2 = O(e^x)$ as $x \to \infty$ because $\dfrac{e^x + x^2}{e^x} \to 1$ as $x \to \infty$.

(c) $x = O(e^x)$ as $x \to \infty$ because $\dfrac{x}{e^x} \to 0$ as $x \to \infty$.   ∎

If you look at the definitions again, you will see that $f = o(g)$ implies $f = O(g)$ for functions that are positive for x sufficiently large. Also, if f and g grow at the same rate, then $f = O(g)$ and $g = O(f)$ (Exercise 11).

Sequential vs. Binary Search

Computer scientists often measure the efficiency of an algorithm by counting the number of steps a computer must take to execute the algorithm. There can be significant differences in how efficiently algorithms perform, even if they are designed to accomplish the same task. These differences are often described in big-oh notation. Here is an example.

Webster's Third New International Dictionary lists about 26,000 words that begin with the letter *a*. One way to look up a word, or to learn if it is not there, is to read through the list one word at a time until you either find the word or determine that it is not there. This method, called sequential search, makes no particular use of the words' alphabetical arrangement. You are sure to get an answer, but it might take 26,000 steps.

Another way to find the word or to learn it is not there is to go straight to the middle of the list (give or take a few words). If you do not find the word, then go to the middle of the half that contains it and forget about the half that does not. (You know which half contains it because you know the list is ordered alphabetically.) This method eliminates roughly 13,000 words in a single step. If you do not find the word on the second try, then jump to the middle of the half that contains it. Continue this way until you have either found the word or divided the list in half so many times there are no words left. How many times do you have to divide the list to find the word or learn that it is not there? At most 15, because

$$(26{,}000/2^{15}) < 1.$$

That certainly beats a possible 26,000 steps.

For a list of length *n*, a sequential search algorithm takes on the order of *n* steps to find a word or determine that it is not in the list. A binary search, as the second algorithm is called, takes on the order of $\log_2 n$ steps. The reason is that if $2^{m-1} < n \le 2^m$, then $m - 1 < \log_2 n \le m$, and the number of bisections required to narrow the list to one word will be at most $m = \lceil \log_2 n \rceil$, the integer ceiling for $\log_2 n$.

Big-oh notation provides a compact way to say all this. The number of steps in a sequential search of an ordered list is $O(n)$; the number of steps in a binary search is $O(\log_2 n)$. In our example, there is a big difference between the two (26,000 vs. 15), and the difference can only increase with *n* because *n* grows faster than $\log_2 n$ as $n \to \infty$ (as in Example 1d).

EXERCISES 7.6

Comparisons with the Exponential e^x

1. Which of the following functions grow faster than e^x as $x \to \infty$? Which grow at the same rate as e^x? Which grow slower?

a. $x + 3$ **b.** $x^3 + \sin^2 x$

c. $\sqrt{x}$ **d.** 4^x

e. $(3/2)^x$ **f.** $e^{x/2}$

g. $e^x/2$ **h.** $\log_{10} x$

2. Which of the following functions grow faster than e^x as $x \to \infty$? Which grow at the same rate as e^x? Which grow slower?

a. $10x^4 + 30x + 1$ **b.** $x \ln x - x$

c. $\sqrt{1 + x^4}$ **d.** $(5/2)^x$

e. e^{-x} **f.** xe^x

g. $e^{\cos x}$ **h.** e^{x-1}

Comparisons with the Power x^2

3. Which of the following functions grow faster than x^2 as $x \to \infty$? Which grow at the same rate as x^2? Which grow slower?

a. $x^2 + 4x$ **b.** $x^5 - x^2$

c. $\sqrt{x^4 + x^3}$ **d.** $(x + 3)^2$

e. $x \ln x$ **f.** 2^x

g. $x^3 e^{-x}$ **h.** $8x^2$

4. Which of the following functions grow faster than x^2 as $x \to \infty$? Which grow at the same rate as x^2? Which grow slower?

a. $x^2 + \sqrt{x}$ **b.** $10x^2$

c. $x^2 e^{-x}$ **d.** $\log_{10}(x^2)$

e. $x^3 - x^2$ **f.** $(1/10)^x$

g. $(1.1)^x$ **h.** $x^2 + 100x$

Comparisons with the Logarithm ln x

5. Which of the following functions grow faster than $\ln x$ as $x \to \infty$? Which grow at the same rate as $\ln x$? Which grow slower?

a. $\log_3 x$ **b.** $\ln 2x$

c. $\ln \sqrt{x}$ **d.** $\sqrt{x}$

e. x **f.** $5 \ln x$

g. $1/x$ **h.** e^x

6. Which of the following functions grow faster than $\ln x$ as $x \to \infty$? Which grow at the same rate as $\ln x$? Which grow slower?

a. $\log_2 (x^2)$ **b.** $\log_{10} 10x$

c. $1/\sqrt{x}$ **d.** $1/x^2$

e. $x - 2 \ln x$ **f.** e^{-x}

g. $\ln (\ln x)$ **h.** $\ln (2x + 5)$

Ordering Functions by Growth Rates

7. Order the following functions from slowest growing to fastest growing as $x \to \infty$.

a. e^x **b.** x^x

c. $(\ln x)^x$ **d.** $e^{x/2}$

8. Order the following functions from slowest growing to fastest growing as $x \to \infty$.

a. 2^x **b.** x^2

c. $(\ln 2)^x$ **d.** e^x

Big-oh and Little-oh; Order

9. True, or false? As $x \to \infty$,

a. $x = o(x)$ **b.** $x = o(x + 5)$

c. $x = O(x + 5)$ **d.** $x = O(2x)$

e. $e^x = o(e^{2x})$ **f.** $x + \ln x = O(x)$

g. $\ln x = o(\ln 2x)$ **h.** $\sqrt{x^2 + 5} = O(x)$

10. True, or false? As $x \to \infty$,

a. $\dfrac{1}{x + 3} = O\left(\dfrac{1}{x}\right)$ **b.** $\dfrac{1}{x} + \dfrac{1}{x^2} = O\left(\dfrac{1}{x}\right)$

c. $\dfrac{1}{x} - \dfrac{1}{x^2} = o\left(\dfrac{1}{x}\right)$ **d.** $2 + \cos x = O(2)$

e. $e^x + x = O(e^x)$ **f.** $x \ln x = o(x^2)$

g. $\ln (\ln x) = O(\ln x)$ **h.** $\ln (x) = o(\ln (x^2 + 1))$

11. Show that if positive functions $f(x)$ and $g(x)$ grow at the same rate as $x \to \infty$, then $f = O(g)$ and $g = O(f)$.

12. When is a polynomial $f(x)$ of smaller order than a polynomial $g(x)$ as $x \to \infty$? Give reasons for your answer.

13. When is a polynomial $f(x)$ of at most the order of a polynomial $g(x)$ as $x \to \infty$? Give reasons for your answer.

14. What do the conclusions we drew in Section 2.4 about the limits of rational functions tell us about the relative growth of polynomials as $x \to \infty$?

Other Comparisons

T **15.** Investigate

$$\lim_{x \to \infty} \frac{\ln (x + 1)}{\ln x} \quad \text{and} \quad \lim_{x \to \infty} \frac{\ln (x + 999)}{\ln x}.$$

Then use l'Hôpital's Rule to explain what you find.

16. (*Continuation of Exercise 15.*) Show that the value of

$$\lim_{x \to \infty} \frac{\ln (x + a)}{\ln x}$$

is the same no matter what value you assign to the constant a. What does this say about the relative rates at which the functions $f(x) = \ln (x + a)$ and $g(x) = \ln x$ grow?

17. Show that $\sqrt{10x + 1}$ and $\sqrt{x + 1}$ grow at the same rate as $x \to \infty$ by showing that they both grow at the same rate as $\sqrt{x}$ as $x \to \infty$.

18. Show that $\sqrt{x^4 + x}$ and $\sqrt{x^4 - x^3}$ grow at the same rate as $x \to \infty$ by showing that they both grow at the same rate as x^2 as $x \to \infty$.

19. Show that e^x grows faster as $x \to \infty$ than x^n for any positive integer n, even $x^{1,000,000}$. (*Hint:* What is the nth derivative of x^n?)

20. **The function e^x outgrows any polynomial** Show that e^x grows faster as $x \to \infty$ than any polynomial

$$a_n x^n + a_{n-1} x^{n-1} + \cdots + a_1 x + a_0.$$

21. a. Show that $\ln x$ grows slower as $x \to \infty$ than $x^{1/n}$ for any positive integer n, even $x^{1/1,000,000}$.

T **b.** Although the values of $x^{1/1,000,000}$ eventually overtake the values of $\ln x$, you have to go way out on the x-axis before this happens. Find a value of x greater than 1 for which $x^{1/1,000,000} > \ln x$. You might start by observing that when $x > 1$ the equation $\ln x = x^{1/1,000,000}$ is equivalent to the equation $\ln (\ln x) = (\ln x)/1,000,000$.

T **c.** Even $x^{1/10}$ takes a long time to overtake $\ln x$. Experiment with a calculator to find the value of x at which the graphs of $x^{1/10}$ and $\ln x$ cross, or, equivalently, at which $\ln x = 10 \ln (\ln x)$. Bracket the crossing point between powers of 10 and then close in by successive halving.

T **d.** (*Continuation of part (c).*) The value of x at which $\ln x = 10 \ln (\ln x)$ is too far out for some graphers and root finders to identify. Try it on the equipment available to you and see what happens.

22. **The function $\ln x$ grows slower than any polynomial** Show that $\ln x$ grows slower as $x \to \infty$ than any nonconstant polynomial.

Algorithms and Searches

23. a. Suppose you have three different algorithms for solving the same problem and each algorithm takes a number of steps that is of the order of one of the functions listed here:

$$n \log_2 n, \quad n^{3/2}, \quad n(\log_2 n)^2.$$

Which of the algorithms is the most efficient in the long run? Give reasons for your answer.

T **b.** Graph the functions in part (a) together to get a sense of how rapidly each one grows.

24. Repeat Exercise 23 for the functions

$$n, \quad \sqrt{n} \log_2 n, \quad (\log_2 n)^2.$$

T **25.** Suppose you are looking for an item in an ordered list one million items long. How many steps might it take to find that item with a sequential search? A binary search?

T **26.** You are looking for an item in an ordered list 450,000 items long (the length of *Webster's Third New International Dictionary*). How many steps might it take to find the item with a sequential search? A binary search?

7.7 Inverse Trigonometric Functions

Inverse trigonometric functions arise when we want to calculate angles from side measurements in triangles. They also provide useful antiderivatives and appear frequently in the solutions of differential equations. This section shows how these functions are defined, graphed, and evaluated, how their derivatives are computed, and why they appear as important antiderivatives.

Defining the Inverses

The six basic trigonometric functions are not one-to-one (their values repeat periodically). However we can restrict their domains to intervals on which they are one-to-one. The sine function increases from -1 at $x = -\pi/2$ to $+1$ at $x = \pi/2$. By restricting its domain to the interval $[-\pi/2, \pi/2]$ we make it one-to-one, so that it has an inverse $\sin^{-1} x$ (Figure 7.16). Similar domain restrictions can be applied to all six trigonometric functions.

Domain restrictions that make the trigonometric functions one-to-one

Function	Domain	Range
$\sin x$	$[-\pi/2, \pi/2]$	$[-1, 1]$
$\cos x$	$[0, \pi]$	$[-1, 1]$

FIGURE 7.16 The graph of $y = \sin^{-1} x$.

$\tan x$	$(-\pi/2, \pi/2)$	$(-\infty, \infty)$	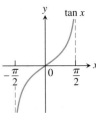
$\cot x$	$(0, \pi)$	$(-\infty, \infty)$	
$\sec x$	$[0, \pi/2) \cup (\pi/2, \pi]$	$(-\infty, -1] \cup [1, \infty)$	
$\csc x$	$[-\pi/2, 0) \cup (0, \pi/2]$	$(-\infty, -1] \cup [1, \infty)$	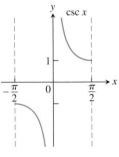

Since these restricted functions are now one-to-one, they have inverses, which we denote by

$$y = \sin^{-1} x \qquad \text{or} \qquad y = \arcsin x$$
$$y = \cos^{-1} x \qquad \text{or} \qquad y = \arccos x$$
$$y = \tan^{-1} x \qquad \text{or} \qquad y = \arctan x$$
$$y = \cot^{-1} x \qquad \text{or} \qquad y = \text{arccot}\, x$$
$$y = \sec^{-1} x \qquad \text{or} \qquad y = \text{arcsec}\, x$$
$$y = \csc^{-1} x \qquad \text{or} \qquad y = \text{arccsc}\, x$$

These equations are read "y equals the arcsine of x" or "y equals arcsin x" and so on.

CAUTION The -1 in the expressions for the inverse means "inverse." It does *not* mean reciprocal. For example, the *reciprocal* of $\sin x$ is $(\sin x)^{-1} = 1/\sin x = \csc x$.

The graphs of the six inverse trigonometric functions are shown in Figure 7.17. We can obtain these graphs by reflecting the graphs of the restricted trigonometric functions through the line $y = x$, as in Section 7.1. We now take a closer look at these functions and their derivatives.

Domain: $-1 \leq x \leq 1$
Range: $-\dfrac{\pi}{2} \leq y \leq \dfrac{\pi}{2}$

(a)

Domain: $-1 \leq x \leq 1$
Range: $0 \leq y \leq \pi$

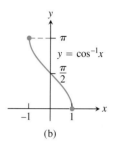

(b)

Domain: $-\infty < x < \infty$
Range: $-\dfrac{\pi}{2} < y < \dfrac{\pi}{2}$

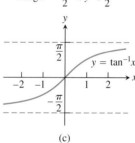

(c)

Domain: $x \leq -1$ or $x \geq 1$
Range: $0 \leq y \leq \pi, y \neq \dfrac{\pi}{2}$

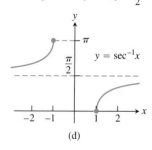

(d)

Domain: $x \leq -1$ or $x \geq 1$
Range: $-\dfrac{\pi}{2} \leq y \leq \dfrac{\pi}{2}, y \neq 0$

(e)

Domain: $-\infty < x < \infty$
Range: $0 < y < \pi$

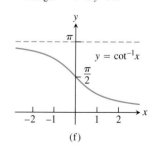

(f)

FIGURE 7.17 Graphs of the six basic inverse trigonometric functions.

The Arcsine and Arccosine Functions

The arcsine of x is the angle in $[-\pi/2, \pi/2]$ whose sine is x. The arccosine is an angle in $[0, \pi]$ whose cosine is x.

> **DEFINITION   Arcsine and Arccosine Functions**
>
> $y = \sin^{-1} x$ is the number in $[-\pi/2, \pi/2]$ for which $\sin y = x$.
>
> $y = \cos^{-1} x$ is the number in $[0, \pi]$ for which $\cos y = x$.

(a)

(b)

FIGURE 7.18   The graphs of (a) $y = \sin x$, $-\pi/2 \le x \le \pi/2$, and (b) its inverse, $y = \sin^{-1} x$. The graph of $\sin^{-1} x$, obtained by reflection across the line $y = x$, is a portion of the curve $x = \sin y$.

The "Arc" in Arc Sine and Arc Cosine

The accompanying figure gives a geometric interpretation of $y = \sin^{-1} x$ and $y = \cos^{-1} x$ for radian angles in the first quadrant. For a unit circle, the equation $s = r\theta$ becomes $s = \theta$, so central angles and the arcs they subtend have the same measure. If $x = \sin y$, then, in addition to being the angle whose sine is x, y is also the length of arc on the unit circle that subtends an angle whose sine is x. So we call y "the arc whose sine is x."

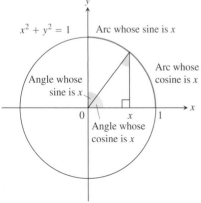

The graph of $y = \sin^{-1} x$ (Figure 7.18) is symmetric about the origin (it lies along the graph of $x = \sin y$). The arcsine is therefore an odd function:

$$\sin^{-1}(-x) = -\sin^{-1} x. \tag{1}$$

The graph of $y = \cos^{-1} x$ (Figure 7.19) has no such symmetry.

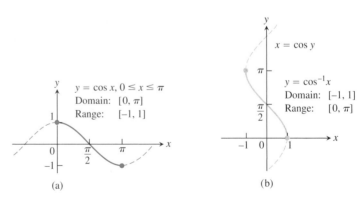

FIGURE 7.19   The graphs of (a) $y = \cos x$, $0 \le x \le \pi$, and (b) its inverse, $y = \cos^{-1} x$. The graph of $\cos^{-1} x$, obtained by reflection across the line $y = x$, is a portion of the curve $x = \cos y$.

Known values of $\sin x$ and $\cos x$ can be inverted to find values of $\sin^{-1} x$ and $\cos^{-1} x$.

EXAMPLE 1   Common Values of $\sin^{-1} x$

x	$\sin^{-1} x$
$\sqrt{3}/2$	$\pi/3$
$\sqrt{2}/2$	$\pi/4$
$1/2$	$\pi/6$
$-1/2$	$-\pi/6$
$-\sqrt{2}/2$	$-\pi/4$
$-\sqrt{3}/2$	$-\pi/3$

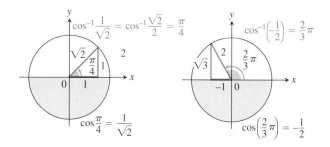

The angles come from the first and fourth quadrants because the range of $\sin^{-1} x$ is $[-\pi/2, \pi/2]$. ∎

EXAMPLE 2   Common Values of $\cos^{-1} x$

x	$\cos^{-1} x$
$\sqrt{3}/2$	$\pi/6$
$\sqrt{2}/2$	$\pi/4$
$1/2$	$\pi/3$
$-1/2$	$2\pi/3$
$-\sqrt{2}/2$	$3\pi/4$
$-\sqrt{3}/2$	$5\pi/6$

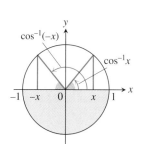

The angles come from the first and second quadrants because the range of $\cos^{-1} x$ is $[0, \pi]$. ∎

Identities Involving Arcsine and Arccosine

As we can see from Figure 7.20, the arccosine of x satisfies the identity

$$\cos^{-1} x + \cos^{-1}(-x) = \pi, \tag{2}$$

or

$$\cos^{-1}(-x) = \pi - \cos^{-1} x. \tag{3}$$

Also, we can see from the triangle in Figure 7.21 that for $x > 0$,

$$\sin^{-1} x + \cos^{-1} x = \pi/2. \tag{4}$$

Equation (4) holds for the other values of x in $[-1, 1]$ as well, but we cannot conclude this from the triangle in Figure 7.21. It is, however, a consequence of Equations (1) and (3) (Exercise 131).

FIGURE 7.20 $\cos^{-1} x$ and $\cos^{-1}(-x)$ are supplementary angles (so their sum is π).

FIGURE 7.21 $\sin^{-1} x$ and $\cos^{-1} x$ are complementary angles (so their sum is $\pi/2$).

Inverses of tan x, cot x, sec x, and csc x

The arctangent of x is an angle whose tangent is x. The arccotangent of x is an angle whose cotangent is x.

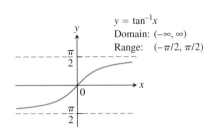

$y = \tan^{-1}x$
Domain: $(-\infty, \infty)$
Range: $(-\pi/2, \pi/2)$

FIGURE 7.22 The graph of $y = \tan^{-1} x$.

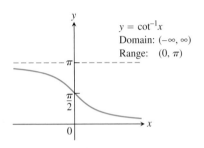

$y = \cot^{-1}x$
Domain: $(-\infty, \infty)$
Range: $(0, \pi)$

FIGURE 7.23 The graph of $y = \cot^{-1} x$.

$y = \sec^{-1}x$
Domain: $|x| \geq 1$
Range: $[0, \pi/2) \cup (\pi/2, \pi]$

FIGURE 7.24 The graph of $y = \sec^{-1} x$.

$y = \csc^{-1}x$
Domain: $|x| \geq 1$
Range: $[-\pi/2, 0) \cup (0, \pi/2]$

FIGURE 7.25 The graph of $y = \csc^{-1} x$.

> **DEFINITION** **Arctangent and Arccotangent Functions**
>
> $y = \tan^{-1} x$ is the number in $(-\pi/2, \pi/2)$ for which $\tan y = x$.
>
> $y = \cot^{-1} x$ is the number in $(0, \pi)$ for which $\cot y = x$.

We use open intervals to avoid values where the tangent and cotangent are undefined.

The graph of $y = \tan^{-1} x$ is symmetric about the origin because it is a branch of the graph $x = \tan y$ that is symmetric about the origin (Figure 7.22). Algebraically this means that

$$\tan^{-1}(-x) = -\tan^{-1} x;$$

the arctangent is an odd function. The graph of $y = \cot^{-1} x$ has no such symmetry (Figure 7.23).

The inverses of the restricted forms of $\sec x$ and $\csc x$ are chosen to be the functions graphed in Figures 7.24 and 7.25.

CAUTION There is no general agreement about how to define $\sec^{-1} x$ for negative values of x. We chose angles in the second quadrant between $\pi/2$ and π. This choice makes $\sec^{-1} x = \cos^{-1}(1/x)$. It also makes $\sec^{-1} x$ an increasing function on each interval of its domain. Some tables choose $\sec^{-1} x$ to lie in $[-\pi, -\pi/2)$ for $x < 0$ and some texts choose it to lie in $[\pi, 3\pi/2)$ (Figure 7.26). These choices simplify the formula for the derivative (our formula needs absolute value signs) but fail to satisfy the computational equation $\sec^{-1} x = \cos^{-1}(1/x)$. From this, we can derive the identity

$$\sec^{-1} x = \cos^{-1}\left(\frac{1}{x}\right) = \frac{\pi}{2} - \sin^{-1}\left(\frac{1}{x}\right) \tag{5}$$

by applying Equation (4).

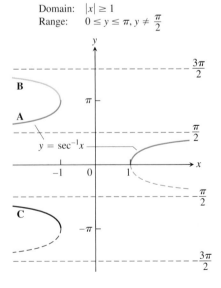

Domain: $|x| \geq 1$
Range: $0 \leq y \leq \pi, y \neq \dfrac{\pi}{2}$

FIGURE 7.26 There are several logical choices for the left-hand branch of $y = \sec^{-1} x$. With choice **A**, $\sec^{-1} x = \cos^{-1}(1/x)$, a useful identity employed by many calculators.

x	$\tan^{-1}x$
$\sqrt{3}$	$\pi/3$
1	$\pi/4$
$\sqrt{3}/3$	$\pi/6$
$-\sqrt{3}/3$	$-\pi/6$
-1	$-\pi/4$
$-\sqrt{3}$	$-\pi/3$

EXAMPLE 3   Common Values of $\tan^{-1}x$

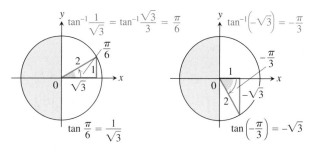

The angles come from the first and fourth quadrants because the range of $\tan^{-1}x$ is $(-\pi/2, \pi/2)$.   ∎

EXAMPLE 4   Find $\cos\alpha$, $\tan\alpha$, $\sec\alpha$, $\csc\alpha$, and $\cot\alpha$ if

$$\alpha = \sin^{-1}\frac{2}{3}.$$

Solution   This equation says that $\sin\alpha = 2/3$. We picture α as an angle in a right triangle with opposite side 2 and hypotenuse 3 (Figure 7.27). The length of the remaining side is

$$\sqrt{(3)^2 - (2)^2} = \sqrt{9 - 4} = \sqrt{5}. \qquad \text{Pythagorean theorem}$$

We add this information to the figure and then read the values we want from the completed triangle:

$$\cos\alpha = \frac{\sqrt{5}}{3}, \quad \tan\alpha = \frac{2}{\sqrt{5}}, \quad \sec\alpha = \frac{3}{\sqrt{5}}, \quad \csc\alpha = \frac{3}{2}, \quad \cot\alpha = \frac{\sqrt{5}}{2}. \qquad ∎$$

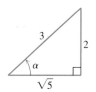

FIGURE 7.27 If $\alpha = \sin^{-1}(2/3)$, then the values of the other basic trigonometric functions of α can be read from this triangle (Example 4).

EXAMPLE 5   Find $\sec\left(\tan^{-1}\dfrac{x}{3}\right)$.

Solution   We let $\theta = \tan^{-1}(x/3)$ (to give the angle a name) and picture θ in a right triangle with

$$\tan\theta = \text{opposite/adjacent} = x/3.$$

The length of the triangle's hypotenuse is

$$\sqrt{x^2 + 3^2} = \sqrt{x^2 + 9}.$$

Thus,

$$\sec\left(\tan^{-1}\frac{x}{3}\right) = \sec\theta$$

$$= \frac{\sqrt{x^2 + 9}}{3}. \qquad \sec\theta = \frac{\text{hypotenuse}}{\text{adjacent}} \qquad ∎$$

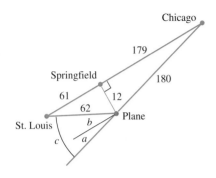

FIGURE 7.28 Diagram for drift correction (Example 6), with distances rounded to the nearest mile (drawing not to scale).

EXAMPLE 6   Drift Correction

During an airplane flight from Chicago to St. Louis the navigator determines that the plane is 12 mi off course, as shown in Figure 7.28. Find the angle a for a course parallel to the original, correct course, the angle b, and the correction angle $c = a + b$.

Solution

$$a = \sin^{-1}\frac{12}{180} \approx 0.067 \text{ radian} \approx 3.8°$$

$$b = \sin^{-1}\frac{12}{62} \approx 0.195 \text{ radian} \approx 11.2°$$

$$c = a + b \approx 15°. \qquad \blacksquare$$

The Derivative of $y = \sin^{-1} u$

We know that the function $x = \sin y$ is differentiable in the interval $-\pi/2 < y < \pi/2$ and that its derivative, the cosine, is positive there. Theorem 1 in Section 7.1 therefore assures us that the inverse function $y = \sin^{-1} x$ is differentiable throughout the interval $-1 < x < 1$. We cannot expect it to be differentiable at $x = 1$ or $x = -1$ because the tangents to the graph are vertical at these points (see Figure 7.29).

We find the derivative of $y = \sin^{-1} x$ by applying Theorem 1 with $f(x) = \sin x$ and $f^{-1}(x) = \sin^{-1} x$.

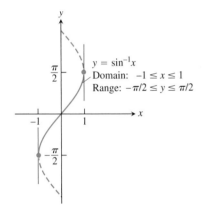

FIGURE 7.29 The graph of $y = \sin^{-1} x$.

$$(f^{-1})'(x) = \frac{1}{f'(f^{-1}(x))} \qquad \text{Theorem 1}$$

$$= \frac{1}{\cos(\sin^{-1} x)} \qquad f'(u) = \cos u$$

$$= \frac{1}{\sqrt{1 - \sin^2(\sin^{-1} x)}} \qquad \cos u = \sqrt{1 - \sin^2 u}$$

$$= \frac{1}{\sqrt{1 - x^2}} \qquad \sin(\sin^{-1} x) = x$$

Alternate Derivation: Instead of applying Theorem 1 directly, we can find the derivative of $y = \sin^{-1} x$ using implicit differentiation as follows:

$$\sin y = x \qquad y = \sin^{-1} x \Leftrightarrow \sin y = x$$

$$\frac{d}{dx}(\sin y) = 1 \qquad \text{Derivative of both sides with respect to } x$$

$$\cos y \frac{dy}{dx} = 1 \qquad \text{Chain Rule}$$

$$\frac{dy}{dx} = \frac{1}{\cos y} \qquad \begin{array}{l}\text{We can divide because } \cos y > 0 \\ \text{for } -\pi/2 < y < \pi/2.\end{array}$$

$$= \frac{1}{\sqrt{1 - x^2}} \qquad \cos y = \sqrt{1 - \sin^2 y}$$

No matter which derivation we use, we have that the derivative of $y = \sin^{-1} x$ with respect to x is

$$\frac{d}{dx}(\sin^{-1} x) = \frac{1}{\sqrt{1 - x^2}}.$$

If u is a differentiable function of x with $|u| < 1$, we apply the Chain Rule to get

$$\frac{d}{dx}(\sin^{-1} u) = \frac{1}{\sqrt{1 - u^2}}\frac{du}{dx}, \qquad |u| < 1.$$

EXAMPLE 7   Applying the Derivative Formula

$$\frac{d}{dx}(\sin^{-1} x^2) = \frac{1}{\sqrt{1 - (x^2)^2}} \cdot \frac{d}{dx}(x^2) = \frac{2x}{\sqrt{1 - x^4}}$$ ∎

The Derivative of $y = \tan^{-1} u$

We find the derivative of $y = \tan^{-1} x$ by applying Theorem 1 with $f(x) = \tan x$ and $f^{-1}(x) = \tan^{-1} x$. Theorem 1 can be applied because the derivative of $\tan x$ is positive for $-\pi/2 < x < \pi/2$.

$$
\begin{aligned}
(f^{-1})'(x) &= \frac{1}{f'(f^{-1}(x))} & \text{Theorem 1}\\[2mm]
&= \frac{1}{\sec^2(\tan^{-1} x)} & f'(u) = \sec^2 u\\[2mm]
&= \frac{1}{1 + \tan^2(\tan^{-1} x)} & \sec^2 u = 1 + \tan^2 u\\[2mm]
&= \frac{1}{1 + x^2} & \tan(\tan^{-1} x) = x
\end{aligned}
$$

The derivative is defined for all real numbers. If u is a differentiable function of x, we get the Chain Rule form:

$$\frac{d}{dx}(\tan^{-1} u) = \frac{1}{1 + u^2}\frac{du}{dx}.$$

EXAMPLE 8   A Moving Particle

A particle moves along the x-axis so that its position at any time $t \geq 0$ is $x(t) = \tan^{-1}\sqrt{t}$. What is the velocity of the particle when $t = 16$?

Solution

$$v(t) = \frac{d}{dt}\tan^{-1}\sqrt{t} = \frac{1}{1 + (\sqrt{t})^2} \cdot \frac{d}{dt}\sqrt{t} = \frac{1}{1 + t} \cdot \frac{1}{2\sqrt{t}}$$

When $t = 16$, the velocity is

$$v(16) = \frac{1}{1 + 16} \cdot \frac{1}{2\sqrt{16}} = \frac{1}{136}.$$ ∎

The Derivative of $y = \sec^{-1} u$

Since the derivative of $\sec x$ is positive for $0 < x < \pi/2$ and $\pi/2 < x < \pi$, Theorem 1 says that the inverse function $y = \sec^{-1} x$ is differentiable. Instead of applying the formula in Theorem 1 directly, we find the derivative of $y = \sec^{-1} x$, $|x| > 1$, using implicit differentiation and the Chain Rule as follows:

$$y = \sec^{-1} x$$

$$\sec y = x \qquad\qquad \text{Inverse function relationship}$$

$$\frac{d}{dx}(\sec y) = \frac{d}{dx} x \qquad\qquad \text{Differentiate both sides.}$$

$$\sec y \tan y \frac{dy}{dx} = 1 \qquad\qquad \text{Chain Rule}$$

$$\frac{dy}{dx} = \frac{1}{\sec y \tan y} \qquad\qquad \begin{array}{l}\text{Since } |x| > 1, y \text{ lies in} \\ (0, \pi/2) \cup (\pi/2, \pi) \text{ and} \\ \sec y \tan y \neq 0.\end{array}$$

To express the result in terms of x, we use the relationships

$$\sec y = x \qquad \text{and} \qquad \tan y = \pm\sqrt{\sec^2 y - 1} = \pm\sqrt{x^2 - 1}$$

to get

$$\frac{dy}{dx} = \pm \frac{1}{x\sqrt{x^2 - 1}}.$$

Can we do anything about the $\pm$ sign? A glance at Figure 7.30 shows that the slope of the graph $y = \sec^{-1} x$ is always positive. Thus,

$$\frac{d}{dx} \sec^{-1} x = \begin{cases} + \dfrac{1}{x\sqrt{x^2 - 1}} & \text{if } x > 1 \\[3mm] - \dfrac{1}{x\sqrt{x^2 - 1}} & \text{if } x < -1. \end{cases}$$

With the absolute value symbol, we can write a single expression that eliminates the "$\pm$" ambiguity:

$$\frac{d}{dx} \sec^{-1} x = \frac{1}{|x|\sqrt{x^2 - 1}}.$$

If u is a differentiable function of x with $|u| > 1$, we have the formula

$$\frac{d}{dx}(\sec^{-1} u) = \frac{1}{|u|\sqrt{u^2 - 1}} \frac{du}{dx}, \qquad |u| > 1.$$

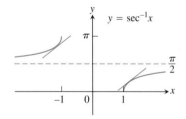

FIGURE 7.30   The slope of the curve $y = \sec^{-1} x$ is positive for both $x < -1$ and $x > 1$.

EXAMPLE 9 Using the Formula

$$\frac{d}{dx}\sec^{-1}(5x^4) = \frac{1}{|5x^4|\sqrt{(5x^4)^2 - 1}}\frac{d}{dx}(5x^4)$$

$$= \frac{1}{5x^4\sqrt{25x^8 - 1}}(20x^3) \qquad 5x^4 > 0$$

$$= \frac{4}{x\sqrt{25x^8 - 1}}$$

∎

Derivatives of the Other Three

We could use the same techniques to find the derivatives of the other three inverse trigonometric functions—arccosine, arccotangent, and arccosecant—but there is a much easier way, thanks to the following identities.

Inverse Function–Inverse Cofunction Identities

$$\cos^{-1} x = \pi/2 - \sin^{-1} x$$

$$\cot^{-1} x = \pi/2 - \tan^{-1} x$$

$$\csc^{-1} x = \pi/2 - \sec^{-1} x$$

We saw the first of these identities in Equation (4). The others are derived in a similar way. It follows easily that the derivatives of the inverse cofunctions are the negatives of the derivatives of the corresponding inverse functions. For example, the derivative of $\cos^{-1} x$ is calculated as follows:

$$\frac{d}{dx}(\cos^{-1} x) = \frac{d}{dx}\left(\frac{\pi}{2} - \sin^{-1} x\right) \qquad \text{Identity}$$

$$= -\frac{d}{dx}(\sin^{-1} x)$$

$$= -\frac{1}{\sqrt{1 - x^2}} \qquad \text{Derivative of arcsine}$$

EXAMPLE 10 A Tangent Line to the Arccotangent Curve

Find an equation for the line tangent to the graph of $y = \cot^{-1} x$ at $x = -1$.

Solution First we note that

$$\cot^{-1}(-1) = \pi/2 - \tan^{-1}(-1) = \pi/2 - (-\pi/4) = 3\pi/4.$$

The slope of the tangent line is

$$\frac{dy}{dx}\bigg|_{x=-1} = -\frac{1}{1 + x^2}\bigg|_{x=-1} = -\frac{1}{1 + (-1)^2} = -\frac{1}{2},$$

so the tangent line has equation $y - 3\pi/4 = (-1/2)(x + 1)$.

∎

The derivatives of the inverse trigonometric functions are summarized in Table 7.3.

TABLE 7.3   Derivatives of the inverse trigonometric functions

1. $\dfrac{d(\sin^{-1} u)}{dx} = \dfrac{du/dx}{\sqrt{1 - u^2}}, \quad |u| < 1$

2. $\dfrac{d(\cos^{-1} u)}{dx} = -\dfrac{du/dx}{\sqrt{1 - u^2}}, \quad |u| < 1$

3. $\dfrac{d(\tan^{-1} u)}{dx} = \dfrac{du/dx}{1 + u^2}$

4. $\dfrac{d(\cot^{-1} u)}{dx} = -\dfrac{du/dx}{1 + u^2}$

5. $\dfrac{d(\sec^{-1} u)}{dx} = \dfrac{du/dx}{|u|\sqrt{u^2 - 1}}, \quad |u| > 1$

6. $\dfrac{d(\csc^{-1} u)}{dx} = \dfrac{-du/dx}{|u|\sqrt{u^2 - 1}}, \quad |u| > 1$

Integration Formulas

The derivative formulas in Table 7.3 yield three useful integration formulas in Table 7.4. The formulas are readily verified by differentiating the functions on the right-hand sides.

TABLE 7.4   Integrals evaluated with inverse trigonometric functions

The following formulas hold for any constant $a \neq 0$.

1. $\displaystyle\int \frac{du}{\sqrt{a^2 - u^2}} = \sin^{-1}\left(\frac{u}{a}\right) + C$ (Valid for $u^2 < a^2$)

2. $\displaystyle\int \frac{du}{a^2 + u^2} = \frac{1}{a}\tan^{-1}\left(\frac{u}{a}\right) + C$ (Valid for all u)

3. $\displaystyle\int \frac{du}{u\sqrt{u^2 - a^2}} = \frac{1}{a}\sec^{-1}\left|\frac{u}{a}\right| + C$ (Valid for $|u| > a > 0$)

The derivative formulas in Table 7.3 have $a = 1$, but in most integrations $a \neq 1$, and the formulas in Table 7.4 are more useful.

EXAMPLE 11   Using the Integral Formulas

(a) $\displaystyle\int_{\sqrt{2}/2}^{\sqrt{3}/2} \frac{dx}{\sqrt{1 - x^2}} = \sin^{-1} x \,\Big]_{\sqrt{2}/2}^{\sqrt{3}/2}$

$$= \sin^{-1}\left(\frac{\sqrt{3}}{2}\right) - \sin^{-1}\left(\frac{\sqrt{2}}{2}\right) = \frac{\pi}{3} - \frac{\pi}{4} = \frac{\pi}{12}$$

(b) $\int_0^1 \dfrac{dx}{1 + x^2} = \tan^{-1} x \Big]_0^1 = \tan^{-1}(1) - \tan^{-1}(0) = \dfrac{\pi}{4} - 0 = \dfrac{\pi}{4}$

(c) $\int_{2/\sqrt{3}}^{\sqrt{2}} \dfrac{dx}{x\sqrt{x^2 - 1}} = \sec^{-1} x \Big]_{2/\sqrt{3}}^{\sqrt{2}} = \dfrac{\pi}{4} - \dfrac{\pi}{6} = \dfrac{\pi}{12}$ ■

EXAMPLE 12 Using Substitution and Table 7.4

(a) $\int \dfrac{dx}{\sqrt{9 - x^2}} = \int \dfrac{dx}{\sqrt{(3)^2 - x^2}} = \sin^{-1}\left(\dfrac{x}{3}\right) + C$ Table 7.4 Formula 1, with $a = 3, u = x$

(b) $\int \dfrac{dx}{\sqrt{3 - 4x^2}} = \dfrac{1}{2}\int \dfrac{du}{\sqrt{a^2 - u^2}}$ $a = \sqrt{3}, u = 2x$, and $du/2 = dx$

$\qquad = \dfrac{1}{2}\sin^{-1}\left(\dfrac{u}{a}\right) + C$ Formula 1

$\qquad = \dfrac{1}{2}\sin^{-1}\left(\dfrac{2x}{\sqrt{3}}\right) + C$ ■

EXAMPLE 13 Completing the Square

Evaluate

$$\int \frac{dx}{\sqrt{4x - x^2}}.$$

Solution The expression $\sqrt{4x - x^2}$ does not match any of the formulas in Table 7.4, so we first rewrite $4x - x^2$ by completing the square:

$$4x - x^2 = -(x^2 - 4x) = -(x^2 - 4x + 4) + 4 = 4 - (x - 2)^2.$$

Then we substitute $a = 2, u = x - 2$, and $du = dx$ to get

$\int \dfrac{dx}{\sqrt{4x - x^2}} = \int \dfrac{dx}{\sqrt{4 - (x - 2)^2}}$

$\qquad = \int \dfrac{du}{\sqrt{a^2 - u^2}}$ $a = 2, u = x - 2$, and $du = dx$

$\qquad = \sin^{-1}\left(\dfrac{u}{a}\right) + C$ Table 7.4, Formula 1

$\qquad = \sin^{-1}\left(\dfrac{x - 2}{2}\right) + C$ ■

EXAMPLE 14 Completing the Square

Evaluate

$$\int \frac{dx}{4x^2 + 4x + 2}.$$

Solution We complete the square on the binomial $4x^2 + 4x$:

$$4x^2 + 4x + 2 = 4(x^2 + x) + 2 = 4\left(x^2 + x + \frac{1}{4}\right) + 2 - \frac{4}{4}$$

$$= 4\left(x + \frac{1}{2}\right)^2 + 1 = (2x + 1)^2 + 1.$$

Then,

$$\int \frac{dx}{4x^2 + 4x + 2} = \int \frac{dx}{(2x + 1)^2 + 1} = \frac{1}{2}\int \frac{du}{u^2 + a^2} \qquad \begin{array}{l} a = 1, u = 2x + 1, \\ \text{and } du/2 = dx \end{array}$$

$$= \frac{1}{2} \cdot \frac{1}{a} \tan^{-1}\left(\frac{u}{a}\right) + C \qquad \text{Table 7.4, Formula 2}$$

$$= \frac{1}{2} \tan^{-1}(2x + 1) + C \qquad a = 1, u = 2x + 1 \qquad \blacksquare$$

EXAMPLE 15 Using Substitution

Evaluate

$$\int \frac{dx}{\sqrt{e^{2x} - 6}}.$$

Solution

$$\int \frac{dx}{\sqrt{e^{2x} - 6}} = \int \frac{du/u}{\sqrt{u^2 - a^2}} \qquad \begin{array}{l} u = e^x, du = e^x\, dx, \\ dx = du/e^x = du/u, \\ a = \sqrt{6} \end{array}$$

$$= \int \frac{du}{u\sqrt{u^2 - a^2}}$$

$$= \frac{1}{a} \sec^{-1}\left|\frac{u}{a}\right| + C \qquad \text{Table 7.4, Formula 3}$$

$$= \frac{1}{\sqrt{6}} \sec^{-1}\left(\frac{e^x}{\sqrt{6}}\right) + C \qquad \blacksquare$$

EXERCISES 7.7

Common Values of Inverse Trignonometric Functions

Use reference triangles like those in Examples 1–3 to find the angles in Exercises 1–12.

1. **a.** $\tan^{-1} 1$ **b.** $\tan^{-1}(-\sqrt{3})$ **c.** $\tan^{-1}\left(\frac{1}{\sqrt{3}}\right)$

2. **a.** $\tan^{-1}(-1)$ **b.** $\tan^{-1}\sqrt{3}$ **c.** $\tan^{-1}\left(\frac{-1}{\sqrt{3}}\right)$

3. **a.** $\sin^{-1}\left(\frac{-1}{2}\right)$ **b.** $\sin^{-1}\left(\frac{1}{\sqrt{2}}\right)$ **c.** $\sin^{-1}\left(\frac{-\sqrt{3}}{2}\right)$

4. **a.** $\sin^{-1}\left(\frac{1}{2}\right)$ **b.** $\sin^{-1}\left(\frac{-1}{\sqrt{2}}\right)$ **c.** $\sin^{-1}\left(\frac{\sqrt{3}}{2}\right)$

5. **a.** $\cos^{-1}\left(\frac{1}{2}\right)$ **b.** $\cos^{-1}\left(\frac{-1}{\sqrt{2}}\right)$ **c.** $\cos^{-1}\left(\frac{\sqrt{3}}{2}\right)$

6. **a.** $\cos^{-1}\left(\frac{-1}{2}\right)$ **b.** $\cos^{-1}\left(\frac{1}{\sqrt{2}}\right)$ **c.** $\cos^{-1}\left(\frac{-\sqrt{3}}{2}\right)$

7. a. $\sec^{-1}(-\sqrt{2})$ **b.** $\sec^{-1}\left(\dfrac{2}{\sqrt{3}}\right)$ **c.** $\sec^{-1}(-2)$

8. a. $\sec^{-1}\sqrt{2}$ **b.** $\sec^{-1}\left(\dfrac{-2}{\sqrt{3}}\right)$ **c.** $\sec^{-1}2$

9. a. $\csc^{-1}\sqrt{2}$ **b.** $\csc^{-1}\left(\dfrac{-2}{\sqrt{3}}\right)$ **c.** $\csc^{-1}2$

10. a. $\csc^{-1}(-\sqrt{2})$ **b.** $\csc^{-1}\left(\dfrac{2}{\sqrt{3}}\right)$ **c.** $\csc^{-1}(-2)$

11. a. $\cot^{-1}(-1)$ **b.** $\cot^{-1}(\sqrt{3})$ **c.** $\cot^{-1}\left(\dfrac{-1}{\sqrt{3}}\right)$

12. a. $\cot^{-1}(1)$ **b.** $\cot^{-1}(-\sqrt{3})$ **c.** $\cot^{-1}\left(\dfrac{1}{\sqrt{3}}\right)$

Trigonometric Function Values

13. Given that $\alpha = \sin^{-1}(5/13)$, find $\cos\alpha$, $\tan\alpha$, $\sec\alpha$, $\csc\alpha$, and $\cot\alpha$.

14. Given that $\alpha = \tan^{-1}(4/3)$, find $\sin\alpha$, $\cos\alpha$, $\sec\alpha$, $\csc\alpha$, and $\cot\alpha$.

15. Given that $\alpha = \sec^{-1}(-\sqrt{5})$, find $\sin\alpha$, $\cos\alpha$, $\tan\alpha$, $\csc\alpha$, and $\cot\alpha$.

16. Given that $\alpha = \sec^{-1}(-\sqrt{13}/2)$, find $\sin\alpha$, $\cos\alpha$, $\tan\alpha$, $\csc\alpha$, and $\cot\alpha$.

Evaluating Trigonometric and Inverse Trigonometric Terms

Find the values in Exercises 17–28.

17. $\sin\left(\cos^{-1}\left(\dfrac{\sqrt{2}}{2}\right)\right)$ **18.** $\sec\left(\cos^{-1}\dfrac{1}{2}\right)$

19. $\tan\left(\sin^{-1}\left(-\dfrac{1}{2}\right)\right)$ **20.** $\cot\left(\sin^{-1}\left(-\dfrac{\sqrt{3}}{2}\right)\right)$

21. $\csc(\sec^{-1}2) + \cos(\tan^{-1}(-\sqrt{3}))$

22. $\tan(\sec^{-1}1) + \sin(\csc^{-1}(-2))$

23. $\sin\left(\sin^{-1}\left(-\dfrac{1}{2}\right) + \cos^{-1}\left(-\dfrac{1}{2}\right)\right)$

24. $\cot\left(\sin^{-1}\left(-\dfrac{1}{2}\right) - \sec^{-1}2\right)$

25. $\sec(\tan^{-1}1 + \csc^{-1}1)$ **26.** $\sec(\cot^{-1}\sqrt{3} + \csc^{-1}(-1))$

27. $\sec^{-1}\left(\sec\left(-\dfrac{\pi}{6}\right)\right)$ (The answer is *not* $-\pi/6$.)

28. $\cot^{-1}\left(\cot\left(-\dfrac{\pi}{4}\right)\right)$ (The answer is *not* $-\pi/4$.)

Finding Trigonometric Expressions

Evaluate the expressions in Exercises 29–40.

29. $\sec\left(\tan^{-1}\dfrac{x}{2}\right)$ **30.** $\sec(\tan^{-1}2x)$

31. $\tan(\sec^{-1}3y)$ **32.** $\tan\left(\sec^{-1}\dfrac{y}{5}\right)$

33. $\cos(\sin^{-1}x)$ **34.** $\tan(\cos^{-1}x)$

35. $\sin(\tan^{-1}\sqrt{x^2 - 2x})$, $x \geq 2$

36. $\sin\left(\tan^{-1}\dfrac{x}{\sqrt{x^2 + 1}}\right)$ **37.** $\cos\left(\sin^{-1}\dfrac{2y}{3}\right)$

38. $\cos\left(\sin^{-1}\dfrac{y}{5}\right)$ **39.** $\sin\left(\sec^{-1}\dfrac{x}{4}\right)$

40. $\sin\sec^{-1}\left(\dfrac{\sqrt{x^2 + 4}}{x}\right)$

Limits

Find the limits in Exercises 41–48. (If in doubt, look at the function's graph.)

41. $\lim\limits_{x \to 1^-} \sin^{-1}x$ **42.** $\lim\limits_{x \to -1^+} \cos^{-1}x$

43. $\lim\limits_{x \to \infty} \tan^{-1}x$ **44.** $\lim\limits_{x \to -\infty} \tan^{-1}x$

45. $\lim\limits_{x \to \infty} \sec^{-1}x$ **46.** $\lim\limits_{x \to -\infty} \sec^{-1}x$

47. $\lim\limits_{x \to \infty} \csc^{-1}x$ **48.** $\lim\limits_{x \to -\infty} \csc^{-1}x$

Finding Derivatives

In Exercises 49–70, find the derivative of y with respect to the appropriate variable.

49. $y = \cos^{-1}(x^2)$ **50.** $y = \cos^{-1}(1/x)$

51. $y = \sin^{-1}\sqrt{2}\,t$ **52.** $y = \sin^{-1}(1 - t)$

53. $y = \sec^{-1}(2s + 1)$ **54.** $y = \sec^{-1}5s$

55. $y = \csc^{-1}(x^2 + 1)$, $x > 0$

56. $y = \csc^{-1}\dfrac{x}{2}$

57. $y = \sec^{-1}\dfrac{1}{t}$, $0 < t < 1$ **58.** $y = \sin^{-1}\dfrac{3}{t^2}$

59. $y = \cot^{-1}\sqrt{t}$ **60.** $y = \cot^{-1}\sqrt{t - 1}$

61. $y = \ln(\tan^{-1}x)$ **62.** $y = \tan^{-1}(\ln x)$

63. $y = \csc^{-1}(e^t)$ **64.** $y = \cos^{-1}(e^{-t})$

65. $y = s\sqrt{1 - s^2} + \cos^{-1}s$ **66.** $y = \sqrt{s^2 - 1} - \sec^{-1}s$

67. $y = \tan^{-1}\sqrt{x^2 - 1} + \csc^{-1}x$, $x > 1$

68. $y = \cot^{-1}\dfrac{1}{x} - \tan^{-1}x$ **69.** $y = x\sin^{-1}x + \sqrt{1 - x^2}$

70. $y = \ln(x^2 + 4) - x\tan^{-1}\left(\dfrac{x}{2}\right)$

Evaluating Integrals

Evaluate the integrals in Exercises 71–94.

71. $\displaystyle\int \dfrac{dx}{\sqrt{9 - x^2}}$ **72.** $\displaystyle\int \dfrac{dx}{\sqrt{1 - 4x^2}}$

73. $\displaystyle\int \frac{dx}{17 + x^2}$

74. $\displaystyle\int \frac{dx}{9 + 3x^2}$

75. $\displaystyle\int \frac{dx}{x\sqrt{25x^2 - 2}}$

76. $\displaystyle\int \frac{dx}{x\sqrt{5x^2 - 4}}$

77. $\displaystyle\int_0^1 \frac{4\,ds}{\sqrt{4 - s^2}}$

78. $\displaystyle\int_0^{3\sqrt{2}/4} \frac{ds}{\sqrt{9 - 4s^2}}$

79. $\displaystyle\int_0^2 \frac{dt}{8 + 2t^2}$

80. $\displaystyle\int_{-2}^2 \frac{dt}{4 + 3t^2}$

81. $\displaystyle\int_{-1}^{-\sqrt{2}/2} \frac{dy}{y\sqrt{4y^2 - 1}}$

82. $\displaystyle\int_{-2/3}^{-\sqrt{2}/3} \frac{dy}{y\sqrt{9y^2 - 1}}$

83. $\displaystyle\int \frac{3\,dr}{\sqrt{1 - 4(r - 1)^2}}$

84. $\displaystyle\int \frac{6\,dr}{\sqrt{4 - (r + 1)^2}}$

85. $\displaystyle\int \frac{dx}{2 + (x - 1)^2}$

86. $\displaystyle\int \frac{dx}{1 + (3x + 1)^2}$

87. $\displaystyle\int \frac{dx}{(2x - 1)\sqrt{(2x - 1)^2 - 4}}$

88. $\displaystyle\int \frac{dx}{(x + 3)\sqrt{(x + 3)^2 - 25}}$

89. $\displaystyle\int_{-\pi/2}^{\pi/2} \frac{2\cos\theta\,d\theta}{1 + (\sin\theta)^2}$

90. $\displaystyle\int_{\pi/6}^{\pi/4} \frac{\csc^2 x\,dx}{1 + (\cot x)^2}$

91. $\displaystyle\int_0^{\ln\sqrt{3}} \frac{e^x\,dx}{1 + e^{2x}}$

92. $\displaystyle\int_1^{e^{\pi/4}} \frac{4\,dt}{t(1 + \ln^2 t)}$

93. $\displaystyle\int \frac{y\,dy}{\sqrt{1 - y^4}}$

94. $\displaystyle\int \frac{\sec^2 y\,dy}{\sqrt{1 - \tan^2 y}}$

Evaluate the integrals in Exercises 95–104.

95. $\displaystyle\int \frac{dx}{\sqrt{-x^2 + 4x - 3}}$

96. $\displaystyle\int \frac{dx}{\sqrt{2x - x^2}}$

97. $\displaystyle\int_{-1}^0 \frac{6\,dt}{\sqrt{3 - 2t - t^2}}$

98. $\displaystyle\int_{1/2}^1 \frac{6\,dt}{\sqrt{3 + 4t - 4t^2}}$

99. $\displaystyle\int \frac{dy}{y^2 - 2y + 5}$

100. $\displaystyle\int \frac{dy}{y^2 + 6y + 10}$

101. $\displaystyle\int_1^2 \frac{8\,dx}{x^2 - 2x + 2}$

102. $\displaystyle\int_2^4 \frac{2\,dx}{x^2 - 6x + 10}$

103. $\displaystyle\int \frac{dx}{(x + 1)\sqrt{x^2 + 2x}}$

104. $\displaystyle\int \frac{dx}{(x - 2)\sqrt{x^2 - 4x + 3}}$

Evaluate the integrals in Exercises 105–112.

105. $\displaystyle\int \frac{e^{\sin^{-1} x}\,dx}{\sqrt{1 - x^2}}$

106. $\displaystyle\int \frac{e^{\cos^{-1} x}\,dx}{\sqrt{1 - x^2}}$

107. $\displaystyle\int \frac{(\sin^{-1} x)^2\,dx}{\sqrt{1 - x^2}}$

108. $\displaystyle\int \frac{\sqrt{\tan^{-1} x}\,dx}{1 + x^2}$

109. $\displaystyle\int \frac{dy}{(\tan^{-1} y)(1 + y^2)}$

110. $\displaystyle\int \frac{dy}{(\sin^{-1} y)\sqrt{1 - y^2}}$

111. $\displaystyle\int_{\sqrt{2}}^2 \frac{\sec^2(\sec^{-1} x)\,dx}{x\sqrt{x^2 - 1}}$

112. $\displaystyle\int_{2/\sqrt{3}}^2 \frac{\cos(\sec^{-1} x)\,dx}{x\sqrt{x^2 - 1}}$

Limits

Find the limits in Exercises 113–116.

113. $\displaystyle\lim_{x\to 0} \frac{\sin^{-1} 5x}{x}$

114. $\displaystyle\lim_{x\to 1^+} \frac{\sqrt{x^2 - 1}}{\sec^{-1} x}$

115. $\displaystyle\lim_{x\to\infty} x\tan^{-1}\frac{2}{x}$

116. $\displaystyle\lim_{x\to 0} \frac{2\tan^{-1} 3x^2}{7x^2}$

Integration Formulas

Verify the integration formulas in Exercises 117–120.

117. $\displaystyle\int \frac{\tan^{-1} x}{x^2}\,dx = \ln x - \frac{1}{2}\ln(1 + x^2) - \frac{\tan^{-1} x}{x} + C$

118. $\displaystyle\int x^3\cos^{-1} 5x\,dx = \frac{x^4}{4}\cos^{-1} 5x + \frac{5}{4}\int \frac{x^4\,dx}{\sqrt{1 - 25x^2}}$

119. $\displaystyle\int (\sin^{-1} x)^2\,dx = x(\sin^{-1} x)^2 - 2x + 2\sqrt{1 - x^2}\sin^{-1} x + C$

120. $\displaystyle\int \ln(a^2 + x^2)\,dx = x\ln(a^2 + x^2) - 2x + 2a\tan^{-1}\frac{x}{a} + C$

Initial Value Problems

Solve the initial value problems in Exercises 121–124.

121. $\dfrac{dy}{dx} = \dfrac{1}{\sqrt{1 - x^2}}, \quad y(0) = 0$

122. $\dfrac{dy}{dx} = \dfrac{1}{x^2 + 1} - 1, \quad y(0) = 1$

123. $\dfrac{dy}{dx} = \dfrac{1}{x\sqrt{x^2 - 1}}, \quad x > 1; \quad y(2) = \pi$

124. $\dfrac{dy}{dx} = \dfrac{1}{1 + x^2} - \dfrac{2}{\sqrt{1 - x^2}}, \quad y(0) = 2$

Applications and Theory

125. You are sitting in a classroom next to the wall looking at the blackboard at the front of the room. The blackboard is 12 ft long and starts 3 ft from the wall you are sitting next to. Show that your viewing angle is

$$\alpha = \cot^{-1}\frac{x}{15} - \cot^{-1}\frac{x}{3}$$

if you are x ft from the front wall.

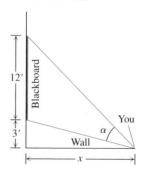

126. The region between the curve $y = \sec^{-1} x$ and the x-axis from $x = 1$ to $x = 2$ (shown here) is revolved about the y-axis to generate a solid. Find the volume of the solid.

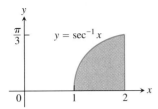

127. The slant height of the cone shown here is 3 m. How large should the indicated angle be to maximize the cone's volume?

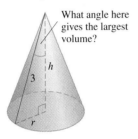

What angle here gives the largest volume?

128. Find the angle α.

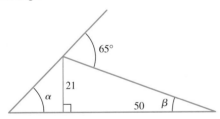

129. Here is an informal proof that $\tan^{-1} 1 + \tan^{-1} 2 + \tan^{-1} 3 = \pi$. Explain what is going on.

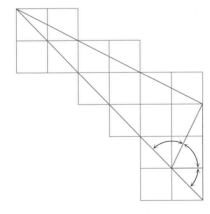

130. Two derivations of the identity $\sec^{-1}(-x) = \pi - \sec^{-1} x$

a. (*Geometric*) Here is a pictorial proof that $\sec^{-1}(-x) = \pi - \sec^{-1} x$. See if you can tell what is going on.

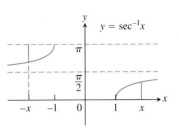

b. (*Algebraic*) Derive the identity $\sec^{-1}(-x) = \pi - \sec^{-1} x$ by combining the following two equations from the text:

$$\cos^{-1}(-x) = \pi - \cos^{-1} x \qquad \text{Eq. (3)}$$
$$\sec^{-1} x = \cos^{-1}(1/x) \qquad \text{Eq. (5)}$$

131. The identity $\sin^{-1} x + \cos^{-1} x = \pi/2$ Figure 7.21 establishes the identity for $0 < x < 1$. To establish it for the rest of $[-1, 1]$, verify by direct calculation that it holds for $x = 1, 0$, and -1. Then, for values of x in $(-1, 0)$, let $x = -a$, $a > 0$, and apply Eqs. (1) and (3) to the sum $\sin^{-1}(-a) + \cos^{-1}(-a)$.

132. Show that the sum $\tan^{-1} x + \tan^{-1}(1/x)$ is constant.

Which of the expressions in Exercises 133–136 are defined, and which are not? Give reasons for your answers.

133. a. $\tan^{-1} 2$ **b.** $\cos^{-1} 2$

134. a. $\csc^{-1}(1/2)$ **b.** $\csc^{-1} 2$

135. a. $\sec^{-1} 0$ **b.** $\sin^{-1}\sqrt{2}$

136. a. $\cot^{-1}(-1/2)$ **b.** $\cos^{-1}(-5)$

137. (*Continuation of Exercise 125.*) You want to position your chair along the wall to maximize your viewing angle α. How far from the front of the room should you sit?

138. What value of x maximizes the angle θ shown here? How large is θ at that point? Begin by showing that $\theta = \pi - \cot^{-1} x - \cot^{-1}(2 - x)$.

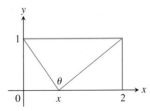

139. Can the integrations in (a) and (b) both be correct? Explain.

a. $\displaystyle\int \frac{dx}{\sqrt{1 - x^2}} = \sin^{-1} x + C$

b. $\displaystyle\int \frac{dx}{\sqrt{1 - x^2}} = -\int -\frac{dx}{\sqrt{1 - x^2}} = -\cos^{-1} x + C$

140. Can the integrations in (a) and (b) both be correct? Explain.

a. $\displaystyle\int \frac{dx}{\sqrt{1 - x^2}} = -\int -\frac{dx}{\sqrt{1 - x^2}} = -\cos^{-1} x + C$

b. $\int \dfrac{dx}{\sqrt{1 - x^2}} = \int \dfrac{-du}{\sqrt{1 - (-u)^2}}$ $\begin{aligned} x &= -u, \\ dx &= -du \end{aligned}$

$\qquad\qquad = \int \dfrac{-du}{\sqrt{1 - u^2}}$

$\qquad\qquad = \cos^{-1} u + C$

$\qquad\qquad = \cos^{-1}(-x) + C$ $u = -x$

141. Use the identity

$$\csc^{-1} u = \frac{\pi}{2} - \sec^{-1} u$$

to derive the formula for the derivative of $\csc^{-1} u$ in Table 7.3 from the formula for the derivative of $\sec^{-1} u$.

142. Derive the formula

$$\frac{dy}{dx} = \frac{1}{1 + x^2}$$

for the derivative of $y = \tan^{-1} x$ by differentiating both sides of the equivalent equation $\tan y = x$.

143. Use the Derivative Rule in Section 7.1, Theorem 1, to derive

$$\frac{d}{dx} \sec^{-1} x = \frac{1}{|x| \sqrt{x^2 - 1}}, \quad |x| > 1.$$

144. Use the identity

$$\cot^{-1} u = \frac{\pi}{2} - \tan^{-1} u$$

to derive the formula for the derivative of $\cot^{-1} u$ in Table 7.3 from the formula for the derivative of $\tan^{-1} u$.

145. What is special about the functions

$$f(x) = \sin^{-1} \frac{x - 1}{x + 1}, \quad x \geq 0, \quad \text{and} \quad g(x) = 2 \tan^{-1} \sqrt{x}?$$

Explain.

146. What is special about the functions

$$f(x) = \sin^{-1} \frac{1}{\sqrt{x^2 + 1}} \quad \text{and} \quad g(x) = \tan^{-1} \frac{1}{x}?$$

Explain.

147. Find the volume of the solid of revolution shown here.

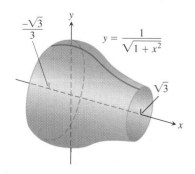

$-\dfrac{\sqrt{3}}{3}$

$y = \dfrac{1}{\sqrt{1 + x^2}}$

$\sqrt{3}$

148. Arc length Find the length of the curve $y = \sqrt{1 - x^2}$, $-1/2 \leq x \leq 1/2$.

Volumes by Slicing

Find the volumes of the solids in Exercises 149 and 150.

149. The solid lies between planes perpendicular to the x-axis at $x = -1$ and $x = 1$. The cross-sections perpendicular to the x-axis are

a. circles whose diameters stretch from the curve $y = -1/\sqrt{1 + x^2}$ to the curve $y = 1/\sqrt{1 + x^2}$.

b. vertical squares whose base edges run from the curve $y = -1/\sqrt{1 + x^2}$ to the curve $y = 1/\sqrt{1 + x^2}$.

150. The solid lies between planes perpendicular to the x-axis at $x = -\sqrt{2}/2$ and $x = \sqrt{2}/2$. The cross-sections perpendicular to the x-axis are

a. circles whose diameters stretch from the x-axis to the curve $y = 2/\sqrt[4]{1 - x^2}$.

b. squares whose diagonals stretch from the x-axis to the curve $y = 2/\sqrt[4]{1 - x^2}$.

T Calculator and Grapher Explorations

151. Find the values of

a. $\sec^{-1} 1.5$ **b.** $\csc^{-1}(-1.5)$ **c.** $\cot^{-1} 2$

152. Find the values of

a. $\sec^{-1}(-3)$ **b.** $\csc^{-1} 1.7$ **c.** $\cot^{-1}(-2)$

In Exercises 153–155, find the domain and range of each composite function. Then graph the composites on separate screens. Do the graphs make sense in each case? Give reasons for your answers. Comment on any differences you see.

153. a. $y = \tan^{-1}(\tan x)$ **b.** $y = \tan(\tan^{-1} x)$

154. a. $y = \sin^{-1}(\sin x)$ **b.** $y = \sin(\sin^{-1} x)$

155. a. $y = \cos^{-1}(\cos x)$ **b.** $y = \cos(\cos^{-1} x)$

156. Graph $y = \sec(\sec^{-1} x) = \sec(\cos^{-1}(1/x))$. Explain what you see.

157. Newton's serpentine Graph Newton's serpentine, $y = 4x/(x^2 + 1)$. Then graph $y = 2\sin(2\tan^{-1} x)$ in the same graphing window. What do you see? Explain.

158. Graph the rational function $y = (2 - x^2)/x^2$. Then graph $y = \cos(2\sec^{-1} x)$ in the same graphing window. What do you see? Explain.

159. Graph $f(x) = \sin^{-1} x$ together with its first two derivatives. Comment on the behavior of f and the shape of its graph in relation to the signs and values of f' and f''.

160. Graph $f(x) = \tan^{-1} x$ together with its first two derivatives. Comment on the behavior of f and the shape of its graph in relation to the signs and values of f' and f''.

7.8 Hyperbolic Functions

The hyperbolic functions are formed by taking combinations of the two exponential functions e^x and e^{-x}. The hyperbolic functions simplify many mathematical expressions and they are important in applications. For instance, they are used in problems such as computing the tension in a cable suspended by its two ends, as in an electric transmission line. They also play an important role in finding solutions to differential equations. In this section, we give a brief introduction to hyperbolic functions, their graphs, how their derivatives are calculated, and why they appear as important antiderivatives.

Even and Odd Parts of the Exponential Function

Recall the definitions of even and odd functions from Section 1.4, and the symmetries of their graphs. An even function f satisfies $f(-x) = f(x)$, while an odd function satisfies $f(-x) = -f(x)$. Every function f that is defined on an interval centered at the origin can be written in a unique way as the sum of one even function and one odd function. The decomposition is

$$f(x) = \underbrace{\frac{f(x) + f(-x)}{2}}_{\text{even part}} + \underbrace{\frac{f(x) - f(-x)}{2}}_{\text{odd part}}.$$

If we write e^x this way, we get

$$e^x = \underbrace{\frac{e^x + e^{-x}}{2}}_{\text{even part}} + \underbrace{\frac{e^x - e^{-x}}{2}}_{\text{odd part}}.$$

The even and odd parts of e^x, called the hyperbolic cosine and hyperbolic sine of x, respectively, are useful in their own right. They describe the motions of waves in elastic solids and the temperature distributions in metal cooling fins. The centerline of the Gateway Arch to the West in St. Louis is a weighted hyperbolic cosine curve.

Definitions and Identities

The hyperbolic cosine and hyperbolic sine functions are defined by the first two equations in Table 7.5. The table also lists the definitions of the hyperbolic tangent, cotangent, secant, and cosecant. As we will see, the hyperbolic functions bear a number of similarities to the trigonometric functions after which they are named. (See Exercise 84 as well.)

The notation cosh x is often read "kosh x," rhyming with "gosh x," and sinh x is pronounced as if spelled "cinch x," rhyming with "pinch x."

Hyperbolic functions satisfy the identities in Table 7.6. Except for differences in sign, these resemble identities we already know for trigonometric functions.

The second equation is obtained as follows:

$$2 \sinh x \cosh x = 2\left(\frac{e^x - e^{-x}}{2}\right)\left(\frac{e^x + e^{-x}}{2}\right)$$

$$= \frac{e^{2x} - e^{-2x}}{2}$$

$$= \sinh 2x.$$

TABLE 7.5 The six basic hyperbolic functions

FIGURE 7.31

Hyperbolic sine of x: $\quad \sinh x = \dfrac{e^x - e^{-x}}{2}$

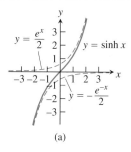

(a)

Hyperbolic cosine of x: $\quad \cosh x = \dfrac{e^x + e^{-x}}{2}$

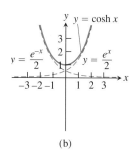

(b)

Hyperbolic tangent: $\quad \tanh x = \dfrac{\sinh x}{\cosh x} = \dfrac{e^x - e^{-x}}{e^x + e^{-x}}$

Hyperbolic cotangent: $\quad \coth x = \dfrac{\cosh x}{\sinh x} = \dfrac{e^x + e^{-x}}{e^x - e^{-x}}$

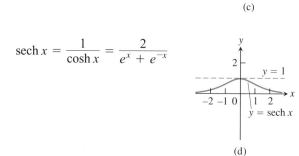

(c)

Hyperbolic secant: $\quad \operatorname{sech} x = \dfrac{1}{\cosh x} = \dfrac{2}{e^x + e^{-x}}$

(d)

Hyperbolic cosecant: $\quad \operatorname{csch} x = \dfrac{1}{\sinh x} = \dfrac{2}{e^x - e^{-x}}$

(e)

TABLE 7.6 Identities for hyperbolic functions

$\cosh^2 x - \sinh^2 x = 1$

$\sinh 2x = 2 \sinh x \cosh x$

$\cosh 2x = \cosh^2 x + \sinh^2 x$

$\cosh^2 x = \dfrac{\cosh 2x + 1}{2}$

$\sinh^2 x = \dfrac{\cosh 2x - 1}{2}$

$\tanh^2 x = 1 - \operatorname{sech}^2 x$

$\coth^2 x = 1 + \operatorname{csch}^2 x$

The other identities are obtained similarly, by substituting in the definitions of the hyperbolic functions and using algebra. Like many standard functions, hyperbolic functions and their inverses are easily evaluated with calculators, which have special keys or keystroke sequences for that purpose.

Derivatives and Integrals

The six hyperbolic functions, being rational combinations of the differentiable functions e^x and e^{-x}, have derivatives at every point at which they are defined (Table 7.7). Again, there are similarities with trigonometric functions. The derivative formulas in Table 7.7 lead to the integral formulas in Table 7.8.

TABLE 7.7 Derivatives of hyperbolic functions
$\dfrac{d}{dx}(\sinh u) = \cosh u \,\dfrac{du}{dx}$
$\dfrac{d}{dx}(\cosh u) = \sinh u \,\dfrac{du}{dx}$
$\dfrac{d}{dx}(\tanh u) = \operatorname{sech}^2 u \,\dfrac{du}{dx}$
$\dfrac{d}{dx}(\coth u) = -\operatorname{csch}^2 u \,\dfrac{du}{dx}$
$\dfrac{d}{dx}(\operatorname{sech} u) = -\operatorname{sech} u \tanh u \,\dfrac{du}{dx}$
$\dfrac{d}{dx}(\operatorname{csch} u) = -\operatorname{csch} u \coth u \,\dfrac{du}{dx}$

TABLE 7.8 Integral formulas for hyperbolic functions
$\displaystyle\int \sinh u \, du = \cosh u + C$
$\displaystyle\int \cosh u \, du = \sinh u + C$
$\displaystyle\int \operatorname{sech}^2 u \, du = \tanh u + C$
$\displaystyle\int \operatorname{csch}^2 u \, du = -\coth u + C$
$\displaystyle\int \operatorname{sech} u \tanh u \, du = -\operatorname{sech} u + C$
$\displaystyle\int \operatorname{csch} u \coth u \, du = -\operatorname{csch} u + C$

The derivative formulas are derived from the derivative of e^u:

$$\frac{d}{dx}(\sinh u) = \frac{d}{dx}\left(\frac{e^u - e^{-u}}{2}\right) \qquad \text{Definition of } \sinh u$$

$$= \frac{e^u \, du/dx + e^{-u} \, du/dx}{2} \qquad \text{Derivative of } e^u$$

$$= \cosh u \frac{du}{dx} \qquad \text{Definition of } \cosh u$$

This gives the first derivative formula. The calculation

$$\frac{d}{dx}(\operatorname{csch} u) = \frac{d}{dx}\left(\frac{1}{\sinh u}\right) \qquad \text{Definition of } \operatorname{csch} u$$

$$= -\frac{\cosh u}{\sinh^2 u}\frac{du}{dx} \qquad \text{Quotient Rule}$$

$$= -\frac{1}{\sinh u}\frac{\cosh u}{\sinh u}\frac{du}{dx} \qquad \text{Rearrange terms.}$$

$$= -\operatorname{csch} u \coth u \frac{du}{dx} \qquad \text{Definitions of } \operatorname{csch} u \text{ and } \coth u$$

gives the last formula. The others are obtained similarly.

EXAMPLE 1   Finding Derivatives and Integrals

(a) $\dfrac{d}{dt}\left(\tanh \sqrt{1+t^2}\right) = \mathrm{sech}^2 \sqrt{1=t^2} \cdot \dfrac{d}{dt}\left(\sqrt{1+t^2}\right)$

$\qquad\qquad\qquad\qquad = \dfrac{t}{\sqrt{1+t^2}}\,\mathrm{sech}^2 \sqrt{1+t^2}$

(b) $\displaystyle\int \coth 5x\,dx = \int \dfrac{\cosh 5x}{\sinh 5x}\,dx = \dfrac{1}{5}\int \dfrac{du}{u}$
$\qquad\qquad\qquad\qquad\qquad\qquad\qquad\qquad\qquad\qquad$ $u = \sinh 5x,$
$\qquad\qquad\qquad\qquad\qquad\qquad\qquad\qquad\qquad\qquad$ $du = 5\cosh 5x\,dx$

$\qquad\qquad\qquad = \dfrac{1}{5}\ln|u| + C = \dfrac{1}{5}\ln|\sinh 5x| + C$

(c) $\displaystyle\int_0^1 \sinh^2 x\,dx = \int_0^1 \dfrac{\cosh 2x - 1}{2}\,dx$
$\qquad\qquad\qquad\qquad\qquad\qquad\qquad\qquad\qquad\qquad$ Table 7.6

$\qquad\qquad\qquad = \dfrac{1}{2}\int_0^1 (\cosh 2x - 1)\,dx = \dfrac{1}{2}\left[\dfrac{\sinh 2x}{2} - x\right]_0^1$

$\qquad\qquad\qquad = \dfrac{\sinh 2}{4} - \dfrac{1}{2} \approx 0.40672$
$\qquad\qquad\qquad\qquad\qquad\qquad\qquad\qquad\qquad\qquad$ Evaluate with
$\qquad\qquad\qquad\qquad\qquad\qquad\qquad\qquad\qquad\qquad$ a calculator

(d) $\displaystyle\int_0^{\ln 2} 4e^x \sinh x\,dx = \int_0^{\ln 2} 4e^x \dfrac{e^x - e^{-x}}{2}\,dx = \int_0^{\ln 2} (2e^{2x} - 2)\,dx$

$\qquad\qquad\qquad = \left[e^{2x} - 2x\right]_0^{\ln 2} = (e^{2\ln 2} - 2\ln 2) - (1 - 0)$

$\qquad\qquad\qquad = 4 - 2\ln 2 - 1$

$\qquad\qquad\qquad \approx 1.6137$ ∎

Inverse Hyperbolic Functions

The inverses of the six basic hyperbolic functions are very useful in integration. Since $d(\sinh x)/dx = \cosh x > 0$, the hyperbolic sine is an increasing function of x. We denote its inverse by

$$y = \sinh^{-1} x.$$

For every value of x in the interval $-\infty < x < \infty$, the value of $y = \sinh^{-1} x$ is the number whose hyperbolic sine is x. The graphs of $y = \sinh x$ and $y = \sinh^{-1} x$ are shown in Figure 7.32a.

The function $y = \cosh x$ is not one-to-one, as we can see from the graph in Figure 7.31b. The restricted function $y = \cosh x, x \geq 0$, however, is one-to-one and therefore has an inverse, denoted by

$$y = \cosh^{-1} x.$$

For every value of $x \geq 1, y = \cosh^{-1} x$ is the number in the interval $0 \leq y < \infty$ whose hyperbolic cosine is x. The graphs of $y = \cosh x, x \geq 0$, and $y = \cosh^{-1} x$ are shown in Figure 7.32b.

Like $y = \cosh x$, the function $y = \mathrm{sech}\, x = 1/\cosh x$ fails to be one-to-one, but its restriction to nonnegative values of x does have an inverse, denoted by

$$y = \mathrm{sech}^{-1} x.$$

For every value of x in the interval $(0, 1], y = \mathrm{sech}^{-1} x$ is the nonnegative number whose hyperbolic secant is x. The graphs of $y = \mathrm{sech}\, x, x \geq 0$, and $y = \mathrm{sech}^{-1} x$ are shown in Figure 7.32c.

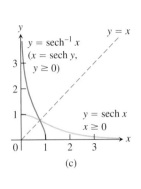

FIGURE 7.32 The graphs of the inverse hyperbolic sine, cosine, and secant of x. Notice the symmetries about the line $y = x$.

The hyperbolic tangent, cotangent, and cosecant are one-to-one on their domains and therefore have inverses, denoted by

$$y = \tanh^{-1} x, \qquad y = \coth^{-1} x, \qquad y = \operatorname{csch}^{-1} x.$$

These functions are graphed in Figure 7.33.

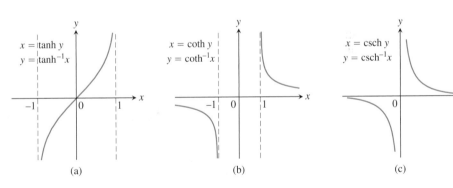

FIGURE 7.33 The graphs of the inverse hyperbolic tangent, cotangent, and cosecant of x.

TABLE 7.9 Identities for inverse hyperbolic functions

$$\operatorname{sech}^{-1} x = \cosh^{-1} \frac{1}{x}$$

$$\operatorname{csch}^{-1} x = \sinh^{-1} \frac{1}{x}$$

$$\coth^{-1} x = \tanh^{-1} \frac{1}{x}$$

Useful Identities

We use the identities in Table 7.9 to calculate the values of $\operatorname{sech}^{-1} x$, $\operatorname{csch}^{-1} x$, and $\coth^{-1} x$ on calculators that give only $\cosh^{-1} x$, $\sinh^{-1} x$, and $\tanh^{-1} x$. These identities are direct consequences of the definitions. For example, if $0 < x \le 1$, then

$$\operatorname{sech}\left(\cosh^{-1}\left(\frac{1}{x}\right)\right) = \frac{1}{\cosh\left(\cosh^{-1}\left(\frac{1}{x}\right)\right)} = \frac{1}{\left(\frac{1}{x}\right)} = x$$

so

$$\cosh^{-1}\left(\frac{1}{x}\right) = \operatorname{sech}^{-1} x$$

since the hyperbolic secant is one-to-one on $(0, 1]$.

Derivatives and Integrals

The chief use of inverse hyperbolic functions lies in integrations that reverse the derivative formulas in Table 7.10.

TABLE 7.10 Derivatives of inverse hyperbolic functions

$$\frac{d(\sinh^{-1} u)}{dx} = \frac{1}{\sqrt{1 + u^2}}\frac{du}{dx}$$

$$\frac{d(\cosh^{-1} u)}{dx} = \frac{1}{\sqrt{u^2 - 1}}\frac{du}{dx}, \qquad u > 1$$

$$\frac{d(\tanh^{-1} u)}{dx} = \frac{1}{1 - u^2}\frac{du}{dx}, \qquad |u| < 1$$

$$\frac{d(\coth^{-1} u)}{dx} = \frac{1}{1 - u^2}\frac{du}{dx}, \qquad |u| > 1$$

$$\frac{d(\operatorname{sech}^{-1} u)}{dx} = \frac{-du/dx}{u\sqrt{1 - u^2}}, \qquad 0 < u < 1$$

$$\frac{d(\operatorname{csch}^{-1} u)}{dx} = \frac{-du/dx}{|u|\sqrt{1 + u^2}}, \qquad u \neq 0$$

The restrictions $|u| < 1$ and $|u| > 1$ on the derivative formulas for $\tanh^{-1} u$ and $\coth^{-1} u$ come from the natural restrictions on the values of these functions. (See Figure 7.33a and b.) The distinction between $|u| < 1$ and $|u| > 1$ becomes important when we convert the derivative formulas into integral formulas. If $|u| < 1$, the integral of $1/(1 - u^2)$ is $\tanh^{-1} u + C$. If $|u| > 1$, the integral is $\coth^{-1} u + C$.

We illustrate how the derivatives of the inverse hyperbolic functions are found in Example 2, where we calculate $d(\cosh^{-1} u)/dx$. The other derivatives are obtained by similar calculations.

EXAMPLE 2 Derivative of the Inverse Hyperbolic Cosine

Show that if u is a differentiable function of x whose values are greater than 1, then

$$\frac{d}{dx}(\cosh^{-1} u) = \frac{1}{\sqrt{u^2 - 1}}\frac{du}{dx}.$$

Solution   First we find the derivative of $y = \cosh^{-1} x$ for $x > 1$ by applying Theorem 1 with $f(x) = \cosh x$ and $f^{-1}(x) = \cosh^{-1} x$. Theorem 1 can be applied because the derivative of $\cosh x$ is positive for $0 < x$.

$$(f^{-1})'(x) = \frac{1}{f'(f^{-1}(x))} \qquad \text{Theorem 1}$$

$$= \frac{1}{\sinh(\cosh^{-1} x)} \qquad f'(u) = \sinh u$$

$$= \frac{1}{\sqrt{\cosh^2(\cosh^{-1} x) - 1}} \qquad \begin{array}{l} \cosh^2 u - \sinh^2 u = 1, \\ \sinh u = \sqrt{\cosh^2 u - 1} \end{array}$$

$$= \frac{1}{\sqrt{x^2 - 1}} \qquad \cosh(\cosh^{-1} x) = x$$

In short,

$$\frac{d}{dx}(\cosh^{-1} x) = \frac{1}{\sqrt{x^2 - 1}}.$$

The Chain Rule gives the final result:

$$\frac{d}{dx}(\cosh^{-1} u) = \frac{1}{\sqrt{u^2 - 1}} \frac{du}{dx}. \qquad \blacksquare$$

Instead of applying Theorem 1 directly, as in Example 2, we could also find the derivative of $y = \cosh^{-1} x, x > 1$, using implicit differentiation and the Chain Rule:

$$y = \cosh^{-1} x$$

$$x = \cosh y \qquad \text{Equivalent equation}$$

$$1 = \sinh y \frac{dy}{dx} \qquad \begin{array}{l} \text{Implicit differentiation} \\ \text{with respect to } x, \text{ and} \\ \text{the Chain Rule} \end{array}$$

$$\frac{dy}{dx} = \frac{1}{\sinh y} = \frac{1}{\sqrt{\cosh^2 y - 1}} \qquad \begin{array}{l} \text{Since } x > 1, y > 0 \\ \text{and } \sinh y > 0 \end{array}$$

$$= \frac{1}{\sqrt{x^2 - 1}}. \qquad \cosh y = x$$

With appropriate substitutions, the derivative formulas in Table 7.10 lead to the integration formulas in Table 7.11. Each of the formulas in Table 7.11 can be verified by differentiating the expression on the right-hand side.

EXAMPLE 3   Using Table 7.11

Evaluate

$$\int_0^1 \frac{2 \, dx}{\sqrt{3 + 4x^2}}.$$

TABLE 7.11 Integrals leading to inverse hyperbolic functions

1. $\displaystyle\int \frac{du}{\sqrt{a^2 + u^2}} = \sinh^{-1}\left(\frac{u}{a}\right) + C,$ $\qquad a > 0$

2. $\displaystyle\int \frac{du}{\sqrt{u^2 - a^2}} = \cosh^{-1}\left(\frac{u}{a}\right) + C,$ $\qquad u > a > 0$

3. $\displaystyle\int \frac{du}{a^2 - u^2} = \begin{cases} \dfrac{1}{a}\tanh^{-1}\left(\dfrac{u}{a}\right) + C & \text{if } u^2 < a^2 \\[2mm] \dfrac{1}{a}\coth^{-1}\left(\dfrac{u}{a}\right) + C, & \text{if } u^2 > a^2 \end{cases}$

4. $\displaystyle\int \frac{du}{u\sqrt{a^2 - u^2}} = -\frac{1}{a}\operatorname{sech}^{-1}\left(\frac{u}{a}\right) + C,$ $\qquad 0 < u < a$

5. $\displaystyle\int \frac{du}{u\sqrt{a^2 + u^2}} = -\frac{1}{a}\operatorname{csch}^{-1}\left|\frac{u}{a}\right| + C,$ $\qquad u \neq 0 \text{ and } a > 0$

Solution The indefinite integral is

$$\int \frac{2\,dx}{\sqrt{3 + 4x^2}} = \int \frac{du}{\sqrt{a^2 + u^2}} \qquad u = 2x, \quad du = 2\,dx, \quad a = \sqrt{3}$$

$$= \sinh^{-1}\left(\frac{u}{a}\right) + C \qquad \text{Formula from Table 7.11}$$

$$= \sinh^{-1}\left(\frac{2x}{\sqrt{3}}\right) + C.$$

Therefore,

$$\int_0^1 \frac{2\,dx}{\sqrt{3 + 4x^2}} = \sinh^{-1}\left(\frac{2x}{\sqrt{3}}\right)\Big]_0^1 = \sinh^{-1}\left(\frac{2}{\sqrt{3}}\right) - \sinh^{-1}(0)$$

$$= \sinh^{-1}\left(\frac{2}{\sqrt{3}}\right) - 0 \approx 0.98665.$$

■

EXERCISES 7.8

Hyperbolic Function Values and Identities

Each of Exercises 1–4 gives a value of $\sinh x$ or $\cosh x$. Use the definitions and the identity $\cosh^2 x - \sinh^2 x = 1$ to find the values of the remaining five hyperbolic functions.

1. $\sinh x = -\dfrac{3}{4}$

2. $\sinh x = \dfrac{4}{3}$

3. $\cosh x = \dfrac{17}{15}, \quad x > 0$

4. $\cosh x = \dfrac{13}{5}, \quad x > 0$

Rewrite the expressions in Exercises 5–10 in terms of exponentials and simplify the results as much as you can.

5. $2\cosh(\ln x)$

6. $\sinh(2\ln x)$

7. $\cosh 5x + \sinh 5x$

8. $\cosh 3x - \sinh 3x$

9. $(\sinh x + \cosh x)^4$

10. $\ln(\cosh x + \sinh x) + \ln(\cosh x - \sinh x)$

11. Use the identities

$$\sinh (x + y) = \sinh x \cosh y + \cosh x \sinh y$$
$$\cosh (x + y) = \cosh x \cosh y + \sinh x \sinh y$$

to show that

a. $\sinh 2x = 2 \sinh x \cosh x$

b. $\cosh 2x = \cosh^2 x + \sinh^2 x$.

12. Use the definitions of $\cosh x$ and $\sinh x$ to show that

$$\cosh^2 x - \sinh^2 x = 1.$$

Derivatives

In Exercises 13–24, find the derivative of y with respect to the appropriate variable.

13. $y = 6 \sinh \dfrac{x}{3}$

14. $y = \dfrac{1}{2} \sinh (2x + 1)$

15. $y = 2\sqrt{t} \tanh \sqrt{t}$

16. $y = t^2 \tanh \dfrac{1}{t}$

17. $y = \ln (\sinh z)$

18. $y = \ln (\cosh z)$

19. $y = \operatorname{sech} \theta (1 - \ln \operatorname{sech} \theta)$

20. $y = \operatorname{csch} \theta (1 - \ln \operatorname{csch} \theta)$

21. $y = \ln \cosh v - \dfrac{1}{2} \tanh^2 v$

22. $y = \ln \sinh v - \dfrac{1}{2} \coth^2 v$

23. $y = (x^2 + 1) \operatorname{sech} (\ln x)$

(*Hint:* Before differentiating, express in terms of exponentials and simplify.)

24. $y = (4x^2 - 1) \operatorname{csch} (\ln 2x)$

In Exercises 25–36, find the derivative of y with respect to the appropriate variable.

25. $y = \sinh^{-1} \sqrt{x}$

26. $y = \cosh^{-1} 2\sqrt{x + 1}$

27. $y = (1 - \theta) \tanh^{-1} \theta$

28. $y = (\theta^2 + 2\theta) \tanh^{-1} (\theta + 1)$

29. $y = (1 - t) \coth^{-1} \sqrt{t}$

30. $y = (1 - t^2) \coth^{-1} t$

31. $y = \cos^{-1} x - x \operatorname{sech}^{-1} x$

32. $y = \ln x + \sqrt{1 - x^2} \operatorname{sech}^{-1} x$

33. $y = \operatorname{csch}^{-1} \left(\dfrac{1}{2} \right)^{\theta}$

34. $y = \operatorname{csch}^{-1} 2^{\theta}$

35. $y = \sinh^{-1} (\tan x)$

36. $y = \cosh^{-1} (\sec x), \quad 0 < x < \pi/2$

Integration Formulas

Verify the integration formulas in Exercises 37–40.

37. a. $\displaystyle \int \operatorname{sech} x \, dx = \tan^{-1} (\sinh x) + C$

b. $\displaystyle \int \operatorname{sech} x \, dx = \sin^{-1} (\tanh x) + C$

38. $\displaystyle \int x \operatorname{sech}^{-1} x \, dx = \dfrac{x^2}{2} \operatorname{sech}^{-1} x - \dfrac{1}{2} \sqrt{1 - x^2} + C$

39. $\displaystyle \int x \coth^{-1} x \, dx = \dfrac{x^2 - 1}{2} \coth^{-1} x + \dfrac{x}{2} + C$

40. $\displaystyle \int \tanh^{-1} x \, dx = x \tanh^{-1} x + \dfrac{1}{2} \ln (1 - x^2) + C$

Indefinite Integrals

Evaluate the integrals in Exercises 41–50.

41. $\displaystyle \int \sinh 2x \, dx$

42. $\displaystyle \int \sinh \dfrac{x}{5} \, dx$

43. $\displaystyle \int 6 \cosh \left(\dfrac{x}{2} - \ln 3 \right) dx$

44. $\displaystyle \int 4 \cosh (3x - \ln 2) \, dx$

45. $\displaystyle \int \tanh \dfrac{x}{7} \, dx$

46. $\displaystyle \int \coth \dfrac{\theta}{\sqrt{3}} \, d\theta$

47. $\displaystyle \int \operatorname{sech}^2 \left(x - \dfrac{1}{2} \right) dx$

48. $\displaystyle \int \operatorname{csch}^2 (5 - x) \, dx$

49. $\displaystyle \int \dfrac{\operatorname{sech} \sqrt{t} \tanh \sqrt{t} \, dt}{\sqrt{t}}$

50. $\displaystyle \int \dfrac{\operatorname{csch} (\ln t) \coth (\ln t) \, dt}{t}$

Definite Integrals

Evaluate the integrals in Exercises 51–60.

51. $\displaystyle \int_{\ln 2}^{\ln 4} \coth x \, dx$

52. $\displaystyle \int_{0}^{\ln 2} \tanh 2x \, dx$

53. $\displaystyle \int_{-\ln 4}^{-\ln 2} 2e^{\theta} \cosh \theta \, d\theta$

54. $\displaystyle \int_{0}^{\ln 2} 4e^{-\theta} \sinh \theta \, d\theta$

55. $\displaystyle \int_{-\pi/4}^{\pi/4} \cosh (\tan \theta) \sec^2 \theta \, d\theta$

56. $\displaystyle \int_{0}^{\pi/2} 2 \sinh (\sin \theta) \cos \theta \, d\theta$

57. $\displaystyle \int_{1}^{2} \dfrac{\cosh (\ln t)}{t} \, dt$

58. $\displaystyle \int_{1}^{4} \dfrac{8 \cosh \sqrt{x}}{\sqrt{x}} \, dx$

59. $\displaystyle \int_{-\ln 2}^{0} \cosh^2 \left(\dfrac{x}{2} \right) dx$

60. $\displaystyle \int_{0}^{\ln 10} 4 \sinh^2 \left(\dfrac{x}{2} \right) dx$

Evaluating Inverse Hyperbolic Functions and Related Integrals

When hyperbolic function keys are not available on a calculator, it is still possible to evaluate the inverse hyperbolic functions by expressing them as logarithms, as shown here.

$$\sinh^{-1} x = \ln \left(x + \sqrt{x^2 + 1} \right), \qquad -\infty < x < \infty$$

$$\cosh^{-1} x = \ln \left(x + \sqrt{x^2 + 1} \right), \qquad x \geq 1$$

$$\tanh^{-1} x = \dfrac{1}{2} \ln \dfrac{1 + x}{1 - x}, \qquad |x| < 1$$

$$\operatorname{sech}^{-1} x = \ln \left(\dfrac{1 + \sqrt{1 - x^2}}{x} \right), \qquad 0 < x \leq 1$$

$$\operatorname{csch}^{-1} x = \ln \left(\dfrac{1}{x} + \dfrac{\sqrt{1 + x^2}}{|x|} \right), \qquad x \neq 0$$

$$\coth^{-1} x = \dfrac{1}{2} \ln \dfrac{x + 1}{x - 1}, \qquad |x| > 1$$

Use the formulas in the box here to express the numbers in Exercises 61–66 in terms of natural logarithms.

61. $\sinh^{-1}(-5/12)$

62. $\cosh^{-1}(5/3)$

63. $\tanh^{-1}(-1/2)$

64. $\coth^{-1}(5/4)$

65. $\operatorname{sech}^{-1}(3/5)$

66. $\operatorname{csch}^{-1}(-1/\sqrt{3})$

Evaluate the integrals in Exercises 67–74 in terms of

  a. inverse hyperbolic functions.

  b. natural logarithms.

67. $\displaystyle\int_0^{2\sqrt{3}} \frac{dx}{\sqrt{4+x^2}}$

68. $\displaystyle\int_0^{1/3} \frac{6\,dx}{\sqrt{1+9x^2}}$

69. $\displaystyle\int_{5/4}^2 \frac{dx}{1-x^2}$

70. $\displaystyle\int_0^{1/2} \frac{dx}{1-x^2}$

71. $\displaystyle\int_{1/5}^{3/13} \frac{dx}{x\sqrt{1-16x^2}}$

72. $\displaystyle\int_1^2 \frac{dx}{x\sqrt{4+x^2}}$

73. $\displaystyle\int_0^{\pi} \frac{\cos x\,dx}{\sqrt{1+\sin^2 x}}$

74. $\displaystyle\int_1^e \frac{dx}{x\sqrt{1+(\ln x)^2}}$

Applications and Theory

75. a. Show that if a function f is defined on an interval symmetric about the origin (so that f is defined at $-x$ whenever it is defined at x), then

$$f(x) = \frac{f(x)+f(-x)}{2} + \frac{f(x)-f(-x)}{2}. \qquad (1)$$

Then show that $(f(x)+f(-x))/2$ is even and that $(f(x)-f(-x))/2$ is odd.

  b. Equation (1) simplifies considerably if f itself is (i) even or (ii) odd. What are the new equations? Give reasons for your answers.

76. Derive the formula $\sinh^{-1}x = \ln\left(x + \sqrt{x^2+1}\right)$, $-\infty < x < \infty$. Explain in your derivation why the plus sign is used with the square root instead of the minus sign.

77. Skydiving If a body of mass m falling from rest under the action of gravity encounters an air resistance proportional to the square of the velocity, then the body's velocity t sec into the fall satisfies the differential equation

$$m\frac{dv}{dt} = mg - kv^2,$$

where k is a constant that depends on the body's aerodynamic properties and the density of the air. (We assume that the fall is short enough so that the variation in the air's density will not affect the outcome significantly.)

  a. Show that

$$v = \sqrt{\frac{mg}{k}}\tanh\left(\sqrt{\frac{gk}{m}}\,t\right)$$

satisfies the differential equation and the initial condition that $v = 0$ when $t = 0$.

  b. Find the body's *limiting velocity*, $\lim_{t\to\infty} v$.

  c. For a 160-lb skydiver ($mg = 160$), with time in seconds and distance in feet, a typical value for k is 0.005. What is the diver's limiting velocity?

78. Accelerations whose magnitudes are proportional to displacement Suppose that the position of a body moving along a coordinate line at time t is

  a. $s = a\cos kt + b\sin kt$

  b. $s = a\cosh kt + b\sinh kt$.

Show in both cases that the acceleration d^2s/dt^2 is proportional to s but that in the first case it is directed toward the origin, whereas in the second case it is directed away from the origin.

79. Tractor trailers and the tractrix When a tractor trailer turns into a cross street or driveway, its rear wheels follow a curve like the one shown here. (This is why the rear wheels sometimes ride up over the curb.) We can find an equation for the curve if we picture the rear wheels as a mass M at the point $(1, 0)$ on the x-axis attached by a rod of unit length to a point P representing the cab at the origin. As the point P moves up the y-axis, it drags M along behind it. The curve traced by M—called a *tractrix* from the Latin word *tractum*, for "drag"—can be shown to be the graph of the function $y = f(x)$ that solves the initial value problem

Differential equation: $\quad\dfrac{dy}{dx} = -\dfrac{1}{x\sqrt{1-x^2}} + \dfrac{x}{\sqrt{1-x^2}}$

Initial condition: $\quad y = 0 \quad$ when $\quad x = 1$.

Solve the initial value problem to find an equation for the curve. (You need an inverse hyperbolic function.)

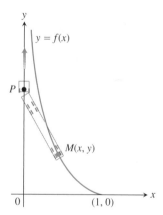

80. Area Show that the area of the region in the first quadrant enclosed by the curve $y = (1/a)\cosh ax$, the coordinate axes, and the line $x = b$ is the same as the area of a rectangle of height $1/a$ and length s, where s is the length of the curve from $x = 0$ to $x = b$. (See accompanying figure.)

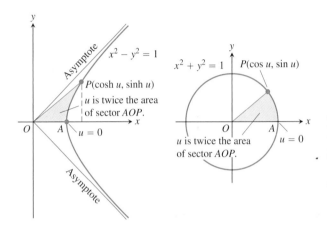

b. Differentiate both sides of the equation in part (a) with respect to u to show that

$$A'(u) = \frac{1}{2}.$$

c. Solve this last equation for $A(u)$. What is the value of $A(0)$? What is the value of the constant of integration C in your solution? With C determined, what does your solution say about the relationship of u to $A(u)$?

One of the analogies between hyperbolic and circular functions is revealed by these two diagrams (Exercise 84).

81. Volume   A region in the first quadrant is bounded above by the curve $y = \cosh x$, below by the curve $y = \sinh x$, and on the left and right by the y-axis and the line $x = 2$, respectively. Find the volume of the solid generated by revolving the region about the x-axis.

82. Volume   The region enclosed by the curve $y = \operatorname{sech} x$, the x-axis, and the lines $x = \pm \ln \sqrt{3}$ is revolved about the x-axis to generate a solid. Find the volume of the solid.

83. Arc length   Find the length of the segment of the curve $y = (1/2) \cosh 2x$ from $x = 0$ to $x = \ln \sqrt{5}$.

84. The hyperbolic in hyperbolic functions   In case you are wondering where the name *hyperbolic* comes from, here is the answer: Just as $x = \cos u$ and $y = \sin u$ are identified with points (x, y) on the unit circle, the functions $x = \cosh u$ and $y = \sinh u$ are identified with points (x, y) on the right-hand branch of the unit hyperbola, $x^2 - y^2 = 1$.

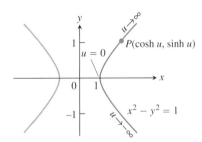

Since $\cosh^2 u - \sinh^2 u = 1$, the point $(\cosh u, \sinh u)$ lies on the right-hand branch of the hyperbola $x^2 - y^2 = 1$ for every value of u (Exercise 84).

Another analogy between hyperbolic and circular functions is that the variable u in the coordinates $(\cosh u, \sinh u)$ for the points of the right-hand branch of the hyperbola $x^2 - y^2 = 1$ is twice the area of the sector AOP pictured in the accompanying figure. To see why this is so, carry out the following steps.

a. Show that the area $A(u)$ of sector AOP is

$$A(u) = \frac{1}{2} \cosh u \sinh u - \int_1^{\cosh u} \sqrt{x^2 - 1} \, dx.$$

85. A minimal surface   Find the area of the surface swept out by revolving about the x-axis the curve $y = 4 \cosh (x/4)$, $-\ln 16 \le x \le \ln 81$.

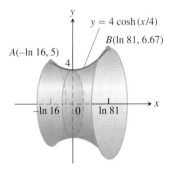

It can be shown that, of all continuously differentiable curves joining points A and B in the figure, the curve $y = 4 \cosh (x/4)$ generates the surface of least area. If you made a rigid wire frame of the end-circles through A and B and dipped them in a soap-film solution, the surface spanning the circles would be the one generated by the curve.

T 86. a. Find the centroid of the curve $y = \cosh x$, $-\ln 2 \le x \le \ln 2$.

b. Evaluate the coordinates to two decimal places. Then sketch the curve and plot the centroid to show its relation to the curve.

Hanging Cables

87. Imagine a cable, like a telephone line or TV cable, strung from one support to another and hanging freely. The cable's weight per unit length is w and the horizontal tension at its lowest point is a vector of length H. If we choose a coordinate system for the plane of the cable in which the x-axis is horizontal, the force of gravity is straight down, the positive y-axis points straight up, and the lowest point of the cable lies at the point $y = H/w$ on the y-axis (see accompanying figure), then it can be shown that the cable lies along the graph of the hyperbolic cosine

$$y = \frac{H}{w} \cosh \frac{w}{H} x.$$

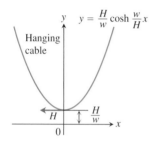

Such a curve is sometimes called a **chain curve** or a **catenary**, the latter deriving from the Latin *catena*, meaning "chain."

a. Let $P(x, y)$ denote an arbitrary point on the cable. The next accompanying figure displays the tension at P as a vector of length (magnitude) T, as well as the tension H at the lowest point A. Show that the cable's slope at P is

$$\tan \phi = \frac{dy}{dx} = \sinh \frac{w}{H} x.$$

b. Using the result from part (a) and the fact that the horizontal tension at P must equal H (the cable is not moving), show that $T = wy$. Hence, the magnitude of the tension at $P(x, y)$ is exactly equal to the weight of y units of cable.

88. (*Continuation of Exercise 87.*) The length of arc AP in the Exercise 87 figure is $s = (1/a) \sinh ax$, where $a = w/H$. Show that the coordinates of P may be expressed in terms of s as

$$x = \frac{1}{a} \sinh^{-1} as, \qquad y = \sqrt{s^2 + \frac{1}{a^2}}.$$

89. **The sag and horizontal tension in a cable**   The ends of a cable 32 ft long and weighing 2 lb/ft are fastened at the same level to posts 30 ft apart.

a. Model the cable with the equation

$$y = \frac{1}{a} \cosh ax, \quad -15 \le x \le 15.$$

Use information from Exercise 88 to show that a satisfies the equation

$$16a = \sinh 15a. \tag{2}$$

T b. Solve Equation (2) graphically by estimating the coordinates of the points where the graphs of the equations $y = 16a$ and $y = \sinh 15a$ intersect in the ay-plane.

T c. Solve Equation (2) for a numerically. Compare your solution with the value you found in part (b).

d. Estimate the horizontal tension in the cable at the cable's lowest point.

T e. Using the value found for a in part (c), graph the catenary

$$y = \frac{1}{a} \cosh ax$$

over the interval $-15 \le x \le 15$. Estimate the sag in the cable at its center.

Chapter 7   Questions to Guide Your Review

1. What functions have inverses? How do you know if two functions f and g are inverses of one another? Give examples of functions that are (are not) inverses of one another.

2. How are the domains, ranges, and graphs of functions and their inverses related? Give an example.

3. How can you sometimes express the inverse of a function of x as a function of x?

4. Under what circumstances can you be sure that the inverse of a function f is differentiable? How are the derivatives of f and f^{-1} related?

5. What is the natural logarithm function? What are its domain, range, and derivative? What arithmetic properties does it have? Comment on its graph.

6. What is logarithmic differentiation? Give an example.

7. What integrals lead to logarithms? Give examples. What are the integrals of $\tan x$ and $\cot x$?

8. How is the exponential function e^x defined? What are its domain, range, and derivative? What laws of exponents does it obey? Comment on its graph.

9. How are the functions a^x and $\log_a x$ defined? Are there any restrictions on a? How is the graph of $\log_a x$ related to the graph of $\ln x$? What truth is there in the statement that there is really only one exponential function and one logarithmic function?

10. Describe some of the applications of base 10 logarithms.

11. What is the law of exponential change? How can it be derived from an initial value problem? What are some of the applications of the law?

12. How do you compare the growth rates of positive functions as $x \to \infty$?

13. What roles do the functions e^x and $\ln x$ play in growth comparisons?

14. Describe big-oh and little-oh notation. Give examples.

15. Which is more efficient—a sequential search or a binary search? Explain.

16. How are the inverse trigonometric functions defined? How can you sometimes use right triangles to find values of these functions? Give examples.

17. What are the derivatives of the inverse trigonometric functions? How do the domains of the derivatives compare with the domains of the functions?

18. What integrals lead to inverse trigonometric functions? How do substitution and completing the square broaden the application of these integrals?

19. What are the six basic hyperbolic functions? Comment on their domains, ranges, and graphs. What are some of the identities relating them?

20. What are the derivatives of the six basic hyperbolic functions? What are the corresponding integral formulas? What similarities do you see here with the six basic trigonometric functions?

21. How are the inverse hyperbolic functions defined? Comment on their domains, ranges, and graphs. How can you find values of $\text{sech}^{-1} x$, $\text{csch}^{-1} x$, and $\coth^{-1} x$ using a calculator's keys for $\cosh^{-1} x$, $\sinh^{-1} x$, and $\tanh^{-1} x$?

22. What integrals lead naturally to inverse hyperbolic functions?

Chapter 7 Practice Exercises

Differentiation

In Exercises 1–24, find the derivative of y with respect to the appropriate variable.

1. $y = 10e^{-x/5}$

2. $y = \sqrt{2}e^{\sqrt{2}x}$

3. $y = \frac{1}{4}xe^{4x} - \frac{1}{16}e^{4x}$

4. $y = x^2e^{-2/x}$

5. $y = \ln(\sin^2\theta)$

6. $y = \ln(\sec^2\theta)$

7. $y = \log_2(x^2/2)$

8. $y = \log_5(3x - 7)$

9. $y = 8^{-t}$

10. $y = 9^{2t}$

11. $y = 5x^{3.6}$

12. $y = \sqrt{2}x^{-\sqrt{2}}$

13. $y = (x + 2)^{x+2}$

14. $y = 2(\ln x)^{x/2}$

15. $y = \sin^{-1}\sqrt{1 - u^2}, \quad 0 < u < 1$

16. $y = \sin^{-1}\left(\frac{1}{\sqrt{v}}\right), \quad v > 1$ **17.** $y = \ln\cos^{-1}x$

18. $y = z\cos^{-1}z - \sqrt{1 - z^2}$

19. $y = t\tan^{-1}t - \frac{1}{2}\ln t$

20. $y = (1 + t^2)\cot^{-1}2t$

21. $y = z\sec^{-1}z - \sqrt{z^2 - 1}, \quad z > 1$

22. $y = 2\sqrt{x - 1}\,\sec^{-1}\sqrt{x}$

23. $y = \csc^{-1}(\sec\theta), \quad 0 < \theta < \pi/2$

24. $y = (1 + x^2)e^{\tan^{-1}x}$

Logarithmic Differentiation

In Exercises 25–30, use logarithmic differentiation to find the derivative of y with respect to the appropriate variable.

25. $y = \dfrac{2(x^2 + 1)}{\sqrt{\cos 2x}}$

26. $y = \sqrt[10]{\dfrac{3x + 4}{2x - 4}}$

27. $y = \left(\dfrac{(t + 1)(t - 1)}{(t - 2)(t + 3)}\right)^5, \quad t > 2$

28. $y = \dfrac{2u2^u}{\sqrt{u^2 + 1}}$

29. $y = (\sin\theta)^{\sqrt{\theta}}$

30. $y = (\ln x)^{1/(\ln x)}$

Integration

Evaluate the integrals in Exercises 31–78.

31. $\displaystyle\int e^x\sin(e^x)\,dx$

32. $\displaystyle\int e^t\cos(3e^t - 2)\,dt$

33. $\int e^x \sec^2 (e^x - 7) \, dx$

34. $\int e^y \csc (e^y + 1) \cot (e^y + 1) \, dy$

35. $\int \sec^2 (x) e^{\tan x} \, dx$

36. $\int \csc^2 x \, e^{\cot x} \, dx$

37. $\int_{-1}^{1} \frac{dx}{3x - 4}$

38. $\int_{1}^{e} \frac{\sqrt{\ln x}}{x} \, dx$

39. $\int_{0}^{\pi} \tan \frac{x}{3} \, dx$

40. $\int_{1/6}^{1/4} 2 \cot \pi x \, dx$

41. $\int_{0}^{4} \frac{2t}{t^2 - 25} \, dt$

42. $\int_{-\pi/2}^{\pi/6} \frac{\cos t}{1 - \sin t} \, dt$

43. $\int \frac{\tan (\ln v)}{v} \, dv$

44. $\int \frac{dv}{v \ln v}$

45. $\int \frac{(\ln x)^{-3}}{x} \, dx$

46. $\int \frac{\ln (x - 5)}{x - 5} \, dx$

47. $\int \frac{1}{r} \csc^2 (1 + \ln r) \, dr$

48. $\int \frac{\cos (1 - \ln v)}{v} \, dv$

49. $\int x 3^{x^2} \, dx$

50. $\int 2^{\tan x} \sec^2 x \, dx$

51. $\int_{1}^{7} \frac{3}{x} \, dx$

52. $\int_{1}^{32} \frac{1}{5x} \, dx$

53. $\int_{1}^{4} \left(\frac{x}{8} + \frac{1}{2x} \right) dx$

54. $\int_{1}^{8} \left(\frac{2}{3x} - \frac{8}{x^2} \right) dx$

55. $\int_{-2}^{-1} e^{-(x+1)} \, dx$

56. $\int_{-\ln 2}^{0} e^{2w} \, dw$

57. $\int_{0}^{\ln 5} e^r (3e^r + 1)^{-3/2} \, dr$

58. $\int_{0}^{\ln 9} e^\theta (e^\theta - 1)^{1/2} \, d\theta$

59. $\int_{1}^{e} \frac{1}{x} (1 + 7 \ln x)^{-1/3} \, dx$

60. $\int_{e}^{e^2} \frac{1}{x \sqrt{\ln x}} \, dx$

61. $\int_{1}^{3} \frac{(\ln (v + 1))^2}{v + 1} \, dv$

62. $\int_{2}^{4} (1 + \ln t) t \ln t \, dt$

63. $\int_{1}^{8} \frac{\log_4 \theta}{\theta} \, d\theta$

64. $\int_{1}^{e} \frac{8 \ln 3 \log_3 \theta}{\theta} \, d\theta$

65. $\int_{-3/4}^{3/4} \frac{6 \, dx}{\sqrt{9 - 4x^2}}$

66. $\int_{-1/5}^{1/5} \frac{6 \, dx}{\sqrt{4 - 25x^2}}$

67. $\int_{-2}^{2} \frac{3 \, dt}{4 + 3t^2}$

68. $\int_{\sqrt{3}}^{3} \frac{dt}{3 + t^2}$

69. $\int \frac{dy}{y \sqrt{4y^2 - 1}}$

70. $\int \frac{24 \, dy}{y \sqrt{y^2 - 16}}$

71. $\int_{\sqrt{2/3}}^{2/3} \frac{dy}{|y| \sqrt{9y^2 - 1}}$

72. $\int_{-2/\sqrt{5}}^{-\sqrt{6}/\sqrt{5}} \frac{dy}{|y| \sqrt{5y^2 - 3}}$

73. $\int \frac{dx}{\sqrt{-2x - x^2}}$

74. $\int \frac{dx}{\sqrt{-x^2 + 4x - 1}}$

75. $\int_{-2}^{-1} \frac{2 \, dv}{v^2 + 4v + 5}$

76. $\int_{-1}^{1} \frac{3 \, dv}{4v^2 + 4v + 4}$

77. $\int \frac{dt}{(t + 1) \sqrt{t^2 + 2t - 8}}$

78. $\int \frac{dt}{(3t + 1) \sqrt{9t^2 + 6t}}$

Solving Equations with Logarithmic or Exponential Terms

In Exercises 79–84, solve for y.

79. $3^y = 2^{y+1}$

80. $4^{-y} = 3^{y+2}$

81. $9e^{2y} = x^2$

82. $3^y = 3 \ln x$

83. $\ln (y - 1) = x + \ln y$

84. $\ln (10 \ln y) = \ln 5x$

Evaluating Limits

Find the limits in Exercises 85–96.

85. $\lim_{x \to 0} \frac{10^x - 1}{x}$

86. $\lim_{\theta \to 0} \frac{3^\theta - 1}{\theta}$

87. $\lim_{x \to 0} \frac{2^{\sin x} - 1}{e^x - 1}$

88. $\lim_{x \to 0} \frac{2^{-\sin x} - 1}{e^x - 1}$

89. $\lim_{x \to 0} \frac{5 - 5 \cos x}{e^x - x - 1}$

90. $\lim_{x \to 0} \frac{4 - 4e^x}{xe^x}$

91. $\lim_{t \to 0^+} \frac{t - \ln (1 + 2t)}{t^2}$

92. $\lim_{x \to 4} \frac{\sin^2 (\pi x)}{e^{x-4} + 3 - x}$

93. $\lim_{t \to 0^+} \left(\frac{e^t}{t} - \frac{1}{t} \right)$

94. $\lim_{y \to 0^+} e^{-1/y} \ln y$

95. $\lim_{x \to \infty} \left(1 + \frac{3}{x} \right)^x$

96. $\lim_{x \to 0^+} \left(1 + \frac{3}{x} \right)^x$

Comparing Growth Rates of Functions

97. Does f grow faster, slower, or at the same rate as g as $x \to \infty$? Give reasons for your answers.

   a. $f(x) = \log_2 x$, $g(x) = \log_3 x$

   b. $f(x) = x$, $g(x) = x + \frac{1}{x}$

   c. $f(x) = x/100$, $g(x) = xe^{-x}$

   d. $f(x) = x$, $g(x) = \tan^{-1} x$

   e. $f(x) = \csc^{-1} x$, $g(x) = 1/x$

   f. $f(x) = \sinh x$, $g(x) = e^x$

98. Does f grow faster, slower, or at the same rate as g as $x \to \infty$? Give reasons for your answers.

   a. $f(x) = 3^{-x}$, $g(x) = 2^{-x}$

   b. $f(x) = \ln 2x$, $g(x) = \ln x^2$

   c. $f(x) = 10x^3 + 2x^2$, $g(x) = e^x$

   d. $f(x) = \tan^{-1}(1/x)$, $g(x) = 1/x$

   e. $f(x) = \sin^{-1}(1/x)$, $g(x) = 1/x^2$

   f. $f(x) = \mathrm{sech}\, x$, $g(x) = e^{-x}$

99. True, or false? Give reasons for your answers.

a. $\dfrac{1}{x^2} + \dfrac{1}{x^4} = O\left(\dfrac{1}{x^2}\right)$ **b.** $\dfrac{1}{x^2} + \dfrac{1}{x^4} = O\left(\dfrac{1}{x^4}\right)$

c. $x = o(x + \ln x)$ **d.** $\ln(\ln x) = o(\ln x)$

e. $\tan^{-1} x = O(1)$ **f.** $\cosh x = O(e^x)$

100. True, or false? Give reasons for your answers.

a. $\dfrac{1}{x^4} = O\left(\dfrac{1}{x^2} + \dfrac{1}{x^4}\right)$ **b.** $\dfrac{1}{x^4} = o\left(\dfrac{1}{x^2} + \dfrac{1}{x^4}\right)$

c. $\ln x = o(x + 1)$ **d.** $\ln 2x = O(\ln x)$

e. $\sec^{-1} x = O(1)$ **f.** $\sinh x = O(e^x)$

Theory and Applications

101. The function $f(x) = e^x + x$, being differentiable and one-to-one, has a differentiable inverse $f^{-1}(x)$. Find the value of df^{-1}/dx at the point $f(\ln 2)$.

102. Find the inverse of the function $f(x) = 1 + (1/x), x \neq 0$. Then show that $f^{-1}(f(x)) = f(f^{-1}(x)) = x$ and that

$$\left.\frac{df^{-1}}{dx}\right|_{f(x)} = \frac{1}{f'(x)}.$$

In Exercises 103 and 104, find the absolute maximum and minimum values of each function on the given interval.

103. $y = x \ln 2x - x$, $\left[\dfrac{1}{2e}, \dfrac{e}{2}\right]$

104. $y = 10x(2 - \ln x)$, $(0, e^2]$

105. Area   Find the area between the curve $y = 2(\ln x)/x$ and the x-axis from $x = 1$ to $x = e$.

106. Area

a. Show that the area between the curve $y = 1/x$ and the x-axis from $x = 10$ to $x = 20$ is the same as the area between the curve and the x-axis from $x = 1$ to $x = 2$.

b. Show that the area between the curve $y = 1/x$ and the x-axis from ka to kb is the same as the area between the curve and the x-axis from $x = a$ to $x = b$ $(0 < a < b, k > 0)$.

107. A particle is traveling upward and to the right along the curve $y = \ln x$. Its x-coordinate is increasing at the rate $(dx/dt) = \sqrt{x}$ m/sec. At what rate is the y-coordinate changing at the point $(e^2, 2)$?

108. A girl is sliding down a slide shaped like the curve $y = 9e^{-x/3}$. Her y-coordinate is changing at the rate $dy/dt = (-1/4)\sqrt{9 - y}$ ft/sec. At approximately what rate is her x-coordinate changing when she reaches the bottom of the slide at $x = 9$ ft? (Take e^3 to be 20 and round your answer to the nearest ft/sec.)

109. The rectangle shown here has one side on the positive y-axis, one side on the positive x-axis, and its upper right-hand vertex on the curve $y = e^{-x^2}$. What dimensions give the rectangle its largest area, and what is that area?

110. The rectangle shown here has one side on the positive y-axis, one side on the positive x-axis, and its upper right-hand vertex on the curve $y = (\ln x)/x^2$. What dimensions give the rectangle its largest area, and what is that area?

111. The functions $f(x) = \ln 5x$ and $g(x) = \ln 3x$ differ by a constant. What constant? Give reasons for your answer.

112. a. If $(\ln x)/x = (\ln 2)/2$, must $x = 2$?

b. If $(\ln x)/x = -2 \ln 2$, must $x = 1/2$?

Give reasons for your answers.

113. The quotient $(\log_4 x)/(\log_2 x)$ has a constant value. What value? Give reasons for your answer.

T 114. $\log_x (2)$ **vs.** $\log_2 (x)$ How does $f(x) = \log_x (2)$ compare with $g(x) = \log_2 (x)$? Here is one way to find out.

a. Use the equation $\log_a b = (\ln b)/(\ln a)$ to express $f(x)$ and $g(x)$ in terms of natural logarithms.

b. Graph f and g together. Comment on the behavior of f in relation to the signs and values of g.

T 115. Graph the following functions and use what you see to locate and estimate the extreme values, identify the coordinates of the inflection points, and identify the intervals on which the graphs are concave up and concave down. Then confirm your estimates by working with the functions' derivatives.

a. $y = (\ln x)/\sqrt{x}$ **b.** $y = e^{-x^2}$ **c.** $y = (1 + x)e^{-x}$

T 116. Graph $f(x) = x \ln x$. Does the function appear to have an absolute minimum value? Confirm your answer with calculus.

117. What is the age of a sample of charcoal in which 90% of the carbon-14 originally present has decayed?

118. Cooling a pie   A deep-dish apple pie, whose internal temperature was 220°F when removed from the oven, was set out on a breezy 40°F porch to cool. Fifteen minutes later, the pie's internal temperature was 180°F. How long did it take the pie to cool from there to 70°F?

119. Locating a solar station   You are under contract to build a solar station at ground level on the east–west line between the two buildings shown here. How far from the taller building should you place the station to maximize the number of hours it will be in the sun on a day when the sun passes directly overhead? Begin by observing that

$$\theta = \pi - \cot^{-1} \frac{x}{60} - \cot^{-1} \frac{50 - x}{30}.$$

Then find the value of x that maximizes θ.

120. A round underwater transmission cable consists of a core of copper wires surrounded by nonconducting insulation. If x denotes the ratio of the radius of the core to the thickness of the insulation, it is known that the speed of the transmission signal is given by the equation $v = x^2 \ln (1/x)$. If the radius of the core is 1 cm, what insulation thickness h will allow the greatest transmission speed?

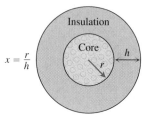

Chapter 7 Additional and Advanced Exercises

Limits

Find the limits in Exercises 1–6.

1. $\lim\limits_{b \to 1^-} \int_0^b \dfrac{dx}{\sqrt{1 - x^2}}$

2. $\lim\limits_{x \to \infty} \dfrac{1}{x} \int_0^x \tan^{-1} t \, dt$

3. $\lim\limits_{x \to 0^+} (\cos \sqrt{x})^{1/x}$

4. $\lim\limits_{x \to \infty} (x + e^x)^{2/x}$

5. $\lim\limits_{n \to \infty} \left(\dfrac{1}{n + 1} + \dfrac{1}{n + 2} + \cdots + \dfrac{1}{2n} \right)$

6. $\lim\limits_{n \to \infty} \dfrac{1}{n} \left(e^{1/n} + e^{2/n} + \cdots + e^{(n-1)/n} + e^{n/n} \right)$

7. Let $A(t)$ be the area of the region in the first quadrant enclosed by the coordinate axes, the curve $y = e^{-x}$, and the vertical line $x = t, t > 0$. Let $V(t)$ be the volume of the solid generated by revolving the region about the x-axis. Find the following limits.

a. $\lim\limits_{t \to \infty} A(t)$ **b.** $\lim\limits_{t \to \infty} V(t)/A(t)$ **c.** $\lim\limits_{t \to 0^+} V(t)/A(t)$

8. Varying a logarithm's base

a. Find $\lim \log_a 2$ as $a \to 0^+, 1^-, 1^+$, and ∞.

T b. Graph $y = \log_a 2$ as a function of a over the interval $0 < a \le 4$.

Theory and Examples

9. Find the areas between the curves $y = 2(\log_2 x)/x$ and $y = 2(\log_4 x)/x$ and the x-axis from $x = 1$ to $x = e$. What is the ratio of the larger area to the smaller?

T 10. Graph $f(x) = \tan^{-1} x + \tan^{-1}(1/x)$ for $-5 \le x \le 5$. Then use calculus to explain what you see. How would you expect f to behave beyond the interval $[-5, 5]$? Give reasons for your answer.

11. For what $x > 0$ does $x^{(x^x)} = (x^x)^x$? Give reasons for your answer.

T 12. Graph $f(x) = (\sin x)^{\sin x}$ over $[0, 3\pi]$. Explain what you see.

13. Find $f'(2)$ if $f(x) = e^{g(x)}$ and $g(x) = \int_2^x \dfrac{t}{1 + t^4} dt$.

14. a. Find df/dx if

$$f(x) = \int_1^{e^x} \frac{2 \ln t}{t} dt.$$

b. Find $f(0)$.

c. What can you conclude about the graph of f? Give reasons for your answer.

15. The figure here shows an informal proof that

$$\tan^{-1} \frac{1}{2} + \tan^{-1} \frac{1}{3} = \frac{\pi}{4}.$$

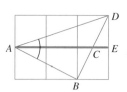

How does the argument go? (*Source:* "Behold! Sums of Arctan," by Edward M. Harris, *College Mathematics Journal*, Vol. 18, No. 2, Mar. 1987, p. 141.)

16. $\pi^e < e^{\pi}$

a. Why does the accompanying figure "prove" that $\pi^e < e^{\pi}$? (*Source:* "Proof Without Words," by Fouad Nakhil, *Mathematics Magazine*, Vol. 60, No. 3, June 1987, p. 165.)

b. The accompanying figure assumes that $f(x) = (\ln x)/x$ has an absolute maximum value at $x = e$. How do you know it does?

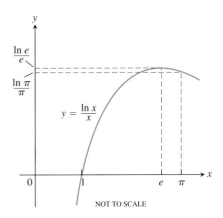

NOT TO SCALE

17. Use the accompanying figure to show that

$$\int_0^{\pi/2} \sin x \, dx = \frac{\pi}{2} - \int_0^1 \sin^{-1} x \, dx.$$

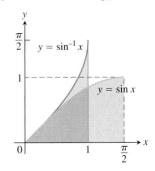

18. Napier's inequality Here are two pictorial proofs that

$$b > a > 0 \quad \Rightarrow \quad \frac{1}{b} < \frac{\ln b - \ln a}{b - a} < \frac{1}{a}.$$

Explain what is going on in each case.

a.

b.

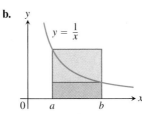

(*Source:* Roger B. Nelson, *College Mathematics Journal*, Vol. 24, No. 2, March 1993, p. 165.)

19. Even-odd decompositions

a. Suppose that g is an even function of x and h is an odd function of x. Show that if $g(x) + h(x) = 0$ for all x then $g(x) = 0$ for all x and $h(x) = 0$ for all x.

b. Use the result in part (a) to show that if $f(x) = f_E(x) + f_O(x)$ is the sum of an even function $f_E(x)$ and an odd function $f_O(x)$, then

$$f_E(x) = (f(x) + f(-x))/2 \quad \text{and} \quad f_O(x) = (f(x) - f(-x))/2.$$

c. What is the significance of the result in part (b)?

20. Let g be a function that is differentiable throughout an open interval containing the origin. Suppose g has the following properties:

i. $g(x + y) = \dfrac{g(x) + g(y)}{1 - g(x)g(y)}$ for all real numbers x, y, and $x + y$ in the domain of g.

ii. $\lim\limits_{h \to 0} g(h) = 0$

iii. $\lim\limits_{h \to 0} \dfrac{g(h)}{h} = 1$

a. Show that $g(0) = 0$.

b. Show that $g'(x) = 1 + [g(x)]^2$.

c. Find $g(x)$ by solving the differential equation in part (b).

Applications

21. Center of mass Find the center of mass of a thin plate of constant density covering the region in the first and fourth quadrants enclosed by the curves $y = 1/(1 + x^2)$ and $y = -1/(1 + x^2)$ and by the lines $x = 0$ and $x = 1$.

22. Solid of revolution The region between the curve $y = 1/(2\sqrt{x})$ and the x-axis from $x = 1/4$ to $x = 4$ is revolved about the x-axis to generate a solid.

a. Find the volume of the solid.

b. Find the centroid of the region.

23. The Rule of 70 If you use the approximation $\ln 2 \approx 0.70$ (in place of $0.69314\ldots$), you can derive a rule of thumb that says, "To estimate how many years it will take an amount of money to double when invested at r percent compounded continuously, divide r into 70." For instance, an amount of money invested at 5% will double in about $70/5 = 14$ years. If you want it to double in 10 years instead, you have to invest it at $70/10 = 7\%$. Show how the Rule of 70 is derived. (A similar "Rule of 72" uses 72 instead of 70, because 72 has more integer factors.)

24. Free fall in the fourteenth century In the middle of the fourteenth century, Albert of Saxony (1316–1390) proposed a model of free fall that assumed that the velocity of a falling body was proportional to the distance fallen. It seemed reasonable to think that a body that had fallen 20 ft might be moving twice as fast as a body that had fallen 10 ft. And besides, none of the instruments in use at the time were accurate enough to prove otherwise. Today we can see just how far off Albert of Saxony's model was by solving the initial value problem implicit in his model. Solve the problem and compare your solution graphically with the equation $s = 16t^2$. You will see that it describes a motion that starts too slowly at first and then becomes too fast too soon to be realistic.

25. **The best branching angles for blood vessels and pipes**   When a smaller pipe branches off from a larger one in a flow system, we may want it to run off at an angle that is best from some energy-saving point of view. We might require, for instance, that energy loss due to friction be minimized along the section AOB shown in the accompanying figure. In this diagram, B is a given point to be reached by the smaller pipe, A is a point in the larger pipe up-stream from B, and O is the point where the branching occurs. A law due to Poiseuille states that the loss of energy due to friction in nonturbulent flow is proportional to the length of the path and inversely proportional to the fourth power of the radius. Thus, the loss along AO is $(kd_1)/R^4$ and along OB is $(kd_2)/r^4$, where k is a constant, d_1 is the length of AO, d_2 is the length of OB, R is the ra-dius of the larger pipe, and r is the radius of the smaller pipe. The angle θ is to be chosen to minimize the sum of these two losses:

$$L = k\frac{d_1}{R^4} + k\frac{d_2}{r^4}.$$

In our model, we assume that $AC = a$ and $BC = b$ are fixed. Thus we have the relations

$$d_1 + d_2 \cos\theta = a \quad d_2 \sin\theta = b,$$

so that

$$d_2 = b \csc\theta,$$
$$d_1 = a - d_2 \cos\theta = a - b \cot\theta.$$

We can express the total loss L as a function of θ:

$$L = k\left(\frac{a - b\cot\theta}{R^4} + \frac{b\csc\theta}{r^4}\right).$$

a. Show that the critical value of θ for which $dL/d\theta$ equals zero is

$$\theta_c = \cos^{-1}\frac{r^4}{R^4}.$$

b. If the ratio of the pipe radii is $r/R = 5/6$, estimate to the nearest degree the optimal branching angle given in part (a).

The mathematical analysis described here is also used to explain the angles at which arteries branch in an animal's body. (See *Introduction to Mathematics for Life Scientists*, Second Edition, by E. Batschelet [New York: Springer-Verlag, 1976].)

T **26. Group blood testing**   During World War II it was necessary to administer blood tests to large numbers of recruits. There are two standard ways to administer a blood test to N people. In method 1, each person is tested separately. In method 2, the blood samples of x people are pooled and tested as one large sample. If the test is negative, this one test is enough for all x people. If the test is pos-itive, then each of the x people is tested separately, requiring a to-tal of $x + 1$ tests. Using the second method and some probability theory it can be shown that, on the average, the total number of tests y will be

$$y = N\left(1 - q^x + \frac{1}{x}\right).$$

With $q = 0.99$ and $N = 1000$, find the integer value of x that minimizes y. Also find the integer value of x that maximizes y. (This second result is not important to the real-life situation.) The group testing method was used in World War II with a savings of 80% over the individual testing method, but not with the given value of q.

APPENDICES

A.1   Mathematical Induction

Many formulas, like

$$1 + 2 + \cdots + n = \frac{n(n + 1)}{2},$$

can be shown to hold for every positive integer n by applying an axiom called the *mathematical induction principle*. A proof that uses this axiom is called a *proof by mathematical induction* or a *proof by induction*.

The steps in proving a formula by induction are the following:

1. Check that the formula holds for $n = 1$.
2. Prove that if the formula holds for any positive integer $n = k$, then it also holds for the next integer, $n = k + 1$.

The induction axiom says that once these steps are completed, the formula holds for all positive integers n. By Step 1 it holds for $n = 1$. By Step 2 it holds for $n = 2$, and therefore by Step 2 also for $n = 3$, and by Step 2 again for $n = 4$, and so on. If the first domino falls, and the kth domino always knocks over the $(k + 1)$st when it falls, all the dominoes fall.

From another point of view, suppose we have a sequence of statements S_1, $S_2, \ldots, S_n, \ldots$, one for each positive integer. Suppose we can show that assuming any one of the statements to be true implies that the next statement in line is true. Suppose that we can also show that S_1 is true. Then we may conclude that the statements are true from S_1 on.

EXAMPLE 1   Use mathematical induction to prove that for every positive integer n,

$$1 + 2 + \cdots + n = \frac{n(n + 1)}{2}.$$

Solution   We accomplish the proof by carrying out the two steps above.

1. The formula holds for $n = 1$ because

$$1 = \frac{1(1 + 1)}{2}.$$

2. If the formula holds for $n = k$, does it also hold for $n = k + 1$? The answer is yes, as we now show. If

$$1 + 2 + \cdots + k = \frac{k(k + 1)}{2},$$

then

$$1 + 2 + \cdots + k + (k + 1) = \frac{k(k + 1)}{2} + (k + 1) = \frac{k^2 + k + 2k + 2}{2}$$

$$= \frac{(k + 1)(k + 2)}{2} = \frac{(k + 1)((k + 1) + 1)}{2}.$$

The last expression in this string of equalities is the expression $n(n + 1)/2$ for $n = (k + 1)$.

The mathematical induction principle now guarantees the original formula for all positive integers n.   ∎

In Example 4 of Section 5.2 we gave another proof for the formula giving the sum of the first n integers. However, proof by mathematical induction is more general. It can be used to find the sums of the squares and cubes of the first n integers (Exercises 9 and 10). Here is another example.

EXAMPLE 2   Show by mathematical induction that for all positive integers n,

$$\frac{1}{2^1} + \frac{1}{2^2} + \cdots + \frac{1}{2^n} = 1 - \frac{1}{2^n}.$$

Solution   We accomplish the proof by carrying out the two steps of mathematical induction.

1. The formula holds for $n = 1$ because

$$\frac{1}{2^1} = 1 - \frac{1}{2^1}.$$

2. If

$$\frac{1}{2^1} + \frac{1}{2^2} + \cdots + \frac{1}{2^k} = 1 - \frac{1}{2^k},$$

then

$$\frac{1}{2^1} + \frac{1}{2^2} + \cdots + \frac{1}{2^k} + \frac{1}{2^{k+1}} = 1 - \frac{1}{2^k} + \frac{1}{2^{k+1}} = 1 - \frac{1 \cdot 2}{2^k \cdot 2} + \frac{1}{2^{k+1}}$$

$$= 1 - \frac{2}{2^{k+1}} + \frac{1}{2^{k+1}} = 1 - \frac{1}{2^{k+1}}.$$

Thus, the original formula holds for $n = (k + 1)$ whenever it holds for $n = k$.

With these steps verified, the mathematical induction principle now guarantees the formula for every positive integer n.   ∎

Other Starting Integers

Instead of starting at $n = 1$ some induction arguments start at another integer. The steps for such an argument are as follows.

1. Check that the formula holds for $n = n_1$ (the first appropriate integer).
2. Prove that if the formula holds for any integer $n = k \geq n_1$, then it also holds for $n = (k + 1)$.

Once these steps are completed, the mathematical induction principle guarantees the formula for all $n \geq n_1$.

EXAMPLE 3   Show that $n! > 3^n$ if n is large enough.

Solution   How large is large enough? We experiment:

n	1	2	3	4	5	6	7
$n!$	1	2	6	24	120	720	5040
3^n	3	9	27	81	243	729	2187

It looks as if $n! > 3^n$ for $n \geq 7$. To be sure, we apply mathematical induction. We take $n_1 = 7$ in Step 1 and complete Step 2.
  Suppose $k! > 3^k$ for some $k \geq 7$. Then

$$(k + 1)! = (k + 1)(k!) > (k + 1)3^k > 7 \cdot 3^k > 3^{k+1}.$$

Thus, for $k \geq 7$,

$$k! > 3^k \quad \text{implies} \quad (k + 1)! > 3^{k+1}.$$

The mathematical induction principle now guarantees $n! \geq 3^n$ for all $n \geq 7$.   ∎

EXERCISES A.1

1. Assuming that the triangle inequality $|a + b| \leq |a| + |b|$ holds for any two numbers a and b, show that

$$|x_1 + x_2 + \cdots + x_n| \leq |x_1| + |x_2| + \cdots + |x_n|$$

for any n numbers.

2. Show that if $r \neq 1$, then

$$1 + r + r^2 + \cdots + r^n = \frac{1 - r^{n+1}}{1 - r}$$

for every positive integer n.

3. Use the Product Rule, $\dfrac{d}{dx}(uv) = u\dfrac{dv}{dx} + v\dfrac{du}{dx}$, and the fact that $\dfrac{d}{dx}(x) = 1$ to show that $\dfrac{d}{dx}(x^n) = nx^{n-1}$ for every positive integer n.

4. Suppose that a function $f(x)$ has the property that $f(x_1 x_2) = f(x_1) + f(x_2)$ for any two positive numbers x_1 and x_2. Show that

$$f(x_1 x_2 \cdots x_n) = f(x_1) + f(x_2) + \cdots + f(x_n)$$

for the product of any n positive numbers $x_1, x_2 \ldots, x_n$.

5. Show that

$$\frac{2}{3^1} + \frac{2}{3^2} + \cdots + \frac{2}{3^n} = 1 - \frac{1}{3^n}$$

for all positive integers n.

6. Show that $n! > n^3$ if n is large enough.

7. Show that $2^n > n^2$ if n is large enough.

8. Show that $2^n \geq 1/8$ for $n \geq -3$.

9. **Sums of squares**   Show that the sum of the squares of the first n positive integers is

$$\frac{n\left(n + \dfrac{1}{2}\right)(n + 1)}{3}.$$

10. **Sums of cubes**   Show that the sum of the cubes of the first n positive integers is $(n(n + 1)/2)^2$.

11. **Rules for finite sums**   Show that the following finite sum rules hold for every positive integer n.

a. $\displaystyle\sum_{k=1}^{n}(a_k + b_k) = \sum_{k=1}^{n} a_k + \sum_{k=1}^{n} b_k$

b. $\displaystyle\sum_{k=1}^{n} (a_k - b_k) = \sum_{k=1}^{n} a_k - \sum_{k=1}^{n} b_k$

d. $\displaystyle\sum_{k=1}^{n} a_k = n \cdot c$ (if a_k has the constant value c)

c. $\displaystyle\sum_{k=1}^{n} ca_k = c \cdot \sum_{k=1}^{n} a_k$ (Any number c)

12. Show that $|x^n| = |x|^n$ for every positive integer n and every real number x.

A.2   Proofs of Limit Theorems

This appendix proves Theorem 1, Parts 2–5, and Theorem 4 from Section 2.2.

THEOREM 1   Limit Laws

If L, M, c, and k are real numbers and

$$\lim_{x \to c} f(x) = L \quad \text{and} \quad \lim_{x \to c} g(x) = M, \quad \text{then}$$

1. *Sum Rule:* $\displaystyle\lim_{x \to c} \Big(f(x) + g(x) \Big) = L + M$

2. *Difference Rule:* $\displaystyle\lim_{x \to c} \Big(f(x) - g(x) \Big) = L - M$

3. *Product Rule:* $\displaystyle\lim_{x \to c} \Big(f(x) \cdot g(x) \Big) = L \cdot M$

4. *Constant Multiple Rule:* $\displaystyle\lim_{x \to c} \Big(kf(x) \Big) = kL$ (any number k)

5. *Quotient Rule:* $\displaystyle\lim_{x \to c} \frac{f(x)}{g(x)} = \frac{L}{M},$ if $M \neq 0$

6. *Power Rule:*   If r and s are integers with no common factor and $s \neq 0$, then

$$\lim_{x \to c} \Big(f(x) \Big)^{r/s} = L^{r/s}$$

provided that $L^{r/s}$ is a real number. (If s is even, we assume that $L > 0$.)

We proved the Sum Rule in Section 2.3 and the Power Rule is proved in more advanced texts. We obtain the Difference Rule by replacing $g(x)$ by $-g(x)$ and M by $-M$ in the Sum Rule. The Constant Multiple Rule is the special case $g(x) = k$ of the Product Rule. This leaves only the Product and Quotient Rules.

Proof of the Limit Product Rule   We show that for any $\epsilon > 0$ there exists a $\delta > 0$ such that for all x in the intersection D of the domains of f and g,

$$0 < |x - c| < \delta \quad \Rightarrow \quad |f(x)g(x) - LM| < \epsilon.$$

Suppose then that ϵ is a positive number, and write $f(x)$ and $g(x)$ as

$$f(x) = L + (f(x) - L), \qquad g(x) = M + (g(x) - M).$$

Multiply these expressions together and subtract LM:

$$f(x) \cdot g(x) - LM = (L + (f(x) - L))(M + (g(x) - M)) - LM$$

$$= LM + L(g(x) - M) + M(f(x) - L)$$

$$+ (f(x) - L)(g(x) - M) - LM$$

$$= L(g(x) - M) + M(f(x) - L) + (f(x) - L)(g(x) - M). \quad (1)$$

Since f and g have limits L and M as $x \to c$, there exist positive numbers δ_1, δ_2, δ_3, and δ_4 such that for all x in D

$$
\begin{aligned}
0 < |x - c| < \delta_1 &\implies |f(x) - L| < \sqrt{\epsilon/3} \\
0 < |x - c| < \delta_2 &\implies |g(x) - M| < \sqrt{\epsilon/3} \\
0 < |x - c| < \delta_3 &\implies |f(x) - L| < \epsilon/(3(1 + |M|)) \\
0 < |x - c| < \delta_4 &\implies |g(x) - M| < \epsilon/(3(1 + |L|))
\end{aligned}
\quad (2)
$$

If we take δ to be the smallest numbers δ_1 through δ_4, the inequalities on the right-hand side of the Implications (2) will hold simultaneously for $0 < |x - c| < \delta$. Therefore, for all x in D, $0 < |x - c| < \delta$ implies

$$|f(x) \cdot g(x) - LM| \qquad \text{\small Triangle inequality}$$
$$\text{\small applied to Equation (1)}$$

$$\leq |L||g(x) - M| + |M||f(x) - L| + |f(x) - L||g(x) - M|$$

$$\leq (1 + |L|)|g(x) - M| + (1 + |M|)|f(x) - L| + |f(x) - L||g(x) - M|$$

$$< \frac{\epsilon}{3} + \frac{\epsilon}{3} + \sqrt{\frac{\epsilon}{3}}\sqrt{\frac{\epsilon}{3}} = \epsilon. \qquad \text{\small Values from (2)}$$

This completes the proof of the Limit Product Rule. ∎

Proof of the Limit Quotient Rule   We show that $\lim_{x \to c} (1/g(x)) = 1/M$. We can then conclude that

$$\lim_{x \to c} \frac{f(x)}{g(x)} = \lim_{x \to c} \left(f(x) \cdot \frac{1}{g(x)} \right) = \lim_{x \to c} f(x) \cdot \lim_{x \to c} \frac{1}{g(x)} = L \cdot \frac{1}{M} = \frac{L}{M}$$

by the Limit Product Rule.

Let $\epsilon > 0$ be given. To show that $\lim_{x \to c} (1/g(x)) = 1/M$, we need to show that there exists a $\delta > 0$ such that for all x.

$$0 < |x - c| < \delta \implies \left| \frac{1}{g(x)} - \frac{1}{M} \right| < \epsilon.$$

Since $|M| > 0$, there exists a positive number δ_1 such that for all x

$$0 < |x - c| < \delta_1 \implies |g(x) - M| < \frac{M}{2}. \quad (3)$$

For any numbers A and B it can be shown that $|A| - |B| \leq |A - B|$ and $|B| - |A| \leq |A - B|$, from which it follows that $||A| - |B|| \leq |A - B|$. With $A = g(x)$ and $B = M$, this becomes

$$||g(x)| - |M|| \leq |g(x) - M|,$$

which can be combined with the inequality on the right in Implication (3) to get, in turn,

$$\left| |g(x)| - |M| \right| < \frac{|M|}{2}$$

$$-\frac{|M|}{2} < |g(x)| - |M| < \frac{|M|}{2}$$

$$\frac{|M|}{2} < |g(x)| < \frac{3|M|}{2}$$

$$|M| < 2|g(x)| < 3|M|$$

$$\frac{1}{|g(x)|} < \frac{2}{|M|} < \frac{3}{|g(x)|} \tag{4}$$

Therefore, $0 < |x - c| < \delta_1$ implies that

$$\left| \frac{1}{g(x)} - \frac{1}{M} \right| = \left| \frac{M - g(x)}{Mg(x)} \right| \leq \frac{1}{|M|} \cdot \frac{1}{|g(x)|} \cdot |M - g(x)|$$

$$< \frac{1}{|M|} \cdot \frac{2}{|M|} \cdot |M - g(x)|. \quad \text{Inequality (4)} \tag{5}$$

Since $(1/2)|M|^2\epsilon > 0$, there exists a number $\delta_2 > 0$ such that for all x

$$0 < |x - c| < \delta_2 \quad \Rightarrow \quad |M - g(x)| < \frac{\epsilon}{2}|M|^2. \tag{6}$$

If we take δ to be the smaller of δ_1 and δ_2, the conclusions in (5) and (6) both hold for all x such that $0 < |x - c| < \delta$. Combining these conclusions gives

$$0 < |x - c| < \delta \quad \Rightarrow \quad \left| \frac{1}{g(x)} - \frac{1}{M} \right| < \epsilon.$$

This concludes the proof of the Limit Quotient Rule.   ■

THEOREM 4   The Sandwich Theorem

Suppose that $g(x) \leq f(x) \leq h(x)$ for all x in some open interval I containing c, except possibly at $x = c$ itself. Suppose also that $\lim_{x \to c} g(x) = \lim_{x \to c} h(x) = L$. Then $\lim_{x \to c} f(x) = L$.

Proof for Right-Hand Limits   Suppose $\lim_{x \to c^+} g(x) = \lim_{x \to c^+} h(x) = L$. Then for any $\epsilon > 0$ there exists a $\delta > 0$ such that for all x the interval $c < x < c + \delta$ is contained in I and the inequality implies

$$L - \epsilon < g(x) < L + \epsilon \quad \text{and} \quad L - \epsilon < h(x) < L + \epsilon.$$

These inequalities combine with the inequality $g(x) \leq f(x) \leq h(x)$ to give

$$L - \epsilon < g(x) \leq f(x) \leq h(x) < L + \epsilon,$$

$$L - \epsilon < f(x) < L + \epsilon,$$

$$-\epsilon < f(x) - L < \epsilon.$$

Therefore, for all x, the inequality $c < x < c + \delta$ implies $|f(x) - L| < \epsilon$.   ■

Proof for Left-Hand Limits Suppose $\lim_{x \to c^-} g(x) = \lim_{x \to c^-} h(x) = L$. Then for any $\epsilon > 0$ there exists a $\delta > 0$ such that for all x the interval $c - \delta < x < c$ is contained in I and the inequality implies

$$L - \epsilon < g(x) < L + \epsilon \qquad \text{and} \qquad L - \epsilon < h(x) < L + \epsilon.$$

We conclude as before that for all $x, c - \delta < x < c$ implies $|f(x) - L| < \epsilon$. ∎

Proof for Two-Sided Limits If $\lim_{x \to c} g(x) = \lim_{x \to c} h(x) = L$, then $g(x)$ and $h(x)$ both approach L as $x \to c^+$ and as $x \to c^-$; so $\lim_{x \to c^+} f(x) = L$ and $\lim_{x \to c^-} f(x) = L$. Hence $\lim_{x \to c} f(x)$ exists and equals L. ∎

EXERCISES A.2

1. Suppose that functions $f_1(x)$, $f_2(x)$, and $f_3(x)$ have limits L_1, L_2, and L_3, respectively, as $x \to c$. Show that their sum has limit $L_1 + L_2 + L_3$. Use mathematical induction (Appendix 1) to generalize this result to the sum of any finite number of functions.

2. Use mathematical induction and the Limit Product Rule in Theorem 1 to show that if functions $f_1(x)$, $f_2(x)$, ..., $f_n(x)$ have limits L_1, L_2, ..., L_n as $x \to c$, then

$$\lim_{x \to c} f_1(x) f_2(x) \cdot \cdots \cdot f_n(x) = L_1 \cdot L_2 \cdot \cdots \cdot L_n.$$

3. Use the fact that $\lim_{x \to c} x = c$ and the result of Exercise 2 to show that $\lim_{x \to c} x^n = c^n$ for any integer $n > 1$.

4. **Limits of polynomials** Use the fact that $\lim_{x \to c}(k) = k$ for any number k together with the results of Exercises 1 and 3 to show that $\lim_{x \to c} f(x) = f(c)$ for any polynomial function

$$f(x) = a_n x^n + a_{n-1} x^{n-1} + \cdots + a_1 x + a_0.$$

5. **Limits of rational functions** Use Theorem 1 and the result of Exercise 4 to show that if $f(x)$ and $g(x)$ are polynomial functions and $g(c) \neq 0$, then

$$\lim_{x \to c} \frac{f(x)}{g(x)} = \frac{f(c)}{g(c)}.$$

6. **Composites of continuous functions** Figure A.1 gives the diagram for a proof that the composite of two continuous functions is continuous. Reconstruct the proof from the diagram. The statement to be proved is this: If f is continuous at $x = c$ and g is continuous at $f(c)$, then $g \circ f$ is continuous at c.

   Assume that c is an interior point of the domain of f and that $f(c)$ is an interior point of the domain of g. This will make the limits involved two-sided. (The arguments for the cases that involve one-sided limits are similar.)

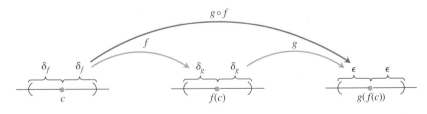

FIGURE A.1 The diagram for a proof that the composite of two continuous functions is continuous.

A.3 Commonly Occurring Limits

This appendix verifies limits (4)–(6) in Theorem 5 of Section 11.1.

Limit 4: If $|x| < 1$, $\lim_{n \to \infty} x^n = 0$ We need to show that to each $\epsilon > 0$ there corresponds an integer N so large that $|x^n| < \epsilon$ for all n greater than N. Since $\epsilon^{1/n} \to 1$, while

$|x| < 1$, there exists an integer N for which $\epsilon^{1/N} > |x|$. In other words,

$$|x^N| = |x|^N < \epsilon. \tag{1}$$

This is the integer we seek because, if $|x| < 1$, then

$$|x^n| < |x^N| \quad \text{for all } n > N. \tag{2}$$

Combining (1) and (2) produces $|x^n| < \epsilon$ for all $n > N$, concluding the proof. ∎

Limit 5: For any number x, $\displaystyle\lim_{n \to \infty} \left(1 + \frac{x}{n}\right)^n = e^x$ Let

$$a_n = \left(1 + \frac{x}{n}\right)^n.$$

Then

$$\ln a_n = \ln\left(1 + \frac{x}{n}\right)^n = n \ln\left(1 + \frac{x}{n}\right) \to x,$$

as we can see by the following application of l'Hôpital's Rule, in which we differentiate with respect to n:

$$\lim_{n \to \infty} n \ln\left(1 + \frac{x}{n}\right) = \lim_{n \to \infty} \frac{\ln(1 + x/n)}{1/n}$$

$$= \lim_{n \to \infty} \frac{\left(\dfrac{1}{1 + x/n}\right) \cdot \left(-\dfrac{x}{n^2}\right)}{-1/n^2} = \lim_{n \to \infty} \frac{x}{1 + x/n} = x.$$

Apply Theorem 4, Section 11.1, with $f(x) = e^x$ to conclude that

$$\left(1 + \frac{x}{n}\right)^n = a_n = e^{\ln a_n} \to e^x.$$ ∎

Limit 6: For any number x, $\displaystyle\lim_{n \to \infty} \frac{x^n}{n!} = 0$ Since

$$-\frac{|x|^n}{n!} \leq \frac{x^n}{n!} \leq \frac{|x|^n}{n!},$$

all we need to show is that $|x|^n/n! \to 0$. We can then apply the Sandwich Theorem for Sequences (Section 11.1, Theorem 2) to conclude that $x^n/n! \to 0$.

The first step in showing that $|x|^n/n! \to 0$ is to choose an integer $M > |x|$, so that $(|x|/M) < 1$. By Limit 4, just proved, we then have $(|x|/M)^n \to 0$. We then restrict our attention to values of $n > M$. For these values of n, we can write

$$\frac{|x|^n}{n!} = \frac{|x|^n}{1 \cdot 2 \cdot \cdots \cdot M \cdot \underbrace{(M+1)(M+2) \cdot \cdots \cdot n}_{(n-M) \text{ factors}}}$$

$$\leq \frac{|x|^n}{M! M^{n-M}} = \frac{|x|^n M^M}{M! M^n} = \frac{M^M}{M!} \left(\frac{|x|}{M}\right)^n.$$

Thus,

$$0 \le \frac{|x|^n}{n!} \le \frac{M^M}{M!}\left(\frac{|x|}{M}\right)^n.$$

Now, the constant $M^M/M!$ does not change as n increases. Thus the Sandwich Theorem tells us that $|x|^n/n! \to 0$ because $(|x|/M)^n \to 0$.   ∎

A.4   Theory of the Real Numbers

A rigorous development of calculus is based on properties of the real numbers. Many results about functions, derivatives, and integrals would be false if stated for functions defined only on the rational numbers. In this appendix we briefly examine some basic concepts of the theory of the reals that hint at what might be learned in a deeper, more theoretical study of calculus.

Three types of properties make the real numbers what they are. These are the **algebraic, order,** and **completeness** properties. The algebraic properties involve addition and multiplication, subtraction and division. They apply to rational or complex numbers as well as to the reals.

The structure of numbers is built around a set with addition and multiplication operations. The following properties are required of addition and multiplication.

A1 $a + (b + c) = (a + b) + c$ for all a, b, c.

A2 $a + b = b + a$ for all a, b, c.

A3   There is a number called "0" such that $a + 0 = a$ for all a.

A4   For each number a, there is a b such that $a + b = 0$.

M1 $a(bc) = (ab)c$ for all a, b, c.

M2 $ab = ba$ for all a, b.

M3   There is a number called "1" such that $a \cdot 1 = a$ for all a.

M4   For each nonzero a, there is a b such that $ab = 1$.

D $a(b + c) = ab + bc$ for all a, b, c.

A1 and M1 are *associative laws*, A2 and M2 are *commutativity laws*, A3 and M3 are *identity laws*, and D is the *distributive law*. Sets that have these algebraic properties are examples of **fields**, and are studied in depth in the area of theoretical mathematics called abstract algebra.

The **order** properties allow us to compare the size of any two numbers. The order properties are

O1   For any a and b, either $a \le b$ or $b \le a$ or both.

O2   If $a \le b$ and $b \le a$ then $a = b$.

O3   If $a \le b$ and $b \le c$ then $a \le c$.

O4   If $a \le b$ then $a + c \le b + c$.

O5   If $a \le b$ and $0 \le c$ then $ac \le bc$.

O3 is the *transitivity law*, and O4 and O5 relate ordering to addition and multiplication.

We can order the reals, the integers, and the rational numbers, but we cannot order the complex numbers (see Appendix A.5). There is no reasonable way to decide whether a number like $i = \sqrt{-1}$ is bigger or smaller than zero. A field in which the size of any two elements can be compared as above is called an **ordered field**. Both the rational numbers and the real numbers are ordered fields, and there are many others.

We can think of real numbers geometrically, lining them up as points on a line. The **completeness property** says that the real numbers correspond to all points on the line, with no "holes" or "gaps." The rationals, in contrast, omit points such as $\sqrt{2}$ and π, and the integers even leave out fractions like $1/2$. The reals, having the completeness property, omit no points.

What exactly do we mean by this vague idea of missing holes? To answer this we must give a more precise description of completeness. A number M is an **upper bound** for a set of numbers if all numbers in the set are smaller than or equal to M. M is a **least upper bound** if it is the smallest upper bound. For example, $M = 2$ is an upper bound for the negative numbers. So is $M = 1$, showing that 2 is not a least upper bound. The least upper bound for the set of negative numbers is $M = 0$. We define a **complete** ordered field to be one in which every nonempty set bounded above has a least upper bound.

If we work with just the rational numbers, the set of numbers less than $\sqrt{2}$ is bounded, but it does not have a rational least upper bound, since any rational upper bound M can be replaced by a slightly smaller rational number that is still larger than $\sqrt{2}$. So the rationals are not complete. In the real numbers, a set that is bounded above always has a least upper bound. The reals are a complete ordered field.

The completeness property is at the heart of many results in calculus. One example occurs when searching for a maximum value for a function on a closed interval $[a, b]$, as in Section 4.1. The function $y = x - x^3$ has a maximum value on $[0, 1]$ at the point x satisfying $1 - 3x^2 = 0$, or $x = \sqrt{1/3}$. If we limited our consideration to functions defined only on rational numbers, we would have to conclude that the function has no maximum, since $\sqrt{1/3}$ is irrational (Figure A.2). The Extreme Value Theorem (Section 4.1), which implies that continuous functions on closed intervals $[a, b]$ have a maximum value, is not true for functions defined only on the rationals.

The Intermediate Value Theorem implies that a continuous function f on an interval $[a, b]$ with $f(a) < 0$ and $f(b) > 0$ must be zero somewhere in $[a, b]$. The function values cannot jump from negative to positive without there being some point x in $[a, b]$ where $f(x) = 0$. The Intermediate Value Theorem also relies on the completeness of the real numbers and is false for continuous functions defined only on the rationals. The function $f(x) = 3x^2 - 1$ has $f(0) = -1$ and $f(1) = 2$, but if we consider f only on the rational numbers, it never equals zero. The only value of x for which $f(x) = 0$ is $x = \sqrt{1/3}$, an irrational number.

We have captured the desired properties of the reals by saying that the real numbers are a complete ordered field. But we're not quite finished. Greek mathematicians in the school of Pythagoras tried to impose another property on the numbers of the real line, the condition that all numbers are ratios of integers. They learned that their effort was doomed when they discovered irrational numbers such as $\sqrt{2}$. How do we know that our efforts to specify the real numbers are not also flawed, for some unseen reason? The artist Escher drew optical illusions of spiral staircases that went up and up until they rejoined themselves at the bottom. An engineer trying to build such a staircase would find that no structure realized the plans the architect had drawn. Could it be that our design for the reals contains some subtle contradiction, and that no construction of such a number system can be made?

We resolve this issue by giving a specific description of the real numbers and verifying that the algebraic, order, and completeness properties are satisfied in this model. This

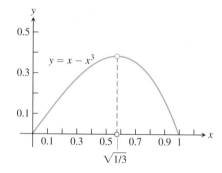

FIGURE A.2 The maximum value of $y = x - x^3$ on $[0, 1]$ occurs at the irrational number $x = \sqrt{1/3}$.

is called a **construction** of the reals, and just as stairs can be built with wood, stone, or steel, there are several approaches to constructing the reals. One construction treats the reals as all the infinite decimals,

$$a.d_1d_2d_3d_4\ldots$$

In this approach a real number is an integer a followed by a sequence of decimal digits $d_1, d_2, d_3, \ldots$, each between 0 and 9. This sequence may stop, or repeat in a periodic pattern, or keep going forever with no pattern. In this form, $2.00, 0.3333333\ldots$ and $3.1415926535898\ldots$ represent three familiar real numbers. The real meaning of the dots "$\ldots$" following these digits requires development of the theory of sequences and series, as in Chapter 11. Each real number is constructed as the limit of a sequence of rational numbers given by its finite decimal approximations. An infinite decimal is then the same as a series

$$a + \frac{d_1}{10} + \frac{d_2}{100} + \cdots.$$

This decimal construction of the real numbers is not entirely straightforward. It's easy enough to check that it gives numbers that satisfy the completeness and order properties, but verifying the algebraic properties is rather involved. Even adding or multiplying two numbers requires an infinite number of operations. Making sense of division requires a careful argument involving limits of rational approximations to infinite decimals.

A different approach was taken by Richard Dedekind (1831–1916), a German mathematician, who gave the first rigorous construction of the real numbers in 1872. Given any real number x, we can divide the rational numbers into two sets: those less than or equal to x and those greater. Dedekind cleverly reversed this reasoning and defined a real number to be a division of the rational numbers into two such sets. This seems like a strange approach, but such indirect methods of constructing new structures from old are common in theoretical mathematics.

These and other approaches (see Appendix A.5) can be used to construct a system of numbers having the desired algebraic, order, and completeness properties. A final issue that arises is whether all the constructions give the same thing. Is it possible that different constructions result in different number systems satisfying all the required properties? If yes, which of these is the real numbers? Fortunately, the answer turns out to be no. The reals are the only number system satisfying the algebraic, order, and completeness properties.

Confusion about the nature of real numbers and about limits caused considerable controversy in the early development of calculus. Calculus pioneers such as Newton, Leibniz, and their successors, when looking at what happens to the difference quotient

$$\frac{\Delta y}{\Delta x} = \frac{f(x + \Delta x) - f(x)}{\Delta x}$$

as each of Δy and Δx approach zero, talked about the resulting derivative being a quotient of two infinitely small quantities. These "infinitesimals," written dx and dy, were thought to be some new kind of number, smaller than any fixed number but not zero. Similarly, a definite integral was thought of as a sum of an infinite number of infinitesimals

$$f(x) \cdot dx$$

as x varied over a closed interval. While the approximating difference quotients $\Delta y / \Delta x$ were understood much as today, it was the quotient of infinitesimal quantities, rather than a limit, that was thought to encapsulate the meaning of the derivative. This way of thinking led to logical difficulties, as attempted definitions and manipulations of infinitesimals ran into contradictions and inconsistencies. The more concrete and computable difference quotients did not cause such trouble, but they were thought of merely as useful calculation tools. Difference quotients were used to work out the numerical value of the derivative and to derive general formulas for calculation, but were not considered to be at the heart of the question of what the derivative actually was. Today we realize that the logical problems associated with infinitesimals can be avoided by *defining* the derivative to be the limit of its approximating difference quotients. The ambiguities of the old approach are no longer present, and in the standard theory of calculus, infinitesimals are neither needed nor used.

A.5   Complex Numbers

Complex numbers are expressions of the form $a + ib$, where a and b are real numbers and i is a symbol for $\sqrt{-1}$. Unfortunately, the words "real" and "imaginary" have connotations that somehow place $\sqrt{-1}$ in a less favorable position in our minds than $\sqrt{2}$. As a matter of fact, a good deal of imagination, in the sense of *inventiveness*, has been required to construct the *real* number system, which forms the basis of the calculus (see Appendix A.4). In this appendix we review the various stages of this invention. The further invention of a complex number system is then presented.

The Development of the Real Numbers

The earliest stage of number development was the recognition of the **counting numbers** $1, 2, 3, \ldots$, which we now call the **natural numbers** or the **positive integers**. Certain simple arithmetic operations can be performed with these numbers without getting outside the system. That is, the system of positive integers is **closed** under the operations of addition and multiplication. By this we mean that if m and n are any positive integers, then

$$m + n = p \quad \text{and} \quad mn = q \tag{1}$$

are also positive integers. Given the two positive integers on the left side of either equation in (1), we can find the corresponding positive integer on the right side. More than this, we can sometimes specify the positive integers m and p and find a positive integer n such that $m + n = p$. For instance, $3 + n = 7$ can be solved when the only numbers we know are the positive integers. But the equation $7 + n = 3$ cannot be solved unless the number system is enlarged.

The number zero and the negative integers were invented to solve equations like $7 + n = 3$. In a civilization that recognizes all the **integers**

$$\ldots, -3, -2, -1, 0, 1, 2, 3, \ldots, \tag{2}$$

an educated person can always find the missing integer that solves the equation $m + n = p$ when given the other two integers in the equation.

Suppose our educated people also know how to multiply any two of the integers in the list (2). If, in Equations (1), they are given m and q, they discover that sometimes they can find n and sometimes they cannot. Using their imagination, they may be

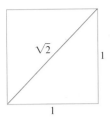

FIGURE A.3 With a straightedge and compass, it is possible to construct a segment of irrational length.

inspired to invent still more numbers and introduce fractions, which are just ordered pairs m/n of integers m and n. The number zero has special properties that may bother them for a while, but they ultimately discover that it is handy to have all ratios of integers m/n, excluding only those having zero in the denominator. This system, called the set of **rational numbers**, is now rich enough for them to perform the **rational operations** of arithmetic:

> **1. (a)** addition
>   **(b)** subtraction
>
> **2. (a)** multiplication
>   **(b)** division

on any two numbers in the system, *except that they cannot divide by zero* because it is meaningless.

The geometry of the unit square (Figure A.3) and the Pythagorean theorem showed that they could construct a geometric line segment that, in terms of some basic unit of length, has length equal to $\sqrt{2}$. Thus they could solve the equation

$$x^2 = 2$$

by a geometric construction. But then they discovered that the line segment representing $\sqrt{2}$ is an incommensurable quantity. This means that $\sqrt{2}$ cannot be expressed as the ratio of two *integer* multiples of some unit of length. That is, our educated people could not find a rational number solution of the equation $x^2 = 2$.

There *is* no rational number whose square is 2. To see why, suppose that there were such a rational number. Then we could find integers p and q with no common factor other than 1, and such that

$$p^2 = 2q^2. \tag{3}$$

Since p and q are integers, p must be even; otherwise its product with itself would be odd. In symbols, $p = 2p_1$, where p_1 is an integer. This leads to $2p_1{}^2 = q^2$ which says q must be even, say $q = 2q_1$, where q_1 is an integer. This makes 2 a factor of both p and q, contrary to our choice of p and q as integers with no common factor other than 1. Hence there is no rational number whose square is 2.

Although our educated people could not find a rational solution of the equation $x^2 = 2$, they could get a sequence of rational numbers

$$\frac{1}{1}, \quad \frac{7}{5}, \quad \frac{41}{29}, \quad \frac{239}{169}, \quad \dots, \tag{4}$$

whose squares form a sequence

$$\frac{1}{1}, \quad \frac{49}{25}, \quad \frac{1681}{841}, \quad \frac{57{,}121}{28{,}561}, \quad \dots, \tag{5}$$

that converges to 2 as its limit. This time their imagination suggested that they needed the concept of a limit of a sequence of rational numbers. If we accept the fact that an increasing sequence that is bounded from above always approaches a limit (Theorem 6, Section 11.1) and observe that the sequence in (4) has these properties, then we want it to have a limit L. This would also mean, from (5), that $L^2 = 2$, and hence L is *not* one of our rational numbers. If to the rational numbers we further add the limits of all bounded increasing sequences of rational numbers, we arrive at the system of all "real" numbers. The word *real* is placed in quotes because there is nothing that is either "more real" or "less real" about this system than there is about any other mathematical system.

The Complex Numbers

Imagination was called upon at many stages during the development of the real number system. In fact, the art of invention was needed at least three times in constructing the systems we have discussed so far:

1. The *first invented* system: the set of *all integers* as constructed from the counting numbers.

2. The *second invented* system: the set of *rational numbers m/n* as constructed from the integers.

3. The *third invented* system: the set of all *real numbers x* as constructed from the rational numbers.

These invented systems form a hierarchy in which each system contains the previous system. Each system is also richer than its predecessor in that it permits additional operations to be performed without going outside the system:

1. In the system of all integers, we can solve all equations of the form

$$x + a = 0, \tag{6}$$

where a can be any integer.

2. In the system of all rational numbers, we can solve all equations of the form

$$ax + b = 0, \tag{7}$$

provided a and b are rational numbers and $a \neq 0$.

3. In the system of all real numbers, we can solve all of Equations (6) and (7) and, in addition, all quadratic equations

$$ax^2 + bx + c = 0 \quad \text{having} \quad a \neq 0 \quad \text{and} \quad b^2 - 4ac \geq 0. \tag{8}$$

You are probably familiar with the formula that gives the solutions of Equation (8), namely,

$$x = \frac{-b \pm \sqrt{b^2 - 4ac}}{2a}, \tag{9}$$

and are familiar with the further fact that when the discriminant, $b^2 - 4ac$, is negative, the solutions in Equation (9) do *not* belong to any of the systems discussed above. In fact, the very simple quadratic equation

$$x^2 + 1 = 0$$

is impossible to solve if the only number systems that can be used are the three invented systems mentioned so far.

Thus we come to the *fourth invented* system, the set of *all complex numbers* $a + ib$. We could dispense entirely with the symbol i and use the ordered pair notation (a, b). Since, under algebraic operations, the numbers a and b are treated somewhat differently, it is essential to keep the *order* straight. We therefore might say that the **complex number system** consists of the set of all ordered pairs of real numbers (a, b), together with the rules by which they are to be equated, added, multiplied, and so on, listed below. We will use both the (a, b) notation and the notation $a + ib$ in the discussion that follows. We call a the **real part** and b the **imaginary part** of the complex number (a, b).

We make the following definitions.

Equality

$a + ib = c + id$ Two complex numbers (a, b)

if and only if   and (c, d) are *equal* if and only

$a = c$ and $b = d$.   if $a = c$ and $b = d$.

Addition

$(a + ib) + (c + id)$ The *sum* of the two complex

$= (a + c) + i(b + d)$ numbers (a, b) and (c, d) is the

                              complex number $(a + c, b + d)$.

Multiplication

$(a + ib)(c + id)$ The *product* of two complex

$= (ac - bd) + i(ad + bc)$ numbers (a, b) and (c, d) is the

                              complex number $(ac - bd, ad + bc)$.

$c(a + ib) = ac + i(bc)$ The product of a real number c

                              and the complex number (a, b) is

                              the complex number (ac, bc).

The set of all complex numbers (a, b) in which the second number b is zero has all the properties of the set of real numbers a. For example, addition and multiplication of $(a, 0)$ and $(c, 0)$ give

$$(a, 0) + (c, 0) = (a + c, 0),$$

$$(a, 0) \cdot (c, 0) = (ac, 0),$$

which are numbers of the same type with imaginary part equal to zero. Also, if we multiply a "real number" $(a, 0)$ and the complex number (c, d), we get

$$(a, 0) \cdot (c, d) = (ac, ad) = a(c, d).$$

In particular, the complex number $(0, 0)$ plays the role of *zero* in the complex number system, and the complex number $(1, 0)$ plays the role of *unity* or *one*.

The number pair $(0, 1)$, which has real part equal to zero and imaginary part equal to one, has the property that its square,

$$(0, 1)(0, 1) = (-1, 0),$$

has real part equal to minus one and imaginary part equal to zero. Therefore, in the system of complex numbers (a, b) there is a number $x = (0, 1)$ whose square can be added to unity $= (1, 0)$ to produce zero $= (0, 0)$, that is,

$$(0, 1)^2 + (1, 0) = (0, 0).$$

The equation

$$x^2 + 1 = 0$$

therefore has a solution $x = (0, 1)$ in this new number system.

You are probably more familiar with the $a + ib$ notation than you are with the notation (a, b). And since the laws of algebra for the ordered pairs enable us to write

$$(a, b) = (a, 0) + (0, b) = a(1, 0) + b(0, 1),$$

while $(1, 0)$ behaves like unity and $(0, 1)$ behaves like a square root of minus one, we need not hesitate to write $a + ib$ in place of (a, b). The i associated with b is like a tracer element that tags the imaginary part of $a + ib$. We can pass at will from the realm of ordered pairs (a, b) to the realm of expressions $a + ib$, and conversely. But there is nothing less "real" about the symbol $(0, 1) = i$ than there is about the symbol $(1, 0) = 1$, once we have learned the laws of algebra in the complex number system of ordered pairs (a, b).

To reduce any rational combination of complex numbers to a single complex number, we apply the laws of elementary algebra, replacing i^2 wherever it appears by -1. Of course, we cannot divide by the complex number $(0, 0) = 0 + i0$. But if $a + ib \neq 0$, then we may carry out a division as follows:

$$\frac{c + id}{a + ib} = \frac{(c + id)(a - ib)}{(a + ib)(a - ib)} = \frac{(ac + bd) + i(ad - bc)}{a^2 + b^2}.$$

The result is a complex number $x + iy$ with

$$x = \frac{ac + bd}{a^2 + b^2}, \qquad y = \frac{ad - bc}{a^2 + b^2},$$

and $a^2 + b^2 \neq 0$, since $a + ib = (a, b) \neq (0, 0)$.

The number $a - ib$ that is used as multiplier to clear the i from the denominator is called the **complex conjugate** of $a + ib$. It is customary to use $\bar{z}$ (read "z bar") to denote the complex conjugate of z; thus

$$z = a + ib, \qquad \bar{z} = a - ib.$$

Multiplying the numerator and denominator of the fraction $(c + id)/(a + ib)$ by the complex conjugate of the denominator will always replace the denominator by a real number.

EXAMPLE 1   Arithmetic Operations with Complex Numbers

(a) $(2 + 3i) + (6 - 2i) = (2 + 6) + (3 - 2)i = 8 + i$

(b) $(2 + 3i) - (6 - 2i) = (2 - 6) + (3 - (-2))i = -4 + 5i$

(c) $(2 + 3i)(6 - 2i) = (2)(6) + (2)(-2i) + (3i)(6) + (3i)(-2i)$

$$= 12 - 4i + 18i - 6i^2 = 12 + 14i + 6 = 18 + 14i$$

(d) $\dfrac{2 + 3i}{6 - 2i} = \dfrac{2 + 3i}{6 - 2i}\dfrac{6 + 2i}{6 + 2i}$

$$= \frac{12 + 4i + 18i + 6i^2}{36 + 12i - 12i - 4i^2}$$

$$= \frac{6 + 22i}{40} = \frac{3}{20} + \frac{11}{20}i$$ ■

Argand Diagrams

There are two geometric representations of the complex number $z = x + iy$:

1.   as the point $P(x, y)$ in the xy-plane

2.   as the vector $\overrightarrow{OP}$ from the origin to P.

In each representation, the x-axis is called the **real axis** and the y-axis is the **imaginary axis**. Both representations are **Argand diagrams** for $x + iy$ (Figure A.4).

In terms of the polar coordinates of x and y, we have

$$x = r \cos \theta, \qquad y = r \sin \theta,$$

FIGURE A.4   This Argand diagram represents $z = x + iy$ both as a point $P(x, y)$ and as a vector $\overrightarrow{OP}$.

and

$$z = x + iy = r(\cos\theta + i\sin\theta). \tag{10}$$

We define the **absolute value** of a complex number $x + iy$ to be the length r of a vector $\overrightarrow{OP}$ from the origin to $P(x, y)$. We denote the absolute value by vertical bars; thus,

$$|x + iy| = \sqrt{x^2 + y^2}.$$

If we always choose the polar coordinates r and θ so that r is nonnegative, then

$$r = |x + iy|.$$

The polar angle θ is called the **argument** of z and is written $\theta = \arg z$. Of course, any integer multiple of 2π may be added to θ to produce another appropriate angle.

The following equation gives a useful formula connecting a complex number z, its conjugate $\bar{z}$, and its absolute value $|z|$, namely,

$$z \cdot \bar{z} = |z|^2.$$

Euler's Formula

The identity

$$e^{i\theta} = \cos\theta + i\sin\theta,$$

called **Euler's formula**, enables us to rewrite Equation (10) as

$$z = re^{i\theta}.$$

This formula, in turn, leads to the following rules for calculating products, quotients, powers, and roots of complex numbers. It also leads to Argand diagrams for $e^{i\theta}$. Since $\cos\theta + i\sin\theta$ is what we get from Equation (10) by taking $r = 1$, we can say that $e^{i\theta}$ is represented by a unit vector that makes an angle θ with the positive x-axis, as shown in Figure A.5.

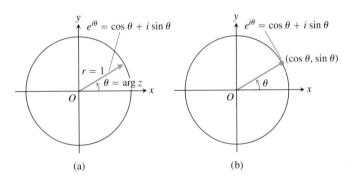

FIGURE A.5 Argand diagrams for $e^{i\theta} = \cos\theta + i\sin\theta$ (a) as a vector and (b) as a point.

Products

To multiply two complex numbers, we multiply their absolute values and add their angles. Let

$$z_1 = r_1 e^{i\theta_1}, \qquad z_2 = r_2 e^{i\theta_2}, \tag{11}$$

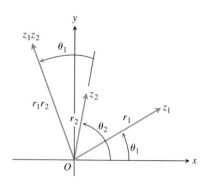

FIGURE A.6 When z_1 and z_2 are multiplied, $|z_1 z_2| = r_1 \cdot r_2$ and arg $(z_1 z_2) = \theta_1 + \theta_2$.

so that

$$|z_1| = r_1, \quad \arg z_1 = \theta_1; \quad |z_2| = r_2, \quad \arg z_2 = \theta_2.$$

Then

$$z_1 z_2 = r_1 e^{i\theta_1} \cdot r_2 e^{i\theta_2} = r_1 r_2 e^{i(\theta_1 + \theta_2)}$$

and hence

$$|z_1 z_2| = r_1 r_2 = |z_1| \cdot |z_2|$$
$$\arg (z_1 z_2) = \theta_1 + \theta_2 = \arg z_1 + \arg z_2. \tag{12}$$

Thus, the product of two complex numbers is represented by a vector whose length is the product of the lengths of the two factors and whose argument is the sum of their arguments (Figure A.6). In particular, from Equation (12) a vector may be rotated counterclockwise through an angle θ by multiplying it by $e^{i\theta}$. Multiplication by i rotates 90°, by -1 rotates 180°, by $-i$ rotates 270°, and so on.

EXAMPLE 2 Finding a Product of Complex Numbers

Let $z_1 = 1 + i, z_2 = \sqrt{3} - i$. We plot these complex numbers in an Argand diagram (Figure A.7) from which we read off the polar representations

$$z_1 = \sqrt{2} e^{i\pi/4}, \quad z_2 = 2e^{-i\pi/6}.$$

Then

$$z_1 z_2 = 2\sqrt{2} \exp\left(\frac{i\pi}{4} - \frac{i\pi}{6}\right) = 2\sqrt{2} \exp\left(\frac{i\pi}{12}\right)$$

$$= 2\sqrt{2}\left(\cos\frac{\pi}{12} + i\sin\frac{\pi}{12}\right) \approx 2.73 + 0.73i.$$

The notation $\exp(A)$ stands for e^A.

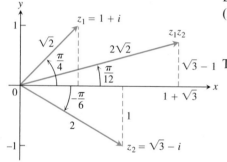

FIGURE A.7 To multiply two complex numbers, multiply their absolute values and add their arguments.

Quotients

Suppose $r_2 \neq 0$ in Equation (11). Then

$$\frac{z_1}{z_2} = \frac{r_1 e^{i\theta_1}}{r_2 e^{i\theta_2}} = \frac{r_1}{r_2} e^{i(\theta_1 - \theta_2)}.$$

Hence

$$\left|\frac{z_1}{z_2}\right| = \frac{r_1}{r_2} = \frac{|z_1|}{|z_2|} \quad \text{and} \quad \arg\left(\frac{z_1}{z_2}\right) = \theta_1 - \theta_2 = \arg z_1 - \arg z_2.$$

That is, we divide lengths and subtract angles for the quotient of complex numbers.

EXAMPLE 3 Let $z_1 = 1 + i$ and $z_2 = \sqrt{3} - i$, as in Example 2. Then

$$\frac{1 + i}{\sqrt{3} - i} = \frac{\sqrt{2} e^{i\pi/4}}{2e^{-i\pi/6}} = \frac{\sqrt{2}}{2} e^{5\pi i/12} \approx 0.707\left(\cos\frac{5\pi}{12} + i\sin\frac{5\pi}{12}\right)$$

$$\approx 0.183 + 0.683i.$$

Powers

If n is a positive integer, we may apply the product formulas in Equation (12) to find

$$z^n = z \cdot z \cdot \cdots \cdot z. \qquad \text{\textit{n} factors}$$

With $z = re^{i\theta}$, we obtain

$$z^n = (re^{i\theta})^n = r^n e^{i(\theta + \theta + \cdots + \theta)} \qquad \text{\textit{n} summands}$$

$$= r^n e^{in\theta}. \tag{13}$$

The length $r = |z|$ is raised to the nth power and the angle $\theta = \arg z$ is multiplied by n.

If we take $r = 1$ in Equation (13), we obtain De Moivre's Theorem.

De Moivre's Theorem

$$(\cos \theta + i \sin \theta)^n = \cos n\theta + i \sin n\theta. \tag{14}$$

If we expand the left side of De Moivre's equation above by the Binomial Theorem and reduce it to the form $a + ib$, we obtain formulas for $\cos n\theta$ and $\sin n\theta$ as polynomials of degree n in $\cos \theta$ and $\sin \theta$.

EXAMPLE 4   If $n = 3$ in Equation (14), we have

$$(\cos \theta + i \sin \theta)^3 = \cos 3\theta + i \sin 3\theta.$$

The left side of this equation expands to

$$\cos^3 \theta + 3i \cos^2 \theta \sin \theta - 3 \cos \theta \sin^2 \theta - i \sin^3 \theta.$$

The real part of this must equal $\cos 3\theta$ and the imaginary part must equal $\sin 3\theta$. Therefore,

$$\cos 3\theta = \cos^3 \theta - 3 \cos \theta \sin^2 \theta,$$

$$\sin 3\theta = 3 \cos^2 \theta \sin \theta - \sin^3 \theta. \qquad \blacksquare$$

Roots

If $z = re^{i\theta}$ is a complex number different from zero and n is a positive integer, then there are precisely n different complex numbers $w_0, w_1, \ldots, w_{n-1}$, that are nth roots of z. To see why, let $w = \rho e^{i\alpha}$ be an nth root of $z = re^{i\theta}$, so that

$$w^n = z$$

or

$$\rho^n e^{in\alpha} = re^{i\theta}.$$

Then

$$\rho = \sqrt[n]{r}$$

is the real, positive nth root of r. For the argument, although we cannot say that $n\alpha$ and θ must be equal, we can say that they may differ only by an integer multiple of 2π. That is,

$$n\alpha = \theta + 2k\pi, \qquad k = 0, \pm 1, \pm 2, \ldots.$$

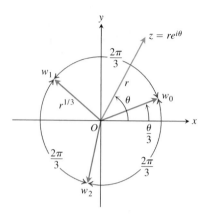

FIGURE A.8 The three cube roots of $z = re^{i\theta}$.

Therefore,

$$\alpha = \frac{\theta}{n} + k\frac{2\pi}{n}.$$

Hence, all the nth roots of $z = re^{i\theta}$ are given by

$$\sqrt[n]{re^{i\theta}} = \sqrt[n]{r} \exp i\left(\frac{\theta}{n} + k\frac{2\pi}{n}\right), \qquad k = 0, \pm1, \pm2, \dots. \qquad (15)$$

There might appear to be infinitely many different answers corresponding to the infinitely many possible values of k, but $k = n + m$ gives the same answer as $k = m$ in Equation (15). Thus, we need only take n consecutive values for k to obtain all the different nth roots of z. For convenience, we take

$$k = 0, 1, 2, \dots, n - 1.$$

All the nth roots of $re^{i\theta}$ lie on a circle centered at the origin and having radius equal to the real, positive nth root of r. One of them has argument $\alpha = \theta/n$. The others are uniformly spaced around the circle, each being separated from its neighbors by an angle equal to $2\pi/n$. Figure A.8 illustrates the placement of the three cube roots, w_0, w_1, w_2, of the complex number $z = re^{i\theta}$.

EXAMPLE 5 Finding Fourth Roots

Find the four fourth roots of -16.

Solution As our first step, we plot the number -16 in an Argand diagram (Figure A.9) and determine its polar representation $re^{i\theta}$. Here, $z = -16$, $r = +16$, and $\theta = \pi$. One of the fourth roots of $16e^{i\pi}$ is $2e^{i\pi/4}$. We obtain others by successive additions of $2\pi/4 = \pi/2$ to the argument of this first one. Hence,

$$\sqrt[4]{16 \exp i\pi} = 2 \exp i\left(\frac{\pi}{4}, \frac{3\pi}{4}, \frac{5\pi}{4}, \frac{7\pi}{4}\right),$$

and the four roots are

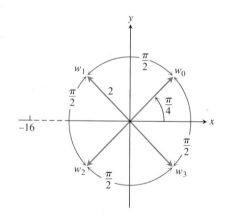

FIGURE A.9 The four fourth roots of -16.

$$w_0 = 2\left[\cos\frac{\pi}{4} + i\sin\frac{\pi}{4}\right] = \sqrt{2}(1 + i)$$

$$w_1 = 2\left[\cos\frac{3\pi}{4} + i\sin\frac{3\pi}{4}\right] = \sqrt{2}(-1 + i)$$

$$w_2 = 2\left[\cos\frac{5\pi}{4} + i\sin\frac{5\pi}{4}\right] = \sqrt{2}(-1 - i)$$

$$w_3 = 2\left[\cos\frac{7\pi}{4} + i\sin\frac{7\pi}{4}\right] = \sqrt{2}(1 - i). \qquad \blacksquare$$

The Fundamental Theorem of Algebra

One might say that the invention of $\sqrt{-1}$ is all well and good and leads to a number system that is richer than the real number system alone; but where will this process end? Are we also going to invent still more systems so as to obtain $\sqrt[4]{-1}$, $\sqrt[6]{-1}$, and so on? But it turns out this is not necessary. These numbers are already expressible in terms of the complex number system $a + ib$. In fact, the Fundamental Theorem of Algebra says that with the introduction of the complex numbers we now have enough numbers to factor every polynomial into a product of linear factors and so enough numbers to solve every possible polynomial equation.

The Fundamental Theorem of Algebra

Every polynomial equation of the form

$$a_n z^n + a_{n-1} z^{n-1} + \cdots + a_1 z + a_0 = 0,$$

in which the coefficients $a_0, a_1, \ldots, a_n$ are any complex numbers, whose degree n is greater than or equal to one, and whose leading coefficient a_n is not zero, has exactly n roots in the complex number system, provided each multiple root of multiplicity m is counted as m roots.

A proof of this theorem can be found in almost any text on the theory of functions of a complex variable.

EXERCISES A.5

Operations with Complex Numbers

1. **How computers multiply complex numbers** Find $(a, b) \cdot (c, d) = (ac - bd, ad + bc)$.
   a. $(2, 3) \cdot (4, -2)$
   b. $(2, -1) \cdot (-2, 3)$
   c. $(-1, -2) \cdot (2, 1)$

   (This is how complex numbers are multiplied by computers.)

2. Solve the following equations for the real numbers, x and y.
   a. $(3 + 4i)^2 - 2(x - iy) = x + iy$
   b. $\left(\dfrac{1 + i}{1 - i}\right)^2 + \dfrac{1}{x + iy} = 1 + i$
   c. $(3 - 2i)(x + iy) = 2(x - 2iy) + 2i - 1$

Graphing and Geometry

3. How may the following complex numbers be obtained from $z = x + iy$ geometrically? Sketch.
   a. $\bar{z}$
   b. $\overline{(-z)}$
   c. $-z$
   d. $1/z$

4. Show that the distance between the two points z_1 and z_2 in an Argand diagram is $|z_1 - z_2|$.

In Exercises 5–10, graph the points $z = x + iy$ that satisfy the given conditions.

5. a. $|z| = 2$ b. $|z| < 2$ c. $|z| > 2$
6. $|z - 1| = 2$ 7. $|z + 1| = 1$
8. $|z + 1| = |z - 1|$ 9. $|z + i| = |z - 1|$
10. $|z + 1| \geq |z|$

Express the complex numbers in Exercises 11–14 in the form $re^{i\theta}$, with $r \geq 0$ and $-\pi < \theta \leq \pi$. Draw an Argand diagram for each calculation.

11. $\left(1 + \sqrt{-3}\right)^2$ 12. $\dfrac{1 + i}{1 - i}$

13. $\dfrac{1 + i\sqrt{3}}{1 - i\sqrt{3}}$ 14. $(2 + 3i)(1 - 2i)$

Powers and Roots

Use De Moivre's Theorem to express the trigonometric functions in Exercises 15 and 16 in terms of $\cos \theta$ and $\sin \theta$.

15. $\cos 4\theta$ 16. $\sin 4\theta$

17. Find the three cube roots of 1.

18. Find the two square roots of i.

19. Find the three cube roots of $-8i$.

20. Find the six sixth roots of 64.

21. Find the four solutions of the equation $z^4 - 2z^2 + 4 = 0$.

22. Find the six solutions of the equation $z^6 + 2z^3 + 2 = 0$.

23. Find all solutions of the equation $x^4 + 4x^2 + 16 = 0$.

24. Solve the equation $x^4 + 1 = 0$.

Theory and Examples

25. **Complex numbers and vectors in the plane** Show with an Argand diagram that the law for adding complex numbers is the same as the parallelogram law for adding vectors.

26. **Complex arithmetic with conjugates** Show that the conjugate of the sum (product, or quotient) of two complex numbers, z_1 and z_2, is the same as the sum (product, or quotient) of their conjugates.

27. **Complex roots of polynomials with real coefficients come in complex-conjugate pairs**

a. Extend the results of Exercise 26 to show that $f(\bar{z}) = \overline{f(z)}$ if

$$f(z) = a_n z^n + a_{n-1} z^{n-1} + \cdots + a_1 z + a_0$$

   is a polynomial with real coefficients $a_0, \ldots, a_n$.

b. If z is a root of the equation $f(z) = 0$, where $f(z)$ is a polynomial with real coefficients as in part (a), show that the conjugate $\bar{z}$ is also a root of the equation. (*Hint:* Let $f(z) = u + iv = 0$; then both u and v are zero. Use the fact that $f(\bar{z}) = \overline{f(z)} = u - iv$.)

28. **Absolute value of a conjugate** Show that $|\bar{z}| = |z|$.

29. **When $\mathbf{z} = \bar{\mathbf{z}}$** If z and $\bar{z}$ are equal, what can you say about the location of the point z in the complex plane?

30. **Real and imaginary parts** Let $\text{Re}(z)$ denote the real part of z and $\text{Im}(z)$ the imaginary part. Show that the following relations hold for any complex numbers z, z_1, and z_2.

a. $z + \bar{z} = 2\text{Re}(z)$ b. $z - \bar{z} = 2i\text{Im}(z)$

c. $|\text{Re}(z)| \le |z|$

d. $|z_1 + z_2|^2 = |z_1|^2 + |z_2|^2 + 2\text{Re}(z_1\bar{z}_2)$

e. $|z_1 + z_2| \le |z_1| + |z_2|$

A.6   The Distributive Law for Vector Cross Products

In this appendix, we prove the Distributive Law

$$\mathbf{u} \times (\mathbf{v} + \mathbf{w}) = \mathbf{u} \times \mathbf{v} + \mathbf{u} \times \mathbf{w}$$

which is Property 2 in Section 12.4.

Proof To derive the Distributive Law, we construct $\mathbf{u} \times \mathbf{v}$ a new way. We draw $\mathbf{u}$ and $\mathbf{v}$ from the common point O and construct a plane M perpendicular to $\mathbf{u}$ at O (Figure A.10). We then project $\mathbf{v}$ orthogonally onto M, yielding a vector $\mathbf{v}'$ with length $|\mathbf{v}| \sin \theta$. We rotate $\mathbf{v}'$ 90° about $\mathbf{u}$ in the positive sense to produce a vector $\mathbf{v}''$. Finally, we multiply $\mathbf{v}''$ by the

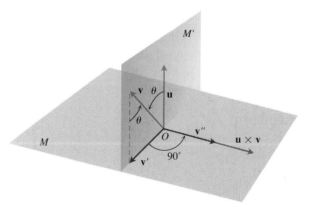

FIGURE A.10 As explained in the text, $\mathbf{u} \times \mathbf{v} = |\mathbf{u}|\mathbf{v}''$.

length of $\mathbf{u}$. The resulting vector $|\mathbf{u}|\mathbf{v}''$ is equal to $\mathbf{u} \times \mathbf{v}$ since $\mathbf{v}''$ has the same direction as $\mathbf{u} \times \mathbf{v}$ by its construction (Figure A.10) and

$$|\mathbf{u}||\mathbf{v}''| = |\mathbf{u}||\mathbf{v}'| = |\mathbf{u}||\mathbf{v}|\sin\theta = |\mathbf{u} \times \mathbf{v}|.$$

Now each of these three operations, namely,

1. projection onto M
2. rotation about $\mathbf{u}$ through $90°$
3. multiplication by the scalar $|\mathbf{u}|$

when applied to a triangle whose plane is not parallel to $\mathbf{u}$, will produce another triangle. If we start with the triangle whose sides are $\mathbf{v}$, $\mathbf{w}$, and $\mathbf{v} + \mathbf{w}$ (Figure A.11) and apply these three steps, we successively obtain the following:

1. A triangle whose sides are $\mathbf{v}'$, $\mathbf{w}'$, and $(\mathbf{v} + \mathbf{w})'$ satisfying the vector equation

$$\mathbf{v}' + \mathbf{w}' = (\mathbf{v} + \mathbf{w})'$$

2. A triangle whose sides are $\mathbf{v}''$, $\mathbf{w}''$, and $(\mathbf{v} + \mathbf{w})''$ satisfying the vector equation

$$\mathbf{v}'' + \mathbf{w}'' = (\mathbf{v} + \mathbf{w})''$$

(the double prime on each vector has the same meaning as in Figure A.10)

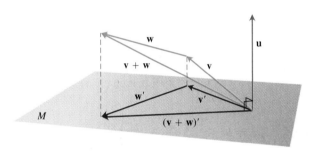

FIGURE A.11 The vectors, $\mathbf{v}$, $\mathbf{w}$, $\mathbf{v} + \mathbf{w}$, and their projections onto a plane perpendicular to $\mathbf{u}$.

3. A triangle whose sides are $|\mathbf{u}|\mathbf{v}''$, $|\mathbf{u}|\mathbf{w}''$, and $|\mathbf{u}|(\mathbf{v} + \mathbf{w})''$ satisfying the vector equation

$$|\mathbf{u}|\mathbf{v}'' + |\mathbf{u}|\mathbf{w}'' = |\mathbf{u}|(\mathbf{v} + \mathbf{w})''.$$

Substituting $|\mathbf{u}|\mathbf{v}'' = \mathbf{u} \times \mathbf{v}$, $|\mathbf{u}|\mathbf{w}'' = \mathbf{u} \times \mathbf{w}$, and $|\mathbf{u}|(\mathbf{v} + \mathbf{w})'' = \mathbf{u} \times (\mathbf{v} + \mathbf{w})$ from our discussion above into this last equation gives

$$\mathbf{u} \times \mathbf{v} + \mathbf{u} \times \mathbf{w} = \mathbf{u} \times (\mathbf{v} + \mathbf{w}),$$

which is the law we wanted to establish. ∎

A.7 The Mixed Derivative Theorem and the Increment Theorem

This appendix derives the Mixed Derivative Theorem (Theorem 2, Section 14.3) and the Increment Theorem for Functions of Two Variables (Theorem 3, Section 14.3). Euler first published the Mixed Derivative Theorem in 1734, in a series of papers he wrote on hydrodynamics.

> **THEOREM 2** The Mixed Derivative Theorem
>
> If $f(x, y)$ and its partial derivatives f_x, f_y, f_{xy}, and f_{yx} are defined throughout an open region containing a point (a, b) and are all continuous at (a, b), then
> $$f_{xy}(a, b) = f_{yx}(a, b).$$

Proof The equality of $f_{xy}(a, b)$ and $f_{yx}(a, b)$ can be established by four applications of the Mean Value Theorem (Theorem 4, Section 4.2). By hypothesis, the point (a, b) lies in the interior of a rectangle R in the xy-plane on which f, f_x, f_y, f_{xy}, and f_{yx} are all defined. We let h and k be the numbers such that the point $(a + h, b + k)$ also lies in R, and we consider the difference

$$\Delta = F(a + h) - F(a), \tag{1}$$

where

$$F(x) = f(x, b + k) - f(x, b). \tag{2}$$

We apply the Mean Value Theorem to F, which is continuous because it is differentiable. Then Equation (1) becomes

$$\Delta = hF'(c_1), \tag{3}$$

where c_1 lies between a and $a + h$. From Equation (2).

$$F'(x) = f_x(x, b + k) - f_x(x, b),$$

so Equation (3) becomes

$$\Delta = h[f_x(c_1, b + k) - f_x(c_1, b)]. \tag{4}$$

Now we apply the Mean Value Theorem to the function $g(y) = f_x(c_1, y)$ and have

$$g(b + k) - g(b) = kg'(d_1),$$

or

$$f_x(c_1, b + k) - f_x(c_1, b) = kf_{xy}(c_1, d_1)$$

for some d_1 between b and $b + k$. By substituting this into Equation (4), we get

$$\Delta = hkf_{xy}(c_1, d_1) \tag{5}$$

for some point (c_1, d_1) in the rectangle R' whose vertices are the four points (a, b), $(a + h, b)$, $(a + h, b + k)$, and $(a, b + k)$. (See Figure A.12.)

By substituting from Equation (2) into Equation (1), we may also write

$$\begin{aligned}
\Delta &= f(a + h, b + k) - f(a + h, b) - f(a, b + k) + f(a, b) \\
&= [f(a + h, b + k) - f(a, b + k)] - [f(a + h, b) - f(a, b)] \\
&= \phi(b + k) - \phi(b), \tag{6}
\end{aligned}$$

where

$$\phi(y) = f(a + h, y) - f(a, y). \tag{7}$$

The Mean Value Theorem applied to Equation (6) now gives

$$\Delta = k\phi'(d_2) \tag{8}$$

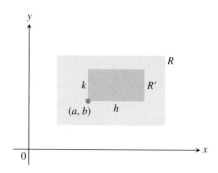

FIGURE A.12 The key to proving $f_{xy}(a, b) = f_{yx}(a, b)$ is that no matter how small R' is, f_{xy} and f_{yx} take on equal values somewhere inside R' (although not necessarily at the same point).

for some d_2 between b and $b + k$. By Equation (7),

$$\phi'(y) = f_y(a + h, y) - f_y(a, y). \tag{9}$$

Substituting from Equation (9) into Equation (8) gives

$$\Delta = k[f_y(a + h, d_2) - f_y(a, d_2)].$$

Finally, we apply the Mean Value Theorem to the expression in brackets and get

$$\Delta = khf_{yx}(c_2, d_2) \tag{10}$$

for some c_2 between a and $a + h$.

Together, Equations (5) and (10) show that

$$f_{xy}(c_1, d_1) = f_{yx}(c_2, d_2), \tag{11}$$

where (c_1, d_1) and (c_2, d_2) both lie in the rectangle R' (Figure A.12). Equation (11) is not quite the result we want, since it says only that f_{xy} has the same value at (c_1, d_1) that f_{yx} has at (c_2, d_2). The numbers h and k in our discussion, however, may be made as small as we wish. The hypothesis that f_{xy} and f_{yx} are both continuous at (a, b) means that $f_{xy}(c_1, d_1) = f_{xy}(a, b) + \epsilon_1$ and $f_{yx}(c_2, d_2) = f_{yx}(a, b) + \epsilon_2$, where each of $\epsilon_1, \epsilon_2 \to 0$ as both $h, k \to 0$. Hence, if we let h and $k \to 0$, we have $f_{xy}(a, b) = f_{yx}(a, b)$. ∎

The equality of $f_{xy}(a, b)$ and $f_{yx}(a, b)$ can be proved with hypotheses weaker than the ones we assumed. For example, it is enough for $f, f_x,$ and f_y to exist in R and for f_{xy} to be continuous at (a, b). Then f_{yx} will exist at (a, b) and equal f_{xy} at that point.

THEOREM 3   The Increment Theorem for Functions of Two Variables

Suppose that the first partial derivatives of $z = f(x, y)$ are defined throughout an open region R containing the point (x_0, y_0) and that f_x and f_y are continuous at (x_0, y_0). Then the change $\Delta z = f(x_0 + \Delta x, y_0 + \Delta y) - f(x_0, y_0)$ in the value of f that results from moving from (x_0, y_0) to another point $(x_0 + \Delta x, y_0 + \Delta y)$ in R satisfies an equation of the form

$$\Delta z = f_x(x_0, y_0)\Delta x + f_y(x_0, y_0)\Delta y + \epsilon_1 \Delta x + \epsilon_2 \Delta y,$$

in which each of $\epsilon_1, \epsilon_2 \to 0$ as both $\Delta x, \Delta y \to 0$.

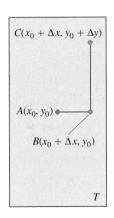

FIGURE A.13 The rectangular region T in the proof of the Increment Theorem. The figure is drawn for Δx and Δy positive, but either increment might be zero or negative.

Proof   We work within a rectangle T centered at $A(x_0, y_0)$ and lying within R, and we assume that Δx and Δy are already so small that the line segment joining A to $B(x_0 + \Delta x, y_0)$ and the line segment joining B to $C(x_0 + \Delta x, y_0 + \Delta y)$ lie in the interior of T (Figure A.13).

We may think of Δz as the sum $\Delta z = \Delta z_1 + \Delta z_2$ of two increments, where

$$\Delta z_1 = f(x_0 + \Delta x, y_0) - f(x_0, y_0)$$

is the change in the value of f from A to B and

$$\Delta z_2 = f(x_0 + \Delta x, y_0 + \Delta y) - f(x_0 + \Delta x, y_0)$$

is the change in the value of f from B to C (Figure A.14).

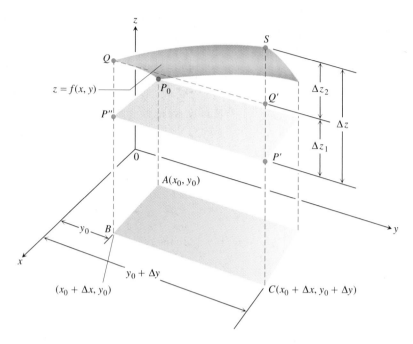

FIGURE A.14   Part of the surface $z = f(x, y)$ near $P_0(x_0, y_0, f(x_0, y_0))$. The points P_0, P', and P'' have the same height $z_0 = f(x_0, y_0)$ above the xy-plane. The change in z is $\Delta z = P'S$. The change

$$\Delta z_1 = f(x_0 + \Delta x, y_0) - f(x_0, y_0),$$

shown as $P''Q = P'Q'$, is caused by changing x from x_0 to $x_0 + \Delta x$ while holding y equal to y_0. Then, with x held equal to $x_0 + \Delta x$,

$$\Delta z_2 = f(x_0 + \Delta x, y_0 + \Delta y) - f(x_0 + \Delta x, y_0)$$

is the change in z caused by changing y_0 from $y_0 + \Delta y$, which is represented by $Q'S$? The total change in z is the sum of Δz_1 and Δz_2.

On the closed interval of x-values joining x_0 to $x_0 + \Delta x$, the function $F(x) = f(x, y_0)$ is a differentiable (and hence continuous) function of x, with derivative

$$F'(x) = f_x(x, y_0).$$

By the Mean Value Theorem (Theorem 4, Section 4.2), there is an x-value c between x_0 and $x_0 + \Delta x$ at which

$$F(x_0 + \Delta x) - F(x_0) = F'(c)\Delta x$$

or

$$f(x_0 + \Delta x, y_0) - f(x_0, y_0) = f_x(c, y_0)\Delta x$$

or

$$\Delta z_1 = f_x(c, y_0)\Delta x. \tag{12}$$

Similarly, $G(y) = f(x_0 + \Delta x, y)$ is a differentiable (and hence continuous) function of y on the closed y-interval joining y_0 and $y_0 + \Delta y$, with derivative

$$G'(y) = f_y(x_0 + \Delta x, y).$$

Hence, there is a y-value d between y_0 and $y_0 + \Delta y$ at which

$$G(y_0 + \Delta y) - G(y_0) = G'(d)\Delta y$$

or

$$f(x_0 + \Delta x, y_0 + \Delta y) - f(x_0 + \Delta x, y) = f_y(x_0 + \Delta x, d)\Delta y$$

or

$$\Delta z_2 = f_y(x_0 + \Delta x, d)\Delta y. \tag{13}$$

Now, as both Δx and $\Delta y \to 0$, we know that $c \to x_0$ and $d \to y_0$. Therefore, since f_x and f_y are continuous at (x_0, y_0), the quantities

$$\epsilon_1 = f_x(c, y_0) - f_x(x_0, y_0),$$
$$\epsilon_2 = f_y(x_0 + \Delta x, d) - f_y(x_0, y_0) \tag{14}$$

both approach zero as both Δx and $\Delta y \to 0$.

Finally,

$$\begin{aligned}
\Delta z &= \Delta z_1 + \Delta z_2 \\
&= f_x(c, y_0)\Delta x + f_y(x_0 + \Delta x, d)\Delta y && \text{From Equations (12) and (13)} \\
&= [f_x(x_0, y_0) + \epsilon_1]\Delta x + [f_y(x_0, y_0) + \epsilon_2]\Delta y && \text{From Equation (14)} \\
&= f_x(x_0, y_0)\Delta x + f_y(x_0, y_0)\Delta y + \epsilon_1\Delta x + \epsilon_2\Delta y,
\end{aligned}$$

where both ϵ_1 and $\epsilon_2 \to 0$ as both Δx and $\Delta y \to 0$, which is what we set out to prove. ∎

Analogous results hold for functions of any finite number of independent variables. Suppose that the first partial derivatives of $w = f(x, y, z)$ are defined throughout an open region containing the point (x_0, y_0, z_0) and that f_x, f_y, and f_z are continuous at (x_0, y_0, z_0). Then

$$\begin{aligned}
\Delta w &= f(x_0 + \Delta x, y_0 + \Delta y, z_0 + \Delta z) - f(x_0, y_0, z_0) \\
&= f_x\Delta x + f_y\Delta y + f_z\Delta z + \epsilon_1\Delta x + \epsilon_2\Delta y + \epsilon_3\Delta z, \tag{15}
\end{aligned}$$

where $\epsilon_1, \epsilon_2, \epsilon_3 \to 0$ as $\Delta x, \Delta y$, and $\Delta z \to 0$.

The partial derivatives f_x, f_y, f_z in Equation (15) are to be evaluated at the point (x_0, y_0, z_0).

Equation (15) can be proved by treating Δw as the sum of three increments,

$$\Delta w_1 = f(x_0 + \Delta x, y_0, z_0) - f(x_0, y_0, z_0) \tag{16}$$

$$\Delta w_2 = f(x_0 + \Delta x, y_0 + \Delta y, z_0) - f(x_0 + \Delta x, y_0, z_0) \tag{17}$$

$$\Delta w_3 = f(x_0 + \Delta x, y_0 + \Delta y, z_0 + \Delta z) - f(x_0 + \Delta x, y_0 + \Delta y, z_0), \tag{18}$$

and applying the Mean Value Theorem to each of these separately. Two coordinates remain constant and only one varies in each of these partial increments $\Delta w_1, \Delta w_2, \Delta w_3$. In Equation (17), for example, only y varies, since x is held equal to $x_0 + \Delta x$ and z is held equal to z_0. Since $f(x_0 + \Delta x, y, z_0)$ is a continuous function of y with a derivative f_y, it is subject to the Mean Value Theorem, and we have

$$\Delta w_2 = f_y(x_0 + \Delta x, y_1, z_0)\Delta y$$

for some y_1 between y_0 and $y_0 + \Delta y$.

A.8   The Area of a Parallelogram's Projection on a Plane

This appendix proves the result needed in Section 16.5 that $|(\mathbf{u} \times \mathbf{v}) \cdot \mathbf{p}|$ is the area of the projection of the parallelogram with sides determined by $\mathbf{u}$ and $\mathbf{v}$ onto any plane whose normal is $\mathbf{p}$. (See Figure A.15.)

THEOREM

The area of the orthogonal projection of the parallelogram determined by two vectors $\mathbf{u}$ and $\mathbf{v}$ in space onto a plane with unit normal vector $\mathbf{p}$ is

$$\text{Area} = |(\mathbf{u} \times \mathbf{v}) \cdot \mathbf{p}|.$$

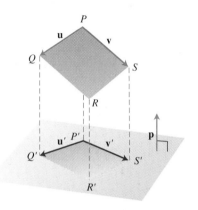

FIGURE A.15   The parallelogram determined by two vectors $\mathbf{u}$ and $\mathbf{v}$ in space and the orthogonal projection of the parallelogram onto a plane. The projection lines, orthogonal to the plane, lie parallel to the unit normal vector $\mathbf{p}$.

Proof   In the notation of Figure A.15, which shows a typical parallelogram determined by vectors $\mathbf{u}$ and $\mathbf{v}$ and its orthogonal projection onto a plane with unit normal vector $\mathbf{p}$,

$$\mathbf{u} = \overrightarrow{PP'} + \mathbf{u}' + \overrightarrow{Q'Q}$$
$$= \mathbf{u}' + \overrightarrow{PP'} - \overrightarrow{QQ'} \qquad (\overrightarrow{Q'Q} = -\overrightarrow{QQ'})$$
$$= \mathbf{u}' + s\mathbf{p}. \qquad \text{(For some scalar } s \text{ because } (\overrightarrow{PP'} - \overrightarrow{QQ'}) \text{ is parallel to } \mathbf{p})$$

Similarly,

$$\mathbf{v} = \mathbf{v}' + t\mathbf{p}$$

for some scalar t. Hence,

$$\mathbf{u} \times \mathbf{v} = (\mathbf{u}' + s\mathbf{p}) \times (\mathbf{v}' + t\mathbf{p})$$
$$= (\mathbf{u}' \times \mathbf{v}') + s(\mathbf{p} \times \mathbf{v}') + t(\mathbf{u}' \times \mathbf{p}) + st\underbrace{(\mathbf{p} \times \mathbf{p})}_{0}. \qquad (1)$$

The vectors $\mathbf{p} \times \mathbf{v}'$ and $\mathbf{u}' \times \mathbf{p}$ are both orthogonal to $\mathbf{p}$. Hence, when we dot both sides of Equation (1) with $\mathbf{p}$, the only nonzero term on the right is $(\mathbf{u}' \times \mathbf{v}') \cdot \mathbf{p}$. That is,

$$(\mathbf{u} \times \mathbf{v}) \cdot \mathbf{p} = (\mathbf{u}' \times \mathbf{v}') \cdot \mathbf{p}.$$

In particular,

$$|(\mathbf{u} \times \mathbf{v}) \cdot \mathbf{p}| = |(\mathbf{u}' \times \mathbf{v}') \cdot \mathbf{p}|. \qquad (2)$$

The absolute value on the right is the volume of the box determined by $\mathbf{u}'$, $\mathbf{v}'$, and $\mathbf{p}$. The height of this particular box is $|\mathbf{p}| = 1$, so the box's volume is numerically the same as its base area, the area of parallelogram $P'Q'R'S'$. Combining this observation with Equation (2) gives

$$\text{Area of } P'Q'R'S' = |(\mathbf{u}' \times \mathbf{v}') \cdot \mathbf{p}| = |(\mathbf{u} \times \mathbf{v}) \cdot \mathbf{p}|,$$

which says that the area of the orthogonal projection of the parallelogram determined by $\mathbf{u}$ and $\mathbf{v}$ onto a plane with unit normal vector $\mathbf{p}$ is $|(\mathbf{u} \times \mathbf{v}) \cdot \mathbf{p}|$. This is what we set out to prove.   ∎

FIGURE A.16   Example 1 calculates the area of the orthogonal projection of parallelogram $PQRS$ on the xy-plane.

EXAMPLE 1   Finding the Area of a Projection

Find the area of the orthogonal projection onto the xy-plane of the parallelogram determined by the points $P(0, 0, 3)$, $Q(2, -1, 2)$, $R(3, 2, 1)$, and $S(1, 3, 2)$ (Figure A.16).

Solution With

$$\mathbf{u} = \overrightarrow{PQ} = 2\mathbf{i} - \mathbf{j} - \mathbf{k}, \qquad \mathbf{v} = \overrightarrow{PS} = \mathbf{i} + 3\mathbf{j} - \mathbf{k}, \qquad \text{and} \qquad \mathbf{p} = \mathbf{k},$$

we have

$$(\mathbf{u} \times \mathbf{v}) \cdot \mathbf{p} = \begin{vmatrix} 2 & -1 & -1 \\ 1 & 3 & -1 \\ 0 & 0 & 1 \end{vmatrix} = \begin{vmatrix} 2 & -1 \\ 1 & 3 \end{vmatrix} = 7,$$

so the area is $|(\mathbf{u} \times \mathbf{v}) \cdot \mathbf{p}| = |7| = 7.$ ∎

A.9 Basic Algebra, Geometry, and Trigonometry Formulas

Algebra

Arithmetic Operations

$$a(b + c) = ab + ac, \qquad \frac{a}{b} \cdot \frac{c}{d} = \frac{ac}{bd}$$

$$\frac{a}{b} + \frac{c}{d} = \frac{ad + bc}{bd}, \qquad \frac{a/b}{c/d} = \frac{a}{b} \cdot \frac{d}{c}$$

Laws of Signs

$$-(-a) = a, \qquad \frac{-a}{b} = -\frac{a}{b} = \frac{a}{-b}$$

Zero Division by zero is not defined.

$$\text{If } a \neq 0: \frac{0}{a} = 0, \quad a^0 = 1, \quad 0^a = 0$$

$$\text{For any number } a: \ a \cdot 0 = 0 \cdot a = 0$$

Laws of Exponents

$$a^m a^n = a^{m+n}, \qquad (ab)^m = a^m b^m, \qquad (a^m)^n = a^{mn}, \qquad a^{m/n} = \sqrt[n]{a^m} = \left(\sqrt[n]{a}\right)^m$$

If $a \neq 0$,

$$\frac{a^m}{a^n} = a^{m-n}, \quad a^0 = 1, \quad a^{-m} = \frac{1}{a^m}.$$

The Binomial Theorem For any positive integer n,

$$(a + b)^n = a^n + na^{n-1}b + \frac{n(n-1)}{1 \cdot 2} a^{n-2}b^2$$

$$+ \frac{n(n-1)(n-2)}{1 \cdot 2 \cdot 3} a^{n-3}b^3 + \cdots + nab^{n-1} + b^n.$$

For instance,

$$(a + b)^2 = a^2 + 2ab + b^2, \qquad (a - b)^2 = a^2 - 2ab + b^2$$

$$(a + b)^3 = a^3 + 3a^2b + 3ab^2 + b^3, \qquad (a - b)^3 = a^2 - 3a^2b + 3ab^2 - b^3.$$

Factoring the Difference of Like Integer Powers, $n > 1$

$$a^n - b^n = (a - b)(a^{n-1} + a^{n-2}b + a^{n-3}b^2 + \cdots + ab^{n-2} + b^{n-1})$$

For instance,

$$a^2 - b^2 = (a - b)(a + b),$$

$$a^3 - b^3 = (a - b)(a^2 + ab + b^2),$$

$$a^4 - b^4 = (a - b)(a^3 + a^2b + ab^2 + b^3).$$

Completing the Square If $a \neq 0$,

$$ax^2 + bx + c = a\left(x^2 + \frac{b}{a}x\right) + c$$

$$= a\left(x^2 + \frac{b}{a}x + \frac{b^2}{4a^2} - \frac{b^2}{4a^2}\right) + c$$

$$= a\left(x^2 + \frac{b}{a}x + \frac{b^2}{4a^2}\right) + a\left(-\frac{b^2}{4a^2}\right) + c$$

$$= a\underbrace{\left(x^2 + \frac{b}{a}x + \frac{b^2}{4a^2}\right)}_{\text{This is } \left(x + \frac{b}{2a}\right)^2.} + \underbrace{c - \frac{b^2}{4a}}_{\text{Call this part } C.}$$

$$= au^2 + C \qquad (u = x + (b/2a))$$

The Quadratic Formula If $a \neq 0$ and $ax^2 + bx + c = 0$, then

$$x = \frac{-b \pm \sqrt{b^2 - 4ac}}{2a}.$$

Geometry

Formulas for area, circumference, and volume: (A = area, B = area of base, C = circumference, S = lateral area or surface area, V = volume)

Triangle   **Similar Triangles**   **Pythagorean Theorem**

$$A = \frac{1}{2}bh$$

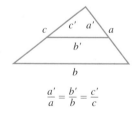

$$\frac{a'}{a} = \frac{b'}{b} = \frac{c'}{c}$$

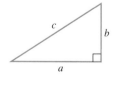

$$a^2 + b^2 = c^2$$

Parallelogram

$A = bh$

Trapezoid

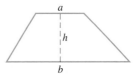

$A = \frac{1}{2}(a + b)h$

Circle

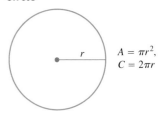

$A = \pi r^2,$
$C = 2\pi r$

Any Cylinder or Prism with Parallel Bases

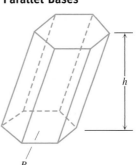

$V = Bh$

Right Circular Cylinder

$V = \pi r^2 h$
$S = 2\pi rh = \text{Area of side}$

Any Cone or Pyramid

$V = \frac{1}{3}Bh$

Right Circular Cone

$V = \frac{1}{3}\pi r^2 h$
$S = \pi rs = \text{Area of side}$

Sphere

$V = \frac{4}{3}\pi r^3, S = 4\pi r^2$

Trigonometry Formulas

Definitions and Fundamental Identities

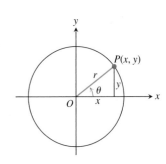

Sine: $\sin \theta = \dfrac{y}{r} = \dfrac{1}{\csc \theta}$

Cosine: $\cos \theta = \dfrac{x}{r} = \dfrac{1}{\sec \theta}$

Tangent: $\tan \theta = \dfrac{y}{x} = \dfrac{1}{\cot \theta}$

Identities

$$\sin(-\theta) = -\sin\theta, \quad \cos(-\theta) = \cos\theta$$

$$\sin^2\theta + \cos^2\theta = 1, \quad \sec^2\theta = 1 + \tan^2\theta, \quad \csc^2\theta = 1 + \cot^2\theta$$

$$\sin 2\theta = 2\sin\theta\cos\theta, \quad \cos 2\theta = \cos^2\theta - \sin^2\theta$$

$$\cos^2\theta = \frac{1 + \cos 2\theta}{2}, \quad \sin^2\theta = \frac{1 - \cos 2\theta}{2}$$

$$\sin(A + B) = \sin A\cos B + \cos A\sin B$$

$$\sin(A - B) = \sin A\cos B - \cos A\sin B$$

$$\cos(A + B) = \cos A\cos B - \sin A\sin B$$

$$\cos(A - B) = \cos A\cos B + \sin A\sin B$$

$$\tan(A + B) = \frac{\tan A + \tan B}{1 - \tan A\tan B}, \quad \tan(A - B) = \frac{\tan A - \tan B}{1 + \tan A\tan B}$$

$$\sin\left(A - \frac{\pi}{2}\right) = -\cos A, \quad \cos\left(A - \frac{\pi}{2}\right) = \sin A$$

$$\sin\left(A + \frac{\pi}{2}\right) = \cos A, \quad \cos\left(A + \frac{\pi}{2}\right) = -\sin A$$

$$\sin A\sin B = \frac{1}{2}\cos(A - B) - \frac{1}{2}\cos(A + B)$$

$$\cos A\cos B = \frac{1}{2}\cos(A - B) + \frac{1}{2}\cos(A + B)$$

$$\sin A\cos B = \frac{1}{2}\sin(A - B) + \frac{1}{2}\sin(A + B)$$

$$\sin A + \sin B = 2\sin\frac{1}{2}(A + B)\cos\frac{1}{2}(A - B)$$

$$\sin A - \sin B = 2\cos\frac{1}{2}(A + B)\sin\frac{1}{2}(A - B)$$

$$\cos A + \cos B = 2\cos\frac{1}{2}(A + B)\cos\frac{1}{2}(A - B)$$

$$\cos A - \cos B = -2\sin\frac{1}{2}(A + B)\sin\frac{1}{2}(A - B)$$

Trigonometric Functions

Radian Measure

Degrees	Radians

$$\frac{s}{r} = \frac{\theta}{1} = \theta \quad \text{or} \quad \theta = \frac{s}{r},$$

$$180° = \pi \text{ radians.}$$

The angles of two common triangles, in degrees and radians.

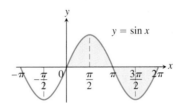

Domain: $(-\infty, \infty)$
Range: $[-1, 1]$

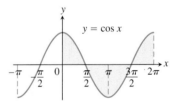

Domain: $(-\infty, \infty)$
Range: $[-1, 1]$

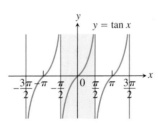

Domain: All real numbers except odd
integer multiples of $\pi/2$
Range: $(-\infty, \infty)$

Domain: $x \neq \pm\dfrac{\pi}{2}, \pm\dfrac{3\pi}{2}, \ldots$
Range: $(-\infty, -1] \cup [1, \infty)$

Domain: $x \neq 0, \pm\pi, \pm 2\pi, \ldots$
Range: $(-\infty, -1] \cup [1, \infty)$

Domain: $x \neq 0, \pm\pi, \pm 2\pi, \ldots$
Range: $(-\infty, \infty)$

ANSWERS

CHAPTER 1

Section 1.1, pp. 7–8

1. $0.\overline{1}, 0.\overline{2}, 0.\overline{3}, 0.\overline{8}, 0.\overline{9}$ or 1

3. **(a)** Not necessarily true　**(b)** True　**(c)** True　**(d)** True
(e) True　**(f)** True　**(g)** True　**(h)** True

5. $x < -2$

7. $x \le \dfrac{5}{4}$

9. $x \le -\dfrac{1}{3}$

11. $x < -\dfrac{6}{7}$

13. ± 3　**15.** $-\dfrac{1}{2}, -\dfrac{9}{2}$　**17.** $\dfrac{7}{6}, \dfrac{25}{6}$

19. $-2 < x < 2$

21. $-2 \le t \le 4$

23. $1 < y < \dfrac{11}{3}$

25. $0 \le z \le 10$

27. $\dfrac{2}{7} < x < \dfrac{2}{5}$ or $\dfrac{10}{35} < x < \dfrac{14}{35}$

29. $(-\infty, -2] \cup [2, \infty)$

31. $(-\infty, 0) \cup (2, \infty)$

33. $(-\infty, -3] \cup [1, \infty)$

35. $(-\sqrt{2}, \sqrt{2})$　**37.** $(-3, -2) \cup (2, 3)$　**39.** $(-1, 3)$

41. $(0, 1)$　**43.** $a \ge 0$; any negative real number

47. $-\dfrac{1}{2} < x \le 3$

Section 1.2, pp. 16–19

1. $2, -4; 2\sqrt{5}$　**3.** $-4.9, 0; 4.9$　**5.** Unit circle

7. The circle centered at the origin with points less than a radius of $\sqrt{3}$ and its interior

9. $m_\perp = -\dfrac{1}{3}$

11. $m_\perp$ is undefined.

13. **(a)** $x = -1$　**(b)** $y = 4/3$

15. **(a)** $x = 0$　**(b)** $y = -\sqrt{2}$

17. $y = -x$　**19.** $y = -\dfrac{x}{5} + \dfrac{23}{5}$　**21.** $y = -\dfrac{5}{4}x + 6$

23. $y = -9$　**25.** $y = 4x + 4$　**27.** $y = -\dfrac{2}{5}x + 1$

29. $y = -\dfrac{x}{2} + 12$

31. x-intercept $= 4$, y-intercept $= 3$

33. x-intercept $= \sqrt{3}$, y-intercept $= -\sqrt{2}$

35. Yes. The lines are perpendicular because their slopes, $-A/B$ and B/A, are negative reciprocals of one another.

37. $(3, -3)$ **39.** $(-2, -9)$

41. $x^2 + (y - 2)^2 = 4$

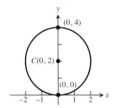

43. $(x + 1)^2 + (y - 5)^2 = 10$

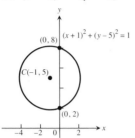

45. $(x + \sqrt{3})^2 + (y + 2)^2 = 4$

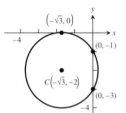

47. $(x + 2)^2 + (y - 2)^2 = 4$

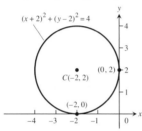

49. $x^2 + (y - 3/2)^2 = 25/4$

51. $(x - 2)^2 + (y + 2)^2 = 8$

53.

55.

57.

59.

61. Exterior points of a circle of radius $\sqrt{7}$, centered at the origin

63. A circle of radius 2, centered at $(1, 0)$, together with its interior

65. The washer between the circles $x^2 + y^2 = 1$ and $x^2 + y^2 = 4$ (points with distance from the origin between 1 and 2)

67. The interior points of a circle centered at $(0, -3)$ with a radius of 3 that lie above the line $y = -3$

69. $(x + 2)^2 + (y - 1)^2 < 6$ **71.** $x^2 + y^2 \leq 2, \quad x \geq 1$

73. $\left(\dfrac{1}{\sqrt{5}}, \dfrac{2}{\sqrt{5}}\right), \quad \left(-\dfrac{1}{\sqrt{5}}, -\dfrac{2}{\sqrt{5}}\right)$

75. $\left(\dfrac{1 - \sqrt{5}}{2}, \dfrac{3 - \sqrt{5}}{2}\right), \quad \left(\dfrac{1 + \sqrt{5}}{2}, \dfrac{3 + \sqrt{5}}{2}\right)$

77. $\left(-\dfrac{1}{\sqrt{3}}, -\dfrac{1}{3}\right), \quad \left(\dfrac{1}{\sqrt{3}}, -\dfrac{1}{3}\right)$

79. $\left(\dfrac{1}{2}, -\dfrac{\sqrt{3}}{2}\right), \quad \left(\dfrac{1}{2}, \dfrac{\sqrt{3}}{2}\right)$

81. (a) ≈ -2.5 degrees/inch   **(b)** ≈ -16.1 degrees/inch
(c) ≈ -8.3 degrees/inch   **83.** 5.97 atm

85. Yes: $C = F = -40°$

91.

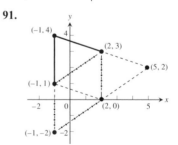

93. $k = -8, \quad k = 1/2$

Section 1.3, pp. 26–28

1. $D: (-\infty, \infty), \quad R: [1, \infty)$ **3.** $D: (0, \infty), \quad R: (0, \infty)$

5. $D: [-2, 2], \quad R: [0, 2]$

7. (a) Not a function of x because some values of x have two values of y **(b)** A function of x because for every x there is only one possible y

9. (a) No **(b)** No **(c)** No **(d)** $(0, 1]$

11. $A = \dfrac{\sqrt{3}}{4}x^2, \quad p = 3x$

13. $x = \dfrac{d}{\sqrt{3}}, \quad A = 2d^2, \quad V = \dfrac{d^3}{3\sqrt{3}}$

15. $(-\infty, \infty)$ **17.** $(-\infty, \infty)$

19. $(-\infty, 0) \cup (0, \infty)$

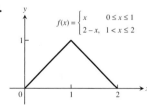

21. (a) For each positive value of x, there are two values of y.   **(b)** For each value of $x \neq 0$, there are two values of y.

23.

$f(x) = \begin{cases} x & 0 \le x \le 1 \\ 2 - x, & 1 < x \le 2 \end{cases}$

25.

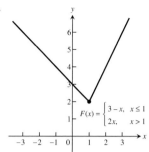

$F(x) = \begin{cases} 3 - x, & x \le 1 \\ 2x, & x > 1 \end{cases}$

27. (a) $f(x) = \begin{cases} x, & 0 \le x \le 1 \\ -x + 2, & 1 < x \le 2 \end{cases}$

(b) $f(x) = \begin{cases} 2, & 0 \le x < 1 \\ 0, & 1 \le x < 2 \\ 2, & 2 \le x < 3 \\ 0, & 3 \le x \le 4 \end{cases}$

29. (a) $f(x) = \begin{cases} -x, & -1 \le x < 0 \\ 1, & 0 < x \le 1 \\ -\frac{1}{2}x + \frac{3}{2}, & 1 < x < 3 \end{cases}$

(b) $f(x) = \begin{cases} \frac{1}{2}x, & -2 \le x \le 0 \\ -2x + 2, & 0 < x \le 1 \\ -1, & 1 < x \le 3 \end{cases}$

31. (a) $(-2, 0) \cup (4, \infty)$

33. (a) $0 \le x < 1$ **(b)** $-1 < x \le 0$

35. Yes   **37.** $V = x(14 - 2x)(22 - 2x)$

39. (a) Because the circumference of the original circle was 8π and a piece of length x was removed

(b) $r = \dfrac{8\pi - x}{2\pi} = 4 - \dfrac{x}{2\pi}$

(c) $h = \sqrt{16 - r^2} = \dfrac{\sqrt{16\pi x - x^2}}{2\pi}$

(d) $V = \dfrac{1}{3}\pi r^2 h = \dfrac{(8\pi - x)^2\sqrt{16\pi x - x^2}}{24\pi^2}$

Section 1.4, pp. 37–38

1. (a) linear, algebraic, polynomial of degree 1   **(b)** power, algebraic   **(c)** rational, algebraic   **(d)** exponential

3. (a) rational, algebraic   **(b)** algebraic   **(c)** trigonometric   **(d)** logarithmic

5. (a) h **(b)** f **(c)** g

7. Symmetric about the origin   Dec. $-\infty < x < \infty$

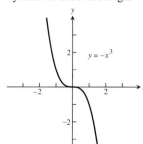

9. Symmetric about the origin

Inc. $-\infty < x < 0$ and $0 < x < \infty$

11. Symmetric about the y-axis

Dec. $-\infty < x \le 0$;
inc. $0 \le x < \infty$

13. Symmetric about the origin

Inc. $-\infty < x < \infty$

15. No symmetry

Dec. $0 \le x < \infty$

17. Symmetric about the y-axis

Dec. $-\infty < x \le 0$;
inc. $0 \le x < \infty$

19. Even   **21.** Even   **23.** Odd   **25.** Even   **27.** Neither
29. Neither

31. (a) The graph supports the assumption that y is proportional to x. The constant of proportionality is estimated from the slope of the line, which is 0.166.

(b) The graph supports the assumption that y is proportional to $x^{1/2}$. The constant of proportionality is estimated from the slope of the line, which is 2.03.

33. (a) $k \approx 1.1$ **(b)** $k \approx 0.059$
35. (a)

(b) $k \approx 0.87$
(c) Using $y = 0.87x$ with $x = 13$, we get $y = 11.31$.

Section 1.5, pp. 45–48

1. $D_f : -\infty < x < \infty$, $D_g : x \ge 1$, $R_f : -\infty < y < \infty$,
   $R_g : y \ge 0$, $D_{f+g} = D_{f \cdot g} = D_g$, $R_{f+g} : y \ge 1$, $R_{f \cdot g} : y \ge 0$
3. $D_f : -\infty < x < \infty$, $D_g : -\infty < x < \infty$, $R_f : y = 2$,
   $R_g : y \ge 1$, $D_{f/g} : -\infty < x < \infty$, $R_{f/g} : 0 < y \le 2$,
   $D_{g/f} : -\infty < x < \infty$, $R_{g/f} : y \ge 1/2$
5. (a) 2   **(b)** 22   **(c)** $x^2 + 2$ **(d)** $x^2 + 10x + 22$ **(e)** 5
   (f) -2 **(g)** $x + 10$ **(h)** $x^4 - 6x^2 + 6$

7. (a) $\dfrac{4}{x^2} - 5$ **(b)** $\dfrac{4}{x^2} - 5$ **(c)** $\left(\dfrac{4}{x} - 5\right)^2$ **(d)** $\left(\dfrac{1}{4x - 5}\right)^2$

   (e) $\dfrac{1}{4x^2 - 5}$ **(f)** $\dfrac{1}{(4x - 5)^2}$

9. (a) $f(g(x))$ **(b)** $j(g(x))$ **(c)** $g(g(x))$ **(d)** $j(j(x))$
(e) $g(h(f(x)))$ **(f)** $h(j(f(x)))$

11.

	$g(x)$	$f(x)$	$f \circ g(x)$
(a)	$x - 7$	$\sqrt{x}$	$\sqrt{x - 7}$
(b)	$x + 2$	$3x$	$3x + 6$
(c)	x^2	$\sqrt{x - 5}$	$\sqrt{x^2 - 5}$
(d)	$\dfrac{x}{x - 1}$	$\dfrac{x}{x - 1}$	x
(e)	$\dfrac{1}{x - 1}$	$1 + \dfrac{1}{x}$	x
(f)	$\dfrac{1}{x}$	$\dfrac{1}{x}$	x

13. (a) $f(g(x)) = \sqrt{\dfrac{1}{x} + 1}$, $g(f(x)) = \dfrac{1}{\sqrt{x + 1}}$

(b) $D_{f \circ g} = (0, \infty), D_{g \circ f} = (-1, \infty)$

(c) $R_{f \circ g} = (1, \infty), R_{g \circ f} = (0, \infty)$

15. (a) $y = -(x + 7)^2$ **(b)** $y = -(x - 4)^2$
17. (a) Position 4 **(b)** Position 1 **(c)** Position 2 **(d)** Position 3
19. $(x + 2)^2 + (y + 3)^2 = 49$ **21.** $y + 1 = (x + 1)^3$

23. $y = \sqrt{x + 0.81}$ **25.** $y = 2x$

27. $y - 1 = \dfrac{1}{x - 1}$ **29.**

31. **33.**

35. **37.**

39. **41.**

43. **45.**

47.

49. (a) $D : [0, 2], \quad R : [2, 3]$ **(b)** $D : [0, 2], \quad R : [-1, 0]$

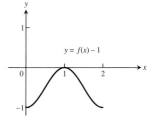

(c) $D : [0, 2], \quad R : [0, 2]$

$y = 2f(x)$

(d) $D : [0, 2], \quad R : [-1, 0]$

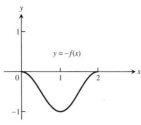

$y = -f(x)$

(e) $D : [-2, 0], \quad R : [0, 1]$

$y = f(x + 2)$

(f) $D : [1, 3], R : [0, 1]$

$y = f(x - 1)$

(g) $D : [-2, 0], \quad R : [0, 1]$

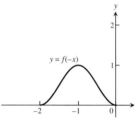

$y = f(-x)$

(h) $D : [-1, 1], \quad R : [0, 1]$

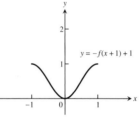

$y = -f(x + 1) + 1$

51. $y = 3x^2 - 3$ **53.** $y = \dfrac{1}{2} + \dfrac{1}{2x^2}$ **55.** $y = \sqrt{4x + 1}$

57. $y = \sqrt{4 - \dfrac{x^2}{4}}$ **59.** $y = 1 - 27x^3$

61.

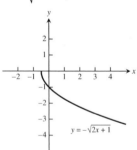

$y = -\sqrt{2x + 1}$

63.

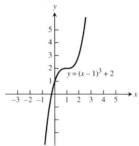

$y = (x - 1)^3 + 2$

65.

$y = \dfrac{1}{2x} - 1$

67.

$y = -\sqrt[3]{x}$

69.

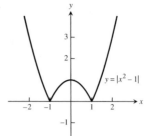

$y = |x^2 - 1|$

71.

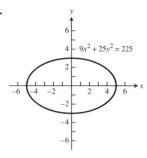

$9x^2 + 25y^2 = 225$

73.

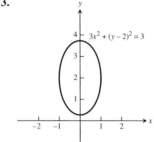

$3x^2 + (y - 2)^2 = 3$

75.

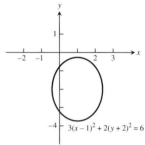

$3(x - 1)^2 + 2(y + 2)^2 = 6$

77. $\dfrac{(x + 4)^2}{16} + \dfrac{(y - 3)^2}{9} = 1$ Center: $(-4, 3)$

The major axis is the line segment between $(-8, 3)$ and $(0, 3)$.

$\dfrac{(x + 4)^2}{16} + \dfrac{(y - 3)^2}{9} = 1$

79. (a) Odd   **(b)** Odd   **(c)** Odd   **(d)** Even   **(e)** Even
(f) Even   **(g)** Even   **(h)** Even   **(i)** Odd

Section 1.6, pp. 56–58

1. (a) 8π m   **(b)** $\dfrac{55\pi}{9}$ m   **3.** 8.4 in.

5.

θ	$-\pi$	$-2\pi/3$	0	$\pi/2$	$3\pi/4$
$\sin\theta$	0	$-\dfrac{\sqrt{3}}{2}$	0	1	$\dfrac{1}{\sqrt{2}}$
$\cos\theta$	-1	$-\dfrac{1}{2}$	1	0	$-\dfrac{1}{\sqrt{2}}$
$\tan\theta$	0	$\sqrt{3}$	0	UND	-1
$\cot\theta$	UND	$\dfrac{1}{\sqrt{3}}$	UND	0	-1
$\sec\theta$	-1	-2	1	UND	$-\sqrt{2}$
$\csc\theta$	UND	$-\dfrac{2}{\sqrt{3}}$	UND	1	$\sqrt{2}$

7. $\cos x = -4/5$, $\tan x = -3/4$

9. $\sin x = -\dfrac{\sqrt{8}}{3}$, $\tan x = -\sqrt{8}$

11. $\sin x = -\dfrac{1}{\sqrt{5}}$, $\cos x = -\dfrac{2}{\sqrt{5}}$

13. Period π

15. Period 2

17. Period 6

19. Period 2π

21. Period 2π

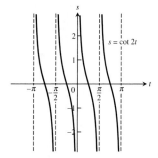

23. Period $\pi/2$, symmetric about the origin

25. Period 4, symmetric about the y-axis

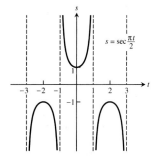

29. $D: (-\infty, \infty)$, $R: y = -1, 0, 1$

39. $-\cos x$ **41.** $-\cos x$ **43.** $\dfrac{\sqrt{6} + \sqrt{2}}{4}$ **45.** $\dfrac{1 + \sqrt{3}}{2\sqrt{2}}$

47. $\dfrac{2 + \sqrt{2}}{4}$ **49.** $\dfrac{2 - \sqrt{3}}{4}$ **55.** $c = \sqrt{7} \approx 2.646$

59. $a = 1.464$

61. $A = 2, B = 2\pi, C = -\pi, D = -1$

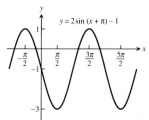

63. $A = -\dfrac{2}{\pi}, B = 4, C = 0, D = \dfrac{1}{\pi}$

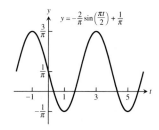

65. **(a)** 37 **(b)** 365 **(c)** Right 101 **(d)** Up 25

Section 1.7, pp. 66–68

1. d) **3.** d)

5. $[-3, 5]$ by $[-15, 40]$

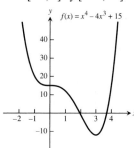

7. $[-3, 6]$ by $[-250, 50]$

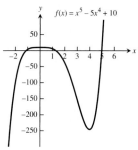

9. $[-3, 3]$ by $[-6, 6]$

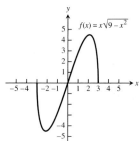

11. $[-2, 6]$ by $[-5, 4]$

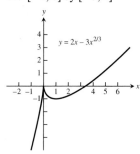

13. $[-2, 8]$ by $[-5, 10]$

$y = 5x^{2/5} - 2x$

15. $[-3, 3]$ by $[0, 10]$

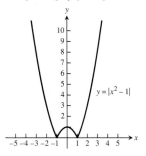

$y = |x^2 - 1|$

27. $[-100\pi, 100\pi]$ by $[-1.25, 1.25]$

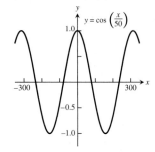

$y = \cos\left(\frac{x}{50}\right)$

17. $[-15, 5]$ by $[-10, 10]$

$y = \frac{x+3}{x+2}$

19. $[-4, 4]$ by $[0, 3]$

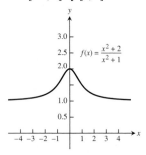

$f(x) = \frac{x^2 + 2}{x^2 + 1}$

29. $\left[-\dfrac{\pi}{15}, \dfrac{\pi}{15}\right]$ by $[-0.25, 0.25]$

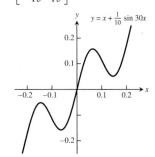

$y = x + \frac{1}{10}\sin 30x$

21. $[-10, 10]$ by $[-6, 6]$

$f(x) = \frac{x-1}{x^2 - x - 6}$

23. $[-6, 10]$ by $[-6, 6]$

$f(x) = \frac{6x^2 - 15x + 6}{4x^2 - 10x}$

31.

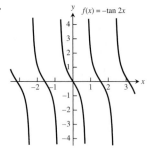

$(x+1)^2 + (y-2)^2 = 9$

33.

$f(x) = -\tan 2x$

25. $\left[-\dfrac{\pi}{125}, \dfrac{\pi}{125}\right]$ by $[-1.25, 1.25]$

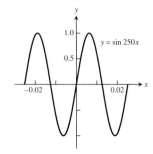

$y = \sin 250x$

35.

$f(x) = \sin 2x + \cos 3x$

37.

$y = \dfrac{1}{x-3}$

39.

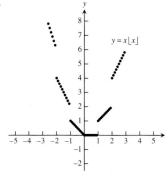

$y = x\lfloor x \rfloor$

41. (a) $y = 1059.14x - 2074972.23$
  (b) $m = 1059.14$; this is the amount the compensation will increase by each year.
  (c)

  (d) \$53,899.17

43. (a) $y = 0.0866x^2 - 1.9701x + 50.0594$
  (b)

  (c) If the speed is 72 mph, the approximate stopping distance is 367.50 ft. If the speed is 85 mph, the approximate stopping distance is 522.67 ft.

(d) $y = -140.4121 + 6.889x$

If the speed is 72 mph, the approximate stopping distance is 355.60 ft. If the speed is 85 mph, the approximate stopping distance is 445.15 ft
The quadratic regression equation is a better fit.

Practice Exercises, pp. 69–70

1. $x \geq -2$

3. $x > 6$

5. $-8, 6$ **7.** $x < -1$ or $x > 5$ **9.** $(0, 11)$
11. No, no two sides have the same length; no, no two sides are perpendicular
13. $y = 3x - 9$ **15.** $x = 0$ **17.** $y = 2$ **19.** $y = -3x + 3$
21. $y = -\dfrac{4}{3}x - \dfrac{20}{3}$ **23.** $y = \dfrac{2}{3}x + \dfrac{8}{3}$
25. $A = \pi r^2, C = 2\pi r, A = \dfrac{C^2}{4\pi}$ **27.** $x = \tan\theta, y = \tan^2\theta$
29. Origin **31.** Neither **33.** Even **35.** Even **37.** Odd
39. Neither **41. (a)** Domain: all reals **(b)** Range: $[-2, \infty)$
43. (a) Domain: $[-4, 4]$ **(b)** Range: $[0, 4]$
45. (a) Domain: all reals **(b)** Range: $(-3, \infty)$
47. (a) Domain: all reals **(b)** Range: $[-3, 1]$
49. (a) Domain: $(3, \infty)$ **(b)** Range: all reals
51. (a) Domain: $[-4, 4]$ **(b)** Range: $[0, 2]$
53. $f(x) = \begin{cases} 1 - x, & 0 \leq x < 1 \\ 2 - x, & 1 \leq x \leq 2 \end{cases}$
55. (a) 1 **(b)** $\dfrac{1}{\sqrt{2.5}} = \sqrt{\dfrac{2}{5}}$ **(c)** $x, x \neq 0$
  (d) $\dfrac{1}{\sqrt{1/\sqrt{x+2}+2}}$
57. (a) $(f \circ g)(x) = -x, x \geq -2, (g \circ f)(x) = \sqrt{4 - x^2}$
  (b) Domain $(f \circ g)$: $[-2, \infty)$, domain $(g \circ f)$: $[-2, 2]$
  (c) Range $(f \circ g)$: $(-\infty, 2]$, range $(g \circ f)$: $[0, 2]$

59. Replace the portion for $x < 0$ with mirror image of the portion for $x > 0$ to make the new graph symmetric with respect to the y-axis.

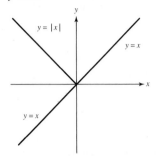

61. It does not change it.

63. Adds the mirror image of the portion for $x > 0$ to make the new graph symmetric with respect to the y-axis

65. Reflects the portion for $y < 0$ across the x-axis

67. Reflects the portion for $y < 0$ across the x-axis

69. Period π

71. Period 2

73.

75. (a) $a = 1$ $b = \sqrt{3}$ (b) $a = 2\sqrt{3}/3$ $c = 4\sqrt{3}/3$

77. (a) $a = \dfrac{b}{\tan B}$ (b) $c = \dfrac{a}{\sin A}$

79. ≈ 16.98 m **81.** (b) 4π

Additional and Advanced Exercises, pp. 71–72

1. (a)

(b)

(c)

(d)

3. Yes. For instance: $f(x) = 1/x$ and $g(x) = 1/x$, or $f(x) = 2x$ and $g(x) = x/2$, or $f(x) = e^x$ and $g(x) = \ln x$.

5. If $f(x)$ is odd, then $g(x) = f(x) - 2$ is not odd. Nor is $g(x)$ even, unless $f(x) = 0$ for all x. If f is even, then $g(x) = f(x) - 2$ is also even.

7.

9. $\sqrt{2}$ **11.** 3/4 **13.** $3\sqrt{15}/16$ **27.** $-4 < m < 0$

CHAPTER 2

Section 2.1, pp. 81–84

1. (a) Does not exist. As x approaches 1 from the right, $g(x)$ approaches 0. As x approaches 1 from the left, $g(x)$ approaches 1. There is no single number L that all the values $g(x)$ get arbitrarily close to as $x \to 1$. (b) 1 (c) 0

3. (a) True (b) True (c) False
(d) False (e) False (f) True

5. As x approaches 0 from the left, $x/|x|$ approaches -1. As x approaches 0 from the right, $x/|x|$ approaches 1. There is no single number L that the function values all get arbitrarily close to as $x \to 0$.

7. Nothing can be said. **9.** No; no; no

11. (a) $f(x) = (x^2 - 9)/(x + 3)$

x	-3.1	-3.01	-3.001	-3.0001	-3.00001	-3.000001
$f(x)$	-6.1	-6.01	-6.001	-6.0001	-6.00001	-6.000001

x	-2.9	-2.99	-2.999	-2.9999	-2.99999	-2.999999
$f(x)$	-5.9	-5.99	-5.999	-5.9999	-5.99999	-5.999999

(c) $\lim\limits_{x \to -3} f(x) = -6$

13. (a) $G(x) = (x + 6)/(x^2 + 4x - 12)$

x	-5.9	-5.99	-5.999	-5.9999
$G(x)$	$-.126582$	$-.1251564$	$-.1250156$	$-.1250015$

-5.99999	-5.999999
$-.1250001$	$-.1250000$

x	-6.1	-6.01	-6.001	-6.0001
$G(x)$	$-.123456$	$-.124843$	$-.124984$	$-.124998$

-6.00001	-6.000001
$-.124999$	$-.124999$

(c) $\lim\limits_{x \to -6} G(x) = -1/8 = -0.125$

15. (a) $f(x) = (x^2 - 1)/(|x| - 1)$

x	-1.1	-1.01	-1.001	-1.0001	-1.00001	-1.000001
$f(x)$	2.1	2.01	2.001	2.0001	2.00001	2.000001

x	$-.9$	$-.99$	$-.999$	$-.9999$	$-.99999$	$-.999999$
$f(x)$	1.9	1.99	1.999	1.9999	1.99999	1.999999

(c) $\lim\limits_{x \to -1} f(x) = 2$

17. (a) $g(\theta) = (\sin \theta)/\theta$

θ	$.1$	$.01$	$.001$	$.0001$	$.00001$	$.000001$
$g(\theta)$	$.998334$	$.999983$	$.999999$	$.999999$	$.999999$	$.999999$

θ	$-.1$	$-.01$	$-.001$	$-.0001$	$-.00001$	$-.000001$
$g(\theta)$	$.998334$	$.999983$	$.999999$	$.999999$	$.999999$	$.999999$

$\lim\limits_{\theta \to 0} g(\theta) = 1$

19. (a) $f(x) = x^{1/(1-x)}$

x	$.9$	$.99$	$.999$	$.9999$	$.99999$	$.999999$
$f(x)$	$.348678$	$.366032$	$.367695$	$.367861$	$.367877$	$.367879$

x	1.1	1.01	1.001	1.0001	1.00001	1.000001
$f(x)$	$.385543$	$.369711$	$.368063$	$.367897$	$.367881$	$.367878$

$\lim\limits_{x \to 1} f(x) \approx 0.36788$

21. 4   **23.** 0   **25.** 9   **27.** $\pi/2$ **29.** (a) 19   (b) 1

31. (a) $-\dfrac{4}{\pi}$ (b) $-\dfrac{3\sqrt{3}}{\pi}$ **33.** 1

35. Graphs can shift during a press run, so your estimates may not completely agree with these.

(a)

PQ_1	PQ_2	PQ_3	PQ_4
43	46	49	50

The appropriate units are m/sec.

(b) $\approx$ 50 m/sec or 180 km/h

37. (a)

(b) $\approx$ \$56,000/year
(c) $\approx$ \$42,000/year

39. (a) 0.414213, 0.449489, $(\sqrt{1 + h} - 1)/h$ (b) $g(x) = \sqrt{x}$

$1 + h$	1.1	1.01	1.001	1.0001
$\sqrt{1 + h}$	1.04880	1.004987	1.0004998	1.0000499
$(\sqrt{1 + h} - 1)/h$	0.4880	0.4987	0.4998	0.499

1.00001	1.000001
1.000005	1.0000005
0.5	0.5

(c) 0.5   (d) 0.5

Section 2.2, pp. 89–91

1. -9 **3.** 4   **5.** -8 **7.** 5/8   **9.** 5/2   **11.** 27   **13.** 16
15. 3/2   **17.** 3/2   **19.** 1/10   **21.** -7 **23.** 3/2   **25.** $-1/2$
27. 4/3   **29.** 1/6   **31.** 4   **33.** 1/2   **35.** 3/2
37. (a) Quotient Rule   (b) Difference and Power Rules
(c) Sum and Constant Multiple Rules
39. (a) -10 (b) -20 (c) -1 (d) 5/7
41. (a) 4   (b) -21 (c) -12 (d) $-7/3$
43. 2   **45.** 3   **47.** $1/(2\sqrt{7})$ **49.** $\sqrt{5}$
51. (a) The limit is 1.   **53.** $c = 0, 1, -1$; The limit is 0 at $c = 0$, and 1 at $c = 1, -1$ **55.** 7   **57.** (a) 5   (b) 5

Section 2.3, pp. 98–101

1. $\delta = 2$

3. $\delta = 1/2$

5. $\delta = 1/18$

7. $\delta = 0.1$ **9.** $\delta = 7/16$ **11.** $\delta = \sqrt{5} - 2$ **13.** $\delta = 0.36$
15. $(3.99, 4.01)$, $\delta = 0.01$ **17.** $(-0.19, 0.21)$, $\delta = 0.19$
19. $(3, 15)$, $\delta = 5$ **21.** $(10/3, 5)$, $\delta = 2/3$
23. $(-\sqrt{4.5}, -\sqrt{3.5})$, $\delta = \sqrt{4.5} - 2 \approx 0.12$
25. $(\sqrt{15}, \sqrt{17})$, $\delta = \sqrt{17} - 4 \approx 0.12$

27. $\left(2 - \dfrac{0.03}{m}, 2 + \dfrac{0.03}{m}\right)$, $\delta = \dfrac{0.03}{m}$

29. $\left(\dfrac{1}{2} - \dfrac{c}{m}, \dfrac{c}{m} + \dfrac{1}{2}\right)$, $\delta = \dfrac{c}{m}$

31. $L = -3$, $\delta = 0.01$ **33.** $L = 4$, $\delta = 0.05$

35. $L = 4$, $\delta = 0.75$

55. [3.384, 3.387]. To be safe, the left endpoint was rounded up and the right endpoint rounded down.

59. The limit does not exist as x approaches 3.

Section 2.4, pp. 111–114

1. (a) True   **(b)** True   **(c)** False   **(d)** True   **(e)** True
   (f) True   **(g)** False   **(h)** False   **(i)** False   **(j)** False
   (k) True   **(l)** False

3. (a) 2, 1   **(b)** No, $\lim\limits_{x\to 2^{+}} f(x) \neq \lim\limits_{x\to 2^{-}} f(x)$ **(c)** 3, 3
   (d) Yes, 3

5. (a) No   **(b)** Yes, 0   **(c)** No

7. (a)   **(b)** 1, 1   **(c)** Yes, 1

$y = \begin{cases} x^3, & x \neq 1 \\ 0, & x = 1 \end{cases}$

9. (a) $D: 0 \le x \le 2, R: 0 < y \le 1$ and $y = 2$.
   (b) $(0, 1) \cup (1, 2)$ **(c)** $x = 2$ **(d)** $x = 0$

$y = \begin{cases} \sqrt{1 - x^2}, & 0 \le x < 1 \\ 1, & 1 \le x < 2 \\ 2, & x = 2 \end{cases}$

11. $\sqrt{3}$ **13.** 1   **15.** $2/\sqrt{5}$ **17. (a)** 1   **(b)** -1
19. (a) 1   **(b)** 2/3   **21.** 1   **23.** 3/4   **25.** 2   **27.** 1/2
29. 2   **31.** 1   **33.** 1/2   **35.** 3/8   **37. (a)** -3 **(b)** -3
39. (a) 1/2   **(b)** 1/2   **41. (a)** $-5/3$ **(b)** $-5/3$ **43.** 0
45. -1 **47. (a)** 2/5   **(b)** 2/5   **49. (a)** 0   **(b)** 0
51. (a) 7   **(b)** 7   **53. (a)** 0   **(b)** 0   **55. (a)** $-2/3$
   (b) $-2/3$ **57.** 0   **59.** 1   **61.** ∞ **69.** 1

73. $\delta = \epsilon^2$, $\lim\limits_{x\to 5^{+}} \sqrt{x - 5} = 0$

77. (a) 400   **(b)** 399   **(c)** The limit does not exist.

79. 1   **81.** 3/2   **83.** 3

Section 2.5, pp. 122–123

1. ∞ **3.** $-\infty$ **5.** $-\infty$ **7.** ∞ **9. (a)** ∞ **(b)** $-\infty$
11. ∞ **13.** ∞ **15.** $-\infty$ **17. (a)** ∞ **(b)** $-\infty$

(c) $-\infty$ **(d)** ∞ **19. (a)** $-\infty$ **(b)** ∞ **(c)** 0
(d) 3/2   **21. (a)** $-\infty$ **(b)** 1/4   **(c)** 1/4   **(d)** 1/4
(e) It will be $-\infty$.   **23. (a)** $-\infty$ **(b)** ∞ **25. (a)** ∞
(b) ∞ **(c)** ∞ **(d)** ∞

27.

$y = \dfrac{1}{x - 1}$

$x = 1$

29.

$y = \dfrac{1}{2x + 4}$

$x = -2$

31.

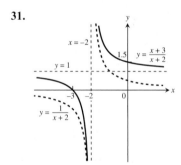

$x = -2$ $y = \dfrac{x + 3}{x + 2}$ $y = 1$ $y = \dfrac{1}{x + 2}$

33.

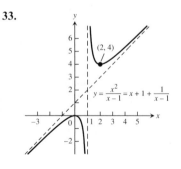

$(2, 4)$

$y = \dfrac{x^2}{x - 1} = x + 1 + \dfrac{1}{x - 1}$

35.

37.

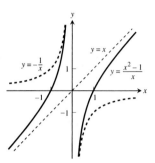

39. Here is one possibility.

41. Here is one possibility.

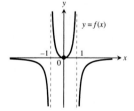

43. Here is one possibility.

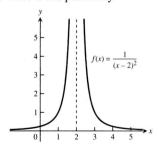

45. Here is one possibility.

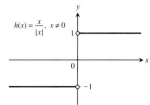

51. **(a)** For every positive real number B there exists a corresponding number $\delta > 0$ such that for all x
$$x_0 - \delta < x < x_0 \Rightarrow f(x) > B.$$

(b) For every negative real number $-B$ there exists a corresponding number $\delta > 0$ such that for all x
$$x_0 < x < x_0 + \delta \Rightarrow f(x) < -B.$$

(c) For every negative real number $-B$ there exists a corresponding number $\delta > 0$ such that for all x
$$x_0 - \delta < x < x_0 \Rightarrow f(x) < -B.$$

57.

59.

61.

63.

$y = x^{2/3} + \dfrac{1}{x^{1/3}}$

9. $y = 12x + 16$

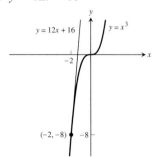

$y = 12x + 16$

$y = x^3$

$(-2, -8)$

Section 2.6, pp. 132–134

1. No; discontinuous at $x = 2$; not defined at $x = 2$
3. Continuous   **5. (a)** Yes   **(b)** Yes   **(c)** Yes   **(d)** Yes
7. (a) No   **(b)** No   **9.** 0   **11.** 1, nonremovable; 0, removable   **13.** All x except $x = 2$ **15.** All x except $x = 3, x = 1$ **17.** All x **19.** All x except $x = 0$
21. All x except $x = n\pi/2$, n any integer   **23.** All x except $n\pi/2$, n an odd integer   **25.** All $x \geq -3/2$ **27.** All x
29. 0; continuous at $x = \pi$ **31.** 1; continuous at $y = 1$
33. $\sqrt{2}/2$; continuous at $t = 0$ **35.** $g(3) = 6$
37. $f(1) = 3/2$ **39.** $a = 4/3$
63. $x \approx 1.8794, -1.5321, -0.3473$
65. $x \approx 1.7549$ **67.** $x \approx 3.5156$ **69.** $x \approx 0.7391$

Section 2.7, pp. 140–141

1. $P_1: m_1 = 1, P_2: m_2 = 5$ **3.** $P_1: m_1 = 5/2, P_2: m_2 = -1/2$
5. $y = 2x + 5$

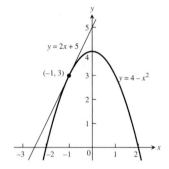

$y = 2x + 5$

$(-1, 3)$

$y = 4 - x^2$

7. $y = x + 1$

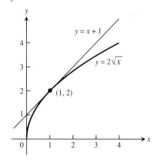

$y = x + 1$

$y = 2\sqrt{x}$

$(1, 2)$

11. $m = 4, y - 5 = 4(x - 2)$
13. $m = -2, y - 3 = -2(x - 3)$
15. $m = 12, y - 8 = 12(t - 2)$
17. $m = \dfrac{1}{4}, y - 2 = \dfrac{1}{4}(x - 4)$
19. $m = -10$ **21.** $m = -1/4$ **23.** $(-2, -5)$
25. $y = -(x + 1), y = -(x - 3)$ **27.** 19.6 m/sec
29. 6π **31.** Yes   **33.** Yes   **35. (a)** Nowhere
37. (a) At $x = 0$ **39. (a)** Nowhere   **41. (a)** At $x = 1$
43. (a) At $x = 0$

Practice Exercises, pp. 142–143

1. At $x = -1$: $\lim\limits_{x \to -1^-} f(x) = \lim\limits_{x \to -1^+} f(x) = 1$, so $\lim\limits_{x \to -1} f(x) = 1 = f(-1)$; continuous at $x = -1$

At $x = 0$: $\lim\limits_{x \to 0^-} f(x) = \lim\limits_{x \to 0^+} f(x) = 0$, so $\lim\limits_{x \to 0} f(x) = 0$. However, $f(0) \neq 0$, so f is discontinuous at $x = 0$. The discontinuity can be removed by redefining $f(0)$ to be 0.

At $x = 1$: $\lim\limits_{x \to 1^-} f(x) = -1$ and $\lim\limits_{x \to 1^+} f(x) = 1$, so $\lim\limits_{x \to 1} f(x)$ does not exist. The function is discontinuous at $x = 1$, and the discontinuity is not removable.

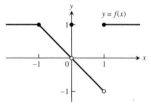

$y = f(x)$

3. (a) -21 **(b)** 49   **(c)** 0   **(d)** 1   **(e)** 1   **(f)** 7
   (g) -7 **(h)** $-\dfrac{1}{7}$ **5.** 4
7. (a) $(-\infty, +\infty)$ **(b)** $[0, \infty)$ **(c)** $(-\infty, 0)$ and $(0, \infty)$
   (d) $(0, \infty)$
9. (a) Does not exist   **(b)** 0
11. $\dfrac{1}{2}$ **13.** $2x$ **15.** $-\dfrac{1}{4}$ **17.** 2   **19.** 0   **21.** $\dfrac{2}{5}$ **23.** 0
25. $-\infty$ **27.** 0   **29.** 1   **31.** No in both cases, because $\lim\limits_{x \to 1} f(x)$ does not exist, and $\lim\limits_{x \to -1} f(x)$ does not exist.
37. (b) 1.324717957

Additional and Advanced Exercises, pp. 144–146

3. 0; the left-hand limit was needed because the function is undefined for $v > c$.   **5.** $65 < t < 75$; within $5°F$

13. (a) B **(b)** A **(c)** A **(d)** A

21. (a) $\lim_{a \to 0} r_+(a) = 0.5$, $\lim_{a \to -1^+} r_+(a) = 1$

(b) $\lim_{a \to 0} r_-(a)$ does not exist, $\lim_{a \to -1^+} r_-(a) = 1$

25. 0   **27.** 1   **29.** 4

CHAPTER 3

Section 3.1, pp. 155–159

1. $-2x, 6, 0, -2$ **3.** $-\dfrac{2}{t^3}, 2, -\dfrac{1}{4}, -\dfrac{2}{3\sqrt{3}}$

5. $\dfrac{3}{2\sqrt{30}}, \dfrac{3}{2\sqrt{3}}, \dfrac{1}{2}, \dfrac{3}{2\sqrt{2}}$ **7.** $6x^2$ **9.** $\dfrac{1}{(2t+1)^2}$

11. $\dfrac{-1}{2(q+1)\sqrt{q+1}}$ **13.** $1 - \dfrac{9}{x^2}, 0$ **15.** $3t^2 - 2t, 5$

17. $\dfrac{-4}{(x-2)\sqrt{x-2}}$, $y - 4 = -\dfrac{1}{2}(x-6)$ **19.** 6

21. $1/8$ **23.** $\dfrac{-1}{(x+2)^2}$ **25.** $\dfrac{-1}{(x-1)^2}$ **27.** b   **29.** d

31. (a) $x = 0, 1, 4$ **(b)**

33.

35. Since $\lim_{x \to 0^+} f'(x) = 1$ while $\lim_{x \to 0^-} f'(x) = 0$, $f(x)$ is not differentiable at $x = 0$.

37. Since $\lim_{x \to 1^+} f'(x) = 2$ while $\lim_{x \to 1^-} f'(x) = 1/2$, $f(x)$ is not differentiable at $x = 1$.

39. (a) $-3 \le x \le 2$ **(b)** None   **(c)** None

41. (a) $-3 \le x < 0, 0 < x \le 3$ **(b)** None   **(c)** $x = 0$

43. (a) $-1 \le x < 0, 0 < x \le 2$ **(b)** $x = 0$ **(c)** None

45. (a) $y' = -2x$ **(c)** $x < 0, x = 0, x > 0$
(d) $-\infty < x < 0, 0 < x < \infty$

47. (a) $y' = x^2$
(b)

(c) $x \ne 0, x = 0$, none   **(d)** $-\infty < x < \infty$, none

49. $y' = 3x^2$ is never negative

51. Yes, $y + 16 = -(x - 3)$ is tangent at $(3, -16)$

53. No, the function $y = \lfloor x \rfloor$ does not satisfy the intermediate value property of derivatives.

55. Yes, $(-f)'(x) = -(f'(x))$

57. For $g(t) = mt$ and $h(t) = t$, $\lim_{t \to 0} \dfrac{g(t)}{h(t)} = m$, which need not be zero.

Section 3.2, pp. 169–171

1. $\dfrac{dy}{dx} = -2x, \dfrac{d^2y}{dx^2} = -2$

3. $\dfrac{ds}{dt} = 15t^2 - 15t^4, \dfrac{d^2s}{dt^2} = 30t - 60t^3$

5. $\dfrac{dy}{dx} = 4x^2 - 1, \dfrac{d^2y}{dx^2} = 8x$

7. $\dfrac{dw}{dz} = -\dfrac{6}{z^3} + \dfrac{1}{z^2}, \dfrac{d^2w}{dz^2} = \dfrac{18}{z^4} - \dfrac{2}{z^3}$

9. $\dfrac{dy}{dx} = 12x - 10 + 10x^{-3}, \dfrac{d^2y}{dx^2} = 12 - 30x^{-4}$

11. $\dfrac{dr}{ds} = \dfrac{-2}{3s^3} + \dfrac{5}{2s^2}, \dfrac{d^2r}{ds^2} = \dfrac{2}{s^4} - \dfrac{5}{s^3}$

13. $y' = -5x^4 + 12x^2 - 2x - 3$

15. $y' = 3x^2 + 10x + 2 - \dfrac{1}{x^2}$ **17.** $y' = \dfrac{-19}{(3x-2)^2}$

19. $g'(x) = \dfrac{x^2 + x + 4}{(x + 0.5)^2}$ **21.** $\dfrac{dv}{dt} = \dfrac{t^2 - 2t - 1}{(1 + t^2)^2}$

23. $f'(s) = \dfrac{1}{\sqrt{s}(\sqrt{s} + 1)^2}$ **25.** $v' = -\dfrac{1}{x^2} + 2x^{-3/2}$

27. $y' = \dfrac{-4x^3 - 3x^2 + 1}{(x^2 - 1)^2(x^2 + x + 1)^2}$

29. $y' = 2x^3 - 3x - 1, y'' = 6x^2 - 3, y''' = 12x, y^{(4)} = 12$, $y^{(n)} = 0$ for $n \ge 5$

31. $y' = 2x - 7x^{-2}, y'' = 2 + 14x^{-3}$

33. $\dfrac{dr}{d\theta} = 3\theta^{-4}, \dfrac{d^2r}{d\theta^2} = -12\theta^{-5}$

35. $\dfrac{dw}{dz} = -z^{-2} - 1, \dfrac{d^2w}{dz^2} = 2z^{-3}$

37. $\dfrac{dp}{dq} = \dfrac{1}{6}q + \dfrac{1}{6}q^{-3} + q^{-5}, \dfrac{d^2p}{dq^2} = \dfrac{1}{6} - \dfrac{1}{2}q^{-4} - 5q^{-6}$

39. (a) 13 **(b)** −7 **(c)** 7/25 **(d)** 20

41. (a) $y = -\dfrac{x}{8} + \dfrac{5}{4}$ **(b)** $m = -4$ at $(0, 1)$

(c) $y = 8x - 15, y = 8x + 17$

43. $y = 4x, y = 2$ **45.** $a = 1, b = 1, c = 0$

47. (a) $y = 2x + 2,$ **(c)** $(2, 6)$

49. $P'(x) = na_nx^{n-1} + (n-1)a_{n-1}x^{n-2} + \cdots + 2a_2x + a_1$

51. The Product Rule is then the Constant Multiple Rule, so the latter is a special case of the Product Rule.

53. (a) $\dfrac{d}{dx}(uvw) = uvw' + uv'w + u'vw$

(b) $\dfrac{d}{dx}(u_1u_2u_3u_4) = u_1u_2u_3u_4' + u_1u_2u_3'u_4 + u_1u_2'u_3u_4 +$

$u_1'u_2u_3u_4$

(c) $\dfrac{d}{dx}(u_1 \cdots u_n) = u_1u_2 \cdots u_{n-1}u_n' + u_1u_2 \cdots u_{n-2}u_{n-1}'u_n +$

$\cdots + u_1'u_2 \cdots u_n$

55. $\dfrac{dP}{dV} = -\dfrac{nRT}{(V - nb)^2} + \dfrac{2an^2}{V^3}$

Section 3.3, pp. 179–183

1. (a) −2 m, −1 m/sec **(b)** 3 m/sec, 1 m/sec; 2 m/sec², 2 m/sec² **(c)** changes direction at $t = 3/2$ sec

3. (a) −9 m, −3 m/sec **(b)** 3 m/sec, 12 m/sec; 6 m/sec², −12 m/sec² **(c)** no change in direction

5. (a) −20 m, −5 m/sec **(b)** 45 m/sec, (1/5) m/sec; 140 m/sec², (4/25) m/sec² **(c)** no change in direction

7. (a) $a(1) = -6$ m/sec², $a(3) = 6$ m/sec² **(b)** $v(2) = 3$ m/sec **(c)** 6 m

9. Mars: ≈ 7.5 sec, Jupiter: ≈ 1.2 sec **11.** $g_s = 0.75$ m/sec²

13. (a) $v = -32t, |v| = 32t$ ft/sec, $a = -32$ ft/sec² **(b)** $t \approx 3.3$ sec **(c)** $v \approx -107.0$ ft/sec

15. (a) $t = 2, t = 7$ **(b)** $3 \le t \le 6$

(c) **(d)**

17. (a) 190 ft/sec **(b)** 2 sec **(c)** 8 sec, 0 ft/sec, **(d)** 10.8 sec, 90 ft/sec **(e)** 2.8 sec

(f) greatest acceleration happens 2 sec after launch

(g) constant acceleration between 2 and 10.8 sec, −32 ft/sec²

19. (a) $\dfrac{4}{7}$ sec, 280 cm/sec **(b)** 560 cm/sec, 980 cm/sec²

(c) 29.75 flashes/sec

21. $C = $ position, $A = $ velocity, $B = $ acceleration

23. (a) \$110/machine **(b)** \$80 **(c)** \$79.90

25. (a) $b'(0) = 10^4$ bacteria/h **(b)** $b'(5) = 0$ bacteria/h **(c)** $b'(10) = -10^4$ bacteria/h

27. (a) $\dfrac{dy}{dt} = \dfrac{t}{12} - 1$ **(b)** The largest value of $\dfrac{dy}{dt}$ is 0 m/h when $t = 12$ and the smallest value of $\dfrac{dy}{dt}$ is −1 m/h, when $t = 0$.

(c)

29. $t = 25$ sec $\qquad D = \dfrac{6250}{9}$ m

31.

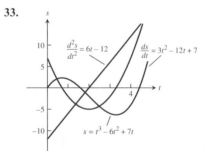

(a) $v = 0$ when $t = 6.25$ sec. **(b)** $v > 0$ when $0 \le t < 6.25 \Rightarrow$ body moves up; $v < 0$ when $6.25 < t \le 12.5 \Rightarrow$ body moves down. **(c)** Body changes direction at $t = 6.25$ sec. **(d)** Body speeds up on (6.25, 12.5] and slows down on [0, 6.25). **(e)** The body is moving fastest at the endpoints $t = 0$ and $t = 12.5$ when it is traveling 200 ft/sec. It's moving slowest at $t = 6.25$ when the speed is 0. **(f)** When $t = 6.25$ the body is $s = 625$ m from the origin and farthest away.

33.

(a) $v = 0$ when $t = \dfrac{6 \pm \sqrt{15}}{3}$ sec.

(b) $v < 0$ when $\dfrac{6 - \sqrt{15}}{3} < t < \dfrac{6 + \sqrt{15}}{3} \Rightarrow$ body moves

left; $v > 0$ when $0 \le t < \dfrac{6 - \sqrt{15}}{3}$ or $\dfrac{6 + \sqrt{15}}{3} < t \le 4 \Rightarrow$

body moves right.

(c) Body changes direction at $t = \dfrac{6 \pm \sqrt{15}}{3}$ sec.

(d) Body speeds up on $\left(\dfrac{6 - \sqrt{15}}{3}, 2\right) \cup \left(\dfrac{6 + \sqrt{15}}{3}, 4\right]$ and

slows down on $\left[0, \dfrac{6 - \sqrt{15}}{3}\right) \cup \left(2, \dfrac{6 + \sqrt{15}}{3}\right)$.

(e) The body is moving fastest at $t = 0$ and $t = 4$ when it is

moving 7 units/sec and slowest at $t = \dfrac{6 \pm \sqrt{15}}{3}$ sec.

(f) When $t = \dfrac{6 + \sqrt{15}}{3}$ the body is at position $s \approx -6.303$

units and farthest from the origin.

35. (a) It takes 135 sec.   **(b)** Average speed $= \dfrac{\Delta F}{\Delta t} = \dfrac{5 - 0}{73 - 0} =$

$\dfrac{5}{73} \approx 0.068$ furlongs/sec.   **(c)** Using a centered difference

quotient, the horse's speed is approximately (Section 3.4, Exer-

cise 53) $\dfrac{\Delta F}{\Delta t} = \dfrac{4 - 2}{59 - 33} = \dfrac{2}{26} = \dfrac{1}{13} \approx 0.077$ furlongs/sec.

(d) The horse is running the fastest during the last furlong
(between 9th and 10th furlong markers). This furlong takes only
11 sec to run, which is the least amount of time for a furlong.
(e) The horse accelerates the fastest during the first furlong
(between markers 0 and 1).

Section 3.4, pp. 188–190

1. $-10 - 3 \sin x$ **3.** $-\csc x \cot x - \dfrac{2}{\sqrt{x}}$ **5.** 0

7. $\dfrac{-\csc^2 x}{(1 + \cot x)^2}$ **9.** $4 \tan x \sec x - \csc^2 x$ **11.** $x^2 \cos x$

13. $\sec^2 t - 1$ **15.** $\dfrac{-2 \csc t \cot t}{(1 - \csc t)^2}$ **17.** $-\theta(\theta \cos \theta + 2 \sin \theta)$

19. $\sec \theta \csc \theta (\tan \theta - \cot \theta) = \sec^2 \theta - \csc^2 \theta$

21. $\sec^2 q$ **23.** $\sec^2 q$ **25. (a)** $2 \csc^3 x - \csc x$
(b) $2 \sec^3 x - \sec x$

27.

(graph with $y = \sin x$, lines $y = -x - \pi$, $y = x$, $y = -1$, point $(3\pi/2, -1)$; x-axis marked $-3\pi/2, -\pi, -\pi/2, \pi/2, 3\pi/2, 2$)

29.

(graph with $y = \sec x$, points $(-\pi/3, 2)$, $(\pi/4, \sqrt{2})$, values $\sqrt{2}$, lines $y = -2\sqrt{3}x - \dfrac{2\sqrt{3}\pi}{3} + 2$, $y = \sqrt{2}x - \dfrac{\sqrt{2}\pi}{4} + \sqrt{2}$; x-axis marked $-\pi/2, -\pi/3, 0, \pi/4, \pi/2$)

31. Yes, at $x = \pi$ **33.** No

35. $\left(-\dfrac{\pi}{4}, -1\right); \left(\dfrac{\pi}{4}, 1\right)$

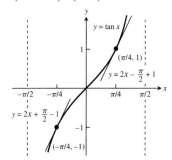

(graph of $y = \tan x$ with tangent lines $y = 2x - \dfrac{\pi}{2} + 1$ at $(\pi/4, 1)$ and $y = 2x + \dfrac{\pi}{2} - 1$ at $(-\pi/4, -1)$; x-axis marked $-\pi/2, -\pi/4, \pi/4, \pi/2$)

37. (a) $y = -x + \pi/2 + 2$ **(b)** $y = 4 - \sqrt{3}$
39. 0 **41.** -1 **43.** 0
45. $-\sqrt{2}$ m/sec, $\sqrt{2}$ m/sec, $\sqrt{2}$ m/sec^2, $\sqrt{2}$ m/sec^3
47. $c = 9$ **49.** $\sin x$

Section 3.5, pp. 201–205

1. $12x^3$ **3.** $3 \cos (3x + 1)$ **5.** $-\sin (\sin x) \cos x$
7. $10 \sec^2 (10x - 5)$

9. With $u = (2x + 1), y = u^5 : \dfrac{dy}{dx} = \dfrac{dy}{du} \dfrac{du}{dx} = 5u^4 \cdot 2 =$

$10(2x + 1)^4$

11. With $u = (1 - (x/7)), y = u^{-7} : \dfrac{dy}{dx} = \dfrac{dy}{du} \dfrac{du}{dx} =$

$-7u^{-8} \cdot \left(-\dfrac{1}{7}\right) = \left(1 - \dfrac{x}{7}\right)^{-8}$

13. With $u = ((x^2/8) + x - (1/x)), y = u^4 : \dfrac{dy}{dx} = \dfrac{dy}{du} \dfrac{du}{dx} =$

$4u^3 \cdot \left(\dfrac{x}{4} + 1 + \dfrac{1}{x^2}\right) = 4\left(\dfrac{x^2}{8} + x - \dfrac{1}{x}\right)^3 \left(\dfrac{x}{4} + 1 + \dfrac{1}{x^2}\right)$

15. With $u = \tan x, y = \sec u : \dfrac{dy}{dx} = \dfrac{dy}{du} \dfrac{du}{dx} =$

$(\sec u \tan u)(\sec^2 x) = \sec (\tan x) \tan (\tan x) \sec^2 x$

17. With $u = \sin x, y = u^3 : \dfrac{dy}{dx} = \dfrac{dy}{du} \dfrac{du}{dx} = 3u^2 \cos x =$

$3 \sin^2 x (\cos x)$

19. $-\dfrac{1}{2\sqrt{3 - t}}$ **21.** $\dfrac{4}{\pi} (\cos 3t - \sin 5t)$ **23.** $\dfrac{\csc \theta}{\cot \theta + \csc \theta}$

25. $2x \sin^4 x + 4x^2 \sin^3 x \cos x + \cos^{-2} x + 2x \cos^{-3} x \sin x$

27. $(3x - 2)^6 - \dfrac{1}{x^3 \left(4 - \dfrac{1}{2x^2}\right)^2}$ **29.** $\dfrac{(4x + 3)^3(4x + 7)}{(x + 1)^4}$

31. $\sqrt{x} \sec^2 (2\sqrt{x}) + \tan (2\sqrt{x})$ **33.** $\dfrac{2 \sin \theta}{(1 + \cos \theta)^2}$

35. $\dfrac{dr}{d\theta} = -2 \sin (\theta^2) \sin 2\theta + 2\theta \cos (2\theta) \cos (\theta^2)$

37. $\dfrac{dq}{dt} = \left(\dfrac{t+2}{2(t+1)^{3/2}}\right)\cos\left(\dfrac{t}{\sqrt{t+1}}\right)$

39. $2\pi \sin(\pi t - 2)\cos(\pi t - 2)$ **41.** $\dfrac{8\sin(2t)}{(1+\cos 2t)^5}$

43. $-2\cos(\cos(2t-5))(\sin(2t-5))$

45. $\left(1 + \tan^4\left(\dfrac{t}{12}\right)\right)^2\left(\tan^3\left(\dfrac{t}{12}\right)\sec^2\left(\dfrac{t}{12}\right)\right)$

47. $-\dfrac{t\sin(t^2)}{\sqrt{1+\cos(t^2)}}$ **49.** $\dfrac{6}{x^3}\left(1+\dfrac{1}{x}\right)\left(1+\dfrac{2}{x}\right)$

51. $2\csc^2(3x-1)\cot(3x-1)$ **53.** $5/2$ **55.** $-\pi/4$ **57.** 0

59. (a) $2/3$ **(b)** $2\pi + 5$ **(c)** $15 - 8\pi$ **(d)** $37/6$ **(e)** -1
   (f) $\sqrt{2}/24$ **(g)** $5/32$ **(h)** $-5/(3\sqrt{17})$ **61.** 5

63. (a) 1 **(b)** 1 **65. (a)** $y = \pi x + 2 - \pi$ **(b)** $\pi/2$

67.

69.

71.

73.

75.

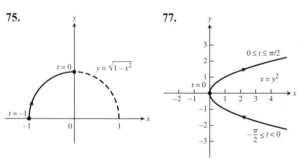

77.

79. (a) $x = a\cos t,\ y = -a\sin t,\ 0 \le t \le 2\pi$
   (b) $x = a\cos t,\ y = a\sin t,\ 0 \le t \le 2\pi$
   (c) $x = a\cos t,\ y = -a\sin t,\ 0 \le t \le 4\pi$
   (d) $x = a\cos t,\ y = a\sin t,\ 0 \le t \le 4\pi$
81. Possible answer: $x = -1 + 5t,\ y = -3 + 4t,\ 0 \le t \le 1$
83. Possible answer: $x = t^2 + 1,\ y = t,\ t \le 0$
85. Possible answer: $x = 2 - 3t,\ y = 3 - 4t,\ t \ge 0$

87. $y = -x + 2,\ \left.\dfrac{d^2y}{dx^2}\right|_{t=\pi/4} = -\sqrt{2}$

89. $y = x + \dfrac{1}{4},\ \left.\dfrac{d^2y}{dx^2}\right|_{t=1/4} = -2$

91. $y = x - 4,\ \left.\dfrac{d^2y}{dx^2}\right|_{t=-1} = \dfrac{1}{2}$

93. $y = 2,\ \left.\dfrac{d^2y}{dx^2}\right|_{t=\pi/2} = -1$

95. It multiplies the velocity, acceleration, and jerk by 2, 4, and 8, respectively.

97. $v(6) = \dfrac{2}{5}$ m/sec, $a(6) = -\dfrac{4}{125}$ m/sec^2

107. $\left(\dfrac{\sqrt{2}}{2}, 1\right)$, $y = 2x$ at $t = 0$, $y = -2x$ at $t = \pi$

Section 3.6, pp. 211–213

1. $\dfrac{9}{4}x^{5/4}$ **3.** $\dfrac{2^{1/3}}{3x^{2/3}}$ **5.** $\dfrac{7}{2(x+6)^{1/2}}$ **7.** $-(2x+5)^{-3/2}$

9. $\dfrac{2x^2+1}{(x^2+1)^{1/2}}$ **11.** $\dfrac{ds}{dt} = \dfrac{2}{7}t^{-5/7}$

13. $\dfrac{dy}{dt} = -\dfrac{4}{3}(2t+5)^{-5/3}\cos[(2t+5)^{-2/3}]$

15. $f'(x) = \dfrac{-1}{4\sqrt{x}(1-\sqrt{x})}$

17. $h'(\theta) = -\dfrac{2}{3}(\sin 2\theta)(1 + \cos 2\theta)^{-2/3}$ **19.** $\dfrac{-2xy - y^2}{x^2 + 2xy}$

21. $\dfrac{1 - 2y}{2x + 2y - 1}$ **23.** $\dfrac{-2x^3 + 3x^2y - xy^2 + x}{x^2y - x^3 + y}$

25. $\dfrac{1}{y(x+1)^2}$ **27.** $\cos^2 y$ **29.** $\dfrac{-\cos^2(xy) - y}{x}$

31. $\dfrac{-y^2}{y\sin\left(\dfrac{1}{y}\right) - \cos\left(\dfrac{1}{y}\right) + xy}$ **33.** $-\dfrac{\sqrt{r}}{\sqrt{\theta}}$ **35.** $\dfrac{-r}{\theta}$

37. $y' = -\dfrac{x}{y},\ y'' = \dfrac{-y^2 - x^2}{y^3}$

39. $y' = \dfrac{x+1}{y},\ y'' = \dfrac{y^2 - (x+1)^2}{y^3}$

41. $y' = \dfrac{\sqrt{y}}{\sqrt{y}+1},\ y'' = \dfrac{1}{2(\sqrt{y}+1)^3}$

43. -2 **45.** $(-2, 1): m = -1, (-2, -1): m = 1$

47. (a) $y = \dfrac{7}{4}x - \dfrac{1}{2}$,   **(b)** $y = -\dfrac{4}{7}x + \dfrac{29}{7}$

49. (a) $y = 3x + 6$,   **(b)** $y = -\dfrac{1}{3}x + \dfrac{8}{3}$

51. (a) $y = \dfrac{6}{7}x + \dfrac{6}{7}$,   **(b)** $y = -\dfrac{7}{6}x - \dfrac{7}{6}$

53. (a) $y = -\dfrac{\pi}{2}x + \pi$,   **(b)** $y = \dfrac{2}{\pi}x - \dfrac{2}{\pi} + \dfrac{\pi}{2}$

55. (a) $y = 2\pi x - 2\pi$, **(b)** $y = -\dfrac{x}{2\pi} + \dfrac{1}{2\pi}$

57. Points: $(-\sqrt{7}, 0)$ and $(\sqrt{7}, 0)$, Slope: -2

59. $m = -1$ at $\left(\dfrac{\sqrt{3}}{4}, \dfrac{\sqrt{3}}{2}\right)$, $m = \sqrt{3}$ at $\left(\dfrac{\sqrt{3}}{4}, \dfrac{1}{2}\right)$

61. $(-3, 2): m = -\dfrac{27}{8}; (-3, -2): m = \dfrac{27}{8}; (3, 2): m = \dfrac{27}{8};$

$(3, -2): m = -\dfrac{27}{8}$

63. 0 **65.** -6 **67. (a)** False **(b)** True **(c)** True
(d) True **69.** $(3, -1)$

73. $\dfrac{dy}{dx} = \dfrac{y^3 + 2xy}{x^2 + 3xy^2}$, $\dfrac{dx}{dy} = -\dfrac{x^2 + 3xy^2}{y^3 + 2xy}$, $\dfrac{dx}{dy} = \dfrac{1}{dy/dx}$

Section 3.7, pp. 218–221

1. $\dfrac{dA}{dt} = 2\pi r \dfrac{dr}{dt}$ **3. (a)** $\dfrac{dV}{dt} = \pi r^2 \dfrac{dh}{dt}$ **(b)** $\dfrac{dV}{dt} = 2\pi hr \dfrac{dr}{dt}$

(c) $\dfrac{dV}{dt} = \pi r^2 \dfrac{dh}{dt} + 2\pi hr \dfrac{dr}{dt}$ **5. (a)** 1 volt/sec

(b) $-\dfrac{1}{3}$ amp/sec **(c)** $\dfrac{dR}{dt} = \dfrac{1}{I}\left(\dfrac{dV}{dt} - \dfrac{V}{I}\dfrac{dI}{dt}\right)$

(d) $3/2$ ohms/sec, R is increasing.

7. (a) $\dfrac{dS}{dt} = \dfrac{x}{\sqrt{x^2 + y^2}}\dfrac{dx}{dt}$

(b) $\dfrac{dS}{dt} = \dfrac{x}{\sqrt{x^2 + y^2}}\dfrac{dx}{dt} + \dfrac{y}{\sqrt{x^2 + y^2}}\dfrac{dy}{dt}$

(c) $\dfrac{dx}{dt} = -\dfrac{y}{x}\dfrac{dy}{dt}$

9. (a) $\dfrac{dA}{dt} = \dfrac{1}{2}ab\cos\theta\dfrac{d\theta}{dt}$

(b) $\dfrac{dA}{dt} = \dfrac{1}{2}ab\cos\theta\dfrac{d\theta}{dt} + \dfrac{1}{2}b\sin\theta\dfrac{da}{dt}$

(c) $\dfrac{dA}{dt} = \dfrac{1}{2}ab\cos\theta\dfrac{d\theta}{dt} + \dfrac{1}{2}b\sin\theta\dfrac{da}{dt} + \dfrac{1}{2}a\sin\theta\dfrac{db}{dt}$

11. (a) 14 cm²/sec, increasing **(b)** 0 cm/sec, constant
(c) $-14/13$ cm/sec, decreasing
13. (a) -12 ft/sec **(b)** -59.5 ft²/sec **(c)** -1 rad/sec
15. 20 ft/sec

17. (a) $\dfrac{dh}{dt} = 11.19$ cm/min **(b)** $\dfrac{dr}{dt} = 14.92$ cm/min

19. (a) $\dfrac{-1}{24\pi}$ m/min **(b)** $r = \sqrt{26y - y^2}$ m,

(c) $\dfrac{dr}{dt} = -\dfrac{5}{288\pi}$ m/min

21. 1 ft/min, 40π ft²/min **23.** 11 ft/sec **25.** Increasing at
466/1681 L/min **27.** 1 rad/sec **29.** -5 m/sec

31. -1500 ft/sec **33.** $\dfrac{5}{72\pi}$ in./min, $\dfrac{10}{3}$ in.²/min

35. 7.1 in./min **37. (a)** $-32/\sqrt{13} \approx -8.875$ ft/sec,
(b) $d\theta_1/dt = -8/65$ rad/sec, $d\theta_2/dt = 8/65$ rad/sec

(c) $d\theta_1/dt = -1/6$ rad/sec, $d\theta_2/dt = 1/6$ rad/sec

Section 3.8, pp. 231–234

1. $L(x) = 10x - 13$ **3.** $L(x) = 2$ **5.** $2x$ **7.** -5

9. $\dfrac{1}{12}x + \dfrac{4}{3}$ **11. (a)** $L(x) = x$ **(b)** $L(x) = \pi - x$

13. (a) $L(x) = 1$ **(b)** $L(x) = 2 - 2\sqrt{3}\left(x + \dfrac{\pi}{3}\right)$

15. $f(0) = 1$. Also, $f'(x) = k(1 + x)^{k-1}$, so $f'(0) = k$. This
means the linearization at $x = 0$ is $L(x) = 1 + kx$.

17. (a) 1.01 **(b)** 1.003

19. $\left(3x^2 - \dfrac{3}{2\sqrt{x}}\right)dx$ **21.** $\dfrac{2 - 2x^2}{(1 + x^2)^2}dx$

23. $\dfrac{1 - y}{3\sqrt{y} + x}dx$ **25.** $\dfrac{5}{2\sqrt{x}}\cos(5\sqrt{x})\,dx$

27. $\left(4x^2\right)\sec^2\left(\dfrac{x^3}{3}\right)dx$

29. $\dfrac{3}{\sqrt{x}}(\csc(1 - 2\sqrt{x})\cot(1 - 2\sqrt{x}))\,dx$

31. (a) .41 **(b)** .4 **(c)** .01
33. (a) .231 **(b)** .2 **(c)** .031
35. (a) $-1/3$ **(b)** $-2/5$ **(c)** $1/15$
37. $dV = 4\pi r_0^2\,dr$ **39.** $dS = 12x_0\,dx$ **41.** $dV = 2\pi r_0 h\,dr$
43. (a) 0.08π m² **(b)** 2% **45.** $dV \approx 565.5$ in.³

47. $\dfrac{1}{3}\%$ **49.** 0.05%

51. The ratio equals 37.87, so a change in the acceleration of gravity
on the moon has about 38 times the effect that a change of the
same magnitude has on Earth.
53. 3% **55.** 3%

59. $\displaystyle\lim_{x\to 0}\dfrac{\sqrt{1 + x}}{1 + \left(\dfrac{x}{2}\right)} = \dfrac{\sqrt{1 + 0}}{1 + \left(\dfrac{0}{2}\right)} = \dfrac{1}{1} = 1$ **65.** $0.07c$

Practice Exercises, pp. 235–240

1. $5x^4 - 0.25x + 0.25$ **3.** $3x(x - 2)$
5. $2(x + 1)(2x^2 + 4x + 1)$
7. $3(\theta^2 + \sec\theta + 1)^2(2\theta + \sec\theta\tan\theta)$

9. $\dfrac{1}{2\sqrt{t}\left(1 + \sqrt{t}\right)^2}$ **11.** $2\sec^2 x\tan x$

13. $8\cos^3(1 - 2t)\sin(1 - 2t)$ **15.** $5(\sec t)(\sec t + \tan t)^5$

17. $\dfrac{\theta\cos\theta + \sin\theta}{\sqrt{2\theta\sin\theta}}$ **19.** $\dfrac{\cos\sqrt{2\theta}}{\sqrt{2\theta}}$

21. $x\csc\left(\dfrac{2}{x}\right) + \csc\left(\dfrac{2}{x}\right)\cot\left(\dfrac{2}{x}\right)$

23. $\dfrac{1}{2}x^{1/2}\sec(2x)^2\left[16\tan(2x)^2 - x^{-2}\right]$

25. $-10x\csc^2(x^2)$ **27.** $8x^3\sin(2x^2)\cos(2x^2) + 2x\sin^2(2x^2)$

29. $\dfrac{-(t + 1)}{8t^3}$ **31.** $\dfrac{1 - x}{(x + 1)^3}$ **33.** $\dfrac{-1}{2x^2\left(1 + \dfrac{1}{x}\right)^{1/2}}$

35. $\dfrac{-2\sin\theta}{(\cos\theta - 1)^2}$ **37.** $3\sqrt{2x+1}$ **39.** $-9\left[\dfrac{5x + \cos 2x}{(5x^2 + \sin 2x)^{5/2}}\right]$

41. $-\dfrac{y+2}{x+3}$ **43.** $\dfrac{-3x^2 - 4y + 2}{4x - 4y^{1/3}}$ **45.** $-\dfrac{y}{x}$

47. $\dfrac{1}{2y(x+1)^2}$ **49.** $\dfrac{dp}{dq} = \dfrac{6q - 4p}{3p^2 + 4q}$

51. $\dfrac{dr}{ds} = (2r - 1)(\tan 2s)$

53. (a) $\dfrac{d^2y}{dx^2} = \dfrac{-2xy^3 - 2x^4}{y^5}$ **(b)** $\dfrac{d^2y}{dx^2} = \dfrac{-2xy^2 - 1}{x^4y^3}$

55. (a) 7 **(b)** -2 **(c)** 5/12 **(d)** 1/4 **(e)** 12 **(f)** 9/2 **(g)** 3/4

57. 0 **59.** $\sqrt{3}$ **61.** $-\dfrac{1}{2}$ **63.** $\dfrac{-2}{(2t+1)^2}$

65. (a)

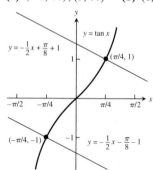

$f(x) = \begin{cases} x^2, & -1 \le x < 0 \\ -x^2, & 0 \le x < 1 \end{cases}$

(b) Yes **(c)** Yes

67. (a)

$y = \begin{cases} x, & 0 \le x \le 1 \\ 2 - x, & 1 < x \le 2 \end{cases}$

(b) Yes **(c)** No

69. $\left(\dfrac{5}{2}, \dfrac{9}{4}\right)$ and $\left(\dfrac{3}{2}, -\dfrac{1}{4}\right)$ **71.** $(-1, 27)$ and $(2, 0)$

73. (a) $(-2, 16), (3, 11)$ **(b)** $(0, 20), (1, 7)$

75.

$y = \tan x$

$y = -\dfrac{1}{2}x + \dfrac{\pi}{8} + 1$

$(\pi/4, 1)$

$(-\pi/4, -1)$

$y = -\dfrac{1}{2}x - \dfrac{\pi}{8} - 1$

77. $\dfrac{1}{4}$ **79.** 4 **81.** Tangent: $y = -\dfrac{1}{4}x + \dfrac{9}{4}$, normal: $y = 4x - 2$

83. Tangent: $y = 2x - 4$, normal: $y = -\dfrac{1}{2}x + \dfrac{7}{2}$

85. Tangent: $y = -\dfrac{5}{4}x + 6$, normal: $y = \dfrac{4}{5}x - \dfrac{11}{5}$

87. $(1, 1): m = -\dfrac{1}{2}; (1, -1):$ m not defined

89. $y = \left(\dfrac{\sqrt{3}}{2}\right)x + \dfrac{1}{4}, \dfrac{1}{4}$ **91.** $B =$ graph of f, $A =$ graph of f'

93.

(graph: $y = f(x)$ with points $(-1, 2)$, $(4, 3)$, $(6, 1)$)

95. (a) 0, 0 **(b)** 1700 rabbits, $\approx$1400 rabbits

97. -1 **99.** 1/2 **101.** 4 **103.** 1

107. (a) $\dfrac{dS}{dt} = (4\pi r + 2\pi h)\dfrac{dr}{dt}$ **(b)** $\dfrac{dS}{dt} = 2\pi r\dfrac{dh}{dt}$

(c) $\dfrac{dS}{dt} = (4\pi r + 2\pi h)\dfrac{dr}{dt} + 2\pi r\dfrac{dh}{dt}$

(d) $\dfrac{dr}{dt} = -\dfrac{r}{2r + h}\dfrac{dh}{dt}$

109. $-40 \text{ m}^2/\text{sec}$ **111.** 0.02 ohm/sec **113.** 22 m/sec

115. (a) $r = \dfrac{2}{5}h$ **(b)** $-\dfrac{125}{144\pi}$ ft/min

117. (a) $\dfrac{3}{5}$ km/sec or 600 m/sec **(b)** $\dfrac{18}{\pi}$ rpm

119. (a) $L(x) = 2x + \dfrac{\pi - 2}{2}$

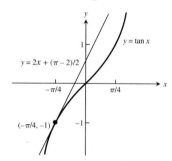

$y = 2x + (\pi - 2)/2$, $y = \tan x$, $(-\pi/4, -1)$

(b) $L(x) = -\sqrt{2}x + \dfrac{\sqrt{2}(4 - \pi)}{4}$

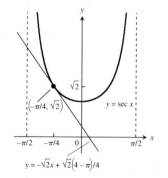

$\left(-\pi/4, \sqrt{2}\right)$, $y = \sec x$, $y = -\sqrt{2}x + \sqrt{2}(4 - \pi)/4$

121. $L(x) = 1.5x + 0.5$ **123.** $dS = \dfrac{\pi r h_0}{\sqrt{r^2 + h_0^2}}\, dh$

125. (a) 4%   **(b)** 8%   **(c)** 12%

Additional and Advanced Exercises, pp. 240–243

1. (a) $\sin 2\theta = 2 \sin \theta \cos \theta$; $2 \cos 2\theta = 2 \sin \theta\,(-\sin \theta) +$ $\cos \theta\,(2 \cos \theta)$; $2 \cos 2\theta = -2 \sin^2 \theta + 2 \cos^2 \theta$; $\cos 2\theta =$ $\cos^2 \theta - \sin^2 \theta$

  (b) $\cos 2\theta = \cos^2 \theta - \sin^2 \theta$; $-2 \sin 2\theta =$ $2 \cos \theta\,(-\sin \theta) - 2 \sin \theta\,(\cos \theta)$; $\sin 2\theta =$ $\cos \theta \sin \theta + \sin \theta \cos \theta$; $\sin 2\theta = 2 \sin \theta \cos \theta$

3. (a) $a = 1, b = 0, c = -\dfrac{1}{2}$ **(b)** $b = \cos a, c = \sin a$

5. $h = -4, k = \dfrac{9}{2}, a = \dfrac{5\sqrt{5}}{2}$

7. (a) $0.09y$ **(b)** Increasing at 1% per year

9. Answers will vary. Here is one possibility.

11. (a) 2 sec, 64 ft/sec   **(b)** 12.31 sec, 393.85 ft

15. (a) $m = -\dfrac{b}{\pi}$ **(b)** $m = -1, b = \pi$

17. (a) $a = \dfrac{3}{4}, b = \dfrac{9}{4}$ **19.** f odd $\Rightarrow f'$ is even

23. h' is defined but not continuous at $x = 0$; k' is defined *and* continuous at $x = 0$.

27. (a) 0.8156 ft   **(b)** 0.00613 sec   **(c)** It will lose about 8.83 min/day.

CHAPTER 4

Section 4.1, pp. 252–255

1. Absolute minimum at $x = c_2$; absolute maximum at $x = b$
3. Absolute maximum at $x = c$; no absolute minimum
5. Absolute minimum at $x = a$; absolute maximum at $x = c$
7. Local minimum at $(-1, 0)$; local maximum at $(1, 0)$
9. Maximum at $(0, 5)$ **11.** (c)   **13.** (d)
15. Absolute maximum: -3; absolute minimum: $-19/3$

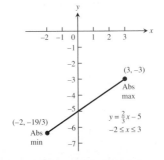

17. Absolute maximum: 3; absolute minimum: -1

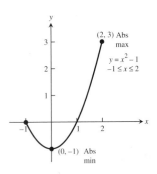

19. Absolute maximum: -0.25; absolute minimum: -4

21. Absolute maximum: 2; absolute minimum: -1

23. Absolute maximum: 2; absolute minimum: 0

25. Absolute maximum: 1; absolute minimum: -1

27. Absolute maximum: $2/\sqrt{3}$; absolute minimum: 1

29. Absolute maximum: 2; absolute minimum: -1

31. Increasing on $(0, 8)$, decreasing on $(-1, 0)$; absolute maximum: 16 at $x = 8$; absolute minimum: 0 at $x = 0$

33. Increasing on $(-32, 1)$; absolute maximum: 1 at $\theta = 1$; absolute minimum: -8 at $\theta = -32$

35. Minimum value is 1 at $x = 2$.

37. Local maximum at $(-2, 17)$; local minimum at $\left(\dfrac{4}{3}, -\dfrac{41}{27}\right)$

39. Minimum value is 0 at $x = -1$ and $x = 1$.

41. There is a local minimum at $(0, 1)$.

43. Maximum value is $\dfrac{1}{2}$ at $x = 1$; minimum value is $-\dfrac{1}{2}$ at $x = -1$.

45.

Critical point	Derivative	Extremum	Value
$x = -\dfrac{4}{5}$	0	Local max	$\dfrac{12}{25} 10^{1/3} = 1.034$
$x = 0$	Undefined	Local min	0

47.

Critical point	Derivative	Extremum	Value
$x = -2$	Undefined	Local max	0
$x = -\sqrt{2}$	0	Minimum	-2
$x = \sqrt{2}$	0	Maximum	2
$x = 2$	Undefined	Local min	0

49.

Critical point	Derivative	Extremum	Value
$x = 1$	Undefined	Minimum	2

51.

Critical point	Derivative	Extremum	Value
$x = -1$	0	Maximum	5
$x = 1$	Undefined	Local min	1
$x = 3$	0	Maximum	5

53. **(a)** No

(b) The derivative is defined and nonzero for $x \neq 2$. Also, $f(2) = 0$ and $f(x) > 0$ for all $x \neq 2$.

(c) No, because $(-\infty, \infty)$ is not a closed interval.

(d) The answers are the same as parts (a) and (b) with 2 replaced by a.

55. **(a)** $C(x) = 0.3\sqrt{16 + x^2} + 0.2(9 - x)$ million dollars, where $0 \leq x \leq 9$ mi. To minimize the cost of construction, the pipeline should be placed from the docking facility to point B, 3.58 mi along the shore from point A, and then along the shore from point B to the refinery.

(b) In theory, the underwater pipe cost per mile p would have to be infinite to justify running the pipe directly from the docking facility to point A (i.e., for x_c to be zero). For all values of $p > 0.218864$, there is always an x_c in $(0, 9)$ that will give a minimum value for C. This is proved by looking at $C''(x_c) = \dfrac{16p}{(16 + x_c^2)^{3/2}}$, which is always positive for $p > 0$.

57. The length of pipeline is $L(x) = \sqrt{4 + x^2} + \sqrt{25 + (10 - x)^2}$ for $0 \leq x \leq 10$. $x = \dfrac{20}{7} \approx 2.857$ mi along the coast from Town A to Town B.

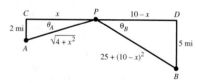

59. **(a)** Maximum value is 144 at $x = 2$.

(b) The largest volume of the box is 144 cubic units, and it occurs when $x = 2$.

61. The largest possible area is $A\left(\dfrac{5}{\sqrt{2}}\right) = \dfrac{25}{4}$ cm^2.

63. $\dfrac{v_0{}^2}{2g} + s_0$ **65.** Yes   **67.** g assumes a local maximum at $-c$.

69. **(a)** $f'(x) = 3ax^2 + 2bx + c$ is a quadratic, so it can have 0, 1, or 2 zeros, which would be the critical points of f. Examples: The function $f(x) = x^3 - 3x$ has two critical points at $x = -1$ and $x = 1$.

The function $f(x) = x^3 - 1$ has one critical point at $x = 0$.

The function $f(x) = x^3 + x$ has no critical points.

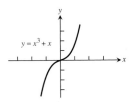

(b) Two or none

71. Maximum value is 11 at $x = 5$; minimum value is 5 on the interval $[-3, 2]$; local maximum at $(-5, 9)$.

73. Maximum value is 5 on the interval $[3, \infty)$; minimum value is -5 on the interval $(-\infty, -2]$.

Section 4.2, pp. 260–262

1. $1/2$ **3.** 1   **5.** Does not; f is not differentiable at the interior domain point $x = 0$.   **7.** Does

11. (a)

i)

ii)

iii)

iv)

23. Yes   **25. (a)** 4   **(b)** 3   **(c)** 3

27. (a) $\dfrac{x^2}{2} + C$ **(b)** $\dfrac{x^3}{3} + C$ **(c)** $\dfrac{x^4}{4} + C$

29. (a) $\dfrac{1}{x} + C$ **(b)** $x + \dfrac{1}{x} + C$ **(c)** $5x - \dfrac{1}{x} + C$

31. (a) $-\dfrac{1}{2}\cos 2t + C$ **(b)** $2\sin\dfrac{t}{2} + C$

(c) $-\dfrac{1}{2}\cos 2t + 2\sin\dfrac{t}{2} + C$

33. $f(x) = x^2 - x$ **35.** $r(\theta) = 8\theta + \cot\theta - 2\pi - 1$

37. $s = 4.9t^2 + 5t + 10$ **39.** $s = \dfrac{1 - \cos(\pi t)}{\pi}$

41. $s = 16t^2 + 20t + 5$ **43.** $s = \sin(2t) - 3$

45. If $T(t)$ is the temperature of the thermometer at time t, then $T(0) = -19\,°C$ and $T(14) = 100\,°C$. From the Mean Value Theorem, there exists a $0 < t_0 < 14$ such that

$$\frac{T(14) - T(0)}{14 - 0} = 8.5\,°C/\text{sec} = T'(t_0),$$ the rate at which the

temperature was changing at $t = t_0$ as measured by the rising mercury on the thermometer.

47. Because its average speed was approximately 7.667 knots, and by the Mean Value Theorem, it must have been going that speed at least once during the trip.

51. The conclusion of the Mean Value Theorem yields

$$\frac{\dfrac{1}{b} - \dfrac{1}{a}}{b - a} = -\frac{1}{c^2} \Rightarrow c^2\left(\frac{a - b}{ab}\right) = a - b \Rightarrow c = \sqrt{ab}.$$

55. $f(x)$ must be zero at least once between a and b by the Intermediate Value Theorem. Now suppose that $f(x)$ is zero twice between a and b. Then, by the Mean Value Theorem, $f'(x)$ would have to be zero at least once between the two zeros of $f(x)$, but this can't be true since we are given that $f'(x) \neq 0$ on this interval. Therefore, $f(x)$ is zero once and only once between a and b.

61. $1.09999 \le f(0.1) \le 1.1$

Section 4.3, pp. 266–267

1. (a) $0, 1$ **(b)** increasing on $(-\infty, 0)$ and $(1, \infty)$, decreasing on $(0, 1)$ **(c)** local maximum at $x = 0$, local minimum at $x = 1$

3. (a) $-2, 1$ **(b)** increasing on $(-2, 1)$ and $(1, \infty)$, decreasing on $(-\infty, -2)$ **(c)** no local maximum, local minimum at $x = -2$

5. (a) $-2, 1, 3$ **(b)** increasing on $(-2, 1)$ and $(3, \infty)$, decreasing on $(-\infty, -2)$ and $(1, 3)$ **(c)** local maximum at $x = 1$, local minima at $x = -2, 3$

7. (a) $-2, 0$ **(b)** increasing on $(-\infty, -2)$ and $(0, \infty)$, decreasing on $(-2, 0)$ **(c)** local maximum at $x = -2$, local minimum at $x = 0$

9. (a) Increasing on $(-\infty, -1.5)$, decreasing on $(-1.5, \infty)$ **(b)** local maximum: 5.25 at $t = -1.5$ **(c)** absolute maximum: 5.25 at $t = -1.5$

11. (a) Decreasing on $(-\infty, 0)$, increasing on $(0, 4/3)$, decreasing on $(4/3, \infty)$ **(b)** local minimum at $x = 0$ $(0, 0)$, local maximum at $x = 4/3$ $(4/3, 32/27)$ **(c)** no absolute extrema

13. (a) Decreasing on $(-\infty, 0)$, increasing on $(0, 1/2)$, decreasing on $(1/2, \infty)$ **(b)** local minimum at $\theta = 0$ $(0, 0)$, local maximum at $\theta = 1/2$ $(1/2, 1/4)$ **(c)** no absolute extrema

15. (a) Increasing on $(-\infty, \infty)$, never decreasing   **(b)** no local extrema   **(c)** no absolute extrema

17. (a) Increasing on $(-2, 0)$ and $(2, \infty)$, decreasing on $(-\infty, -2)$ and $(0, 2)$ **(b)** local maximum: 16 at $x = 0$, local minimum: 0 at $x = \pm 2$ **(c)** no absolute maximum; absolute minimum: 0 at $x = \pm 2$

19. (a) Increasing on $(-\infty, -1)$, decreasing on $(-1, 0)$, increasing on $(0, 1)$, decreasing on $(1, \infty)$ **(b)** local maximum at $x = \pm 1$ $(1, 0.5)$, $(-1, 0.5)$, local minimum at $x = 0$ $(0, 0)$ **(c)** absolute maximum: $1/2$ at $x = \pm 1$; no absolute minimum

21. (a) Decreasing on $(-2\sqrt{2}, -2)$, increasing on $(-2, 2)$, decreasing on $(2, 2\sqrt{2})$ **(b)** local minima: $g(-2) = -4, g(2\sqrt{2}) = 0$; local maxima: $g(-2\sqrt{2}) = 0, g(2) = 4$ **(c)** absolute maximum: 4 at $x = 2$; absolute minimum: -4 at $x = -2$

23. (a) Increasing on $(-\infty, 1)$, decreasing when $1 < x < 2$, decreasing when $2 < x < 3$, discontinuous at $x = 2$, increasing on $(3, \infty)$ **(b)** local minimum at $x = 3$ $(3, 6)$, local maximum at $x = 1$ $(1, 2)$ **(c)** no absolute extrema

25. (a) Increasing on $(-2, 0)$ and $(0, \infty)$, decreasing on $(-\infty, -2)$ **(b)** local minimum: $-6\sqrt[3]{2}$ at $x = -2$ **(c)** no absolute maximum; absolute minimum: $-6\sqrt[3]{2}$ at $x = -2$

27. (a) Increasing on $\left(-\infty, -2/\sqrt{7}\right)$ and $\left(2/\sqrt{7}, \infty\right)$, decreasing on $\left(-2/\sqrt{7}, 0\right)$ and $\left(0, 2/\sqrt{7}\right)$ **(b)** local maximum: $24\sqrt[3]{2}/7^{7/6} \approx 3.12$ at $x = -2/\sqrt{7}$; local minimum: $-24\sqrt[3]{2}/7^{7/6} \approx -3.12$ at $x = 2/\sqrt{7}$ **(c)** no absolute extrema

29. (a) Local maximum: 1 at $x = 1$; local minimum: 0 at $x = 2$ **(b)** absolute maximum: 1 at $x = 1$; no absolute minimum

31. (a) Local maximum: 1 at $x = 1$; local minimum: 0 at $x = 2$ **(b)** no absolute maximum; absolute minimum: 0 at $x = 2$

33. (a) Local maxima: -9 at $t = -3$ and 16 at $t = 2$; local minimum: -16 at $t = -2$ **(b)** absolute maximum: 16 at $t = 2$; no absolute minimum

35. (a) Local minimum: 0 at $x = 0$ **(b)** no absolute maximum; absolute minimum: 0 at $x = 0$

37. (a) Local minimum: $(\pi/3) - \sqrt{3}$ at $x = 2\pi/3$; local maximum: 0 at $x = 0$; local maximum: π at $x = 2\pi$

39. (a) Local minimum: 0 at $x = \pi/4$

41. Local maximum: 3 at $\theta = 0$; local minimum: -3 at $\theta = 2\pi$

43.

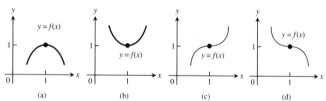

(a)   (b)   (c)   (d)

45. (a)   **(b)**

47. Rising

Section 4.4, pp. 274–277

1. Local maximum: 3/2 at $x = -1$, local minimum: -3 at $x = 2$, point of inflection at $(1/2, -3/4)$, rising on $(-\infty, -1)$ and $(2, \infty)$, falling on $(-1, 2)$, concave up on $(1/2, \infty)$, concave down on $(-\infty, 1/2)$

3. Local maximum: 3/4 at $x = 0$, local minimum: 0 at $x = \pm 1$, points of inflection at $\left(-\sqrt{3}, \dfrac{3\sqrt[3]{4}}{4}\right)$ and $\left(\sqrt{3}, \dfrac{3\sqrt[3]{4}}{4}\right)$, rising on $(-1, 0)$ and $(1, \infty)$, falling on $(-\infty, -1)$ and $(0, 1)$, concave up on $(-\infty, -\sqrt{3})$ and $(\sqrt{3}, \infty)$, concave down on $(-\sqrt{3}, \sqrt{3})$

5. Local maxima: $-2\pi/3 + \sqrt{3}/2$ at $x = -2\pi/3$; $\dfrac{\pi}{3} + \dfrac{\sqrt{3}}{2}$ at $x = \dfrac{\pi}{3}$, local minima: $-\dfrac{\pi}{3} - \dfrac{\sqrt{3}}{2}$ at $x = -\dfrac{\pi}{3}$; $2\pi/3 - \sqrt{3}/2$ at $x = \dfrac{2\pi}{3}$, points of inflection at $(-\pi/2, -\pi/2), (0, 0)$, and $(\pi/2, \pi/2)$, rising on $(-\pi/3, \pi/3)$, falling on $(-2\pi/3, -\pi/3)$ and $(\pi/3, 2\pi/3)$, concave up on $(-\pi/2, 0)$ and $(\pi/2, 2\pi/3)$, concave down on $(-2\pi/3, -\pi/2)$ and $(0, \pi/2)$

7. Local maxima: 1 at $x = -\dfrac{\pi}{2}$ and $x = \dfrac{\pi}{2}$; 0 at $x = -2\pi$ and $x = 2\pi$; local minima: -1 at $x = -\dfrac{3\pi}{2}$ and $x = \dfrac{3\pi}{2}$, 0 at $x = 0$, points of inflection at $(-\pi, 0)$ and $(\pi, 0)$, rising on $(-3\pi/2, -\pi/2), (0, \pi/2)$ and $(3\pi/2, 2\pi)$, falling on $(-2\pi, -3\pi/2), (-\pi/2, 0)$ and $(\pi/2, 3\pi/2)$, concave up on $(-2\pi, -\pi)$ and $(\pi, 2\pi)$, concave down on $(-\pi, \pi)$

9.

11.

13.

15.

17.

19.

21.

23.

25.

27.

29.

31.

33.

35.

37.

39.

41. $y'' = 1 - 2x$

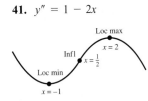

43. $y'' = 3(x - 3)(x - 1)$

45. $y'' = 3(x - 2)(x + 2)$

47. $y'' = 4(4 - x)(5x^2 - 16x + 8)$

49. $y'' = 2 \sec^2 x \tan x$

51. $y'' = -\dfrac{1}{2} \csc^2 \dfrac{\theta}{2}, \; 0 < \theta < 2\pi$

53. $y'' = 2 \tan \theta \sec^2 \theta, \; -\dfrac{\pi}{2} < \theta < \dfrac{\pi}{2}$

55. $y'' = -\sin t, \; 0 \le t \le 2\pi$

57. $y'' = -\dfrac{2}{3}(x + 1)^{-5/3}$

59. $y'' = \dfrac{1}{3}x^{-2/3} + \dfrac{2}{3}x^{-5/3}$

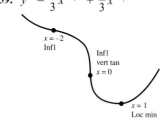

61. $y'' = \begin{cases} -2, & x < 0 \\ 2, & x > 0 \end{cases}$

63.

65.

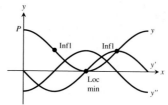

67.

Point	y'	y''
P	$-$	$+$
Q	$+$	0
R	$+$	$-$
S	0	$-$
T	$-$	$-$

69.

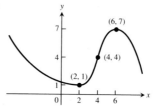

73. $\approx$ 60 thousand units   **75.** Local minimum at $x = 2$, inflection points at $x = 1$ and $x = 5/3$ **79.** $b = -3$

81. (a) $\left(-\dfrac{b}{2a}, \dfrac{4ac - b^2}{4a} \right)$ **(b)** concave up if $a > 0$, concave down if $a < 0$

85. The zeros of $y' = 0$ and $y'' = 0$ are extrema and points of inflection, respectively. Inflection at $x = 3$, local maximum at $x = 0$, local minimum at $x = 4$.

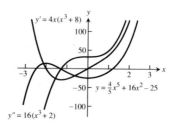

87. The zeros of $y' = 0$ and $y'' = 0$ are extrema and points of inflection, respectively. Inflection at $x = -\sqrt[3]{2}$, local maximum at $x = -2$, local minimum at $x = 0$.

91. (b) $f'(x) = 3x^2 + k$; $-12k$; positive if $k < 0$, negative if $k > 0$, 0 if $k = 0$; f' has two zeros if $k < 0$, one zero if $k = 0$, no zeros if $k > 0$; that is, the sign of k controls the number of local extrema.

93. (b) A cusp since $\lim_{x \to 0^-} y' = \infty$ and $\lim_{x \to 0^+} y' = -\infty$

95. Yes, the graph of y' crosses through zero near -3, so y has a horizontal tangent near -3.

Section 4.5, pp. 285–292

1. 16 in., 4 in. by 4 in.   **3. (a)** $(x, 1 - x)$

(b) $A(x) = 2x(1 - x)$ **(c)** $\dfrac{1}{2}$ square units, 1 by $\dfrac{1}{2}$

5. $\dfrac{14}{3} \times \dfrac{35}{3} \times \dfrac{5}{3}$ in., $\dfrac{2450}{27}$ in.^{3} **7.** 80,000 m^2; 400 m by 200 m

9. (a) The optimum dimensions of the tank are 10 ft on the base edges and 5 ft deep.

(b) Minimizing the surface area of the tank minimizes its weight for a given wall thickness. The thickness of the steel walls would likely be determined by other considerations such as structural requirements.

11. 9×18 in.   **13.** $\dfrac{\pi}{2}$ **15.** $h : r = 8 : \pi$

17. (a) $V(x) = 2x(24 - 2x)(18 - 2x)$ **(b)** Domain: $(0, 9)$

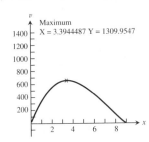

(c) Maximum volume ≈ 1309.95 in.^{3} when $x \approx 3.39$ in.

(d) $V'(x) = 24x^2 - 336x + 864$, so the critical point is at $x = 7 - \sqrt{13}$, which confirms the result in part (c).

(e) $x = 2$ in. or $x = 5$ in.

19. ≈ 2418.40 cm^3

21. (a) $h = 24$, $w = 18$

(b)

23. If r is the radius of the hemisphere, h the height of the cylinder, and V the volume, then $r = \left(\dfrac{3V}{8\pi}\right)^{1/3}$ and $h = \left(\dfrac{3V}{\pi}\right)^{1/3}$.

25. (b) $x = \dfrac{51}{8}$ **(c)** $L \approx 11$ in.

27. Radius $= \sqrt{2}$ m, height $= 1$ m, volume $\dfrac{2\pi}{3}$ m^3

31. (a) $v(0) = 96$ ft/sec   **(b)** 256 ft at $t = 3$ sec
(c) Velocity when $s = 0$ is $v(7) = -128$ ft/sec

33. ≈ 46.87 ft   **35. (a)** $6 \times 6\sqrt{3}$ in.

37. (a) $10\pi \approx 31.42$ cm/sec; when $t = 0.5$ sec, 1.5 sec, 2.5 sec, 3.5 sec; $s = 0$, acceleration is 0   **(b)** 10 cm from rest position; speed is 0

39. (a) $s = ((12 - 12t)^2 + 64t^2)^{1/2}$ **(b)** -12 knots, 8 knots
(c) No   **(e)** $4\sqrt{13}$. This limit is the square root of the sums of the squares of the individual speeds.

41. $x = \dfrac{a}{2}$, $v = \dfrac{ka^2}{4}$ **43.** $\dfrac{c}{2} + 50$

45. (a) $\sqrt{\dfrac{2km}{h}}$ **(b)** $\sqrt{\dfrac{2km}{h}}$

49. (a) The cabinetmaker should order px units of material to have enough until the next delivery.

(c) Average cost per day $= \dfrac{\left(d + \dfrac{ps}{2}x^2\right)}{x} = \dfrac{d}{x} + \dfrac{ps}{2}x$;

$x^* = \sqrt{\dfrac{2d}{ps}}$; $px^* = \sqrt{\dfrac{2pd}{s}}$ gives a minimum.

(d) The line and hyperbola intersect when $\dfrac{d}{x} = \dfrac{ps}{2}x$. For

$x > 0$, $x_{\text{intersection}} = \sqrt{\dfrac{2d}{ps}} = x^*$. The average cost per day is minimized when the average daily cost of delivery is equal to the average daily cost of storage.

51. $M = \dfrac{C}{2}$ **57. (a)** $y = -1$

59. (a) The minimum distance is $\dfrac{\sqrt{5}}{2}$.

(b) The minimum distance is from the point $(3/2, 0)$ to the point $(1, 1)$ on the graph of $y = \sqrt{x}$, and this occurs at the value $x = 1$, where $D(x)$, the distance squared, has its minimum value.

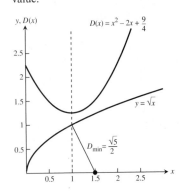

61. (a) $V(x) = \dfrac{\pi}{3}\left(\dfrac{2\pi a - x}{2\pi}\right)^2 \sqrt{a^2 - \left(\dfrac{2\pi a - x}{2\pi}\right)^2}$

(b) When $a = 4$: $r = \dfrac{4\sqrt{6}}{3}$, $h = \dfrac{4\sqrt{3}}{3}$; when $a = 5$:

$r = \dfrac{5\sqrt{6}}{3}$, $h = \dfrac{5\sqrt{3}}{3}$; when $a = 6$: $r = 2\sqrt{6}$, $h = 2\sqrt{3}$;

when $a = 8$: $r = \dfrac{8\sqrt{6}}{3}$, $h = \dfrac{8\sqrt{3}}{3}$

(c) Since $r = \dfrac{a\sqrt{6}}{3}$ and $h = \dfrac{a\sqrt{3}}{3}$, the relationship is $\dfrac{r}{h} = \sqrt{2}$.

Section 4.6, pp. 298–299

1. $\dfrac{1}{4}$ **3.** $\dfrac{5}{7}$ **5.** $\dfrac{1}{2}$ **7.** 0   **9.** 1   **11.** $\sqrt{2}$ **13.** $+1$

15. -1 **17.** $\dfrac{1}{2}$ **19.** 3   **21.** *na*   **23.** $-\dfrac{1}{2}$ **25.** 0   **27.** 3

29. 1   **31.** (b) is correct, but (a) is not.

33. $c = \dfrac{27}{10}$ **35.** -1

Section 4.7, pp. 305–306

1. $x_2 = -\dfrac{5}{3}, \dfrac{13}{21}$ **3.** $x_2 = -\dfrac{51}{31}, \dfrac{5763}{4945}$ **5.** $x_2 = \dfrac{2387}{2000}$

7. x, and all later approximations will equal x_0.

9.

$y = \begin{cases} \sqrt{x} \,, & x \geq 0 \\ \sqrt{-x}, & x < 0 \end{cases}$

11. The points of intersection of $y = x^3$ and $y = 3x + 1$ or $y = x^3 - 3x$ and $y = 1$ have the same x-values as the roots of part (i) or the solutions of part (iv).   **15.** 1.165561185

17. (a) Two   **(b)** 0.35003501505249 and -1.0261731615301

19. ± 1.3065629648764, ± 0.5411961001462 **21.** $x \approx 0.45$

23. The root is 1.17951.

25. (a) For $x_0 = -2$ or $x_0 = -0.8$, $x_i \to -1$ as i gets large.
    (b) For $x_0 = -0.5$ or $x_0 = 0.25$, $x_i \to 0$ as i gets large.
    (c) For $x_0 = 0.8$ or $x_0 = 2$, $x_i \to 1$ as i gets large.
    (d) For $x_0 = -\sqrt{21}/7$ or $x_0 = \sqrt{21}/7$, Newton's method does not converge. The values of x_i alternate between $-\sqrt{21}/7$ and $\sqrt{21}/7$ as i increases.

27. Answers will vary with machine speed.   **29.** 2.45, 0.000245

Section 4.8, pp. 314–318

1. (a) x^2 **(b)** $\dfrac{x^3}{3}$ **(c)** $\dfrac{x^3}{3} - x^2 + x$

3. (a) x^{-3} **(b)** $-\dfrac{1}{3}x^{-3}$ **(c)** $-\dfrac{1}{3}x^{-3} + x^2 + 3x$

5. (a) $-\dfrac{1}{x}$ **(b)** $-\dfrac{5}{x}$ **(c)** $2x + \dfrac{5}{x}$

7. (a) $\sqrt{x^3}$ **(b)** $\sqrt{x}$ **(c)** $\dfrac{2\sqrt{x^3}}{3} + 2\sqrt{x}$

9. (a) $x^{2/3}$ **(b)** $x^{1/3}$ **(c)** $x^{-1/3}$

11. (a) $\cos(\pi x)$ **(b)** $-3\cos x$ **(c)** $-\dfrac{1}{\pi}\cos(\pi x) + \cos(3x)$

13. (a) $\tan x$ **(b)** $2\tan\left(\dfrac{x}{3}\right)$ **(c)** $-\dfrac{2}{3}\tan\left(\dfrac{3x}{2}\right)$

15. (a) $-\csc x$ **(b)** $\dfrac{1}{5}\csc(5x)$ **(c)** $2\csc\left(\dfrac{\pi x}{2}\right)$

17. $\dfrac{x^2}{2} + x + C$ **19.** $t^3 + \dfrac{t^2}{4} + C$ **21.** $\dfrac{x^4}{2} - \dfrac{5x^2}{2} + 7x + C$

23. $-\dfrac{1}{x} - \dfrac{x^3}{3} - \dfrac{x}{3} + C$ **25.** $\dfrac{3}{2}x^{2/3} + C$

27. $\dfrac{2}{3}x^{3/2} + \dfrac{3}{4}x^{4/3} + C$ **29.** $4y^2 - \dfrac{8}{3}y^{3/4} + C$

31. $x^2 + \dfrac{2}{x} + C$ **33.** $2\sqrt{t} - \dfrac{2}{\sqrt{t}} + C$ **35.** $-2\sin t + C$

37. $-21\cos\dfrac{\theta}{3} + C$ **39.** $3\cot x + C$ **41.** $-\dfrac{1}{2}\csc\theta + C$

43. $4\sec x - 2\tan x + C$ **45.** $-\dfrac{1}{2}\cos 2x + \cot x + C$

47. $\dfrac{t}{2} + \dfrac{\sin 4t}{8} + C$ **49.** $\tan\theta + C$

51. $-\cot x - x + C$ **53.** $-\cos\theta - \theta + C$

61. (a) Wrong: $\dfrac{d}{dx}\left(\dfrac{x^2}{2}\sin x + C\right) = \dfrac{2x}{2}\sin x + \dfrac{x^2}{2}\cos x = $

    $x\sin x + \dfrac{x^2}{2}\cos x$

(b) Wrong: $\dfrac{d}{dx}(-x\cos x + C) = -\cos x + x\sin x$

(c) Right: $\dfrac{d}{dx}(-x\cos x + \sin x + C) = -\cos x + x\sin x + \cos x = x\sin x$

63. (a) Wrong: $\dfrac{d}{dx}\left(\dfrac{(2x+1)^3}{3} + C\right) = \dfrac{3(2x+1)^2(2)}{3} = 2(2x+1)^2$

(b) Wrong: $\dfrac{d}{dx}((2x+1)^3 + C) = 3(2x+1)^2(2) = 6(2x+1)^2$

(c) Right: $\dfrac{d}{dx}((2x+1)^3 + C) = 6(2x+1)^2$

65. (b)   **67.** $y = x^2 - 7x + 10$ **69.** $y = -\dfrac{1}{x} + \dfrac{x^2}{2} - \dfrac{1}{2}$

71. $y = 9x^{1/3} + 4$ **73.** $s = t + \sin t + 4$

75. $r = \cos(\pi\theta) - 1$ **77.** $v = \dfrac{1}{2}\sec t + \dfrac{1}{2}$

79. $y = x^2 - x^3 + 4x + 1$ **81.** $r = \dfrac{1}{t} + 2t - 2$

83. $y = x^3 - 4x^2 + 5$ **85.** $y = -\sin t + \cos t + t^3 - 1$

87. $y = 2x^{3/2} - 50$ **89.** $y = x - x^{4/3} + \dfrac{1}{2}$

91. $y = -\sin x - \cos x - 2$

93. **(a) (i)** 33.2 units, **(ii)** 33.2 units, **(iii)** 33.2 units   **(b)** True

95. $t = 88/k, k = 16$

97. **(a)** $v = 10t^{3/2} - 6t^{1/2}$ **(b)** $s = 4t^{5/2} - 4t^{3/2}$

101. **(a)** $-\sqrt{x} + C$ **(b)** $x + C$ **(c)** $\sqrt{x} + C$

(d) $-x + C$ **(e)** $x - \sqrt{x} + C$ **(f)** $-x - \sqrt{x} + C$

Practice Exercises, pp. 318–321

1. No   **3.** No minimum; absolute maximum: $f(1) = 16$; critical points: $x = 1$ and $11/3$ **5.** Yes, except at $x = 0$ **7.** No

11. **(b)** one

13. **(b)** 0.8555 99677 2   **19.** Global minimum value of $\dfrac{1}{2}$ at $x = 2$

21. **(a)** $t = 0, 6, 12$ **(b)** $t = 3, 9$ **(c)** $6 < t < 12$

(d) $0 < t < 6, 12 < t < 14$

23.

25.

27.

29.

31.

33. **(a)** Local maximum at $x = 4$, local minimum at $x = -4$, inflection point at $x = 0$

(b)

35. **(a)** Local maximum at $x = 0$, local minima at $x = -1$ and $x = 2$, inflection points at $x = \left(1 \pm \sqrt{7}\right)/3$

(b)

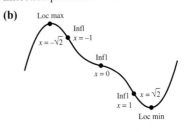

37. **(a)** Local maximum at $x = -\sqrt{2}$, local minimum at $x = \sqrt{2}$, inflection points at $x = \pm 1$ and 0

(b)

43.

45.

47.

49.

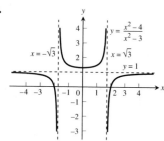

51. 5   **53.** 0   **55.** 1   **57.** 3/7   **59.** 0   **61.** 1

63. (a) $0, 36$ **(b)** $18, 18$ **65.** 54 square units

67. height $= 2$, radius $= \sqrt{2}$

69. $x = 5 - \sqrt{5}$ hundred ≈ 276 tires,
$y = 2(5 - \sqrt{5})$ hundred ≈ 553 tires

71. Dimensions: base is 6 in. by 12 in., height $= 2$ in.;
maximum volume $= 144$ in.^{3}

73. $x_5 = 2.1958\,23345$ **75.** $\dfrac{x^4}{4} + \dfrac{5}{2}x^2 - 7x + C$

77. $2t^{3/2} - \dfrac{4}{t} + C$ **79.** $-\dfrac{1}{r+5} + C$

81. $(\theta^2 + 1)^{3/2} + C$ **83.** $\dfrac{1}{3}(1 + x^4)^{3/4} + C$

85. $10 \tan \dfrac{s}{10} + C$ **87.** $-\dfrac{1}{\sqrt{2}} \csc \sqrt{2}\,\theta + C$

89. $\dfrac{1}{2}x - \sin \dfrac{x}{2} + C$ **91.** $y = x - \dfrac{1}{x} - 1$

93. $r = 4t^{5/2} + 4t^{3/2} - 8t$

Additional and Advanced Exercises, pp. 322–324

1. The function is constant on the interval.

3. The extreme points will not be at the end of an open interval.

5. (a) A local minimum at $x = -1$, points of inflection at $x = 0$
and $x = 2$ **(b)** A local maximum at $x = 0$ and local minima
at $x = -1$ and $x = 2$, points of inflection at $x = \dfrac{1 \pm \sqrt{7}}{3}$

9. No   **11.** $a = 1, b = 0, c = 1$ **13.** Yes   **15.** Drill the
hole at $y = h/2$.

17. $r = \dfrac{RH}{2(H - R)}$ for $H > 2R$, $r = R$ if $H \le 2R$

19. (a) $\frac{10}{3}$ **(b)** $\frac{5}{3}$ **(c)** $\frac{1}{2}$ **(d)** 0   **(e)** $-\frac{1}{2}$ **(f)** 1   **(g)** $\frac{1}{2}$
(h) 3

21. (a) $\dfrac{c - b}{2e}$ **(b)** $\dfrac{c + b}{2}$ **(c)** $\dfrac{b^2 - 2bc + c^2 + 4ae}{4e}$
(d) $\dfrac{c + b + t}{2}$

23. $m_0 = 1 - \dfrac{1}{q}, m_1 = \dfrac{1}{q}$

25. (a) $k = -38.72$ **(b)** 25 ft

27. Yes, $y = x + C$ **29.** $v_0 = \dfrac{2\sqrt{2}}{3}b^{3/4}$

CHAPTER 5

Section 5.1, pp. 333–335

1. (a) 0.125   **(b)** 0.21875   **(c)** 0.625   **(d)** 0.46875
3. (a) 1.066667   **(b)** 1.283333   **(c)** 2.666667   **(d)** 2.083333
5. $0.3125, 0.328125$ **7.** $1.5, 1.574603$
9. (a) 87 in.   **(b)** 87 in.
11. (a) 3490 ft   **(b)** 3840 ft
13. (a) 74.65 ft/sec   **(b)** 45.28 ft/sec   **(c)** 146.59 ft
15. $\dfrac{31}{16}$ **17.** 1

19. (a) Upper $= 758$ gal, lower $= 543$ gal
(b) Upper $= 2363$ gal, lower $= 1693$ gal
(c) ≈ 31.4 h, ≈ 32.4 h

21. (a) 2   **(b)** $2\sqrt{2} \approx 2.828$
(c) $8 \sin\left(\dfrac{\pi}{8}\right) \approx 3.061$
(d) Each area is less than the area of the circle, π. As n
increases, the polygon area approaches π.

Section 5.2, pp. 342–343

1. $\dfrac{6(1)}{1 + 1} + \dfrac{6(2)}{2 + 1} = 7$

3. $\cos(1)\pi + \cos(2)\pi + \cos(3)\pi + \cos(4)\pi = 0$

5. $\sin \pi - \sin \dfrac{\pi}{2} + \sin \dfrac{\pi}{3} = \dfrac{\sqrt{3} - 2}{2}$

7. All of them   **9.** b   **11.** $\displaystyle\sum_{k=1}^{6} k$ **13.** $\displaystyle\sum_{k=1}^{4} \frac{1}{2^k}$

15. $\displaystyle\sum_{k=1}^{5} (-1)^{k+1} \frac{1}{k}$

17. (a) -15 (b) 1 (c) 1 (d) -11 (e) 16

19. (a) 55 (b) 385 (c) 3025

21. -56 **23.** -73 **25.** 240 **27.** 3376

29. (a)   (b)

31. (a)

(b)

(c)

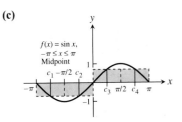

33. 1.2

35. $\dfrac{2}{3} + \dfrac{3n-1}{6n^2}, \dfrac{2}{3}$

37. $12 + \dfrac{27n+9}{2n^2}, 12$

39. $\dfrac{5}{6} + \dfrac{6n+1}{6n^2}, \dfrac{5}{6}$

Section 5.3, pp. 352–356

1. $\displaystyle\int_0^2 x^2\, dx$ **3.** $\displaystyle\int_{-7}^5 (x^2 - 3x)\, dx$ **5.** $\displaystyle\int_2^3 \frac{1}{1-x}\, dx$

7. $\displaystyle\int_{-\pi/4}^0 \sec x\, dx$

9. (a) 0 (b) -8 (c) -12 (d) 10 (e) -2 (f) 16

11. (a) 5 (b) $5\sqrt{3}$ (c) -5 (d) -5

13. (a) 4 (b) -4 **15.** Area $= 21$ square units

17. Area $= 9\pi/2$ square units   **19.** Area $= 2.5$ square units

21. Area $= 3$ square units   **23.** $b^2/4$ **25.** $b^2 - a^2$ **27.** $1/2$

29. $3\pi^2/2$ **31.** $7/3$ **33.** $1/24$ **35.** $3a^2/2$ **37.** $b/3$

39. -14 **41.** 10 **43.** -2 **45.** $-7/4$ **47.** 7 **49.** 0

51. Using n subintervals of length $\Delta x = b/n$ and right-endpoint values:
$$\text{Area} = \int_0^b 3x^2\, dx = b^3$$

53. Using n subintervals of length $\Delta x = b/n$ and right-endpoint values:
$$\text{Area} = \int_0^b 2x\, dx = b^2$$

55. $\text{av}(f) = 0$ **57.** $\text{av}(f) = -2$ **59.** $\text{av}(f) = 1$

61. (a) $\text{av}(g) = -1/2$ (b) $\text{av}(g) = 1$ (c) $\text{av}(g) = 1/4$

63. $a = 0$ and $b = 1$ maximize the integral.

65. Upper bound $= 1$, lower bound $= 1/2$

67. For example, $\displaystyle\int_0^1 \sin(x^2)\, dx \le \int_0^1 dx = 1$

69. $\displaystyle\int_a^b f(x)\, dx \ge \int_a^b 0\, dx = 0$ **71.** Upper bound $= 1/2$

Section 5.4, pp. 365–368

1. 6 **3.** 8 **5.** 1 **7.** $5/2$ **9.** 2 **11.** $2\sqrt{3}$ **13.** 0

15. $-\pi/4$ **17.** $\dfrac{2\pi^3}{3}$ **19.** $-8/3$ **21.** $-3/4$

23. $\sqrt{2} - \sqrt[4]{8} + 1$ **25.** 16 **27.** $(\cos\sqrt{x})\left(\dfrac{1}{2\sqrt{x}}\right)$

29. $4t^5$ **31.** $\sqrt{1 + x^2}$ **33.** $-\frac{1}{2}x^{-1/2}\sin x$ **35.** 1

37. 28/3 **39.** 1/2 **41.** 51/4 **43.** π **45.** $\dfrac{\sqrt{2}\pi}{2}$

47. d, since $y' = \dfrac{1}{x}$ and $y(\pi) = \displaystyle\int_\pi^\pi \frac{1}{t}\,dt - 3 = -3$

49. b, since $y' = \sec x$ and $y(0) = \displaystyle\int_0^0 \sec t\,dt + 4 = 4$

51. $y = \displaystyle\int_2^x \sec t\,dt + 3$ **53.** $s = \displaystyle\int_{t_0}^t f(x)\,dx + s_0$

55. $\dfrac{2}{3}bh$ **57.** \$9.00

59. (a) $v = \dfrac{ds}{dt} = \dfrac{d}{dt}\displaystyle\int_0^t f(x)\,dx = f(t) \Rightarrow v(5) = f(5) = 2$ m/sec

(b) $a = df/dt$ is negative since the slope of the tangent line at $t = 5$ is negative.

(c) $s = \displaystyle\int_0^3 f(x)\,dx = \frac{1}{2}(3)(3) = \frac{9}{2}$ m since the integral is the area of the triangle formed by $y = f(x)$, the x-axis, and $x = 3$.

(d) $t = 6$ since after $t = 6$ to $t = 9$, the region lies below the x-axis.

(e) At $t = 4$ and $t = 7$, since there are horizontal tangents there.

(f) Toward the origin between $t = 6$ and $t = 9$ since the velocity is negative on this interval. Away from the origin between $t = 0$ and $t = 6$ since the velocity is positive there.

(g) Right or positive side, because the integral of f from 0 to 9 is positive, there being more area above the x-axis than below.

63. $2x - 2$ **65.** $-3x + 5$

67. (a) True. Since f is continuous, g is differentiable by Part 1 of the Fundamental Theorem of Calculus.

(b) True: g is continuous because it is differentiable.

(c) True, since $g'(1) = f(1) = 0$.

(d) False, since $g''(1) = f'(1) > 0$.

(e) True, since $g'(1) = 0$ and $g''(1) = f'(1) > 0$.

(f) False: $g''(x) = f'(x) > 0$, so g'' never changes sign.

(g) True, since $g'(1) = f(1) = 0$ and $g'(x) = f(x)$ is an increasing function of x (because $f'(x) > 0$).

Section 5.5, pp. 374–376

1. $-\dfrac{1}{3}\cos 3x + C$ **3.** $\dfrac{1}{2}\sec 2t + C$ **5.** $-(7x - 2)^{-4} + C$

7. $-6(1 - r^3)^{1/2} + C$

9. $\dfrac{1}{3}(x^{3/2} - 1) - \dfrac{1}{6}\sin(2x^{3/2} - 2) + C$

11. (a) $-\dfrac{1}{4}(\cot^2 2\theta) + C$ (b) $-\dfrac{1}{4}(\csc^2 2\theta) + C$

13. $-\dfrac{1}{3}(3 - 2s)^{3/2} + C$ **15.** $\dfrac{2}{5}(5s + 4)^{1/2} + C$

17. $-\dfrac{2}{5}(1 - \theta^2)^{5/4} + C$ **19.** $-\dfrac{1}{3}(7 - 3y^2)^{3/2} + C$

21. $(-2/(1 + \sqrt{x})) + C$ **23.** $\dfrac{1}{3}\sin(3z + 4) + C$

25. $\dfrac{1}{3}\tan(3x + 2) + C$ **27.** $\dfrac{1}{2}\sin^6\left(\dfrac{x}{3}\right) + C$

29. $\left(\dfrac{r^3}{18} - 1\right)^6 + C$ **31.** $-\dfrac{2}{3}\cos(x^{3/2} + 1) + C$

33. $\sec\left(v + \dfrac{\pi}{2}\right) + C$ **35.** $\dfrac{1}{2\cos(2t + 1)} + C$

37. $-\dfrac{2}{3}(\cot^3 y)^{1/2} + C$ **39.** $-\sin\left(\dfrac{1}{t} - 1\right) + C$

41. $-\dfrac{\sin^2(1/\theta)}{2} + C$ **43.** $\dfrac{(s^3 + 2s^2 - 5s + 5)^2}{2} + C$

45. $\dfrac{1}{16}(1 + t^4)^4 + C$

47. $\dfrac{1}{5}(x^2 + 1)^{5/2} - \dfrac{1}{3}(x^2 + 1)^{3/2} + C$

49. (a) $-\dfrac{6}{2 + \tan^3 x} + C$ (b) $-\dfrac{6}{2 + \tan^3 x} + C$

(c) $-\dfrac{6}{2 + \tan^3 x} + C$

51. $\dfrac{1}{6}\sin\sqrt{3(2r - 1)^2 + 6} + C$

53. $s = \dfrac{1}{2}(3t^2 - 1)^4 - 5$

55. $s = 4t - 2\sin\left(2t + \dfrac{\pi}{6}\right) + 9$

57. $s = \sin\left(2t - \dfrac{\pi}{2}\right) + 100t + 1$

59. 6 m **63.** b) 399 Volts

Section 5.6, pp. 383–387

1. (a) 14/3 (b) 2/3

3. (a) 1/2 (b) −1/2

5. (a) 15/16 (b) 0

7. (a) 0 (b) 1/8

9. (a) 4 (b) 0

11. (a) 1/6 (b) 1/2

13. (a) 0 (b) 0

15. $2\sqrt{3}$ **17.** 3/4 **19.** $3^{5/2} - 1$ **21.** 3 **23.** $\pi/3$

25. 16/3 **27.** $2^{5/2}$ **29.** $\pi/2$ **31.** 128/15 **33.** 4/3

35. 5/6 **37.** 38/3 **39.** 49/6 **41.** 32/3 **43.** 48/5

45. 8/3 **47.** 8 **49.** 5/3 (There are three intersection points.)

51. 18 **53.** 243/8 **55.** 8/3 **57.** 2 **59.** 104/15

61. 56/15 **63.** 4 **65.** $\dfrac{4}{3} - \dfrac{4}{\pi}$ **67.** $\pi/2$ **69.** 2 **71.** 1/2

73. 1

75. (a) $\left(\pm\sqrt{c}, c\right)$ (b) $c = 4^{2/3}$ (c) $c = 4^{2/3}$

77. 11/3 **79.** 3/4 **81.** Neither **83.** $F(6) - F(2)$

85. (a) −3 (b) 3

87. $I = a/2$

Practice Exercises, pp. 388–391

1. (a) about 680 ft   **(b)** h (feet)

3. (a) $-1/2$ **(b)** 31   **(c)** 13   **(d)** 0

5. $\int_{1}^{5} (2x - 1)^{-1/2} dx = 2$ **7.** $\int_{-\pi}^{0} \cos \frac{x}{2} dx = 2$

9. (a) 4   **(b)** 2   **(c)** -2 **(d)** -2π **(e)** 8/5

11. 8/3   **13.** 62   **15.** 1   **17.** 1/6   **19.** 18   **21.** 9/8

23. $\frac{\pi^2}{32} + \frac{\sqrt{2}}{2} - 1$ **25.** 4   **27.** $\frac{8\sqrt{2} - 7}{6}$

29. Min: -4, max: 0, area: 27/4   **31.** 6/5

35. $y = \int_{5}^{x} \left(\frac{\sin t}{t}\right) dt - 3$ **37.** $-4(\cos x)^{1/2} + C$

39. $\theta^2 + \theta + \sin(2\theta + 1) + C$ **41.** $\frac{t^3}{3} + \frac{4}{t} + C$

43. $-\frac{1}{3}\cos(2t^{3/2}) + C$ **45.** 16   **47.** 2   **49.** 1   **51.** 8

53. $27\sqrt{3}/160$ **55.** $\pi/2$ **57.** $\sqrt{3}$ **59.** $6\sqrt{3} - 2\pi$

61. -1 **63.** 2   **65.** -2 **67.** 1   **69.** $\sqrt{2} - 1$

71. (a) b **(b)** b

75. 25°F   **77.** $\sqrt{2 + \cos^3 x}$ **79.** $\frac{-6}{3 + x^4}$ **81.** Yes

83. $-\sqrt{1 + x^2}$

85. cost $\approx$ \$10,899 using a lower sum estimate

87. 600, \$18.00   **89.** 300, \$6.00

Additional and Advanced Exercises, pp. 391–394

1. (a) Yes   **(b)** No

5. (a) 1/4   **(b)** $\sqrt[3]{12}$

7. $f(x) = \frac{x}{\sqrt{x^2 + 1}}$ **9.** $y = x^3 + 2x - 4$

11. 36/5

13. $\frac{1}{2} - \frac{2}{\pi}$

15. 13/3

17. 1/2   **19.** 2/x

21. $\frac{\sin 4y}{\sqrt{y}} - \frac{\sin y}{2\sqrt{y}}$ **23.** 1/6   **25.** $\int_{0}^{1} f(x)\, dx$

29. (a) 0   **(b)** -1 **(c)** $-\pi$ **(d)** $x = 1$

(e) $y = 2x + 2 - \pi$ **(f)** $x = -1, x = 2$ **(g)** $[-2\pi, 0]$

CHAPTER 6

Section 6.1, pp. 405–409

1. (a) $A(x) = \pi(1 - x^2)$ **(b)** $A(x) = 4(1 - x^2)$
   (c) $A(x) = 2(1 - x^2)$ **(d)** $A(x) = \sqrt{3}(1 - x^2)$

3. 16   **5.** $\frac{16}{3}$ **7. (a)** $2\sqrt{3}$ **(b)** 8   **9.** 8π

11. (a) $s^2 h$ **(b)** $s^2 h$ **13.** $\frac{2\pi}{3}$ **15.** $4 - \pi$ **17.** $\frac{32\pi}{5}$

19. 36π **21.** π **23.** $\pi\left(\frac{\pi}{2} + 2\sqrt{2} - \frac{11}{3}\right)$ **25.** 2π

27. 2π **29.** 3π **31.** $\pi^2 - 2\pi$ **33.** $\frac{2\pi}{3}$ **35.** $\frac{117\pi}{5}$

37. $\pi(\pi - 2)$ **39.** $\frac{4\pi}{3}$ **41.** 8π **43.** $\frac{7\pi}{6}$

45. (a) 8π **(b)** $\frac{32\pi}{5}$ **(c)** $\frac{8\pi}{3}$ **(d)** $\frac{224\pi}{15}$

47. (a) $\frac{16\pi}{15}$ **(b)** $\frac{56\pi}{15}$ **(c)** $\frac{64\pi}{15}$

49. $V = 2a^2 b\pi^2$ **51. (a)** $V = \frac{\pi h^2(3a - h)}{3}$ **(b)** $\frac{1}{120\pi}$ m/sec

55. $V = 3308$ cm³

57. (a) $c = \frac{2}{\pi}$ **(b)** $c = 0$
   (c)

Section 6.2, pp. 414–416

1. 6π **3.** 2π **5.** $\frac{14\pi}{3}$ **7.** 8π **9.** $\frac{5\pi}{6}$ **11.** $\frac{7\pi}{15}$

13. (b) 4π **15.** $\frac{16\pi}{15}(3\sqrt{2} + 5)$ **17.** $\frac{8\pi}{3}$ **19.** $\frac{4\pi}{3}$

21. $\frac{16\pi}{3}$ **23. (a)** $\frac{6\pi}{5}$ **(b)** $\frac{4\pi}{5}$ **(c)** 2π **(d)** 2π

25. (a) About the x-axis: $V = \dfrac{2\pi}{15}$; about the y-axis: $V = \dfrac{\pi}{6}$

(b) About the x-axis: $V = \dfrac{2\pi}{15}$; about the y-axis: $V = \dfrac{\pi}{6}$

27. (a) $\dfrac{5\pi}{3}$ (b) $\dfrac{4\pi}{3}$ (c) 2π (d) $\dfrac{2\pi}{3}$

29. (a) $\dfrac{4\pi}{15}$ (b) $\dfrac{7\pi}{30}$ **31.** (a) $\dfrac{24\pi}{5}$ (b) $\dfrac{48\pi}{5}$

33. (a) $\dfrac{9\pi}{16}$ (b) $\dfrac{9\pi}{16}$

35. Disk: 2 integrals; washer: 2 integrals; shell: 1 integral

Section 6.3, pp. 423–424

1. $\dfrac{5\sqrt{10}}{3}$ **3.** 7   **5.** $\dfrac{21}{2}$ **7.** 12   **9.** $\dfrac{53}{6}$ **11.** $\dfrac{123}{32}$

13. $\dfrac{99}{8}$ **15.** 2   **17.** (a) $\displaystyle\int_{-1}^{2}\sqrt{1 + 4x^2}\,dx$ (c) ≈ 6.13

19. (a) $\displaystyle\int_{0}^{\pi}\sqrt{1 + \cos^2 y}\,dy$ (c) ≈ 3.82

21. (a) $\displaystyle\int_{-1}^{3}\sqrt{1 + (y + 1)^2}\,dy$ (c) ≈ 9.29

23. (a) $\displaystyle\int_{0}^{\pi/6}\sec x\,dx$ (c) ≈ 0.55

25. Yes, $f(x) = \pm x + C$ where C is any real number.

27. (a) $y = \sqrt{x}$ from $(1, 1)$ to $(4, 2)$

(b) Only one. We know the derivative of the function and the value of the function at one value of x.

29. (a) π (b) π

Section 6.4, pp. 434–435

1. 4 ft   **3.** $(L/4, L/4)$ **5.** $M_0 = 8, M = 8, \bar{x} = 1$

7. $M_0 = 15/2, M = 9/2, \bar{x} = 5/3$

9. $M_0 = 73/6, M = 5, \bar{x} = 73/30$ **11.** $M_0 = 3, M = 3, \bar{x} = 1$

13. $\bar{x} = 0, \bar{y} = 12/5$ **15.** $\bar{x} = 1, \bar{y} = -3/5$

17. $\bar{x} = 16/105, \bar{y} = 8/15$ **19.** $\bar{x} = 0, \bar{y} = \pi/8$

21. $\bar{x} = 1, \bar{y} = -2/5$ **23.** $\bar{x} = \bar{y} = \dfrac{2}{4 - \pi}$

25. $\bar{x} = 3/2, \bar{y} = 1/2$

27. (a) $\dfrac{224\pi}{3}$ (b) $\bar{x} = 2, \bar{y} = 0$

(c)

31. $\bar{x} = \bar{y} = 1/3$ **33.** $\bar{x} = a/3, \bar{y} = b/3$ **35.** $13\delta/6$

37. $\bar{x} = 0, \bar{y} = \dfrac{a\pi}{4}$

Section 6.5, pp. 444–447

1. (a) $2\pi\displaystyle\int_{0}^{\pi/4}\tan x\sqrt{1 + \sec^4 x}\,dx$ (c) ≈ 3.84

3. (a) $2\pi\displaystyle\int_{1}^{2}\dfrac{1}{y}\sqrt{1 + y^{-4}}\,dy$ (c) ≈ 5.02

5. (a) $2\pi\displaystyle\int_{1}^{4}(3 - \sqrt{x})^2\sqrt{1 + (1 - 3x^{-1/2})^2}\,dx$ (c) ≈ 63.37

7. (a) $2\pi\displaystyle\int_{0}^{\pi/3}\left(\int_{0}^{y}\tan t\,dt\right)\sec y\,dy$ (c) ≈ 2.08

9. $4\pi\sqrt{5}$ **11.** $3\pi\sqrt{5}$ **13.** $98\pi/81$ **15.** 2π

17. $\pi\left(\sqrt{8} - 1\right)/9$ **19.** $35\pi\sqrt{5}/3$ **21.** $253\pi/20$

25. $2\pi\displaystyle\int_{-\pi/2}^{\pi/2}(\cos x)\sqrt{1 + \sin^2 x}\,dx$

27. Order 226.2 liters of each color.   **31.** $5\sqrt{2}\pi$ **33.** $8\pi^2$

35. $52\pi/3$ **37.** $3\pi\sqrt{5}$ **41.** $V = 32\pi, S = 32\sqrt{2}\pi$

43. $4\pi^2$ **45.** $\bar{x} = 0, \bar{y} = \dfrac{2a}{\pi}$ **47.** $\bar{x} = 0, \bar{y} = \dfrac{4b}{3\pi}$

49. $\sqrt{2}\pi a^3(4 + 3\pi)/6$ **51.** $\dfrac{2a^3}{3}$

Section 6.6, pp. 452–455

1. 400 N·m   **3.** 4 cm, 0.08 J

5. (a) 7238 lb/in.   (b) 905 in.-lb, 2714 in.-lb   **7.** 780 J

9. 72,900 ft-lb   **13.** 160 ft-lb

15. (a) 1,497,600 ft-lb   (b) 1 hr, 40 min   (d) At 62.26 lb/ft³: a) 1,494,240 ft-lb b) 1 hr, 40.1 min At 62.59 lb/ft³: a) 1,502,160 ft-lb b) 1 hr, 40.1 min

17. 37,306 ft-lb   **19.** 7,238,229.47 ft-lb

21. (a) 34,583 ft-lb   (b) 53,483 ft-lb   **23.** 15,073,100.75 J

27. 85.1 ft-lb   **29.** 64.6 ft-lb   **31.** 110.6 ft-lb

33. (a) $r(y) = 60 - \sqrt{50^2 - (y - 325)^2}$ for $325 \le y \le 375$ ft

(b) $\Delta V \approx \pi[60 - \sqrt{2500 - (y - 325)^2}]^2\,\Delta y$

(c) $W = 6.3358 \cdot 10^7$ ft-lb

35. 91.32 in.-oz   **37.** 5.144×10^{10} J

Section 6.7, pp. 459–461

1. 1684.8 lb   **3.** 2808 lb   **5.** (a) 1164.8 lb   (b) 1194.7 lb

7. 1309 lb   **9.** 41.6 lb   **11.** (a) 93.33 lb   (b) 3 ft

13. 1035 ft³   **15.** $wb/2$

17. No. The tank will overflow because the movable end will have moved only $3\frac{1}{3}$ ft by the time the tank is full.

19. 4.2 lb   **21.** (a) 374.4 lb   (b) 7.5 in.   (c) No

Practice Exercises, pp. 461–464

1. $\dfrac{9\pi}{280}$ **3.** π^2 **5.** $\dfrac{72\pi}{35}$

7. (a) 2π **(b)** π **(c)** $12\pi/5$ **(d)** $26\pi/5$
9. (a) 8π **(b)** $1088\pi/15$ **(c)** $512\pi/15$
11. $\pi\left(3\sqrt{3} - \pi\right)/3$
13. (a) $16\pi/15$ **(b)** $8\pi/5$ **(c)** $8\pi/3$ **(d)** $32\pi/5$
15. $\dfrac{28\pi}{3}$ ft^3 **17.** $\dfrac{10}{3}$ **19.** $\dfrac{285}{8}$ **21.** 10 **23.** $\dfrac{9\pi}{2}$
25. $\bar{x} = 0, \bar{y} = 8/5$ **27.** $\bar{x} = 3/2, \bar{y} = 12/5$
29. $\bar{x} = 9/5, \bar{y} = 11/10$ **31.** $28\pi\sqrt{2}/3$ **33.** 4π
35. $76\pi/3$ **37.** 4640 J **39.** 10 ft-lb, 30 ft-lb
41. 418,208.81 ft-lb **43.** 22,500π ft-lb, 257 sec
45. 332.8 lb **47.** 2196.48 lb **49.** $216w_1 + 360w_2$

Additional and Advanced Exercises, pp. 464–465

1. $f(x) = \sqrt{\dfrac{2x - a}{\pi}}$ **3.** $f(x) = \sqrt{C^2 - 1}\,x + a$, where $C \geq 1$
5. $\bar{x} = 0, \bar{y} = \dfrac{n}{2n + 1}$, $(0, 1/2)$
9. (a) $\bar{x} = \bar{y} = 4(a^2 + ab + b^2)/(3\pi(a + b))$
(b) $(2a/\pi, 2a/\pi)$

11. $28/3$ **13.** $\dfrac{4h\sqrt{3mh}}{3}$ **15.** ≈ 2329.6 lb
17. (a) $2h/3$ **(b)** $(6a^2 + 8ah + 3h^2)/(6a + 4h)$

CHAPTER 7

Section 7.1, 473–475

1. One-to-one **3.** Not one-to-one **5.** One-to-one
7. D: $(0, 1]$ R: $[0, \infty)$

9. D: $[-1, 1]$ R: $[-\pi/2, \pi/2]$

11. (a) Symmetric about the line $y = x$

13. $f^{-1}(x) = \sqrt{x - 1}$ **15.** $f^{-1}(x) = \sqrt[3]{x + 1}$
17. $f^{-1}(x) = \sqrt{x} - 1$
19. $f^{-1}(x) = \sqrt[5]{x}$; domain: $-\infty < x < \infty$; range: $-\infty < y < \infty$
21. $f^{-1}(x) = 5\sqrt{x - 1}$; domain: $-\infty < x < \infty$; range: $-\infty < y < \infty$
23. $f^{-1}(x) = \dfrac{1}{\sqrt{x}}$; domain: $x > 0$; range: $y > 0$
25. (a) $f^{-1}(x) = \dfrac{x}{2} - \dfrac{3}{2}$
(b)

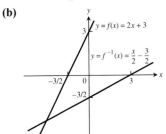

(c) $2, 1/2$
27. (a) $f^{-1}(x) = -\dfrac{x}{4} + \dfrac{5}{4}$
(b)

(c) $-4, -1/4$
29. (b)

(c) Slope of f at $(1, 1)$: 3; slope of g at $(1, 1)$: $1/3$; slope of f at $(-1, -1)$: 3; slope of g at $(-1, -1)$: $1/3$
(d) $y = 0$ is tangent to $y = x^3$ at $x = 0$; $x = 0$ is tangent to $y = \sqrt[3]{x}$ at $x = 0$

31. $1/9$ **33.** 3

35. (a) $f^{-1}(x) = \dfrac{1}{m}x$

(b) The graph of f^{-1} is the line through the origin with slope $1/m$.

37. (a) $f^{-1}(x) = x - 1$

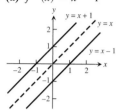

(b) $f^{-1}(x) = x - b$. The graph of f^{-1} is a line parallel to the graph of f. The graphs of f and f^{-1} lie on opposite sides of the line $y = x$ and are equidistant from that line.

(c) Their graphs will be parallel to one another and lie on opposite sides of the line $y = x$ equidistant from that line.

41. Increasing, therefore one-to-one; $df^{-1}/dx = \dfrac{1}{9}x^{-2/3}$

43. Decreasing, therefore one-to-one; $df^{-1}/dx = -\dfrac{1}{3}x^{-2/3}$

Section 7.2, pp. 484–485

1. (a) $\ln 3 - 2\ln 2$ (b) $2(\ln 2 - \ln 3)$ (c) $-\ln 2$,
(d) $\dfrac{2}{3}\ln 3$ (e) $\ln 3 + \dfrac{1}{2}\ln 2$ (f) $\dfrac{1}{2}(3\ln 3 - \ln 2)$

3. (a) $\ln 5$ (b) $\ln(x - 3)$ (c) $\ln(t^2)$

5. $1/x$ **7.** $2/t$ **9.** $-1/x$ **11.** $\dfrac{1}{\theta + 1}$ **13.** $3/x$

15. $2(\ln t) + (\ln t)^2$ **17.** $x^3 \ln x$ **19.** $\dfrac{1 - \ln t}{t^2}$

21. $\dfrac{1}{x(1 + \ln x)^2}$ **23.** $\dfrac{1}{x \ln x}$ **25.** $2\cos(\ln\theta)$

27. $-\dfrac{3x + 2}{2x(x + 1)}$ **29.** $\dfrac{2}{t(1 - \ln t)^2}$ **31.** $\dfrac{\tan(\ln\theta)}{\theta}$

33. $\dfrac{10x}{x^2 + 1} + \dfrac{1}{2(1 - x)}$ **35.** $2x \ln|x| - x\ln\dfrac{|x|}{\sqrt{2}}$ **37.** $\ln\left(\dfrac{2}{3}\right)$

39. $\ln|y^2 - 25| + C$ **41.** $\ln 3$ **43.** $(\ln 2)^2$ **45.** $\dfrac{1}{\ln 4}$

47. $\ln|6 + 3\tan t| + C$ **49.** $\ln 2$ **51.** $\ln 27$

53. $\ln(1 + \sqrt{x}) + C$

55. $\left(\dfrac{1}{2}\right)\sqrt{x(x + 1)}\left(\dfrac{1}{x} + \dfrac{1}{x + 1}\right) = \dfrac{2x + 1}{2\sqrt{x(x + 1)}}$

57. $\left(\dfrac{1}{2}\right)\sqrt{\dfrac{t}{t + 1}}\left(\dfrac{1}{t} - \dfrac{1}{t + 1}\right) = \dfrac{1}{2\sqrt{t}(t + 1)^{3/2}}$

59. $\sqrt{\theta + 3}\,(\sin\theta)\left(\dfrac{1}{2(\theta + 3)} + \cot\theta\right)$

61. $t(t + 1)(t + 2)\left[\dfrac{1}{t} + \dfrac{1}{t + 1} + \dfrac{1}{t + 2}\right] = 3t^2 + 6t + 2$

63. $\dfrac{\theta + 5}{\theta\cos\theta}\left[\dfrac{1}{\theta + 5} - \dfrac{1}{\theta} + \tan\theta\right]$

65. $\dfrac{x\sqrt{x^2 + 1}}{(x + 1)^{2/3}}\left[\dfrac{1}{x} + \dfrac{x}{x^2 + 1} - \dfrac{2}{3(x + 1)}\right]$

67. $\dfrac{1}{3}\sqrt[3]{\dfrac{x(x - 2)}{x^2 + 1}}\left(\dfrac{1}{x} + \dfrac{1}{x - 2} - \dfrac{2x}{x^2 + 1}\right)$

69. (a) Max $= 0$ at $x = 0$, min $= -\ln 2$ at $x = \pi/3$
(b) Max $= 1$ at $x = 1$, min $= \cos(\ln 2)$ at $x = 1/2$ and $x = 2$

71. $\ln 16$ **73.** $4\pi\ln 4$ **75.** $\pi\ln 16$

77. (a) $6 + \ln 2$ (b) $8 + \ln 9$

79. (a) $\bar{x} \approx 1.44, \bar{y} \approx 0.36$

(b)

81. $y = x + \ln|x| + 2$ **83.** (b) 0.00469

Section 7.3, pp. 493–495

1. (a) 7.2 (b) $\dfrac{1}{x^2}$ (c) $\dfrac{x}{y}$

3. (a) 1 (b) 1 (c) $-x^2 - y^2$

5. e^{2t+4} **7.** $e^{5t} + 40$ **9.** $y = 2xe^x + 1$

11. (a) $k = \ln 2$ (b) $k = (1/10)\ln 2$ (c) $k = 1000\ln a$

13. (a) $t = -10\ln 3$ (b) $t = -\dfrac{\ln 2}{k}$ (c) $t = \dfrac{\ln .4}{\ln .2}$

15. $4(\ln x)^2$ **17.** $-5e^{-5x}$ **19.** $-7e^{(5-7x)}$ **21.** xe^x

23. $x^2 e^x$ **25.** $2e^\theta\cos\theta$ **27.** $2\theta e^{-\theta^2}\sin(e^{-\theta^2})$

29. $\dfrac{1 - t}{t}$ **31.** $1/(1 + e^\theta)$ **33.** $e^{\cos t}(1 - t\sin t)$

35. $(\sin x)/x$ **37.** $\dfrac{ye^y\cos x}{1 - ye^y\sin x}$ **39.** $\dfrac{2e^{2x} - \cos(x + 3y)}{3\cos(x + 3y)}$

41. $\dfrac{1}{3}e^{3x} - 5e^{-x} + C$ **43.** 1 **45.** $8e^{(x+1)} + C$ **47.** 2

49. $2e^{\sqrt{r}} + C$ **51.** $-e^{-t^2} + C$ **53.** $-e^{1/x} + C$ **55.** e

57. $\dfrac{1}{\pi}e^{\sec\pi t} + C$ **59.** 1 **61.** $\ln(1 + e^r) + C$

63. $y = 1 - \cos(e^t - 2)$ **65.** $y = 2(e^{-x} + x) - 1$

67. Maximum: 1 at $x = 0$, minimum: $2 - 2\ln 2$ at $x = \ln 2$

69. Abs max of $1/(2e)$ assumed at $x = 1/\sqrt{e}$

71. 2 **73.** $y = e^{x/2} - 1$

75. (a) $\dfrac{d}{dx}(x\ln x - x + C) = x\cdot\dfrac{1}{x} + \ln x - 1 + 0 = \ln x$

(b) $\dfrac{1}{e - 1}$

77. (b) $|\text{error}| \approx 0.02140$ **79.** 2.71828183

Section 7.4, pp. 500–502

1. (a) 7 (b) $\sqrt{2}$ (c) 75 (d) 2 (e) 0.5 (f) -1

3. (a) $\sqrt{x}$ (b) x^2 (c) $\sin x$ **5.** (a) $\dfrac{\ln 3}{\ln 2}$ (b) 3 (c) 2

7. $x = 12$ **9.** $x = 3$ or $x = 2$ **11.** $2^x \ln x$

13. $\left(\dfrac{\ln 5}{2\sqrt{s}}\right)5^{\sqrt{s}}$ 15. $\pi x^{(\pi-1)}$ 17. $-\sqrt{2}\cos\theta^{(\sqrt{2}-1)}\sin\theta$

19. $7^{\sec\theta}(\ln 7)^2(\sec\theta\tan\theta)$ 21. $(3\cos 3t)(2^{\sin 3t})\ln 2$

23. $\dfrac{1}{\theta\ln 2}$ 25. $\dfrac{3}{x\ln 4}$ 27. $\dfrac{2(\ln r)}{r(\ln 2)(\ln 4)}$

29. $\dfrac{-2}{(x+1)(x-1)}$ 31. $\sin(\log_7\theta)+\dfrac{1}{\ln 7}\cos(\log_7\theta)$

33. $\dfrac{1}{\ln 5}$ 35. $\dfrac{1}{t}(\log_2 3)3^{\log_2 t}$ 37. $\dfrac{1}{t}$

39. $(x+1)^x\left(\dfrac{x}{x+1}+\ln(x+1)\right)$ 41. $(\sqrt{t})^t\left(\dfrac{\ln t}{2}+\dfrac{1}{2}\right)$

43. $(\sin x)^x(\ln\sin x+x\cot x)$ 45. $(x^{\ln x})\left(\dfrac{\ln x^2}{x}\right)$

47. $\dfrac{5^x}{\ln 5}+C$ 49. $\dfrac{1}{2\ln 2}$ 51. $\dfrac{1}{\ln 2}$ 53. $\dfrac{6}{\ln 7}$ 55. 32760

57. $\dfrac{3x^{(\sqrt{3}+1)}}{\sqrt{3}+1}+C$ 59. $3^{\sqrt{2}+1}$ 61. $\dfrac{1}{\ln 10}\left(\dfrac{(\ln x)^2}{2}\right)+C$

63. $2(\ln 2)^2$ 65. $\dfrac{3\ln 2}{2}$ 67. $\ln 10$ 69. $(\ln 10)\ln|\ln x|+C$

71. $\ln(\ln x), x>1$ 73. $-\ln x$ 75. $2\ln 5$
77. $[10^{-7.44}, 10^{-7.37}]$ 79. $k=10$
81. (a) 10^{-7} (b) 7   (c) 1:1   83. $x\approx -0.76666$
85. (a) $L(x)=1+(\ln 2)x\approx 0.69x+1$
87. (a) 1.89279   (b) -0.35621   (c) 0.94575   (d) -2.80735
   (e) 5.29595   (f) 0.97041   (g) -1.03972   (h) -1.61181
91. $1/e$ 93. 1   95. $1/e$ 97. $e^{1/2}$ 99. 1

Section 7.5, pp. 508–511

1. (a) -0.00001   (b) 10,536 years   (c) 82%
3. 54.88 g   5. 59.8 ft   7. 2.8147498×10^{14}
9. (a) 8 years   (b) 32.02 years   11. 15.28 years
13. (a) $A_0 e^{0.2}$ (b) 17.33 years; 27.47 years
15. 4.50%   17. 0.585 days
21. (a) 17.5 min.   (b) 13.26 min.
23. -3°C   25. About 6659 years   27. 41 years old

Section 7.6, pp. 515–517

1. (a) slower   (b) slower   (c) slower   (d) faster
   (e) slower   (f) slower   (g) same   (h) slower
3. (a) same   (b) faster   (c) same   (d) same   (e) slower
   (f) faster   (g) slower   (h) same
5. (a) same   (b) same   (c) same   (d) faster   (e) faster
   (f) same   (g) slower   (h) faster
7. d, a, c, b
9. (a) false   (b) false   (c) true   (d) true   (e) true
   (f) true   (g) false   (h) true
13. When the degree of f is less than or equal to the degree of g.
15. 1, 1
21. (b) $\ln(e^{17000000})=17,000,000<(e^{17\times10^6})^{1/10^6}$
$$=e^{17}\approx 24,154,952.75$$
   (c) $x\approx 3.4306311\times 10^{15}$
   (d) They cross at $x\approx 3.4306311\times 10^{15}$

23. (a) The algorithm that takes $O(n\log_2 n)$ steps
25. It could take one million for a sequential search; at most 20 steps for a binary search.

Section 7.7, pp. 530–534

1. (a) $\pi/4$ (b) $-\pi/3$ (c) $\pi/6$
3. (a) $-\pi/6$ (b) $\pi/4$ (c) $-\pi/3$
5. (a) $\pi/3$ (b) $3\pi/4$ (c) $\pi/6$
7. (a) $3\pi/4$ (b) $\pi/6$ (c) $2\pi/3$
9. (a) $\pi/4$ (b) $-\pi/3$ (c) $\pi/6$
11. (a) $3\pi/4$ (b) $\pi/6$ (c) $2\pi/3$

13. $\cos\alpha=\dfrac{12}{13}, \tan\alpha=\dfrac{5}{12}, \sec\alpha=\dfrac{13}{12}, \csc\alpha=\dfrac{13}{5}, \cot\alpha=\dfrac{12}{5}$

15. $\sin\alpha=\dfrac{2}{\sqrt{5}}, \cos\alpha=-\dfrac{1}{\sqrt{5}}, \tan\alpha=-2, \csc\alpha=\dfrac{\sqrt{5}}{2},$
$\cot\alpha=-\dfrac{1}{2}$

17. $1/\sqrt{2}$ 19. $-1/\sqrt{3}$ 21. $\dfrac{4+\sqrt{3}}{2\sqrt{3}}$ 23. 1

25. $-\sqrt{2}$ 27. $\pi/6$ 29. $\dfrac{\sqrt{x^2+4}}{2}$ 31. $\sqrt{9y^2-1}$

33. $\sqrt{1-x^2}$ 35. $\dfrac{\sqrt{x^2-2x}}{x-1}$ 37. $\dfrac{\sqrt{9-4y^2}}{3}$

39. $\dfrac{\sqrt{x^2-16}}{x}$ 41. $\pi/2$ 43. $\pi/2$ 45. $\pi/2$

47. 0   49. $\dfrac{-2x}{\sqrt{1-x^4}}$ 51. $\dfrac{\sqrt{2}}{\sqrt{1-2t^2}}$

53. $\dfrac{1}{|2s+1|\sqrt{s^2+s}}$ 55. $\dfrac{-2x}{(x^2+1)\sqrt{x^4+2x^2}}$

57. $\dfrac{-1}{\sqrt{1-t^2}}$ 59. $\dfrac{-1}{2\sqrt{t}(1+t)}$ 61. $\dfrac{1}{(\tan^{-1}x)(1+x^2)}$

63. $\dfrac{-e^t}{|e^t|\sqrt{(e^t)^2-1}}=\dfrac{-1}{\sqrt{e^{2t}-1}}$ 65. $\dfrac{-2s^n}{\sqrt{1-s^2}}$ 67. 0

69. $\sin^{-1}x$ 71. $\sin^{-1}\dfrac{x}{7}+C$ 73. $\dfrac{1}{\sqrt{17}}\tan^{-1}\dfrac{x}{\sqrt{17}}+C$

75. $\dfrac{1}{\sqrt{2}}\sec^{-1}\left|\dfrac{5x}{\sqrt{2}}\right|+C$ 77. $2\pi/3$ 79. $\pi/16$

81. $-\pi/12$ 83. $\dfrac{3}{2}\sin^{-1}2(r-1)+C$

85. $\dfrac{\sqrt{2}}{2}\tan^{-1}\left(\dfrac{x-1}{\sqrt{2}}\right)+C$ 87. $\dfrac{1}{4}\sec^{-1}\left|\dfrac{2x-1}{2}\right|+C$

89. π 91. $\pi/12$ 93. $\dfrac{1}{2}\sin^{-1}y^2+C$ 95. $\sin^{-1}(x-2)+C$

97. π 99. $\dfrac{1}{2}\tan^{-1}\left(\dfrac{y-1}{2}\right)+C$ 101. 2π

103. $\sec^{-1}|x+1|+C$ 105. $e^{\sin^{-1}x}+C$ 107. $\dfrac{1}{3}(\sin^{-1}(x))^3+C$

109. $\ln|\tan^{-1}y|+C$ 111. $\sqrt{3}-1$ 113. 5   115. 2

121. $y=\sin^{-1}x$ 123. $y=\sec^{-1}x+\dfrac{2\pi}{3}, x>1$

127. $\theta = \cos^{-1}\left(\dfrac{1}{\sqrt{3}}\right) \approx 54.7°$

133. (a) Defined; there is an angle whose tangent is 2.
(b) Not defined; there is no angle whose cosine is 2.

135. (a) Not defined; no angle has secant 0.
(b) Not defined; no angle has sine $\sqrt{2}$.

137. $3\sqrt{5}$ ft.

139. Yes, $\sin^{-1}(x)$ and $-\cos^{-1}(x)$ differ by the constant $\pi/2$.

147. $\pi^2/2$ **149. (a)** $\pi^2/2$ **(b)** 2π

151. (a) 0.84107   **(b)** -0.72973 **(c)** 0.46365

153. (a) Domain: all real numbers except those having the form $\dfrac{\pi}{2} + k\pi$ where k is an integer; range: $-\pi/2 < y < \pi/2$.
(b) Domain: $-\infty < x < \infty$; range: $-\infty < y < \infty$

155. (a) Domain: $-\infty < x < \infty$; range: $0 \le y \le \pi$
(b) Domain: $-1 \le x \le 1$; range: $-1 \le y \le 1$

157. The graphs are identical.

Section 7.8, pp. 542–546

1. $\cosh x = 5/4$, $\tanh x = -3/5$, $\coth x = -5/3$,
$\operatorname{sech} x = 4/5$, $\operatorname{csch} x = -4/3$

3. $\sinh x = 8/15$, $\tanh x = 8/17$, $\coth x = 17/8$, $\operatorname{sech} x = 15/17$,
$\operatorname{csch} x = 15/8$

5. $x + \dfrac{1}{x}$ **7.** e^{5x} **9.** e^{4x} **13.** $2\cosh\dfrac{x}{3}$

15. $\operatorname{sech}^2\sqrt{t} + \dfrac{\tanh\sqrt{t}}{\sqrt{t}}$ **17.** $\coth z$

19. $(\ln \operatorname{sech}\theta)(\operatorname{sech}\theta\tanh\theta)$ **21.** $\tanh^3 v$ **23.** 2

25. $\dfrac{1}{2\sqrt{x}(1+x)}$ **27.** $\dfrac{1}{1+\theta} - \tanh^{-1}\theta$

29. $\dfrac{1}{2\sqrt{t}} - \coth^{-1}\sqrt{t}$ **31.** $-\operatorname{sech}^{-1}x$ **33.** $\dfrac{\ln 2}{\sqrt{1 + \left(\frac{1}{2}\right)^{2\theta}}}$

35. $|\sec x|$ **41.** $\dfrac{\cosh 2x}{2} + C$

43. $12\sinh\left(\dfrac{x}{2} - \ln 3\right) + C$ **45.** $7\ln|e^{x/7} + e^{-x/7}| + C$

47. $\tanh\left(x - \dfrac{1}{2}\right) + C$ **49.** $-2\operatorname{sech}\sqrt{t} + C$ **51.** $\ln\dfrac{5}{2}$

53. $\dfrac{3}{32} + \ln 2$ **55.** $e - e^{-1}$ **57.** 3/4   **59.** $\dfrac{3}{8} + \ln\sqrt{2}$

61. $\ln(2/3)$ **63.** $\dfrac{-\ln 3}{2}$ **65.** $\ln 3$

67. (a) $\sinh^{-1}(\sqrt{3})$ **(b)** $\ln(\sqrt{3} + 2)$

69. (a) $\coth^{-1}(2) - \coth^{-1}(5/4)$ **(b)** $\left(\dfrac{1}{2}\right)\ln\left(\dfrac{1}{3}\right)$

71. (a) $-\operatorname{sech}^{-1}\left(\dfrac{12}{13}\right) + \operatorname{sech}^{-1}\left(\dfrac{4}{5}\right)$

(b) $-\ln\left(\dfrac{1 + \sqrt{1 - (12/13)^2}}{(12/13)}\right) + \ln\left(\dfrac{1 + \sqrt{1 - (4/5)^2}}{(4/5)}\right) =$
$-\ln\left(\dfrac{3}{2}\right) + \ln(2) = \ln(4/3)$

73. (a) 0   **(b)** 0

75. (b) i) $f(x) = \dfrac{2f(x)}{2} + 0 = f(x)$, ii) $f(x) = 0 + \dfrac{2f(x)}{2} = f(x)$

77. (b) $\sqrt{\dfrac{mg}{k}}$ **(c)** $80\sqrt{5} \approx 178.89$ ft/sec

79. $y = \operatorname{sech}^{-1}(x) - \sqrt{1 - x^2}$ **81.** 2π **83.** $\dfrac{6}{5}$

85. $16\pi\ln 6 + \dfrac{455\pi}{9}$

89. (c) $a \approx 0.0417525$ **(d)** ≈ 47.90 lb

Practice Exercises, pp. 547–550

1. $-2e^{-x/5}$ **3.** xe^{4x} **5.** $\dfrac{2\sin\theta\cos\theta}{\sin^2\theta} = 2\cot\theta$ **7.** $\dfrac{2}{(\ln 2)x}$

9. $-8^{-t}(\ln 8)$ **11.** $18x^{2.6}$

13. $(x + 2)^{x+2}(\ln(x + 2) + 1)$ **15.** $-\dfrac{1}{\sqrt{1 - u^2}}$

17. $\dfrac{-1}{\sqrt{1 - x^2}\cos^{-1}x}$ **19.** $\tan^{-1}(t) + \dfrac{t}{1 + t^2} - \dfrac{1}{2t}$

21. $\dfrac{1 - z}{\sqrt{z^2 - 1}} + \sec^{-1}z$ **23.** -1

25. $\dfrac{2(x^2 + 1)}{\sqrt{\cos 2x}}\left[\dfrac{2x}{x^2 + 1} + \tan 2x\right]$

27. $5\left[\dfrac{(t + 1)(t - 1)}{(t - 2)(t + 3)}\right]^5\left[\dfrac{1}{t + 1} + \dfrac{1}{t - 1} - \dfrac{1}{t - 2} - \dfrac{1}{t + 3}\right]$

29. $\dfrac{1}{\sqrt{\theta}}(\sin\theta)^{\sqrt{\theta}}\left(\dfrac{\ln\sqrt{\sin\theta}}{2} + \theta\cot\theta\right)$ **31.** $-\cos e^x + C$

33. $\tan(e^x - 7) + C$ **35.** $e^{\tan x} + C$ **37.** $\dfrac{-\ln 7}{3}$

39. $\ln 8$ **41.** $\ln(9/25)$ **43.** $-[\ln|\cos(\ln v)|] + C$

45. $-\dfrac{1}{2}(\ln x)^{-2} + C$ **47.** $-\cot(1 + \ln r) + C$

49. $\dfrac{1}{2\ln 3}(3^x) + C$ **51.** $3\ln 7$ **53.** $15/16 + \ln 2$

55. $e - 1$ **57.** 1/6   **59.** 9/14

61. $\dfrac{1}{3}\left[(\ln 4)^3 - (\ln 2)^3\right]$ or $\dfrac{7}{3}(\ln 2)^3$ **63.** $\dfrac{9\ln 2}{4}$ **65.** π

67. $\pi/\sqrt{3}$ **69.** $\sec^{-1}|2y| + C$ **71.** $\pi/12$

73. $\sin^{-1}(x + 1) + C$ **75.** $\pi/2$ **77.** $\dfrac{1}{3}\sec^{-1}\left(\dfrac{t + 1}{3}\right) + C$

79. $y = \dfrac{\ln 2}{\ln(3/2)}$ **81.** $y = \ln x - \ln 3$ **83.** $y = \dfrac{1}{1 - e^x}$

85. $\ln 10$ **87.** $\ln 2$ **89.** 5   **91.** $-\infty$ **93.** 1   **95.** e^3

97. (a) same rate   **(b)** same rate   **(c)** faster   **(d)** faster
(e) same rate   **(f)** same rate

99. (a) true   **(b)** false   **(c)** false   **(d)** true   **(e)** true
(f) true

101. 1/3

103. Absolute maximum $= 0$ at $x = e/2$, absolute minimum $= -0.5$
at $x = 0.5$

105. 1   **107.** $1/e$ m/sec

109. $1/\sqrt{2}$ units long by $1/\sqrt{e}$ units high, $A = 1/\sqrt{2e} \approx 0.43$ units^2

111. $\ln 5x - \ln 3x = \ln(5/3)$ **113.** 1/2

115. **(a)** Absolute maximum of $2/e$ at $x = e^2$, inflection point $(e^{8/3}, (8/3)e^{-4/3})$, concave up on $(e^{8/3}, \infty)$, concave down on $(0, e^{8/3})$

   (b) Absolute maximum of 1 at $x = 0$, inflection points $(\pm 1/\sqrt{2}, 1/\sqrt{e})$, concave up on $(-\infty, -1/\sqrt{2}) \cup (1/\sqrt{2}, \infty)$, concave down on $(-1/\sqrt{2}, 1/\sqrt{2})$

   (c) Absolute maximum of 1 at $x = 0$, inflection point $(1, 2/e)$, concave up on $(1, \infty)$, concave down on $(-\infty, 1)$

117. 18,935 years   **119.** $20(5 - \sqrt{17})$ m

Additional and Advanced Exercises, pp. 550–552

1. $\pi/2$ **3.** $1/\sqrt{e}$ **5.** $\ln 2$ **7. (a)** 1   **(b)** $\pi/2$ **(c)** π

9. $\dfrac{1}{\ln 2}, \dfrac{1}{2\ln 2}$, $2:1$ **11.** $x = 2$ **13.** $2/17$

21. $\bar{x} = \dfrac{\ln 4}{\pi}, \bar{y} = 0$ **25. (b)** $61°$

INDEX